ENCYCLOPEDIA OF
AUSTRALIAN WILDLIFE

ENCYCLOPEDIA OF AUSTRALIAN WILDLIFE

Published by Reader's Digest (Australia) Pty Ltd
80 Bay Street Ultimo, NSW 2007
www.readersdigest.com.au

First edition 1997, reprinted 1998. Revised edition 2005.

Encyclopedia of Australian wildlife.

Includes index.
ISBN 1 876689 34 X.

1. Animals - Australia - Encyclopedias.
2. Zoology - Australia - Encyclopedias.
I. Reader's Digest (Australia).

591.99403

Colour separations by Rainbow Graphic Arts Co. Ltd, Hong Kong
and Sinnott Bros, Sydney
Printing and binding in China by Toppan Printing Co., (H.K.) Ltd

We are interested in receiving your comments on the contents of this
book. Write to: The Editor, General Books Editorial, Reader's Digest
(Australia) Pty Limited, GPO Box 4353, Sydney, NSW 2001
or email us at bookeditors.au@readersdigest.com

To order additional copies of the *Encyclopedia of
Australian Wildlife* call 1300 303 210 (Australia)
or 0800 540 032 (New Zealand) or email us at
customerservice@au.readersdigest.com

ENCYCLOPEDIA OF
AUSTRALIAN WILDLIFE

READER'S DIGEST, SYDNEY

CONTRIBUTORS

COMMISSIONING EDITOR Louise Egerton, BSc

MAJOR CONSULTANTS
MAMMALS Chris Dickman, BSc (Hons), PhD
BIRDS Graeme Phipps, BSc
REPTILES AND AMPHIBIANS Hal Cogger, AM, BSc, MSc, PhD, Hon DSc
FISHES Graham Edgar, PhD
INVERTEBRATES Noel Tait, BSc, MSc, PhD
INTRODUCTION Alex Ritchie, BSc, PhD; Robyn Stutchbury BSc (Hons),
Grad.Cert. SciComm.

PROJECT EDITORS Fiona Doig, Janet Healey

ART EDITORS James Marks, Kylie Mulquin, Sue Rawkins,
Suzanne Keating

EDITORS Maggi Aldhamland, Fiona Doig, Gillian Hewitt,
Emma Johnson, Judith Simpson

PICTURE RESEARCHERS Annette Crueger, Debra Wager

INDEXER Diane Harriman

ILLUSTRATORS Martin Camm, Marje Crosby-Fairall,
Andrew Davies, Jon Gittoes, Ray Grinaway, Karen Lloyd-Jones,
James McKinnon, Tony Oliver, Ray Sim

PRODUCTION MANAGER Janelle Garside

GENERAL BOOKS EDITORIAL
EDITORIAL DIRECTOR Elaine Russell
MANAGING EDITOR Rosemary McDonald

SPECIALIST CONTRIBUTORS

Gerry Allen, PhD, Curator of Aquatic Zoology, Western Australian Museum
Michael Archer, BA, PhD, School of Biological Science, University of New South Wales
Peter Banks, BSc (Hons), PhD, New South Wales National Parks and Wildlife Service
J M de Bavay, BSc, Department of Zoology, University of New England
Carrie Bengston, BAppSc, DipEd
Isobel Bennett, AO, BSc, author and marine biologist
Dan Bickel, PhD, Research Scientist, Australian Museum
Walter Boles, BSE (Hons),

Scientific Officer and Collection Manager (Birds), Australian Museum
David Briscoe, BSc (Hons), PhD, School of Biological Sciences, Macquarie University
Bert Brunet, natural history writer
Clay Bryce, DipAppSc (Biol), RBI, Western Australian Museum
Michael Bryden, BVSc, DScVM, PhD, DSc, Department of Veterinary Anatomy, University of Sydney
Brian Bush, Snakes Harmful & Harmless, Stoneville, WA
Mike Calver, BSc (Hons), PhD, DipEd, School of Biological Sciences, Murdoch University

John Cann, Honorary Adviser, Queensland Museum
Terry Carless, Honorary Assistant, Queensland Museum
P H J Castle, PhD, School of Biological Sciences, Victoria University of Wellington
Liana Christensen, BA, MA, science writer and editor
Michelle Christie, BSc (Hons), Research Associate, Australian Museum
Hal Cogger, AM, BSc, MSc, PhD, Hon DSc, John Evans Memorial Fellow, Australian Museum
C D Creagh, BSc, science writer and editor
Andrew Cribb, BA, science writer and editor

Toni Davis
Stephen Debus, BA, DipNatRes, DipEd, MSc, Department of Zoology, University of New England
Chris Dickman, BSc (Hons), PhD, Institute of Wildlife Research, University of Sydney
Nick Drayson
Graham Edgar, PhD, Department of Zoology, University of Tasmania
Peter Eggler, BSc (Hons), Australian Museum
Mark Eldridge, BSc (Hons), PhD, School of Biological Sciences, Macquarie University
Tish Ennis, BSc, Australian Museum

Murray Clement Evans, BNatRes (Hons), MResSci, Ecosystem Management, University of New England

Tim Flannery, PhD, Principal Research Scientist, Australian Museum

Tony Friend, BSc (Hons), PhD, Principal Research Scientist, WA Department of Conservation and Land Management

Judith Gillespie, BSc, Exhibit Planning Officer, Taronga Zoo, Sydney

Martin F Gomon, BSc, MSc, PhD, Senior Curator (Ichthyology), Museum of Victoria

Alastair Graham, BSc (Hons), CSIRO Division of Marine Research, Hobart

Phillip Hadlington, BSc (Agric)

Bruce Halliday, PhD, Principal Research Scientist (Acarology), CSIRO Entomology, Canberra

Neil Hermes, BSc (Hons)

Mark Hindell, BSc (Hons), PhD, Department of Zoology, University of Tasmania

Paul Horner, BSc, Curator of Terrestrial Vertebrates, Museum and Art Gallery of the Northern Territory

Professor Ian D Hume, BSc (Agric), PhD, DSc, School of Biological Sciences, University of Sydney

Barry Hutchins, BSc, BSc (Hons), PhD, Department of Aquatic Zoology, Museum of Western Australia

Mark Hutchinson, BSc (Hons), PhD, Curator of Reptiles and Amphibians, South Australian Museum

Glen J Ingram, BSc, PhD, Senior Curator (Vertebrates), Queensland Museum

Walter Ivantsoff, PhD, School of Biological Sciences, Macquarie University

Tessa Ivison, Curatorial Assistant (Birds), Australian Museum

George Jackson, BSc (Hons), PhD, Department of Marine Biology, James Cook University, Townsville

Peter John Jarman, BA, PhD, Department of Ecosystem Management, University of New England

Chris Johnson, BNatRes, PhD, Department of Ecology and Tropical Ecology, James Cook University, Townsville

Ken Johnson, BRurSc, PhD, GradDip (Public Admin)

Menna E Jones, BSc (Hons), PhD, Department of Zoology, University of Tasmania

Patricia J Kailola, BSc (Hons), DipEd (DC), PhD (Zool), CertAppSci (Fish), fisheries consultant

John Keesing, BSc (Hons), PhD, Aquatic Sciences, South Australian Research and Development Institute

Anne Kerle, BA (Hons), PhD, consultant biologist; Research Associate, University of Canberra

David Knowles, field naturalist; writer; photographer

Lucien E Koch, MSc, PhD, School of Environmental Biology, Curtin University of Technology

Patricia Kott, AO, PhD, DSc, Hon DSc, FAI Biol, Honorary Associate, Queensland Museum

Rudie Kuiter, Research Associate, Zoology Department, Museum of Victoria; Associate (Fish), Australian Museum

Helen K Larson, BA, MSc, Curator of Fishes, Museum and Art Gallery of the Northern Territory

Peter Last, BSc (Hons), PhD, CSIRO Division of Marine Research, Hobart

K A Lazenby-Cohen, PhD

Luke K-P Leung, PhD, School of Biological Sciences, University of Sydney

Warren Lewington, naturalist

Murray Littlejohn, BSc (Hons), PhD, MSc, Department of Zoology, University of Melbourne

N W Longmore, Associate (Birds), Australian Museum

Tim Low, BSc, environmental consultant; nature writer

Genevieve Lyon, BA, GradDip, MPhil

Karen McGhee, BSc

Paul Mahon, BSc (Hons), Institute of Wildlife Research, University of Sydney

Michael Mahony, BA, DipEd, PhD, Department of Biological Sciences, University of Newcastle

Jane Miller

Nicola Mitchell, BSc (Hons), Department of Zoology, University of Adelaide

Robin Murray

Anne Musser, PhD

Mark Norman, PhD, Department of Zoology, University of Melbourne

William S Osborne, PhD, Applied Ecology Research Group, University of Canberra

Julian Pepperell, BSc (Hons), PhD, Pepperell Research & Consulting, Caringbah, NSW

Graeme Phipps, BSc, zoo and museum consultant; biologist; writer; publisher

Gary C B Poore, PhD, Museum of Victoria

Robert Porter, MSc, Manager, Australian Reptile Park, Gosford

Ian Caesar Potter, BA, PhD, School of Biological and Environmental Sciences, Murdoch University

David Priddel, BSc (Hons), PhD, New South Wales National Parks and Wildlife Service

Jacquie Recsei, fauna consultant

Greg Richards, BAppSc, wildlife consultant

Stephen J Richards, BA (Hons), Department of Zoology and Tropical Ecology, James Cook University, Townsville

Professor Barry J Richardson, BSc (Hons), PhD, School of Science, University of Western Sydney, Richmond

J Dale Roberts, PhD, Department of Zoology, University of Western Australia

Peter Roberts, BA

Louise Rodgerson, BSc (Hons), PhD, Department of Biological Sciences, University of Wollongong

Peter Rowland, freelance writer

Barry C Russell, BSc, MSc (Hons), PhD, Research and Collections, Museum and Art Gallery of the Northern Territory

Tony Saunders, BSc, DipEd

John Scanlon, BSc (Hons), PhD, School of Biological Sciences, University of New South Wales

Bronwen Scott, BSc (Hons), PhD, Department of Zoology and Tropical Ecology, James Cook University, Townsville

Glenn Shea, BVSc, PhD, Department of Veterinary Science, University of Sydney; Australian Museum

James M Shields, BSc, BA, MT, MSc (For), PhD, Native Forests Division, State Forests of New South Wales

Richard Shine, BSc, PhD, DSc, Department of Evolutionary Biology, University of Sydney

Jeff Short, BSc, MSc, CSIRO Division of Wildlife and Ecology, Perth

Lindsay Smith, Southern Oceans Seabird Study Association

Richard Southgate, BNatRes, MSc, Parks and Wildlife Commission of the Northern Territory

John Stevens, BSc (Hons), PhD, Principal Research Scientist, CSIRO Division of Marine Research, Hobart

Phil Straw, BSc, Projects Coordinator, Royal Australian Ornithologists Union

Liz Sutherland, BSc (Hons), Institute of Wildlife Research, University of Sydney

Gerry Swan, Associate, Australian Museum; President, Herpetology Society; Editor, Herpetofauna

Noel Tait, BSc, MSc, PhD, School of Biological Sciences, Macquarie University

James Miln Thomson, DSc, DSc (Hons), FI Biol Australia, FI Biol UK

Karen Thumm, BA (Hons)

Colin Trainor, BAppSci (Hons), MSc, Department of Biological Sciences, Northern Territory University; Parks and Wildlife Commission of the Northern Territory

Michael J Tyler, AO, MSc, Department of Zoology, University of Adelaide

Frederik van Gessel, member of RAOU, ABSA, NSW FOC, HBOC, Wader Study Group

Steve Van Dyck, BSc, MSc, Queensland Museum

Graeme Watson, BSc, PhD, Department of Zoology, University of Melbourne

Grahame Webb, BSc, PhD, Director, Wildlife Management International Pty Ltd, Northern Territory

Alan Williams, PhD, CSIRO Division of Marine Research, Hobart

Dick Williams, BSc, MSc, PhD, Australian Antarctic Division, Department of Environment, Sport and Territories, Tasmania

Steve Wilson, wildlife photographer and writer; part-time information officer, Queensland Museum

John Winter, PhD, Massey Creek Ecology Centre, Queensland

Geoff Witten, BSc (Hons), MSc, PhD, Department of Anatomy and Physiology, Royal Melbourne Institute of Technology

David Wurst, BNatRes, Parks and Wildlife Commission of the Northern Territory

Gordon Kenneth Yearsley, BSc (Hons), CSIRO Division of Marine Research, Hobart

Jock Young, BSc, MSc, CSIRO Division of Marine Research, Hobart

Paul Zborowski, BAppSci, entomologist; science photographer and writer

Richard G Zweifel, BA, PhD, Curator Emeritus, Department of Herpetology and Ichthyology, American Museum of Natural History, New York

CONTENTS

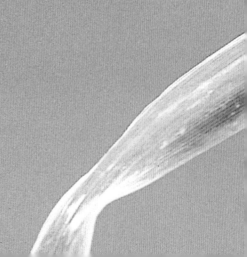

USING THIS BOOK

Animals are grouped into six principal chapters: mammals, birds, reptiles, amphibians, fishes and invertebrates. Within each chapter, the animals are grouped at the classification level that best lends itself to a description of the animals concerned. The classification levels that determine the groupings vary from chapter to chapter, and sometimes within a chapter: for example, mammals, birds, reptiles, amphibians and fishes all belong to the phylum Chordata, but the invertebrate group contains many phyla – eleven for worms alone. So worms form a major invertebrate group, with each phylum constituting a subgroup, but for mammals the major grouping is by subclass (for example, placental mammals) and the subgrouping is by order (for example, bats).

Turn to the table of contents (pages 4–7) to find the main groupings and subgroupings, and consult the index (pages 613–638) to find the page references for individual entries.

DISTRIBUTION

■ DUGONG

DUGONG

The dugong (*Dugong dugon*) is not related in any way to either seals or whales but belongs to the order Sirenia, the sea cows. There are only two families in this group – the manatees, which are found only in the northern hemisphere, and the dugongs of the Indian Ocean and

the south-western and the dugong is of the family Dugo

These gentle herbs warm, shallow coas the northern half of Shark Bay in the we Queensland–New S der in the east. The extend further dow indeed, they were c spread throughout

Dugongs can weig and grow up to 3 m measurements are of large dolphins, b dumpier than dolp rounded, downwar and broad, flexible perfectly adapted f grasses. Their nostr front of their heads when the animal is Unlike their norther manatees, which ha that of the platypus dolphin-like tails. T bronze-grey with a lack a dorsal fin bu flippers for steering feeding, and for gra

A GENTLE THREATEN
Good hearing and a the dugong's only pr predators – large sha crocodiles, killer wha

---

THIS TYPE OF HEADING and the text that follows describe the important characteristics of a major animal group – in this case, the daytime birds of prey (the hawks and eagles and the falcons), which have the group name 'raptors'.

AERIAL HUNTER
The wedge-tailed eagle's long, broad wings provide maximum lift on updraughts and agility near ground level.

ILLUSTRATIONS show important features that cannot be illustrated photographically. In this example, the drawings illustrate the aerodynamic design of a raptor's wings (top); the special characteristics of a raptor's vision (centre); and the locking mechanism of a raptor's claws (bottom).

EAGLE EYES
Raptors' eyeballs have two fields of extremely acute vision, called foveas. The sideways-directed foveas (red) scan large areas separately, and the forward-directed foveas (green) focus on prey together.

LOCKED CLAWS
As a raptor's claw closes, a tendon attached to the claw locks it into position by catching on corrugations inside the tendon sheath.

friction pad on tendon

corrugations on tendon sheath

RAPTORS

Raptors are birds of prey that have s intense eyes and powerful clawed fe larger than the male. They belong to Accipitridae, which contains the haw Falconidae, which contains the falco

All raptors except the letter-winge day. Some feed mainly on insects an carrion, but most Australian species introduced rats, mice, rabbits and bi locusts. The name of their order is F

Raptors have extremely keen eye-sight – about twice as acute as that of humans. Their eyes are very large and are set slightly further forward than those of most birds. This gives them binocular vision – an essential attribute for judging distances.

Their eyes are also extremely sensitive to movement, and their high visual resolution enables them to distinguish even motionless animals from their surroundings. Once they spot their prey, they can rapidly adjust the lenses in their eyes to focus on the creature as it moves among obstacles. The presence of a raptor is often betrayed by alarm calls from other birds.

Nesting and nurturing
Most hawks and eagles build stick nests in trees, while falcons lay on a cliff ledge, in a tree hollow, or in an abandoned eagle nest. Before mating, which occurs on the nest or a nearby perch, the male performs aerobatics and presents food or nesting materials to females in midair to show off his prowess and hunting ability. Clutches range from five or six eggs for small hawks to one or two for large eagles.

The eggs hatch within a month in small species and within six weeks in large ones. The young of the smaller species spend about a month in the nest before flying, while those of large eagles take up to three months to leave the nest.

The female incubates the eggs and cares for the chicks, and the male provides food until the young are large enough to be left and the female can hunt again.

Deadly talons
Raptors living in open country hover in the air searching for their prey, while those living in wooded country perch in foliage ready to pounce.

Hawks and eagles clutch their prey strongly in their feet, crushing it and driving their talons through the vital organs. Falcons strike their victim a heavy blow with their feet or grasp it with their feet and bite through the vertebrae at the base of its skull.

Once they have secured their victim, raptors anchor it to a perch with their feet and then pluck and shred it with their beak. The indigestible remains, such as bones, fur and feathers, are later regurgitated as a pellet, or casting. Scientists often use these castings to analyse what the raptor has eaten.

Aerodynamic engineering
Raptors have broad wings in order to maximise their lift in thermal updraughts and provide agility near the ground. Their wing tip feathers separate like fingers to increase stability and reduce stalling speed, permitting a slow, searching flight.

KILLING ONLY TO EAT
This peregrine falcon is about to start feeding on a pigeon it has just caught. Raptors store any surplus food, retrieving and consuming it later.

Hawks that live in forested regions and give rapid chase have short wings for precision flying between tree trunks and for rapid acceleration in attack. Those that soar in the open have long wings for gliding. Smaller hovering kites (which are hawks) have more pointed wings to give them a buoyant, flapping flight. Falcons have long pointed wings for swift aerial pursuit.

A tail increases drag when flying, but it is invaluable for steering and braking, so species that need good manoeuvrability in the air or in dense cover have long tails, while those that fly swiftly or have little need for tight manoeuvres generally have short tails.

DISTRIBUTION

■ AUSTRALIAN SEA-LION
■ AUSTRALIAN FUR-SEAL

■ NEW ZEALAND FUR-SEAL

SEALS

Seals belong to the same order as the terrestrial carnivorous mammals – dogs, cats, foxes and bears. Unlike the other carnivores, however, seals have adapted to a life at sea, though they still come ashore to breed. Instead of land legs, they have two pairs of flippers, which they use in effortless, lithe swimming.

Like those of whales and dugongs, the ancestors of seals were land mammals that returned to the sea. Seals evolved from two separate groups of land mammals, and from these developed two families – the eared seals and the 'true' seals.
Order: Carnivora

CARNIVOROUS MAMMAL OF THE SEA
While seals, such as this Weddell seal, may look ungainly on land, they are acrobatic swimmers and skilful hunters.

even living in cities. They are most frequently seen in flight, often circling high in the sky, but some hide in trees and rarely fly high.

Of about 220 hawk and eagle species in the world, there are 18 in Australia, all of them native. Five of these birds – the black-shouldered kite, the letter-winged kite, the square-tailed kite, the black-breasted buzzard and the red goshawk – are unique to Australia.
Family: Accipitridae

OSPREY ■
Large brown and white hawks, about 60 cm long with a wingspan of about 160 cm, ospreys are fish-eaters. They live right around the Australian coastline, but they are much more common in the north than in the south.

The osprey circles and hovers over inshore waters and estuaries or perches on tall, dead trees, scouring the water for signs of movement. When it catches sight of potential prey it plummets into the water feet first, often disappearing below the surface before rising into the air with its catch. It also hunts upriver, and in wet years it will occasionally move some distance inland over rivers or freshwater lakes.

It builds a huge stick nest in a tall dead or partly dead tree, or sometimes on artificial structures such as electricity transmission poles. The female lays two to four eggs from late autumn to early spring.
Scientific name: Pandion haliaetus

stick
living
betwe
Scient

BLA
KITI
This i
like h
90 cm
It live

■ Os
Ospre
each y
The b
trees,

THESE HEADINGS provide an instant key to the grouping of animals within chapters and major sections: on this page, a quick glance at the top bar tells you that seals belong to the placental mammal group within the larger group called mammals.

BOXES highlight features of general interest about a variety of topics – for example, the exploitation of species in the past (as here), fascinating evolutionary developments, or simply unusual and interesting facts.

THIS TYPE OF HEADING gives the common name of an animal or group of animals, and the text that follows describes the animal's appearance, habitat, distribution and life cycle. The symbol ■ after the heading indicates that the entry is accompanied by a photograph, and the symbol also appears against the caption heading.

partner while mating. Like all herbivores, dugongs have large stomachs and long intestines with which to digest their food.

A dugong's lifestyle does not demand speed and they average less than 10 km an hour, though they can reach 22 km an hour in short bursts. Nor do they need to be able to dive deeply; instead, their dense bones enable them to stay on the sea bottom while feeding. They generally spend one to ten minutes under water before coming up for air.

Dugongs sometimes gather in herds of hundreds of individuals, though large groups are becoming less common as their habitat diminishes and their numbers dwindle. They have a similar lifespan to humans and produce only one young at a time, with up to seven years between births. Calves start feeding on seagrasses when they are very young but continue to drink their mother's milk for about a year and a half after birth.

With the exception of Aboriginal and Torres Strait Islander hunters, it is illegal to hunt dugongs in Australian waters. Nevertheless, the species is under threat, mainly because of habitat loss, either through coastal development or boat traffic, and – perhaps most crucially – because of hunting and incidental capture in fishing nets.
Order: Sirenia; Family: Dugongidae

SEAL HUNTING

In the eighteenth and early nineteenth centuries, hunting seals for their pelts and blubber was a major business, and the Australian fur-seal, pictured below, was particularly prized. British seal hunters arrived in Australia in 1798 and French and American vessels soon followed. With the taking of nursing mothers and young, seal stocks fell rapidly.

State protection began in Western Australia in 1892, and by 1925 seals were generally protected, but seal populations took decades to return to reasonable numbers. Today both State and Federal legislation prohibits seal harvesting in Australian waters.

EARED SEALS

Although this family of seals is at least 12 million years old, it did not reach the southern hemisphere until about five million years ago. Today, eared seals are represented in Australian waters by the Australian sea-lion and the Australian and New Zealand fur-seals. The subantarctic fur-seal is a common vagrant and the antarctic fur-seal swims in Australian regions of Antarctica.

Four features distinguish the eared seals from the 'true' seals: eared seals have small external ears; they move on land using all four limbs; they have larger necks than the 'true' seals; and their teeth are similar to those of terrestrial carnivores.
Family: Otariidae

AUSTRALIAN SEA-LION ■

Most sea-lion species live in the warmer Pacific waters and do not have the dense underfur that characterises the fur-seals. The Australian sea-lion is no exception, though it occurs further south. These seals live on islands along the southern coast –

from The Pages off South Australia to Houtman Abrolhos off Western Australia. Unlike other eared seals, they breed only every 17–18 months, rather than during a specific season, and different groups pup at different times. An embryo is normally conceived directly after the mother has pupped, and begins to develop eight or nine months later.

Australian sea-lions prefer inaccessible breeding sites on the sheltered sides of islands, and the pups generally hide in vegetation and rock holes. Breeding sites have 'toddlers' pools' where the pups learn to swim.

Sea-lions have blunt snouts, small, furled ears, and large front limbs. Males are brown or black with lighter fur on their head. Females have silver-grey backs and creamy yellow bellies. Males weigh about 300 kg and average 2.1 metres long; females weigh about 80 kg and average 1.6 metres long. Australian sea-lions eat fishes and squids, and in turn are preyed upon by sharks.
Scientific name: Neophoca cinerea

AUSTRALIAN FUR-SEAL

Male Australian fur-seals average 2.16 metres in length and females 1.6 metres. Females average only 77 kg as against an average 279 kg for males. Males are dark brown or grey, females are paler with a fawn or cream bib, and pups are black with some silver. Adults dive to at least 200 metres in search of prey. On land they usually shuffle but they can break into a fast gallop.

These fur-seals live in large groups. They gather on rocky ledges and reefs and tolerate an unusual degree of body contact with one another. Their range runs from northern New South Wales to southern Tasmania and across to South Australia.

■ NEW ZEALAND FUR-SEAL
Despite their common name, these creatures occur on many islands off the coasts of South Australia, south-west Tasmania and southern Western Australia.

In November and December these fur-seals come ashore, females and immature males congregating and successful males establishing territories. Males maintain these territories more by bark than by bite, though aggressive displays turn to violence if boundaries are ignored. During this time females give birth to one offspring, each mother recognising her pup by smell and sound. About a week after giving birth the mother becomes receptive to the territorial males and chooses a mate. She then goes to sea to feed on squids, fishes, octopuses and rock lobsters, returning intermittently to suckle her pup.
Scientific name: Artocephalus pusillus

NEW ZEALAND FUR-SEAL ■

New Zealand fur-seal males average 2 metres in length, females about 1.4 metres. They are sometimes mistaken for Australian fur-seals, but they weigh much less, with males averaging 152 kg and females about 42 kg. Adults are grey to brown and

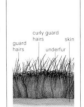

curly guard hairs   skin
guard hairs   underfur

KEEPING WARM AND DRY
The fur-seal's luxuriant coat consists of long guard hairs over a layer of curly guard hairs, beneath which grows dense underfur. This undercoat is waterproofed by secreted oils and sweat and never becomes wet.

■ AUSTRALIAN SEA-LIONS
Both sexes can be aggressive during breeding, sometimes killing pups and running after humans who approach too closely. Outside the breeding season sea-lions come ashore on sandy beaches and are easier to observe.

103

THIS TYPE OF HEADING and the text that follows describe the characteristics of a subgroup within a major group: this example explains that seals are carnivorous placental mammals that belong to the same main group as foxes and bears but have developed various adaptations for survival at sea.

THIS TYPE OF HEADING is used, in some sections, to describe a smaller group within a subgroup: in this example, eared seals differ in important ways from 'true' seals, and the differences are explained in the text that follows the heading.

PHOTOGRAPHS illustrate most of the individual animal species and groups described. The symbol ■ against the caption heading indicates that the photograph relates to a specific entry; photographs without the symbol illustrate a broader animal grouping.

in the canopy of a ... two or three eggs ...ber and January. ...viceda subcristata

...OULDERED

...grey and white, gull-... a wingspan of about ...ly about 35 cm long. ...and lightly wooded

...heir seaside nests ...sticks and seaweed. ...and nest in tall, dead ...becoming scarce.

the mainland and in Tasmania.

The black-shouldered kite eats rodents, particularly the introduced house mouse. When hunting, it flies with quick wingbeats and long glides on gracefully upcurved wings. Stopping to hover suspended in one position, it flutters its wings, lowering its yellow feet and peering down. When it sights a mouse it gradually flutters down within range, and then, at the last moment, pounces with its wings held high above its back and catches its prey in its talons.

Once caught, the mouse is carried to a high perch and swallowed

These kites prey widely on the house mouse, an introduced species, and in mouse plague years the kites may rear two broods of young.

DISTRIBUTION

OSPREY

PACIFIC BAZA

BLACK-SHOULDERED KITE

155

DISTRIBUTION MAPS are provided for mammals, birds, reptiles and amphibians, except those found only on islands or in Australia's Antarctic territories or waters. The maps are based on the most recent information available, but remote or inaccessible parts of Australia may house as yet unreported animal populations.

THE ANIMAL KINGDOM

The variety of animal life is enormous. Well over a million species have been discovered, and some scientists estimate that ten times this number are yet to be recognised. For each of the species so far named we have at least some information, such as what they look like and where they live. But how do we organise this information so that we can quickly find out what an animal is called, which are its closest relatives and what else is known about it?

Biologists who work on classification are known as taxonomists and they do two important things: they identify, describe and name new species; and they arrange them into groups according to how they believe the new species are related to other animals.

The Linnaean system
The classification system that scientists use today is based on a scheme proposed in 1758 by the Swedish naturalist Karl von Linné (1707–1778). Species names are based on Latin, Greek or nowadays, on Latinised English. Linné used Latin because it was at that time the international scientific language.

Linné's aim was to incorporate all living things into an unchanging design. His groupings were based on degrees of similarity, very similar species being placed in the same genus, very different animals in different phyla.

In 1859, a century after Linné, Charles Darwin published *The Origin of Species* – the theory of evolution by natural selection. This theory stressed a changing rather than an unchanging world, where organisms living at a specific time could give rise to a variety of new types at a later time, or could go extinct. It radically changed the way scientists viewed the living world, but the Linnaean system is still the basis of our way of classifying animals.

The same species in different parts of the world may have different common names, or different species may have the same common names. The Linnaean system avoids such confusions. For example, there are small red-breasted birds in Europe, North America and Australia; all are known as robins, but their Latin names show that they are not related. Of all the categories in the Linnaean system, only the species has a sound natural basis.

How taxonomy works
A **species** is a group of organisms that can breed with one another in the wild to produce fertile offspring: members of different species cannot interbreed to produce fertile offspring. Broader categories, such as genus or family, are based on a scientific assessment of how closely or distantly related animals are.

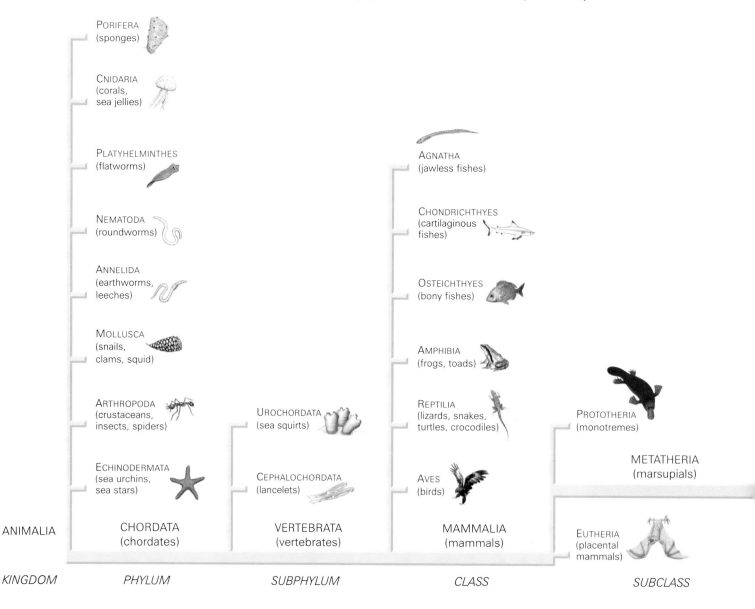

PORIFERA (sponges)

CNIDARIA (corals, sea jellies)

PLATYHELMINTHES (flatworms)

NEMATODA (roundworms)

ANNELIDA (earthworms, leeches)

MOLLUSCA (snails, clams, squid)

ARTHROPODA (crustaceans, insects, spiders)

ECHINODERMATA (sea urchins, sea stars)

UROCHORDATA (sea squirts)

CEPHALOCHORDATA (lancelets)

AGNATHA (jawless fishes)

CHONDRICHTHYES (cartilaginous fishes)

OSTEICHTHYES (bony fishes)

AMPHIBIA (frogs, toads)

REPTILIA (lizards, snakes, turtles, crocodiles)

AVES (birds)

PROTOTHERIA (monotremes)

METATHERIA (marsupials)

EUTHERIA (placental mammals)

ANIMALIA

CHORDATA (chordates)

VERTEBRATA (vertebrates)

MAMMALIA (mammals)

KINGDOM   PHYLUM   SUBPHYLUM   CLASS   SUBCLASS

A species name is prefixed by the name of its **genus**: for example, *Macropus rufus*. The first part (the genus) denotes the group to which the species is most closely related. The second part is the species name. Here, the two words form the unique name of the red kangaroo.

The classification system then groups animals into larger and larger categories. Related genera (plural of genus) are placed in the same **family**, related families in the same **order**, related orders in the same **class**, and related classes in the same **phylum**. Together, all the phyla make up the animal **kingdom**.

Species classified in the same genus have a common ancestor in the reasonably recent past, remembering that 'reasonably recent' can mean tens of millions of years along the evolutionary timeframe! At the other end of the scale, the common ancestor of classes of animals placed in the same phylum may go back hundreds of millions of years.

With over a million species already classified, and many more yet to be discovered and named, taxonomists have created subgroups between the major taxonomic categories. For example, a phylum can be split into subphyla, a class into subclasses and so on.

Sometimes populations of the same species from different places are so different that they are given subspecific names: for example, the echidna of eastern mainland Australia is named *Tachyglossus aculeatus aculeatus* ('spiny long-tongue'), while its relative in Tasmania, which has developed far more hair between its spines as an adaptation to living in a colder climate, is named *Tachyglossus aculeatus setosus* ('spiny, hairy, long-tongue').

Taxonomy and technology

A taxonomist's hardest task is to work out the relationships among the large groups: for example, is a sea star (phylum Echinodermata)

more closely related to a sea jelly (Cnidaria) or a whale (Chordata)? To answer such questions, taxonomists compare the embryonic development of animals and analyse their DNA – the chemical that codes for inheritance. DNA analysis can also reveal fine differences between related species and is used to study relationships between species of the same genus.

Taxonomists have many techniques at their disposal. Powerful microscopes allow minute details of animals' bodies and cells to be examined: some animals are so similar that only analysis of their chemical molecules can determine whether they belong to the same species or a different one. Computer programs have been designed to compare similarities and differences among organisms, and computer networks allow taxonomists around the world to share information instantaneously. Every year, new discoveries help to fill in the missing pieces in the fossil record.

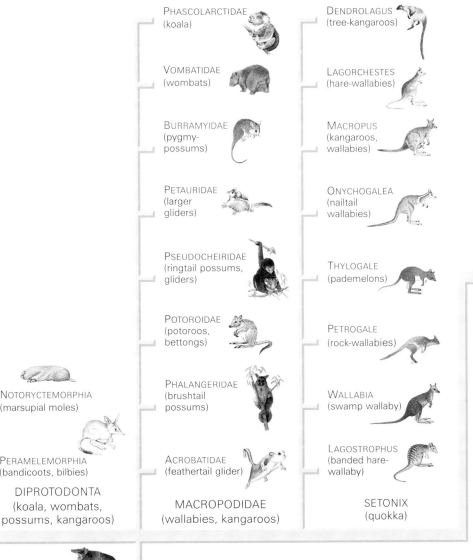

SETONIX BRACHYURUS (quokka)

PHASCOLARCTIDAE (koala)

VOMBATIDAE (wombats)

BURRAMYIDAE (pygmy-possums)

PETAURIDAE (larger gliders)

PSEUDOCHEIRIDAE (ringtail possums, gliders)

POTOROIDAE (potoroos, bettongs)

PHALANGERIDAE (brushtail possums)

ACROBATIDAE (feathertail glider)

NOTORYCTEMORPHIA (marsupial moles)

PERAMELEMORPHIA (bandicoots, bilbies)

DIPROTODONTA (koala, wombats, possums, kangaroos)

MACROPODIDAE (wallabies, kangaroos)

DASYUROMORPHIA (carnivorous marsupials)

TARSIPEDIDAE (honey possum)

DENDROLAGUS (tree-kangaroos)

LAGORCHESTES (hare-wallabies)

MACROPUS (kangaroos, wallabies)

ONYCHOGALEA (nailtail wallabies)

THYLOGALE (pademelons)

PETROGALE (rock-wallabies)

WALLABIA (swamp wallaby)

LAGOSTROPHUS (banded hare-wallaby)

SETONIX (quokka)

THE CLASSIFICATION OF THE QUOKKA
The quokka has a spine, which places it in the phylum Chordata. Its spine is made up of vertebrae, placing it in the subphylum Vertebrata. It is furred and suckles its young, so it fits into the class Mammalia, and its pouch makes it a member of the subclass Marsupialia. It has only one pair of lower front teeth, a prerequisite for the order Diprotodontia, and powerful hind legs with a strong fourth toe, a characteristic of the family Macropodidae. Its small size, short tail, grizzled fur and short, rounded ears identify it as *Setonix brachyurus*, the 'short-tailed bristle-claw' – the quokka. It is the only species in the genus *Setonix* and has no surviving related species.

ORDER   *FAMILY*   *GENUS*   *SPECIES*

WHERE AUSTRALIAN ANIMALS LIVE

A complex interplay of the history of the continent with its present geology and climate determines where Australian animals live. The rainforests along the east coast and the animals that live there have evolved from the ancient forests of Gondwana, isolated over millions of years from the influences of other landmasses. Australia is the flattest, driest (after Antarctica) continent in the world, with some of the oldest and least fertile soils. These conditions determine plant growth – and it is on plants that animals ultimately depend for food. Their survival also depends on how they meet the climatic and seasonal challenges of their habitats.

The habitats of Australia's animals extend from Antarctica to the tropics, encompassing oceans, seashores, lakes, rivers, swamps, coastal heathlands, mountain forests, alpine meadows, woodlands, shrublands and the dry grasslands of the interior.

South of the Tropic of Capricorn, in the temperate forests and woodlands of eastern Australia, rain falls year-round; summers are warm or hot and winters are mild to cool but may be really cold in the high country. North of the Tropic, temperature and annual rainfall increase, but in the woodlands of Cape York and the Top End, summers are very wet and there is a long dry season in winter. The temperate forests of southern Western Australia have cool, rainy winters and warm or hot, dry summers. The arid interior includes the spinifex or hummock grasslands, shrublands and tussock grasslands; rainfall is sparse and sporadic, falling mainly in winter in the south and in summer in the north. Within these broad-scale environments there are many smaller habitats.

Marine environments and seashores
Australia's oceans have a great diversity of animal life. Reefs of colourful and variously shaped corals occur in the warmer northern waters, providing homes for worms, molluscs, crustaceans, sea stars and fishes, while sea snakes and turtles navigate the waters around the reefs. Enormous numbers of individual fishes are found in the cooler southern

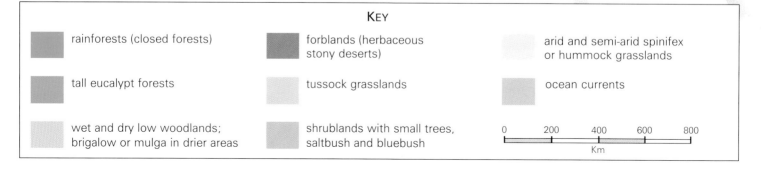

KEY		
rainforests (closed forests)	forblands (herbaceous stony deserts)	arid and semi-arid spinifex or hummock grasslands
tall eucalypt forests	tussock grasslands	ocean currents
wet and dry low woodlands; brigalow or mulga in drier areas	shrublands with small trees, saltbush and bluebush	0 200 400 600 800 Km

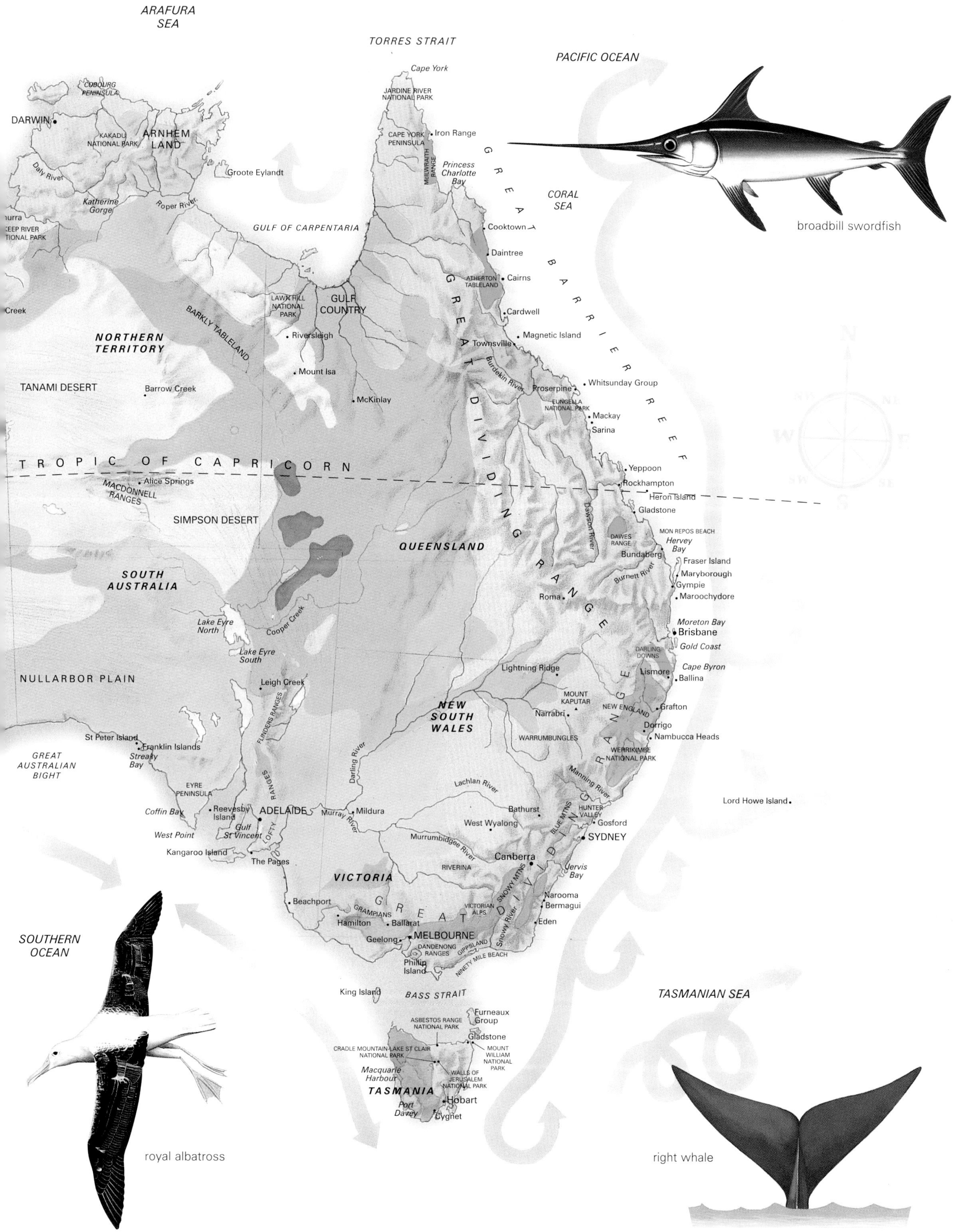

TORRES STRAIT

PACIFIC OCEAN

Cape York

JARDINE RIVER
NATIONAL PARK

COBOURG
PENINSULA

DARWIN

KAKADU
NATIONAL PARK

ARNHEM
LAND

CAPE YORK
PENINSULA

Iron Range

MCILWRAITH
RANGE

Daly River

Groote Eylandt

*Princess
Charlotte
Bay*

CORAL
SEA

Katherine
Gorge

KEEP RIVER
NATIONAL PARK

urra

Roper River

GULF OF CARPENTARIA

Cooktown

Daintree

Creek

ATHERTON
TABLELAND

Cairns

BARKLY TABLELAND

LAWN HILL
NATIONAL
PARK

GULF
COUNTRY

Cardwell

Magnetic Island

NORTHERN
TERRITORY

Riversleigh

Townsville

Burdekin River

TANAMI DESERT

Barrow Creek

Mount Isa

McKinlay

Whitsunday Group

Proserpine

EUNGELLA
NATIONAL PARK

Mackay

Sarina

T R O P I C   O F   C A P R I C O R N

Yeppoon

Alice Springs

MACDONNELL
RANGES

Rockhampton

Heron Island

SIMPSON DESERT

Gladstone

SOUTH
AUSTRALIA

QUEENSLAND

DAWES
RANGE

MON REPOS BEACH

*Hervey
Bay*

Bundaberg

Fraser Island

Lake Eyre
North

Cooper Creek

Burnett River

Maryborough

Lake Eyre
South

Roma

Gympie

Maroochydore

NULLARBOR PLAIN

Lightning Ridge

Moreton Bay

Brisbane

DARLING
DOWNS

Gold Coast

Leigh Creek

Lismore

Cape Byron

Ballina

St Peter Island

Franklin Islands

*Streaky
Bay*

MOUNT
KAPUTAR

NEW ENGLAND

Grafton

NEW
SOUTH
WALES

Narrabri

Dorrigo

*GREAT
AUSTRALIAN
BIGHT*

Nambucca Heads

WARRUMBUNGLES

WERRIKIMBE
NATIONAL PARK

EYRE
PENINSULA

Lord Howe Island

Coffin Bay

Reevesby
Island

ADELAIDE

Murray River

Mildura

Manning River

Lachlan River

Bathurst

HUNTER
VALLEY

BLUE MTNS

Gosford

West Point

*Gulf
St Vincent*

West Wyalong

Kangaroo Island

Murrumbidgee River

SYDNEY

The Pages

RIVERINA

Canberra

*Jervis
Bay*

VICTORIA

SNOWY MTNS

Narooma

Bermagui

Beachport

GRAMPIANS

VICTORIAN
ALPS

Snowy River

Eden

Hamilton

Ballarat

Geelong

MELBOURNE

DANDENONG
RANGES

GIPPSLAND

Philip
Island

NINETY MILE BEACH

King Island

BASS STRAIT

*Furneaux
Group*

ASBESTOS RANGE
NATIONAL PARK

Gladstone

CRADLE MOUNTAIN LAKE ST CLAIR
NATIONAL PARK

MOUNT
WILLIAM
NATIONAL
PARK

*Macquarie
Harbour*

WALLS OF
JERUSALEM
NATIONAL PARK

TASMANIA

Hobart

*Port
Davey*

Cygnet

TASMANIAN SEA

royal albatross

broadbill swordfish

right whale

15

seas, which are also rich in the plankton that feed the great baleen whales. Vast shoals of small fishes such as pilchards provide food for seals and sea birds.

In the shallower inshore habitats, the dugong grazes on seagrass beds, and salt-water crocodiles patrol the northern waters and estuaries, which are often fringed by mangrove swamps that form valuable animal habitats. Many invertebrates, fishes, reptiles and birds (such as the mangrove kingfisher) live exclusively in mangroves, where shel-tered shallow waters act as nurseries for the juveniles of many fish species and crustaceans such as prawns.

The pools, ledges, boulders and seaweeds of the rocky shores are habitats for sea snails, sea stars and sea urchins, worms, sponges, sea anemones, crustaceans and fishes. On open sandy beaches, spaces between sand grains give shelter to a variety of creatures, such as beach worms and pipis. However, many of these creatures are so little known that they have no common names.

Freshwater environments

Water is essential to all living things. Freshwater occurs in greatly varying quan-tities depending on rainfall. It forms lakes, rivers and streams, which might be perma-nent in areas of higher rainfall but which are usually ephemeral, or temporary, in the more arid regions where many animals become apparent only after rain. When conditions are dry, the shield-shrimp's eggs are scattered by the wind, but when it rains they hatch in puddles and develop rapidly to mate and lay more eggs before the water dries up. Desert burrowing frogs and freshwater crabs enter a state of suspended animation underground when watercourses dry up, and it may be years before fresh rains awaken them to feed, breed and renew the cycle.

In the desert around Alice Springs are waterholes where black-fronted dotterels pick among the pebbles for food, dragonflies dart above the shoreline vegetation and, in the evenings, cave bats flutter above the water and rock-wallabies emerge from boulder piles to graze and drink. In the semi-arid zones, springs sustain species of snails and fresh-water fishes, with some being found nowhere other than the shallow spring waters.

In arid regions, lakes may be very salty, so only a few aquatic animals can survive; a crustacean called the brine shrimp is one of these. However, when there is sufficient rain to fill the lakes, fishes, crustaceans, worms and other animals quickly breed and form food for millions of water birds.

Streams that start off in mountains, rush through gullies to form rivers that might flow through rainforests, tall forests or low wood-lands and eventually to the sea.

Mountains

The Snowy Mountains are Australia's only truly alpine area, where animals must survive in snow cover for several months of the year.

SHRUBLAND is one of the most extensive types of vegetation in Australia. It includes small areas of coastal heathland and vast regions of saltbush and bluebush, with scattered, low eucalyptus trees or acacias.

TALL FORESTS are dominated by massive eucalypts in hilly areas of high rainfall near the coast. The canopy is thin, and low-growing plants thrive in the sunlight on the forest floor.

SPINIFEX OR HUMMOCK GRASSLANDS cover about a quarter of Australia. Annual rainfall is often less than 125 mm and hummock grasses are the mainstay of the ecological system.

Many invertebrate species of the high country are found nowhere else on the continent. Among the vertebrates, the best known are the black-and-yellow corroboree frog, found in marshlands above the tree-line and along creeks in the lower forests, and the dainty mountain pygmy-possum – the only mar-supial that hibernates. It was known only from fossils until a live animal was found at Mount Hotham in 1966. Since then, it has also been found living near Mount Kosciuszko.

Rainforests

Rainforests probably house the largest num-ber of species of land animals, particularly in the tropics. In the northern rainforests, cassowaries pick over the forest floor for fruits. Another fruit-eater, the wompoo pigeon, rarely alights on the ground. These forests are also home to many marsupials, including the striped possum and the green ringtail possum, which are found nowhere else. Tree-kangaroos clamber along branches

RAINFORESTS are scattered along the mountains of eastern Australia. Mosses and ferns abound in the dim light that filters through the dense canopy.

FORBLANDS are barren-looking stony deserts with a few scattered saltbushes but, when the rains come, many types of herbs germinate and blossom overnight.

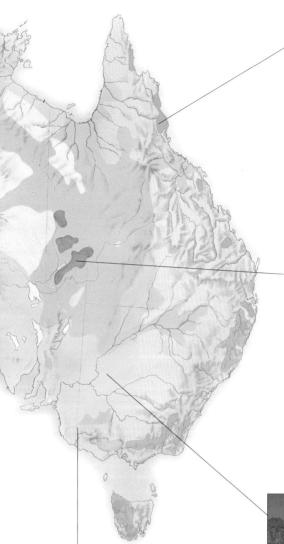

LOW WOODLANDS cover much of eastern Australia's near-coastal region. They are usually open and bright, with many shrubs and grasses growing beneath the trees.

TUSSOCK GRASSLANDS are open environments dominated by grass-like plants, often with exposed soil among the clumps. Saltbush, bluebush and acacias provide a little shade.

More widespread inhabitants of tall forests are koalas, common wombats and ringtail possums. Damp gullies in the forests of south-eastern Australia house superb lyre-birds. By day, the canopy may echo with the sound of gang-gangs cracking open seeds and fruits, while by night arboreal mammals and roosting birds fall prey to powerful owls.

Low woodlands

Low woodlands are home to a great variety of Australian animals. Some, like grey and red kangaroos, ringtail and brushtail possums and spotted grass frogs, have ranges that also extend into both the tall forests and the drier shrublands and grasslands of the interior. For others, such as quolls, yellow robins, yellow-footed marsupial mice and superb blue wrens, low woodland is their major home.

Semi arid and arid

The shrublands, an open habitat also known as scrub, is a generally harsher environment than forests and woodlands. It supports a surprising number of parrots, including the scarlet-breasted and mallee ringneck parrots, as well as birds that spend most of their time on the ground, such as the mallee fowl and the plains wanderers. The many varieties of insects that thrive in these conditions are an important part of the diet of lizards such as geckoes, which feed in and among the shrubs.

Tussock grasses are a feature of arid regions. Native rodents, such as Forrest's mouse and the long-haired rat, search for food among the clumps of tussocky grass while overhead, letter-winged kites scan the ground for unwary rodents or hare-wallabies.

Spinifex or hummock grasslands of the arid and semi-arid zones have more ant species than anywhere else in Australia. Spinifex birds, grasswrens and spinifex pigeons peck and flit among the clumps of spinifex, while the calls of chiming wedgebills sometimes fill the air. Desert rodents like hopping mice and the spinifex mouse, marsupials like the bilby and reptiles such as the thorny devil live among the clumps. Many of these animals have evolved burrowing or nocturnal lifestyles to avoid heat and water loss.

In this arid and semi-arid zone there are more ant species than anywhere else in Australia. Reptiles here have also diversified remarkably: there may be up to 120 species in just one area of this country – equal to the numbers found throughout the entire tropical east coast. These include the perentie, which can grow to 2.5 metres and emerges from rock crevices to feed on other reptiles, and insects, small mammals and birds.

Forblands is the name given to small but spectacular plant communities along the Queensland–South Australian border and in the Ashburton Range of Western Australia. These are the stony deserts. When the rains come, they burst into flower, and animals from surrounding shrublands and tussock grasslands move into the forblands to graze and feed on the seeds.

and the smallest of the macropods, the musky rat-kangaroo, forages on the forest floor or climbs with its unique grasping big toe.

The rainforests on the Queensland–New South Wales border support endangered pouched frogs – the males raise the young in pouches on their sides. Some insects are most diverse in rainforest areas: the forests around Cairns and the Queensland–New South Wales border house up to 140 butterfly species. Multitides of unnamed invertebrate species await discovery in the ferns and mosses that cloak the trees in the canopy and in the leaf litter beneath them.

Tall forests

Mammals of the tall forests include rare and endangered species, such as Leadbeaters possum in the Central Highlands of Victoria, the long-footed potoroo, found in east Gippsland and a tiny area of south-eastern New South Wales, and the numbat of Western Australia.

HOW ANIMALS EVOLVED

HOW ANIMALS EVOLVED

Australia's living animals, from the heavily armoured desert-dwelling thorny devil to the reclusive subterranean marsupial mole, are among the most distinctive in the world, mainly because of their long history of evolutionary change on a large island continent that became isolated from all other landmasses 45–35 million years ago. The fossil animals of Australia include many of the first, last and most fascinating examples of a wide range of creatures, from the oldest known life forms to Earth's largest dinosaurs.

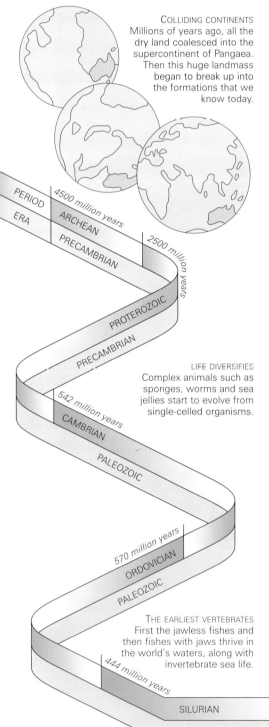

COLLIDING CONTINENTS
Millions of years ago, all the dry land coalesced into the supercontinent of Pangaea. Then this huge landmass began to break up into the formations that we know today.

LIFE DIVERSIFIES
Complex animals such as sponges, worms and sea jellies start to evolve from single-celled organisms.

THE EARLIEST VERTEBRATES
First the jawless fishes and then fishes with jaws thrive in the world's waters, along with invertebrate sea life.

While Australia was still part of the supercontinent of Gondwana, many of its creatures were closely related to those of other lands. But after separating from Antarctica, its land and freshwater animals parted company and kind with those of the rest of the world. Australia's fossil creatures include thousands of unique kinds, as well as many of the first, oldest and biggest examples in the world.

Charles Darwin and the origin of species

In 1836, HMS *Beagle* brought Charles Darwin to Australia. It was a critical time in Darwin's life: he had studied living and fossil animals of many lands and had discovered that some of the extinct animals of, for example South America, most closely resembled the living animals of that continent, rather than animals from somewhere else on Earth. He reasoned that this pattern could be explained if the creatures of South America had gradually changed from one generation to the next over long periods, so that the living animals of South America differed from – but still most closely resembled – ancestors from the same land. Today the idea seems obvious, but at the time it was instrumental in the development of Darwin's theory of the origin of species.

Darwin observed the same pattern in Australia. Extinct animals whose bones were being found in Wellington Caves, New South Wales, were clearly kangaroos, wombats and other marsupials that more closely resembled the living creatures of Australia than those of any other landmass. In this fossil record there were no bones of rhinoceroses, giraffes, buffaloes, elephants, badgers, cats or any of the animal groups typical of the fossil records of the northern continents. Living kangaroos, possums and wombats, Darwin reasoned, must be the evolutionary descendants of pre-existing creatures known only from Australia.

Darwin's basic notions still provide the best explanation for the diversity of life on Earth. When Darwin published *The Origin of Species* in 1859, the fossil record was not well known

and 'missing links' were the order of the day, but as the fossil record grew, many thousands of examples of evolutionary change were documented. Some of the most interesting of these examples came from Australia.

A self-checking process

Every time a new individual is born or an old one dies, the population it belongs to changes because the frequency of features in that population, from hair colour to tiny tooth detail, alters. Change of this kind is the grist for the evolutionary mill, but when biologists talk about evolution, most are describing how life originated and subsequently changed, or the fossil record and what it tells us about the history of life, or the dynamic processes by which new kinds of living creatures evolve from pre-existing kinds. This is the process Darwin described as 'the origin of species'.

The science of evolution is a body of many hypotheses that together make up the theory of evolution. Each hypothesis purports to be the best explanation for some aspect of the natural world, such as why kangaroos lick their forearms when they are hot or why some male carnivorous marsupials die after mating. But each hypothesis has to be tested and discarded if it fails the test; this is the self-checking process of science.

First, observations are made about the world. A hypothesis is then developed to explain the cause or origin of what is observed. It is tested and, if it survives the testing, is retested. If it does not withstand testing, the hypothesis is discarded or is modified and tested again. If it is discarded, a new

A GENTLE DEVIL
The thorny devil (*Moloch horridus*) is harmless, despite its savage-looking conical spines. It has adapted to desert existence by evolving a method of absorbing water through its skin.

The first amphibians evolve and start to populate the land.

PERIOD				
ERA				

4500 million years
ARCHEAN
PRECAMBRIAN

2500 million years
PROTEROZOIC
PRECAMBRIAN

542 million years
CAMBRIAN
PALEOZOIC

570 million years
ORDOVICIAN
PALEOZOIC

444 million years

SILURIAN	DEVONIAN	CARBONIFEROUS	PERMIAN
	416 million years	360 million years	299 million years

PALEOZOIC

HALF AS OLD AS TIME
The world's most ancient creatures are 3500 million-year-old bacteria that form dome-shaped stromatolites preserved as fossils. Stromatolites are still forming in favourable environments, such as Shark Bay, Western Australia.

hypothesis that better explains all the observations is developed and the whole process is repeated. Modern, dynamic evolutionary theory is made up of many thousands of hypotheses that have been subjected to this process.

There are four broad concepts involved in evolutionary theory. First, that living things produce more offspring than there are resources available to them. Thus they face a continual struggle for survival. Second, the individuals found within a population vary. Some of this variation is inherited; it reflects variations in genetic make-up or genotype. Third, the variants best adapted to local conditions are most likely to survive and to successfully reproduce themselves (often called 'survival of the fittest'). Fourth, to the extent that their adaptations are inheritable, these will be passed onto their offspring.

The first life forms
Laboratory experiments simulating the conditions on Earth 3500 million years ago have resulted in the spontaneous production of all the major classes of organic molecules, or building blocks that make up life. Such experiments have not yet produced a self-replicating living organism, but many of the key prerequisites have been achieved in a remarkably short time – and research goes on.

No one knows exactly how life first started, but these experiments suggest that, given the right conditions, the spontaneous origin of life is a highly probable event.

The geological record of Earth reinforces this conclusion. Earth's oldest sedimentary rocks, which formed in water, are 3800 million years old. By this time, Earth was cool enough for water to persist on its surface. A mere 300 million years later, bacteria appear in the fossil record. Simple cells evidently appeared very soon, once conditions were right for the evolution of life on Earth – a good reason for believing that Earth is unlikely to be the only planet in the universe that can sustain life.

How living things change
Once life had originated, it could change in several ways. The first is mutation – a simple error in the replication process of the genetic material. Some mutations are neutral: that is, they do not affect the organism's ability to function. Others can interfere with survival functions. For example, misshapen teeth may interfere with an animal's ability to eat, so that the individual dies or is seriously weakened, so the mutation is not passed on. Still others can be beneficial; for example, mutations in bacteria often make them resistant to antibiotics that previously killed them – a clear benefit to the bacteria, if not to the organisms they attack. Beneficial mutations often begin as neutral mutations that are unimportant when they first occur but become advantageous if aspects of the environment change. For example, a mutation that increases the density of fur may be of no consequence to animals living in mild climates, but if the climate cools it could become beneficial.

Life forms can also change, without involving mutations, by sexual reproduction, in which the genetic material of one individual is combined with the genetic material of another. Genetic variation in a species is markedly increased by this process. Further, if there has been a damaging mutation on one of the chromosomes, its failure to function properly can be corrected by the introduction of a normal chromosome during sexual exchange. This 'repair mechanism' may well be one of the main reasons why sexual reproduction developed in the first place.

What determines survival
Living creatures normally give birth to more young than can survive; for example, a female brown antechinus has eight offspring a year, but on average only two survive to breed the following year. 'Natural selection' was the term Charles Darwin used to describe the environmental factors that determine which young survive and reproduce themselves. There are four kinds of natural selection.

Random natural selection has nothing to do with the genetic 'fitness' of the individual; for example, a bushfire may consume a koala in one tree but miss another in the next tree. This kind of natural selection does not result in long-term change in the population.

Stabilising selection maintains the current form of the species by rejecting mutations that produce forms or behaviours outside a 'normal' range. An example of stabilising selection would be a mutation in the timing of sexual maturity of an insect that relies on a

The dinosaurs appear and rule Earth for 140 million years.

Australia's unique animal species are already recognisable.

Humans arrive in Australia.

245 million years	200 million years	145.6 million years	65 million years	2 million years
TRIASSIC	JURASSIC	CRETACEOUS	TERTIARY	QUATERNARY
MESOZOIC			CAINOZOIC	

FOOTPRINTS IN THE SANDS OF TIME

Some traces of dinosaur life in Australia suggest that our continent may once have been the home of some of the largest dinosaurs in the world. Near Broome in Western Australia, an oddly shaped rockpool in Cretaceous sandstone is believed to be the print of an enormous carnivorous dinosaur that planted its feet here 130 million years ago.

food source that is available only at a specific time of the year. Individuals that mature sexually outside that time will fail to raise young that would perpetuate the mutation.

Directional selection changes the features of a population in one direction. For example, if one lot of rainbow bee-eaters were inclined to lay their eggs in nests in tree hollows while others were inclined to lay them in holes in the ground, an increase in the abundance of a tree snake that hunted prey in tree hollows would probably lead to an increase in the percentage of rainbow bee-eaters that nested in holes in the ground. Another fascinating example is the peppered moth of Europe: the colour mutations of this moth in the eighteenth and nineteenth centuries were a direct response to the increased levels of soot produced by new manufacturing industries during and after the Industrial Revolution.

Diversifying selection divides one form or behaviour into two. An example would be a possum that has two kinds of food available to it, plant sap and leaves. Individual possums with mutations that produce thick lower incisor teeth with pointed ends might be favourably selected because of their superior ability to gouge wounds in the tree's wood. At the same time, individuals that produced slightly flatter and sharper incisors might be favourably selected because of their superior ability to crop leaves. Continued selection

along these lines could lead to the evolution of two distinct populations of possums with different dental characteristics and different feeding behaviours.

Where new species come from

Species are groups of individuals that can breed with each other but not with members of other species. For example, the dingo, the wolf and all domestic dogs belong to the species *Canis lupus* because they can interbreed. Conversely, the western ringtail possum (*Pseudocheirus occidentalis*), though very similar to the common ringtail possum (*P. peregrinus*) and until recently thought to be the same species, is now known to be reproductively isolated. Fossil species are recognised as different if they exhibit physical differences comparable to those that distinguish living species. New species can arise in several ways, all involving some form of reproductive isolation of part of an ancestral population.

A group can become isolated from its ancestral population if a geographic barrier, such as a river, develops inside the range of the population. Over time, unique mutations can accumulate in the two populations, so that even if they are reunited they will not be able to interbreed. This process was probably the origin of many species pairs in Australia, such as the eastern grey kangaroo (*Macropus giganteus*) and the western grey kangaroo (*M. fuliginosus*). Presumably an ancestral species split into two populations when large deserts developed in South Australia, and the two groups mutated so differently that they are now reproductively isolated, even though they overlap in western New South Wales.

New species can also originate without geographic isolation. For example, cell division may accidentally double or even treble the number of chromosomes, and any individuals with this condition are instantly isolated reproductively from all others except similarly mutated individuals. Almost half of modern flowering plants and many worms,

crustaceans, insects, molluscs, fishes and amphibians speciated in this way.

Another form of speciation without geographic isolation is exemplified in the North American apple maggot fly (*Rhagoletis pomonella*). This species raised its young in hawthorn fruits, which ripened between early September and early November, so any flies that matured sexually outside this period failed to reproduce. But in 1865, about a century after apples were introduced into North America, apple maggot fly larvae were found in apples, which begin to ripen in North America in late July. Flies that matured early suddenly had a new food source. In the ensuing century, the ancestral apple maggot fly divided into two kinds, a hawthorn specialist and an apple specialist; over a mere hundred years, one species had evolved into two.

The ever-changing web of life

Studies of life from molecular biology to anatomy have confirmed the evolutionary web that binds all living things together. The fossil record provides evidence of many 'missing links' between living branches, as well as evidence of extinct branches.

If we could view life in its four dimensions (length, width, height and time), the physical connections between all living things, along the time dimension, would be clear. 'Life' is one creature, which has been growing and changing shape through space and time for 3500 million years. Like a colossal amoeba, it continually reshapes itself in response to changes in the environments it occupies. While bits of it stretch back into the past, other bits push into the future. This concept is called the four-dimensional bioblob of life.

A CONTROVERSIAL MARSUPIAL
Marsupial moles are placed in their own order and family of marsupial mammals. Their ancestry goes back 50 million years or more. It was only recently discovered there are two species, not just one. Pictured is *Notoryctes typhlops*.

THE FIRST ANIMALS

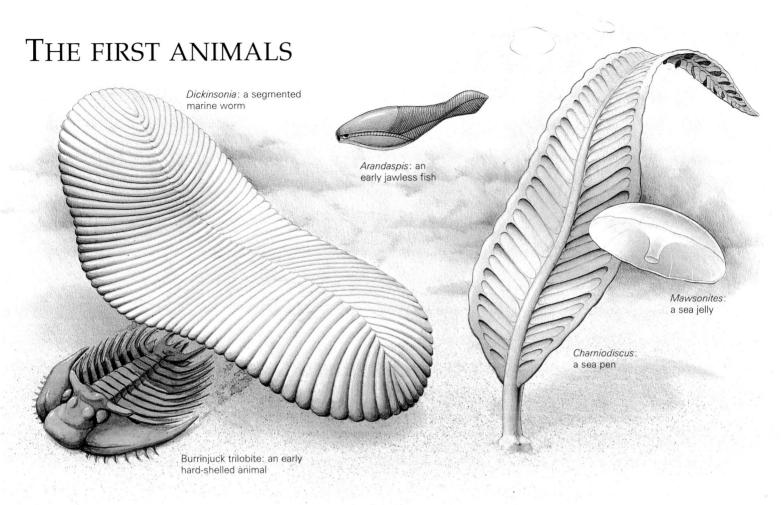

Dickinsonia: a segmented marine worm

Arandaspis: an early jawless fish

Mawsonites: a sea jelly

Charniodiscus: a sea pen

Burrinjuck trilobite: an early hard-shelled animal

PRECAMBRIAN TIME began with the formation of the Earth about 4500 million years ago and ended 544 million years ago. Scientists divide the Precambrian era into the Archean period, during which the solar system formed and the Earth's crust and atmosphere developed, and the Proterozoic period, which saw the evolution of multi-cellular organisms. The Paleozoic era encompassed the Cambrian, Ordovician, Silurian, Devonian, Carboniferous and Permian periods, during which fishes multiplied in the seas and fresh waters and insects, amphibians and reptiles began to colonise the land. The Mesozoic era spanned the Triassic, Jurassic and Cretaceous periods, and witnessed the rule of the dinosaurs. The Cainozoic era, during which mammals diversified and took over the dominant role of the dinosaurs, is divided into a Tertiary period (the Paleocene, Eocene, Oligocene, Miocene and Pliocene epochs) and a Quaternary period (the Pleistocene and Holocene epochs).

Fossil treasures of South Australia
Fossil traces of animals from the Ural Mountains in Asia may be as much as a thousand million years old, but no animals of this age are known from Australia. Before the evolution of hard parts (external and internal skeletons), soft-bodied animals were rarely preserved as fossils, so the soft-bodied animals preserved in the 570 million-year-old

Precambrian sandstones of Ediacara in South Australia are very special. Ediacaran-type fossils are now known from other areas of the world, including Namibia, Newfoundland and Byelorussia.

Among the fossil treasures of Ediacara, *Inaria* appears to have been a sea anemone (an anthozoan) and, if so, it is the world's oldest known example. *Tribrachidium* may have been a primitive sea jelly, though it has also been interpreted as a forerunner of the echinoderms (the spiny-skinned group that includes the sea stars and the sea urchins). Because of its three curved lobes, *Tribrachidium* is sometimes called a trilobozoan. *Mawsonites* was a much larger sea jelly, 10–12.5 cm in diameter. *Charniodiscus* was a sea pen that was rooted by its base into the sandy sea floor and waved like a leaf in the current; the Ediacaran specimen is the earliest record for this group. *Arkuna*, a small, disc-like animal with five-rayed symmetry, appears to be the world's oldest echinoderm. *Dickinsonia* was a segmented water-dwelling worm that swam along slowly, undulating like a wide banner in a wave-like up-and-down pattern. *Parvancorina*, a small creature 2 cm long that looked rather like a horseshoe crab, may have been a forerunner of the crustaceans. *Precambridium*, a small and mysterious arthropod-like creature, may have been related (and possibly ancestral) to the trilobites of the Paleozoic era.

LATE PRECAMBRIAN TO DEVONIAN: 570–410 MILLION YEARS AGO

Ediacara, a Precambrian fossil site in the Flinders Ranges of South Australia, was once covered by a shallow sea. It has yielded many fossils of soft-bodied Precambrian animals dated to 570 million years. *Dickinsonia costata* was a wide, flattened, segmented crawling or swimming worm about 7 cm long. *Charniodiscus arboreus* was a sea pen 30 cm long; Ediacara has the earliest record for this group. *Mawsonites spriggi* was a large sea jelly; like a modern sea jelly, it propelled itself through the water with rhythmic pulses of its translucent bell, which was marked by radial lobes.

At Mount Watt in the Northern Territory, Ordovician fossils dated 470 million years old include *Arandaspis prionotolepis*, an early bony-skinned jawless fish that probably scavenged its food from the floor of a shallow inland sea.

Trilobites were abundant, diverse marine organisms living from Cambrian to Silurian times (520–410 million years ago). They had a hard external skeleton with a head shield, a flexible thorax comprised of many narrow segments and a small tail shield. *Leonaspis*, from early Devonian rocks (410 million years old) in Burrinjuck, NSW, was very spiny.

WATERS TEEMING WITH LIFE

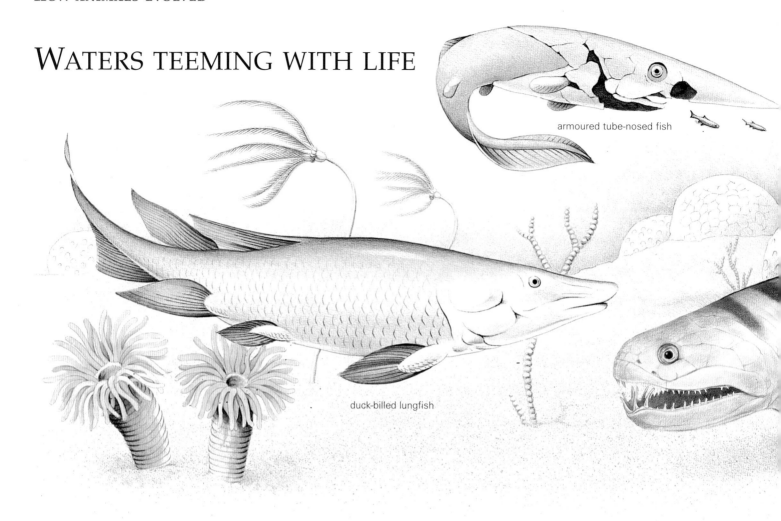

armoured tube-nosed fish

duck-billed lungfish

ROCKS 544–245 MILLION YEARS OLD were formed in the Paleozoic era. The beginning of this era was marked all around the world by a rapid increase in hard-shelled animals such as bivalves, snails, brachiopods, arthropods, echinoderms and corals – groups that are still common today. There were also many other less familiar groups of invertebrates, including the predatory, squid-like nautiloids, the trilobites, the net-like graptolites and the mysterious conodonts, which appear to be the earliest chordates (animals with a nerve chord).

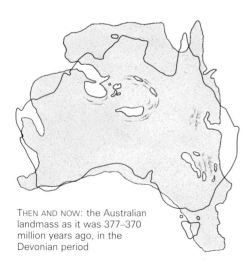

One of the most famous early Paleozoic sites in the world is the Cambrian Burgess Shale of Canada (about 530 million years old), a World Heritage fossil site, where marine creatures of astonishing diversity have been preserved. This period in Earth's history appears to mark a high point in the evolutionary diversity of animals.

Although less well known, a comparably aged deposit on Kangaroo Island, off the coast of South Australia, has yielded some of the same kinds of bizarre creatures, including *Anomalocaris*, a ferocious predatory arthropod without clear relationships to other groups. Most still surviving groups, or phyla, of invertebrates had made an appearance in Australia's inland seas by the end of Cambrian time (570 million years ago).

Tales of trilobites

Of all invertebrate fossils, the trilobites are among the most fascinating. After possibly evolving from one of the Precambrian arthropod-like creatures such as the Ediacaran *Precambridium*, they diversified rapidly to fill the rocks of the early Palaeozoic age. Some had huge eyes, others were blind; some burrowed, some swam, some floated; some scavenged, some were predators; some rolled up when threatened, others were protected by masses of spines; some were no bigger than a pinhead, others were over half a metre long. Trilobites began to decline in diversity and

abundance until they vanished at the end of the Paleozoic era, which was a time of widespread and severe extinctions in many groups. Among the best known Australian trilobites are those that are preserved in colourful millions in Cambrian rocks near Beetle Creek, Queensland, such as the 8 cm-long *Xystridura*.

Australia's famous fishes

Four kinds of extremely primitive fishes – among the world's oldest – from a deposit 470 million years old at Mount Watt in the Northern Territory were the first vertebrates of the Ordovician period to be found in the Southern Hemisphere. They included the bony-skinned jawless fish known as *Arandaspis*. Fossils of the world's oldest known shark-like fishes in early Ordovician rocks in the Amadeus Basin in the Northern Territory also provide the world's earliest record of jawed fishes.

Australian fishes from the Devonian period (416–360 million years ago) are famous worldwide because of their remarkable state of preservation. In particular, the amazingly diverse fishes from Gogo Station in the Kimberley region of Western Australia are among the best preserved in the world.

Many of Australia's ancient fishes belonged to groups that were once very widespread. *Groenlandaspis*, a Devonian freshwater fish, was first described from bony plates found

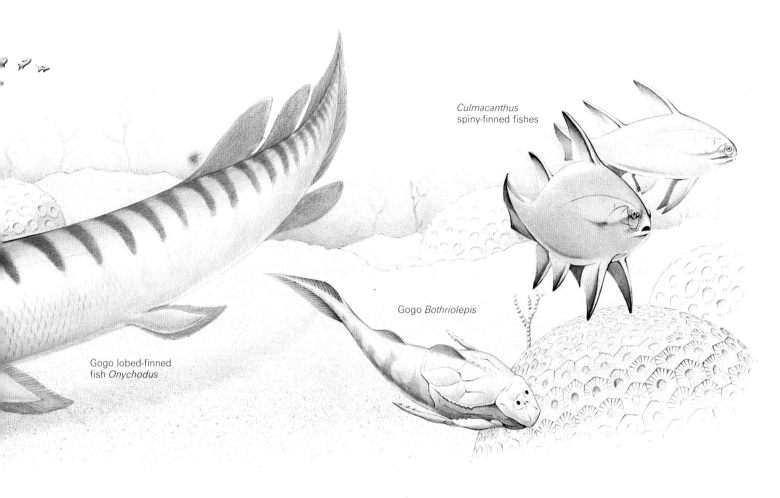

Culmacanthus
spiny-finned fishes

Gogo Bothriolepis

Gogo lobed-finned
fish Onychodus

in Greenland. It was later discovered in
Devonian sediments in Ireland, England,
Turkey, Iran, Antarctica, and finally Australia,
in many late Devonian localities in New
South Wales and Victoria.

Early expeditions onto dry land
Several other significant events in Paleozoic
animal evolution first took place in Australia.
What appears to be fossil bone from late
Cambrian deposits in the Georgina Basin,
Queensland, may represent the world's
first vertebrates (animals with backbones).

The creatures of the early Paleozoic
Cambrian and Ordovician periods were all
restricted to the seas but, by the late Silurian
(about 420 million years ago), plants, such
as Cooksonia in Australia, had begun to
invade the land. Roots broke down rock
into soil, freeing nutrients that at first
would have acted like pollutants when
washed into the sea, and hungry animals
soon followed the plants onto land.

A late Silurian trackway 420 million years
old from near Kalbarri, Western Australia,
proves that at least two kinds of arthropods
were making regular forays out of water onto
sandflats next to rivers. These trackways are
the oldest direct evidence in the world for the
invasion of land by animals. The first kind of
tracks were made by predatory eurypterids,
or 'sea scorpions', some of which reached
lengths of nearly a metre. The second may

have been made by euthycarcinoids, which
may have been the ancestors of insects.
Another 13 kinds of animals that left tracks
in this riverine sand are less easy to identify.

Australia's contribution to understanding
the origin of amphibians includes an early
Devonian sandstone trackway – possibly
400 million years old – with 23 prints, from
GlenIsla Homestead in Victoria. If the age is
correct, this is the world's earliest evidence
for the emergence of vertebrates from water
and the earliest evidence for amphibians –
the most primitive four-footed creatures.

The possibility that amphibians first
evolved in the Australian sector of Pangaea,
the global supercontinent of the time, has
received recent support from the discovery
of early freshwater amphibians from the
late Paleozoic Carboniferous period at
Ducabrook, in Queensland – the first
Carboniferous four-footed animals known
from the Southern Hemisphere.

The end of the Paleozoic era
The close of this era was marked by rapidly
changing climates, by fusion of the continents
into the giant supercontinent Pangaea and by
the most significant mass extinction event
in the history of Earth – the late Permian
extinction event. This occurred about 245
million years ago. It has been estimated that
80 per cent of Earth's sea creatures became
extinct during this crisis.

DEVONIAN: 410–370 MILLION YEARS AGO

By Devonian times the earliest amphibians
had begun to colonise the land, but animal
life was still most abundant in the seas and
fresh waters. On the sheltered side of a
Devonian reef, sponges and corals on the
sandy or muddy sea floor provided hiding
places, feeding stations and camouflage.

The duck-billed lungfish (Griphognathus
whitei) had a long snout like a duck's bill,
with which it probed the silty bottom for
food. It was heavy-bodied with large scales
and scaled, lobed, movable fins. The
armoured tube-nosed fish (Rolfosteus can-
ningensis) was a fast-moving predator that
swam around near the surface of the water
hunting for smaller fishes. The Gogo onychodus (Onychodus sp.) lurked in ambush
for smaller fishes, as do moray eels. Its jaw
was equipped with many long, sharp teeth
and was generously hinged for a wide gape.
The front part of the Gogo bothriolepis
(Bothriolepis sp.) was encased in bony
armour, but its back parts were free and
provided mobility. It propped itself up
on the sea floor with its armoured front
fins. The spiny-finned fish (Culmacanthus
species) was a deep-bodied fish with spiny
spikes on its dorsal and paired fins.

THE AGE OF GIANT REPTILES

Rapator, flesh-eating dinosaur

Minmi, armoured dinosaur

Steropodon, monotreme mammal

pliosaur

THEN AND NOW: the Australian landmass as it was 119–114 million years ago, in the late Cretaceous period

ROCKS BETWEEN THE AGES OF 245 and 65 million years belong to the period in Earth's history known as the Mesozoic era. The Mesozoic era dawned over a warm Earth whose continents were fused together in the large landmass known as Pangaea, and at this time Australia shared the same basic kinds of animals with all other landmasses, but very early in the Mesozoic era Pangaea began to break up. Even so, Australia remained attached to a large fragmenting southern landmass called Gondwana, which comprised Africa, India, South America and Antarctica.

During the Triassic period (between 245 and 208 million years ago), the land animals of Australia included a wide variety of very strange amphibians and reptiles. The early Triassic red mudstones of the Arcadia Formation at Rewan, Queensland, have yielded thousands of fossils, about 90 per cent of which represent complex-toothed amphibians (labyrinthodonts), such as *Parotosuchus*, which looked like a crocodile. There are also lungfish; metre-long predatory fishes such as *Saurichthys*; 15 cm-long reptiles distantly related to turtles; primitive lizard-like reptiles such as *Kadimakara*; the lizard-like *Kudnu*; the somewhat crocodile-like reptile *Kalisuchus*; and a mammal-like reptile from the group that later evolved into mammals.

In Australia, not many land animals of the Jurassic period (208–146 million years ago) are known. One of the few is *Rhoetosaurus*, a middle Jurassic dinosaur from Queensland. *Rhoetosaurus* was 7 metres long and weighed 20 tonnes. At 170 million years old, it is one of the world's oldest known sauropods.

The kingdom of the dinosaurs

Around the world, this was also the time when both the earliest mammals and the earliest dinosaurs evolved. Although both groups started out in the Triassic period, dinosaurs soon outstripped their furred mammalian competitors, and went on to dominate the land until the end of the era.

Australia's animals of the Cretaceous period (146–65 million years ago) are much better known than those of the Jurassic period. In the early Cretaceous period (146–97 million years ago), vertebrates living in and around the shallow inland bodies of water that divided Australia's dry land into three landmasses included huge reptiles as well as predatory fishes and giant ammonites.

One of the most extraordinary marine predators of all time was *Kronosaurus*, a short-necked pliosaur from marine rocks 120 million years old near Hughenden, Queensland. Over 13 metres long, with a tooth-filled head a quarter the length of its body, *Kronosaurus* was one of the largest and most ferocious marine reptiles known from anywhere in the world.

Most land animals at this time were dinosaurs. The largest presently known dinosaurs come from Argentinian rocks 100 million years old; *Argentinosaurus*, a plant-eater weighing 100 tonnes, was the largest animal known to have walked on land, and *Giganotosaurus*, a flesh-eater weighing 8 tonnes and measuring 12 metres, was one of the largest known land-dwelling carnivores. But these records may one day be dwarfed by Australian discoveries: some dinosaur footprints and trackways from early Cretaceous sandstone deposits in north-west Western Australia are larger than any known from anywhere else in the world.

Muttaburrasaurus,
bird-footed dinosaur

Austrosaurus,
sauropod
dinosaur

pterosaur

Dinosaurs may have dominated the early Cretaceous period, but there were also monotremes such as *Steropodon* and *Kollikodon*. Archaic birds, probably toothed, and winged pterosaurs flew overhead, while the last of the labyrinthodont amphibians clung to survival in the cold waters of Victoria. Buzzing about all of them were flying and crawling insects, the group of arthropods that benefited most spectacularly by the rise of flowering plants.

From early Cretaceous rocks near Inverloch, Victoria, an ankle bone of *Allosaurus*, a flesh-eater 5–6 metres long, shows that this group lived here at least 20 million years after all the world's other allosaurs became extinct, suggesting that the Australian part of Gondwana may have been a refuge for some groups.

Dinosaurs in the dark
Dinosaurs and other early Cretaceous vertebrates found in the sandstones of Dinosaur Cove, on the south coast of Victoria, offer some insights into how dinosaurs may have survived in very difficult conditions. Dinosaur Cove was within the Antarctic Circle at the time, so temperatures would have been low (averaging –5 to +5 C) and it would have been dark for half the year.

Fulgurotherium, a plant-eater 1–2 metres long, occurred at the same time in Lightning Ridge, New South Wales, suggesting that it may have migrated northward at the coldest times of the year. The chicken-sized, kangaroo-like *Leaellynasaura* had large eye sockets and optic lobes that may have enabled it to see in the near-dark.

A moment of terror
About 100 million years ago, in the early Cretaceous period, Lark Quarry, near Winton in Queensland, was the scene of a prehistoric drama. Many small plant-eating dinosaurs and several small meat-eaters were feeding on the edge of a mud flat when a large flesh-eating carnosaur bore down on them. Analysis of the 3300 tracks shows that the predator moved in at about 7 kilometres an hour. The plant-eaters fled at 20 kilometres an hour and the carnivores at 12 kilometres an hour. Some were so confused and terrified that they ran up behind, imprinting their tracks over those of the charging predator.

The end of the Mesozoic era
The Cretaceous period – and the Mesozoic era – probably ended when a giant meteor struck Earth, most likely somewhere near central America. This collision would have hurled so much dust into the atmosphere that the sun would have been obscured for months or even years, causing havoc in most of the world's ecosystems. During the ensuing mass extinction, ammonites, the giant marine reptiles, most of the dinosaurs and many other groups were rushed into extinction.

EARLY CRETACEOUS: 120 MILLION YEARS AGO

Conifers such as kauri pines dominated the landscape in this period and flowering plants started to appear. Much of central Australia was covered with shallow seas

Rapator (*Rapator ornitholestoides*) was a ferocious carnivorous dinosaur. The bird-footed dinosaur *Muttaburrasaurus langdoni*, a plant-eater, usually went on all fours but could raise itself on its hind legs to reach for branches. Austrosaurus (*Austrosaurus mackillopi*) was large and long-necked; it browsed on foliage plucked from the tops of trees. Minmi (*Minmi paravertebra*) had armoured plates in its skin and crocodile-like scutes on its back and flanks; despite its fierce appearance, it was a toothless plant-eater, cropping vegetation with its beak.

Running among the dinosaurs were cat-sized egg-laying monotremes such as *Steropodon galmani*, the ancestor of the platypus and the echidnas. The giant pliosaur *Kronosaurus queenslandicus* was a huge (over 13 metres long) marine predator with powerful jaws and a large, flat head. A fish-eating pterosaur tentatively named *Ornithocheirus* glided above the water surface on wings formed from webs of skin attached to its elongated fourth fingers.

The age of mammals

Riversleigh
Darcius

Silvabestius
with young

mihirung with chicks

tube-nosed bandicoot

THE CAINOZOIC ERA (65 million years ago to the present) is often referred to as the age of mammals. With the disappearance of nonflying dinosaurs, winged pterosaurs and giant marine reptiles, smaller vertebrates on all continents suddenly became the inheritors of the world.

Among the many animal groups that began the struggle for dominance were birds and mammals. Birds (which are dinosaurs that survived the late Cretaceous extinction event) filled the daytime skies, trees and water surfaces. Mammals dominated the night skies, overran the land and evolved into giant

THEN AND NOW: the Australian landmass as it was 20 million years ago, in the Miocene period

predators in the seas. Soon all the niches left empty at the end of the Cretaceous period were once more occupied.

Throughout the Cainozoic era, the climate of Australia went through cycles of climatic change from icehouse to greenhouse conditions and back again. This climatic cycle periodically suppressed and then encouraged animal diversity. The early Eocene period (about 56 million years ago), the early to middle Miocene period (23–14 million years ago) and the early Pliocene period (about 5 million years ago) were times of greenhouse conditions with wet, lush and diverse communities. At other times, including those of modern Australia, climates were cooler and drier and animal communities less diverse.

The mammals arrive

Australia's history of the rise of terrestrial animals in the early Cainozoic era is less well known than that of any other continent except Antarctica. As it is currently understood, the story of Australia's mammals began well before the end of the Mesozoic era with early Cretaceous monotremes – egg-laying mammals that today are unique to Australia.

Living monotremes (echidnas and the platypus) are famous among mammals for many reasons, including their ability to 'see' electricity and their habit of laying eggs. The fossil record of echidnas is sparse, but that of the platypus and platypus-like creatures

goes back 120 million years to the early Cretaceous deposits at Lightning Ridge, New South Wales, where cat-sized monotremes such as *Steropodon* coexisted with dinosaurs.

The discovery in 1972 of teeth of Australia's oldest platypus, the 24 million-year-old late Oligocene *Obdurodon*, in two areas of South Australia was followed by the discovery in 1985 of a complete skull of another kind of *Obdurodon* in sediments 17 million years old at a site at Riversleigh, Queensland.

In 1992 an early Paleocene platypus 63 million years old was discovered in Argentinian fossil deposits, showing that platypuses once existed in South America, and it seems likely that they will eventually be found in fossil deposits in Antarctica.

Marsupials arrived from South America by way of Antarctica some time between 70 and 55 million years ago, and rapidly came to dominate Australia's mammal communities.

Fascinating finds at Murgon

Though little is known about animal life on this continent 65–24 million years ago, fossil finds at Murgon, a site in Queensland, shed some light on the evolution of Australian animals in the early Cainozoic era.

At 55 million years old, the animals whose remains lie in the early Eocene clays of Murgon may well have been in direct communication with those of Antarctica, and Antarctic animals, in turn, with the animals

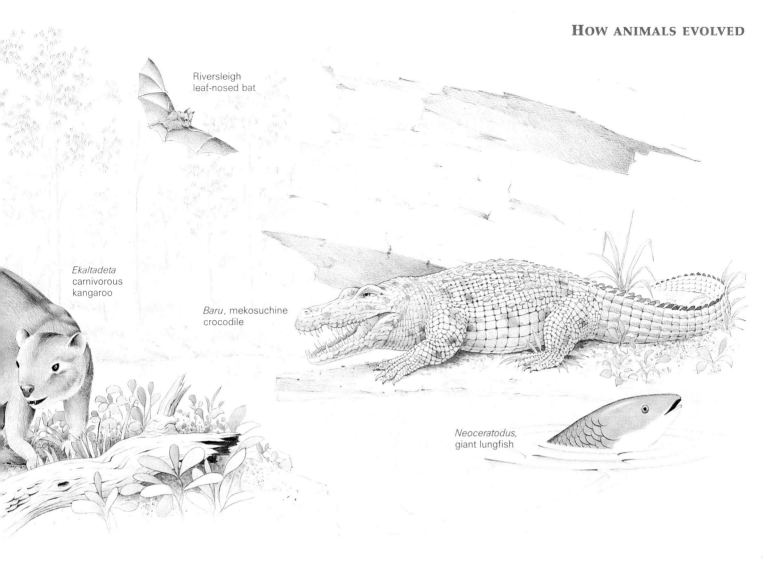

Riversleigh
leaf-nosed bat

Ekaltadeta
carnivorous
kangaroo

Baru, mekosuchine
crocodile

Neoceratodus,
giant lungfish

of South America. One of the first mammals discovered at Murgon, in 1983, was *Thylaco-tinga*, a bizarre group of marsupials that resembled others known from about the same time from Argentina and earlier from Peru.

Other finds at Murgon included crocodiles ancestral to a group once unique to Australia and New Caledonia; soft-shelled turtles, which no longer occur in Australia; madtsoid snakes, a group of primitive, nonvenomous constrictors that occurred in several regions of Gondwana; a possible salamander-like amphibian; frogs referable to modern genera; the world's oldest songbirds; an archaic insect-eating bat older than any other so far found in the Southern Hemisphere; a marsupial closely resembling others from the same time in Argentina and representing a group that molecular biologists had surmised were the original stock for Australia's marsupials; a primitive bandicoot (the only 'modern' mammal group recognised in the deposit); and several tiny insectivorous marsupials whose relationships to other groups are unclear.

Marsupials versus placental mammals
The most startling discovery of all at Murgon was *Tingamarra*, a placental mammal that resembles the contemporary condylarths of South America, North America and Eurasia.

Tingamarra was important because it had often been assumed that marsupials managed to dominate Australia only because early

terrestrial placental mammals failed to reach this continent. The presence of *Tingamarra* at Murgon, however, suggests that both groups were in Australia from the start, and that on this continent the marsupials outcompeted the early placental mammals.

Travelling north
Perhaps the biggest crisis faced by these early Australians took place under their feet. Before 45 million years ago, Australia was still directly connected with Antarctica. Antarctica at that time was a mild and vegetated continent that was in turn still attached to South America. This connection is reflected in the many South American-type creatures discovered in the Murgon clays.

When the link with Antarctica was severed, some time between 45 and 35 million years ago, Australia began a long phase – at least 20 million years – of evolutionary isolation as it drifted northward through the Indian Ocean. It was during this time that many of Australia's most distinctive and unusual creatures evolved.

As the Australian continent approached south-eastern Asia, about 15 million years ago, its 'prow' began to buckle and eventually became the highlands of New Guinea. This gave northern animal groups such as elapid snakes, goannas, rodents – and eventually humans – the opportunity to board the docking 'southern ark'.

**EARLY MIOCENE:
23–20 MILLION YEARS AGO**

Northern Australia at this time was covered with lush lowland rainforest in which lived the ancestors of Australia's distinctive modern vertebrate population.

The Riversleigh darcius (*Darcius* sp.) was possum-like, with a fluffy tail and thick fur, a short face and large forward-directed eyes. The tube-nosed bandicoot (not yet scientifically named) looked like its modern descendants but had a long, slender snout. The silvabestius (*Silvabestius johnnilandi*) had a backward-opening pouch and a short, tapering tail; it was sheep-sized and its fur resembled that of a kangaroo. The now-extinct mihirungs were large, heavily built, flightless birds, rather like an emu. The carnivorous kangaroo *Ekaltadeta ima* had hind legs shorter than those of modern kangaroos and it had not developed its tail as a balancing tool. The Riversleigh leaf-nosed bat (*Brachipposideros nooraleebus*) had an ornate, fleshy, horseshoe-shaped noseleaf. The mekosuchine crocodile (*Baru darrowi*) was heavy-bodied and very big (5–6 metres long) with a proportionately large head and deep snout. It had sharp, compressed teeth. The giant lungfish (*Neoceratodus gregoryi*) raised its head from the water to breathe air.

TOWARD TODAY'S ANIMALS

Palorchestes, marsupial 'tapir'

eastern long-beaked echidna

Megalania, giant goanna

Meiolania, Lord Howe Island horned turtle

B Y THE EARLY MIOCENE PERIOD, representatives of most of Australia's extant groups of vertebrate animals were living alongside representatives of older Gondwanan groups, but by the end of the Miocene period many of the early and middle Miocene groups had died out, leaving the field to the Pliocene and Pleistocene groups that are the clear forerunners of Australia's distinctive modern animals.

Remarkable reptiles

Most of Australia's prehistoric crocodiles belonged to a group known as mekosuchines. Some, such as the 8 metre *Pallimnarchus*, from the Pliocene and Pleistocene periods,

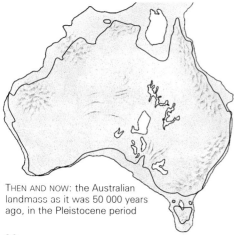

THEN AND NOW: the Australian landmass as it was 50 000 years ago, in the Pleistocene period

lived in the water and hunted from there, in much the same way as Australia's living crocodiles do today. Others hunted their prey on land: for example, *Quinkana* from the Pleistocene of Queensland, found at Bluff Downs, reached at least 3–4 metres in length.

Even stranger were the 1–2 metre Miocene forms from the Riversleigh site, and *Mekosuchus* from late Pleistocene deposits in New Caledonia. These forms seem to have been tree-climbing crocodiles that hunted birds and other tree-dwelling creatures.

Among the strangest of Australian fossil reptiles are the horned tortoises (meiolaniids), a group also known from Cretaceous and Eocene deposits in South America. Most had spiked tail clubs as well as horns. Of the Australian forms, the Lord Howe Island horned turtle (*Meiolania platyceps*) from Lord Howe Island beach deposits of the late Pleistocene period, almost 2 metres long, was the best known. The recently described early Miocene horned tortoise *Warkalania* from Riversleigh (20 million years old) was among the smallest known and had the smallest horns. A more primitive type named *Ninjemys* may have been twice the size of the Lord Howe Island species; *Ninjemys* had larger horns than *Warkalania*, and persisted into the Pleistocene period of Queensland.

A most exciting experience for a palaeontologist is to witness the 'resurrection' of an extinct species. The describer of the fossil

turtle *Emydura lavarackorum* first discovered and named the turtle from 80 cm fossil shells excavated from river gravels 30 000–20 000 years old at the Riversleigh site. The next year, while he was swimming in Lawn Hill Gorge in the same region of north-western Queensland, he found himself being stared at by a still-living *Emydura lavarackorum*. Recovering from the shock, he captured the turtle for a closer examination, which confirmed that the supposedly extinct species was indeed still alive and well.

Today, pythons are Australia's most common nonvenomous snakes, but before about 15 million years ago a very different and unrelated group of more massive constrictor snakes, the madtsoiids, far outnumbered the pythons. The last surviving madtsoiid, from 50 000 years ago, was the 5–6 metre *Wonambi* from Naracoorte in South Australia, where it appears to have survived in climates surprisingly cold for such a large reptile.

The oldest known Australian madtsoiids are the early Eocene forms from the Murgon site, which are closely related to Cretaceous to Eocene madtsoiids from South America, Africa and Madagascar.

Birds that could not fly

All the southern continents have produced large flightless birds, collectively known as ratites. The emu and cassowary of Australia, the kiwi of New Zealand, the

Thylacoleo, marsupial lion

short-faced kangaroos

giant constrictor snake

tiger quoll

ostrich of Africa and the rhea of South America still survive, but others, including the dromornithid ('thunder bird') of Australia, are extinct.

The 8 million-year-old late Miocene *Dromornis*, from Alcoota, Northern Territory, at a height of up to 3 metres and weighing more than 500 kilograms, may have been not only the largest of the ratites, but the largest – or at least the heaviest – bird in the world.

Flying mammals
One of the first of many fossil bats discovered in the limestone deposits of the Riversleigh site was the 24–15 million-year-old bat *Brachipposideros*. It was rather like the living orange horseshoe-bat (*Rhinonicteris aurantius*), but it bore just as close a resemblance to other kinds of *Brachipposideros* known from similar-aged deposits in France.

This overlap suggests that bats moved between Eurasia and Australia long before Australia collided with south-eastern Asia.

Flesh-eating kangaroos
Today's kangaroos are gentle plant-eaters, apart from some kinds that will occasionally eat eggs and small animals, but this was not always the case. Study of Pliocene and Pleistocene rat-kangaroos suggests that marks on their teeth were made by fragments of bone, not plant. The subsequent discovery and study of the slightly smaller Miocene

Ekaltadeta from Riversleigh, Queensland, suggest that it also was a carnivore.

Another recent discovery in Oligocene to Miocene sediments at the Riversleigh site has been called 'Fangaroo' because, although it was clearly a kangaroo that ate plants, it had enormous canine teeth that were quite unlike those of any other known kangaroo; it may have used these teeth to defend itself against flesh-eating kangaroos such as the contemporaneous *Ekaltadeta*.

Giants and dwarfs
A mysterious trend that characterised the animals of almost all continents during the Pleistocene period was gigantism: the evolution of giant representatives in many groups. Gigantism seemed to begin about 15 million years ago and culminated 50 000 years ago with the largest marsupials as well as huge lizards, crocodiles and snakes.

The reasons for this trend are not clear, nor are the reasons for what has been called post-Pleistocene dwarfing, which has taken place during the past 40 000 years. Although some giants, such as the marsupial lions, became extinct, others simply began to shrink, often in proportion to their absolute size; for example, the late Pleistocene giant grey kangaroo shrank by nearly 30 per cent to become the living eastern grey kangaroo, whereas the late Pleistocene devil shrank only about 15 per cent to become the modern Tasmanian Devil.

MAMMALS

MAMMALS EVOLVED FROM REPTILES some 220–180 million years ago, and have become the most successful group of animals on the planet. Mammals (class Mammalia) occur all over Australia and on many of its islands, but the greatest diversity of species is found in the coastal forests. The wet tropics of northern Queensland are particularly rich in mammalian life, but many species are also found in northern New South Wales and in the south-west of Western Australia. Some of the early mammal groups are now extinct, but three subclasses survive, and Australia and New Guinea share the distinction of being home to all three.

MIGHTY AND MINIATURE Land mammals range in size from diminutive marsupials and bats, some weighing as little as 3 grams, to the huge swamp buffalo, which can weigh as much as 1200 kg.

The subclass Prototheria consists of the monotremes – the platypus and the echidnas, both unique to Australasia. Alone among modern mammals, the platypus and echidnas lay eggs, their young entering the outside world by slitting the shell with a specialised egg-tooth. Members of the subclass Marsupialia, the marsupials, occur in the Americas but achieve their highest diversity in Australia, while members of the subclass Eutheria, the placental mammals, occur worldwide. About 88 per cent of Australia's land mammals are restricted to this continent.

The composition of the mammalian wildlife of Australia is distinctive, but it has not always been so. Fossil evidence demonstrates that monotremes have been present in Australia for over 100 million years, but one ancient form of platypus lived in South America some 61 million years ago. Marsupial fossils have been found in all the world's continents, including Antarctica; in fact, the oldest known marsupial fossils are from north-eastern China. At over 125 million years old, they are more than double the age of Australia's oldest marsupial fossils, which date back to 55 million years ago. At that time, bats first entered Australia, crossing a substantial ocean barrier to arrive in the north-west or in Cape York.

Waves of invasion

Australia's native rodents arrived here more recently than the bats, in two waves of invasion: the ancestors of the first wave island-hopped from South-East Asia about 6 million years ago, whereas the forebears of the second wave arrived less than a million years ago, probably by crossing a land bridge between Cape York Peninsula and New Guinea.

The dingo was brought to Australia by Asian sailors about 4000–3500 years ago, and over the past 200 years European settlers have introduced a further 25 placental mammal species.

Mammal characteristics

Mammals are very diverse, but all species produce milk to feed their young and have hair and a unique jaw structure. Unlike their reptile ancestors, mammals are warm-blooded – that is, internal metabolic processes keep their body temperature constant – and they have larger brains relative to body size.

Milk producers

The production of milk is known as lactation. Milk is a highly nutritious liquid that is the first source of food for the newborn. It is produced in mammary glands and in most species is expressed through the mother's nipples, but in the platypus and the echidnas it is secreted over the skin of the belly and drains to the young on tufts of hair. The number of nipples varies from two in koalas and wombats to 12 or 13 in small marsupials such as planigales.

Lactation allows young mammals to grow fast and they are relatively large at independence. The combined weight of a litter of antechinuses at weaning can be three times that of their mother, and suckling echidnas can increase their body weight by 20 per cent in less than two hours – though they may have to wait several days between feeds – because echidna milk is exceptionally rich, containing as much as 55 per cent solid food. Kangaroos can suckle two young of different ages at the same time: the nipple used by the newborn gives milk that is virtually free of fat, whereas the older joey sucks milk that contains 20 per cent fat.

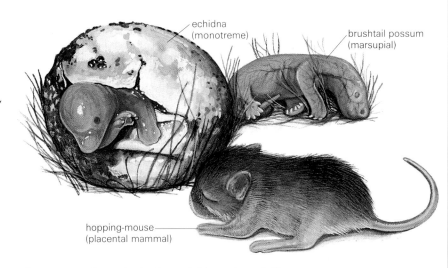

echidna
(monotreme)

brushtail possum
(marsupial)

hopping-mouse
(placental mammal)

Coats of fur

Hair is reduced on the sleek bodies of marine mammals, but on most land mammals it forms a dense fur that covers the body.

Hair is important in keeping mammals warm, but it has other functions too. The light hair of red kangaroos reflects sunlight, helping the animals to keep cool in the harsh outback. The long, dark fur of the water-rat traps oily secretions from the skin to make a waterproof barrier that keeps the animal dry while swimming. In echidnas the hairs on the back have been modified to form hard, sharp spines that repel predators. In many Australian mammals the body hair can come in a dazzling array of colours and patterns that give their owners a very distinctive appearance.

The better to eat you with

Unlike the lower jaw of its reptilian ancestors, which consisted of several bones, a mammal's lower jaw has only one main bone and is hinged to the skull in a unique way.

Mammals have developed three basic kinds of teeth for different functions. At the front of the mouth are the incisors, used for biting food or gnawing tough, fibrous material. The canines, behind the incisors, are for piercing or stabbing, and are especially well developed in carnivorous mammals. The cheek teeth, which are used for grinding up food before swallowing it, are usually of two types: the blunt grinding teeth, or molars, are right at the back, and the sharper premolars are just in front of them.

There are many variations on this basic pattern. Rodents, for instance, do not have canine teeth, and many do not have premolars. Beaked whales have only two or four teeth in the lower jaw and none in the upper, and the teeth of female beaked whales do not erupt. In the platypus, only the young have any teeth at all, and these soon fall out.

The arrangement of the teeth in a single mammal species is usually quite constant, but the numbers and arrangement of teeth vary considerably from species to species. These differences allow mammals to exploit a remarkably broad range of foods, from leaves and fruits to seeds, insects and even bones. In species that eat only soft foods or liquids, such as the honey possum, the teeth may be small or few.

The numbers of different kinds of teeth are described using a formula that is written as the number of teeth of each kind on one half of the upper jaw over the corresponding number in the lower jaw. For example, the dental formula for most rodents is: incisors 1/1, canines 0/0, premolars 0/0, molars 3/3. For the usually more toothy marsupials, the formula is: incisors 5/4, canines 1/1, premolars 3/3, molars 4/4.

The teeth of mammals are useful in classifying modern species and, because they fossilise, teeth can also provide important clues to the evolutionary history of mammals.

Devastation in the deserts

Australia has the worst record in the world for the loss of mammal species: since European settlement in 1788, some 24 species are known to have become extinct, and many others have vanished from large parts of their ranges.

Small to medium-sized mammals in the arid zone have been most seriously affected, mainly because of changes in the landscape brought about partly by land clearing for agriculture and partly by the abandonment of traditional Aboriginal burning patterns, which created a mosaic of resources needed by many native mammals. As well, introduced species, such as foxes and cats, prey upon small mammals, and others, such as rabbits, sheep and cattle, compete with them for food and habitat.

BRINGING UP BABY
Monotremes are almost embryonic on hatching from the egg, as are marsupials when they emerge from their mother's cloaca and climb into her pouch. Placental mammals are more highly developed at birth, but all mammals are dependent on their parents when they are born.

MARINE MAMMALS
Seals, which live in coastal waters and often haul themselves onto Australia's southern shores, are quite large mammals, but in deeper waters the blue whale dwarfs every mammal that has ever lived.

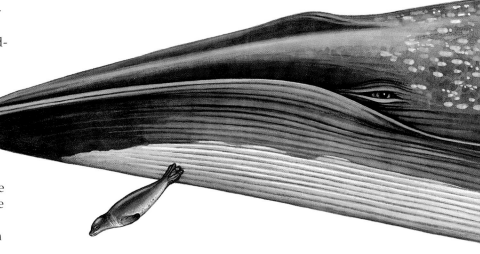

MONOTREMES

Monotremes (order Monotremata) are perhaps the oldest of the three subclasses of living mammals: monotremes, marsupials and eutherians or placental mammals. Up to five species survive – the platypus, the short-beaked echidna and up to three species of long-beaked echidna. Monotremes were once thought to be survivors of a group that developed from reptiles and evolved into marsupials and then into placental mammals. However, it is now widely accepted that the three main groups of modern mammals evolved independently from early reptile-like mammals.

FOSSIL RELATIVES
The present-day platypus is the only surviving member of its family, but fossils of at least four extinct platypus species have been found.

MILK PRODUCTION
Young monotremes lap milk that oozes from the ducts of a pair of mammary glands that open onto the mother's belly.

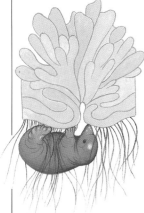

Monotremes are the only mammals that lay eggs and have no teats, though – like all other mammals – they do produce milk for their young. Instead of suckling from nipples, the young lap milk secreted from ducts opening onto two circular patches on the mother's belly. Monotreme eggs are soft-shelled and similar to reptile eggs. The mother incubates them for about ten days. Growth inside the egg is very limited and the young are undeveloped and totally dependent when they hatch.

Monotremata means 'with one hole', describing the opening – the cloaca – used to pass waste products and for reproductive functions: the male's penis protrudes from it during mating, and the female lays eggs via this channel. Marsupials, reptiles and birds also have a cloaca.

Despite these non-mammalian features, monotremes have most of the characteristics typical of mammals, including fur and the ability to maintain a constant body temperature by internal metabolic processes. Modern monotremes do not have whiskers, external ears or teeth, but these features may not have been missing in earlier monotremes:

young platypuses, for instance, do have teeth, but they quickly fall out. The structure of these teeth is distinctive, and has been important in identifying monotreme fossils.

Living monotremes
Experts continue to debate why so few monotreme species exist, when almost 300 marsupials and thousands of placental mammals survive. It was once thought that the answer related to their brain power.

In general, mammals have greater learning ability than other animals, and this is believed to have played an important part in their evolutionary success. Scientists once thought that it was inferior brain power that resulted in the extinction of most monotreme species, but this theory is no longer supported by those who study these animals.

The surviving monotremes have complex behaviour, are very adaptable, and may live for more than ten years. They are now thought to be at least as 'smart' as the carnivorous marsupials. They probably escaped extinction because their lifestyle did not bring them into serious competition with other mammals.

Fossil monotremes
Scientists have long suggested that monotremes are an ancient group of animals that must once have been much more diverse and widespread than they are today. Recent fossil discoveries have begun to confirm this hypothesis, and the truth about how extensive monotremes were, and the variety of forms they took, has started to emerge.

Until the mid 1980s there was no fossil evidence that the group existed earlier than about 20 million years ago. Then an opalised jaw fragment containing three molars from a platypus-like creature was found at Lightning Ridge, New South Wales. It was dated at 110 million years, when Australia was still linked to South America and Antarctica in the remnant of the supercontinent Gondwana. This meant that monotremes were on Earth at the same time as the dinosaurs – and about the same time as the oldest known placental and marsupial mammals, both of which date back to about 125 million years ago. In the 1990s a fossil tooth 61–63 million years old from an extinct platypus-like creature was found in southern Argentina, proving that monotremes once occurred outside Australia and New Guinea. In 1994, Lightning Ridge yielded the opalised jaw of another monotreme – about 110 million years old – that was quite unlike previous platypus-like fossils. It belonged to an unknown monotreme family, and was informally called 'hotcrossbunodon' because the teeth resembled hot cross buns!

Almost certainly there are many more exciting clues about ancient monotremes waiting to be found.

AN ADAPTABLE SURVIVOR
The short-beaked echidna (*Tachyglossus aculeatus*), one of four echidna species, occurs in Australia and New Guinea. It is the only native Australian mammal found throughout the continent.

PLATYPUS

When a dried platypus skin was sent to Britain in 1798, it was thought to be a hoax – a duck's bill and feet attached to a rabbit's body. But Sir Joseph Banks saw two more skins in 1800 and declared: '… suspicions … are now completely dissipated.'

Because few people are fortunate enough to see a platypus in the wild, there is a misconception that this shy and often nocturnal creature is rare, but the species is quite common, though it is regarded as vulnerable because it relies on healthy freshwater systems, which are threatened by human development and pollution.

Platypuses live in permanent fresh-water streams, rivers and lakes in eastern Australia. They can withstand conditions from the hot humidity of tropical rainforests to the snowy winters of high altitudes. They are found from far north Queensland to south-eastern South Australia and Tasmania. South Australia's platypus population has been badly depleted and reintroductions are being attempted there. Platypuses

RIVER-BANK BURROW
Platypuses lead mostly solitary lives. When not in the water, they rest in simple residential bur-rows dug into the banks of watercourses.

also occur naturally on King Island in Bass Strait, and have been intro-duced into Kangaroo Island.

Platypus home ranges overlap sig-nificantly, so that a relatively large number of these animals sometimes live along the same stretch of water.

Much of the platypus's body is covered with long, flattened guard hairs over a denser underfur that remains dry even when the creature is under water for long periods.

Aquatic dining
Platypuses eat insects, molluscs, crustaceans, and sometimes frogs. They store their catch in cheek pouches until they surface, and then float while they grind the food between the hard plates on their upper and lower jaws.

When submerged, a platypus gains information from its bill (see box, 'Bills of fare'). It also uses its bill, which is shaped like a duck's, to snap at prey and to sift small inver-tebrates from sediments. Unlike a duck's bill, however, the platypus's bill is pliable and very sensitive.

Looks and little ones
On average, males weigh 1.7 kg and are about 50 cm long. Females weigh 0.9 kg and are 43 cm long. Just above the heel of each hind leg, males have hollow poisonous spurs, about 1.5 cm long, that are connected to glands in the thighs. Because these glands become active when males reach maturity, and are largest during the breeding season, it is thought that males use their spurs as weapons when they fight over breeding territories and females.

Platypuses mate in water in late winter and spring. Males play no parental role. Females dig a nursery burrow up to 20 metres long, ending in a nesting chamber padded with damp plant matter. They lay up to three leathery eggs 17 mm long.

The female has no pouch, and it is thought that she lies on her back to incubate the eggs between her stom-ach and curled-up tail. The young hatch after about ten days and feed on milk oozing from two patches of skin on the mother's belly. Juveniles leave the burrow at four months.
Family: Ornithorhynchidae;
Scientific name: *Ornithorhynchus anatinus*

AQUATIC EFFICIENCY
The platypus feeds in water, where it spends about half its time. It can catch up to nearly half its body weight in prey in a single night.

BILLS OF FARE

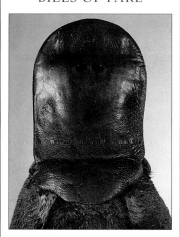

Platypuses often forage at night in murky water. They close their eyes and ears while they are submerged and locate prey with their bill, the skin of which contains electroreceptors. Muscle activity in all animals generates electric current, and the platypus's bill detects this electricity in such creatures as yabbies. The bill is also extremely sensitive to touch.

Similar electroreceptive appara-tus has been found at the tip of the snout of the short-beaked echidna (page 38). Ants and termites, the echidna's staple diet, are thought to emit weak electrical signals.

tail used as rudder and for fat storage

partially webbed hind feet for steering when swimming

webbed forefeet for swimming: membrane folds back when walking or digging

poisonous spur on mature males

body covered with dense, soft fur

ear and eye within groove that closes for diving

soft, touch-sensitive bill containing electroreceptors

DISTRIBUTION

SHORT-BEAKED
ECHIDNA

EGG LAYING

The female echidna lays
a single soft-shelled egg,
which is then rolled back
into an incubation pouch
formed by the contrac-
tion of muscles. The egg
hatches ten days later.

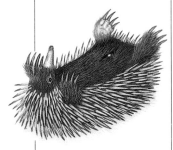

A NURSERY BURROW

This young short-beaked
echidna has begun to
grow prickles, so its
mother has stopped
carrying it in her pouch.
She digs a burrow for
her offspring and returns
every few days to feed it.

ECHIDNAS

Echidnas are readily recognised by
their long, beak-like snouts and the
sharp spines on the sides and backs
of their bodies. The short-beaked
echidna (*Tachyglossus aculeatus*), one
of the four living members of this
family, is found in Australia and New
Guinea. Its larger relatives, the long-
beaked echidnas (*Zaglossus* species)
are restricted to New Guinea, and
appear to eat mainly earthworms.
One species, *Z. bruijnii*, weighs
about 16 kg and can grow up to a
metre long. Several other long-beaked
echidna species, now extinct, were
probably widespread in Australia and
New Guinea up to 10 000 years ago.

The short-beaked echidna is the
only native Australian mammal
distributed throughout the continent.
It can survive in a diverse range of
habitats – from the hot, arid interior
to the chilly Australian Alps, where
it hibernates to survive the winter.

These creatures are reclusive but
quite common. There are five forms,
corresponding to different parts of
their range. Echidnas weigh 2–7 kg
and are 30–45 cm long. Their spines
are interspersed with fur, and in the
Tasmanian form the fur can be so
long that it masks the spines. Young
echidnas have nonvenomous spurs
on the inside of their hind feet, the
purpose of which is uncertain. Males
retain one or both spurs, and females
sometimes retain one. Echidnas have
short tails and no teeth.

Tongue twisters

Short-beaked echidnas feed mainly
on ants and termites by breaking
into their nests. An echidna's tongue
can protrude 18 cm beyond the end
of its snout, and flicks in and out up
to 100 times a minute. It can also
bend at the end in any direction.

PROTECTIVE PRICKLES

In echidnas, some of the dense covering of hair that characterises mammals
has been modified into an armour of
protective spines.

Not only insects adhere to the
tongue. Echidnas also swallow a lot
of dirt, which they excrete in their
droppings. They grind prey between
hard spines on the back of their
tongue and the roof of their mouth
before swallowing it. Echidnas are
unable to digest the tough external
skeletons of insects, so these are also
passed out in their droppings.

Persistent suitors

Echidnas are mostly solitary animals
that inhabit overlapping home
ranges, but they meet in winter
to breed. Sometimes trains of up to
ten males trudge nose-to-tail after
a mature female in a courtship that
can last for 36 days. When ready to
mate, the female crouches down flat
and her suitor or suitors begin digging beside her. Males compete in
head-to-head pushing contests
and vanquished animals leave. The
victor continues digging beside the
female, strokes her spines and tries
to lift her tail for mating in 'foreplay'
that may last for hours.

To mate, the male lies on his side
and extends his penis into the
female's cloaca as the pair push their
tails together. This coupling may last
up to three hours, after which the
animals go their separate ways.

In about four weeks, the female
lays a single egg into a simple pouch
on her abdomen. Some ten days
later, the young echidna, known as a
puggle, hatches. It is less than 1.3 cm

long and weighs about 0.3 grams.
Clinging onto hairs in the pouch, the
puggle laps up milk from the paired
mammary glands and grows at a
great rate, multiplying its body
weight by as much as 500 in 45 days.
When the puggle becomes too prickly
to carry, the mother digs a burrow in
which she leaves it, returning every
few days to give it a meal. The
young echidna emerges from the
burrow at about six months and is
weaned about four weeks later.

LICKING UP ANTS AND TERMITES

This short-beaked echidna is breaking
into an ants' nest with its front paws
and its snout. Echidnas capture their
prey on long, slender, sticky tongues.

Putting the prickles to work

While dingoes occasionally eat them
and goannas may take the young,
echidnas have no real enemies. On
open ground a threatened animal
often curls into a prickly ball, protecting its belly. On soft earth it may
flatten itself horizontally, dig down
with its front paws and, in a flurry
of soil, rapidly disappear.
Family: Tachyglossidae

MARSUPIALS

A marsupial (subclass Marsupialia) is born after quite a short pregnancy, but with its strong front limbs and sense of smell it finds its way from its mother's pelvic opening (cloaca) to her pouch, where it attaches itself to a teat and continues to grow. Most marsupials have pouches, but they are little developed in some and a few have none at all: in the numbat, for instance, the young simply dangle from the mother's teats.

FIRMLY ATTACHED
A month-old kangaroo shows how newborn marsupials grasp the teat in their mother's pouch. A swelling at the end of the teat expands inside the baby's mouth, and because the newborn's lips are joined with skin at the outer edges, the teat becomes wedged into place.

A young marsupial has a short time to develop in its mother's uterus compared with placental mammals, and so it is quite undeveloped when it is born. Marsupials therefore need a longer period of lactation than placental mammals and, during the newborn's development, the milk changes from a dilute fluid high in carbohydrate to a thick liquid high in fat. Even after leaving the pouch permanently, the young drink from the teat for a while.

The pouch provides the newborn with a continuous supply of milk and the warm, humid environment essential for its survival. Young marsupials cannot regulate their body temperature until they are totally furred, and do not leave their mother's pouch until they can generate their own body heat. Pouches are not unique to marsupials – echidnas, for example, also have them – but the pouch is one of the marsupial's most distinctive characteristics.

The varied lives of marsupials
Marsupials are found in terrestrial habitats of every kind. Some, such as the common brushtail possum, have learnt to live with humans and are widespread, but many others are extremely rare and are found only in remote refuges safe from competition and habitat degradation.

Some marsupials, such as the tiny planigales, are insectivorous. Many more, such as the bandicoots and many of the possums, are omnivorous, feeding on plants and animals. The herbivores include 50 living species of kangaroo, wallaby and rat-kangaroo, three wombat species, 12 leaf-eating possum species, the greater glider and the koala.

LIVING ON THE LAND
Marsupials live in burrows, on the ground or up in trees. They differ greatly in size: the smallest – the insect-eating planigale – weighs only 4 grams, while the grass-eating kangaroo weighs up to 80 kg.

All but two marsupial species, the musky rat-kangaroo and the numbat, are nocturnal, though on cold overcast days kangaroos and wombats may graze during daylight. Nocturnal habits minimise contact with day-active predators and are a way for desert species to avoid the intense daytime heat.

Marsupial evolution
Marsupials evolved in China, then moved to North America, but the original stock became extinct at least 100 million years ago. Before then some animals are thought to have 'rafted' their way to South America on floating vegetation, then to have crossed to Australia by way of Antarctica when these three continents formed part of the great continent of Gondwana. They then diversified into the unique fauna that exist today.

South America is still home to about a third of all living marsupials. Most of these are opossums living in trees. One, the Virginia opossum, has reinvaded North America. New Guinea has at least 60 marsupial species. Australia, with 159 species, has the majority of living marsupials.

European settlement has had a profound effect on Australia's marsupials. Ten species have become extinct, and nine species that formerly occurred over much of the mainland now survive only on a few offshore islands. Many others are threatened with extinction. Causes for the decline include competition from introduced herbivores, predation by introduced cats, foxes and dogs, and habitat destruction by farming, logging and urban development. Much current research is directed towards finding ways to reverse the decline in some of the most threatened marsupial species.

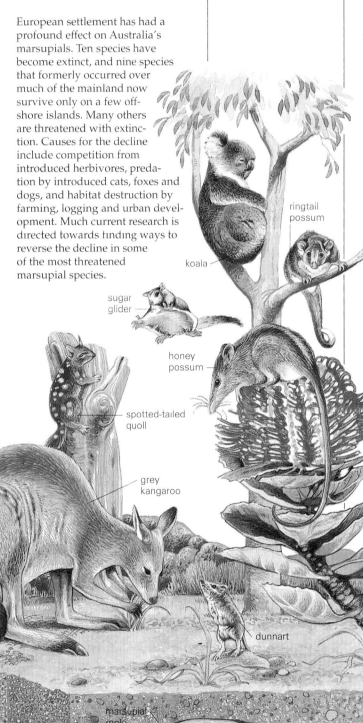

ringtail possum

koala

sugar glider

honey possum

spotted-tailed quoll

grey kangaroo

rock-wallaby

dunnart

wombat

marsupial mole

DISTRIBUTION

KOALA

LIVING ON LEAVES
Eucalypt leaves comprise the koala's entire diet, and only about 35 of Australia's 600 eucalypt species produce first-choice koala foliage. Species preferences change during the year, probably in response to subtle alterations in the chemical composition of the leaves.

KOALA

So unique is the koala that it has not only its own genus but its own family. With its forward-facing eyes, relatively high forehead and upright posture, this is one of Australia's best known marsupials. Wombats are its closest relatives. Both animals have backward-opening pouches.

Although there are fossil koalas in the south-western corner of Western Australia and in central and northern Australia, the koala's present distribution is confined to South Australia, Victoria, New South Wales and Queensland. Male koalas in Victoria average a weight of about 12 kg and a height of 78 cm; females weigh 8.5 kg and are 72 cm high. Koalas from the northern part of their range are smaller: Queensland males average 6.5 kg in weight and 70 cm in length, and females weigh about 5 kg and are 68 cm long. Queensland koalas are light grey, rather than the dark brown of the Victorian form, and have shorter fur and larger ears.

Koalas spend most of their life in trees. They sleep most of the day, usually in a fork in the upper third of the tree. They are solitary animals. Only rarely are two animals found in the same tree, except during mating or when a female is carrying a young koala. Koalas do not use nests or tree hollows for shelter but have

MOVING AMONG THE BRANCHES
Koalas are agile climbers, but because eucalypt woodlands have an open canopy, animals often have to descend to the ground to move from tree to tree.

an extremely well-insulated coat. Because of the absence of a den, a young animal is carried on its mother's back until it grows to about 2 kg in weight.

In a habitat of good quality, females produce one young koala each year. Mating occurs in early summer. After a one-month gestation period, the young koala is born and finds its way to the mother's pouch, where it attaches itself to a teat. The mother produces milk until the young koala is finally weaned in late spring – in fact, females are almost continually lactating. The young koala first pokes its head out of the pouch towards the end of winter. It starts to nibble the leaves its mother is feeding on, and this is how it learns which eucalypt leaves are best. At this time it also feeds on soft liquid faeces, called pap, produced by the mother. This probably inoculates its gut with the right bacteria to digest eucalypt leaves.

Fussy eaters
Koalas live on a highly specialised diet of eucalypt leaves wherever eucalypts grow in relatively undisturbed dry forests and woodlands. Koalas will starve rather than eat eucalypt leaves that are too high in tannins or essential oils, which are part of the tree's defence against being eaten by insects – or koalas. There have been reports of koalas in pine plantations, and they do eat pine needles, but only for short periods as they pass through the area.

Clearing and fragmentation of the koala's habitat for farming, forestry and urban sprawl have reduced this animal's distribution to a small fraction of what it was 200 years ago. The best koala habitat is found in river valleys and river-fed coastal plains, where quality soils yield nutrient-rich foliage only lightly laced with tannins and essential oils. Sadly, these areas are also attractive to farmers and urban developers. Much of the habitat presently occupied by koalas is substandard and can support only low numbers.

Koalas under stress
Much publicity has been given to the high incidence of infection by the bacteria-like organism *Chlamydia* in some koala populations.

Chlamydia infection (chlamydiosis) causes infertility in females and blindness in both sexes. It has been suggested that this disease may be the main threat facing koalas today, but most biologists now agree that chlamydiosis is the result of the more fundamental problem of habitat loss and fragmentation.

Fragmented habitat occurs around centres of human habitation. Koalas subjected to this tend to suffer from nutritional stress, making them susceptible to parasites and diseases, including chlamydiosis. The *Chlamydia* organism is probably present in most koala populations, but in the absence of stress there is an equilibrium and the koalas remain healthy. The wellbeing of wild koalas depends on conservation of remaining habitats and restoration of damaged habitats, rather than the development of vaccines.

Family: Phascolarctidae;
Scientific name: *Phascolarctos cinereus*

WOMBATS

All three species in this family are endemic to Australia. Although closely related to koalas, wombats are grazing animals rather than leaf-eaters. Their sturdy bodies and powerful limbs are adaptations to a burrowing habit. Tunnels any bigger than theirs would be in danger of collapsing in most soil types.

Common wombats typically build burrows in banks or hill slopes, leaving a mound of excavated earth just outside the entrance. The burrow usually descends for 1–5 metres and then the wombat builds a hump as a trap for stormwater and to keep the remainder of the burrow dry. Beyond the hump are one or more sleeping chambers, some lined with bark, twigs, leaves and bracken. Burrows often branch into several tunnels up to 30 metres in extent, with a number of entrances and chambers. The burrow network is occupied by one or two wombats, and each of the burrows is widely separated from the others.

The burrows of hairy-nosed wombats usually consist of loose clusters of extensive tunnels with up to 20 entrances. As many as ten wombats share this network.
Family: Vombatidae

COMMON WOMBAT

On the mainland, common wombats weigh about 30 kg and reach about a metre in length. In Tasmania, they are smaller, at about 20 kg in weight and 85 cm in length. Their bodies are rotund and powerful with a broad skull that they often employ as a battering ram to remove obstructions from the burrow.

◾ COMMON WOMBAT
Wombats are among the world's largest burrowers. Their compact bodies and considerable strength are suited to a life of digging and burrow dwelling.

Common wombats have been known to suffocate intruding dogs or dingoes by squeezing them against the burrow wall. Their tough skin helps them to survive dog bites, and within its burrow the wombat uses its bony lower back as a shield against attack. Common wombats are remarkably swift over moderate distances, and surprisingly flexible; adults 25 cm high at the shoulder can squeeze through 10 cm gaps.

The common wombat is found in south-eastern Australia, but its distribution is patchy, other than in Tasmania and the Australian Alps, where it is still widespread and common. Its habitat is varied, ranging from coastal forest to alpine woodland and grassland.

Wombats spend most of their life in the dark, either in their burrows during the day or out foraging at night. They have poor eyesight, and so must rely on smell and hearing to find food and avoid predators. They graze over large areas on grasses and sedges. Wombats easily uncover alpine grasses blanketed by snow in winter.

Wombats' dental arrangements are unique among marsupials. They have only two incisors on each jaw, and no canines. Both the incisors and the cheek teeth are rootless and continue to grow throughout the animal's life. One side of each molar is free of enamel and wears down much faster than the enamelled side, maintaining a sharp cutting edge for chewing tough plant material.

If food is plentiful, common wombats may breed throughout the year. Gestation lasts a month, and the bean-sized newborn climbs into the pouch, where it develops. At ten months it leaves the pouch but it stays with its mother for another eight to ten months before setting off to establish its own territory.
Scientific name: *Vombatus ursinus*

HAIRY-NOSED WOMBATS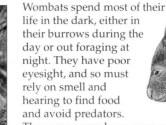

These wombats are distinguished from common wombats by their silky, grey-brown fur and by their large square nose covered with fine hairs. They also have longer ears.

The southern hairy-nosed wombat (*Lasiorhinus latifrons*) is confined to a few small areas in southern Australia, largely on the Nullarbor Plain. The northern hairy-nosed wombat (*L. krefftii*) is found only in Epping Forest National Park, an area of only 300 hectares in central Queensland. It is on the brink of extinction, with fewer than 100 animals remaining.

Both species were formerly found in southern Queensland and New South Wales but grazing stock has removed the grasses on which they feed, drastically reducing their range.
Scientific name: *Lasiorhinus* spp.

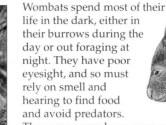 HAIRY-NOSED WOMBATS
The young southern hairy-nosed wombat (*Lasiorhinus latifrons*) stays with its mother for several months after leaving the pouch, and then heads out to establish a territory of its own.

POUCH LIFE
A female wombat's pouch faces backwards, so that the young are protected from flying soil when she is digging. Young wombats leave the pouch for good at ten months of age.

DISTRIBUTION

◾ COMMON WOMBAT

◾ SOUTHERN HAIRY-NOSED WOMBAT
◾ NORTHERN HAIRY-NOSED WOMBAT

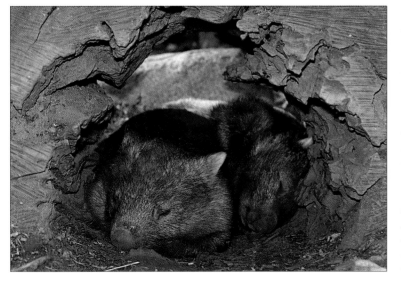

KANGAROOS AND OTHER MACROPODS

There are 41 living members of the macropod family in Australia; 39 are confined to this continent, but the remaining two also occur in New Guinea. Most species are known colloquially as kangaroos or wallabies, but wallaroos, quokkas and pademelons also belong to this family.

Getting around
The name macropod comes from two Greek words meaning 'big-footed'. Members of this family have long, muscular hind legs and large hind feet that enable them to bound along swiftly with their distinctive hopping motion. Elastic ligaments in their hind legs provide the energy for the hop. When they land, their back feet stretch their calf muscles and Achilles tendons, and the recoil from the stretch provides lift for the next hop. The animals hop from and land on two toes: an enlarged fourth toe and a smaller fifth toe. In the course of evolution the first toe has disappeared and the second and third have been modified into a tiny two-clawed toe for grooming.

For slow grazing, the larger macropods use five-footed (pentapedal) motion, supporting themselves on their front legs and tail as they bring their hind legs forward. Their relatively short, feeble front paws have five fingers of equal length, with which they grasp their food, handle their young and support their body while they move on all fours.

Grazing and browsing
Macropods are herbivores. Some, such as the larger kangaroos, graze in open grasslands; others graze and browse in a mixture of habitats; and the remainder browse on leaves in wet forest. As they munch, their cheek teeth wear down. In the larger grazing species, these are replaced with new teeth that grow at the back of their mouth and gradually move forward. At the front of their mouth a narrow arc of six upper incisors cuts the vegetation. This arc encloses a tough pad at the front of the palate, against which two forward-pointing lower incisors, set like knife blades back-to-back, hold the plant matter as it is torn off against the upper incisors. A gap between the incisors and cheek teeth allows the tongue to manipulate food.

The large macropods are usually sedentary and forage in groups. A group's composition, in terms of age and sex, changes sometimes several times a day. Its size can be affected by food and water supplies, the presence of predators or fire outbreaks. Groups of a hundred or more animals often form where food and water are plentiful.

SAFETY IN NUMBERS
Large macropods like these eastern grey kangaroos, forage in loose-knit groups of mixed age and sex for protection from predators such as dingoes.

The smaller species do not forage in groups. Unable to outrun predators, they are more likely to hide – rufous hare-wallabies among spinifex, rock-wallabies between boulders, bridled nailtail wallabies in hollow logs, and many species under bushes.

Male and female
Kangaroos live for 15–20 years, wallabies for 12–15 years. Male and female kangaroos and wallabies are weaned at the same size, but as they grow the sexes begin to differ in shape and size, especially the larger species. After four or five years, females grow little but males grow faster and for longer, developing

DESIGNER TEETH
A macropod uses its forward-pointing lower front teeth (incisors) to grasp plant matter and its top incisors to tear it off. Its cheek teeth chomp on the fodder and its tongue masticates a mouthful in the gap between the cheek teeth and the incisors.

upper incisors

cheek teeth *gap* *lower incisors*

BALANCING ACT
Whether loping quickly along, rearing to fight or gently grazing, the macropod relies on its powerfully muscled tail. When it moves quickly, it takes off from and lands on its toes, with its tail for balance. In a fighting stance, it supports itself on its tail and lashes out with its strong hind legs. To move slowly while grazing it uses its tail as a fifth limb.

calf muscle
Achilles tendon
heel
tibia
foot

Macropods use their calf muscles and Achilles tendons to power their energy-efficient hopping motion. Slow movement brings the tail into play as a fifth limb.

The front legs are level with the head and the back legs and tail push the animal forward.

The tail lifts and slides between the hind legs, forming a tripod with the front legs.

The back legs swing forward in a relaxed fashion and come to rest on either side of the front legs.

longer arms, broader shoulders, larger paws with stouter claws, more muscular arms, shoulders and neck, and tougher belly skin.

In small species, such as quokkas and many rock-wallabies, males are only slightly bigger than females.

Social bonds

All macropod species are polygamous and, apart from the tammar wallaby and the red-necked wallaby, most do not have regular breeding seasons. Males compete with each other to get close to a receptive female, who then mates with the most dominant male. In the larger macropod species, fights can last for half an hour and both males may even be killed. The stakes are high: the winner breeds with most of the females in the group, passing his genes on to the next generation. Smaller species lead more solitary lives in denser habitats, so finding females with which to mate may be a matter of knowledge and experience rather than physical prowess.

Most female kangaroos and wallabies can delay the development of a fertilised egg if they have a joey in their pouch or, in tammar wallabies, if the season is wrong. A month before a joey leaves the pouch, the development of the embryo is reactivated. A day or two before birth, the mother refuses to let the mature joey back into her pouch. She then gives birth to a tiny, hairless joey, 1–2 cm long, which crawls from her cloaca through her fur and into her pouch, where it attaches itself to one of her

four nipples. The newborn joey stays in the pouch for several months, emerging occasionally to exercise. The mother contracts her pouch muscles to prevent the joey from falling or climbing out.

Once outside the pouch, the joey suckles from a special elongated teat. Remarkably, this teat secretes milk suitable for the joey at foot, while the one that the pouch joey uses produces a different formula to satisfy its needs. As its mother forages, the joey follows her or takes cover nearby. Most young macropods are weaned one to five months after leaving the pouch.

Many mothers leave the group and forage alone with their young when it has just emerged from the pouch to avoid harassment from males and also to reduce competition for food. However, this puts the joey at greater risk from predators, and many juveniles are snatched by dingoes, foxes or wedge-tailed eagles. Surviving female joeys often rejoin the group with their mothers, but males disperse in search of new groups.

Species survival

Macropods have evolved a survival technique called embryonic diapause. During prolonged drought, the female's milk dries up, her pouch young dies and she stops suckling. However, she has a dormant embryo, which now begins to develop and is born. She then mates again. The new joey's need for milk is easily met, but if the drought continues the mother's milk fails again and that young also dies, to be replaced by the next. This cycle can be repeated

STAYING COOL
A red kangaroo licks its forearms in a typical gesture. The evaporating saliva draws heat from the tiny blood vessels below the skin to cool the animal's body.

until the female is so run down that she stops ovulating, but when the drought breaks she recovers and the joey currently in her pouch survives.

Macropods and men

The larger macropods have benefited from some human activities, such as tree clearing, provision of water and the suppression of dingoes, but some other species in this family have been driven to local or country-wide extinction by the clearing of vegetation, the destruction of habitat by introduced species such as grazing stock and rabbits, and the predatory activities of foxes and feral cats.
Family: Macropodidae

CARING FOR JOEY
A female red-necked wallaby and her offspring share a moment of affection. The bond between mother and young is not broken until the juvenile is mature enough to fend for itself.

PUGNACIOUS MALES
Two eastern grey kangaroos battle for supremacy. Most fights in the large kangaroo species are between young males in training or trying their luck with older ones, but fighting becomes a life-or-death affair when two mature males vie for the top position in the group.

KANGAROOS, WALLABIES AND WALLAROOS

This large group of macropods contains perhaps the most famous of Australia's native animals, the magnificent red kangaroo, which is the world's largest living marsupial and the most abundant kangaroo in Australia. At the other end of the scale, the group also contains the little parma wallaby, which weighs in at a mere 5–6 kg.
Scientific name: *Macropus* spp.

RED KANGAROO ■

Sometimes known as the marloo, the red kangaroo is restricted to the arid and semi-arid zones of Australia. It lives in most vegetated habitats, especially grasslands and shrub-lands mixed with mulga woodlands where creeks provide waterholes.

Males weigh more than 90 kg and reach a height of about 1.8 metres when sitting up on their haunches.

RED KANGAROO
This magnificent male red kangaroo is absorbed in grooming his chest. The startlingly bright staining on his upper body is caused by secretions of bacteria from skin glands, and is characteristic of large males of this species.

Females are considerably smaller, rarely reaching more than 35 kg in weight and 1.25 metres in height.

Red kangaroos have a distinctive black, drooping, moustache-like mark alongside a broad white patch on each side of their muzzle. Their legs, arms and underside are off-white, and the chest and throat of large males are often stained pink by bacteria-rich secretions from skin glands. Their paws and toes are dark coloured. Despite the name red kangaroo, the females are often called blue fliers. In fact, both sexes can be blue-grey, red or a blend of the two, although most females are blue-grey and most males are red.

These kangaroos prefer short green grass, but also thrive on herbs and nitre bushes (chenopod shrubs). Like other large kangaroos, they forage in the early morning and evening and during the night. They avoid high temperatures and direct sunlight, crouching or lying in the shade of trees or bushes wherever they can catch a breeze. They gener-ally forage in small groups, but in open country where both food and water are plentiful, groups may swell to hundreds of individuals.

Red kangaroos are found in regions where rainfall is low and unpredictable. They breed almost continuously, females mating hours or days after the birth of a joey. In good conditions a female may carry an embryo in delayed development and also have a pouch young and a young at foot that is still suckling. In prolonged drought, however, she may cease ovulating entirely.

GREY KANGAROOS
After leaving the pouch, the eastern grey joey spends eight months with its mother, suckling outside the pouch and becoming used to a diet of grass.

Red kangaroos usually occupy a home territory of about 100 hectares, with males ranging more widely than females. Fire or drought can drive them from their normal range in search of food, and they are some-times attracted to irrigated crops.

From the 1830s to the 1890s, first cattle and then sheep invaded the red kangaroo's range. Numbers of kangaroos declined rapidly, and by 1860 naturalists feared that the species would not survive without protection measures. Then, as range-land development for stock began, kangaroo numbers recovered, especially where dingoes had been eradicated to protect sheep. Uninten-tionally, sheep graziers gave red kangaroos short pasture on which to feed, plentiful watering points and freedom from predators. Threatened by their rising numbers, the graziers then shot and poisoned hundreds of thousands of kangaroos. After the introduction of myxomatosis in the late 1950s to control rabbits, com-mercial trappers hunted kangaroos instead of rabbits for their skins and for pet food. One to two million red kangaroos are now shot each year under strict government control.
Scientific name: *Macropus rufus*

GREY KANGAROOS ■

Until relatively recently, it was believed that there was only one species of grey kangaroo, but two are now recognised: the western grey (*Macropus fuliginosus*) and the eastern grey (*M. giganteus*). The western grey is browner, and is found predominantly in the drier country of the inland and Western Australia. The eastern species is a more uniform grey and frequents a wide variety of habitats, from high mountain forests to semi-arid rangelands in the eastern states. It is the only kangaroo species that is found in Tasmania, where it is considerably rarer than it is on the mainland.

The two species overlap to some extent in the semi-arid inland of western New South Wales and central Queensland, where the western grey is most abundant.

Grey kangaroos are second in size only to red kangaroos. Adult males weigh as much as 70 kg and, sitting on their haunches, are about 1.6 metres tall. Females are a good deal smaller – about 35 kg in weight and up to 1.2 metres tall. Males are slightly darker than females, and are much more muscular.

Female eastern greys may start breeding at 18 months but western greys are able to breed at 14 months, which allows them to respond more rapidly to drought-breaking rains. Mating generally occurs from September to March, with a single offspring born 30–36 days later. The tiny joey makes its way into the pouch, where it suckles for the next 300 days. The joey then stays with its mother for a further eight months, becoming independent at 18 months. Female eastern greys do not mate for six months after they have given birth – and then only if conditions are good – while female western greys will not mate until their previous joey is permanently out of the pouch.

■ WHIPTAIL WALLABY
A striking chocolate-brown face contrasting with a white chest gives this macropod its other common name, the pretty-faced wallaby.

Both grey kangaroo species are gregarious, feeding on grasses and herbs in small groups of two to ten. They generally rest in woodlands during the heat of the day, emerging at dusk to forage on adjacent pastures for up to 14 hours during winter.

Grey kangaroos can travel long distances in search of food. In times of drought they will eat almost any ground vegetation, but in good times they live inside their home ranges, which expand as the country becomes drier. In grazing areas, they often compete with sheep and cattle for forage and water.

Numbers of both species have increased since graziers cleared the land and made the country more drought-resistant: in 1981, it was estimated that there were 1.7 million western greys and 5 million eastern greys in Australia. Population numbers are still greatly influenced by rainfall in the rangelands, and crash during periods of droughts when breeding fails and animals starve. However, grey kangaroos generally last longer than sheep or cattle in these environments because they are better adapted to dry conditions.

In semi-arid and temperate areas, numbers of kangaroos are also influenced by the activities of predators; many juvenile kangaroos fall victim to foxes or wedge-tailed eagles, while dingo packs sometimes take on adults. Both grey kangaroo species may be shot – under licence – for harvesting or as pasture pests, and millions are culled each year.
Scientific name: *Macropus* spp.

WHIPTAIL WALLABY ■
The whiptail wallaby is a slender, long-tailed, long-limbed macropod. Its head, back and upper limbs are fawn-grey, and its lower limbs, its chest, its belly and the base of its undertail are white; the rest of its tail, feet and paws are dark. It has a striking chocolate-brown face mask, accentuated by a broad white stripe running from below its eyes to its muzzle. The tips and bases of its ears are dark brown with white in between. Males weigh 26 kg and are about 1.2 metres tall when sitting on their haunches; females weigh 15 kg and are about 85 cm tall.

Whiptail wallabies are found on the tropical and subtropical east coast, living in woodlands and forests with an open grassy understorey on hills with steep but not rocky slopes. They feed on grasses and are usually seen in small groups of two to ten, but sometimes as many as 50 will congregate.

Hunters used to target whiptails for their beautifully marked fur, and these animals are still shot, under licence, as pasture pests.
Scientific name: *Macropus parryi*

RED-NECKED WALLABY ■
The red-necked wallaby is common in the eucalypt forests of the east coast of mainland Australia and Tasmania. Although it is mostly grey, the rusty colour on its neck and sometimes its rump accounts for its common name. Males are larger than females, weighing 20 kg and reaching a height of 1 metre sitting on their haunches; females reach 14 kg in weight and 80 cm in height.

These wallabies are more solitary than larger kangaroos, and groups are less cohesive. Mothers and young also behave differently. Instead of staying at their mother's side during the first months out of the pouch, juveniles hide and feed near cover while their mothers feed and rest in more open spaces. Juveniles are still frequently taken by dingoes, foxes or eagles. Surviving females often remain in their mother's home range to breed at about 14 months, while males disperse at about 24 months.

Red-necked wallabies eat grasses and herbs, and occasionally leaves. Food availability influences breeding, but most females breed each year. The joey leaves the pouch after 280 days and is weaned within a year.

■ RED-NECKED WALLABY
This wallaby's range extends to the highlands of Tasmania, where winters are long and snow is widespread.

DISTRIBUTION

WHIPTAIL WALLABY

■ RED-NECKED WALLABY

■ PARMA WALLABY
The smallest member of the *Macropus* genus, parma wallabies are often preyed upon by foxes.

Land clearing since European settlement has improved conditions for these wallabies in some areas, as they can rest in forest remnants during the day and move out to feed in the open at nightfall. They cause minor damage to some commercial crops, but they are protected in all states and are secure throughout the major part of their range.
Scientific name: *Macropus rufogriseus*

PARMA WALLABY ■

The back fur of the parma wallaby, or white-throated wallaby, is a grizzled greyish fawn tipped with black, its neck and shoulders are washed with red, its throat is white, and its face is dark with a white stripe. Its paws, feet and slightly crested tail are all dark. Males weigh up to 6 kg and are about 55 cm tall when sitting on their haunches; females weigh 5 kg and are about 50 cm tall.

This wallaby was once found in wet eucalypt forests along the eastern escarpment of the Great Dividing Range in New South Wales, from the northern Bega district to the Clarence River catchment. Its range and habitats overlap those of the red-necked pademelon (page 50). South of Sydney, the parma wallaby has disappeared, but it is still widespread in the forests of Barrington Tops, in the Dorrigo district and in the Gibraltar Range in northern New South Wales.

Parma wallabies are solitary creatures that spend the day in wet forests, foraging at dusk and by night on grasses and herbs in clearings and along the forest edges. These small wallabies frequently fall prey to foxes and even to feral cats. Several radio-collared parma wallabies released from captivity in the Sydney region were killed within a few weeks by foxes.
Scientific name: *Macropus parma*

DISTRIBUTION

■ PARMA WALLABY
■ TAMMAR WALLABY

■ WESTERN BRUSH WALLABY
■ AGILE WALLABY

TAMMAR WALLABY

Most surviving populations of tammar wallabies live on islands, from the Houtman Abrolhos, off Western Australia, to Kangaroo Island, off South Australia. Two former South Australian mainland populations are extinct, and those left in Western Australia are found in remnant scrub. This wallaby's disappearance is due to the clearing of mallee and scrub and to predation by foxes and cats. On Kangaroo Island, settlers harvested the wallabies for skins, and they are still shot as pasture pests.

Kangaroo Island males weigh 7.5–10 kg and are about 70 cm tall when sitting on their haunches, while females average 5.5 kg and are about 55 cm tall. Both sexes have a salt-and-pepper, grey-brown back, with an indistinct dark stripe from their crown to their nose, a pale cheek stripe, an off-white belly, a russet tinge on their fore and hind limbs and along their sides, and long black eyelashes.

Tammar wallabies shelter in dense woody vegetation by day, foraging at night in grassy areas such as cleared pasture. Their diverse diet includes grasses, sedges, herbs and woody plants. On Western Australian islands, where there is no fresh water for much of the year, they survive by drinking seawater.

Tammars are strictly seasonal breeders, at least on Kangaroo Island. The young are born in late January and early February. They stay in the pouch for eight months, and continue to suckle at foot for a few more months. A female mates again a few days after giving birth.

■ AGILE WALLABY
These pretty wallabies have rather short ears and a 'Roman' nose with a high, prominent bridge.

The embryo begins to grow but then stops for ten months until the longest day of the year, 22 December – the summer solstice. It then attaches itself to the wall of the uterus and starts developing again, ready to be born in late January. Young females can mate at only nine or ten months old and while still suckling.
Scientific name: *Macropus eugenii*

WESTERN BRUSH WALLABY

The quick, graceful western brush wallaby is also called the black-gloved wallaby because the ends of its paws and feet are black, in contrast with its fawn lower limbs. The end of its long tail, the top of its head and the backs of its ears are also black, while the rest of its upper body is grey except for a pale face stripe. Males and females weigh about 8 kg and are about 65 cm tall when sitting on their haunches.

These wallabies prefer open forests and woodlands with a grassy understorey. They shelter by day and feed at night, usually in ones or twos. Once widespread and quite abundant in south-western Western Australia, their numbers have fallen as fox numbers have risen, and they are in need of protection. They are also threatened by land clearing.
Scientific name: *Macropus irma*

AGILE WALLABY ■

This is the most common macropod in Australia's wet tropics. Also known as the Kimberley wallaby, the sandy wallaby, the jungle wallaby, the grass wallaby and the river wallaby, it is especially abundant on the coastal flood plains of Arnhem Land.

In the wet season in Arnhem Land, floods drive agile wallabies off the coastal plains and back to the base of the escarpment, where grasses are sparse. As flooding subsides, they return to the plains to eat the freshly sprouting sedges and grasses. Despite these fluctuations in food supplies, agile wallabies breed all year. The young leaves the pouch at seven or eight months, and is weaned at ten months to a year. Females mature at a year old.

Males weigh up to 27 kg and are about 1.2 metres high when sitting on their haunches, while females weigh up to 15 kg and are about 85 cm high. Both sexes are a light sandy fawn, paler on the chest and belly, with a distinct pale hip stripe and a pale cheek stripe beneath a darker eye line. Males develop longer, more heavily muscled arms and broader shoulders.

■ BLACK-STRIPED WALLABY
All but gone from its former range in New South Wales, this wallaby is also disappearing in Queensland as ground cover is cleared to create cattle pasture.

Agile wallabies are commonly preyed upon by dingoes. They form groups of ten to several hundred, and where they are considered too numerous in pasture or sugar cane areas, they may be shot as pests.
Scientific name: *Macropus agilis*

BLACK-STRIPED WALLABY ■

Earlier this century, the black-striped or scrub wallaby was one of the most abundant wallabies of central and southern Queensland and northern New South Wales. It was particularly common in brigalow woodland, but also lived in eucalypt forests. Since then, tens of thousands have been snared and shot every year.

Both sexes are grey-brown, washed with russet on the shoulders and forearms, with an off-white belly, a white hip stripe, and a black stripe running from crown to rump. Large males have muscular shoulders, may weigh 20 kg and are about a metre tall when sitting on their haunches; the largest females weigh 7.5 kg and are little more than 65 cm tall.

Unlike most small wallabies, black-striped wallabies rest and forage in groups of up to a dozen. They spend the day lying in dusty scrapes under bushes or around a small tree, slipping away if disturbed. After dark they travel up to a kilometre to open country, where they forage within 300 metres of cover. They eat mainly grasses. They have a home range of about 90 hectares, but mostly live within an area of 10–15 hectares.
Scientific name: *Macropus dorsalis*

BLACK WALLAROO

Black wallaroos, or black kangaroos, are confined to central and western Arnhem Land. They are quite common within the woodlands, shrub cover and patches of monsoon forests on the Arnhem Land plateau. This solitary animal bounds up and down rocky escarpments with its short, powerful legs, and uses rocks and bushes as daytime shelters.

Although this is the smallest of the wallaroo species, males are still stocky, at 22 kg in weight and about a metre tall when sitting on their haunches. They are black or brown, tinged with russet. Females, weighing 13 kg or more and up to 80 cm tall, are pale grey or grey-brown, with dark paws, feet and tail tip.
Scientific name: *Macropus bernardus*

COMMON WALLAROO ■

The common wallaroo, called the euro in the inland and in Western Australia, is the most widespread macropod. Those in the eastern highlands have shaggy fur; males are purple-grey to black with a reddish black tail and females are silver-grey with a white underside and a cream tail. In the inland they

SURVIVING THE DRY

When drought hits an area, the first thing macropods do, if they can, is move to better foraging sites. Large species, such as the red kangaroo, are able to travel long distances to reach green growth, but smaller species are less mobile, so they extend their usually rather limited diet to include various other plants. All large kangaroos need to drink, and if they cannot travel to water they may dig for it in dry creek beds, as this common wallaroo has done. Smaller species can survive without drinking, obtaining all the moisture they need from their food. They are also able to retain water in their bodies by producing concentrated urine and dry faeces.

have shorter fur and are reddish above; females are paler than males.

Males are stocky, with muscular arms and shoulders. They may weigh as much as 58 kg and are about 1.6 metres tall when sitting on their haunches. Females do not exceed 25 kg and are about 1.2 metres tall.

Common wallaroos usually live in rocky places. They spend the day in caves or crouched against a boulder, emerging in the late afternoon to forage through the night. They eat mainly grasses and can survive on low-protein fodder such as spinifex.

Common wallaroos are widely shot, under licence, as pasture pests, but the remoteness of their habitat protects them from over-shooting.
Scientific name: *Macropus robustus*

ANTILOPINE WALLAROO

These wallaroos are most abundant in the grassy eucalypt woodlands of Australia's monsoonal north. Their habitats, diet and activity cycles are like those of red kangaroos (page 44).

Males are up to 49 kg in weight and are about 1.5 metres tall when sitting on their haunches; females weigh up to 20 kg and are about a metre tall. Both sexes are fawn on

■ COMMON WALLAROOS
In the cool of the evening these wallaroos come out to graze on grasses and shrubs, either alone or in twos or threes.

DISTRIBUTION

■ BLACK-STRIPED WALLABY

■ BLACK WALLAROO

■ COMMON WALLAROO

■ ANTILOPINE WALLAROO

DISTRIBUTION

■ LUMHOLTZ'S
TREE-KANGAROO

■ BENNETT'S
TREE-KANGAROO

the lower sides, grey on the upper back, shoulders and head, and have pale limbs and tail. They are less stocky than other wallaroos and their fur is less shaggy. They usually forage in groups of 6–20 individuals.

Antilopines are quite social. They rest in shade during the day and forage mainly on grasses at night. They live near water, and regularly visit waterholes in the dry season.

Scientific name: Macropus antilopinus

TREE-KANGAROOS

Kangaroos that spend most of their time in trees sound like a rural myth, but two arboreal species are found in the rainforests of north-eastern Australia and there are at least eight more species living in New Guinea. Tree-kangaroo fossils dating back several million years have been discovered as far south as central New South Wales and western Victoria, so these creatures were more widely distributed on the continent in the past.

Tree-kangaroos are found primarily in areas of rainforest. A few species inhabit the lowlands, but most prefer cool mountain forests, where they sleep and forage high in the canopy or browse on lower branches and vines. Males are almost always solitary, but females are often accompanied by a juvenile. Some species are almost entirely arboreal, but one New Guinea species spends a considerable amount of its time on the ground. All tree-kangaroos feed on leaves, and some consume fruits when they are available.

Compared with ground-living kangaroos, tree-kangaroos are squat and thickly furred, with sturdy, muscular forelegs. They use all four limbs to clamber along branches, and have strong, curved claws for gripping. They can leap from branch to branch and are able to jump to the ground from heights of more than 30 metres. They use their exceptionally long tail as a prop and for keeping their balance.

Tree-kangaroos weigh 6.5–17 kg and are 1.2–1.6 metres long; in some species the tail accounts for more than half the animal's length.

Scientific name: Dendrolagus spp.

LUMHOLTZ'S TREE-KANGAROO ■

Lumholtz's tree-kangaroo is among the smallest of the tree-kangaroos; it weighs 5–8 kg and its total length is no more than 1.3 metres. It has a cream belly, an ash-brown back and black hands, feet and face, and its tail darkens noticeably near the tip.

It is found in rainforests and rainforest fringes in Queensland's Atherton Tableland at altitudes of more than 800 metres, resting in the trees in a crouched sitting position during the day and foraging after dark. Occasionally it leaves the forest cover in order to raid crops.

This species is solitary, and males fight savagely if they are caged together. Females bear one young at a time; each remains in the pouch for about 230 days and then stays with its mother for about two years.

Although its distribution is limited, this tree-kangaroo may occur at high densities, even in small patches of rainforest. About 25 per cent of its distribution is inside national parks.

Scientific name: Dendrolagus lumholtzi

■ LUMHOLTZ'S TREE-KANGAROO
Tree-kangaroos are stockier and have denser fur than their terrestrial relatives. Unlike their tree-dwelling ancestors, they do not use their tail for gripping but as a prop and a counterbalance.

FULL-CIRCLE EVOLUTION

Tree-kangaroos are descendants of terrestrial kangaroos, which themselves evolved from arboreal ancestors. As kangaroos adapted to life on the ground, they lost climbing attributes such as a gripping tail and an opposable great toe. When tree-kangaroos began to adapt to trees, they had to make do with the basic terrestrial kangaroo physique.

Tree-kangaroos have large, strong forelimbs that they can raise above their head; hind feet that they can rotate and move independently, allowing the animals to walk along branches rather than hop; and thick limb bones built to withstand the stress of leaping out of the canopy. The gripping ability of the fore-limbs is apparent in Lumholtz's tree-kangaroo, pictured above.

BENNETT'S TREE-KANGAROO

Bennett's tree-kangaroo has a dark brown back; its belly and the underside of its tail are blackish, its neck and shoulders are a bright rusty orange and it is light fawn below. Males are powerful and aggressive animals that grow to about 14 kg in weight and are 1.6 metres long in total. Females weigh 8–10 kg and are about 1.5 metres long.

This species inhabits the Daintree–Cooktown area in far north-eastern Queensland. It is common within its range but is rarely seen because it is so secretive. It usually spends the daytime resting in the canopy of a giant, vine-covered forest tree, but an hour or two after dark it climbs down and begins to forage for the leaves of vines and rainforest trees, and occasionally for fruits.

Males are very territorial, and have ranges that overlap those of two or three females. Females breed annually, carrying their young for nine months in their pouch, and juveniles stay close to their mothers for another two years. Dingoes and scrub pythons prey on the joeys.

Scientific name: Dendrolagus bennettianus

NAILTAIL WALLABIES ▪

Both known species of nailtail wallaby, the bridled nailtail wallaby (*Onychogalea fraenata*) and the northern nailtail wallaby (*O. unguifera*), are small and distinctively marked. These wallabies get their name from a horny spur on the end of their exceptionally long tail, but the function of this spur is a mystery.

Nailtail wallaby numbers have diminished since European settlement. Although the northern nailtail wallaby, which lives in the drier parts of the tropics, is still common in some areas, the bridled nailtail wallaby, an inhabitant of the dry inland, is currently endangered. A third species, the crescent nailtail wallaby (*O. lunata*), is now extinct.

The northern nailtail weighs around 7 kg and sits 55 cm high on its haunches. It is sandy in colour with a dark stripe down its backbone extending to its dark-tipped tail. The bridled nailtail wallaby, so called because of the bridle-shaped pattern of white across its neck and shoulders, weighs about 5 kg and sits about 45 cm high.

During the day, nailtails rest under bushes or logs, lying in a depression that they scratch out with the claws on their forearms. At dusk they move into the open to feed on grasses and herbs, returning to shelter at dawn. When chased, they may escape into a hollow log or the inside of a hollow tree. To avoid detection,

▪ NAILTAIL WALLABY
The bridled nailtail wallaby (*Onychogalea fraenata*) takes its common name from the bridle-like marking across its neck

a bridled nailtail wallaby will often stretch out on its belly in long grass or crawl under a bush. Nailtail wallabies are solitary creatures, though they do sometimes congregate on patches where food is plentiful and several interested males may follow a female that is in season.

Bridled nailtail wallabies breed all year; most pouch young are seen during the wet season, when pasture conditions are most favourable. The breeding cycle of northern nailtails probably follows a similar pattern.
Scientific name: *Onychogalea* spp.

HARE-WALLABIES ▪

Hare-wallabies are a group of small kangaroos – about the size of a rabbit or a hare – that were once common and widespread in drier inland Australia. These delicately built animals have fared very badly since European settlement: only two of the original four species in the genus *Lagorchestes* remain, and one in the genus *Lagostrophus*.

Lagorchestes means dancing hare in Greek; it describes the darting or zigzagging movement of hare-wallabies as they explode from cover when alarmed. They move very fast over short distances, bounding rapidly between clumps of vegetation to escape predators. The nineteenth century English ornithologist John Gould reported that a hare-wallaby chased by dogs came to within 6 metres of him before leaping right over his head. When hare-wallabies are not in a hurry, however, they move on all four legs, their tail dragging limply behind them.

Hare-wallabies are generally brown to red-brown. Their rather long, shaggy fur was once spun into string by Aborigines in some areas. They prefer succulent, nutritious herbs and grasses, selecting only the very best morsels with their front paws, but in very dry conditions they can survive on the harsh, fibrous desert plants, and they have been known to eat insects to supplement their diet. They are adapted to desert conditions and have no need to drink, extracting all the moisture they need from their food.

These solitary animals do not form social groups, even where there are dense populations. Like European hares, they make shallow squats under bushes or tussocks of grass for shelter during the daytime.

The spectacled hare-wallaby (*Lagorchestes conspicillatus*) is named for the area of red fur around its eyes. Adults weigh 1.5–4.5 kg and reach sexual maturity after about a year. They are still relatively common in northern Australia, although in recent years they have disappeared from the more southerly desert areas of central Australia.

The mala, or rufous hare-wallaby (*L. hirsutus*), weighs only 0.8–2 kg and has declined alarmingly in numbers since about 1940. It once occupied the vast spinifex grasslands and associated shrublands of about a third of Australia, but it is now confined to Bernier and Dorre islands in Shark Bay, off the coast of Western Australia, and to a tiny captive population in central Australia. It utters a sharp, high-pitched squeak when disturbed, making it one of the very few kangaroo species that has an alarm call.

It digs a burrow up to the length of a human arm in the soft desert sands to provide protection from the heat and a refuge from the fires that often sweep the desert landscapes. Fire was widely used by Aborigines in hunting the mala, and fire also features in Aboriginal myths and legends about this species.

Both *Lagorchestes* species are nocturnal. Where population numbers are high, they create heavily used 'runways' in the soft desert sands. Feral cats, foxes and fire have been implicated in their decline. The patchy burning patterns created by

▪ HARE-WALLABY
A spectacled hare-wallaby (*Lagorchestes conspicillatus*) enjoys a treat – juicy plant matter is this species' favourite food.

DISTRIBUTION

▪ BRIDLED NAILTAIL WALLABY
▪ NORTHERN NAILTAIL WALLABY

▪ SPECTACLED HARE-WALLABY

THE LAST OF ITS KIND

The little banded hare-wallaby – the last survivor of a great subfamily of kangaroos known as the Sthenurinae – is of great evolutionary interest. Almost 30 species are known from fossils, all of which share similarities in their skull and teeth.

One group of this subfamily, the short-faced kangaroos, had short, broad faces, long forelimbs and a single toe on each foot. The largest of these kangaroos, nearly 3 metres tall and weighing up to 300 kilograms, belonged to the genus *Procoptodon*. Most of the sthenurines probably became extinct near the end of the Pleistocene period, some 35 000 years ago.

The banded hare-wallaby has an unusual arrangement of teeth, in that its lower incisors bite against its upper incisors, unlike any other living macropods. The study of this animal's relationship with its environment is likely to shed light on the way of life of its gigantic extinct relatives. A banded hare-wallaby is illustrated here, alongside a prehistoric *Procoptodon* – the largest kangaroo that ever existed.

■ RED-LEGGED
PADEMELON

■ RED-NECKED
PADEMELON

■ RED-BELLIED
PADEMELON

the Aborigines provided a more favourable environment than the large summer wildfires that are now a feature of the desert landscape.

The banded hare-wallaby (*Lagostrophus fasciatus*), a diminutive, delicate hare-wallaby in a genus of its own, is only about 40 cm long, with a tail that is almost as long again. It is the only member of the kangaroo family that has distinct bands on its back. These are silver and brown and, together with its black crested tail and silvery muzzle and eyebrows, give the animal a most attractive appearance. It lives in dense scrub, several animals often sheltering in the same patch, and feeds on grasses and shrubs.

Today, the banded hare-wallaby is found only on Bernier and Dorre islands in Shark Bay, Western Australia, although in the nineteenth century it extended to the south-west of Western Australia and the Gawler region of South Australia.
Scientific names: *Lagorchestes* spp., *Lagostrophus* sp.

PADEMELONS ■

Pademelons are a group of medium-sized wallabies that are confined to the rainforests and dense eucalypt forests. Three species occur in eastern Australia; a fourth is found only in New Guinea. The name pademelon is probably a corruption of an Aboriginal name from the Sydney area; their scientific name, *Thylogale*, comes from a Greek word meaning pouched weasel.

Adult male pademelons continue to grow throughout life. They reach about 7 kg on average, almost twice the weight of females, and are much more heavily muscled. Sitting on their haunches, however, males are not much higher than females – about 50 cm, compared with about 45 cm. Their heavy build is thought to discourage smaller suitors in the search for receptive females, without the need for a fight. For wallabies, pademelons have short tails.

Keen observers in the dense forests along the eastern coast of Australia occasionally glimpse a pademelon fleeing through the dark understorey. More often, they may hear the pademelon's alarm signal: one or two sharp thumps of the hind feet, alerting others to the approach of danger. Adults make other sounds too, including a gravelly hiss when two contentious animals encounter each other at some favourite spot and a low cluck when a male is courting a receptive female.

Breeding among pademelons occurs throughout the year. The young become sexually mature at 11–18 months, having spent their first 26–30 weeks in the pouch.

Pademelons tend to live along the edges of forests. They are generally solitary, but sometimes gather at favoured feeding areas or at sunny basking sites during cold winter weather. Each pademelon occupies a home range of 5–6 hectares of forest during daylight, but with the fading light it travels rapidly and directly along well-defined pathways, venturing out into more open adjoining country, where feed is more abundant but the danger from dingoes and foxes is greater. Pademelons rarely move more than 70 metres into open grazing country, and if disturbed they quickly bound back to the safety of the trees. They always return to the forest as dawn approaches. In Tasmania their night area may be as much as 2 kilometres from their daytime territory.

Where their forest refuge adjoins pasture or forestry plantations, pademelon populations sometimes increase considerably in size. In extreme situations, their numbers rise to pest proportions and they cause serious crop losses.

None of the pademelon species appears to be in any danger of extinction, though the continued clearing of their forest habitat will reduce the area they occupy.

The red-legged pademelon (*Thylogale stigmatica*) occurs in the rainforests of New South Wales, Queensland and New Guinea. In Australia, it is sometimes found alongside the red-necked pademelon (*T. thetis*), which prefers a drier habitat. Both species are generally brown, with much paler fur on their bellies. Red-legged pademelons eat fallen fruits from the forest floor, but red-necked pademelons prefer more grass in their diet.

The red-bellied pademelon (*T. billardierii*) is generally dark brown with distinctly reddish belly fur. This species is plentiful in the rainforests and eucalypt forests of Tasmania and favours a grassy diet. Red-bellied pademelons once occurred in the coastal regions of Victoria and South Australia, but for reasons that are not yet clear they vanished from these areas early in the twentieth century.
Scientific name: *Thylogale* spp.

■ PADEMELONS
Though extinct in mainland Australia, the red-bellied pademelon (*Thylogale billardierii*) is still common and widespread in Tasmania and on the larger islands of Bass Strait.

QUOKKA

Quokkas are well known on Rottnest Island, Western Australia, where they scrounge food around houses. They are threatened with extinction on the mainland. These solidly built wallabies weigh 2–4 kg. They have have long, thick fur, reddish brown to grey with lighter tips, small ears and short tails and sit no higher than 30 cm on their haunches.

Descriptions by early settlers of the quokka's habitat in south-western Australia show that the animal favoured dense vegetation around swamps and watercourses. The arrival of foxes in Western Australia in the 1920s made these refuges even more important, and removal of that cover by settlers was a virtual death sentence for the quokka populations hiding there. Now, a few scattered remnant colonies of quokkas exist in the forests south of Perth and in the heathland along the southern coast. Fortunately, quokkas are abundant on Bald Island, off the southern coast of Western Australia – like Rottnest, this island is fox-free.

Quokkas browse on low shrubs and succulent plants. Access to water is important for them, and appears to limit numbers on Rottnest Island. They breed only in winter on Rottnest, after rain improves the supply of drinking water and the nutrients in the vegetation on which they feed, but mainland populations breed all year round. One pouch young is produced at a time, and an embryo is stored until conditions are again suitable for breeding. Young are weaned in October, about nine months after birth, and may breed the following January or February.
Scientific name: *Setonix brachyurus*

SWAMP WALLABY

Swamp wallabies are found along the eastern coast of Australia and several offshore islands. They have also been introduced to New Zealand. These animals are the sole surviving species of the genus *Wallabia*, and are genetically distinct from all other kangaroos and wallabies.

These small, stocky animals weigh 13–17 kg, and sit about 70 cm high on their haunches. Their fur is dark brown all over – almost black – though some lighter rusty patches often mark their belly and chest.

Despite their common name, swamp wallabies are most often found in tall, wet eucalypt forest or heath where there is a dense, moist understorey. The wallabies shelter during the day in areas of dense vegetation, resting and feeding on

QUOKKA
In 1696, when the Dutch navigator Willem de Vlamingh saw the quokka in Western Australia, he thought it was a kind of rat, and named Rottnest ('rat nest') Island after the animal. Quokkas are still numerous on the island but are fighting for survival on the mainland.

various grasses, soft shrubs and ferns. Swamp wallabies usually feed on their own and can range over an area of 16 hectares in search of food, but individuals may come together when resting. They feed both during the day and at night, taking short rests between feeds.

During daylight swamp wallabies stay in cover to avoid exposure to dingoes and foxes. In some areas, swamp wallabies may constitute as much as 70 per cent of a dingo's diet. In fact, dingoes hunt juvenile wallabies so heavily and constantly that they may interrupt the wallaby's normal breeding patterns so that, instead of breeding seasonally, females are replacing lost joeys continuously throughout the year. This rapid replacement of young is possible only because females are able to breed while they are still pregnant, mating right up to eight days before the first young is born. Like red kangaroos, swamp wallabies delay the development of the embryo until the pouch young hops out permanently at eight months. The mother continues to wean this juvenile for another seven months.

Population numbers of the swamp wallaby are considered to be secure across its range, although habitat loss through the clearing of land may have caused declines since the time of European settlement. Although it is a common forest inhabitant of the eastern seaboard, surprisingly little is known about Australia's only *Wallabia* species.
Scientific name: *Wallabia bicolor*

SWAMP WALLABY
These wallabies live in wet eucalypt forest or heath where there is enough dense vegetation to provide shelter. They feed on a variety of plants, including grasses, shrubs and ferns.

ROCK-WALLABIES

Rock-wallabies are a group of small Australian macropods. Their habitat includes rocky escarpments, boulder piles and cliffs, where crevices and caves give protection from predators and the elements. Sixteen species live on the Australian mainland and on some offshore islands, but Tasmania has none. The closest relatives of rock-wallabies are the tree-kangaroos and the pademelons.

Colonial living

Rock-wallabies live in colonies of up to 100 animals. Their presence is indicated by droppings on the tops of exposed rocks and around resting sites, or polished rocks along their 'runways'. Although they are largely nocturnal, rock-wallabies sun themselves in the early morning or late afternoon, especially in winter. In summer they stay in their rocky shelters, emerging after dark to feed.

Most rock-wallaby species eat grasses, herbs and the leaves of trees and bushes. In good seasons they feed near their shelters, but when food is scarce they travel kilometres from the safety of the rocks to find it. They do not need to drink regularly.

Rock-wallabies tend to breed continuously, with females producing young all year round. The single joey is born after a month's gestation and makes its way to its mother's pouch, where it attaches itself to one of her four teats. It spends the next six to seven months suckling before emerging from the pouch and being weaned. Males and females reach sexual maturity at 18–24 months and live for up to 15 years. Males are larger and more muscular than females, but the sexes are similarly coloured and marked.

Decreasing numbers

Many rock-wallaby populations in southern and central Australia have disappeared since European settlement, and several species now face extinction. For thousands of years, eagles, pythons and dingoes have preyed on rock-wallabies. They were also hunted by Aborigines. Now they contend with foxes and feral cats, and compete with introduced herbivores such as sheep, goats, cattle and rabbits.

Equipped for rocky habitats

A combination of unique features allows rock-wallabies to traverse rocky terrain or climb almost vertical slopes easily and quickly. Their hind feet are relatively short and broad, with thickly padded, highly granulated soles that give traction on steep, slippery surfaces. The large, protruding central claw present on other macropods' hind feet is reduced in rock-wallabies, so that it does not impede movement.

Rock-wallabies also have powerful hind legs that enable them to jump vertically – more than 2 metres in some species – and their compact bodies are extremely manoeuvrable. As the animal hops, it usually arches its tail upwards for balancing and making tight turns, sometimes in midair. Rock-wallabies can ricochet from vertical surfaces, and perform spectacular acrobatics at high speed to reach seemingly inaccessible sites.

To escape detection, the fur of some species matches the colour of the rocks where they live. In others, striking markings and rich colours make them almost impossible to see against a background of rocks, shadows and vegetation clumps.

Most young macropods, newly emerged from the pouch, follow their mother closely for several months. However, rock-wallaby habitats make such behaviour dangerous for uncoordinated youngsters, and so the offspring is at first left by its mother in a crevice, to which she returns regularly to suckle it.
Scientific name: *Petrogale* spp.

ROCKS AND STONES AND TREES
Rocky outcrops, gorges and boulder piles are rock-wallaby habitats, and they readily climb trees with sloping trunks. Here, an unadorned rock-wallaby peers from a tree, and in the background a yellow-footed rock-wallaby rests on a rock.

■ YELLOW-FOOTED ROCK-WALLABY
The rocky outcrops where these wallabies live create their own microclimate and usually support a greater variety of plants than the surrounding plains.

ALLIED ROCK-WALLABY

The allied rock-wallaby is a grey-brown animal, 3–6 kg in weight and 30–40 cm high, with few distinctive markings. It is widespread in rocky outcrops in the tropical woodlands of north-eastern Queensland, and is commonly seen around Townsville and on Magnetic Island.

Allied rock-wallabies feed mainly on herbs and the leaves of bushes and trees, though after rain they devour new grass shoots. When feeding, individual allied rock-wallabies regularly range over an area of around 12 hectares, but they rarely move more than 2 kilometres from their rock piles. Within their colonies, males and females often form stable long-term relationships. Pairs spend most of their time together, resting, feeding, grooming each other and defending their common territory. However, young born to a paired female are not always fathered by her consort.

Scientific name: *Petrogale assimilis*

BLACK-FOOTED ROCK-WALLABY

The black-footed rock-wallaby consists of five distinct subspecies, some of which may be separate species, as yet unrecognised. They weigh 3–7 kg and are 30–45 cm in height. Most of these rock-wallabies are a dark grey-brown with a white-over-black stripe on each side of their bodies. Despite their common name, few have black feet, so their other common names – the side-striped rock-wallaby and the black-flanked rock-wallaby – are more accurate.

Two of the five subspecies have ten pairs of chromosomes, instead of the more usual 11 pairs. Both are geographically restricted, the first to the west Kimberley region, the other to just three islands in the Recherche Archipelago, Western Australia.

These rock-wallabies were once widespread and common throughout most of central and western Australia, but have declined dramatically since European settlement. While the central Australian form is still numerous in the Macdonnell Ranges, it is extinct at Uluru, Kata Tjuta (the Olgas) and at many other sites in South and Western Australia. In the south-west of Western Australia, these animals are now found only in small numbers in scattered localities, including several offshore islands.

Research has implicated foxes in the decline of the black-footed rock-wallaby. Control of foxes is vital to ensure the survival of the species.

Scientific name: *Petrogale lateralis*

YELLOW-FOOTED ROCK-WALLABY

This is a grey-brown animal with a white underside, a striped tail and orange to yellow forearms, hind legs, feet and tail. It weighs 6–12 kg and stands about 60 cm high.

This species inhabits rocky outcrops in the semi-arid zone, with scattered populations occurring from South Australia through New South Wales into south-western Queensland. There are often permanent water seepages among the rocks, which these wallabies use during dry periods.

Individual yellow-footed rock-wallabies occupy home ranges of 150–200 hectares, usually centered on rocky shelters and often overlapping those of other colony members. After rain, they feed mainly on herbs and grasses. As the country dries, they eat the foliage of bushes and

trees, and during drought they eat dead leaves. In summer, they conserve water by spending the day in their rock shelters, where it can be up to 15°C cooler than outside.

This rock-wallaby has declined over most of its range in the past 200 years. Before the 1920s, thousands were shot in South Australia for sport and for their skins. In addition, much of their habitat has been degraded by introduced animals – rabbits, goats and sheep.

Scientific name: *Petrogale xanthopus*

PROSERPINE ROCK-WALLABY AND UNADORNED ROCK-WALLABY

The Proserpine rock-wallaby (*Petrogale persephone*) is a remarkable, rare animal that was not described until 1982. It is mostly grey, with males weighing up to 9 kg and standing 55 cm high and females weighing 6.5 kg and standing 40 cm tall. It has the smallest distribution of any rock-wallaby, being found only around the coastal Queensland town of Proserpine and on some islands of the Whitsunday group. The Proserpine rock-wallaby is unique among rock-wallabies in that its preferred habitat is rocky outcrops within rainforests. Each day the animals make their way to the forest edge, where they feed in the grassy understorey of the surrounding open woodland.

Being confined to such a small area, the Proserpine rock-wallaby is extremely sensitive to habitat disturbance of any sort. It is threatened by the spread of human settlement.

▓ **BLACK-FOOTED ROCK-WALLABY**
In cooler weather, rock-wallabies often bask in the sunshine in the early morning and at the end of the day.

▓ **ALLIED ROCK-WALLABIES**
Pair-bonding occurs in this species, with males and females forming long-term relationships. Despite this, genetic research has shown that young born to a female in such a relationship are not always fathered by her partner.

DISTRIBUTION

▓ ALLIED ROCK-WALLABY
▓ BLACK-FOOTED ROCK-WALLABY

▓ YELLOW-FOOTED ROCK-WALLABY
▓ PROSERPINE ROCK-WALLABY

■ BRUSH-TAILED
ROCK-WALLABY
Sporting a distinctive
bushy black tail, this
rock-wallaby is found
mainly in a restricted
area of the Great
Dividing Range.

DISTRIBUTION

■ UNADORNED
ROCK-WALLABY
■ BRUSH-TAILED
ROCK-WALLABY
■ SHORT-EARED
ROCK-WALLABY

■ HERBERT'S
ROCK-WALLABY
■ NABARLEK
■ CAPE YORK
ROCK-WALLABY

■ MONJON
■ GODMAN'S
ROCK-WALLABY

The more common and widespread
unadorned rock-wallaby (*P. inornata*)
overlaps the range of the Proserpine
rock-wallaby, and the two species
are sometimes confused. However,
the unadorned rock-wallaby is a
smaller and browner species.
Scientific name: Petrogale spp.

BRUSH-TAILED
ROCK-WALLABY
AND HERBERT'S
ROCK-WALLABY ■

The brush-tailed rock-wallaby
(*Petrogale penicillata*) is large and
mostly dark brown. Males weigh
up to 11 kg and stand 55 cm high.
Females are generally smaller,
weighing a maximum of 8 kg and
standing 50 cm tall.

Brush-tailed rock-wallabies were
originally found in rocky areas
throughout south-eastern Australia,
from rainforest gullies to semi-arid
woodlands. However, their numbers
have declined significantly since
European settlement, with many
populations becoming extinct in
southern and western New South
Wales and in Victoria. From the
1880s to the 1920s, thousands were

shot for their fur and because they
were considered agricultural pests.

The species now remains common
only in certain areas of southern
Queensland and the Great Dividing
Range in northern New South
Wales. A few remnant populations
survive in the Shoalhaven district
and the Warrumbungle Range in
New South Wales and in East
Gippsland and the Grampians in
Victoria, but they are considered
highly endangered.

Brush-tailed rock-wallabies eat
grasses, herbs and foliage. When
feeding, they regularly cover an area
of about 16 hectares. They prefer to
inhabit rocky places that have a
northerly aspect, allowing them
maximum opportunity to warm
themselves in the sun and providing
numerous ledges, caves and crevices
as a choice of rest areas with a wide
variety of escape routes.

In parts of its range, the brush-
tailed rock-wallaby comes into contact with a related species, Herbert's
rock-wallaby (*P. herberti*). Where
the species meet they interbreed,
forming a hybrid rock-wallaby.
Scientific name: Petrogale spp.

OTHER ROCK-WALLABIES ■

Five little-studied rock-wallaby
species are found in the far north of
Australia. Three of these, the short-
eared rock-wallaby (*Petrogale brachyotis*), the nabarlek (*P. concinna*) and
the monjon (*P. burbidgei*), are related
and have overlapping distributions
in the far north-west of Australia.

The short-eared rock-wallaby, up
to 5.5 kg in weight and 38 cm high,
is the largest and most widespread
of these species, being found from
the Kimberley to the east coast of
Arnhem Land. It is a variable species
and some populations are brightly
coloured and distinctively marked.

EVOLUTION IN
ACTION

Rock-wallabies provide a rare
chance to study the process of
speciation – the formation of new
species – because some of these animals have speciated only recently, or
are still doing so.

Rock-wallaby speciation is associated with changes in the number
and shape of the chromosomes. To
take an example, the allied rock-
wallaby (*Petrogale assimilis*), Sharman's
rock-wallaby (*P. sharmani*) and the
Mareeba rock-wallaby (*P. mareeba*),
pictured below, cannot be told apart
by physical characteristics or even
protein analysis. But each of these
species has a unique arrangement
of chromosomes, and when they
are crossbred they produce sterile
male offspring. This indicates that
they are separate species.

The nabarlek, or little rock-wallaby,
is smaller than the short-eared rock-
wallaby; adults weigh 1–1.7 kg. At
1–1.4 kg, the monjon is even smaller.
The monjon is restricted to the
wettest part of the Kimberley, and
the nabarlek occurs in scattered populations in the Kimberley and the
north of the Northern Territory.
Little is known about either species.

The other two little-known species,
are the Cape York rock-wallaby
(*P. coenensis*) and Godman's rock-
wallaby (*P. godmani*). Both weigh
4–5 kg and are 30–40 cm high, and
are found only on Cape York
Peninsula. Godman's rock-wallaby
frequently has a pale tail tip, but is
otherwise similar in coloration to the
allied rock-wallaby (page 53). The
Cape York rock-wallaby is known
only from six adult specimens
collected between 1981 and 1987.
Scientific name: Petrogale spp.

■ MONJON
Found only in the Kimberley, the
monjon is the smallest rock-wallaby of
all. This one is feeding on fallen leaves.

RAT-KANGAROOS

Rat-kangaroos, or potoroids, are not at all like rats, but they do somewhat resemble tiny kangaroos. They have short forearms and a forward-opening pouch, long hind feet and long, furred tails, and most move by hopping. They range in size from the musky rat-kangaroo, which stands about 20 cm high and weighs 500 grams, to the rufous bettong, which weighs 3 kg and is about the size of a cat.

Except for the musky rat-kangaroo, rat-kangaroos are active at night, spending the day in shelters, or in nests that they build for themselves. They eat a wide range of plant material – fruits, roots, stem bases, leaves, seeds and fungi – and many species also hunt for some invertebrates.

Most rat-kangaroos breed year-round and produce one offspring at a time. In all species the reproductive potential of each female is about three offspring a year. Gestation varies from about 21 days for the bettong to 38 days for the long-nosed potoroo – a long period for a marsupial – and the young spend three to four months in the pouch. The musky rat-kangaroo, however, has a different breeding pattern. This species has a distinct breeding season and gives birth to twins and triplets, and its young remain in the pouch for about five months.

At the time of European settlement there were at least 11 potoroid species in Australia, but two of these are now extinct. All the surviving species have suffered range reductions, and loss of habitat has been severe in the case of the burrowing bettong and the Tasmanian bettong. The brush-tailed bettong has also declined dramatically, but is recovering as a result of reintroduction programs in Western Australia and South Australia. Introduced predators, especially the European fox, seem to have played a large part in these declines. Rabbits, too, may have exacerbated the problem, either by competing with rat-kangaroos for food or by being food for foxes, thus maintaining fox populations at high levels and increasing their impact on rat-kangaroos.

Rat-kangaroos have few native predators, although they are sometimes eaten by dingoes and may have been hunted by thylacines. There are records of wedge-tailed eagles preying on rufous bettongs.
Family: Potoroidae

MUSKY RAT-KANGAROO

The tiny musky rat-kangaroo is found in tropical north Queensland and is the only potoroid to live in rainforest. It is unusual in several other ways, too: though it spends most of its time on the ground, it can climb fairly well; it bounds along on four feet rather than hopping on its hind feet; and it gives birth to more than one offspring at a time. In these respects, it represents a link between the kangaroos and the possums; some authorities place it in its own family (Hypsiprymnodontidae).

Musky rat-kangaroos eat fallen fruits, fungi and invertebrates from among the leaf litter. Fruit seems to be the most important part of their diet, especially the fruits of rainforest trees such as quandongs and figs, and the animals lose weight when there is a shortage of fruit during winter and spring. These animals either feed on fruits where they find them or carry them to a hiding place and bury them among the leaf litter, to be recovered and eaten later. This behaviour can be very important for certain rainforest trees, because the animals sometimes forget about these hiding places and the seeds of the buried fruits then germinate at a distance from the parent tree. This may happen only rarely, but it helps these trees to disperse their seeds.

Musky rat-kangaroos are active during the day. At night they sleep in nests made of grass and leaves and hidden in vines or between the buttresses of large trees.

The breeding season lasts from October to April. After the young leave the pouch they remain in a large nest, where their mother visits them periodically in order to suckle them. They become independent after about a year and reach sexual maturity at about two years.
Scientific name: *Hypsiprymnodon moschatus*

DESERT RAT-KANGAROO

There have been no sightings of the desert rat-kangaroo since 1935 and it is probably extinct. It lived in some of the most inhospitable country in Australia: dry, stony plains near Lake Eyre in South Australia and in south-western Queensland.

It spent the day in nests made of leaves and twigs, which it built in shallow excavations, sometimes in the shelter of a bush but often completely in the open. It was small – just under 1 kg and about 30 cm high – and had a sandy coat. It could move at great speed if flushed from its nest, and there are reports of it staying ahead of a galloping horse for several kilometres. Very few Europeans saw it, but it was well known to Aborigines, who could catch it by hand from the nest.
Scientific name: *Caloprymnus campestris*

DISTRIBUTION

■ MUSKY RAT-KANGAROO

■ **MUSKY RAT-KANGAROO**
A young rat-kangaroo forages during the day in the leaf litter on the forest floor. From time to time it will rest in one of its several nests.

A VERSATILE TAIL
This musky rat-kangaroo is demonstrating the rat-kangaroo's ingenious way of collecting nesting materials. It gathers twigs in its mouth and forepaws, lays them on the ground, kicks them backwards, and then carries them to its nesting site in its coiled tail.

DISTRIBUTION

■ RUFOUS BETTONG

■ BRUSH-TAILED BETTONG
■ TASMANIAN BETTONG
■ NORTHERN BETTONG

RUFOUS BETTONG

The largest of the rat-kangaroos, an adult rufous bettong weighs as much as 3 kg and stands about 40 cm high. This species is wide-spread in woodlands and open forests from northern Queensland to northern New South Wales. It lives in a range of forest types, but is most abundant in areas with deep soils and plenty of grass and avoids dense undergrowth. It feeds mostly on the stem bases and roots of perennial grasses.

The rufous bettong spends the day in a spherical nest, about 40 cm in diameter, made of woven grass and often placed in a grass tussock or dug out in a shallow depression. Each individual maintains from three to six nests inside an area of 2–3 hectares. If approached, the bettong remains in its nest until the intruder comes to within 1–2 metres. It then bursts suddenly from the nest and flees straight to another. Each animal places its nests out of sight of other nests and 100 metres or so apart so that it can quickly conceal itself again. If the bettong is forced to flee from a nest, it does not return but builds a new one the next

■ TASMANIAN BETTONGS
Bettongs breed continuously. Females give birth to one offspring at a time and produce two or three young each year.

night. It collects nesting materials in its forepaws and rolls them into a bundle that it carries in its tail.

Rufous bettongs are primarily solitary. Feeding ranges overlap in both sexes, and males briefly approach and sniff any females they come across while feeding. When a female is approaching the time when she is ready to mate, her smell becomes attractive to males and one or two suitors follow her through the night. During the day, however, she continues to nest alone. Males maintain contact with a female on heat by waiting outside her nest early in the evening. There is little open aggression between males at mating; one male seems to have undisputed dominance over all the others.

Young rufous bettongs stay with their mothers for about a month after leaving the pouch, first remaining in the nest for a couple of weeks and then following their mother around as she feeds. Females can breed at only five months – in some cases this is before they are weaned.
Scientific name: *Aepyprymnus rufescens*

OTHER BETTONGS ■

Within the genus *Bettongia* there are four species: the brush-tailed bettong (*B. penicillata*) of south-western Western Australia; the Tasmanian bettong (*B. gaimardi*), found only in Tasmania; the north-ern bettong (*B. tropica*) of north Queensland; and the burrowing bettong (*B. lesueur*), now extinct on the mainland.

The first three species are found in dry, open eucalypt woodlands and forests and are most common in areas where the soil is very infertile, probably because their favourite food – the fruit-bodies of truffles (underground fungi) – is most abun-dant in poor soils. Bettongs also feed on insects, seeds and leaves, and the northern bettong relishes the stem bases of native grasses.

The burrowing bettong lives in open shrublands, grasslands and semi-deserts, and used to be found in such habitats across much of inland Australia. However, it now exists only on four islands off the coast of Western Australia. It is the only rat-kangaroo to live in a bur-row – usually a large warren with many entrances and a complex system of underground passages that is shared by many individuals. This species is more gregarious than other rat-kangaroos, but little is known about its social organisation. It feeds on a wide range of foods, including tubers, bulbs, seeds, nuts, leaves, fruits, termites and fungi.

The northern bettong, the brush-tailed bettong and the Tasmanian bettong resemble the rufous bettong in making nests and maintaining several of them within a small area so that they can escape to a different one if they are frightened by a predator. Members of all three species nest and feed alone.

Bettongia species are pale grey or cinnamon in colour. They are more slender in build than other rat-kangaroos and have longer tails and hind feet. Weighing 1–1.5 kg and standing just over 30 cm high, they are about the size of a rabbit.
Scientific name: *Bettongia* spp.

FOREST FRIENDS

Several rat-kangaroo species, such as potoroos and brush-tailed, northern and Tasmanian bettongs, play a critical role in maintaining the health of the forest because they feed mainly on fungi. Most of the fungi that they eat are truffles, which are widespread in Australia's eucalypt forests. Truffles help such plants as eucalypts and acacias to take up nutrients and water, and may sometimes be essential for their survival.

Truffles grow underground on plant roots, and animals dig for them, as this northern bettong is doing. The animals then disperse truffle spores in their faeces, often some distance from where the truffle was eaten, and the spores then germinate. Truffles are thus moved from one root system to another and are carried to seedlings, helping them to become established.

POTOROOS

There were four potoroos: the broad-faced potoroo (*Potorous platyops*), Gilbert's potoroo (*P. gilbertii*), the long-footed potoroo (*P. longipes*) and the long-nosed potoroo (*P. tridactylus*).

The broad-faced potoroo, 24 cm long, had not been seen last century and is probably extinct. The long-footed potoroo, 40 cm long, was identified 20 years ago in south-eastern Australia; further recent sightings suggest an expanding range. The long-nosed potoroo is found in parts of south-eastern Australia and Tasmania. Gilbert's potoroo has recently been rediscovered in the southern tip of Western Australia, where it was thought to be extinct. Males are about 38 cm long, females a little smaller.

◾ POTOROO
Gilbert's potoroo (*Potorous gilbertii*) was rediscovered in 1994 in Western Australia; the last recorded sighting before that was in 1879.

Potoroos are darker and more heavily built than bettongs; their ears are shorter and more rounded and their tails are shorter. They live in forests with denser undergrowth, although the broad-faced potoroo may have

lived in shrubland. Potoroos feed mostly on fungi, as well as invertebrates and some plant food. They do not build nests; instead they shelter by day in tussocks or under shrubs.
Scientific name: *Potorous* spp.

DISTRIBUTION

LONG-FOOTED POTOROO

◾ LONG-NOSED POTOROO
◾ GILBERT'S POTOROO

MARSUPIAL MOLES

The two elusive species of marsupial moles, 14–18 cm long from snout to tail and weighing about 55 grams, are widespread in Australia's sandy deserts, but they are rarely seen because they live mostly underground. Their natural covering of fine, silky, creamy coloured fur generally becomes golden or reddish, possibly from iron compounds in the sand. Originally thought to be monotremes, later research proved that the marsupial moles share a common heritage with other marsupial families that dates back 50 million years. Their obvious marsupial feature is the pouch.

The two recognised species, the southern marsupial mole (*Notoryctes typhlops*) and the northern marsupial mole (*N. caurinus*) differ genetically and in the shape of the snout shield and tail. They otherwise appear to share many similarities. The species not only have their own family, Notoryctidae, but also their own order, Notoryctemorphia. They are called moles because, like true moles, they burrow underground and have adapted to living there.

Marsupial moles are blind, lack external ears, and have cone-shaped heads with a snout protected by a horny pink shield. Thickened skin also protects the stubby tail. But

front paws of marsupial moles, unlike those of true moles, are spade-like with two flattened claws for digging – an ideal design for a desert-dwelling animals that tunnel through sand rather than make a permanent burrow. This sand-swimming lifestyle probably explains why the male's testicles are tucked safely away between the skin and abdominal wall and the females' pouch opens backwards.

Marsupial moles dine mostly underground on the larvae and pupae of insects such as sawflies, cossid moths and various beetles and ants. They tunnel horizontally 10–20 cm below the surface, and then, inexplicably, suddenly dive vertically to 2.5 metres.

Sand dunes, level areas between the dunes, and sandy soils along river flats are favoured habitats. A marsupial mole is most likely to come to the surface after rain, leaving a telltale pattern of three parallel wavy lines in the sand.

To catch sight of one of Australia's strangest mammals is a rare experience. Despite their reclusive behav-

UNDERGROUND LIVING
Marsupial moles are burrowers and mostly feed underground on insect larvae and pupae, but this one is partially above ground and is devouring a gecko.

iour, these marsupials are familiar to Aborigines: four names for them have been recorded from ten Aboriginal language groups of desert regions spanning parts of South Australia, the Northern Territory and Western Australia.
Order: Notoryctemorphia;
Family: Notoryctidae; Scientific names: *Notoryctes typhlops; N. caurinus*

DISTRIBUTION

◾ MARSUPIAL MOLES

DISTRIBUTION

FEATHERTAIL GLIDER

FEATHERTAIL GLIDER

With a body length of 6.5–8 cm, a tail 7–8 cm long and an average weight of a mere 12 grams, the feathertail glider is the smallest gliding mammal in the world. It is perfectly equipped for gliding from tree to tree in the forest, using its tail, fringed with long stiff hairs that look like the barbs of a feather, as a rudder in flight and for grasping when it alights. With its large serrated toe pads it clings to smooth surfaces, and its binocular vision is a great advantage for night gliding.

The feathertail glider has the teeth of an insect-eater and the brush-tipped tongue of a nectar-eater. Its specialised ear structures have led some researchers to think that its hearing may be sensitive to certain very high and very low frequencies.

This sophisticated physique means that the feathertail glider's habitat needs are quite complex. These little creatures live around the eastern coast of Australia from Cape York Peninsula to eastern South Australia, but they thrive only in areas where companionship, cover, nesting sites, food and climbing surfaces are abundant. They are most often found in tall, mature, moist forests, congregating in loosely associated groups with a shifting membership.

UP, UP AND AWAY!
A feathertail glider steers and brakes with its flattened, fringed tail. Large eyes and binocular vision make it easy for this marsupial to take leaps in the dark, when it is usually active.

They huddle together to keep warm in winter, but huddling must serve other purposes too, because the groups are often larger – up to 20 animals – in summer.

Communal nesting occurs as well, though it is more frequent among relatives. Forty captive animals have been recorded in a single nest, but this would be extreme.

BANQUETING ON BANKSIA
With the serrated pads on its toes and its versatile tail, the feathertail glider clambers easily over flowers in quest of nectar and pollen.

Like the pygmy-possums, feathertail gliders feed on pollen as well as nectar and insects. In turn, they are the prey of currawongs, kookaburras, foxes and cats. Lactating mothers are particularly vulnerable because they often emerge in the late afternoon to look for food and drink.

In the northern parts of their range feathertail gliders breed throughout the year, but southern populations do not breed in autumn or early

Leaping from a tree, the feathertail glider extends its legs, spreading the loose skin along its sides, and glides swiftly downward.

Just before alighting, the glider swoops upward to lose speed, using its tail as a brake, and drops gently onto the tree, gripping with its sharp claws.

winter. Females are likely to have three or four offspring per litter, which are weaned at 14 weeks – a longer period than is usual in such small marsupials. Like kangaroos, feathertail glider females can conceive again immediately after they have given birth and maintain the second conception in suspension until the first litter has been weaned.

The feathertail glider makes an early appearance in the European history of Australia; when it was first described, in 1794, it was named *Didelphus pygmaea*, and it was later joined by the pygmy-possums in the family Burramyidae.

The feathertail glider is also known as the pygmy glider, the pygmy phalanger and the flying mouse, but its most descriptive and commonly used name remains the feathertail glider. After this marsupial was reclassified, it became the sole Australian member of a new family, the Acrobatidae, its only relative being New Guinea's feathertail possum (*Distoechurus pennatus*).
Family: Acrobatidae;
Scientific name: *Acrobates pygmaeus*

HONEY POSSUM

In colonial times, both British and French explorers visited the southern coast of Western Australia. The British stayed, but the French also left their mark. The French described a local marsupial and named it *Tarsipes rostratus* five days before the British described and named the same animal *Tarsipes spenserae*. The first name took scientific precedence, but the animal became commonly known as the honey possum or the honey mouse, or by its indigenous name, noolbenger.

This species is the only member of the family Tarsipedidae. Despite its common names, it is not closely related to either possums or mice, and despite its scientific name, it is not related to the tarsier, a South-East Asian primate that it superficially resembles in having an opposable digit on its hind feet.

The honey possum is the size of a small mouse, weighing 9 grams and averaging 7 cm long, with a tail 8 cm long. Both its tongue and its tail are long and agile. It has a grasping tail, and its tongue has a stiffening keel and a brush-like tip for reaching into flowers to gather pollen and sugar-rich nectar. The honey possum has fewer teeth than other marsupials; it does not require teeth, since it meets its protein needs with pollen.

The heathlands of the south coast of Western Australia are a perfect habitat for nectar-eaters. The area hosts many nectar-producing plants, particularly from the Proteaceae and Myrtaceae families, most of which are found nowhere else in the world. Banksias are a favourite food source for honey possums.

The honey possum has large, close-set eyes that sit almost on the top of its pointed snout. It has

mouse-coloured fur marked with a dark brown stripe along the backbone, bordered by paler stripes. It is seldom seen because of its small size and nocturnal habits. It curls up by day, sometimes sleeping in an abandoned bird's nest, but is not known to build its own nest. At night, honey possums are busy darting among the blossoms. With cold weather or lack of food they become torpid, and will huddle together for warmth.

The honey possum holds two reproduction records. Females bear the smallest of all mammalian young, weighing less than 5 mg, and males have the longest mammalian

spermatozoa – an amazing one-third of a millimetre. The sperm are accommodated in large testes contained in the animal's sizeable furry scrotum. Despite this, males are smaller than females, and several will compete for a receptive female. Although breeding occurs all year, autumn, winter and spring are favoured, with four young usually born. Honey possums can conceive again immediately after birth, but they delay embryonic development at least until after the first litter of young are weaned at ten weeks.
Family: Tarsipedidae;
Scientific name: *Tarsipes rostratus*

A TASTE OF HONEY
An elongated snout and a long, brush-tipped tongue enable the little honey possum to probe flowers for nectar and pollen – its sole source of nourishment.

HANGING OUT FOR A MEAL
A honey possum feasts on pincushion hakea. These very active nocturnal feeders climb, dart and swing from flower to flower by their long tails.

DISTRIBUTION

HONEY POSSUM

COMMON BRUSHTAIL
POSSUM

BRUSHTAIL POSSUMS AND CUSCUSES

BUILT FOR CLIMBING
The common brushtail possum, like all phalangerids, has a strong tail for gripping branches. Its front feet have five clawed toes; on the hind feet the fourth and fifth toes are clawed, the second and third ones are joined together to form a grooming comb, and the big toe is clawless. The dark streak on the chest is one of the animal's scent glands.

Brushtail possums, cuscuses and the scaly-tailed possum belong to the phalangerid family, which is unique to Australia, New Guinea, Sulawesi and offshore islands of these landmasses. Humans introduced the common brushtail possum into New Zealand in the 1830s and distributed some of the cuscuses to islands around New Guinea and Sulawesi.

Like other Australian marsupials, phalangerids represent fauna that inhabited the supercontinent of Gondwana. Two of the brushtail possum species and the scaly-tailed possum are native only to Australia, and the two cuscus species are shared with New Guinea.

■ **COMMON BRUSHTAIL POSSUM**
At about 90 days old, this joey, furless and with eyelids fused, is still attached to the teat. The strong forelimbs were essential for the journey from pelvic area to pouch at birth. Normally the pouch is tightly closed by sphincter muscles.

Phalangerids range from 1.5 kg to 10 kg in weight. All are tree-climbers with clawed feet and gripping tails with a friction pad of naked skin on the underside. Some utter loud calls, and brushtail possums have a wide vocal repertoire and prominent ears for acute hearing. Most eat leaves and fruits, though some take the occasional bird's egg or small animal. All have two chisel-like lower front teeth and six smaller teeth opposite them in the upper jaw; the cheek teeth are ridged for chewing. They have large eyes, usually with vertical pupil slits for night vision.

The forward-facing pouch contains four teats but the normal litter size is one or two. On emergence from the pouch, the young travel piggyback on their mother until they become too big. A sticky, cream coloured, strong-smelling substance produced by glands in the pelvic area is probably common to all family members and used in scent communication.
Family: Phalangeridae

COMMON BRUSHTAIL POSSUM ■
The common brushtail is the best known of the possums because it has adapted to urban living and often comes into contact with people. Its natural habitat is forest land over much of Australia, from rainforests to dry eucalypt woodlands, but it has recently disappeared from much of its former range in the arid centre.

This species has large ears and a fox-like face. It is usually grey with a pale cream belly, but colours

can vary from black in the wetter parts of Tasmania to dark red in the rainforests of Queensland. In southern Australia these possums weigh up to 4.5 kg and have a head and body length of 55 cm and a tail about 40 cm long, but in northern Australia they are half this size.

When climbing in trees, brushtails reach across gaps, using their tail as a fifth limb. They also spend much time on the ground. Leaves, blossoms and fruits form their diet in the wild, but in suburbia they eat all sorts of foods, even meat.

Though usually solitary at night and when sleeping, brushtails keep in contact with one another through sounds and scents. They screech and chatter to warn of predators such as dingoes. When stressed, they make clicking sounds, and the young emit repetitive high-pitched calls when separated from their mother.

Brushtails, particularly males, mark their territory by rubbing their chin and chest glands against objects to leave their scent, and by depositing urine trails. When a brushtail is frightened, a strong-smelling creamy substance oozes from its pelvic area.

Mating occurs in autumn and sometimes also in spring. During the courtship of 30–40 days the male follows the female, calling softly. After 16–18 days of gestation females bear one, rarely two, young. Males take no part in raising the young.

■ COMMON BRUSHTAIL POSSUM
These possums are usually grey, but there are many colour forms. This is a rare light-coloured individual.

large ears

scent
gland

prominent
eyes

clawed toes

grooming toe

big toe

tail with naked
friction pad on
underside

■ MOUNTAIN BRUSHTAIL POSSUM
This species can be distinguished from the common brushtail by its shorter ears and sturdier build.

The young stay in the pouch for five months and are weaned by seven months. Female offspring may stay in their mother's home range; males leave within 12 months of birth.
Scientific name: *Trichosurus vulpecula*

MOUNTAIN BRUSHTAIL POSSUM ■

Similar in appearance to the common brushtail possum, the mountain brushtail possum weighs up to 4.5 kg, and has a head and body length of 50 cm with a 42 cm long tail. It has a restricted range, living only in the rainforests and tall, wet eucalypt forests of the hilly south-eastern mainland, where it replaces the common brushtail. Its diet is similar to that of the common brushtail, though it spends much of its time feeding on the ground. Its day-time den is often inside a fallen log.

The mountain brushtail has well-developed vocal and scent communication. Males and females establish pair bonds that extend beyond courtship and mating, but it is unclear how permanent these are. One offspring is born after 15–17 days of gestation. It spends five to six months in the pouch and suckles for a further two months. The young stay with their parents for 18–36 months and their presence appears to inhibit the rearing of a subsequent offspring.
Scientific name: *Trichosurus caninus*

SCALY-TAILED POSSUM

Little is known about the scaly-tailed possum, which lives in the Kimberley region of north-western Australia in rugged, rocky country. It spends the day in rock crevices, emerging at night to feed on leaves, fruits and blossoms. Within its range it is sparse and patchily distributed.

This possum weighs about 1.5 kg and has a head and body length of about 40 cm and a tail about 30 cm long. Similar in size and appearance to the common brushtail, it has a dark stripe down its back and its tail is covered with scales. The reduced claws on its forelegs and the fleshy pads on its toes are adaptations for rock climbing.

Females become sexually mature at about two years of age and give birth to one or two young at a time, mainly in the dry season, between March and August. The young stay in the pouch for 150–200 days and are weaned after eight months.
Scientific name: *Wyulda squamicaudata*

COMMON SPOTTED CUSCUS ■

The common spotted cuscus sleeps on a branch rather than in a den, and may be active both day and night. It makes a rough sleeping platform by bending a few twigs or leaves under its body. The common spotted cuscus weighs up to 5 kg and has a head and body length of 58 cm and a tail 44 cm long. The skin visible on the face, paws and tail is yellowish. This colour, together with its shorter ears hidden by fur, distinguishes it from the southern common cuscus. Males have grey-brown fur with large cream spots over much of their body; females are grey with a cream patch on their rump.

This species inhabits the rainforests, gallery forests and mangroves of northern Cape York Peninsula and New Guinea. Numbers are sparse

and the animals are difficult to spot. During the day, males are sometimes seen surveying their territories and neighbours from high vantage points.

Up in the canopy, these creatures feed on leaves, fruits, and the occasional lizard or baby bird. They live alone except when the female is ready for mating, when she advertises herself with hissing brays. Her pouch contains four nipples and up to three young have been recorded, but the most common litter size is one.
Scientific name: *Spilocuscus maculatus*

SOUTHERN COMMON CUSCUS

The southern common cuscus is harder to find than the common spotted cuscus because it sleeps in a den during the day and is confined in Australia to the rainforests of the McIlwraith Range and Iron Range areas of Cape York Peninsula. It is widespread in southern New Guinea.

Adults weigh about 2 kg, and have a head and body length of about 40 cm and a tail 30 cm long. Both sexes are greyish brown with a white belly. The end third of their tail is naked. They have a dark stripe running down their back and dark skin on their face, paws and tail. Their ears protrude.

Very little is known of this somewhat shy animal's biology except that it feeds on leaves and fruits and is generally seen alone, and that females usually rear twins in their four-teat pouch. Adults sometimes hiss and grunt fiercely.
Scientific name: *Phalanger mimicus*

DISTRIBUTION

■ MOUNTAIN BRUSHTAIL POSSUM
■ SCALY-TAILED POSSUM
■ COMMON SPOTTED CUSCUS

■ SOUTHERN COMMON CUSCUS

■ COMMON SPOTTED CUSCUS
A male common spotted cuscus peers from its large, red-rimmed eyes, which make it look rather like a monkey.

DISTRIBUTION

- LEADBEATER'S POSSUM
- STRIPED POSSUM

GLIDING POSSUMS

Most of these marsupials, members of the petaurid family, have a thin membrane of loose, furred skin that stretches from wrist to ankle. Jumping between trees, they spread it out; larger species can achieve directional glides of more than 100 metres. In Leadbeater's possum this membrane is rudimentary.

All family members use their long, sharp lower incisors to dig out insects and to slash neat grooves in trunks and branches to release sweet sap, which they then lick off. Their diet also includes nectar, honeydew, pollen, fruits and acacia gum.

Four of the 11 petaurid species are confined to Australia, five live in Papua New Guinea and nearby islands, and two are common to both landmasses. Their habitats range from dry woodlands to rainforests. Some species are solitary; others are highly social.

Territories may be large – up to 60 hectares for striped possums and yellow-bellied gliders – or less than a hectare for small species. All are

nocturnal and live in trees, resting during the day in tree hollows.

While most of these mammals are relatively quiet, yellow-bellied gliders and mating striped possums are extremely vocal. Animals that prey on petaurids include pythons, goannas, owls and cats.
Family: Petauridae

LEADBEATER'S POSSUM

This species is endemic to Australia and lives in the mountain ash forests of Victoria's central highlands. At heights of up to 100 metres, it hunts insects and spiders among flaking bark, flicks up lerps with its lower incisors, licks honeydew from leaves, or descends headfirst to feast on gum exuded from wounds in wattle trunks and branches below.

With a head and body length of 16 cm, a tail at least as long again, and a weight of 130 grams, Leadbeater's possum resembles a sugar glider without a flying membrane. Its tail, however, is grey and club-shaped, being fatter towards the tip.

Although this species lives in family groups of up to eight individuals, only the dominant pair in each group breeds. Females, which bear one or two young twice a year, are more aggressive than males in maintaining the boundaries of their 1–2 hectare territory. A female's growing intolerance of younger maturing females culminates with her driving her female offspring from the group when they are about ten months old and ready to breed themselves.
Scientific name: *Gymnobelideus leadbeateri*

- STRIPED POSSUM
This boldly marked possum lives on insects, which it prises from tree bark with its sharp teeth, its long tongue, and its skewer-like fourth finger.

STRIPED POSSUM

The black and white striped possum is found in Australia in the rainforests of north Queensland and in New Guinea. It is weasel-bodied and bug-eyed, with a disproportionately large head and enormous lower jaw. With a head to body length of about 26 cm and a tail longer still, it weighs up to 520 grams. It smells like fibreglass resin and charges around the rainforest and adjacent woodland tree tops, flicking its tail around its head. When hunting its favourite food – wood-boring insect larvae – the striped possum taps branches and trunks with its especially lumpy wrists, listening for the sound of shuffling grubs below. Then it tears up the grub's tunnel with its incisors, and skewers the insect with one of its enormously elongated fourth fingers.

The striped possum needs a very large home range to provide it, and its one or two young, with enough insects and native fruits to see it through the dry seasons of the tropical north. Not much is known at present about its social and sexual habits. It builds its nests in hollow limbs and in epiphytes – plants such as bromeliads and ferns that grow on tree branches – and is probably solitary, with breeding occurring from late summer to early spring.
Scientific name: *Dactylopsila trivirgata*

THE LEADBEATER CHALLENGE

The endangered status of Leadbeater's possum is a politically sensitive conservation issue, as 75 per cent of its habitat is state forest where timber is being clear-felled. This tiniest of petaurids occupies the tallest of flowering trees, and in 1939 bushfires wiped out 80 per cent of its mountain ash habitat.

Leadbeater's possum requires trees with nesting hollows – that is, trees at least 120 years old. It also needs dense canopy so that it can move rapidly between trees; plentiful peeling bark, which harbours invertebrates and supplies nesting material; and an acacia understorey to provide oozing gum.

At present, these possums nest in dead trees that are still standing after the 1939 fires, but all these trees will probably have fallen by 2075. The challenge is to balance logging rates against the preservation of the Leadbeater's habitat. If logging continues at the present level, by 2025 the Leadbeater's possum population is likely to have dropped by 90 per cent.

SUGAR GLIDER ▤

The sugar glider has a wider distribution than all the other petaurids and is found in a broad north-eastern coastal band in all states and territories, with populations also in New Guinea and nearby islands.

This delicate-looking marsupial weighs 140 grams and is 17 cm long with a slightly longer black-tipped tail. About three in ten individuals have a white tip to this black tail. The sugar glider makes a repetitious 'yip-yip' call when it is disturbed, which is thought to warn other group members of potential danger.

Sugar gliders eat a broad diet and tolerate a wide range of habitats, including rainforest, wet eucalypt forest, woodland, and even backyard gardens. They may consume acacia gum, insects, spiders, nectar, honeydew, manna, lerps, fungi, fruits and pollen, depending on the season. Sugar gliders can withstand the cold by curling up in a leaf-lined tree hollow with up to eleven other family members – adults and their immature offspring.

They identify each other by individual and group scent, and recent research suggests that the scented secretions produced and spread around by the dominant male suppress reproductive activity in other males. Male and female offspring are often evicted from the group before they are 12 months old, making them exceedingly vulnerable to predators. At least half fall prey to owls, cats, foxes, kookaburras and goannas while attempting to find new unoccupied territories.
Scientific name: *Petaurus breviceps*

▤ SQUIRREL GLIDER
Although endangered in Victoria, this gliding possum is one of outer Brisbane's most common marsupials.

SQUIRREL GLIDER ▤

This endemic glider shares many behavioural traits and food preferences with the sugar glider, but the squirrel glider is slightly larger, with a weight of 230 grams, a head and body length of 21 cm, and a tail 27 cm long with a bushier base. It also has a longer face. The squirrel glider rarely enters rainforest. At night its nasal 'n-when' grunt can be heard when it is disturbed.

Squirrel gliders occur in eastern Australia from north Queensland to western Victoria. In Victoria they have been driven into vegetation along roadsides and around pastures by clearing and agriculture and are endangered, but they are abundant in the coastal woodlands of south-eastern Queensland.
Scientific name: *Petaurus norfolcensis*

YELLOW-BELLIED GLIDER

Endemic to Australia, and the largest member of the family, the yellow-bellied glider measures up to 80 cm from nose to tail tip and weighs around 600 grams. It has large naked ears and is dark grey above and white to yellow on its belly. Its dark tail is almost twice as long as its body.

Living only in the mature eucalypt forests of the east coast, they travel long distances to find insects, nectar and sap-producing trees, and can leap up to 120 metres between trees. These glides help to conserve energy.

In tropical Queensland, where food is abundant, groups of gliders have home ranges of about 2–30 hectares, but where resources are more scattered, as in western Victoria, animals usually travel in pairs over home ranges of up to 60 hectares.

The gurgling shrieks of yellow-bellied gliders may be heard at night. By day, V-shaped gashes 5 cm long in eucalypts show where they have been tapping the trunks for sap.
Scientific name: *Petaurus australis*

MAHOGANY GLIDER

This species, endemic to Australia, is now endangered and restricted to a small coastal strip of often swampy, open woodland, 30 km north and 75 km south of Cardwell in north-eastern Queensland. There, 80 per cent of suitable habitat has been cleared, mainly for sugar cane. What remains is mostly unprotected, despite government moves to buy up critical habitats.

Weighing only 350 grams, the mahogany glider has a body length of 25 cm and a tail length of 35 cm. It is grey to mahogany brown on its back and head, and its belly is white, apricot or a rich nut brown. These gliders depend on tropical plants, mostly eucalypts, acacias and grass-trees, for nectar and sap, and also eat invertebrates and lichen. They need a home range of up to 20 hectares.
Scientific name: *Petaurus gracilis*

▤ SUGAR GLIDER
Launching itself with its hind legs, a sugar glider can 'fly' for at least 50 metres between trees. Most petaurids have a thin membrane of loose furred skin between wrist and ankle, and when they jump from tree to tree, they stretch all their limbs to spread this membrane.

DISTRIBUTION

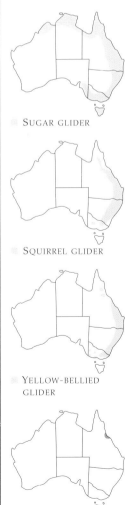

SUGAR GLIDER

SQUIRREL GLIDER

YELLOW-BELLIED GLIDER

▤ MAHOGANY GLIDER

RINGTAIL POSSUMS AND GREATER GLIDER

■ COMMON RINGTAIL POSSUM
Introduced flowers and fruits are a popular meal with the common ringtail possum, which can often be seen after dark in suburban gardens.

These animals are unique to Australia and New Guinea, with all six genera occurring in Australia. They are distinguished by their extreme agility, but the greater glider is the only member of the family that is able to glide. Their scientific name, Pseudocheiridae, means 'with a false hand' – a reference to the structure of their forefeet, which look rather like human hands.

Members of this family are efficient climbers. They have a tail that coils tightly and has a bare-skinned friction pad on its underside at the tip. Their forefeet enable them to hold branches firmly and their hind feet are like a phalangerid's (see 'Built for climbing', page 60), with a clawless big toe and small second and third toes that are fused to form a grooming comb. Most ringtails weigh 1–2 kg and have small ears that are visible beyond their fur.

HOLDING ON TIGHT
Ringtail possums use their tail as an extra limb for climbing. A gap between the second and third finger of their 'hands' allows them to grasp small branches securely.

Ringtails are mainly leaf-eaters, grinding their food with triangular ridges on their cheek teeth. Common ringtails, and possibly other ringtails, eat special soft faecal pellets that they void during the day; they thus digest their food twice, ensuring extraction of maximum nutrition.

Most females have two teats in their pouch, but common and western ringtails have four. Females usually raise one or two young at a time.
Family: Pseudocheiridae

COMMON RINGTAIL POSSUM ■

The common ringtail possum is found in the eucalypt forests and woodlands, coastal tea tree scrub, mangroves and rainforests of eastern Australia, including Tasmania. It builds a football-sized nest – called a drey – in a tree. After dark, these possums walk along interlocking branches and powerlines, family members maintaining contact with soft, twittering calls.

Adults weigh about 1 kg, and have a head and body length of 35 cm, with a tail as long again. Their colour varies from light grey to rich red with darker tan or red limbs. Their tail is tipped with white and they have the largest ears of all ringtails.

The female has four teats, and usually gives birth to twins. These leave the pouch at four months and are weaned at six months. Pair bonds may last from year to year, though a male may associate with a second female. This is the only male possum known to care for its young, carrying them on his back and minding them at night while the mother is feeding. When predators approach, the male calls the young back to the nest.
Scientific name: *Pseudocheirus peregrinus*

WESTERN RINGTAIL POSSUM

The western ringtail possum is a dark grey version of the common ringtail. It is confined to the extreme south-west of Australia, where it is patchily distributed. Its numbers have declined steadily since the early 1900s, and it is now endangered.

The western ringtail prefers peppermint tree leaves but can survive without them. It is most abundant in thick forests with overlapping tree crowns, where it can move without touching the ground. On the coast western ringtails build nests, but inland they live in tree hollows, which provide better insulation from high daytime temperatures. Females generally bear one offspring, and adults do not share dens.
Scientific name: *Pseudocheirus occidentalis*

GREEN RINGTAIL POSSUM

Fine black, yellow and white banding on the hairs of the green ringtail possum give a lime green tinge to its thick fur. Weighing about 1 kg, with a head and body length of up to 37 cm and a tail as long again, this species has two golden stripes down its back, white eye and ear patches, and a short tail with a thick base.

Found only in a small area of north-eastern Queensland, the green ringtail usually stays in rainforest over 300 metres above sea level. It sleeps during the day on an exposed branch and becomes active an hour or two before dusk. The leaves of fig trees and mulberry-leafed stinging trees are its favourite foods. It is solitary except for a brief consort period before mating.
Scientific name: *Pseudochirops archeri*

DAINTREE RIVER RINGTAIL POSSUM ■

This possum inhabits rainforests in Queensland's northern wet tropics at altitudes above 420 metres. It is fawn to dark brown above and

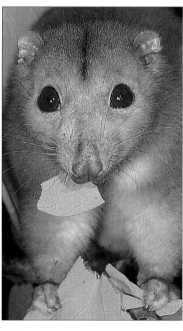

■ DAINTREE RIVER RINGTAIL POSSUM
This species is easy to spot because it loves to eat the leaves of rainforest trees that grow along roadsides.

LEMUROID RINGTAIL POSSUMS
North of Cairns in the Carbine Tableland, there is a population of lemuroids with quite a few white individuals among the usual darker ones.

LEMUROID RINGTAIL POSSUM

Lemuroid ringtail possums frequent rainforest over 450 metres above sea level in north-east Queensland, and their numbers are greatest along the summits of mountain ranges. They weigh about 1 kg, and have a head and body length of 40 cm and a tail about 37 cm long. Most of them are chocolate brown balls of fur with pug-like faces and bushy tails, but one population has a high number of entirely white individuals.

Pairs of lemuroids share a den throughout the year, and the single offspring may remain with its parents until the next young emerges from the pouch. They can be heard at night crashing into dense foliage. They are mostly silent, and their musky smell suggests that scent is important for communication.

Lemuroids are extremely sensitive to rainforest disturbance and rapidly die out in rainforest patches smaller than 75 hectares.

Scientific name: *Hemibelideus lemuroides*

ROCK RINGTAIL POSSUM

Weighing up to 2 kg, with a head and body length of up to 38 cm and a tail about 26 cm long, this is the heaviest of the Australian ringtails. Its tail is tapered, relatively short, and sparsely furred for the last half.

Rock ringtails can be common in their limited habitat of rocky outcrops, cliffs and screes in the Kimberley and Top End regions of northern Australia. Their diet consists of leaves, flowers and fruits of native trees and shrubs.

This species lives in close-knit families, often containing a pair with one young on the back and an older one at heel. Urine and scent from cloacal glands, soft calls and tail tapping on rocks are all possible means of communication. Droppings resembling slightly elongated jellybeans and dark urine stains on rocky ledges are signs of this nocturnal animal's presence, but it quickly retreats into the protection of rocky clefts when disturbed.

Scientific name: *Petropseudes dahli*

creamy white below. Males weigh about 1.5 kg and are about 35 cm long; females are slightly smaller. It feeds on the leaves of rainforest trees.

Though mainly arboreal, Daintree River ringtail possums are cautious climbers and will descend to the ground to cross short gaps between trees. They use their curled tail to carry leaves for lining their nesting hollows. They are mainly silent, but adults occasionally hiss or grunt and the young make a high-pitched repetitive call when they are lost.

Scientific name: *Pseudochirulus cinereus*

HERBERT RIVER RINGTAIL POSSUM

The imposing Herbert River ringtail possum occupies a small rainforest area on the northern coast of Queensland, where it lives over 350 metres above sea level. Its white belly and armbands contrast sharply with its black body. Some individuals lack white markings, but can be identified by their sleek, tapered tail and high-bridged nose.

This possum weighs up to 1.5 kg, and has a head and body length of 40 cm and a tail about 47 cm long. It is nocturnal, using tree hollows and epiphytic plants as daytime dens. It lives on the leaves of rainforest trees.

This species is solitary except in the autumn mating season, when a male follows a female closely for about a month. Females usually bear twins, which they piggyback for two weeks and then often park on low branches during the night.

Scientific name: *Pseudochirulus herbertensis*

☐ COMMON RINGTAIL POSSUM
☒ WESTERN RINGTAIL POSSUM

☒ GREEN RINGTAIL POSSUM

☒ DAINTREE RIVER RINGTAIL POSSUM

☒ HERBERT RIVER RINGTAIL POSSUM

☒ LEMUROID RINGTAIL POSSUM
☐ ROCK RINGTAIL POSSUM

☒ **HERBERT RIVER RINGTAIL POSSUM**
This rainforest ringtail can be identified by its bold white markings and solid, high-arched nose. It is sometimes preyed on by owls and carpet snakes.

DISTRIBUTION

GREATER GLIDER

GREATER GLIDER ■

The greater glider looks like a petaurid, but is in fact closely related to the lemuroid ringtail. Both species have a flap of skin along their sides; in the lemuroid ringtail this flap is suppressed, but in the greater glider it has evolved into an expandable membrane that allows it to glide.

At 1.75 kg, with a head and body length of up to 45 cm and a nonprehensile tail of about 60 cm, it is the longest glider in the world, and one of the clumsiest because its membrane is attached to its elbow rather than its wrist, as in other gliders. Nevertheless, it can glide for up to 100 metres and turn in mid-glide.

Gliding is rarely seen; animals usually seem lethargic. They are

■ GREATER GLIDER
Large ears, a small face and luxuriant fur characterise the greater glider, an inhabitant of eucalypt forests.

recognisable from their large furry ears, small face, long thick fur and bellrope-like tail. Their fur may be dark brown, black, grey or white.

The greater glider inhabits the canopy of the tall eucalypt forests of the east coast, where it feeds on eucalypt leaves and buds and uses a high tree hollow as a daytime den. It is solitary, except when males accompany females before mating; the pair share a den until the single young leaves the pouch about four months after birth.

They communicate by scent rather than sound, and use their cloacal glands, particularly large in males, for marking trees. Their only call is the female's shrill twittering as she nears the den containing her young. She rarely carries the young on her back; once it has left the pouch it is den-bound for four months and then begins to explore its surroundings.
Scientific name: *Petauroides volans*

PYGMY-POSSUMS

Pygmy-possums are tiny nocturnal marsupials. Their relatively large heads feature whiskers, pink noses, big dark eyes and prominent ears, and they have well developed forward-facing pouches.

All are climbers, and eastern and western pygmy-possums can leap from branch to branch. They have long, slender, lightly haired tails for grasping and support and opposable big toes for climbing and clinging. The four species belonging to the genus *Cercartetus* live mainly in trees, but the mountain pygmy-possum of the genus *Burramys* lives and nests on the ground.

Pygmy-possums eat insects, fruits, seeds, pollen, nectar, and sometimes

TINY CLIMBER
Living a mainly solitary existence, the long-tailed pygmy-possum scuttles and leaps among the rainforest foliage in search of food.

even small reptiles. The western, eastern and little pygmy-possums play an important role in pollinating certain types of plants.

There are two species about which very little is known. The rarely seen long-tailed pygmy-possum, or Queensland pygmy-possum (*Cercartetus caudatus*), from the north-east is a solitary species that is also native to New Guinea. Like its relatives, it has perfected the art of 'playing possum' – on cold winter days it may become torpid and be so stiff and cold that it appears to be dead. The little pygmy-possum (*C. lepidus*) from Tasmania and the Victorian–South Australian border region is even more elusive, though it occupies a wide range of habitats. It is the smallest of the pygmy-possums, with an average head and body length of 6.5 cm and a 7 cm tail. This species is sometimes known as the

■ MOUNTAIN PYGMY-POSSUM
This little marsupial lives among rocks on heathlands in the snow country of Victoria and New South Wales.

Tasmanian pygmy-possum, but this is a misleading name for it, as it is also found on the mainland.
Family: Burramyidae

MOUNTAIN PYGMY-POSSUM ■

Both sexes of the mountain pygmy-possum are a similar size – almost twice that of the little pygmy-possum – but there is a large discrepancy in lifespan: males live for less than two years on average, whereas one female has been recorded at more than 12 years old.

Mountain pygmy-possums are the only Australian mammal confined to alpine and subalpine regions, restricted to areas of boulders within

Using its brush-tipped
tongue, this agile little
climber feeds mainly on
nectar and pollen gath-
ered from banksias,
eucalypts and bottle-
brushes. If these are in
short supply it eats soft
fruits and insects.

shrubby heathlands in the snow
country of New South Wales and
Victoria. They spend as much as
seven months of the year curled up
in a ball, hibernating under snow in
small niches among the rocks. In
summer the boulders attract huge
numbers of migratory bogong
moths, which are a favourite food
of mountain pygmy-possums,
and in winter the boulders provide
insulation against the extreme cold.
As well as bogong moths, these
pygmy-possums eat caterpillars,
beetles and spiders and the seeds
and fruits of heathland shrubs.

As the effect of greenhouse
warming reduces the area of
Australia's alpine country, the
mountain pygmy-possum's range
is likewise becoming smaller. This
species' total habitat is now less than
10 square kilometres in extent, and
there is nowhere else for them to go.
Scientific name: *Burramys parvus*

WESTERN PYGMY-POSSUM AND EASTERN PYGMY-POSSUM ■

The ranges of eastern and western
pygmy-possums overlap in the
south-eastern corner of South
Australia and the south-western
corner of Victoria. The two species
are similar but they can be told apart
by the colouring of their fur, as well
as by their size and habitat. The
western species (*Cercartetus concin-
nus*) has a red-brown tinge to its
fawn coat and completely white

belly fur; the eastern species
(*C. nanus*) is fawn and has white-
tipped hairs on its underside.

With a weight of about 24 grams,
a head and body length of 9 cm
and a tail length of 9 cm, the eastern
pygmy-possum is a little bigger than
its slender western cousin, which
weighs about 13 grams and has an
average head and body length of
8 cm and a tail 8.5 cm long.

Western pygmy-possums are
found in mallee heathlands and dry
woodlands where there is plenty of

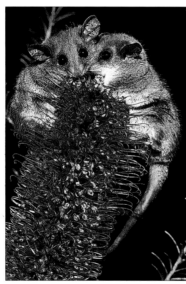

■ EASTERN PYGMY-POSSUMS
Pygmy-possums help to pollinate
certain banksia species. This pair
are feeding on *Banksia ericifolia*.

shrubby undergrowth. During the
day, they curl up and sleep in leaf-
lined nests in tree hollows or among
the leaves of grass-trees. Even when
they are disturbed they do not wake
up, but after dark they emerge alert
to search for fruits, seeds, nectar and
pollen. They use their front paws to
grasp their insect prey, removing
inedible parts such as wings. Eastern
pygmy-possums particularly relish
pollen and nectar, but when these
are not available they make do with
soft fruits and insects. They prefer
wooded habitats such as rainforest
and eucalypt forest.

As they live close to the ground,
western pygmy-possums are easy
prey for feral and domestic cats.
Fortunately they are also prolific
breeders, producing up to three
litters a year, though two is more
common. The maximum litter size
is six. Eastern pygmy-possums also
breed up to three times a year, but
average four young per litter.

Both species groom themselves
thoroughly before, during and after
meals. Until recently, this behaviour
obscured the significant role they
play in pollinating certain banksia
species. Animals trapped overnight
used not to be checked until the
morning, by which stage they had
become relatively free of pollen but,
when the animals were inspected
before they had had a chance
to clean themselves, pollen was
found on their faces.
Scientific name: *Cercartetus* spp.

DISTRIBUTION

■ LONG-TAILED
PYGMY-POSSUM
■ LITTLE PYGMY-POSSUM

■ MOUNTAIN
PYGMY-POSSUM
■ WESTERN
PYGMY-POSSUM

■ EASTERN
PYGMY-POSSUM

CARNIVOROUS MARSUPIALS

This group of marsupials, which scientists sometimes refer to as dasyurids, constitutes the largest family of marsupial mammals. Australia has over 50 dasyurid species, and all but two of them are found only on the Australian mainland or in Tasmania.

AN AGGRESSIVE HUNTER
A northern quoll (*Dasyurus hallucatus*) hungrily devours a hopping mouse. Quolls kill their victim by biting the back of its skull.

FINGERS AND TOES
Dasyurids have five clawed toes on their forefeet and five toes on their hind feet – or four in completely ter-restrial species, since the big toe is reduced or absent. Illustrated here are the feet of the eastern quoll, a ground-dwelling species.

Hairy tails and pointed snouts

Dasyurid means 'hairy-tailed', and members of this family have tails that are either wholly or partially covered in fur. Other characteristics of this group are their distinctive pointed snouts, three pairs of similar-sized lower incisor teeth, well developed canine teeth, and six or seven sharp cheek teeth.

All dasyurids have five toes on their forefeet and their palms are roughly circular. Ground-dwelling dasyurids, including desert species, have long hind feet and their big toes are either reduced or absent. Climbing species have broad ridged or padded hind feet, and their big toes are large and mobile – features that help the animals to cling to vertical surfaces. Some dasyurids, such as the Tasmanian devil, have a permanent pouch, but in many the pouch area is no more than a patch of belly skin that has teats.

The larger dasyurid species include meat in their diet, and Tasmanian devils thrive on little else. Smaller species eat mostly insects and other small invertebrates. This diet is rich in protein and fat, and many species supplement it by licking nectar from flowers. Because insects contain as much as 80 per cent water, dasyurids are frequently able to satisfy their moisture needs from their food intake alone. Several species survive in arid parts of the continent where free water is not available for several months of the year.

Coping with the weather

Dasyurids are found in all environments throughout Australia, from high alpine regions to coastal forests and deserts. At low temperatures – provided there is sufficient food available – some species are able to keep themselves warm by increasing their metabolic rate to eight or nine times the normal level. If food is in short supply, they allow their body temperature to drop and enter a resting state that is known as torpor.

These marsupials are generally nocturnal, but some dasyurids maintain their body heat by sun-bathing or by sharing a nest with some other species. For example, there are records of fat-tailed pseudantechinuses and lesser hairy-footed dunnarts nesting together.

Whenever possible, dasyurids avoid the heat. Most species are uncomfortable at temperatures above 30°C and pant in order to cool down. Those living in the arid zone shelter in burrows by day and forage only during the night, while species that live in tropical forests, such as the Atherton antechinus and the cinnamon antechinus, may rest in nests in the tops of trees, where they catch the breeze.

Population control

Dasyurids have an unusually broad range of life histories. In seasonal environments, breeding is scheduled so that the young are nursed and weaned when food is most plentiful, and some species that breed season-ally have litters of 10–12 young just once a year. In less seasonal environments, such as tropical or arid areas, females have litters of four to eight and give birth at times when food is likely to be in good supply.

The size of most dasyurid populations seems to be largely governed by food availability, but predators, competition, fire and drought also keep populations in check.

Members of the family

Dasyurids are grouped into four subfamilies. The sizeable subfamily Dasyurinae includes the Tasmanian devil, which is the world's largest living marsupial carnivore – roughly the size of a small, stoutly built dog – the quolls, which are considerably smaller than the Tasmanian devil, and a number of species that are smaller still – the mulgara, the ampurta, the kaluta, the kowari, the dibbler and the pseudantechinuses.

The three other subgroups have fewer members. The antechinuses and phascogales are Phascogalinae; the dunnarts and the kultarr, some-times called marsupial mice, are Sminthopsinae; and the smallest of the marsupials – the planigales and the ningauis – are the Planigalinae.
Family: Dasyuridae

KEEPING THE NUMBERS UP
As with most mammals, generally the smaller a dasyurid is, the more offspring it has in a litter. This brown antechinus (*Antechinus stuartii*) is being kept very busy with its nestful of young.

TASMANIAN DEVIL

■ TASMANIAN DEVILS
While they generally forage alone, several Tasmanian devils may feed at the same time on a large carcass, such as that of a wombat.

TASMANIAN DEVIL ■

The Tasmanian devil is endemic to Australia. It disappeared from the Australian mainland after the dingo arrived there and is now restricted to Tasmania, where it inhabits dry eucalypt forests and woodlands, mainly in the north of the island. Male Tasmanian devils weigh about 9 kg and have a head and body length of 65 cm; females are slightly smaller. The sexes are similar in appearance. They have jet black fur, most with white markings, and their fat, coarse-haired tails are slightly less than half the combined length of their head and body. They have a massive head for their body size, with powerful jaws and strong teeth that are ideal for crunching bones – indeed, their generic name, *Sarcophilus*, means 'flesh-lover'.

They owe their common name partly to their colouring and marking and partly to the blood-curdling nocturnal screams that they utter. Though somewhat belligerent, these animals are generally wary.

At night, Tasmanian devils emerge from their burrows to hunt alone for possums, wallabies and wombats, covering distances of up to 8 km a night at a steady lope. All of them can climb trees, but the young are particularly agile and will sometimes catch and eat sleeping birds.

Devils often scavenge food, using their acute sense of smell to locate dead animals, from beached fishes to cows. They consume large carcasses alone or in jostling, growling, screeching groups of up to six. They often squabble and bite, and older animals are frequently quite scarred.

Mating occurs in March and young are born three weeks later. Females carry up to four young in a backward-facing pouch until August, then deposit the now fully furred young in a grass-lined den. They start making forays from the den in November and by the following February they are weaned and independent. Males disperse from their mother's home range.

Devils live for about six years, and females generally breed when they are two years old. Although still common, populations have been depleted in areas by an outbreak of a viral disease that causes severe facial tumours. With the thoughtless introduction of the European fox to Tasmania in 2000, both may pose problems for the security of the Tasmanian devil in the future.
Scientific name: *Sarcophilus harrisii*

CAPABLE CONSUMER
Powerful jaws and strong teeth equip a Tasmanian devil for eating practically every part of its prey. Its droppings are characterised by numerous splinters of bone.

DISTRIBUTION

■ NORTHERN QUOLL
■ EASTERN QUOLL

■ WESTERN QUOLL
□ SPOTTED-TAILED
　QUOLL

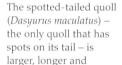

■ QUOLL
The spotted-tailed quoll (*Dasyurus maculatus*) – the only quoll that has spots on its tail – is larger, longer and thinner than other quolls, and has a longer tail.

QUOLLS ■

Quoll is an east coast Aboriginal name for a medium-sized carnivorous marsupial that can be easily recognised by its white spots. Its hairy tail is almost as long as its head and body combined. There are six quoll species, four in Australia and two in New Guinea.

The northern quoll (*Dasyurus hallucatus*) and the western quoll (*D. geoffroii*) were once distributed across the continent, but the ranges of all Australian quolls have declined dramatically since European settlement, and the western quoll is now considered endangered. The largest species, the spotted-tailed quoll (*D. maculatus*) occupies the wetter east and south-east, sharing Tasmania with the eastern quoll (*D. viverrinus*).

Quolls make dens in underground burrows or hollow tree trunks. They mostly hunt alone at night but are sometimes active during the day. Northern and spotted-tailed quolls are good climbers and have a thumb on their hind feet – the western quoll also has this thumb – and their foot pads are ridged for gripping. Quolls have fine, sharp teeth and they kill their prey with a crushing bite to the back of the skull. The size of the prey depends on the size of the quoll: smaller species feed on a mixture of small mammals, birds, insects and fruits; the spotted-tailed quoll's diet consists mostly of medium-sized mammals.

Females live apart from other females in a smaller area than males, whose ranges overlap with those of other quolls of both sexes. The sexes come together only for breeding in late autumn to early winter. The timing of breeding ensures that the young become independent in early summer, when food supplies are at their best. Females carry up to six young – eight in the northern quoll –

■ QUOLL
Once widespread in south-eastern mainland Australia, the eastern quoll (*Dasyurus viverrinus*) now lives only in Tasmania, where it is most common in the eastern half of the island.

in a shallow pouch for about nine weeks, and then leave them in a grass-lined nest in an underground den, returning to suckle them between periods of foraging.

The northern quoll is the smallest of the four species. Males weigh 900 grams and their head and body are a maximum of 31 cm long; females weigh 500 grams and are 30 cm long. The northern quoll's tail is about as long as its combined head and body. This species eats rats, antechinuses, reptiles, worms, beetles and grasshoppers, as well as honey and soft fruits such as figs. Northern quolls frequently climb trees and rocks in their wooded habitats across tropical northern Australia – their species name, *hallucatus*, means 'notable first digit' and refers to their climbing adaptation, the thumb. Populations are highest in broken rocky country, where these quolls are bigger and live longer – up to three years. Living in savanna habitats is more stressful for them, and few animals there live to breed a second year.

Male eastern quolls weigh about 1.3 kg, with a head and body length of 37 cm and a tail 24 cm long. Females weigh about 900 grams, with a head and body length of 34 cm and a tail 22 cm long. Eastern quolls lack the ridged foot pads and

the thumb on the hind feet of some other quolls. Eastern quolls have disappeared from their south-eastern mainland Australian range, and now occur only in Tasmania. They prefer to live in grasslands and open eucalypt forests, reaching their highest densities where pastures border forest. They benefit farmers by consuming large numbers of insect pests, rats and mice. They also eat soft fruits, earthworms, freshwater crustaceans, reptiles, birds and small mammals. Eastern quolls live at altitudes of up to 1100 metres, where they remain active in the snow throughout the winter. These inquisitive animals can be seen at night in Cradle Mountain, Lake St Clair and the Walls of Jerusalem national parks, and around Cygnet in the south, and north of Gladstone in north-eastern Tasmania.

The western counterpart of the eastern quoll is sometimes known by its Western Australian Aboriginal name, chuditch. Both species have a similar diet and are about the same size, though some western quolls grow slightly larger and have a thumb on the hind foot that the eastern quoll lacks. The western quoll used to live in most of Australia's deserts, but became extinct over much of its range between the early 1800s and the 1950s. It now exists only in eucalypt forests, dry woodlands and mallee in the south-west of Western Australia, where fewer than 6000 individuals remain.

Two forms of the spotted-tailed quoll exist. Males of the larger southern form weigh 3.5 kg, have a head and body length of about 50 cm and a tail 43 cm long; females weigh 1.8 kg, with a head and body length of 42 cm and a tail 39 cm long. The smaller form is restricted to the tropical rainforests of northern Queensland. Males weigh l.6 kg, have a head and body length of 40 cm and a tail length of 39 cm; females weigh 1.2 kg, with a head and body length of 38 cm and a tail 36 cm long. Spotted-tailed quolls climb tree trunks and traverse tree canopies to hunt at night. They also move above the forest floor using fallen trees as runways. They live mainly on possums and bandicoots, though they can kill wallabies up to four times their body size; they also eat birds, mice and insects. The best places to see this elusive quoll are in northern and western Tasmania. They sometimes come into bush camp sites, where they appear indifferent to the presence of humans.
Scientific name: *Dasyurus* spp.

■ MULGARA

■ AMPURTA

■ KALUTA
■ KOWARI

MULGARA
AND AMPURTA ■

The mulgara (*Dasycercus cristicauda*) is a pale sandy brown marsupial with a light grey or white belly and a pointed nose. Its tail is slightly more than half the length of its body, and is distinguished by a crest of black hairs that starts at the tip and continues for two-thirds of the tail. Males may reach an overall length of 30 cm; females are a little smaller. Individuals can live for quite a long time – at least seven years.

The mulgara is widespread throughout the centre of Western Australia, the Northern Territory, far

■ KALUTA
This little creature lives among spinifex grasses in the Pilbara region of Western Australia. It supplements its carnivorous diet by licking nectar from flowers.

western Queensland and South Australia, but is usually rare in Western Australia and South Australia. It lives in arid, sandy regions, digging burrows that are sometimes quite complex.

Individuals appear to be solitary and mainly nocturnal, though they sometimes bask in the sun during the day. Mulgaras eat insects, spiders and scorpions, and small vertebrates such as lizards. They require no free water to survive; instead, they produce a concentrated urine from the fluid they obtain from their diet – a useful adaptation to desert life.

Related to the mulgara, the ampurta (*D. hillieri*) is similar in appearance and behaviour. Habitat is the key to telling them apart – ampurtas are found in hard soil areas in south-western Queensland and north-eastern South Australia.
Scientific name: *Dasycercus* spp.

KALUTA ■

The kaluta's chestnut-coloured body is about 10 cm long, and the animal has a thick tail that adds a further 5–6 cm to its overall length. It has a short head, a pointed nose, small ears, and strong, well furred forelimbs.

This marsupial lives in the Pilbara region of Western Australia among spinifex hummocks. Although its distribution is limited, it is common within its range; the fire resistance and unpalatability of spinifex may have helped to protect it.

The kaluta is mainly nocturnal, feeding on small vertebrates and insects. An unusual feature is the

■ MULGARAS
Mulgaras have a varied diet, feeding on large insects, spiders and small lizards. These two are eating a cricket.

way it flicks its tail when making its way about. Like male antechinuses, the male kaluta dies at the end of his first breeding season (see box, 'Live fast, die young', page 73).
Scientific name: *Dasykaluta rosamondae*

KOWARI ■

The kowari is a large-eared grey marsupial with red-tinged fur and a black brush of fur on the end of its tail. Males reach up to 18 cm in head and body length, with a tail of 10–14 cm; females are slightly smaller.

Kowaris inhabit the stony gibber deserts of eastern central Australia, where they dig burrows. They seem to be solitary and nocturnal.

■ KOWARI
Like most animals that are active at night, the kowari has large eyes and long whiskers with which it can feel its way in the dark.

DISTRIBUTION

■ DIBBLER

□ FAT-TAILED
PSEUDANTECHINUS
■ NINGBING
PSEUDANTECHINUS

□ WOOLLEY'S
PSEUDANTECHINUS
■ SANDSTONE
PSEUDANTECHINUS

■ **PSEUDANTECHINUS**
When food is plentiful, the fat-tailed pseudantechinus (*Pseudantechinus macdonnellensis*) feasts, storing fat in its tail for times when there may not be much to eat.

Kowaris prey on insects and small vertebrates, and will also eat the flesh of larger dead animals. If their diet is relatively moist, they do not need free water to survive.

The young stay in the pouch for around two months, and then are carried on their mother's back or left in the nest and fed until they are big enough to fend for themselves.
Scientific name: *Dasyuroides byrnei*

DIBBLER

The dibbler is one of the rarest of the dasyurids. It is now restricted to banksia-dominated heathland in a very small part of southern Western Australia, but it once had a larger range in the south-west. There is evidence that its range was shrinking even before European settlement, but land clearing for farming has accelerated the process.

The dibbler, distinguished by a white ring around its eyes, is about 15 cm long, with a tail length of about 9.5 cm in females and 11.5 cm in males. Its head, back and sides are covered with coarse brownish grey fur tinged with white, and its belly fur is pale cream.

Although it is mainly nocturnal, the dibbler occasionally basks in the sun. It rummages through leaf litter, sniffing out insects with its pointed nose, and climbs trees to take other invertebrates and to supplement its diet with the nectar of banksia flowers.

Both male and female captive dibblers live for two to three years, but all males on Boullanger Island, which lies midway between Perth and Geraldton off the coast of Western Australia, die after their first breeding season, at least in some years. After the short breeding season in March, a female carries up to eight young in her forward-opening pouch for about a month. The young are dependent for three to four months, and are able to breed at 10–11 months.
Scientific name: *Parantechinus apicalis*

PSEUDANTECHINUSES ■

Pseudantechinuses are like antechinuses (page 73) but usually have fatter tails. These are at least three-quarters as long as their head and body length of 8.5–10.5 cm, and act as storage deposits for food when pickings are poor during droughts in desert habitats. They live mainly on insects. Unlike antechinuses, male pseudantechinuses may survive to breed more than once. Little, however, is known about the habits of pseudantechinus species in their natural environment. There are five known pseudantechinus species, of which the most familiar is the fat-tailed pseudantechinus (*Pseudantechinus macdonnellensis*). This particularly attractive marsupial is greyish brown on its back with chestnut patches behind its large ears. Its tail is usually very fat at the base – the more abundant the food, the fatter the tail becomes. Fat-tailed pseudantechinuses range broadly in central and western Australia, living in rocky terrain, sometimes even in termite mounds. Although largely nocturnal, they bask in the sun at times – a habit they share with many desert dwellers.

The ningbing pseudantechinus (*P. ningbing*) from the Kimberley region of northern Western Australia is similar in appearance. It has a hairy base to its tail, the rest of which is sparsely haired and scaly.

Another fat-tailed pseudantechinus is Woolley's pseudantechinus (*P. woolleyae*), which has recently been recognised as a separate species.

■ SANDSTONE PSEUDANTECHINUS
An inhabitant of sandstone country in the Northern Territory, this small sharp-nosed creature has ridged pads on its feet that enable it to scamper with agility over the boulders.

It is lives only in part of Western Australia but occurs in habitats from rocky terrain to sandy plains.

The Carpentarian pseudantechinus (*P. mimulus*) is a smaller version of the fat-tailed pseudantechinus. This species has not been collected on the mainland since 1905. Offshore, on the Sir Edward Pellew group of islands in the Gulf of Carpentaria, it lives on rocky sandstone with spinifex ground cover and a scattering of eucalypts.

Finally, the sandstone pseudantechinus (*P. bilarni*) is a small, sharp-nosed dasyurid, with a body length of 9–12 cm and a slightly longer, slender tail. It has speckled brown fur grading to pale grey on its belly and this is highlighted by reddish patches behind its ears. Females are smaller than males.

The sandstone pseudantechinus is restricted to the scree slopes of the western escarpment of Arnhem Land. Here eucalypt trees and tall grasses are interspersed with sandstone boulders around which the animal hunts and nests. Ridged foot pads enable it to traverse its stony habitat rapidly and effectively. In the dry season, these animals move to areas with thicker canopy cover in order to find more insects in the moist leaf litter.

Breeding occurs from late June to early July, with approximately a quarter of both sexes surviving to breed again the following year.
Scientific name: *Pseudantechinus* spp.

ANTECHINUSES

Antechinuses are small marsupials with brown or grey fur, a pointed nose, long claws on their front paws and sharp, pointed teeth. Some, such as the brown antechinus, have large, prominent eyes; others, such as the dusky antechinus, have comparatively small eyes.

All the members of this genus are 8–16 cm in head and body length, with a tail half to the same length again. Females are always much smaller than males. These marsupials are probably best known for their unusual mating behaviour (see box, 'Live fast, die young').

These creatures are ferocious for their size. They are primarily insectivorous, though some also eat small vertebrates such as lizards. Mainly active at night, they scrabble

LIVE FAST, DIE YOUNG

Antechinuses mate once a year for a season of about two weeks, timed so that the young are weaned when food is abundant.

During this period, males expand their range and are active during the day, and their penis appears to be permanently semi-erect. When a pair meet, the male subdues the female by biting her neck and females, such as the dusky antechinus (*Antechinus swainsonii*) shown below, often have hair missing from the violence of the male's assault. Copulation may last for hours and if the female escapes, the male pursues her. Towards the end of the season males die as a result of suppression of the immune system caused by increased testosterone production.

through leaf litter or run up and down trees searching for their prey. They move with swift, jerky movements and an alert demeanour.

Female antechinuses give birth a month after mating and, depending on the species, have 6–12 young which they carry in an open pouch for five to eight weeks. When these grow too large for the mother to carry, they are placed in a nest until they venture out with their mother at about three months old.

After weaning, male juveniles disperse to new home ranges, but females remain in the area in which they were born. Some females live for more than two years and rear a second litter, but few survive to breed a third time.

Antechinus species vary greatly in behaviour and social organisation and occupy a wide range of habitats, from alpine heathlands, frequented by the densest populations of the dusky antechinus (*Antechinus swainsonii*), to the isolated tropical forests that are the home of the fawn antechinus (*A. bellus*), the palest of all the antechinuses – light grey, with a cream belly and white chin and paws. The rare Atherton antechinus (*A. godmani*), which is found in dense forest at about 1200 metres above sea level in the Atherton region of northern Queensland, has one of the smallest ranges of any Australian mammal. It forages on the ground, relying on its senses of hearing and smell to find its prey, rather than on its small eyes.

By contrast, the most widespread of the antechinuses is the yellow-footed antechinus (*A. flavipes*). This species inhabits a diverse range of habitats, which vary from lush tropical vegetation to dry mulga country, open forests and swamps. The yellow-footed antechinus has slate grey fur on its head, grading to a reddish tinge on its rump and sides. The fur on its belly is often paler, and there are light rings around its large eyes.

The least known of the antechinus species is the cinnamon antechinus (*A. leo*), which has reddish fur like that of the yellow-footed antechinus. This species lives on Cape York Peninsula in inaccessible vine forests that are cut off for part of the year by floods, which makes it a difficult animal to study.

The swamp antechinus (*A. minimus*), which is endangered by loss of habitat, lives in wet heathlands and tussock grasslands and builds its nest at the base of a tussock. In mainland Australia it is found in south-eastern coastal areas, but in

ANTECHINUS
The most widespread member of the *Antechinus* genus, the yellow-footed antechinus (*Antechinus flavipes*), ventures boldly into urban areas, and even comes into houses.

Tasmania it occurs from sea level to subalpine regions at 1000 metres above sea level. The fur of this species is coarse in texture, and grades from grey on the animal's head and shoulders to a rich yellowy brown on its flanks.

Brown antechinuses (*A. stuartii*) nest together in hollows of standing dead trees. Individuals nest in a number of trees, and may visit several nests in a single night. By the mating season, up to 20 animals may be in one nest tree at any one time, males and females apparently bedding down together quite happily. It has recently been discovered that southern populations of what was thought to be the brown antechinus are in fact genetically distinct, and this southern species is now known as the agile antechinus (*A. agilis*). Two further species – discovered even more recently, in 2000 – are the subtropical antechinus (*A. subtropicus*) and the rusty antechinus (*A. adustus*). These species differ from the brown antechinus in colour, size and head shape but are otherwise ecologically quite similar.
Scientific name: *Antechinus* spp.

DISTRIBUTION

- DUSKY ANTECHINUS
- FAWN ANTECHINUS
- ATHERTON ANTECHINUS

- YELLOW-FOOTED ANTECHINUS
- CINNAMON ANTECHINUS
- AGILE ANTECHINUS

- SWAMP ANTECHINUS
- BROWN ANTECHINUS

■ PHASCOGALE
The word phascogale, derived from the Latin for 'pouched weasel', describes two species of tree-dwelling carnivorous marsupial. This is a brush-tailed phascogale (*Phascogale tapoatafa*).

DISTRIBUTION

■ BRUSH-TAILED PHASCOGALE
■ RED-TAILED PHASCOGALE

■ HAIRY-FOOTED DUNNART
■ RED-CHEEKED DUNNART
■ WHITE-TAILED DUNNART

■ CHESTNUT DUNNART
■ LESSER HAIRY-FOOTED DUNNART
■ SANDHILL DUNNART

■ FAT-TAILED DUNNART
■ KAKADU DUNNART
■ BUTLER'S DUNNART

PHASCOGALES ■

There are two phascogale species. The brush-tailed phascogale (*Phascogale tapoatafa*) has a head and body length of 18 cm, and a tail a little longer, covered in short hair at the base but soon sprouting long black hairs. It lives in the open forests and woodlands of eastern, south-western and northern Australia. The red-tailed phascogale (*P. calura*) has a head and body length of 10 cm; the first half of its tail, which is 13 cm long, is covered in short red hairs; the rest has a thin brush of longer black hairs. This marsupial once inhabited arid and semi-arid Australia, but is now found only in remnant patches of long-unburnt vegetation in the Western Australian wheat belt, where it prefers stands of she-oak near old hollow eucalypts.

Brush-tailed phascogales appear to be more solitary than red-tailed phascogales. The latter nest communally in grass and feather-lined tree hollows, under the skirts of live grass trees, or in the broken trunks of dead ones. Both species are nocturnal, living mainly on insects but occasionally taking birds and small mammals. Both are skilful climbers. Brush-tailed phascogales spend most of their time in trees, but red-tailed phascogales also feed extensively on the ground.

Life is short for male phascogales as they die at a year old after a short mating season, while females live for two or three years. Females have eight teats and usually produce seven or eight young in late winter. By summer's end the young have dispersed and set up their own home ranges.
Scientific name: *Phascogale* spp.

DUNNARTS ■

Dunnarts, like antechinuses, look rather like mice – indeed, they are sometimes referred to as marsupial mice. They are not mice, however, but marsupials, carrying their developing young in a tiny fold of belly skin that functions as a pouch.

Dunnarts are nocturnal, spending the daylight hours in burrows that they excavate themselves or in disused ones of other small mammals or dragons. Dunnarts live in a wide variety of habitats, and are perhaps the most successful of Australia's marsupial insectivores. There are 19 species; of these, 17 are endemic to Australia and the other two, the red-cheeked dunnart (*Sminthopsis virginiae*) and the chestnut dunnart (*S. archeri*), also live in southern Papua New Guinea.

Many dunnart species are among the smallest of the marsupials, weighing as little as 10–20 grams. The tiny lesser hairy-footed dunnart (*S. youngsoni*) weighs 9–12 grams when fully grown, and its weaning young are a minuscule 1.5 grams. The head and body length of dunnarts ranges from 5.5 cm to 13.5 cm; their tail can be up to twice as long. Most species have large eyes and large erect or folded ears. They can be distinguished from other small dasyurids by their relatively narrow feet and pointed snouts. Dunnarts have short, sharp teeth that are ideal for crunching the insects and spiders that form the bulk of their diet.

Most mammals need regular food to maintain their body temperature, and are not well suited to Australia's deserts, with their uncertain rainfall and fluctuating food resources. Many dunnart species, however, evolved in these conditions and are successful desert-dwellers. The spinifex grasslands of central Australia, in particular, are home to at least six dunnart species, including the hairy-footed dunnart (*S. hirtipes*), the fat-tailed dunnart (*S. crassicaudata*), the sandhill dunnart (*S. psammophila*), the stripe-faced dunnart (*S. macroura*), the Ooldea dunnart (*S. ooldea*) and the lesser hairy-footed dunnart. The hair on the soles of the hairy-footed dunnart and the lesser hairy-footed dunnart provides traction on loose, sandy surfaces.

One way in which dunnarts flourish in such a hostile environment is by having a flexible breeding pattern. They can mate from late winter

■ DUNNARTS
The common dunnart (*Sminthopsis murina*), widespread in south-eastern Australia, has litters of up to ten young.

to late summer, which allows them to take advantage of flushes of insects brought by unpredictable spring or summer rains. Females may produce six to ten offspring in a litter and, in good conditions, can have two to three litters in a season because they have one of the shortest gestation periods of all mammals; for example, conception to birth for the stripe-faced dunnart takes only 12 days.

The dunnarts' diet of invertebrates has a high water content, so they do not need to drink free water – another adaptation to arid conditions. In addition, many species, such as the fat-tailed dunnart and the stripe-faced dunnart, can store energy as fat in the base of their tails. During short-term food shortages dunnarts, like some other desert dasyurids, enter torpor – a period of low energy use when the animal hibernates.

Not all dunnart species are desert-dwellers. The Kakadu dunnart (S. bindi), the red-cheeked dunnart and the chestnut dunnart all live in the woodlands of the tropical north. In south-eastern Australia the common dunnart (S. murina) is widespread in open forest and heathland, whereas the white-footed dunnart (S. leucopus) occurs in the tussock grasslands, heaths and forests of Tasmania and the southern tip of south-eastern Australia. The Kangaroo Island dunnart (S. aitkeni) occurs only on that island.

Despite their widespread occurrence across Australia, mystery still surrounds the dunnarts. The little long-tailed dunnart (S. dolichura), Gilbert's dunnart (S. gilberti) and the grey-bellied dunnart (S. griseoventer) have only recently been recognised as new species; all were previously mistaken for the common dunnart.

Other species, such as the Julia Creek dunnart (S. douglasi) and Butler's dunnart (S. butleri), occupy such small and isolated areas that few have been caught, and little is known about them. Even some of the more widespread species remain poorly studied: for example, the white-tailed dunnart (S. granulipes) of south-western Western Australia, and the long-tailed dunnart (S. longicaudata), which has quite a large range in rocky country in the western part of inland Australia but is very rare. The long-tailed dunnart is remarkable for its extremely long tail, which it uses as a balancing aid.

Pitfall traps have helped in the search for dunnarts. Pieces of piping are buried vertically in the ground, with a flap of flyscreen wire over the

top to guide the animals into the pipe. These traps are more successful and less harmful than conventional box traps baited with food, and have helped in identifying new species and clarifying the distribution and status of others. Yet there are still many parts of Australia that have not been properly surveyed, and it is possible that more dunnart species are awaiting discovery.
Scientific name: *Sminthopsis* spp.

GOING WALKABOUT

Just imagine having to run across 60 kilometres of sand dunes each night looking for food. Relative to its size, the lesser hairy-footed dunnart does exactly this. In a study made in the Simpson Desert in the south-western corner of Queensland, these tiny creatures were found to travel up to 3 kilometres in a single night.

Perhaps more amazing are the species' movements in response to rain. At the same site, dunnarts were found to travel up to 10 kilometres after localised rain. Almost all movements were toward the rainfall area, even though it may have been 10–20 kilometres away. It is thought that dunnarts may detect rain through their sense of smell.

KULTARR

The kultarr weighs 20–30 grams and its head and body together are 7–10 cm long. Although closely related to the dunnarts, it is distinguishable by its long, brush-tipped tail, usually one and a half times its body length, and its long, slender hind legs, which give it the appearance of a hopping mouse. However, the kultarr does not hop on its hind legs but bounds from hind to front feet. This motion allows it to change direction suddenly – a useful adaptation for avoiding predators.

Primarily an insectivore, the kultarr is found in the deserts of central Australia, favouring gibber plains – stony plains with minimal shrub cover – and open grasslands and shrublands in semi-arid areas. It is sometimes found in association with acacia species and mallee woodlands, but seldom in areas of dense ground cover. The kultarr has been caught well away from these areas, at Cedar Bay in Queensland, north of Cairns, though it is now probably extinct at this location, and a population still survives at the mouth of the Roper River, in the Northern Territory. Neither of these localities is arid, and both are remote from the kultarr's inland habitats. These populations may have survived from a time when the kultarr's distribution was more widespread.

Like dunnarts, the kultarr has a very short gestation period – a mere 12 days. Kultarrs in captivity may breed from July to January, but no births in the wild have been recorded after December. The young are in the pouch for about 30 days, and then either stay in the nest, often a hollow log or disused burrow, or travel around on their mother's back. They become sexually mature after eleven and a half months.
Scientific name: *Antechinomys laniger*

■ **KULTARR**
Adapted to living in desert country, the kultarr is active at night, hunting for cockroaches, crickets and spiders.

DISTRIBUTION

■ STRIPE-FACED DUNNART
■ WHITE-FOOTED DUNNART
■ GILBERT'S DUNNART

■ OOLDEA DUNNART
■ GREY-BELLIED DUNNART
■ COMMON DUNNART

■ LITTLE LONG-TAILED DUNNART
■ JULIA CREEK DUNNART
■ LONG-TAILED DUNNART

■ KULTARR

■ NINGAUI
These diminutive carnivorous marsupials are no bigger than a man's thumb and weigh less than an empty matchbox. A Pilbara ningaui (*Ningaui timealeyi*) is shown here.

DISTRIBUTION

□ WONGAI NINGAUI
■ PILBARA NINGAUI

■ SOUTHERN NINGAUI
□ COMMON PLANIGALE

□ INGRAM'S PLANIGALE

□ NARROW-NOSED
PLANIGALE

□ GILES' PLANIGALE

NINGAUIS ■

There are three ningaui species: the wongai ningaui or inland ningaui (*Ningaui ridei*), the Pilbara ningaui or Ealey's ningaui (*N. timealeyi*) and the southern ningaui (*N. yvonneae*).

All three look like tiny mice with pointed snouts, grey fur, long tails, beady black eyes and very sharp, pointed teeth, but the Pilbara ningaui's fur is more bristly than the fur of the other two species.

Wongai ningauis are found in the entire desert heartland of Australia, while Pilbara ningauis inhabit the semi-arid grasslands of Karijini National Park, near the central coast of Western Australia. Southern ningauis prefer the red and golden inland sands of southern Australia. In the shade of spinifex, mallee or scrub, ningauis quench their thirst with moisture from their food or by licking dew from leaves.

During the day these animals hide in undergrowth and hollow logs or in the abandoned burrows of spiders and lizards. They hunt their prey at night and, like the other dasyurids, they kill their victim by ferociously biting its head.

Wongai ningauis eat spiders, moths, grasshoppers and other small invertebrates. Pilbara ningauis tackle centipedes and cockroaches larger than themselves, while for southern ningauis spiders are the greatest delicacy.

Ningauis generally mate towards the end of winter and bear one to two litters of young through the summer, but few live to breed a second time. These tiny creatures can carry five to eight sucklings on their bellies, and often forage with their young riding on their back.
Scientific name: *Ningaui* spp.

PLANIGALES

There are at least four species of this tiny marsupial. The three desert species do not need to drink water, having adapted their behaviour to an arid environment, but the common planigale lives in moist areas.

Planigales are nocturnal dasyurids that look like miniature house mice but are far more ferocious. They have flattened skulls, beady eyes, pointed noses and long, lightly furred tails. These minute packages of muscle can scuttle around in tiny spaces, such as cracks in rocks and parched ground. There they extract insects from places few other mammals can reach. Sheltering beetles and other invertebrates frequently fall prey to a planigale's 40 or so sharply pointed, snapping teeth.

In these hideouts, temperatures are often considerably lower than on the surface, and planigales forage and nest deep down in the cracks, giving them protection from predators such as owls and feral cats. On the surface, however, many planigales become prey, and up to six at a time have been found in the stomachs of cats.

Although never really common, the so-called common planigale (*Planigale maculata*) is more often seen in leafy nests under sheets of dumped corrugated iron than in more natural surroundings. It favours the grassy woodlands of coastal eastern and northern Australia, but has occasionally been recorded there in rainforests and swamps. Eight or so young pack into the kangaroo-like pouch of a lactating female. Males average a head and body length of 8 cm with a tail almost the same length; females are slightly smaller. This species is significantly larger than

other planigales and its skull is not as flat, but at 11 grams it is still very small for the size of prey it tackles – even a young house mouse is not safe. When in pursuit of invertebrate prey, the common planigale pushes its way through leaf litter and between tall grasses. It pounces on grasshoppers or spiders, and rides its victim until it becomes weak and may be shredded at leisure.

The diminutive Ingram's or long-tailed planigale (*P. ingrami*) weighs less than a 10 cent coin, and has a body no longer than a front door key. It is the smallest marsupial alive and one of the smallest mammals in the world. It forages in the cracking clays of arid western Queensland and, during the dry season, in the deep cracks of the northern monsoonal woodlands and grasslands. In the wet season, however, it moves to higher ground. Ingram's planigale breeds mostly from December to March. The litter of around eight joeys spends six weeks in the pouch before its combined bulk begins to prevent the mother from hunting efficiently. She then leaves the young in a nest, where she feeds and tends them until they become independent at around three months old.

The narrow-nosed planigale (*P. tenuirostris*), resident of the red heart, is a few grams heavier than the long-tailed planigale. Males are 6.5 cm long with a 5.5 cm tail; females are slightly smaller. This species forages among the fissures of western clays to a depth of around 2 metres. Underground, temperature extremes are smoothed out and there may be a difference of 13°C between the surface and the areas where this planigale hunts for more than 70 per cent of its foraging time. Narrow-nosed planigales nest in the cracks and females give birth to an average of six young from July to January. Some raise two litters a year.

Weighing around 10 grams, Giles' planigale (*P. gilesi*) is slightly bigger than the narrow-nosed planigale, with a head and body measuring 7.5 cm and a tail 6.5 cm long. Again, females are smaller. This species also lives in the arid interior. It commonly occurs in the same habitat as the narrow-nosed planigale, but tends to spend more time foraging above ground. Giles' planigale often hunts for only five hours a day; in this time it can eat enough crickets, spiders and small reptiles to keep going. This planigale can travel up to a kilometre in just a few nights. Females often produce two litters in a year.
Scientific name: *Planigale* spp.

Endangered!

Extinction is a natural process, but since European settlement in 1788 Australia has been losing mammal species with unusual rapidity.

The now vanished thylacine, above and left, had a long, slender tail, a broad head with powerful, wide-gaping jaws, and dark stripes marking its coarse, sandy fur.

The causes include predation and competition by various introduced species, and loss of habitat from farming, logging and urban development. In May 1996, 20 mammal species were listed as extinct, 30 as endangered and 18 as vulnerable. Much current research is directed towards finding ways to reverse the decline in the species most at risk.

Island refuges

Some species that have disappeared from their former mainland habitats survive on islands. Burrowing bettongs once lived in most of arid and semi-arid Australia, but the last mainland populations, in the south-west, vanished soon after rabbits and foxes arrived. There were healthy colonies on four islands off Western Australia, so the species is relatively secure and can now be reintroduced into fox-free mainland areas.

Islands have also preserved the brush-tailed bettong, once widely distributed and abundant on the mainland. By 1980, only three mainland populations of this species remained, all in the south-west.

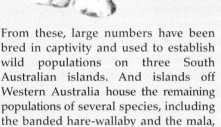

From these, large numbers have been bred in captivity and used to establish wild populations on three South Australian islands. And islands off Western Australia house the remaining populations of several species, including the banded hare-wallaby and the mala, or rufous hare-wallaby.

Lost and found

The rare central rock-rat, which is a medium-sized rock-rat with a particularly hairy tail, was rediscovered in 1996 in the west Macdonnell Ranges near

Alice Springs – until then, it had not been seen since 1960, but fossil deposits suggest that it was once widespread across central and central western Australia on stony spinifex-clad ranges.

Closing the stable door

Australia once had its own 'tiger', the Tasmanian tiger, or thylacine. Today all that is left of Australia's largest carnivorous marsupial are fossils, Aboriginal rock paintings, sketches and historical reports and a few photographs.

The 'pouched dog with a wolf-like head' was about a metre long, and was marked like a tiger. It was a nocturnal hunter of kangaroos and wallabies, and females carried their young in a backward-opening pouch.

Thylacines were once widespread throughout Australia and Papua New Guinea, but they vanished from the mainland 2000–3000 years ago, probably because of competition from dingoes. They were still common in Tasmania when the Europeans arrived, but when they began to kill chickens and sheep the new settlers retaliated, and from 1830 a bounty was placed on the thylacine's head. The last recorded wild thylacine was shot in 1933, and the last captive specimen died in Hobart Zoo in 1936 – ironically, the year the Tasmanian State government declared the thylacine protected. It was too late; there have been no confirmed sightings since.

Another lost species is the Lord Howe Island long-eared bat, known only from a skull. The species appears to have met a sudden demise when it was eaten by rats from a ship wrecked off the island in 1918. Owls that were introduced later to control the rats probably accounted for any remaining bats.

Australia's only surviving populations of the western barred bandicoot, above, and the Shark Bay mouse, right, live on Bernier and Dorre islands in Shark Bay, Western Australia.

■ NUMBAT

OUTDOOR PLAYTIME
When young numbats grow too big to carry around, their mother places them in a burrow. While she is out foraging during the day, they emerge from the burrow from time to time and play near the entrance.

NUMBAT

The numbat is 20–27 cm long and has a bushy tail about 17 cm long. Its thin, coarse fur is reddish brown on the head and shoulders, grading to jet black on the lower back, where there are 4–11 distinct white bands.

Numbats live on termites and hunt when their quarry, which responds to soil temperature, is abundant in the upper soil layers. So, in winter, numbats feed in the middle of the day, and in summer, when the soil is hot by noon, they eat in the morning and just before dusk, and take an afternoon siesta. They find termites with their sensitive noses and use their claws to dig into the insects' tunnels just below the soil surface, or to turn over sticks and expose the termites beneath. The numbat's worm-like tongue can probe several centimetres into a termite gallery.

At night, numbats sleep in nests of grass, leaves or shredded bark, which they construct in hollow logs, dead trees or burrows. They are solitary animals, rarely seen together except in summer around the mating season or in spring, when females still have the young with them.

The production of young is highly synchronised, most mating occurring in the first two weeks of January. Thirteen or 14 days later the pink, hairless young, about 1 cm long, are born. Female numbats have no pouch but the young, usually in litters of four, attach themselves to four nipples on the lower abdomen. By the end of July, when the young are about 5 cm long, the female can leave them in a burrow while she goes out to feed during the day. They emerge from the burrow in September, are weaned by mid October, and have established their own home ranges by late December.

Numbats are now found only in the forests and woodlands of south-western Australia, but in the early days of European settlement they lived in woodlands and grasslands in arid and semi-arid areas across the southern half of the continent. The westward contraction of their range resulted from the introduction of agricultural stock, which trampled the soil, and foxes and cats, which greatly increased predation. As well, burning patterns different from those of the Aborigines may have reduced shelter from predators.

BANDED TERMITE-EATER
So specialised is the numbat for its termite diet – with its sensitive, pointed nose, its sharp claws for digging and its long, thin tongue – that scientists have placed it in a family all of its own.

In the numbat's last stronghold, in the south-west of the continent, land clearing and increasing fox numbers pushed the species towards extinction, and by 1985 numbats survived in only two small areas. Fox baiting and reintroduction programs have reversed this situation, and numbat numbers have begun to recover.
Family: Myrmecobiidae;
Scientific name: *Myrmecobius fasciatus*

BANDICOOTS AND BILBIES

Originally an Indian name for an Asian rat, *Bandicoota indicus*, the word bandicoot was then applied to a group of Australian marsupials that perhaps superficially resemble the Asian rat, at least in body size and coarseness of hair. However, the bandicoot's long snout and many pointed teeth are distinctive. The two extant genera, *Perameles* and *Isoodon*, are externally similar, but members of the former are more slenderly built than a rat, with longer snouts and bigger ears, and some species also have distinctive bands across their rump.

Bandicoots scamper along on four legs, stopping occasionally to sit up on their haunches and look out for

predators, such as dingoes. Their long, sensitive snouts detect food in the form of insects, worms, seeds and berries. These alert night creatures tunnel through undergrowth in a variety of habitats from grasslands to rainforests. When they are alarmed, they can move extremely fast on their powerful hind legs. They use their strong forepaws for scratching and digging around in leaf litter and earth for juicy morsels.

Generally solitary animals, bandicoots rest during the day in well concealed nests, which they construct in shallow depressions that they excavate in the ground. These nests, lined with grasses and twigs, have exits and entrances.

Bandicoots are prolific breeders with gestation periods that are among the shortest of all mammals: a mere 12.5 days for the long-nosed bandicoot. Females have four to eight teats in their backward-opening pouch but usually rear only two to four young in a litter. Most species can breed several times a year, and in favourable conditions females may produce offspring as often as every seven weeks.

Eight members of this family are recognised in Australia. Since the time of European settlement, both the pigfooted bandicoot (*Chaeropus ecaudatus*) and the desert bandicoot (*Perameles eremiana*) appear to have become extinct, and four other

SLENDER FEET
A bandicoot's hind limbs are very like those of the kangaroos, with long, slender feet bearing a grooming claw formed by the fusion of the second and third toes.

species have suffered extensive reductions in range and number.

Bilbies are considered members of the bandicoot family but they have their own subfamily, the Thalacomyinae. The greater bilby is the only surviving member. A slightly smaller close relative, the lesser bilby (*Macrotis leucura*), has not been seen alive in the wild since the mid 1930s, and it is now thought to be extinct.
Family: Peramelidae

GOLDEN BANDICOOT ■

The golden bandicoot looks rather similar to the southern and northern brown bandicoots. Differences in its fur are visible only under a microscope. All three species have short, powerful forelimbs and a long, pointed snout that they use for digging and probing in the soil and leaf litter while foraging for invertebrates such as termites, spiders and insect larvae, and plant matter such as seeds and bulbs. The golden bandicoot is smaller than the other two species; mature males weigh less than 670 grams and females less than 600 grams. Their head and body length is about 30 cm and their tail is about 12 cm long.

Little is known about the golden bandicoot's habits. Present-day populations live in hummock grasslands, heathlands and eucalypt woodlands, and along the margins of rainforests. During the day they nest in shallow depressions under spinifex or dense vegetation, or in rocky crevasses or caves.

A hundred years ago the golden bandicoot's range was extensive, stretching from western New South Wales throughout much of the centre of the continent to Arnhem Land, the Kimberley and the north of Western Australia. The species is

now known only from four islands and a small part of the mainland in the north-western Kimberley.

Barrow Island, off the northern coast of Western Australia, is free from foxes, feral cats and dingoes and supports an estimated 70 000 golden bandicoots. They also inhabit Marchinbar Island, off Arnhem Land. Here, where there are dingoes, but no foxes or feral cats, the bandicoots are more elusive and far less abundant. Their overlapping home ranges cover 10–40 hectares.
Scientific name: *Isoodon auratus*

SOUTHERN BROWN BANDICOOT AND NORTHERN BROWN BANDICOOT ■

The southern brown bandicoot (*Isoodon obesulus*), which has a head and body length of 33 cm and a tail 12 cm long, is a good deal smaller than the northern brown bandicoot (*I. macrourus*), which is 60 cm long

in total. These two species look very similar and are distinguished from other bandicoots by their stockier bodies and smaller, rounder ears.

The northern brown bandicoot inhabits coastal northern Australia; the southern brown bandicoot occurs in the coastal southern mainland and Tasmania. The ranges of the two species meet at the Hawkesbury River in New South Wales, but apparently they do not overlap. Interestingly, however, a separate population of southern brown bandicoots thrives in Cape York alongside three other bandicoot species. This population is quite common in Cape York, perhaps because the Aborigines of this area still use fire in order to maintain patches of young vegetation, which bandicoots find attractive. Bandicoots are still hunted by Aborigines in certain parts of Cape York. They are easily caught in newly burnt areas, as they take refuge in hollow logs.

The southern population of the southern brown bandicoot, by contrast, has suffered a reduction in range since European settlement, probably as a result of changes to the vegetation through clearing. Northern brown bandicoot numbers appear to be relatively unscathed, and the species is common in many coastal suburban areas.

Both species spend the daytime sheltering in hollow logs or in well concealed nests, which they make

■ GOLDEN BANDICOOT
Poised by the back flipper of a female green turtle, this bandicoot is about to eat the eggs that the turtle is laying.

DISTRIBUTION

■ GOLDEN BANDICOOT
■ SOUTHERN BROWN BANDICOOT

■ NORTHERN BROWN BANDICOOT

■ NORTHERN BROWN BANDICOOTS
Females usually have a litter of two to four offspring. Some females mate while carrying pouch-young and can produce several litters in a season.

■ EASTERN BARRED BANDICOOT
Close to extinction on the mainland, this species is still common in Tasmania's grasslands and woodlands.

on the ground from collected leaf litter. They forage during the night, finding worms and other invertebrates with their long, pointed snouts, and dig numerous shallow excavations across their feeding areas. They also feed on fruits, fungi and small vertebrates.
Scientific name: *Isoodon* spp.

EASTERN BARRED BANDICOOT ■

With coarse yellowy brown fur and three or four pale bands striping its hindquarters, the eastern barred bandicoot is perhaps the most eye-catching of all bandicoots. Also known as the Tasmanian barred bandicoot, this marsupial can grow to 35 cm and weighs 500–1450 grams. It is most active at night, using its forefeet to dig small holes in the earth, devouring insects, worms, tubers and bulbs. It prefers grass-land and woodland habitats, and often frequents suburban gardens. It is easily identified by its galloping gait, four-legged leaps, and hisses, grunts and squeaks.

The eastern barred bandicoot mates during most of the year. Females become pregnant again while lactating, and give birth days after weaning the previous litter. Females have eight teats, but litters are never larger than five and rarely more than three. Reproduction may be intense, but life is short – the average lifespan of the species is 18 months to two years.

The eastern barred bandicoot is rare and critically endangered. On the mainland, its distribution has shrunk to one small colony around Hamilton in south-western Victoria. Fortunately, it is still common in Tasmania, particularly in the east and the north. A statewide program of protection, habitat restoration, captive breeding and reintroduction into its former range is under way in a bid to ensure the species' survival.
Scientific name: *Perameles gunnii*

DISTRIBUTION

■ EASTERN BARRED BANDICOOT

■ LONG-NOSED BANDICOOT

WESTERN BARRED BANDICOOT

The delicate appearance of the western barred bandicoot, 20 cm long with a tail 9 cm long, conceals a ferocious temperament. Early this century, eight western barred bandicoots from a remote area were sent by rail to Adelaide in the same cage; when they arrived, all were hairless and dead, having fought and killed each other on the way. In the wild, many western barred bandicoots are partly or completely tailless after an altercation with another of their species.

Once distributed across southern Australia, these bandicoots are now found where cats and foxes are not established – in the low shrublands and hummock grasslands of Bernier and Dorre islands in Shark Bay on the west coast, and more recently re-established at Heirisson Prong on the adjacent mainland. Like most bandicoots, western barreds feed for the most part on invertebrates, which they catch by digging or hunting, though small mammals, reptiles and vegetation such as seeds, roots and herbs also feature in their diet. The stripes across the haunches that give this species its common name are indistinct in island populations, but in eastern areas their markings were so obvious that western barred bandicoots on the Nullarbor Plain were known as zebra rats.

These bandicoots nest in a shallow scrape filled with leaf litter, generally under a low-growing shrub, where they are difficult to detect. The backward-opening pouch of the female western barred bandicoot contains eight nipples, but there are rarely more than three young in a litter. On the islands, breeding stops during the hottest part of the year, but females are able to produce at least two litters before the onset of the following summer. When the young have grown fur, their mother leaves them in the nest at night while she goes out to feed.
Scientific name: *Perameles bougainville*

LONG-NOSED BANDICOOT ■

Small round holes in the earth are sure signs of the presence of long-nosed bandicoots, one of Australia's most widespread and common bandicoots. By day they sleep concealed in shallow burrows lined with dirt and leaves; when a burrow is occupied the entrance is closed and hard to see. By night they forage for insects and plants. Their grunt-like squeak is a common night sound along the eastern coast of Australia, where they prefer the sparsely vegetated floors of rain-forests and woodlands.

Long-nosed bandicoots are grey-brown, with creamy white on their belly, their forefeet and the upper surface of their hind feet. Their rump is not marked with the classic barred pattern, and they have a longer muzzle and longer, more pointed ears than other *Perameles* species. Adult long-nosed bandicoots weigh between 850 and 1100 grams, and have a body length of 31 to 42.5 cm and a coarse tail that measures 12 to 15.5 cm long. Males are slightly larger than females.

■ LONG-NOSED BANDICOOT
These bandicoots forage at night for insects and plant roots, using their forefeet to dig holes just big enough for their long, excavating snouts.

■ GREATER BILBY
This desert-dwelling species was known at one time as the rabbit-eared bandicoot because of its long ears.

Mating, which can occur at any time of the year, is the only time these solitary animals consort with one another. Gestation lasts 12.5 days. Females have eight teats, but rarely bear more than three young.

A newborn long-nosed bandicoot, which weighs a mere 0.25 grams, remains attached to the placenta for several days, growing rapidly inside its mother's backward-facing pouch. Females usually mate again when the young are 50 days old, and give birth to the next litter within days of having weaned the last.
Scientific name: *Perameles nasuta*

GREATER BILBY ■
The greater bilby has long, rabbit-like ears. It is about the same size as a rabbit and its loping gait produces tracks in the sand that look remarkably like those of a rabbit, but its nose, tail and limbs are longer.

The male greater bilby may grow to a weight of 2.5 kg; females are about half this size. Its tail, which is about two-thirds the length of its body and head, is covered with black hair for the first half and is pure white for the remainder, and it has a distinct crest on the upper surface. The greater bilby's mostly ash grey fur is soft and silky to the touch. It has white legs and under-parts, and portions of its feet, nose and ears are pale pink.

Bilbies are now restricted to mulga shrublands and areas of spinifex grassland in the Northern Territory and Western Australia and mitchell grassland in the south-west of Queensland. When conditions are favourable, they produce up to four litters a year, usually with one or

two young in each litter. Gestation takes 14 days and pouch life is about two and a half months. The young are weaned after about three months and can start to reproduce when they are six months old.

Individual bilbies may construct a number of burrows within their home range, but they gather no nesting material. The burrows spiral downwards to a depth of about 2 metres, and the bilby chooses one in which to shelter during daylight. From time to time two adult females or a male and a female may share a burrow, but bilbies mostly prefer to be solitary.

The greater bilby is now thought to be vulnerable to extinction. Its previous distribution neatly corre-sponded with the extent of arid and semi-arid Australia, which encompasses some 70 per cent of the continent, but populations are now extremely scattered and are restricted to the Tanami, Great Sandy and Gibson deserts, with an outlying population in Queensland.
Scientific name: *Macrotis lagotis*

NEW GUINEA BANDICOOTS

New Guinea bandicoots look very similar to members of the Australian bandicoot family, the Peramelidae, but their heads are more cylindrical and they are found in rainforest. Of the eight species that live in New Guinea, only one – the rufous spiny bandicoot – occurs in Australia.
Family: Peroryctidae

RUFOUS SPINY BANDICOOT
During ice ages, much of the world's water freezes and the sea level drops. It is thought that the rufous spiny bandicoot probably arrived in Australia at such a time in the late Pleistocene (about 50 000 years ago), migrating across a land bridge that formed between Cape York and southern New Guinea, but no scientific records were made of it in Australia until 1932.

The rufous spiny bandicoot lives in the rainforests and nearby forests and woodlands of Cape York in northern Queensland.

It is a solitary animal that spends its day sleeping in a hollow log or in a well-concealed nest on the ground, consisting of small heaps of leaf lit-ter entirely covering the occupant. It

AN AUSTRALIAN ICON

Sixty years ago the greater bilby shared the Australian land-scape with many native species, including bettongs, hare-wallabies, possums, numbats and other bandicoots. At least seven species of desert marsupial are now considered extinct, and many others are restricted to offshore islands or more tem-perate regions. From the bilby's decline, much can be learnt about the fate of other extinct and threatened species.

Bilby research shows that it is usually a combination of fac-tors, rather than any one, that tips a population into extinction. Bilbies may overlap with feral cats and dingoes and survive, but if foxes join the predation pressure, it seems that bilby popu-lations cannot survive. Similarly, bilbies can share their habitat with cattle or rabbits but cannot survive where stocking rates are high because heavy grazing may eliminate their food.

The bilby looks very like a rabbit and is a strong contender to replace the rabbit as Australia's Easter icon. The traditional Easter symbols – the rabbit and the egg – represent fertility, but the introduced rabbit is too fertile for Australia and is a pest. Compared with other native mammals, the bilby has excellent reproductive capabilities.

visits the hollows repeatedly but seldom uses a nest more than once.

In the Iron Range area of Cape York, the territory of the rufous spiny bandicoot overlaps those of the northern brown and southern brown bandicoots (page 79) and the long-nosed bandicoot (page 80).

The rufous spiny bandicoot can be distinguished externally from other species by its tail, which is shorter than that of any other bandicoot and is almost hairless. It also has the longest muzzle of any bandicoot in Australia – apparently an adaptation for extracting invertebrates and other items of food from crevices.

Adults weigh 1–2 kg and are about half a metre long. Their fur is blackish above and rufous below, and spiny hairs project from their coarse body fur, which give the animal its common name. Relatively little is known about this tropical bandicoot, though it is common within its limited range.
Scientific name: *Echymipera rufescens*

DISTRIBUTION

■ GREATER BILBY
■ RUFOUS SPINY BANDICOOT

PLACENTAL MAMMALS

The placental mammals, or eutherians, as they are also known, are the most numerous and diverse group of mammals on Earth. They have adapted to most environments, some living on the ground or burrowing into the earth, some living in trees, some flying, and some living entirely in the sea. Because they are so diverse, perhaps the best definition of a placental mammal is any mammal that is neither a marsupial nor a monotreme. Placental mammals belong to the subclass Eutheria.

FURRED SEA-DWELLER
Australian waters are home to several seal species, including the Australian sea-lion. These eutherians have adapted to a life at sea, but they come ashore to breed.

YELLOW DOG DINGO
The most recent native placental mammal to reach Australia is the dingo. It was probably brought here by Asian seafarers about 4000 years ago.

Placental mammals and marsupials diverged from monotremes about 200 million years ago, and placental mammals split from marsupials just after, perhaps 160 million years ago.

The early placental mammals were small insectivores, rather like modern shrews. From this stock, they diversified into many forms as they exploited available resources. Some of today's placental mammals, such as hedgehogs, resemble the primitive insectivorous stock, but others of the 4000 or so living species have adapted to feeding on grasses, fruits, tree leaves, wood, seeds, fungi, lichens, plant saps, plankton and other invertebrates, and vertebrates.

The young of many placental mammals, such as horses and cattle, are large at birth, but some, such as

many of the bat species, are born blind and helpless. Young placental mammals are nourished in the uterus by nutrients that pass from the mother's blood across the connecting placenta for a much longer term of pregnancy, or gestation, than in marsupials. As a result young placental mammals are born at a more mature stage of development than marsupials, and their lactation time is shorter. Despite the different reproductive methods, however, there seems to be little difference between marsupials and placental mammals in the total energy needed for gestation and lactation to produce an independent offspring.

The placental mammals arrived in Australia much later than the monotremes and, going by a 55 million-year-old fossil deposit at Murgon in south-eastern Queensland, at about the same time as the marsupials.

Australia now has about 172 native placental mammals. Most are terrestrial, living on the ground or in trees, and this group includes the bats, the rodents and the dingo. The rest are the ocean-dwelling dugongs, seals, whales and dolphins.

The first arrivals

The first placental mammals to reach Australia were the bats, which have not diversified much since they arrived. Only two of the 25 living Australian bat genera are endemic. Bats are found mainly in the tropics; Cape York has two-thirds of all Australia's 90 or so bat species, but Tasmania has only six.

Rodents came later than bats. The first ones probably arrived, clinging to driftwood, about six million years ago from Asia. A more recent arrival occurred about one million years ago, possibly by crossing a land bridge between New Guinea and Cape York Peninsula. Both entries included only the rat and mouse groups, but these have been highly successful and occupy habitats that range from wet forests to deserts.

AN ADAPTABLE IMMIGRANT
A brown rat carries its young in its mouth. This introduced species quickly populated Australia's coastal cities, living on human food and garbage.

The dingo is the most recent native eutherian to arrive. It is thought to have come to Australia about 4000 years ago, brought by Asian sailors. It now occupies the whole of the mainland, probably with the help of Aborigines, some of whom used it to hunt kangaroos and possums.

New Australians

The First Fleet brought a new wave of placental mammals, both herbivorous and carnivorous. As well as sheep and cattle, introduced herbivores include rabbits and hares, horses and donkeys, camels, pigs, buffaloes and goats, and deer.

Introduced carnivorous placental mammals include foxes, dogs and cats. Cats may have become established even before European settlement, from Asian anglers or from shipwrecks off the Western Australian coast. Foxes were released in the 1860s and spread rapidly in pursuit of the introduced rabbit.

Introduction of these species meant that many small marsupials and native rodents that were once widespread on the mainland are now confined to a few small islands, many of them off the coasts of Western Australia and South Australia, to which cats and foxes have not spread.

BATS

Fossils show that bats evolved as flying animals at least 60 million years ago. They are the only mammals that can truly fly, though some other mammals, such as the sugar gliders (page 63), can glide quite long distances between branches.

Bats' wings are formed in the same way as human arms, except that the bones in the wing are much more elongated, with the strong upper and lower arm bones forming the inner half of the wing and the fingers forming the outer half. These bones support an elastic membrane that is attached both to the wing bones and to the side of the body and the leg. Most bats also have another membrane between their legs, which is supported by their tail.

Bats use their wings not only for flight but also to wrap around themselves when it is cold and to fan themselves when it is hot. When they are at rest they hang upside down by their feet and fold their wings against their body.

Like other mammals, bats are furred and suckle their young at teats on the side of their chest. They usually have a single offspring, but some species may also have twins. Gestation is sometimes up to six months or more. The young are born hairless, and it is a few weeks before they grow their fur. Mothers carry their newborn in flight until they become too heavy. The young are then left at night in a nursery roost while the mother goes foraging. Once a young bat can fly independently, it joins its mother and learns how and where to find food.

There are 74 bat species in Australia, and 15 more are awaiting scientific description. Bats are more common in the tropics than elsewhere, and in one part of Cape York Peninsula 27 species have been recorded. There are two major groups of bat – the fruit-bats and the insectivorous bats. So different are these groups from one another that some scientists think that fruit-bats are more closely related to the primates (of which apes and humans are members) than they are to insect-eating bats.

Big bats ...

The fruit-bats, of which there are 12 species in Australia, belong to the family Pteropodidae in the suborder Megachiroptera – the big bats, or 'megabats'. These are fruit- and nectar-eaters. The most obvious ones

are the flying-foxes, which are frequently seen hanging from branches in their 'camps', or communal roosts, but the group also contains smaller species, such as the tube-nosed bats and the tiny blossom-bats.

Australian fruit-bats use their sharp eyes and their well-developed sense of smell for finding the fruits and flowers that make up their diet.

... and smaller bats

The insect-eating bats are members of the suborder Microchiroptera – little bats, or 'microbats' – to which all other Australian bats belong. Most are quite small: the ghost bat has a wingspan of about a metre but its body is no larger than that of a young guinea pig, and adult bats in the large family of ordinary bats can weigh as little as 3 grams.

Insect-eating bats are able to see, but unlike fruit-bats they use hearing rather than vision to navigate and to detect their insect prey (see 'Blind as a bat?', page 89).

Doing their bit

Bats help to keep their environment thriving in several important ways. Insectivorous bats, for example, help to control insect populations: a recent study of a colony of two million bats in Asia estimated that they ate more than 6000 tonnes of

HUNTING BY EAR
Insect-eating bats use a type of radar to detect their prey. This western false pipistrelle is eating a grasshopper.

insects a year and so were important in controlling insects in nearby vegetable crops. Fruit-bats that feed on nectar pick up pollen on their fur and transfer it from flower to flower, thus assisting in pollination; the flowers of many eucalypts, particularly in northern Australia, produce much of their nectar after dark, which attracts bats to the flowers. And bats that eat native fruits spread the fruit seeds through the forest as they migrate, sometimes over huge distances, from one feeding area to another. Since different fruit-bat species feed at different levels, most rainforest trees and shrubs benefit from pollination or seed dispersal by bats.
Order: Chiroptera

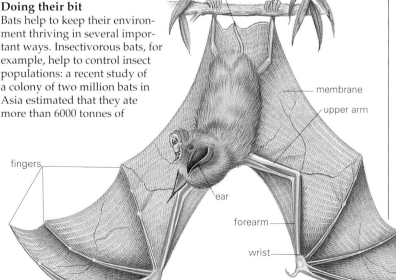

tail | hind foot | membrane | upper arm | fingers | ear | forearm | wrist | thumb

FRUIT-EATERS AND INSECT-EATERS
There are two main groups of bat: the large bats that live on fruits, such as the grey-headed flying-fox, pictured above at the top, and insect-eaters, such as the lesser long-eared bat, bottom, which are somewhat smaller.

HAND-LIKE WINGS
The bone structure of a bat's wing resembles that of an elongated human arm and hand. The bones support a thin, elastic membrane that is attached to the sides of the body and usually extends down the hind legs to the ankles and is further supported by the tail.

■ GREY-HEADED
FLYING-FOX
Sometimes the roosting
colonies, or camps, of
this species are in urban
areas. In most cases, the
same flying-fox camps
have been used through-
out human history.

DISTRIBUTION

GREY-HEADED
FLYING-FOX

SPECTACLED
FLYING-FOX

LITTLE RED
FLYING-FOX

FLYING-FOXES

The best known of the fruit-bats in
Australia, and the largest of all bats,
are the flying-foxes. Some, like the
black flying-fox, can grow to about
the size of a young rabbit, weigh
more than a kilogram and have a
wingspan exceeding one metre.
Even smaller species, such as the
little red flying-fox, can grow to
the size of a guinea pig and weigh
about 300 grams. Most flying-foxes
are mainly black with a mantle, or
collar, that is bright orange, yellowish
or brown, depending on the species.

By day flying-foxes roost in trees
in large colonies called camps.
Camps can be noisy places with
their occupants continually squabbling as they sort out their social
structure, choose mates or look after
their young. The maternity camps

where the young are raised are especially important for the bats' survival because they are the centres for
large regional populations. Other
camps are sometimes left temporarily
unattended, but they are regularly
reoccupied when the migrating bats
arrive to feed on blossoms as they
become locally available.

Flying-foxes feed on the nectar and
pollen of eucalypts, paperbarks and
banksias, and also eat rainforest
fruits such as figs. Some species fly
up to 30 kilometres a night to their
feeding area, and some migrate as
far as 1000 kilometres in a year as
they follow the flowering of eucalypts
up and down the coast. Now that so
much of the forest these bats used
to depend upon for fruit has been
cleared, they also feed in orchards.

Of the seven species known in
Australia, there has been only one
recording of the dusky flying-fox
(*Pteropus brunneus*) – on the Percy
Isles near Mackay – and it is proba-
bly now extinct. Two others, the
large-eared flying-fox (*P. macrotis*)
and the Torresian flying-fox
(*P. banakrisi*), are from the islands
in Torres Strait and are rare.
Suborder: Megachiroptera;
Subfamily: Pteropodinae

GREY-HEADED
FLYING-FOX ■
Grey-headed flying-foxes are found
along the east coast from central
Queensland southwards to
Melbourne. They are black with a
bright orange mantle. These bats
mate between March and April each
year and most of the young are born
around October. For about the first
four weeks of their life the young
are carried by their mother, clinging
onto her teat with specially curved
milk teeth and gripping her fur with
sharp baby claws. As they grow
larger the young are left behind
during the night in special 'creches'

■ SPECTACLED FLYING-FOX
These bats eat mainly light-coloured
rainforest fruits – these are easier to see
at night and tend to be left by birds,
which prefer brightly coloured ones.

in the maternity camp. Once the
offspring are able to fly on their own
and are weaned, at about six months,
they feed with their mother and
learn how to find their own food.
Scientific name: *Pteropus poliocephalus*

SPECTACLED FLYING-FOX ■
Rainforest animals that live only in
far north Queensland, these bats
have their camps normally within
the rainforest or no more than
10 kilometres away. They feed mainly
on rainforest fruits and so closely
interwoven are the lives of spectacled flying-foxes with certain trees
that some plant species may depend
entirely upon these bats for their
regeneration through the growth
of new seedlings. This bat has a
yellowish mantle that is quite distinct against its almost black fur.
Scientific name: *Pteropus conspicillatus*

LITTLE RED FLYING-FOX ■
Sometimes the camps of little red
flying-foxes number several million
bats. They are a nomadic species
that follow the blossoming of eucalypts and paperbarks in the coastal
areas of northern Australia and in
both coastal and inland areas of the
eastern mainland. Local conditions
determine the distance this species

■ LITTLE RED FLYING-FOX
Adept at smelling out flowering
trees, foraging little red flying-foxes
are important pollinators and distri-
butors of seeds in forest ecosystems.

travels and its migration patterns. One population in southern Queensland has an annual circuit, seemingly related to the flowering times of different eucalypts, that takes it from Brisbane westward to Roma in the Great Dividing Range and back. In areas that are drought-prone, the bats migrate nomadically until they find blossoms. Little red flying-foxes in the Gulf Country of northern Queensland have such an erratic food supply that they seem to be nomadic most of the year. These flying-foxes are a rusty brown.
Scientific name: *Pteropus scapulatus*

BLACK FLYING-FOX

Common in the tropical north, this species usually camps in coastal mangroves. One population migrates from New Guinea each year and progressively occupies islands south from Torres Strait from October onwards, apparently following the ripening of the mangoes. It has a reddish brown mantle.
Scientific name: *Pteropus alecto*

BARE-BACKED FRUIT-BAT

Unlike most bats, the bare-backed fruit-bat (*Dobsonia moluccensis*) has wings growing from the middle of its back instead of the sides of its body. This makes it look as if it has no fur, but in fact its fur is beneath its wings. This anatomical feature creates a larger surface area for flight, and this species is able to manoeuvre skilfully and even hover and fly backwards. It roosts, safe from predators such as sea eagles and pythons, in caves or boulder piles, where it prefers dimly lit areas to darkness.

About the size of the similar looking flying-foxes, the bare-backed fruit-bat lives only in northern Cape York and in nearby New Guinea. Being so agile, it can feed in densely vegetated areas, such as deep in the canopy of the rainforest, and along rivers. It prefers native fruits but feeds on eucalypt blossoms as well, and also forages in open forests and woodlands on species such as cycads.

It mates at the end of the wet season, and mothers give birth to one young by the start of the following wet season, when food is abundant. The young are reared in a similar way to flying-foxes, and are weaned after about four or five months.
Suborder: Megachiroptera;
Subfamily: Pteropodinae

TUBE-NOSED BATS ▪

Not all fruit-bat species are large; tube-nosed bats weigh only about 50 grams, which is about the weight of a small egg. They have round heads, large red eyes, tubular nostrils, and yellow spots on their ears and wing membranes. They usually roost alone among the foliage of rainforest trees, where their size and shape, and their habit of hanging by one leg, give them the appearance of dead leaves. This camouflage is enhanced by their yellow spotting, which resembles flecks of sunlight, and the dark stripe that runs down their back like the mid-vein of a leaf.

The most common of the three Australian species of tube-nosed bat (*Nyctimene robinsoni*) that is found along the north-eastern coast of the continent. This species' diet consists largely of the fruits of various understorey plants, but it also feeds in the canopy on fruits such as figs, quandongs and lilly-pillies. It frequently hovers around a shrub or tree while making its choice of delicacies, and then plucks the fruit from the plant before flying to a nearby branch in order to consume it. If the fruit is too large for the bat to carry, it eats it while it is on the tree, tearing out large mouthfuls by opening its jaws wide and piercing

▪ BLOSSOM-BAT
A northern blossom-bat (*Macroglossus minimus*) preens itself with its long tongue adapted for nectar gathering.

the fruit with its teeth. This action forces the bat's upper lip back and its tubular nostrils allow it to go on breathing. These nostrils may also be used for directional smelling.
Suborder: Megachiroptera;
Subfamily: Nyctimeninae

BLOSSOM-BATS ▪

These tiny, mouse-sized bats are important pollinators of rainforest and other tropical plants. They feed on the nectar from flowers of many trees and shrubs, including bananas and banksias, and transfer pollen from one plant to another in the process. For some plants in north Queensland, such as the durian, these bats are the only way in which their genes can be disseminated through the rainforest.

The tongues of blossom-bats are highly adapted for feeding on nectar and can extend to the same length as their head to reach into flowers. The tips of their tongues have fleshy projections for collecting the nectar, and their snouts are long and pointed. Unlike most Australian bats they breed twice a year, one young being born at the start of the wet season and another at the end.

Like many other animals, when food is short or when it is cold, blossom-bats slow down their metabolism and go into a state known as torpor. Torpor is like hibernation, though not as deep or as long-term.

The common blossom-bat (*Syconycteris australis*) lives along the east coast of Australia as far south as central New South Wales, while the northern blossom-bat (*Macroglossus minimus*) lives in the northern tropics. Both species have a similar biology and look like tiny flying-foxes.
Suborder: Megachiroptera;
Subfamily: Macroglossinae

▪ TUBE-NOSED BAT
This picture of an eastern tube-nosed bat (*Nyctimene robinsoni*) illustrates how the tube-nosed bats have evolved nostrils that allow them to breathe easily while gorging on fruits.

DISTRIBUTION

▪ BLACK FLYING-FOX

▪ BARE-BACKED FRUIT-BAT

▪ EASTERN TUBE-NOSED BAT

▪ BLOSSOM-BATS

■ GHOST BAT
These pale, spectral creatures are found only in Áustralia, and fossil records show that they have been here for tens of millions of years.

GHOST BAT ■

The pale fur and wings of the ghost bat (*Macroderma gigas*) account for its name, and it does look quite eerie in flight. With a body about the size of a young guinea pig and a wing-span of about a metre, it is the second largest insectivorous bat in the world. It is sometimes called the false vampire bat. (There are no true vampire bats in Australia.)

These bats feed on large insects and also prey on small animals such as lizards and other bats; at night they even take birds that are sleeping on a branch. To catch a meal, the ghost bat uses its huge ears to listen for sounds of likely prey, such as a rustling in the grass or the chirp of a bird, and then closes in with the aid of its excellent vision and kills its victim with its powerful jaws. It takes the catch to a special roost, often a small cave, to devour it.

Ghost bats used to be widespread throughout Australia, but the southern populations contracted towards the tropics – the only place where ghost bats are found today. This disappearance of the southern populations may have initially been due to the onset of arid conditions and the subsequent reduction of food resources for all predators. The introduction of feral cats and foxes and the reduction of ground vegetation by grazing livestock and rabbits, which have lowered the numbers of suitable prey, may explain the disappearance of the remaining few southern populations.

The ghost bat is an endangered species. There are only 10 000 or so ghost bats left in Australia, and all are centered around their maternity camps, which are either caves or abandoned mine shafts, where the young are born each September to November. Only ten maternity camps have been recorded so far, but there may be some more in northern Queensland.

Except in one or two cases, populations centred around each maternity camp are genetically distinct, so each camp is vital to the conservation of this species. If one of these camps were lost, it would be almost the same as losing a separate species.
Suborder: Microchiroptera;
Family: Megadermatidae

LEAF-NOSED BATS ■

Leaf-nosed bats go through a moult and can be drab brown one season and bright orange the next. In seasons when these small bats are orange, and thousands are roosting together in a cave, they resemble a living carpet tacked to the cave roof. To detect prey, these bats emit their echolocation calls through their nostrils, apparently employing the fleshy flap, called a noseleaf, around their nose to beam the sound.

There are seven leaf-nosed bat species in Australia, most living in the tropical north in caves. These bats are sensitive to humans visiting their caves and some populations have declined as a result of disturbance. Their caves need to be very hot and humid, so there are not many suitable roosts. The few that the bats are able to use are very important conservation sites.

Most leaf-nosed bats give birth at the start of the tropical wet season, when insects are most abundant. They have two pairs of teats but have only one offspring at a time. The two teats at the sides of the chest are for suckling; the other two, between the mother's legs, do not secrete milk and are for the baby to grip on to when the mother is flying. When the baby becomes too heavy it is left behind in a creche at night.

Most leaf-nosed bats weigh about 10 grams and are mouse-sized. The exception is the rare and endangered diadem leaf-nosed bat (*Hipposideros diadema*), at 50 grams. This species has two forms, which may be separate species. One lives in Queensland's wet tropics and the other is found at a few locations in the dry tropics of the Top End. The diadem leaf-nosed bat catches its food, usually large beetles or moths, by hanging from a twig and ambushing prey. It can catch several insects at a time, partially chewing each one and storing the masticated portions in cheek pouches.

The fawn leaf-nosed bat (*H. cervinus*) is found at only a few sites in the northern part of eastern Cape York and the total population is probably less than 5000 animals. Like Semon's leaf-nosed bat

■ LEAF-NOSED BAT
The orange leaf-nosed bat (*Rhinonicteris aurantius*) flies close to the ground in open woodland to catch small moths.

(*H. semoni*) from the same region, it searches for moths and other prey in the rainforest or in dense vegetation along creeks. It has a slow, butterfly-like flight and often goes hunting in small groups.

The dusky leaf-nosed bat (*H. ater*) may weigh as little as 4 grams. This species is widely distributed across northern Australia, with some colonies south of the Tropic of Capricorn. As well as using large limestone caves, this bat lives in sandstone cliff crevices and will share its home with other bat species.

The endangered orange leaf-nosed bat (*Rhinonicteris aurantius*) lives in the north-western dry tropics and moults to a lemon colour. Fossils of close relatives of this species show that these bats were living in Australia about 20 million years ago.
Suborder: Microchiroptera;
Family: Hipposideridae

HORSESHOE BATS

Horseshoe bats resemble leaf-nosed bats in their biology and in the types of roost that they occupy, but the flaps around their nostrils form a more prominent noseleaf. Like the leaf-nosed bats, they use this noseleaf to beam their echolocation calls. Their large ears are tuned to receive the echoes and can move in different directions to give the animal a complete 'picture' of its surroundings. Horseshoe bats feed close to the ground, catching mainly small moths, but occasionally taking beetles and spiders from the ground. They have great manoeuvrability in flight.

There are at least two horseshoe bat species in Australia; a third is presently being studied. The most common is the eastern horseshoe bat (*Rhinolophus megaphyllus*), which weighs around 12 grams and is mouse-sized. This species mainly inhabits the mountain and coastal forests of the Great Dividing Range and is one of the most common bats in the Queensland tropics, where large colonies roost during the day in caves, abandoned mine shafts, under bridges, and occasionally in tree hollows. In southern Australia, only underground roosts can

■ HORSESHOE BAT
The large yellow noseleaf of the large-eared horseshoe bat (*Rhinolophus philippinensis*) sits between its ears and its tiny eyes are almost invisible.

provide the high humidity that these bats need, especially when they are raising their young in summer.

The large-eared horseshoe bat (*R. philippinensis*) is about the same size as the eastern horseshoe bat but it has much larger ears – almost half the size of its body. This species is found only on the eastern side of Cape York Peninsula.
Suborder: Microchiroptera;
Family: Rhinolophidae

SHEATH-TAIL BATS ■

Sheath-tail bats are distributed throughout the world. In Australia, there are eight species divided into two groups, with those in the genus *Taphozous* living in caves and those in the genus *Saccolaimus* living in tree hollows. Sheath-tail bats have a pointed snout, big eyes, and long, tapered wings that allow them to fly very fast. Speed is gained at the cost of manoeuvrability, however, and so they are not as agile as bats with shorter, broader wings. They usually feed in forests or woodlands above the tree canopy, where there are fewer obstructions to avoid.

The common sheath-tail bat (*Taphozous georgianus*) is widely distributed across northern Australia. It usually roosts in the twilight zone at the entrance of caves or in the dimly lit crevices and slits of rocky outcrops. Although common sheath-tail bats

live in the tropics, where insects are normally abundant, they – and probably many other species – build up their body fats in summer to hedge against any scarcity of prey in winter. When insects are in short supply they go into torpor to save energy and become quite sluggish, not feeding again until the nights become warmer. Hill's sheath-tail bat (*T. hilli*), from central Australia, is similar in behaviour and biology.

The coastal sheath-tail bat (*T. australis*) has a very restricted range in northern Queensland and rarely lives further than 5 kilometres from the coast. Most colonies roost in sea caves. Colonies are usually small, less then 20 bats, and for reasons still unknown they seem to prefer

■ SHEATH-TAIL BAT
Favoured roosting sites of the common sheath-tail bat (*Taphozous georgianus*) are in the half light near cave entrances or in rock crevices. Typically, fewer than 20 roost together and individuals regularly move from one cave to another.

DISTRIBUTION

■ HORSESHOE BATS

■ SHEATH-TAIL BATS

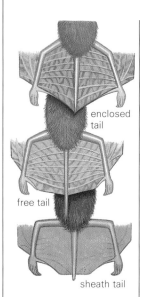

TAIL ARRANGEMENTS
The tails of most insect-eating bats are enclosed to the tip in the membrane that stretches between their legs. In freetail bats the tail is not enclosed in the membrane, and they can tuck the membrane up against their rump and leave their tail exposed. The end of a sheath-tail bat's tail is enclosed for only some of its length.

DISTRIBUTION

FREETAIL BATS

a view of the beach. Coastal development in the tropics is likely to affect populations of this species in the future. Another rare and endangered bat is the Arnhem sheath-tail bat (*T. kapalgensis*), discovered in the late 1970s and found only in Kakadu National Park.

The most widespread sheath-tail bat in the genus *Saccolaimus* is the yellow-bellied sheath-tail bat (*S. flaviventris*), which has black fur on its back, and white, cream or yellow fur below. Other species of the genus are rare and restricted in their distribution, and are endangered. The Papuan sheath-tail bat (*S. mixtus*) inhabits the north of Cape York but is also found in New Guinea. The bare-rumped sheath-tail bat (*S. saccolaimus*) has one form in the Top End and another in north Queensland, which may actually be separate species. The Top End form has black fur on its back and is white or cream underneath, while the Queensland form is reddish brown all over.
Suborder: Microchiroptera;
Family: Emballonuridae

FREETAIL BATS

In Australia there are six described species from this worldwide family of insect-eating bats. All are fast-flying; like the sheath-tail bats, they usually feed above the tree canopy.

Most freetails live in tree hollows or buildings but the northern freetail bat (*Chaerephon jobensis*) occasionally lives in caves, and there is a colony living in jetty pylons at Derby, on the northern coast of Western Australia. Like other freetail bats, the northern freetail flies fast and direct in open spaces, intercepting prey at long ranges with its loud echolocation calls. When commuting between the roost and a feeding area it only calls about every 20 seconds. This is probably to gauge its height above the ground. Small groups have been spotlighted flying about 50 metres above open ground, squabbling with each other and occasionally giving a high-frequency call to check that their height is in unobstructed airspace.

The white-striped freetail bat (*Nyctinomus australis*) is a similar

■ FREETAIL BAT
Freetail bats, such as this southern freetail (*Mormopterus planiceps*), sometimes feed on the ground. At such times they tuck their tail membrane in against their rump for protection.

species with much the same flight behaviour, though at 40 grams it is a little larger than the northern freetail. Roughly at the Tropic of Capricorn there is a neat boundary between the distributions of these two species. This may be maintained by ecological competition because both feed on the same sorts of invertebrates, such as large beetles and moths. The white-striped freetail bat is grotesque, with its wrinkled lips and large ears. Its inner ear margins join together on its muzzle, preventing its ears from folding back in flight. As in most insectivorous bats, its ears are designed for effective echo reception.

This species flies mainly above the canopy, but it also occasionally feeds on the ground on invertebrates such as scorpions. If any other group of bats moved around on the ground they would tear their wings and tail membrane, but in freetail bats the tail membrane is tucked in against the rump, leaving the tail exposed. On the end of the tail most freetails have a bunch of hairs, which the bat probably uses to sense its progress when crawling backwards into its sleeping position.

The other freetail bats are in the genus *Mormopterus*, the taxonomy of which is confused. Four species are scientifically recognised at present, but there may be another five or more with no formal name. They weigh only 8–15 grams and are difficult to identify. All appear to have similar biology. They roost in tree hollows, though in north Queensland they also occupy houses – even when people are living in them. They have thick ears, a wrinkled upper lip and a flattened head that allows them to crawl into small spaces to roost. The

■ FREETAIL BAT
In common with other members of its family, the white-striped freetail bat (*Nyctinomus australis*) has wrinkled lips and large leathery ears.

entry to a roost used by one colony of southern freetails in a low mulga tree was a slit just large enough to accommodate a man's little finger.

There are three types of southern freetail bat (*M. planiceps*). One has shaggy grey fur and is found in the eucalypt forests and woodlands of the south-east, another has short fur and prefers arid regions, and the third is found in southern Western Australia. The same taxonomic problems apply to the little northern freetail bat (*M. loriae*) and Beccari's freetail bat (*M. beccarii*), both of which live in the northern tropics. The rarest of this group, the eastern freetail bat (*M. norfolkensis*) has a very restricted distribution. It seems to be threatened by logging and is listed as an endangered.
Suborder: Microchiroptera;
Family: Molossidae

Blind as a bat?

In fact, bats are far from blind, but they have evolved complex systems of hearing and smell to enable them to navigate and hunt in the dark.

The large group of insect-eating bats have small eyes and use mainly sound to locate their prey and avoid obstacles as they fly. Most fruit-bats, on the other hand, have large eyes and rely on their acute senses of sight and smell for these purposes.

Radar for bats

Many bat species use sound and hearing to map their environment – a system known as echolocation. Like radar or sonar, it works by analysing signals reflected from hard objects.

Imagine calling out in a canyon: if the walls are a long way off the echo takes a long time to return, but if the walls are close the echo returns more quickly. If you timed how long the echo took and divided the time by the speed of sound,

you could work out how far away the canyon walls were. For a human this would involve laborious calculation, but bats do it automatically – and they can do it with a number of objects at the same time, including moving prey.

Bats call at a sound frequency that humans cannot hear. When a bat is simply navigating, it utters about 20 calls a second, but when it homes in on an insect the rate increases to 100 calls a second. Bats that fly fast need information about distant aspects of their environment, so they must call loudly. To avoid deafening themselves, they switch their hearing off when they are calling and turn it on again in time to hear the echo. The mental activity involved is a marvellous example of the capabilities of these fascinating animals.

Sight and smell

Australian fruit-bats navigate using their very powerful sight, and they also have an acute sense of smell for finding food – mainly fruits or flowers. Their sharp eyesight is due to the shape of

An x-ray shows the highly developed inner organs of hearing at the back of a bat's skull that the animal uses to operate its system of echolocation.

their retina; instead of being flat like that of many other animals, it is folded so that more light receptors can be fitted into the eyeball. A fruit-bat's sense of smell is so keen that it can detect a tiny piece of banana from 100 metres away.

The unusual tube-nosed insect bat supplements its radar equipment with a directional smelling apparatus. In cool weather its insect prey do not fly, so the bat uses its sideways-pointing nostrils to locate perfumed flowers, just as humans can work out where a sound is coming from because they have an ear on each side of their head.

The little red flying-fox, above, smells out flowering trees with such accuracy that beekeepers often follow it when they want to move their hives.

In this unusual shot of a rare species, a ghost bat, right, flies back to its roost with a house mouse.

DISTRIBUTION

■ BENTWING BATS

■ PIPISTRELLES

■ FALSE PIPISTRELLES

■ TUBE-NOSED INSECT
BAT

■ **BENTWING BATS**
The biggest known nursery colony of little bentwing bats (*Miniopterus australis*) is in a cave at Mount Etna in central Queensland where over 100 000 bats have been recorded. Their departure from the cave is spectacular, and attracts pythons and green tree frogs to the entrance, where they occasionally snatch a meal from the air. Ghost bats are also seen diving through the outpouring column of bentwing bats to catch prey.

ORDINARY BATS

This family has more species than any other bat family in Australia: 39 have been named so far, and a further five are awaiting scientific names. They are called ordinary bats because most have plain faces without large noseleaves. Most are mouse-sized and weigh 10–15 grams, but in some species the adults are no heavier than 3 grams – about the weight of a book of matches.

There are 11 genera of this family in Australia, most containing both common and abundant species and species that are highly specialised. Some specialised species have a unique way of feeding, others roost only in particular locations, and yet others prefer restricted habitats such as wet gullies or patches of thick forest. They are sensitive to habitat disturbance, which often causes serious conservation problems.
Suborder: Microchiroptera;
Family: Vespertilionidae

BENTWING BATS ■

There are two bentwing bat species in Australia, so called because they fold their very long third finger inside their wing in a different way to other bats. The large bentwing bat (*Miniopterus schreibersii*) lives in forests throughout the east coast and the ranges, and in the woodlands of the Kimberley and the Northern Territory. The little bentwing bat (*M. australis*) is found in the warmer areas of the east coast. Bentwings form large colonies, and live in different caves or mines depending on whether they are breeding or (in the south) hibernating.

In southern regions large bentwing bats mate around late May to early June, just before the winter hibernation period. The embryo develops slowly over winter but grows more rapidly when the bats are active in the spring. In the tropics, where hibernation is unnecessary because insects are available all year round, mating occurs in September. Whether their mothers live in the tropics or the cooler south, all the babies, or 'pups', are born in December.

Nursery caves must have a special domed ceiling where the pups can be kept warm, at around 30°C, by their own trapped body heat. The furless pink young are placed in huge creches, and it has been estimated that they are packed together at a density of 3000 to a square metre. Remarkably, females appear to be able to find their own baby in the crowd when they return to suckle them in the morning.

While warm caves are used for breeding, cooler ones are used for hibernation. These caves can be quite a distance apart, and during the annual cycle to get to them, the bats often travel several hundred kilometres – in some cases as far as 1000 kilometres. They often stop over at other caves or abandoned mines during their migration. The loss of just one cave can upset the species' life cycle, so these caves are very important conservation areas.
Scientific name: *Miniopterus* spp.

PIPISTRELLES AND FALSE PIPISTRELLES

Two pipistrelle species live in Australia's tropical northern woodlands – the rare Cape York pipistrelle (*Pipistrellus adamsi*) in the north-east and the more common northern pipistrelle (*P. westralis*) in the north-west. The northern pipistrelle prefers to feed in mangroves.

There are also two false pipistrelle species, which live only in Australia. Their common name comes from their close relationship to the pipistrelles. The eastern false pipistrelle (*Falsistrellus tasmaniensis*) lives in cool temperate eucalypt forests and can endure quite cold climates – one has even been recorded from the top of Mount Kosciuszko. The western false pipistrelle (*F. mackenziei*) has been recorded only in the forests of south-west Western Australia; like its eastern cousin, it roosts in tree hollows in small colonies of 30 or so. One colony was found in a hollow log on the ground in jarrah forest.
Scientific names: *Pipistrellus* spp. and *Falsistrellus* spp.

TUBE-NOSED INSECT BAT

The extremely rare tube-nosed insect bat lives only in the rainforests of the wet tropics of north Queensland. It has short, broad wings that enable it to fly like a butterfly. Its nostrils are small tubes that point sideways, though they are smaller than those of the tube-nosed fruit-bats (page 85).

Insectivorous bats normally fold their wings at their sides, but the tube-nosed insect bat wraps them around its body like an umbrella to

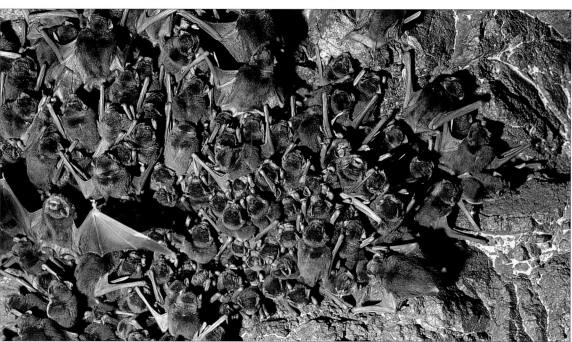

help keep its fur dry in the misty mountain-tops where it prefers to live. This adaptation leads scientists to believe that it may roost during the day among foliage.

Although nights are usually quite warm in the tropics, high up in the mountains it is fairly cool and, as insects stop flying when temperatures fall below 15°C in winter, it is likely that this bat also feeds on the nectar from rainforest flowers – or at least searches the flowers for insects that may be attracted there.
Scientific name: *Murina florium*

LARGE-FOOTED MOUSE-EARED BATS
The three species of large-footed mouse-eared bats are highly specialised. They mainly feed over the smooth surfaces of lakes or ponds, using echolocation to detect the small ripples made by aquatic insects or tiny fish. They then catch their prey by dragging their very long toes through the water and grabbing it with their long claws. So that they can cut smoothly through the water they have flattened bones in their toes instead of round bones like other bats.

Large-footed mouse-eared bats roost in caves or old mine shafts, or under bridges. When they are breeding, each male forms a small territory in the roost, where he defends a harem of several females. The roof of the roosting place usually has small domed pockets where each little group is able to keep its distance from the others.

The species *Myotis moluccarum* is the most widely distributed of the three large-footed mouse-eared bats,

■ VESPADELUS
The tiny eastern forest bat (*Vespadelus pumilus*) feeds in dense, moist forests and roosts in tree hollows.

and ranges along the north coast of Australia southward to about the New South Wales border. *M. macropus* ranges along the coast of New South Wales and Victoria, with some populations living inland on the border between South Australia and Victoria. *M. adversus* has the smallest range of all, being found only in a small pocket centred around Lismore in northern New South Wales.
Scientific name: *Myotis* spp.

WATTLED BATS ■
Among the most common of the ordinary bat species are the wattled bats. They are black with a V-shaped patch of white fur on their undersides. Most live in tree hollows or occasionally, in treeless habitats, in caves. All have a small flap of skin at the rear edge of their mouth, the purpose of which is unknown.

The chocolate wattled bat (*Chalinolobus morio*), named for the colour of its fur, is common in much of southern Australia. Gould's wattled bat (*C. gouldii*), very dark brown on the head and shoulders, occurs over the whole continent except Cape York. The hoary wattled bat (*C. nigrogriseus*), black frosted with grey, is found in northern Australia. All three species live in eucalypt forests and woodlands.

The little pied bat (*C. picatus*), of inland eastern Australia, and the large-eared pied bat (*C. dwyeri*), of south-eastern Queensland and north-eastern New South Wales,

are black with a strip of white fur along their flanks. They appear to prefer caves as daytime roosts, especially the large-eared pied bat. Both species are endangered.
Scientific name: *Chalinolobus* spp.

VESPADELUSES ■
There are nine species in this group, all of which live only in Australia. Most are extremely common, and in most areas several species share the same habitat. In the eucalypt forests of the south-east, three species are generally abundant – the large forest bat (*Vespadelus darlingtoni*), the southern forest bat (*V. regulus*), and the little forest bat (*V. vulturnus*). These bats roost in the hollows of trees and feed on small moths and other small insects. They are tiny: the body of the little forest bat can weigh as little as 3 grams, and even the biggest of the three, the large forest bat, weighs only 8 grams.

Two species occupy the central arid zone – the inland forest bat (*V. baverstocki*), which lives in the hollows of low trees or in buildings, and Finlayson's cave bat (*V. finlaysoni*), which roosts in caves and in the crevices of rocky outcrops.

The eastern cave bat (*V. troughtoni*) is common in the coastal tropics of Queensland but less abundant in the cooler part of its range. These bats, which weigh about 5 grams, feed mainly on mosquitoes and are active only in late afternoon and just after dusk, when mosquitoes are most plentiful. During its lifetime each bat eats hundreds of thousands of these insects – an example of the benefits bats bestow on humans.

So strange is the distribution of the eastern forest bat (*V. pumilus*) that it may one day turn out to be three different species. One population lives in north-eastern New South Wales, another at Kroombit Tops in

■ LARGE-FOOTED MOUSE-EARED BATS

■ WATTLED BATS

■ VESPADELUSES

■ WATTLED BAT
A distinctive black and white bat, the little pied bat (*Chalinolobus picatus*) lives in semi-arid regions in southern Queensland, New South Wales and South Australia and generally roosts in caves.

■ GOLDEN-TIPPED BAT
This bat's woolly fur is tipped with gold and it has golden fur on its arms and thumbs. Its diet consists largely of spiders which it plucks from webs as it flies slowly through dense vegetation.

■ BROAD-NOSED BATS

■ GOLDEN-TIPPED BAT

■ LONG-EARED BATS

south-eastern Queensland, and the third in the mountain rainforests of north Queensland. They roost in tree hollows and commonly bear twins each year, usually in December.

Two other vespadeluses are restricted to the tropics. The western cave bat (*V. caurinus*) is common from the Top End to the Kimberley, but the rare yellow-lipped bat (*V. douglasorum*), which has yellow feet, arms and head, is found only in the high-rainfall areas of the north-western Kimberley region. Small colonies live in caves and bear one offspring during the wet season.
Scientific name: *Vespadelus* spp.

BROAD-NOSED BATS

Broad-nosed bats are common over most of Australia. As their name suggests, all have broad, flat noses. The inland broad-nosed bat (*Scotorepens balstoni*) and the little broad-nosed bat (*S. greyii*) are found throughout most of the continent, especially in the arid zone, where they live in small colonies in tree hollows or in the hollow cores of timber fence posts.

The eastern broad-nosed bat (*S. orion*) and the greater broad-nosed bat (*Scoteanax rueppellii*) have more restricted distributions and live only along the east coast, mainly in forests or woodlands. The northern broad-nosed bat (*Scotorepens sanborni*) lives in coastal forests in the tropical north and east.

All species of broad-nosed bat have one young each year during the summer, but little else is known about their biology.
Scientific name: *Scotorepens* spp. and *Scoteanax rueppellii*

GOLDEN-TIPPED BAT ■

One of the most unusual bats in Australia is the golden-tipped bat, named for the golden fur on its arms and the golden tips on its woolly body fur. Unlike most bats, it can fly in dense tangles of vines, where it searches for spiders as they sit in their webs. These bats have very broad wings that permit them to hover while searching, but entering the vines is still risky for them – they often become draped in cobwebs or tear their wings on thorns.

The golden-tipped bat is sparsely distributed along the east coast of the mainland and has the most unusual roosting behaviour of any bat in Australia; it prefers to crawl into the nests of scrubwrens, which are mossy spherical constructions that usually hang from a branch over a creek bed. The specialised feeding and roosting habits of this bat give rise to concern for the conservation of this unique species.
Scientific name: *Kerivoula papuensis*

■ LONG-EARED BATS
Right, a lesser long-eared bat (*Nyctophilus geoffroyi*) shows the large ears characteristic of this group. Below, a Gould's long-eared bat (*N. gouldi*) flies slowly through its forest habitat.

LONG-EARED BATS ■

Members of this group have extremely large ears that they can fold back when they are at rest. They fly slowly and use their ears to listen for the sounds of the calling insects they catch from bark or leaves. They also eat flying moths and ants. All nine species live in tree hollows, under loose bark, in buildings, and even under old sacks hanging in farm sheds. Tropical long-eared bats often roost in the skirt of dead fronds beneath the foliage of palm and pandanus trees. This adaptable choice of roosts is one reason why they are so common.

Long-eared bats usually give birth to twins once a year in summer, and carry them in flight even when the two babies together are as heavy as the mother. At this stage, however, flight is difficult for the mother, so at night she leaves them in the roost.

Some species, such as the lesser long-eared bat (*Nyctophilus geoffroyi*), are very common and widespread in Australia, whereas others have more restricted distributions. The lesser long-eared bat is one of only two long-eared bat species in Tasmania. The second is the Tasmanian long-eared bat (*N. sherrini*). Both species go into torpor in the colder months.
Scientific name: *Nyctophilus* spp.

RODENTS

Rodents are an enormously successful and diverse group of animals and today there are some 2000 species worldwide, accounting for over 42 per cent of all mammal species. The group includes, among others, mice, rats, squirrels, guinea pigs and hamsters. The relationship of humans to rodents is varied: some rodents are reviled for spreading diseases or eating crops; others are kept as pets or used for medical research; still others, such as the chinchillas, are farmed for their fur; and the capybara of South America, which may reach a weight of 50 kg, is farmed for food.

All rodents have a pair of chisel-shaped incisor teeth in both upper and lower jaws. The front, outer surfaces of these teeth are covered with hard yellow enamel, while the backs are softer. Most rodents eat hard or fibrous vegetable food, such as seeds and leaves, which wears down the backs of the incisors faster than the harder front surfaces so that the teeth are kept sharp. These teeth grow constantly during the animal's life. At the back of their mouth rodents have up to 18 cheek teeth that can grind even the toughest foods. Rodent species that eat softer foods have fewer cheek teeth. Between the incisors and these cheek teeth there is a gap (diastema) where there are no teeth at all.

Rodents in Australia

Rats and mice occur throughout Australia but are most diverse in the arid centre and in spots along the east coast. Other concentrations occur in the extreme south-east, the south-west and the Top End. There are about 58 known species of native rat and mouse, and at least two others are still to be scientifically described. Since European settlement, at least eight species are known to have become extinct, a further 12 are at risk and many others have suffered reductions in range and number.

All Australian rodent species belong to the Muridae family. Most species in this family have three pairs of cheek teeth as well as the two pairs of incisors common to all rodents. Most have long tails; some are naked while others are furred. The Muridae family is the world's largest and most widespread family of mammals, with over 1300 species in some 16 subfamilies. Only two of these subfamilies, however, are represented in Australia.

The vast majority of Australian rodents are from the subfamily Hydromyinae, sometimes referred to as the old endemics, and evolved from a few species that arrived from eastern Indonesia about six million years ago. A further seven species, often called the new endemics, evolved from Asian rats (*Rattus* spp.) that arrived in Australia only a million years ago, or less. These belong to the subfamily Murinae, as do four more recently introduced species – the house mouse, the black rat, the brown rat and the Pacific rat.

Most of the 'old endemics' have slow reproductive rates compared with those of the 'new endemics'. Females have only four teats and usually have litters of between one and four young, sometimes five or six, after gestation periods of up to 38 days. Though some species, such as the fawn-footed melomys, can breed in the same season as their birth, it is not usual. In these slower-breeding species, wild animals can live for three or four years.

HELPLESS AND HAIRLESS
Rodents are born naked and stay in the nest until they are weaned, at one to two months. These are newborn house mice.

Reproductive rates in the Murinae subfamily are much faster. Females have up to 12 teats and rear litters of between four and eight young. The gestation period is 21–24 days, and all species are ready to mate again soon after giving birth. Animals may become sexually mature at one to three months and often breed in the same season as their birth. The new endemics live fast and die young, living to about two years in the wild.

In tropical parts of Australia rodent populations are often stable throughout the year. In seasonal environments in the south-east and south-west, breeding occurs in spring and summer and populations peak in summer and autumn. In arid-zone species, populations can rise and fall rapidly in 'boom and bust' cycles: these are probably driven mainly by the food supply, but they may also be affected by fire, flood rains, drought and other factors.

Population explosions

Many Australian animals are prone to 'boom and bust' cycles, in which populations increase massively and then crash. This pattern is common in arid and semi-arid regions, where droughts tend to be interspersed with unpredictable rainfall, and populations of rodent species in these habitats are likely to explode in this way.

During drought, animals that need free water and fresh vegetation live in small pockets of land at springs or seepages near watercourses. These refuges allow small, stable populations to survive in an otherwise hostile environment and permit colonists to move into surrounding areas when conditions are favourable.

PLAGUE PROPORTIONS
House mice, an introduced species, reach their highest densities where human habitation or agriculture provides a constant supply of food. They are especially common in the grain-producing regions of eastern Australia. On average, a mouse plague occurs once every four years somewhere in this area.

A WELL-TAILED FAMILY
Most rodents have long tails, usually about as long as their bodies or longer. This is a prehensile-tailed rat, which climbs trees with the aid of its tail.

DISTRIBUTION

○ GRASSLAND MELOMYS

■ CAPE YORK MELOMYS
■ FAWN-FOOTED
   MELOMYS

■ PREHENSILE-TAILED
   RAT

A large downpour in the arid zone can trigger rapid and widespread growth of seeds lying dormant in the soil and provide food for animals across vast areas of land, so that animals that could previously survive only in the refuges move across the landscape in great numbers, their populations increased still further by rapid breeding. This response is common in species such as the long-haired rat and the house mouse, which have enormous reproductive potential based on short pregnancies, rapid maturation and large litter sizes. In some desert species, such as the desert mouse

■ MELOMYS
An agile climber, the fawn-footed melomys (*Melomys cervinipes*) moves along tree branches and among vines, browsing on leaves, shoots and fruits.

and the plains rat, rainfall stimulates breeding. Mice can also detect rainfall in dry areas near where rain has fallen, and will migrate as much as 15 kilometres to take advantage of the improved conditions. All these factors can cause populations to boom, and some species can quickly reach plague proportions.

Plague populations move quickly across the landscape, feasting on the sprouting vegetation. Unfortunately for farmers, when the vegetation has been devoured, the hungry animals sometimes move into farmland, destroying crops. As the land dries out and all the plants are either eaten or die, the animals begin to lose condition. Scientists are not sure what causes the great die-off of animals that follows. However, lack of food causes starvation, and unhealthy animals may become more susceptible to diseases and parasites.

Populations of predators, such as birds of prey, foxes, dingoes and feral cats, also boom in response to the large amount of food available, and may play a role in the bust of the rodent populations. Once the rodent populations have begun to crash, the predators must compete to find enough food for themselves. The decrease of the rodent populations can be accelerated by the increased predation pressure, but soon there is not enough prey available and predator populations also crash. Mobile predators, such as birds of prey, can leave the area in search of other prey, but land predators are likely to die of starvation.
Order: Rodentia; Family: Muridae

MELOMYSES ■

These nocturnal rodents spend their day in nests lined with dry leaves in dense vegetation or in hollows, emerging at night to gnaw on plant material. Melomys means 'Melanesian mouse', and most species occur in New Guinea and nearby islands; only four are found in Australia. They have a long, semi-prehensile tail that helps them climb, broad hind feet and fine coats except on their tails, which are virtually hairless. They usually breed throughout the year but can breed seasonally in unfavourable conditions. The female has four teats but usually bears only two or three young.

The grassland melomys (*Melomys burtoni*) has the widest distribution of the four Australian species. In Western Australia and the Northern Territory it occurs mainly in closed forests and woodlands, but in Queensland and northern New South Wales it lives only in heathlands and grasslands – possibly because the forests and woodlands in these regions are occupied by two other melomys species, the Cape York melomys (*M. capensis*) in Cape York and the fawn-footed melomys (*M. cervinipes*) in coastal eastern Australia between Cooktown in Queensland and Gosford in New South Wales. Both these species are similar in appearance and size and differ from the grassland melomys, which is smaller and has longer fur and a hairier tail.

The Bramble Cay melomys (*M. rubicola*) occurs only on a small vegetated coral cay in Torres Strait. Little is known of this species, and it is critically endangered because the cay is being slowly eroded by the sea.
Scientific name: *Melomys* spp.

PREHENSILE-TAILED RAT

This is possibly the most beautiful rat in Australia, with soft, grey body fur, a pure white belly, black rings around its eyes and buff markings on its face. As it moves around the trees and bushes, it wraps its long, prehensile tail around twigs like a corkscrew to give it grip and balance.

It lives in the rainforests of north Queensland and New Guinea and is active during the night, when it forages among the trees. Because of the difficulty of studying an animal at night, and because it does not enter traps, little is known about the habits of this species in Australia, except that it feeds on leaves and fruits and the female raises two to three young at a time.
Scientific name: *Pogonomys mollipilosus*

RODENT SIZE

For biologists, who spend hours in the field measuring their temporary captives, the exact size of a mouse or rat provides important information. The terms 'mouse' and 'rat', however, do not refer to two different types of rodent but merely indicate size: when people came across an unnamed species they simply called it a mouse if it was small and a rat if it was larger.

Most people have an idea of what is 'mouse-size' and what is 'rat-size'. The body and head length of most mice is from 6 cm to 10 cm and they weigh about 10–50 grams. The majority of rats are between 10 cm and 22 cm from nose tip to the base of the tail and they weigh about 50–350 grams.

To illustrate the size range, the largest Australian rodent, the water-rat (*Hydromys chrysogaster*) is shown here, accompanied by the smallest – the delicate mouse (*Pseudomys delicatulus*).

MASKED WHITE-TAILED RAT ▦

This endemic Australian rodent is found in rainforest and is confined to three populations in north Queensland on mountain range summits that are separated by river valleys. With its fawn fur and small body size, it resembles the melomys, but its thick, white-tipped tail identifies it as a member of the genus *Uromys*. When disturbed, both sexes give a rasping, honking call.

Little is known of this creature's habits in the wild because it is rarely found, but it appears to be mainly a ground-dweller and nocturnal, though one has been seen active at midday. It eats hard-shelled nuts and insects. The lesser sooty owl is one of its known predators.
Scientific name: Uromys hadrourus

GIANT WHITE-TAILED RAT ▦

The giant white-tailed rat is one of the largest rodents in Australia; an adult male weighs as much as 1 kilogram and is about 38 cm long – about the size of a small cat. Its coarse body fur is grey except on the belly, where it is pure white. Its long, naked tail is mottled black and white near the base to about two-thirds of the way down, and pure white to the tip. This tail is partially prehensile and the rat uses it to provide grip when climbing. It has a call that is similar to that of the masked white-tailed rat but louder.

It occurs in New Guinea and north Queensland, where it inhabits the

▦ TREE-RAT
The black-footed tree-rat (*Mesembriomys gouldii*) is the largest of the tree-rats. It lives in tropical woodlands and forests and leads a rather solitary existence.

▦ MASKED WHITE-TAILED RAT
Tropical rainforest is the habitat of this rat. Adults have a white throat and chest and a distinctive dark eye ring.

rainforests and extends into neighbouring wooded country along watercourses. It is mostly nocturnal, nesting in a burrow or a tree hollow during the day and foraging on the ground or in the tree tops at night. Because of its size and bold habits, it is the most visible of the rainforest rats. Its staple diet is nuts, fruits and insects, and it can often be heard gnawing through hard-shelled nuts. So powerful are its incisors that it can even open coconut shells.

This rat often invades buildings, where it causes considerable damage by chewing virtually anything it comes across – including electrical wires, water pipes, cupboard doors, tinned food and soap.

It breeds during the wet season and females usually give birth to two or three offspring. Animals can live for at least four years.
Scientific name: *Uromys caudimaculatus*

TREE-RATS ▦

The tropical monsoonal north, from the Pilbara and Kimberley region east to Cape York Peninsula, is home to a variety of tree-rats – large, squirrel-like native rodents that are immediately distinguishable from other rats by their long, brush-tipped tails. The tree-rats all prefer eucalypt woodlands with a grassy understorey and rarely venture into rainforest. They build their nests and gather food in trees, and they also collect dropped food from the

ground, usually scampering up a nearby branch in order to eat it.

The largest of the tree-rats, and one of Australia's heavyweight rodents, is the black-footed tree-rat (*Mesembriomys gouldii*), which weighs up to 900 grams. Its head and body length is about 30 cm, and it is grey with a white-tipped tail 40 cm long. It eats mainly fleshy and hard native fruits and large, tough seeds. The golden-backed tree-rat (*M. macrurus*), about which little is known, is a good deal smaller than the black-footed tree-rat, at about 300 grams in weight and 22 cm in length. It eats fruits, seeds and vegetation.

The brush-tailed tree-rat (*Conilurus penicillatus*) is the smallest of the tree-rats, at about 16 cm long. This rat is grey to golden-brown and has large ears, a blunt face and a long, finely brushed tail. It eats a variety of fruits, seeds and vegetation.
Scientific name: *Mesembriomys* spp. and *Conilurus penicillatus*

DISTRIBUTION

▦ MASKED WHITE-TAILED RAT
□ GOLDEN-BACKED TREE-RAT

▦ GIANT WHITE-TAILED RAT
□ BRUSH-TAILED TREE-RAT

□ BLACK-FOOTED TREE-RAT

▦ GIANT WHITE-TAILED RAT
This rat's tail is partly prehensile – it can curl over a surface and has scales on it that provide a degree of grip when the animal is climbing.

WATER-RAT

FALSE WATER-RAT

FORREST'S MOUSE

LAKELAND DOWNS
MOUSE

■ GREATER
STICK-NEST RAT
This rat builds its conical
communal nest with
sticks as thick as a man's
thumb. The nest may be
up to a metre high and
1.5 metres in diameter,
and substantial enough
to deter dingoes.

WATER-RAT ■

The water-rat has somehow managed to survive in all Australian states, despite heavy exploitation during the depression of the 1930s for its luxurious, soft, muskrat-like fur and the unrelenting efforts of its human neighbours to fill swamps and build protective devices against floods and high tides.

These rats have waterproof fur and webbed hind feet for swimming. Their colour varies from almost black to slate grey above and orange to white below, and their furry tails have a distinctive white tip. Males grow to over 30 cm long, with tails almost as long again, and weigh 600–1200 grams; females are smaller.

They eat a variety of aquatic and terrestrial creatures, from mussels to small mammals. In winter they also sometimes eat plants. They live around water, either fresh or salt, from coastal beaches and mangroves through to the lakes and ephemeral river systems of the dry interior, and make their nest at the end of tunnels in banks. The presence of water-rats can be detected from the piles of discarded food scraps, such as mussel and crab shells, that pile up around their feeding spots.

Most Australian rodents are nocturnal, but the water-rat forages both day and night, possibly because it has difficulty maintaining its body temperature in cold water. To restore its temperature, it spends a considerable amount of time shivering on land, preferably in the sun.

■ WATER-RAT
Lizards, frogs, crayfish, insects – sometimes even swimming water birds – are all part of this powerful hunter's diet.

Female water-rats may breed up to five times a year, each litter comprising three or four young. Populations, however, are usually controlled by the availability of one or two major food items, such as crayfish, and local water-rat extinctions often occur.
Scientific name: *Hydromys chrysogaster*

FALSE WATER-RAT

This small water-rat is found in mangroves, freshwater lagoons, swamps and sedged lakes from the Northern Territory to south-eastern and coastal central Queensland. It usually nests in either large mud mounds built in the reed zone or in simple tunnels in the high-tide bank. At low tide it forages around mangroves and sedgeland for small crustaceans (mainly crabs), marine flatworms, snails and bivalves. It has a head

and body length of about 10 cm, and its silky fur is slate grey flecked with white above and pure white below.

The habitat of this rare species is threatened by urban development and the building of marinas and golf courses. Waste-water treatment plants and the erection of tidal walls are also adding to the pollution of its feeding grounds. Preservation of sedgelands and saltmarshes, avoidance of habitat fragmentation, and maintenance of water levels and quality are vital to this animal's survival.
Scientific name: *Xeromys myoides*

FORREST'S MOUSE AND LAKELAND DOWNS MOUSE

These two plump native mice are grey to brown above and white below, and have short tails. They are so alike in appearance that they can be firmly identified only by a dental examination. Both have small litters of two to four, which are born after about 30 days' gestation and become independent at a month old.

Forrest's mouse (*Leggadina forresti*) occurs in some of Australia's driest habitats – mulga, spinifex, gibber plains and sand dunes in central Australia. It lives on seeds, insects and vegetation, and probably extracts enough water from its food to survive without drinking.

The Lakeland Downs mouse (*L. lakedownensis*), on the other hand, occurs in the seasonally flooded grassy woodlands of the northern coast. Its numbers periodically rise following favourable conditions.
Scientific name: *Leggadina* spp.

GREATER STICK-NEST RAT ■

These fluffy, big-eared native rats are best known for the enormous bonfire-like piles of twigs and branches that they construct as a communal nest.

The greater stick-nest rat is extinct on the mainland because of habitat destruction caused by the spread of sheep and cattle across southern Australia, and until recently was

restricted to East and West Franklin islands, off South Australia. Captive breeding and translocation programs have established populations on Salutation Island, off Western Australia, and Reevesby and St Peters islands, off South Australia. This has doubled the population of greater stick-nest rats to about 2500 individuals, and the species is now considered vulnerable rather than endangered. The establishment of mainland populations continues to be thwarted by predation from cats, foxes and barn owls.
Scientific name: *Leporillus conditor*

ROCK-RATS
Australia's five unique rock-rats are patchily distributed in rocky habitats across northern, central and Western Australia. They range from small mouse-sized animals to large rats. Their fat, carrot-shaped tails and bulging eyes distinguish them from other rats and mice.

The ancestors of rock-rats probably ranged over northern Australia, but with climate changes over millions of years the ideal rock-rat habitat has dwindled to small, widely spread mountain ranges. In this geographical isolation, rock-rats have evolved into several species. The Kimberley rock-rat (*Zyzomys woodwardi*) is the most widespread of the large rock-rats, and occurs in the Kimberley region of Western Australia; the Arnhem Land rock-rat (*Z. maini*) is restricted to a small area of the western Arnhem Land escarpment, including Kakadu National Park; and the rare Carpentarian rock-rat (*Z. palatalis*) occurs in only four gorges at the base of the Gulf of Carpentaria.

These large rock-rats have a habitat of rugged boulder-strewn rock piles covered in monsoon rainforests or broadleaf tropical woodlands. In contrast, the mouse-sized common rock-rat (*Z. argurus*) is widespread and abundant in rocky habitats in much of northern Australia. These tropical rock-rats gnaw woody nuts to reach the seeds within, and their telltale piles of chewed seed coats are occasionally found along cliffs or under overhangs.

The rare central rock-rat (*Z. pedunculatus*), which has a particularly hairy tail, was rediscovered in 1996 in the west Macdonnell Ranges near Alice Springs – until then, it had

■ HOPPING-MOUSE
Mitchell's hopping-mouse (*Notomys mitchellii*), like other members of its genus, forages on all fours but bounds rapidly on its hind limbs when alarmed.

not been seen since 1960. It is intermediate in size between the small common rock-rat and the large rock-rats and, judging from fossil deposits, it was once widespread across central and central western Australia on stony spinifex-clad ranges.
Scientific name: *Zyzomys* spp.

BROAD-TOOTHED RAT ■
The broad-toothed rat is a challenge to researchers who are trying to track its winter movements below thick snow in the upland heathlands, open woodlands and wet eucalypt forests of the south-eastern highlands.

These thickly furred light to dark brown rats do not appear to hibernate, but during the coldest months they nest in small mixed-sex groups, foraging little and staying close to the nesting site. When conditions are less extreme, females aggressively discourage males from entering their home range, which in summer covers up to 3 hectares and is criss-crossed by runways through the dense undergrowth of sedges, shrubs and grasses. When snow blankets the vegetation, these runways remain serviceable and are insulated from biting winds by the snow. The rats continue to use them to reach the grasses, seeds and shrubs that they need to eat in substantial quantities.
Scientific name: *Mastacomys fuscus*

HOPPING-MICE ■
Though they usually move slowly on all four feet with their noses close to the ground looking for food, when they are alarmed or are being chased by a predator, hopping-mice bound rapidly on their hind limbs, and can clear obstacles over 60 cm high.

Their big ears, large eyes and long tails and hind feet distinguish

■ BROAD-TOOTHED RAT
Dense, fluffy fur keeps this inhabitant of Australia's highlands warm when it is out foraging along the 'runways' that it maintains beneath the snow.

hopping-mice from other Australian rodents. They are strictly terrestrial, preferring open or lightly wooded habitats with a thin cover of grass and shrubs. There are five extant species of hopping-mice: the northern hopping-mouse (*Notomys aquilo*), Mitchell's hopping-mouse (*N. mitchellii*) and the spinifex hopping-mouse (*N. alexis*) are sandy brown; the fawn hopping-mouse (*N. cervinus*) is grey to fawn; and the dusky hopping-mouse (*N. fuscus*) is orange. The spinifex, dusky and fawn species live in arid areas, while Mitchell's is most common in semi-arid regions of southern Australia.

They feed at night on seeds, leaves, roots and insects, from which they can extract all the water they need, though fawn hopping-mice may drink salty water. Desert hopping-mice conserve water by huddling in deep, moist burrows by day, and by not sweating. The northern hopping-

■ KIMBERLEY ROCK-RAT
■ ARNHEM LAND ROCK-RAT
■ CARPENTARIAN ROCK-RAT

■ COMMON ROCK-RAT
■ CENTRAL ROCK-RAT
■ BROAD-TOOTHED RAT

■ MITCHELL'S HOPPING-MOUSE
■ FAWN HOPPING-MOUSE

■ SPINIFEX HOPPING-MOUSE
■ NORTHERN HOPPING-MOUSE

■ DUSKY HOPPING-MOUSE

HOME-MAKERS

Like most rodents, pseudo-mice line their nest chambers with plant material. But the five pebble-mound species take home-making a step further and decorate the entrances to their burrows with piles of pebbles. They carry small stones in their mouths and arrange them using their front feet. Most of the stones weigh 1–2 grams, but some may be as much as 10 grams – the weight of the animal itself. The mounds of the western pebble-mound mouse (*P. chapmani*), shown here, can contain thousands of stones and cover up to 9 square metres. No one knows why the mice build these mounds.

DISTRIBUTION

- HASTINGS RIVER MOUSE
- LONG-TAILED MOUSE
- SMOKY MOUSE

- DELICATE MOUSE
- ASH-GREY MOUSE
- PLAINS RAT

- SANDY INLAND MOUSE

mouse, which occurs in coastal Arnhem Land and on the adjacent Groote Eylandt, is probably similar in behaviour to the other four species.

Populations of hopping-mice grow rapidly after fire or heavy rains that produce new growth, but also crash quickly – partly because animals starve or migrate when food supplies dry up, but also because many are taken by foxes, cats and birds of prey.

Females give birth to five young, or occasionally six, and can breed all year, though the rate of reproduction in most species is not fast. Sexual maturity is reached at 60–70 days in the spinifex hopping-mouse and the dusky hopping-mouse and at six months in the fawn hopping-mouse. The spinifex hopping-mouse can increase its numbers many times in a year in good conditions, and will migrate as much as 15 kilometres from a drought area towards rain.
Scientific name: *Notomys* spp.

PSEUDO-MICE

This is the largest genus of Australian native mammals, with 24 species spread around Australia. Pseudo-mice range in size from mouse-size species to the Hastings River mouse (*Pseudomys oralis*), of eastern New South Wales, which reaches a maximum of 17 cm long. Although most prefer heath and semi-arid or arid shrublands, the five pebble-mound species live in open, stony areas (see

- PSEUDO-MOUSE

The elusive Hastings River mouse (*Pseudomys oralis*) is found near creeks in eucalypt forests, where sedges and ferns provide plenty of cover.

box, 'Home-makers'), while the rare Hastings River mouse occurs only in wet forest. The long-tailed mouse (*P. higginsi*), is restricted to Tasmania, where it prefers the wet habitat of the Antarctic beech forests.

Most species eat seeds, leaves, roots and insects, and sometimes fungi. Populations of some pseudo-mice appear to be limited because their food sources are very local. The Hastings River mouse, for example, lives mainly on the leaves of sedges and grasses growing near creeks, and the smoky mouse (*P. fumeus*), of eastern Victoria, has a selective diet of berries, moths, seeds and truffles available in different seasons. In the subalpine parts of its range this species faces a serious food shortage in spring, unless it can find an area where flowers bloom and seed early.

While much is known about some pseudo-mice, other widespread and abundant species are little studied. One such species is the delicate mouse (*P. delicatulus*), a tiny species that occurs across northern Australia in sparse vegetation on coastal dunes where there are no other small mammals. It can reach high numbers after heavy rainfall or intense fire. The ash-grey mouse (*P. albocinereus*), of south-western Australia, is also widespread and locally abundant, but little is known about it. It is thought to be sedentary in some areas but mobile in others, with some individuals moving more than 5 kilometres in just a few days.

Despite their small size and delicate appearance, more than half of all pseudo-mice live in the arid and

semi-arid regions of Australia. They cope with the harsh conditions using a combination of tricks not seen in other desert mammals. Burrows are their first line of defence against the heat. Species that live in open habitats, like the plains rat (*P. australis*), of north-eastern South Australia, and the sandy inland mouse (*P. hermannsburgensis*), which is widespread across central Australia, build burrows up to a metre deep and form underground mazes where up to 20 animals may nest communally, all individuals contributing to burrow maintenance. Their habits often alter in the cooler weather, however, and in winter the sandy inland mouse uses shallower burrows and sunbathes at the burrow entrance on sunny winter mornings.

Limited water is a further problem, and these mice keep humidity high – thus reducing water loss through respiration – by blocking their burrow entrances and by sharing nests. Some species also lack sweat glands. Most desert pseudo-mice survive on dry seeds and produce dry faeces and concentrated urine. Lactating females even eat the faeces and urine of their young to recover some of the water lost in making milk.

Unlike rodents in deserts elsewhere, the pseudo-mice of arid Australia do not hoard food, and will abandon their burrows and go walkabout if conditions become difficult. This is probably because rainfall in arid Australia is less reliable than in other desert environments, so the animals must be flexible in their behaviour.
Scientific name: *Pseudomys* spp.

PALE FIELD RAT

This rat has light yellow-brown fur, large bulging eyes, pink ears and a short tail. It is distributed patchily across the grassy plains of northern and north-eastern Australia, though skeleton finds suggest that it once occupied much of inland Australia.

It builds its nest in termite mounds or burrows and eats grass stems, seeds and roots. It generally lives in refuge areas where food and water are constant, but after heavy rains populations can increase greatly to take advantage of the fresh grass.
Scientific name: *Rattus tunneyi*

DUSKY RAT

Dusky rats live on the monsoonal plains in the north of the Northern Territory, so they cope with flooding in the wet season and drought in the dry. When the rains begin, they invade high ground to shelter in tree roots and logs or to dig burrows in the rain-softened soil. On lower ground they shelter in grass and sedge clumps above the water line, numerous rats sometimes crowding onto tiny patches of ground.

In the dry season they spread over the plains, escaping the heat and predators in the cracks that form in drying soil. They build their nests in these cracks and breed rapidly, the young becoming independent and leaving the nest at three weeks of age. As the ground continues to dry, the cracks in the soil widen and no longer offer protection from predators, so the rats move out onto the surface in search of refuge.

Because of these erratic climatic conditions, dusky rats can become

BUSH RAT

These rats survive bushfires by sheltering in burrows and rock crevices, and then feed on seeds and unburnt plants that they find among the ashes.

rare over much of their range for several years, but they are among the most prolific breeders of all Australian rodents: when conditions are good, females can produce their first litter at only one or two months old, and each litter consists of up to nine young. Dusky rats have coarse dark brown or black fur, becoming grey to pale yellow on the belly.
Scientific name: *Rattus colletti*

CAPE YORK RAT

This rat lives in two areas on Cape York Peninsula and also occurs in New Guinea. Cape York rats have pointed faces with large eyes and ears. The northern forms, on the tip of Cape York, have grey-brown fur, a white underbelly and a brown and white mottled tail, while the southern forms, around Cooktown, are slightly smaller with a plain brown tail and dark rings around their eyes.

Cape York rats forage at night on the forest floor. If disturbed they dash back to their burrow entrances, which are hidden under logs or rotting vegetation. These rats can produce up to three litters of two to five young a year.
Scientific name: *Rattus leucopus*

BUSH RAT

Common in eastern and south-western Australia, this native rat lives in a range of habitats – eucalypt forest, rainforest and coastal heath. It even

lives in alpine woodland, where it stays active throughout the winter by burrowing under the snow. This species has soft brown or grey fur, often much paler on its belly and feet, and large rounded ears.

Bush rats eat whatever food they can find. Those living in forests chew on plant stems and shoots and dig for fungi and insects in the leaf litter, while those living in heaths eat plants in winter and insects, fleshy fruits and seeds in summer.

It is partly because of their varied diet that bush rats are able to survive bushfires. They shelter in burrows and rock crevices during the fire and emerge afterwards to rummage for seeds and unburnt plants. In the weeks and months that follow, they live mainly on the fungi, insects and plant shoots that thrive in the ash.

The highest densities of bush rats occur four or five years after a fire, when the regrowth of shrubs and herbs provides a lush haven. As the habitat returns to 'normal', populations generally decrease.

During the breeding season both sexes expand their territories to increase their chances of finding mates, males sometimes travelling up to 2 kilometres a night in search of females. Females have five or six young per litter, which become independent after four or five weeks and establish their own home ranges.
Scientific name: *Rattus fuscipes*

CANEFIELD RAT

This rat is common in tropical grasslands and swamps in the north-east. Like the Cape York rat, it also lives in New Guinea, but the canefield rat evolved in Australia and travelled north over the land bridge that once

■ PALE FIELD RAT

■ DUSKY RAT
■ CAPE YORK RAT

■ BUSH RAT

■ CANEFIELD RAT

■ CAPE YORK RAT
At night, these rats emerge from their communal burrows in the Queensland rainforest to forage through the leaf litter for insects, fungi, fruits and nuts. This youngster is feasting on fruit.

99

DISTRIBUTION

■ SWAMP RAT
■ LONG-HAIRED RAT

■ BLACK RATS

■ BROWN RAT

■ HOUSE MOUSE

■ BLACK RATS
Black rats have been dispersed by humans around the world so efficiently that they now live on six continents and thousands of islands. This is a European black rat (*Rattus rattus*) in her den with her young.

spanned Torres Strait, whereas the Cape York rat originated in New Guinea and made its way south.

Canefield rats have bristly, long grey fur and feed on grass stems and seeds and some invertebrates. When food is plentiful they reproduce fast. They reach sexual maturity at ten weeks old, have a gestation period of only three weeks and produce six young per litter, so populations can increase dramatically. As a result, these rats have become serious pests in the canefields of north-eastern Queensland, where they gnaw sugar cane stems and leave holes for bacteria to infect the plants, thus reducing the economic value of the crop.
Scientific name: *Rattus sordidus*

SWAMP RAT ■
These rats live in dense, low-lying vegetation, tunnelling through the plants by eating growth that stands in their way. They travel these mazes, by day and at night, searching for the plants and fungi they eat. They have bristly, chocolate-coloured fur, small black ears, black feet and short black tails.

Common in eastern Australia, they usually live along creeks, river flats, swamps and heathlands that occasionally flood. They are not good swimmers, so as the waters rise they paddle to the safety of shrubs or

grasses above the floodwaters. Here they make nests and wait for the water to recede. When it does, they return to the ground and start digging new burrows in which to nest.
Scientific name: *Rattus lutreolus*

LONG-HAIRED RAT
Like many desert animals, the long-haired rat usually forages at night and sleeps during the heat of the day. It lives in hot, dry areas of central and northern Australia and excavates a maze of twisting tunnels with several entrance holes and a number of paths leading to a central nesting chamber lined with grass.

■ SWAMP RAT
These rats live in areas of dense grass, sedge or heath and tunnel through the vegetation by biting away and eating any plants that are in the way.

Long-haired rats, which have grey bristly fur, are also known as plague rats because in certain conditions they breed and spread rapidly. They generally live in small numbers in isolated patches of land where there is a permanent supply of water, plants and seeds, but after heavy rain they move out of their normal range to take advantage of fresh shoots. As they move across the land, they join with individuals from other refuges and their numbers grow. They can produce many young very quickly, and these offspring, which reach maturity within months, reproduce within the season of their birth. In this way, long-haired rats can reach plague proportions, spreading at a rate of 8 kilometres in a day. If native plants are scarce, they feed on agricultural crops.

As the ground dries and the feed disappears, most of the rats die, and their range contracts back to their refuges. Scientists are not sure what causes the animals to die in such numbers. It may be simply starvation and dehydration, but heavy predation by birds of prey, dingoes, foxes, feral cats and snakes may have an impact. A decline in food quality may also cause the rats to become less able to fight diseases.
Scientific name: *Rattus villosissimus*

BLACK RATS ■
The introduced black rats are not always black; they may equally be shades of grey or brown. They are distinguished from native rat species by their slender, long tail and large, erect ears.

The European black rat (*Rattus rattus*) was probably introduced into Australia by the first European settlers, and is now well established in all major towns, cities and ports around the coast, as well as in coastal bushland. It has also spread successfully through agricultural regions of southern Australia, but it has not reached arid inland Australia, probably because it needs to feed on lush vegetation in order to meet its high water requirements.

European black rats use many different habitats and niches, are good climbers and swimmers, and have a generalised, omnivorous diet. Around settlements they eat human food scraps, while in the wild they consume a wide variety of foods, ranging from underground fungi to the occasional bird's egg or nestling.

Since these rats seem to move into habitats newly created by human activity, or into unoccupied niches in bushland, they have had little impact on native small mammal species; indeed, they are often outcompeted in the same habitats.

In addition to the well-known European black rat, a second introduced species, the Asian black rat (*R. tanezumi*), has been identified in Brisbane. The two species are very similar in appearance and behaviour, but they differ genetically.
Scientific name: *Rattus* spp.

PACIFIC RAT

Although it is common in South-East Asia, the Pacific Islands and New Zealand, the Pacific rat is extremely rare in Australia and is known only by a few specimens that were collected during the nineteenth century

■ HOUSE MOUSE
This resourceful introduced rodent makes itself at home wherever it finds an under-utilised habitat, either in the wild or around humans.

from Adele and Murray islands off the north coast of the mainland.

The Pacific rat is small – only about 12 cm long – with a tail at least as long again – and has fibrous, greyish brown fur. It lives close to people, and is thought to have been spread around the Pacific region from its original homeland in Asia by human dispersal. It feeds on seeds, fruits, plants and insects, and thrives around towns, villages, farms and regrowth forests. It is often seen scurrying around houses in search of food, but it is also an energetic climber that takes young birds and eggs from their nests.
Scientific name: *Rattus exulans*

BROWN RAT ■

Brown rats arrived in Australia with early European settlers and are generally found in the major cities along the coast, where they eat human food, scavenging around garbage bins and nibbling their way into grain sacks. Less often they occur outside towns, where they eat anything – seeds, plants, shellfish, birds' eggs and nestlings. Their fierce disposition and large, heavy build make them a resourceful predator of other small mammals.

In the wild, the brown rat is a large, aggressive rat with scruffy brown fur, small eyes and ears, and a thick tail that is often scarred from fighting. Wild brown rats live in deep, complex burrow systems that are often used for many years by successive generations of one family. These rodents prefer to live in large groups, forming a pecking order within the colony that determines each individual's access to food, mates and preferred nesting areas.

Unlike their wild counterparts, the domestic strains of this species, which are popular pets and laboratory research animals, are gentle and inquisitive and come in a variety of fur colours and patterns.
Scientific name: *Rattus norvegicus*

HOUSE MOUSE ■

So successful is the house mouse at moving in to use whatever resources are available that its distribution covers most of the world, including Australia. In the wild, Australian house mice eat insects and seeds, while around humans they eat whatever grain products or leftovers are available.

House mice reach their highest densities where human development and agriculture provide a constant supply of food, but they also live in unsettled areas where there is food

or some other resource that is not being fully used by native species. In Australia they are usually less able to survive in bushland than native species, reaching high numbers only after bushfires or other disturbances have made the environment unsuitable for native species. As soon as native animals return to an area, house mice leave or die.

In agricultural areas house mice frequently reach plague proportions. They are particularly common in the grain-producing areas of eastern Australia – a mouse plague occurs somewhere in this region, on average, once every four years. Plagues in normally dry areas are generally triggered by heavy rainfall followed by regular rain during the next year. In wetter areas of the grain belt, such as northern New South Wales and southern Queensland, however, plagues are triggered by lower than normal rainfall.

House mice produce up to eight young per litter. The young, in turn, are able to reproduce after six or seven weeks, so populations can grow very quickly indeed.
Scientific name: *Mus domesticus*

■ BROWN RAT
This thickset European rodent arrived with the early settlers. Predominantly a city dweller, it prefers to live in large groups and is found at ground level or below – often in sewers.

■ DUGONG

DUGONG

The dugong (*Dugong dugon*) is not related in any way to either seals or whales but belongs to the order Sirenia, the sea cows. There are only two families in this group – the manatees, which are found only in the northern hemisphere, and the dugongs of the Indian Ocean and the south-western Pacific Ocean – and the dugong is the sole member of the family Dugongidae.

These gentle herbivores occur in warm, shallow coastal waters around the northern half of Australia, from Shark Bay in the west to the Queensland–New South Wales border in the east. Their range used to extend further down the east coast; indeed, they were once more widespread throughout the world.

Dugongs can weigh over 500 kg and grow up to 3 metres long. These measurements are similar to those of large dolphins, but dugongs are dumpier than dolphins. They have rounded, downward-facing snouts and broad, flexible mouths that are perfectly adapted for grazing on seagrasses. Their nostrils are near the front of their heads and stay closed when the animal is underwater. Unlike their northern cousins, the manatees, which have tails similar to that of the platypus, dugongs have dolphin-like tails. They are generally bronze-grey with a pale belly. They lack a dorsal fin but use their front flippers for steering, as props when feeding, and for gripping their partner while mating. Like all herbivores, dugongs have large stomachs and long intestines with which to digest their food.

A dugong's lifestyle does not demand speed and they average less than 10 km an hour, though they can reach 22 km an hour in short bursts. Nor do they need to be able to dive deeply; instead, their dense bones enable them to stay on the sea bottom while feeding. They generally spend one to ten minutes under water before coming up for air.

Dugongs sometimes gather in herds of hundreds of individuals, though large groups are becoming less common as their habitat diminishes and their numbers dwindle. They have a similar lifespan to humans and produce only one young at a time, with up to seven years between births. Calves start feeding on seagrasses when they are very young but continue to drink their mother's milk for about a year and a half after birth.

With the exception of Aboriginal and Torres Strait Islander hunters, it is illegal to hunt dugongs in Australian waters. Nevertheless, the species is under threat, mainly because of habitat loss, either through coastal development or boat traffic, and – perhaps most crucially – because of hunting and incidental capture in fishing nets.

A GENTLE THREATENED SPECIES
Good hearing and a tough skin are the dugong's only protection from its predators – large sharks, saltwater crocodiles, killer whales and humans.

Order: Sirenia; Family: Dugongidae

SEALS

■ AUSTRALIAN SEA-LION
■ AUSTRALIAN FUR-SEAL

■ NEW ZEALAND FUR-SEAL

Seals belong to the same order as the terrestrial carnivorous mammals – dogs, cats, foxes and bears. Unlike the other carnivores, however, seals have adapted to a life at sea, though they still come ashore to breed. Instead of land legs, they have two pairs of flippers, which they use in effortless, lithe swimming.

Like those of whales and dugongs, the ancestors of seals were land mammals that returned to the sea. Seals evolved from two separate groups of land mammals, and from these developed two families – the eared seals and the 'true' seals.

Order: Carnivora

CARNIVOROUS MAMMAL OF THE SEA
While seals, such as this Weddell seal, may look ungainly on land, they are acrobatic swimmers and skilful hunters.

In the eighteenth and early nineteenth centuries, hunting seals for their pelts and blubber was a major business, and the Australian fur-seal, pictured below, was particularly prized. British seal hunters arrived in Australia in 1798 and French and American vessels soon followed. With the taking of nursing mothers and young, seal stocks fell rapidly.

State protection began in Western Australia in 1892, and by 1925 seals were generally protected, but seal populations took decades to return to reasonable numbers. Today both state and federal legislation prohibits seal harvesting in Australian waters.

EARED SEALS

Although this family of seals is at least 12 million years old, it did not reach the southern hemisphere until about five million years ago. Today, eared seals are represented in Australian waters by the Australian sea-lion and the Australian and New Zealand fur-seals. The subantarctic fur-seal is a common vagrant and the Antarctic fur-seal swims in Australian regions of Antarctica.

Four features distinguish the eared seals from the 'true' seals: eared seals have small external ears; they move on land using all four limbs; they have larger necks than the 'true' seals; and their teeth are similar to those of terrestrial carnivores.
Family: Otariidae

AUSTRALIAN SEA-LION ■
Most sea-lion species live in the warmer Pacific waters and do not have the dense underfur that characterises the fur-seals. The Australian sea-lion is no exception, though it occurs further south. These seals live on islands along the southern coast –

from The Pages off South Australia to Houtman Abrolhos off Western Australia. Unlike other eared seals, they breed only every 17–18 months, rather than during a specific season, and different groups pup at different times. An embryo is normally conceived directly after the mother has pupped, and begins to develop eight or nine months later.

Australian sea-lions prefer inaccessible breeding sites on the sheltered sides of islands, and the pups generally hide in vegetation and rock holes. Breeding sites have 'toddlers' pools' where the pups learn to swim.

Sea-lions have blunt snouts, small, furled ears, and large front limbs. Males are brown or black with lighter fur on their head. Females have silver-grey backs and creamy yellow bellies. Males weigh about 300 kg and average 2.1 metres long; females weigh about 80 kg and average 1.6 metres long. Australian sea-lions eat fishes and squids, and in turn are preyed upon by sharks.
Scientific name: *Neophoca cinerea*

AUSTRALIAN FUR-SEAL
Male Australian fur-seals average 2.16 metres in length and females 1.6 metres. Females average only 77 kg as against an average 279 kg for males. Males are dark brown or grey, females are paler with a fawn or cream bib, and pups are black with some silver. Adults dive to at least 200 metres in search of prey. On land they usually shuffle but they can break into a fast gallop.

These fur-seals live in large groups. They gather on rocky ledges and reefs and tolerate an unusual degree of body contact with one another. Their range runs from northern New South Wales to southern Tasmania and across to South Australia.

In November and December these fur-seals come ashore, females and immature males congregating and successful males establishing territories. Males maintain these territories more by bark than by bite, though aggressive displays turn to violence if boundaries are ignored. During this time females give birth to one offspring, each mother recognising her pup by smell and sound. About a week after giving birth the mother becomes receptive to the territorial males and chooses a mate. She then goes to sea to feed on squids, fishes, octopuses and rock lobsters, returning intermittently to suckle her pup.
Scientific name: *Arctocephalus pusillus*

NEW ZEALAND FUR-SEAL ■
New Zealand fur-seal males average 2 metres in length, females about 1.4 metres. They are sometimes mistaken for Australian fur-seals, but they weigh much less, with males averaging 152 kg and females about 42 kg. Adults are grey to brown and

Despite their common name, these creatures occur on many islands off the coasts of South Australia, south-west Tasmania and southern Western Australia.

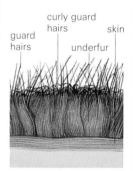

curly guard hairs

guard hairs · skin · underfur

KEEPING WARM AND DRY
The fur-seal's luxuriant coat consists of long guard hairs over a layer of curly guard hairs, beneath which grows dense underfur. This undercoat is waterproofed by secreted oils and sweat and never becomes wet.

Both sexes can be aggressive during breeding, sometimes killing pups and running after humans who approach too closely. Outside the breeding season sea-lions come ashore on sandy beaches and are easier to observe.

■ ELEPHANT SEAL
The foreshortened 'trunk' of the bull elephant seal – an animal that can weigh as much as 3800 kilograms – acts as a soundbox to amplify its roars.

■ SUBANTARCTIC FUR-SEALS
This is one of the most common vagrants to Australian waters and young seals are often washed up on the southern coast. A female and her six-month-old pup are pictured here.

pups are brown or black and are silvered on the head and neck. The New Zealand fur-seal has a longer, more pointed snout than the Australian species, and males have a massive neck and thick mane.

Neptune Island, off West Point in South Australia, is the Australian stronghold of the species, though it also occurs on many other islands off the coasts of South Australia (notably Kangaroo Island), south-west Tasmania and southern Western Australia. These fur-seals prefer rocky ledges with pools and access to shelter in caves or vegetation. Male territorial disputes start with growls and barks and can progress to chest butting and biting. These contests end swiftly when one animal squeals and backs down.

New Zealand fur-seals eat fishes and cephalods, such as octopuses and squids, supplemented by the occasional sea bird. Breeding takes place over five weeks, from late November to early January.
Scientific name: *Arctocephalus forsteri*

SUBANTARCTIC FUR-SEAL ■
The male subantarctic fur-seal has chocolate brown or black fur on its back and yellow fur on its chest and face. If the animal is disturbed, the black fur on its head stands on end. The female is dark grey to brown with paler yellow chest and face markings than the male. These seals are about the same size as New Zealand fur-seals. The only breeding colony in Australian territory is on Macquarie Island in Antarctic waters.
Scientific name: *Arctocephalus tropicalis*

ANTARCTIC FUR-SEAL
This seal lives and breeds in Antarctic waters. Its breeding grounds include at least two Australian territorial islands – Heard Island and

Macquarie Island – and it possibly also breeds on McDonald Island. The Antarctic fur-seal is about the same length as the subantarctic fur-seal, but is much leaner and lighter. Females are silver-grey to brown on their back and pale cream to white on their chest and neck. Males are silver-grey to brown. Both males and females have dark brown bellies. They feed mainly on pelagic fishes, and sometimes squids.
Scientific name: *Arctocephalus gazella*

'TRUE' SEALS

True seals do not have external ears and their hind limbs are directed backwards so that they cannot use them on land. Instead they hump along the ground, dragging their hind parts and back flippers behind them. Their teeth are also quite different from those of the eared seals.

Most true seals prefer the colder seas of the Arctic and Antarctic, but the vagaries of tides and seasons can bring members of this family to Australian shores as vagrants.
Family: Phocidae

ELEPHANT SEAL ■
Females of this huge species weigh an average of 300 kg, while males can weigh a mighty 3800 kg. They once lived on the north-western coast of Tasmania and on King Island in Bass Strait, but since early in the nineteenth century, when hunters exterminated a breeding colony at King Island, only three pups have been born on Australia's coast. From time to time intrepid individuals still reach Australia from subantarctic waters and parts of the Antarctic, and when they do they make quite an impression because of their massive size.
Scientific name: *Mirounga leonina*

■ CRABEATER SEAL
This is another of the more frequent seal visitors to the southern coast of Australia. In fact, these creatures feed on krill rather than crabs.

LEOPARD SEAL
These are the only seals that prey on warm-blooded animals – they eat penguins, krill, carrion, fishes and cephalopods, and also attack young crabeater seals, Weddell seals and elephant seals. Leopard seals live and hunt alone at the edge of the Antarctic pack-ice, but they also frequently visit Australia's southern coasts, and between August and October sometimes become stranded on beaches.
Scientific name: *Hydrurga leptonyx*

CRABEATER SEAL ■
Inhabiting the nutrient-rich waters of the Antarctic, this seal is also the fastest sprinter on ice, reaching up to 25 km an hour. The northernmost crabeater seal recorded in Australian waters reached Nambucca Heads in northern New South Wales.
Scientific name: *Lobodon carcinophagus*

WEDDELL SEAL
This is the most southerly ranging mammal. It is quite at home swimming, eating and mating beneath the ice, using ice holes for breathing and for pulling itself onto the ice. Dives of up 1250 metres take it beyond the range of many whales and dolphins. It is dark brown above and paler below with many spots. It rarely ventures into Australian waters.
Scientific name: *Leptonychotes weddellii*

ROSS SEAL
Australian waters have had only one recorded visit from this species, at Beachport in South Australia. Ross seals prefer to remain close to the polar ice. They have large eyes and their front flippers are almost as big as those of the Australian sea-lion.
Scientific name: *Ommatophoca rossii*

DINGO AND RED FOX

The dingo and the fox belong to a group, the canids, that also includes coyotes, jackals, wolves and domestic dogs. They are carnivores with long snouts, an acute sense of smell, pointed ears and nonretractable claws on their feet. Canids have long been associated with humans, beginning with the first domestication of wolves about 10 000 years ago.

No member of this family is truly native to Australia, though the dingo has lived on the Australian mainland for some 4000 years.

Order: Carnivora; Family: Canidae

DINGO

Dingoes are medium-sized canids weighing about 15 kg and standing about 60 cm high when grown. They have sandy or ginger coats, usually with white on the chest and feet, though there are colour variations such as black and tan or all white.

The dingo is a subspecies of the grey wolf and evolved in Asia probably as a result of domestication by humans. Further selective breeding of the dingo gave rise to many of today's domestic breeds of dog, but in South-East Asia it remained relatively unmanipulated and finally spread throughout the islands of the region, arriving in Australia with Asian seafarers about 4000–3500 years ago. Dingoes spread across mainland Australia, often living in close association with Aborigines, though they never reached Tasmania.

Within a dingo pack there is a strict hierarchy in which one dominant pair is often the only one to breed.

RED FOX
The fox can eat everything, from young kangaroos to berries – which probably explains its success in Australia.

Others in the pack – usually offspring from previous years – help with hunting or rearing pups. Dingoes normally breed once a year, but in drought years they may not breed at all. Up to ten pups are born in early winter and are raised in an underground den. Dingoes howl often, either to signal to other members of the pack or to frighten off rivals.

They commonly prey on kangaroos, wallabies, rabbits, rodents and water birds but will take animals as large as buffaloes or as small as insects; they will also eat fruit. While their impact on small mammals is probably minimal, it is likely that they limit the densities of larger native species, such as red kangaroos and emus, and they may have caused two marsupial carnivore species, the thylacine and Tasmanian devil, to become extinct on the mainland by outcompeting them.

Dingoes also prey on sheep and calves, and this has led to baiting programs and the construction of the 'dingo fence', which is designed to restrict the flow of dingoes into south-eastern Australia. Ironically, it is probably the availability of dead cattle during droughts and the existence of bores dug by graziers that account for the survival of many dingoes through difficult periods.

Dingoes breed successfully with domestic dogs and crossbreeds are becoming common. Today, purebred dingoes survive in only a few areas of Australia, particularly around the Simpson Desert and Arnhem Land. Pure dingoes face probable extinction, not through persecution but through assimilation with domestic dogs.

Scientific name: *Canis lupus dingo*

RED FOX
Initially introduced from Europe into Victoria in 1871 for sport, the fox spread rapidly through south-eastern Australia. It is absent from the far north, but its range is still expanding; in 2000 several foxes were introduced into Tasmania.

Foxes have an extremely diverse diet. They are mainly nocturnal and eat mammals ranging from mice to young grey kangaroos, but they can also live on a diet of berries, insects, birds, reptiles or human refuse. In the Snowy Mountains, for example, foxes survive for much of the summer on bogong moths and grasshoppers. They also prey on newborn lambs.

Foxes are red-brown with a whitish chin, throat, chest and belly. They are about a metre long from snout to tail – their tails accounting for a third of this length. They mate in early winter, and from one to 12 cubs are born in August or September in a den, which is usually in the ground but may be under a rock ledge. Foxes may live in groups of a single male and several related females, and then it is usually the male and an older female that breed, with younger females helping to raise the cubs. The young are sexually mature in the first year and can breed the following winter.

The spread of the fox in Australia coincided with the decline of many now endangered native mammals, such as the numbat and the bilby. Research currently underway on a fox control program based on bait-delivered sterilisation. As the rabbit forms part of the foxes' diet where both species coexist, attempts to control both animals are being integrated.

Scientific name: *Vulpes vulpes*

DINGOES
Like their wolf ancestors, dingoes live and hunt alone or in packs. The members of this pack are busy eating a wallaby carcass.

DISTRIBUTION

DINGO

RED FOX

DISTRIBUTION

FERAL CAT

CAT

The cat (*Felis catus*) is a member of a family that includes tigers, lions and leopards. This carnivore probably evolved from the domestication of the African wild cat in Egypt and the Middle East 8000–4000 years ago. The first European settlers brought cats into eastern Australia

in 1788, but it is also possible cats arrived on the north-west coast of Western Australia earlier than that on Dutch or Indonesian ships. Today, cats live successfully across the whole of mainland Australia, in Tasmania and also on over 40 smaller islands. They occupy all habitats, from urban environments to the core of the central deserts. It is because the cat obtains all the water it needs from its prey that it is able to live in arid regions.

Feral cats are similar in size and appearance to domestic cats, with the colouration and striped pattern-ing known as 'tabby' being the most common type of coat. There is some-times a certain amount of white on the chest, belly or paws. They may

VORACIOUS CONSUMER OF WILDLIFE
Cats are playing a substantial role in the decline of Australian native species, and concerted attempts are being made to eradicate them in the wild.

breed twice a year, usually in spring and then again in late summer.

The diet of feral cats is dominated by small- to medium-sized mammals and they consume vast amounts of native wildlife, though young rab-bits are also an important part of their diet. They also eat birds and reptiles when they are available. Carrion and human refuse are their standby in times of drought and they often move closer to human habitation at these times. Many cats kill more than they are able to eat, and even some well fed pet cats prey heavily on wildlife.

To save what is left of Australia's wildlife scientists are developing broad-scale biological control meth-ods for feral cats. Steps towards responsible cat ownership practices, such as desexing and keeping pet cats inside at night, will also go some way towards protecting native wildlife for the future.
Order: Carnivora; Family: Felidae

RABBIT AND HARE

There are no native members of this family in Australia, but two very successful species were introduced in the early years of European settle-ment – the European rabbit and the brown hare. Rabbits breed rapidly and destroy native habitat, and have been declared vermin in all Australian states. The hare is not so durable nor so destructive, but it can damage agricultural crops.
Order: Lagomorpha; Family: Leporidae

EUROPEAN RABBIT

A native species of the Mediterranean region, European rabbits arrived in Australia with the first European settlers in 1788, but they became established in the wild only after 24 of them were released for hunting purposes on a farm near Geelong in Victoria on Christmas Day 1859; at the same site seven years later, some 15 000 were shot. Within 15 years, rabbits had spread throughout New South Wales; 15 years later they

EUROPEAN RABBITS
Notorious destroyers of native plants, European rabbits now occupy almost all habitats in Australia from high alpine country to sandy deserts, from wet forests to urban parklands.

entered Queensland and South Australia, and by 1900 they had reached Western Australia as well. It was the fastest spread of any colonising vertebrate in history. Today, few parts of Australia south of the tropics are free from rabbits.

Rabbits have transformed the Australian landscape. Grazing like biological chainsaws, they bite close to the ground and suppress native plant growth. They compete with both native herbivores and grazing stock for food, and their abundance supports high numbers of feral predators that prey on small native animals when the rabbits decline.

Females can breed at five months and, with litters every 30 days, pro-duce up to 30–40 young a year when conditions are favourable. When good rains fall in semi-arid areas rabbit numbers explode the next season. In drought, breeding stops and numbers crash, but a few indi-viduals hang on until the next rains.

Rabbits build elaborate tunnel mazes called warrens. As well as providing nests for their young, these warrens protect them from extreme temperatures and from predators. The same warrens are inhabited by succeeding genera-tions, and are an important element

DISTRIBUTION

EUROPEAN RABBIT

in their social hierarchy. Where warrens have been destroyed, rabbit numbers are slow to recover.

In the 1950s CSIRO scientists released the mosquito-spread myxomatosis virus, which caused a huge drop in rabbit numbers, but the development of resistance in a tiny number of survivors gradually rendered the virus less effective.

Calicivirus disease, a new biological control that, like myxomatosis, is specific to rabbits, was released in 1996. Scientists hope to develop a contraceptive for rabbits that will permanently reduce their numbers.
Scientific name: *Oryctolagus cuniculus*

BROWN HARE

Introduced from England into Victoria for hunting in the 1830s, the brown hare became a pest as it rapidly invaded New South Wales and South Australia. However, within 20 years numbers began to decline, perhaps because of competition from rabbits. As livestock made the landscape less favourable, distribution retreated to its present limits.

Larger than the rabbit and weighing about twice as much, the hare feeds on soft grasses, herbs, and occasionally seedlings. It is most abundant in pasture country. It is less frequent west of the Great

Dividing Range and is absent from the western half of Australia. Hares breed rapidly, with females producing 20 young in a good season, but they rarely reach densities of more than one per hectare. They do not burrow, instead sheltering and nesting in grass 'forms'. They range far and wide in search of food and are frequently preyed upon by foxes, cats and birds of prey.

Farmers consider hares a nuisance as they can damage crops, though they are unlikely to compete with livestock. Their impact on native herbivores is unknown.
Scientific name: *Lepus capensis*

HORSE AND DONKEY

This small family of hoofed grazers contains only one genus comprising domestic and wild horses, donkeys, wild asses and zebras. Most species have long been domesticated, and only zebras remain in the wild in large numbers. However, feral populations of horses and donkeys have been successful in Australia.
Order: Perissodactyla; Family: Equidae

BRUMBY

Horses arrived in Australia with European settlers in 1788 and were brought from England during the 1800s for use as farm animals. Today about 300 000 horses, largely originating from abandoned farms, live wild. The Northern Territory and Queensland have by far the largest numbers, mainly scattered across the Gulf of Carpentaria region and the semi-arid interior. The brumbies of the Snowy Mountains that figure in literature and folklore are a small part of the feral horse population, numbering only hundreds.

Brumbies eat mainly grasses but can live on roots and bark in dry times, and will walk long distances

in search of feed. In dry country they can range over 70 square kilometres but they have a strong attachment to their home range. Herds form from time to time, but brumbies generally live in social groups comprising one male, one to three females and their young offspring. The dominant male forces his male offspring out of the harem at about two years of age; the young males then form 'bachelor' groups until they are about four, when they collect their own harems. On average, females produce a foal every two years, but populations fluctuate according to conditions.

Brumbies destroy fences and compete with stock for feed. During drought they can exhaust water before stock arrives. They trample native plants, accelerate soil erosion, compete for food with native herbivores and destroy their burrows and water supplies. They also spread introduced plant species in their dung and manes. As a result, land managers presently control feral horse populations in many areas by trapping, yarding and shooting.
Scientific name: *Equus caballus*

DONKEY

As many as 5 million donkeys live in Australia, primarily in the arid centre and the north. Their ancestors, introduced to Australia in the middle of the nineteenth century, were used on farms and as pack animals. In time they were replaced by motor transport and were released in the wild. Under these conditions they formed large, rapidly growing herds.

Like brumbies, donkeys are hardy and well suited to the dry interior of Australia. They have a diverse diet of mainly grasses but are able to survive on coarser plants than can horses. Donkey populations fluctuate according to environmental conditions. Although females can produce an offspring every year and most of them breed each wet season, the young often die from starvation during times of drought.

Feral donkeys cause similar problems to horses, but the damage is often worse because they form such large groups. Populations are controlled by trapping, yarding and shooting in many regions.
Scientific name: *Equus asinus*

DISTRIBUTION

■ ONE-HUMPED CAMEL

COPING WITH SAND
As protection against
blowing sand, the camel
has long eyelashes and
slit-like nostrils.

CAMEL

The one-humped camel (*Camelus dromedarius*) was introduced into Australia from the Middle East in the 1840s. First used by the ill-fated Burke and Wills expedition into central Australia in the 1860s, these hardy creatures became an essential means of inland transport until they were replaced by motor vehicles. Abandoned and stray camels then formed feral populations that have now spread throughout the sandy deserts of central and Western Australia. Numbers are estimated at well over 100 000. Australia is now the only country in the world where camels live naturally in the wild.

Camels are well adapted to arid conditions. They are very conservative with water, though they will drink up to 200 litres when water is available. They feed on shrubs and trees, selecting those with the highest moisture content, and have large, soft hooves that are ideal for travelling over sand despite their weight, which may be up to 1000 kilograms.

Groups of between two and 12 animals are common, though they sometimes congregate in considerably larger numbers. While females produce only one offspring every two years and breeding ceases during drought, numbers can increase by as much as 15 per cent a year when conditions are good.

Camels are able to destroy fences and sometimes damage waterholes, and land-holders in the areas they frequent consider them a nuisance. Their impact on native plants and wildlife is largely unknown. Due to their low density and remoteness, there are no official control programs for camels, but land-holders often control local populations.

Order: Artiodactyla; Family: Camelidae

SUPERSEDED FORM OF TRANSPORT
The one-humped camel is ideally suited to travelling over sand, and was widely used for inland transport before the arrival of the motor vehicle.

DISTRIBUTION

■ FERAL PIG

PIG

The feral pig (*Sus scrofa*), or 'razorback', seldom bears any resemblance to its pink farm counterparts. Rather, it is a robust, aggressive animal with a brown, black or mottled coat. Adult males weigh 50–170 kg and females 40–100 kg. They have a diverse diet that includes grass, roots and carrion, and they also kill animals such as lambs, calves and small native species. Females breed at eight months old and can produce two litters of about seven piglets every year when conditions are good. However, populations can fall dramatically in times of drought.

Pigs first arrived with the early European settlers, who often turned them out into the swamps and bogs around settlements to fend for themselves. Thus feral populations soon became established – even today, escaped domestic pigs are adding to the feral population. Feral pigs now range over most of New South Wales, Queensland and the northern areas of Western Australia and the Northern Territory. There are also isolated populations along coastal Western Australia, and in southern Victoria and south-eastern South Australia. Since they require moist conditions, they are most abundant in the tropics, but they are also extremely common in the semi-arid rangelands, especially in areas around watercourses.

Feral pigs kill livestock, destroy crops and fencing, and compete for food and water supplies with domestic animals. They also spread various diseases to livestock, foul waterholes and destroy habitats that are used by native species.

Though their flesh is valued as a game meat on the export market, feral pigs are controlled throughout Australia by extensive shooting and poisoning programs.

Order: Artiodactyla; Family: Suidae

BRISTLY BEAST OF THE BUSH
The feral pig consumes small native animals and destroys their habitat, fouls waterholes, spreads disease, kills livestock and destroys crops and fencing.

BUFFALO AND GOAT

All ruminants have a four-chambered stomach to enable these large animals to obtain sufficient nutrition from grass and other vegetation. They all have split hooves, and all males have horns. The females of some species also have horns. There are 137 species from 46 genera in this adaptable family, and there are horned ruminants living in every major habitat type worldwide, from tundra and desert to tropical rainforests.

Australia has no native horned ruminants, but five members of the family have been introduced here. Two – the zebu and the European cow – are domestic species, though even under pastoral management they often roam freely, and are distinguishable from feral groups only because of regular culling, branding and veterinary treatment. The other three species – the Bali banteng, the swamp buffalo and the goat – were also imported for domestic purposes, but are now virtually feral.
Order: Artiodactyla; Family: Bovidae

SWAMP BUFFALO

Swamp buffaloes prefer habitats between forests and flood plains and are found in the far north of the Northern Territory. They spend the early mornings and late afternoons grazing and normally move to wallowing sites at mid-morning. They return after grazing in the afternoon to more or less permanent 'camps'.

Males and females live apart in the dry season, with cows remaining in wooded areas, where shelter and food are plentiful. When grazing, cows take turns to remain near the camp to keep an eye on the young. Bachelor bull herds spend the dry season in drier, less wooded areas.

Groups mingle and mate primarily in the wet season, though mating

may occur up to eight months of the year. Young males are driven out of the female herd and one older bull mates with several cows. Offspring are born 10 or 11 months later.

At maturity, the male possesses huge horns with ridged bases; the female's horns are more curved. Both sexes have grey coats, and white 'socks', and sometimes have a white V below the neck.

Swamp buffaloes are sometimes called water buffaloes, though this is misleading as it is also the common name of a much rarer member of this family. Swamp buffaloes were introduced into Australia in 1826 and by 1985 their numbers had reached 340 000 – more than half the number of free-ranging swamp buffaloes in the world. Such heavy-hoofed animals – they weigh up to 1200 kg – leave their mark, eroding soils, draining wetlands and stripping vegetation. In the dry season they eat whatever vegetation they can find, up to 30 kg a day for a large bull. In the wet season they prefer sedges and aquatic grasses.

A control campaign begun in the 1980s reduced the buffalo population by more than 90 per cent. There is

now interest in its redomestication, since it is adapted to local conditions and provides hides and meat.
Scientific name: *Bubalus bubalis*

GOAT

This is another animal brought to Australia for domestic purposes. Feral goats now live in large areas throughout Australia, especially in semi-arid regions, except in the Northern Territory, where predation by dingoes is too great. Feral populations in most other regions were limited until dingo control programs were introduced. Today goats are numerous and are pests.

A male goat, or billygoat, weighs up to 75 kg and is up to 90 cm tall at the shoulder. Nannygoats are about the same height but weigh less. Goats often have shaggy coats, which can be black, white, brown or a combination of these colours. Both males and females have permanent horns.

Goats may roam widely in search of young grass. They need free water to drink and prefer to browse leaves from shrubs, but they can survive on almost any vegetation. In drought conditions, they can create deserts out of rangelands. This renders pastoral land useless, removes food and shelter for native species and lays soil open to erosion. The goats' hard hooves further degrade the soil.

Females can breed at six months and produce kids every eight months. Only one kid is born initially but twins or triplets are usual thereafter. Despite a 50 per cent mortality rate within the first six months of life, goat populations can increase by 75 per cent within a year.

■ GOATS
In times of drought, goats can strip a landscape of natural vegetation almost as efficiently as a plague of locusts.

■ SWAMP BUFFALO
Introduced from east Asia in the early nineteenth century, the swamp buffalo soon became feral in the Top End of the Northern Territory. These animals wallow in water to cool off and to coat themselves with mud to deter flies and ticks.

DISTRIBUTION

SWAMP BUFFALO

FERAL GOAT

DISTRIBUTION

■ BALI BANTENG

■ BALI BANTENG
This species has recently been declared vulnerable in Asia, so perhaps its presence in Australia will ensure its future.

Ridding Australia of feral goats would prove impossible – they are too widespread for fencing and too wily for complete round-ups. With their ability to breed, it only takes a handful hidden in inaccessible rocky outcrops to quickly recolonise.
Scientific name: *Capra hircus*

BALI BANTENG ■
In 1849, twenty banteng cattle were sent from Bali to a settlement on the Cobourg Peninsula in the far north of Arnhem Land in the Northern Territory. The settlers soon gave up, but the cattle stayed on the peninsula, where the habitat – grasslands and monsoon forests – is similar to their

homeland. A fence across the base of peninsula prevents feral banteng from spreading south. Within this area, commercial hunting keeps numbers in check and provides income for local Aborigines.

These cattle are smaller than domestic breeds. While older bulls are black, most banteng are tan with white 'socks' and dark noses. They have wing-like ears, and both males and females bear horns. Banteng are fertile, have good resistance to parasites, and do relatively little damage to their environment – qualities that make them possible candidates for redomestication in Australia.
Scientific name: *Bos javanicus*

DISTRIBUTION

■ FALLOW DEER

■ RED DEER

■ HOG DEER

■ SAMBAR DEER

■ RUSA DEER

DEER

Only male deer have antlers, and females are usually smaller and more delicate than males. At the age of one, males sport their first small antlers, and while the antlers are growing they are covered with furred skin called velvet. This is shed each year before the mating season and the antlers are shed at the end of the mating season. Each year the antlers regrow, reaching their maximum size at about the sixth regrowth.

Some deer live in herds while others are solitary. Their complex social life includes competition among males for mates, when ritual posturing often develops into full-scale battles.

Australia has no native deer, but six species have been introduced, including the chital (*Axis axis*) from India, which is like a fallow deer. There is one chital population, near Maryvale Creek in Queensland.
Order: Artiodactyla; Family: Cervidae

FALLOW DEER
This English deer was introduced in 1834 and is abundant in Tasmania. On the mainland, where populations are scattered, numbers fluctuate. Traditionally a herd animal, fallow deer in Australia are less social, often sheltering in the forest by day and grazing on pastures by night.

Fallow deer stand 72–98 cm tall at the shoulder and, though many are reddish with white spots, some are plain black or white. During the breeding season, from mid-March, males mark their territory by thrashing their antlers in vegetation and urinating in shallow depressions. Their mating call, a grunt, is easily mistaken for that of the male koala.
Scientific name: *Dama dama*

RED DEER ■
The red deer does well in the cattle country of Queensland, especially around the Brisbane and Mary rivers; populations living in the south-east are less stable.

Males can reach 122 cm at the shoulder and, in the rutting season, bear magnificent many-forked antlers 75–90 cm long. Females are a little smaller and much lighter. Red deer are mainly reddish, but sometimes fade to grey-brown in winter. Their rumps have a light patch.
Scientific name: *Cervus elaphus*

HOG DEER
Australia's hog deer are the only viable wild population of this species outside its native India, Nepal and Sri Lanka. In Australia,

■ RED DEER
This deer needs habitat with adequate water and cover, but it seems to have no major predators apart from humans.

hog deer live in thinly scattered groups in scrublands and tea tree swamps around the south-eastern tip of Victoria. These squat, sheep-sized deer have yellowish or reddish coats that become deep brown in winter. Some feature pale cream spots in summer.

Groups of two or three hog deer graze from dusk to dawn on native grasses, sedges or improved pasture. If startled, each animal flees alone.
Scientific name: *Axis porcinus*

SAMBAR DEER
These large deer are widespread in Asia. Males stand 127 cm high at the shoulder; females are smaller at 109 centimetres. They have dark brown coats and large ears, and bark loudly when alarmed.

Sambar deer live either in small family groups or alone. They are found throughout Gippsland in Victoria and have moved into New South Wales and the Australian Capital Territory wherever there is sufficient forest cover, particularly in mountainous country.
Scientific name: *Cervus unicolor*

RUSA DEER
This is the most recent deer to be introduced into Australia. It has two forms: those from the Moluccas are mainly clustered on northern coastal islands in the Gulf of Carpentaria, while those introduced into southern New South Wales came from Java. Male rusa deer stand 94 cm high at the shoulder and females are 86 cm tall. Males have distinctive antlers shaped like lyres and greyish brown coats of coarse fur.
Scientific name: *Cervus timoriensis*

WHALES AND DOLPHINS

Like all mammals, whales and dolphins, collectively known as cetaceans, are warm-blooded, breathe air and suckle their young. Unlike most mammals, however, they are born and spend their lives in water, most in the oceans but some in bays, estuaries or rivers. Most congregate in groups that vary in number, depending on species, from a few animals to large herds, or pods, of more than a thousand.

More is known about dolphins and porpoises than about the giant whale species, but much of this knowledge comes from studying captive animals.

The cradle of the deep
Some cetaceans travel to warmer climates to breed, females giving birth to well-developed calves after about a year's gestation. Usually only one calf is born, and many species calve only every second year. The young are born under water, close to the surface, and quickly swim to the top for their first breath. They suckle for up to six months, and there is a strong bond between mother and calf. Mothers and other adults protect the young from predators.

Cetaceans have lost the fur of their land-dwelling relatives and instead maintain their body heat by a specially adapted circulatory system and by a layer of fat, or blubber, which also gives them buoyancy.

Whales breathe through a blowhole, rather like a human nostril, on top of their head. They surface only briefly, and they close the blowhole when they are under the surface so that water is not forced into their lungs. The spume from a whale's 'blow' is not water but the whale's breath mixed with secretions from its body. Whales can stay under water for long periods; the sperm

whale, for example, can remain submerged for 90 minutes.

Visibility under water is poor, so whales must rely on their keen hearing to locate food, companions and enemies. They also seem to have a highly developed sense of touch. Their skin is sensitive and easily marked, and marine scientists can often identify individual whales by their distinctive scarring.

Eating and communicating
Cetaceans fall into two groups: the toothed whales (odontocetes), and the baleen whales (mysticetes). Toothed whales, which include the dolphin species, are generally smaller than baleen whales and have only one blowhole, whereas baleen whales have two.

The most obvious difference between the two groups is their feeding

apparatus. All toothed whales have teeth, though some species have as few as one or two and others as many as a hundred in each jaw. They grow one set of teeth, which erupts some time after birth, and these teeth are not replaced when lost. They feed on aquatic creatures such as fishes, squids and cuttlefish.

Baleen whales have no teeth; instead, they have comb-like plates, called baleen plates (see page 119), through which they sieve their food. Baleen whales feed on plankton or small schooling fishes.

The two groups also communicate in different ways. Toothed whales use echolocation, emitting rapid clicks and analysing the echoes. Some species also 'whistle' to communicate with one another. Baleen whales seem to communicate with sounds that can travel hundreds of kilometres under water.
Order: Cetacea

NATURALLY PLAYFUL
There is little difference between whales and dolphins, except their size – dolphins are just small whales. Both the southern right whale and the bottlenose dolphins shown here are acrobatic and active at the surface.

FLIPPERS AND FLUKES
Cetaceans have no hind limbs and their forelimbs are modified into broad flippers. Their tail, flattened at the end into two paddles called flukes, is their main means of propulsion. Some species have elongated jaws – a beak – and some have a dorsal fin while others do not. Many have a rounded forehead, or melon, that contains oily fat.

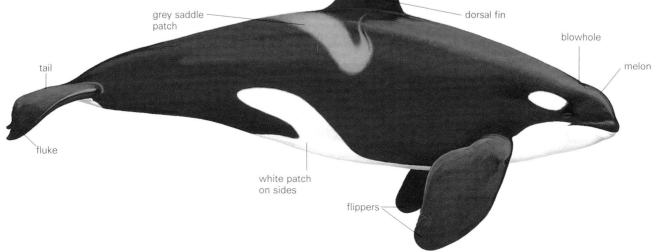

grey saddle patch

dorsal fin

tail

blowhole

melon

fluke

white patch on sides

flippers

DISTRIBUTION

BOTTLENOSE DOLPHIN

COMMON DOLPHIN

RISSO'S DOLPHIN

FRASER'S DOLPHIN

■ BOTTLENOSE DOLPHIN
To exhale, whales and dolphins surface briefly, opening the blowhole on the top of their head, and when they submerge, they close the blowhole (above). The bottlenose dolphin (right) has a short beak and a well defined melon.

DOLPHINS AND CLOSE RELATIVES

These small to medium-sized whales, the delphinidae, are the most abundant and varied of the whale families. They live in seas all around Australia, from the tropics to the Antarctic. Their main food is fishes and cephalopods, but killer whales also eat the flesh of warm-blooded animals such as seals, dolphins, penguins, and even large whales.
Suborder: Odontoceti; Family: Delphinidae

BOTTLENOSE DOLPHIN ■
This is probably the most familiar of all cetaceans because it is the species most commonly kept in marine parks. It adapts successfully to life in these parks, and in some parts of the world several generations have occupied the same facilities.

These dolphins occur around Australia and attain a length of about 2.6 metres, though in other parts of the world they grow up to 4 metres long and 650 kg in weight. They are stockier than the common dolphin, and they have a shorter beak. On each side of their upper and lower jaws there are 18–26 quite large teeth. Like the common dolphin they have a well-defined melon. They are dark to light grey, gradually lightening to white on the belly. In populations that live close inshore, some animals are heavily flecked along the belly.

Bottlenose dolphins congregate in groups of anything from two or three to herds of a thousand or more. Their variable diet includes small fishes, eels, squids and cuttlefish.
Scientific name: *Tursiops truncatus*

COMMON DOLPHIN ■
Common or saddleback dolphins range widely throughout the world in warmer temperate and tropical waters, and live in waters all around Australia. They are among the most

■ COMMON DOLPHIN
Though they are mainly creatures of the open ocean, common dolphins sometimes come close to the shore.

gregarious of the cetaceans, sometimes congregating in enormous herds of several thousand.

They are one of the most beautiful of the delphinidae, with black backs, white underparts and a distinctive figure-of-eight pattern on their flanks. This marking is cream coloured just behind the eye, becoming grey towards the tail. Common dolphins grow to about 2 metres long and are quite robust. They have a well-defined melon and a distinct beak with up to 100 teeth in each jaw. They feed on squids and schools of migrating fishes such as anchovies, herrings and sardines.
Scientific name: *Delphinus delphis*

RISSO'S DOLPHIN
At about 4 metres long, this is one of the largest of the dolphins. It has a large, blunt head, a prominent melon and no beak. It also has a strikingly large dorsal fin. Risso's dolphins are born grey but become brown, and by the time they reach adulthood they are pale grey with darker fins, flippers and flukes. They eat mostly squids and cuttlefish but also small fishes.

Risso's dolphins live in tropical, temperate and subantarctic waters, both inshore and well offshore, frequently over the continental shelf. Although sometimes solitary they usually gather in groups of 25 to several hundred. Small groups of four to five are common in Queensland coastal waters.
Scientific name: *Grampus griseus*

FRASER'S DOLPHIN
This species lives in the open ocean in tropical and subtropical regions, though it has been seen swimming near the coast and it has been washed ashore in Queensland, northern New South Wales and Victoria.

Adults are about 2.6 metres long, grey above and white below, with a light stripe extending from their forehead across their flanks. Their stout dorsal fin has a slightly hooked tip. Herds, which feed on deep-sea fishes, squids and crustaceans, vary in number from less than ten to almost a thousand.
Scientific name: *Lagenodelphis hosei*

PANTROPICAL SPOTTED, STRIPED AND SPINNER DOLPHINS ▪

There are three *Stenella* species in Australian waters – the pantropical spotted dolphin (*S. attenuata*), the spinner dolphin (*S. longirostris*) and the striped dolphin (*S. coeruleoalba*). They are slender and streamlined, though the striped dolphin is stouter than the other two. All three species grow to just over 2 metres long and all have long beaks, especially the spinner dolphin, whose beak is very slender. In all three the melon is separated from the beak by a distinct crease. They are fast swimmers, and spinner dolphins are exceedingly acrobatic – they can spin up to seven times in one leap.

All three species have a dark grey back and a paler belly. Pantropical spotted dolphins have bright white lips and beak. Striped dolphins have striking long black streaks along their sides. The coloration of spinner dolphins is variable.

These dolphins live in the tropical and subtropical zones of both hemispheres, the striped dolphin extending into more temperate regions than the others. Near the coast the three species live together in groups, usually of less than a hundred, but offshore they often gather in thousands. Spotted dolphins feed mainly during the day and spinner dolphins at night, so each species is protected

while resting by the other, active species. Their main food is mid-water fishes and squids. They all feed on tuna, and this has led to large numbers being drowned in the fishing nets from tuna boats.
Scientific name: *Stenella* spp.

ROUGH-TOOTHED DOLPHIN

These dolphins usually stay far offshore, in deep water with surface temperatures of above 25°C. They mainly occur in groups of ten to 20, though sometimes there are as many as several hundred. In Australia sightings have been reported from Barrow Island off Western Australia, the Northern Territory and New South Wales. They feed on small fishes, octopuses and squids. They are avid riders of the bow-waves of ships, and some can exceed speeds of 25 km an hour.

This species does not have a crease where the beak and melon meet. They grow to 2.3 metres long, are dark grey to bluish above and white below, and are compact and sleek.
Scientific name: *Steno bredanensis*

INDO-PACIFIC HUMPBACK DOLPHIN ▪

These dolphins range northward from Carnarvon in Western Australia, around the coast of the Northern Territory and Queensland and south to Ballina in New South Wales. Body colour is almost uniformly grey – dark in younger animals and becoming paler with age. They have a long, slender beak, a distinct, rounded melon, and a low, triangular dorsal fin with a wide base.

Indo-Pacific humpback dolphins usually live in pods of up to six animals, though herds of up to 25 occasionally occur. They are elusive, rising to the surface only briefly to breathe, their beak emerging first, then their head, and then their arched back. They seem to feed mostly on fishes.
Scientific name: *Sousa chinensis*

PYGMY KILLER WHALE

Pygmy killer whales live in tropical and warm subtropical waters worldwide. They normally swim in deep waters in groups of less than 50, but occasionally form herds of up to several hundred. They are one of several species that sometimes become stranded on beaches. They feed mostly on squids and small fishes.

These whales are generally dark grey to black, but in many individuals the lips and an oval patch on the belly are white. In profile, their head is rounded, the upper jaw overhangs the lower, and they do not have a beak. They have long flippers with rounded tips and grow to little more than 2 metres long.
Scientific name: *Feresa attenuata*

▪ INDO-PACIFIC HUMPBACK DOLPHIN
This dolphin remains close to the coast, generally in water less than 20 metres deep; it often enters bays and estuaries and occasionally rivers.

▪ PANTROPICAL SPOTTED DOLPHINS
These pale-bellied dolphins are not born with spots, but spotting develops as they mature.

DISTRIBUTION

▪ SPOTTED, STRIPED AND SPINNER DOLPHINS

▪ ROUGH-TOOTHED DOLPHIN

▪ INDO-PACIFIC HUMPBACK DOLPHIN

▪ PYGMY KILLER WHALE

DISTRIBUTION

■ SHORT-FINNED PILOT WHALE

■ LONG-FINNED PILOT WHALE

■ SOUTHERN RIGHT WHALE DOLPHIN

■ MELON-HEADED WHALE

■ KILLER WHALE

PILOT WHALES

There are two species of pilot whale – the long-finned (*Globicephala melas*) and the short-finned (*G. macrorhynchus*). They have long, sickle-shaped flippers, stocky elongated bodies and backswept dorsal fins that are curved at the tip. They are sometimes called potheads, when their bulging forehead overlaps the tip of their upper jaw. They are black or dark grey and they have no beak.

All long-finned and some short-finned pilot whales have a grey, saddle-shaped patch behind their dorsal fin. An adult male long-finned pilot whale can grow to 7.5 metres and weigh 4000 kg, while females are smaller, at 5.7 metres and 2500 kg. Short-finned pilot whales are smaller, but again males are significantly larger than females. The two species look alike, except that the long-finned whale has longer flippers.

Pilot whales feed mainly on squids but also take schooling fishes. They are gregarious, usually congregating in groups of 10-50, sometimes in herds of several hundred. They frequent deep oceanic waters, occasionally venturing into shallower waters and sometimes becoming stranded on beaches. Long-finned pilot whales occur in the waters of southern Australia, around subantarctic islands and as far south as the edge of the Antarctic Circle. Short-finned pilot whales swim in tropical and temperate waters around Australia, except on the southern coast.
Scientific name: *Globicephala* spp.

SOUTHERN RIGHT WHALE DOLPHIN

These acrobatic dolphins often swim very fast, leaping clear of the water as they travel, and they often ride the bow-waves of ships. They are frequently seen in large herds of a thousand or more, though smaller groups and individuals also occur. They are long and slender with a distinctive marking of black on their back and white on their lower flanks, flippers and head. This is the only dolphin in Australian waters without a dorsal fin. Males grow to 2.9 metres and females to 2.3 metres.

COMING ASHORE

Stranded whales, like this long-finned pilot whale (*Globicephala melas*), are common in Australia, but no one knows quite why they lose their way. Possible reasons include suicide, entering shallow water to rest, confusion of echoes by shallow water, inner-ear parasites interfering with the reception of echoes, brain infections, attempts to use ancient migration routes now closed by geological changes, noise from shipping, pollution, radar and electronic transmissions, phases of the moon, earthquakes and storms, and mistakes made while navigating by the Earth's magnetic field. Some of these suggestions are fanciful, but others are distinct possibilities. Probably a combination of factors is at work.

Southern right whale dolphins occur only in the southern hemisphere, from temperate waters to the Antarctic Circle. They have been sighted south and south-west of Tasmania, where some have stranded, off south-western Australia and in the Great Australian Bight. They feed on oceanic squids and fishes.
Scientific name: *Lissodelphis peronii*

MELON-HEADED WHALE

These whales live in herds of 40–150, occasionally up to 1500, in tropical to temperate waters warmer than 25°C. They frequent deep water, but are sometimes stranded on beaches. They eat squids and small fishes.

They grow to about 2.5 metres and are mainly brownish grey or charcoal. Their forehead is rounded and they do not have a beak, though their snout is pointed. They look like the pygmy killer whale, but the tips of their flippers are more pointed. In many individuals the lips and an oval patch on the belly are white.
Scientific name: *Peponocephala electra*

KILLER WHALE ■

This is by far the largest of the delphinidae. Full-grown males reach 9.6 metres long and weigh more than 9000 kg; females are smaller, at 8.2 metres long and 4800 kilograms.

The killer whale is found worldwide, from the Arctic and Antarctic to the equator, in both inshore and offshore waters. It has striking black and white markings with a grey saddle just behind its dorsal fin, which in males may be almost 2 metres tall.

Killer whales live in pods of one to about 50 individuals. Some groups are sedentary, others nomadic. Sedentary animals feed mainly on fishes, while nomadic ones feed on a range of prey, including squids, penguins, seals, dolphins and porpoises.

Killer whales have been seen to attack large whales, including the largest of all – the blue whale. In such instances they display a high degree of social coordination, and hunting behaviour seems to be learned by younger whales from older members of the pod.

Killer whales are very vocal. They produce three different types of sounds – echolocation clicks, whistles and pulsed calls. Each pod has its distinct dialect of calls. Despite their fearsome reputation, there is no record of a human death from a killer whale attack in the wild.
Scientific name: *Orcinus orca*

FALSE KILLER WHALE
This is one of several species of oceanic whales that have a tendency to swim ashore and strand in large numbers. They live in tropical and temperate waters worldwide, and normally remain some distance from shore, approaching land only where the continental shelf is narrow. They feed on squids and fishes, and sometimes attack sea birds and dolphins.

Usually occurring in small to medium-sized groups, they sometimes form herds of several hundred. They often swim at high

speed, leaping right out of the water, and they also like to bow-ride.

False killer whales are sometimes mistaken for melon-headed whales because of their dark colouring, prominent dorsal fin and rounded beak, but they are longer and slimmer and have a distinct hump halfway down their flipper.
Scientific name: *Pseudorca crassidens*

DUSKY AND HOURGLASS DOLPHINS
Two species of the genus *Lagenorhynchus* occur in Australian waters – the dusky dolphin (*L. obscurus*) and the hourglass dolphin (*L. cruciger*). They are small species that grow to about 2 metres and weigh about 115 kg. Both have a barely discernible beak, a curved forehead that houses the melon, and a tall dorsal fin. In the hourglass dolphin this fin is hooked with a pointed tip, but it is only slightly hooked and rather blunt in the dusky dolphin.

The dusky dolphin is blue-black, turquoise and white, while the hourglass dolphin is black above and white below with a white hourglass-shaped pattern along its flanks.

These dolphins are confined to the southern hemisphere. Dusky dol-

phins live in temperate and subantarctic waters and have been sighted off Tasmania and near Kangaroo Island in South Australia. Hourglass dolphins live in subantarctic and Antarctic waters. They are rarely seen and relatively little is known about them, but they have been recorded in the Southern Ocean and near subantarctic islands to the south of Australia.

Both species are fast swimmers. Hourglass dolphins generally swim in pods of one to eight and dusky dolphins in groups of 20 or so, though herds of more than a hundred have been observed. Dusky dolphins feed on squids and small fishes, but the food preferences of hourglass dolphins are unknown.
Scientific name: *Lagenorhynchus* spp.

BEAKED WHALES

Beaked whales live in deep water far from land and so are rarely seen. The little that is known about them comes from studying dead specimens that have been washed ashore. With the exception of shepherd's beaked whale (*Tasmacetus shepherdi*), they have only one or two teeth in the lower jaw, and none in the upper. Their long beaks, together with their few teeth and the anatomy of the mouth and throat suggest that beaked whales take in prey, mainly squids, by sucking them into their mouths. In beaked whales the dorsal fin curves backward.
Suborder: Odontoceti; Family: Ziphiidae

MESOPLODON BEAKED WHALES
Eight species of this rarely seen genus have been recorded in Australian waters, mostly as strandings. They inhabit offshore waters and are rarely seen. The only certain evidence for the existence of Longman's beaked whale (*Mesoplodon pacificus*) is two skulls, one found in Queensland, the other in Somalia, though reports suggest it persists into the tropical Indo-Pacific.

Other beaked whales are the strap-toothed (*M. layardii*), the ginkgo-toothed (*M. ginkgodens*), Blainville's (*M. densirostris*), Hector's (*M. hectori*), Andrews' (*M. bowdoini*), Gray's (*M. grayi*) and True's (*M. mirus*).

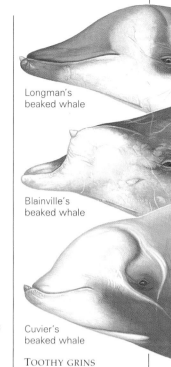
Longman's beaked whale

Blainville's beaked whale

Cuvier's beaked whale

TOOTHY GRINS
A beak-shaped skull and only two or four teeth in the lower jaw characterise the beaked whales, but only males grow teeth. In females the teeth do not erupt.

DISTRIBUTION

FALSE KILLER WHALE

DUSKY DOLPHIN

MESOPLODON BEAKED WHALES

DUSKY DOLPHINS
Great acrobats, these small compact dolphins are strikingly marked with a white or pale grey blaze on their sides.

■ SPERM WHALE
This large, deep-diving whale has a huge head about a third the size of its body.

DISTRIBUTION

■ CUVIER'S BEAKED WHALE

■ SPERM WHALE

■ PYGMY SPERM WHALE

■ DWARF SPERM WHALE

Some species prey on oceanic squids and fishes, and it is thought that all dive to great depths. All are 4–5.5 metres long, though the skull size of Longman's suggests that it may be as long as 9 metres.

The teeth of these species emerge through the gums only in males. In some species they are barely discernible, yet the entire tooth, most of which is beneath the gum, is massive. The teeth of the male strap-toothed whale emerge in the lower jaw and curve over the upper jaw, reaching a length of 30 cm and eventually restricting the opening of the jaws. The ginkgo-toothed whale's teeth emerge in the shape of leaves of the ginkgo tree. Most mesoplodon whales are scarred, suggesting that they use their teeth in fighting.
Scientific name: *Mesoplodon* spp.

CUVIER'S BEAKED WHALE
These whales, which occur in all seas and oceans, except in polar regions, are among the most common beaked whales. Strandings occur all around Australia but sea sightings are infrequent.

Both males and females grow to about 7 metres and weigh about 2500 kg. Males are often scarred from battles over females. These whales are usually alone, but groups of up to 25 have been sighted. They eat squids and deep-sea fishes.
Scientific name: *Ziphius cavirostris*

WHAT A FLUKE
Whales can be identified by their tail flukes, which vary in size and shape.

SPERM WHALE ■

This family has only one species – the sperm whale (*Physeter catodon*), which is found in all oceans of the world. It has stout, conical teeth in its lower jaw, with females having fewer and smaller teeth.

Adult males may be 18 metres long and weigh 60 000 kg, while females reach 12 metres and 45 000 kg. Most sperm whales are dark grey with white lips and whitish blotches on their belly. Occasionally they are pale grey or white. The dorsal fin is low, thick and rounded, set far down the back, and the tail has a crenulated edge. The blowhole is on the upper left-hand side of the snout, and the blow is angled forwards.

The sperm whale's forehead houses the spermaceti organ, the function of which is not fully understood. It is like a large, thick-walled bladder and contains what early whalers believed to be sperm, but is, in fact, an oil that takes on a waxy quality when removed from the whale's body. The oil was formerly used to bind the aromas of perfumes and as a machine lubricant.

Sperm whales usually live in matriarchal pods consisting of females of all ages and immature males. When males are six to eight years old they leave the family group and form their own, known as bachelor pods. At 15–20 years old, they leave the bachelor pod and join pods of mature males. An average pod might comprise 25 animals, though very large gatherings of up to thousands have been reported.

Sperm whales live in water deeper than 200 metres, near the continental shelf. Here they feed mostly on squids, for which they dive. Dives often exceed 60 minutes, and there are records of sperm whales submerging for longer than 130 minutes and diving deeper than 3100 metres. Females and young males remain in warmer waters all year, and in Australian waters venture little further south than the water around Tasmania. Adult males in this part of the world inhabit the colder waters of the Southern Ocean and move north only to join other groups in the breeding season, between late winter and spring.
Suborder: Odontoceti;
Family: Physeteridae

PYGMY AND DWARF SPERM WHALES

These are small to medium-sized whales with a protruding forehead and a small lower jaw. Their forehead houses a modified spermaceti organ resembling that of the sperm whale. Also like sperm whales, they have teeth in the lower jaw only, but these are pointed and backcurved. The blowhole is on top of the snout.

There are only two species in this family and both the pygmy sperm whale (*Kogia breviceps*) and the dwarf sperm whale (*K. simus*) have been recorded in Australia. Similar in appearance, they were considered a single species until recently. They are dark grey above and whitish grey below. Their head is short and squarish in profile and they have a crescent-shaped mark on the side of their head. At 3 metres long and weighing 360 kg, the pygmy sperm whale is larger than the dwarf sperm whale, which is about 2.7 metres long and weighs 200 kilograms. The pygmy sperm whale has a longer head but a tiny dorsal fin. The dwarf sperm whale has a tall dorsal fin in the middle of the back and two creases under the throat.

Both species occur individually and in small groups. They often lie motionless at the surface, and are usually seen only in calm, clear conditions. They swim in all the world's oceans, in temperate, subtropical and tropical waters. Dwarf sperm whales approach the coast more often than pygmy sperm whales. Both species feed mostly on squids and octopuses.
Suborder: Odontoceti; Family: Kogiidae

sperm whale   humpback whale   right whale   blue whale

WHITE WHALES

These are small to medium-sized toothed whales with a blunt, bulbous forehead. The family contains three species, but only one – the Irrawaddy dolphin (*Orcaella brevirostris*) – occurs in Australian waters.

In some parts of the world the Irrawaddy dolphin inhabits fresh water, but in Australia it lives in salt water close to shore, or in estuaries. It ranges northward from about Port Hedland in the west and Mackay in the east. It has no beak, but its prominent melon overlaps its mouth. Its small, triangular dorsal fin has a rounded tip and its blowhole is left of the midline. Its discernible neck is more flexible than in most cetaceans. Adults grow to 2.5 metres and are usually pale grey, occasionally dark grey to blue grey.

These dolphins are not particularly active. Groups of up to six are the norm, though sometimes as many as 15 are seen. They feed on small fishes and crustaceans.
Suborder: Odontoceti;
Family: Monodontidae

RORQUALS

This family of baleen whales includes some of the biggest animals ever to appear on Earth. They have broad, flat heads and pointed snouts and their dorsal fin is set well back on their body. Females are normally slightly larger than males.

Their most distinctive feature is the any folds of skin, called throat grooves, that extend from below their lower jaw to just behind their flippers. These throat grooves are pleated like an accordion and expand during feeding. Rorquals feed on schools of small fishes or shoals of krill by dropping their lower jaw and lunging into their prey. Under the weight and volume of the water scooped up, the whale's elastic throat distends and, with mouth closed, it raises its huge muscular tongue to push water through its baleen plates, sieving out the water and retaining the food.

Rorquals are fast swimmers, and most make long migrations between their tropical breeding and polar feeding grounds. All six species occur off the Australian coast.
Suborder: Mysticeti;
Family: Balaenopteridae

MINKE WHALE ▪

The cigar-shaped minke whale is the smallest of the rorquals, rarely exceeding 10 metres in length. It is dark grey or black above and white below, with shading around its flippers. Its tall, sickle-shaped dorsal fin is positioned well back on its body.

Feeding mostly on planktonic krill in cold productive polar waters, it usually migrates to warmer latitudes to mate and give birth. The North Pacific minke whale seems to be the exception, neither migrating nor depending on crustaceans for

▪ MINKE WHALE
This whale is known for its speed in the water, and is celebrated on the Great Barrier Reef for approaching boats, swimmers and divers.

food, but instead eating small schooling fishes like anchovies and herrings. Minkes are themselves preyed upon by killer whales, to such an extent that up to 85 per cent of a killer whale's diet in the Antarctic may consist of minkes.

Minkes commonly strand on Australian shores. The southern population is estimated at 700 000 to 850 000; so it would appear that the annual permitted Japanese take of 300 minkes is having little impact on the survival of the species.
Scientific name: *Balaenoptera acutorostrata*

FIN WHALE ▪

At 22 metres long, the fin whale is the world's second largest whale; it is probably also the fastest rorqual, having been recorded travelling at over 30 km an hour. Numbers in the southern hemisphere have been estimated at around 500 000 fin whales before whaling began and around 25 000 when protective measures were introduced in 1975. No increase has been detected since.

Fin whales migrate great distances – up to 20 000 km between their polar feeding grounds and their tropical or subtropical breeding areas. When feeding they congregate in groups of a hundred or more.
Scientific name: *Balaenoptera physalus*

IRRAWADDY DOLPHIN

MINKE WHALE

FIN WHALE

▪ FIN WHALES
Feeding at the surface, fin whales turn on their sides, throw one flipper in the air and scoop huge gulps of krill or fishes into their sieve-like expandable mouths.

DISTRIBUTION

SEI WHALE

HUMPBACK WHALE

TROPICAL WHALE

SEI WHALE

Like other baleen whales, the sei migrates vast distances between its summer feeding grounds in cold waters and its winter breeding grounds in the tropics. Its main diet is crustaceans, but it also eats fishes and squids. A typical day's catch, usually made by skimming open-mouthed along the surface, may amount to a tonne of mixed seafood.

The sei has a dark grey back, often covered with white oval scars, and its dorsal fin forms a 40° angle with its back. Females reach about 21 metres in length and males about 18 metres. In the open ocean it is difficult to tell this species from tropical whales. However, stranded sei whales are distinguished from other species by their baleen, which is less than 75 cm long and metallic black, with a fringe of fine white hairs and bristles along the inner edge.
Scientific name: Balaenoptera borealis

HUMPBACK WHALE

Humpback whales, which reach 11.5–15 metres in length, migrate annually up and down the east and west coasts of Australia. After leaving their summer Antarctic feeding grounds, they fast during the winter in the warm waters of the tropics, where they breed. Along the way they can be observed from land or a boat, at places like Cape Byron on the east coast and Shark Bay on the west coast. In late June, at the height of the northern migration, as many as 30 humpbacks may be seen in a single day along the south-east Queensland or northern New South Wales coast. The humpback's predictable migratory habits took this gigantic, inoffensive package of blood-and-bone, meatmeal and oil to the verge of extinction. In eastern Australia alone, the tiny whaling stations at Tangalooma and Byron Bay took a total of 7423 humpback whales between 1952 and 1962, after which operations were closed down, simply because quotas could not be

HUMPBACK WHALE
As the humpback exhales, a low, bushy 'blow' spurts from the twin blowholes on the top of its head.

filled. When protective measures were at last introduced in 1963, the estimated population of east coast humpbacks had fallen from 10 000 to about a hundred.

Today, the population of humpbacks in eastern waters is increasing at an average annual rate of about 12 per cent, and their numbers have recovered to an estimated total of around 2000. Numbers on the west coast are also recovering.
Scientific name: Megaptera novaeangliae

TROPICAL WHALE

Also called Bryde's whale, this species lives in reasonably warm waters, around 20°C. It often comes in close to land, and commonly strands along Australian shores. It is 15 metres long, and can be distinguished at close range by the three ridges that run roughly parallel along the length of its head to its blowholes, and by its baleen, which is short (45 cm maximum) and grey with coarse, stiff, dark bristles.

These whales are great fish-feeders, taking pilchards and anchovies and also krill. Rather than making north–south migrations with other rorquals, these whales appear to undertake inshore–offshore migrations in order to follow the seasonal abundance of foods.
Scientific name: Balaenoptera edeni

BREACHING

Whales and dolphins sometimes launch themselves out of the water head first and fall back again with a splash. This is called breaching and often, when one animal breaches, others in the herd follow. Some of the smaller species can leap very high, twisting and somersaulting before they re-enter the water. Even some of the larger whales, like the humpback below, manage to raise two-thirds of their body from the water. No one is sure why whales breach – it could be a courtship display, or a way of herding fishes, a challenge to others in the herd, or a form of signalling.

BLUE WHALE

The blue whale is the largest whale on Earth. It is also close to extinction. So extraordinary was the yield of oil from a mature blue whale that 300 000 were killed between 1915 and 1965. In 1966 it became a protected species. Today, there are so few northern blue whales that they are virtually impossible to find. In the southern hemisphere there are less than a thousand – a number so low that scientists are unable to predict their survival.

Blue whales are a bluish grey mottled with light grey and white. They are born, after a gestation of 11–12 months, measuring about 7 metres and weighing around 8 tonnes. Newborns drink about 600 litres of concentrated milk a day, and can double their weight in a week. They are weaned at about seven months. At 23–27 metres long and weighing 100–120 tonnes, a mature adult consumes around 4 tonnes of polar krill a day in summer, then migrates to fast and breed in subtropical and tropical waters. It may make the return trip 80 or 90 times in its life.
Scientific name: *Balaenoptera musculus*

RIGHT WHALES

These huge baleen whales have an enormous lower lip that encloses the long, delicate baleen plates that are attached to their arching upper jaw. Their heads are very large, as are their flippers, their backs are broad, and they have no dorsal fin. Also characteristic of this family are the callosities – raised, whitish patches of thick rough skin, like giant warts – that grow on their head and chin. Like all baleen whales, they have two blowholes.
Suborder: Mysticeti; Family: Balaenidae

SOUTHERN RIGHT WHALE ■

The species seen in Australia, the southern right whale, is black or dark brown, with white blotches on its belly and sometimes on its head. Newborn calves are often grey or white. An adult is about 16 metres long and weighs 80 tonnes; females grow slightly larger than males. Individual whales are distinguished by the pattern of the callosities that encrust the top of their head and the edges of their lower jaw. Their 'blow' is V-shaped when viewed from in front or behind.

Southern right whales occur all around the world between latitudes 30°S and 60°S. In summer, they migrate from their winter breeding areas to warmer latitudes. Breeding animals are seen close inshore along the southern coast of Australia, the largest concentration being at Head of Bight in South Australia.

These marine giants feed on tiny invertebrates called copepods, and to a lesser extent on krill, which they skim from the sea surface as they plough through clouds of plankton with partially open mouths.

Southern right whales were abundant up to the beginning of the nineteenth century, but widespread and intensive whaling has reduced their numbers drastically. Populations have recovered somewhat in the past 10–20 years, but these whales are still considered threatened.
Scientific name: *Eubalaena australis*

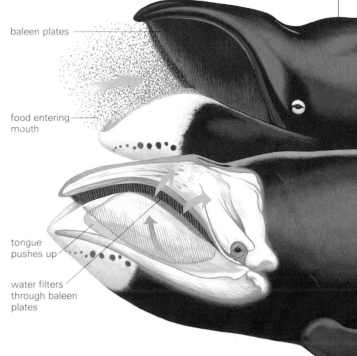

baleen plates

food entering mouth

tongue pushes up

water filters through baleen plates

PYGMY RIGHT WHALE

This family contains one species, the pygmy right whale (*Caperea marginata*). Like the right whale, it has a huge lower lip to accommodate the baleen plates that are attached to its upper jaw. This species is considerably smaller than the right whales, however, and has a dorsal fin.

This whale occurs only in the southern hemisphere, between latitudes 30°S and 52°S. At sea, it can be mistaken for a minke whale, and perhaps for this reason there are few confirmed sightings. However, strandings are frequent enough to suggest that the species is not rare in southern Australian waters.

The pygmy right whale is the smallest of all the baleen whales – adults are about 6 metres long and weigh about 4 tonnes. Its small, hooked dorsal fin is set well back on its body, and it has two throat grooves. This whale swims more like a dolphin than a great whale, filtering small invertebrates through its baleen plates. It is apparently solitary for the most part, but small herds of up to eight individuals have been reported.
Suborder: Mysticeti;
Family: Neobalaenidae

■ SOUTHERN RIGHT WHALE
During the breeding season, female southern right whales and their calves are usually seen close to the shore.

FILTERING SYSTEM
As a baleen whale closes its mouth, it raises its huge, muscular tongue, pushing water out through the baleen plates and retaining the food – rather like the action of an upside down coffee-plunger.

DISTRIBUTION

■ BLUE WHALE

■ SOUTHERN RIGHT WHALE

■ PYGMY RIGHT WHALE

BIRDS

THE EARLY BIRD
Fine-grained limestone in southern Germany preserved the skeleton of *Archaeopteryx*, the first-known bird, almost intact for 150 million years.

THERE ARE OVER 9000 BIRD SPECIES in the world, of which about 800 are found in or around Australia and its island territories. Birds are easy to see, since they are abundant and often quite large, and their ability to fly has enabled them to penetrate almost every habitat on Earth, including the frozen wastes of Antarctica and the vast expanses of treeless deserts.

Archaeopteryx is the name that scientists have given to the earliest fossil of a bird so far discovered. It was a colourful animal, about the size of a modern pigeon, that lived some 150 million years ago. This fossil had both reptile- and bird-like features and, had it not been for its feathers, *Archaeopteryx* would probably have been classified as a small dinosaur. Feathers, which are the hallmark of all birds, are, in fact, modified scales.

Archaeopteryx could fly – though not very well – and its flight feathers were very like those of modern birds.

THE CHICKEN OR THE EGG?
A bird's egg protects the embryo from predators as well as providing the fluid environment and the food that the embryo needs to reach a stage where it can survive outside the egg. A typical embryonic development is illustrated below.

Geologically speaking, birds are younger than mammals by about 100 million years. Their closest living relatives are the reptiles, with which they share an important feature: the 'land egg' that both types of creatures lay. The significance of the land egg is that the embryo and a large yolk are enclosed in a protective membrane, the amnion, which is in turn encased in a water-resistant shell. This evolutionary development meant that the animals did not need to be in a watery environment to reproduce. Unlike reptiles, birds incubate their eggs.

Birds also differ from reptiles in that, like mammals, they are endothermic, or warm-blooded, meaning that they maintain a constant body temperature by internal metabolic processes, rather than by absorbing heat from the atmosphere. In order to fuel this internal furnace of energy they must eat frequently. Perhaps the main advantage of being warm-blooded is that it enables an animal to remain active in all habitats and during all seasons.

Birds have a well-developed brain, a finely tuned nervous system and acute senses of vision, hearing and balance. They also have an efficient respiratory system and a high-pressure circulatory system driven by a four-chambered heart. Instead of teeth, they have stones or grit in their gizzard, or gut; these stones grind up food, and digestion is fast. The oesophagus of many birds has a muscular sac called a crop in which the birds can store food, to be regurgitated later to feed their young.

Most of the features unique to birds are related to their ability to fly. Structurally, they are remarkable uniform, both internally and exter-

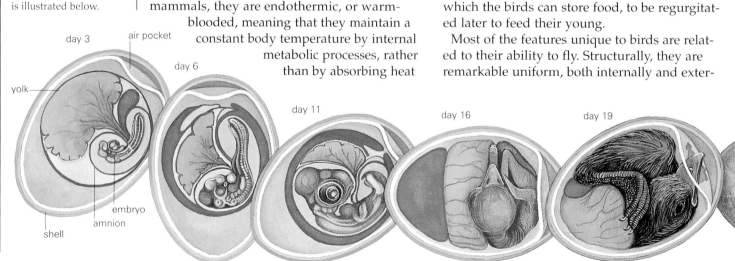

day 3
air pocket
day 6
day 11
day 16
day 19
yolk
embryo
amnion
shell

nally. They are basically four-limbed animals, but their forelimbs, or arms, have been modified to form wings. The 'hand' and 'finger' bones are fused, forming a structure for the attachment of the primary flight feathers, and the secondary flight feathers are attached to the 'forearm'. The tailbones are shortened and fused to form the 'parson's nose', which is an anchor point for the tail feathers. In all but the ratites, the breastbone has a large keel for the attachment of powerful flight muscles.

The mating game

Over 90 per cent of birds are monogamous – that is, one male to one female. In short-lived birds, such as songbirds, the pair bond lasts for only one breeding season, but in longer-lived species, such as albatrosses, the relationship is more permanent and may last for life.

In some species the females can rear the chicks without the help of the males and polygamous mating systems develop, in which a male mates with more than one female.

Males and females of monogamous species tend to be similar in size and colour, but in polygamous species males are usually bigger and more brightly coloured than females.

The choice of territory is linked almost entirely to the availability of resources such as food and nest sites. It is most often the males that set up territories, usually by singing and sometimes by display. These expressions of ownership deter rival males and attract females, but the price is a large expenditure of energy and time.

Mapping migration

Many birds migrate long distances to their breeding territories, and there is much speculation about their unerring sense of direction.

Some birds are virtually independent when they hatch, but others need parental care for some time before they are ready to leave the nest.

independent chick (precocial)

day 21

dependent chick (altricial)

LIGHT AND STRONG
A bird's bones are thin and hollow and are reinforced inside with struts, making the skeleton light but very strong. The breast muscles that it uses for flight are also exceptionally powerful.

They may orient themselves by the sun, and birds that migrate at night may steer by the positions of sunset and the stars. Radar observation suggests that when birds migrate in overcast conditions and cannot use astronomical clues, they may rely on Earth's magnetic field as a map. The sense of smell may also play a part, though it is not acute in birds.

Learning about birds

Capturing, banding and releasing birds – and more recently, satellite tracking – yields much information about their movements and life cycles. To capture the birds, nearly invisible mist nets are set across areas where birds fly. Expert handlers quickly disentangle captured birds, place them in individual cotton bags and make a note of species, measurements, sex, age and any other features, such as whether the bird is moulting. A small, lightweight, numbered metal band is wrapped around one leg with banding pliers before the bird is released. In Australia, the data sheets recording the information are sent to the Australian Bird and Bat Banding Scheme headquarters in Canberra.

Recaptured banded birds are recorded in the same way and the band numbers sent to headquarters. Over time, much of the life history of a species can be pieced together in this way.

RATITES

Ratites – the group that includes ostriches, cassowaries and emus are large flightless birds with long necks and legs and rudimentary wings. They are probably not an early group from which flying birds evolved, but developed from flying ancestors on islands where there were no terrestrial predators and hence no need for the escape mechanism of flight. They are called ratites (from *ratis*, the Latin word for raft) because they have a flat, raft-shaped breastbone, whereas most birds have a breastbone with a pointed keel to provide attachment for the pectoral muscles that they need for flight.

There are five families in the order Struthioniformes: African ostriches, South American rheas, Australian emus, the cassowaries of Australia and New Guinea, and the kiwis of New Zealand.

cross-section of emu's bowl-shaped breastbone

keel

cross-section of gull's keeled breastbone

WINGING IT
The emu's breastbone is shaped like a shallow bowl and has no keel to support the powerful muscles needed for flying. In contrast, the Pacific gull's breastbone is strongly keeled to provide an anchor for flight muscles.

OSTRICH

The flightless ostrich, the world's largest living bird, can weigh as much as 150 kg and can reach a height of 2.5 metres. It is introduced, being native to the open desert and semidesert areas of southern Africa.

Ostriches were imported to New South Wales, Victoria and South Australia towards the end of the nineteenth century to be farmed for their plumes, but when this trade collapsed during the 1930s the ostriches were released. In the wild they gradually declined in number, and the feral ostrich group in South Australia probably no longer exists.

The male ostrich is distinguished by the handsome black plumes on its body and its white wing and tail feathers. The grey or brown female is smaller and less striking than the male. The ostrich can sprint at up to 50 kilometres an hour on its long, powerful legs and two toes. Its eyes are large and fringed by long lashes, and its neck, though it looks bare, is covered in down.

Ostriches are mainly herbivorous, feeding on grasses as well as leaves, flowers and seeds. They travel alone, but may also congregate in large but loosely organised groups in desert areas where food is concentrated. They may also inhabit less arid areas, where food is in more plentiful supply.

Ostriches generally breed at the onset of the rains, but when there is sufficient food they may breed during the dry season. The male prepares a shallow scrape in the ground. A dominant female, known as the major hen, accepts one of a number of nests and lays about ten eggs, and up to five minor hens lay 10–30 eggs between them in the same nest. Excess eggs laid by the minor hens are not incubated. The major hen sits on the selected eggs during the day, and the male takes over incubation duty at night.

The chicks hatch after about 42 days. They leave the nest within a day or two and depart with the adults, often merging with other groups. At one year old the chicks have almost reached adult height, and within three to four years they are capable of breeding.
Family: Struthionidae;
Scientific name: *Struthio camelus*

OSTRICHES
These southern African birds were brought to Australia in the nineteenth century and farmed to provide plumes for women's hats and feather boas.

SOUTHERN CASSOWARY

The southern cassowary is a resident of the north-eastern rainforests of Queensland. It stands 1.5–2 metres high and is easily recognised by the tall, bony helmet, or casque, on the top of its head; by its vivid blue bare neck and face; and by its red lower back neck. Its heavy body is covered in shining black plumes, and pink wattles hang from the lower front of its feet. Its legs are stocky and its feet have three toes, the inner one in the form of a spike.

The females are larger than the males, and are dominant – a female can drive away a male by simply stretching her neck in threat. Males threaten by raising their neck and body in order to appear larger.

Cassowaries are mainly solitary and appear to be territorial. They form well-defined tracks to their regular food sources. Their diet includes rainforest fruits such as quandongs, lilly pillies and laurels, as well as fungi, insects, flowers, and snails taken from ground litter and low vegetation. They are especially fond of large fleshy fruits or fruits that have a single big seed.

During the breeding season (June to October) females tolerate males, and pairing lasts until egg-laying finishes about a month later. The nest, made by the male, is a scrape in the ground lined with vegetation. The female lays three to four green eggs, but plays no part in incubating them or caring for the chicks. After laying the first clutch, she may then pair and mate again with up to three more males during the season.

The eggs take 47–54 days to hatch. After hatching, the chicks stay with their father for about nine months. Newly hatched chicks are covered in down, with a reddish brown crown and three dark brown stripes down their body. Later the stripes are replaced by grey-brown juvenile plumage and then by immature plumage – a mixture of juvenile and adult plumage.

The future of this species is uncertain because of interference with its habitat – a serious problem not only for the birds but for many plant species. The southern cassowary is the only large, native, ground-living, fruit-eating bird in the Queensland rainforests. Seeds pass through the bird's body intact, and in this way it disperses the seeds of more than a hundred plants. In most tropical forests, entire groups of birds and mammals carry out this role, but in Australia the cassowary may be the only seed-disperser in its habitat;

■ SOUTHERN CASSOWARY
The bony projection on the cassowary's head is called a casque. Faced with an intruder, this big rainforest bird puffs out its feathers and hisses vehemently.

the loss of the species could mean the loss of the only method of seed-dispersal for many rainforest plants.
Family: Casuariidae;
Scientific name: *Casuarius casuarius*

EMU

This large flightless bird is endemic to Australia. Adults weigh 30–45 kg and stand 1.6–1.9 metres high, and are distinguished by shaggy grey-brown plumage parted down the centre of their back. The sparse black feathering on their crown continues down their neck until it merges into bare bluish skin that also covers their throat and face. Halfway down the front of their neck is an inflatable air sac that the birds use for making a variety of sounds. Their legs are long and grey, their bill short and wide. Of all living ratites, emus have the most rudimentary wings.

There were once emu species in Tasmania and on Kangaroo Island and King Island, but they are now extinct. The sole extant species is found over most of the mainland, particularly in pastoral areas, but it is seldom seen in unsettled arid areas or rainforests and never in heavily populated areas.

Emus eat the leaves, fruits, flowers and shoots of native plants, and also insects. They are nomadic, remaining in one place only when food and water are available throughout the year. In Western Australia they migrate seasonally, moving south into areas of winter rainfall and north into areas of summer rainfall.

Breeding usually takes place in autumn and winter, when adequate nourishment has enabled the adults to build up their body fat. Couples stay together for several months before the larger, more dominant females lay clutches of 5–15 blue-green eggs, which the males then incubate, eating and drinking little while they do so.

The chicks hatch after 53–61 days; when they leave the nest after two to seven days they can feed themselves. They stay close to their father for six to seven months; during this time he can be aggressive. After three to four months, darker immature plumage replaces their cream, tan and black striped down. Adult plumage appears after about six months, and the birds are sexually mature at two years old.

In the past emus have been seen as agricultural pests, and in 1932 many were shot in Western Australia in a concerted effort at extermination. They are still registered as pests in Western Australia, but are protected in other states.
Family: Dromaiidae; Scientific name: *Dromaius novaehollandiae*

DISTRIBUTION

■ OSTRICH
■ SOUTHERN CASSOWARY

■ EMU

■ EMU
If they feel threatened, emus can produce brief spurts of speed of up to 50 kilometres an hour. They will walk considerable distances in search of food and water: in the course of a year an individual may cover several hundred kilometres.

TUNNELLING UP
This newborn malleefowl is ready to tunnel its way up through its incubator mound to the open air. Hatchlings are alert, with open eyes, strong legs and a downy covering. They can fly after a day and feed themselves within a few days.

DISTRIBUTION

MALLEEFOWL

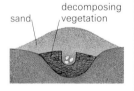

A NOVEL NURSERY
The malleefowl uses decomposing vegetation and the warmth of the sun to incubate its eggs. The male checks the temperature of the mound by poking his beak below ground level, and adds to or digs away the insulating layer of sand as required.

MOUND-BUILDERS AND TRUE QUAILS

Fowl-like birds with short, rounded wings, the mound-builders and the quails are the two families belonging to the order Galliformes that occur in Australia. They are ground-feeding birds that scratch around in the soil for seeds and vegetable matter with their strong feet, which have three toes pointing forward and one pointing backward.

Both mound-builders and quails are related to the domestic chicken, and many of their relatives are popular game birds – for example, pheasants, partridges and guineafowl.

MOUND-BUILDERS

The large, stocky mound-builders, or incubator birds, have short, broad wings, powerful legs and strong feet. Essentially ground-dwelling, they move by walking slowly, taking flight only when they are alarmed.

Mound-builders have a unique method of nesting and incubation. Instead of using body heat to keep their eggs warm, they bury them beneath sand that is warmed by decomposing organic material, volcanic activity or the sun.

Undisturbed by the parents, the eggs incubate for several months. Their very thin shells allow gases to pass in and out in the conditions of reduced oxygen underground. The chicks hatch from eggs that may be buried as much as a metre underground, and they can take many hours to dig their way out.

Mound-builder chicks are the most developed of all young birds. They emerge from the nest fully feathered and are able to run quickly. Within hours, most can maintain their own body heat efficiently, feed independently and fly strongly – capabilities that are essential to them, as they receive no parental care.

Mound-builder species occur in Australia, New Guinea, Indonesia and the Philippines, and on many small Pacific islands. Most species are threatened by human collection of eggs, habitat destruction, and the presence of introduced predators such as foxes and cats.

Three mound-builder species are found in Australia: the Australian brush-turkey, the malleefowl and the orange-footed scrubfowl.
Family: Megapodiidae

MALLEEFOWL
Stocky and stout-legged, this bird weighs about 2.2 kg and grows to 60 cm long. Its upper body is covered in bold 'eyes' of white, black and reddish brown, a patterning that helps to conceal the bird in the dappled light of its natural habitat.

Confined to southern mainland Australia, the malleefowl is the only mound-building bird that lives in arid areas. It drinks when water is available, but is able to survive quite well on the moisture that it obtains from its diet of seeds, fruits, herbs and invertebrates.

The malleefowl was once found in various habitats but now lives mainly in dry mallee woodlands

MALLEEFOWL
The male malleefowl spends much of his time working on the nest mound to keep it at the correct temperature to incubate the eggs, either scooping sand out or piling additional sand on top.

dominated by low-growing eucalypts. Its decline is due largely to land clearance, grazing by domestic stock and predation by foxes.

Malleefowl construct incubation mounds, usually 2–5 metres wide and about a metre high. Some mounds, used repeatedly over many decades, are as much as 12 metres in diameter. Each contains a core of damp leaf litter, which decomposes to produce the necessary heat.

Vegetation decomposes slowly in arid habitats, so the malleefowl uses solar radiation to supplement the heat produced by decomposition. During late summer, the male bird opens the mound in the morning and spreads the sand so that it can be warmed by the sun. As the day progresses, he rakes the warmed sand gradually back onto the nest. This procedure is repeated almost daily until the low temperatures of autumn force the birds to abandon nesting for the season.

Within a few months the birds begin to prepare for the following season. At first the female usually helps to build the mound, but once it is completed she spends much of her time finding the food necessary for egg production. In a season, a female may produce up to 35 eggs, totalling three times her body weight.
Scientific name: *Leipoa ocellata*

 AUSTRALIAN BRUSH-TURKEY
The Australian brush-turkey is mainly a ground-dweller, but it flies into trees to roost and to escape danger.

AUSTRALIAN BRUSH-TURKEY

Found only in Australia, this mound-builder inhabits coastal rainforests from Queensland to central New South Wales, in some areas extending inland into drier forests. These birds are usually wary, but those accustomed to humans often become quite tame, and the species is increasingly being seen around picnic areas and in suburban gardens.

The Australian brush-turkey is large and black and grows to about 70 cm long. It has a large fan-shaped tail and a bright red head and neck. It lives on seeds, fruits, insects, snails and other invertebrates. These birds usually feed alone or in pairs, but gather at dusk in communal roosts, where they perch in trees 5–20 metres above the ground.

Each male constructs an incubation mound of soil and decaying vegetation, usually about 1–2 metres high and 3–7 metres wide, in a shady part of the forest. Some mounds are used repeatedly for many years, so they can become very large and contain many tonnes of material. The male defends the mound vigorously against rival males but allows

females access for laying when the temperature is right. Several females may lay in a single mound. The chicks are solitary when they first emerge, but later join social groups.
Scientific name: *Alectura lathami*

ORANGE-FOOTED SCRUBFOWL

The orange-footed scrubfowl, or jungle fowl, has a crest, a short tail, and large orange legs and feet. It is common in rainforest, riverine forest and mangroves in Indonesia and southern New Guinea. In Australia, it occurs across the far north from Western Australia to Cape York Peninsula, and on many islands off the north Queensland coast.

Scrubfowl are a mere 40 cm long, but they build incubation mounds of soil and decaying vegetation that can be up to 15 metres in diameter and several metres high. Pairs tend their mounds all year, constantly turning and replenishing the organic matter. Several pairs often share the same mound. Scrubfowl are shy but can be very vocal – adults can often be heard calling, particularly at night during the spring breeding season.
Scientific name: *Megapodius reinwardt*

DISTRIBUTION

 AUSTRALIAN BRUSH-TURKEY

 ORANGE-FOOTED SCRUBFOWL

TRUE QUAILS

This family includes three native Australian species and four introduced species: the feral chicken (*Gallus gallus*), the common pheasant (*Phasianus colchicus*), the peafowl (*Pavo cristatus*) and the Californian quail (*Lophortyx californicus*), introduced into King Island and Norfolk Island in the nineteenth century. All of the introduced species occur only sporadically in the wild in Australia.

The rounded wings of quails are very small in relation to their body, which suggests that these birds are incapable of making long flights. However, the Eurasian quail (*Coturnix coturnix*) is migratory, and the native stubble quail (*C. pectoralis*) can travel up to 1100 kilometres, according to banding records.

Quails nest on the ground under bushes or tussocks in simple scrapes, which they line with grass. The female lays and incubates clutches of 4–11 pale coffee-coloured eggs with dark spots. When food is plentiful, she may raise two or three broods in succession. The chicks run around only hours after hatching, and are fed by their parents.
Family: Phasianidae

NATIVE QUAILS

The three native species are the stubble quail (*Coturnix pectoralis*), the brown or swamp quail (*C. ypsilophora*) and the king quail (*C. chinensis*). These heavily built ground-dwelling quails have short tails and bills, short stout legs and small heads.

Button-quails (pages 166–8) look like true quails, but the two species are not closely related. One difference is the number of toes: all other native quails have four, three pointing forwards and one pointing backwards, but button-quails have only three, all pointing forwards.

Native quails are nomadic, feeding on grass seeds, herbaceous leaves and insects. They eat the seeds of introduced plants and feed on crops such as lucerne. King quails and brown quails prefer streamside vegetation, wet heaths and swamps. Stubble quails are found in better drained country, but not in forests.

 NATIVE QUAIL
This male king quail is caring for its chick. King quails live in tall, dense grass in swampy country. If disturbed, they crouch down rather than fly away.

Stubble quails are found all over the Australian mainland except in the far north, the north-west and the central west. Brown quails live between the coast and the interior from northern Western Australia around to eastern South Australia, including Tasmania, and in the south of Western Australia. King quails are found in northern Western Australia and the Northern Territory and along the east coast from Cape York Peninsula to western Victoria.
Scientific name: *Coturnix* spp.

DISTRIBUTION

 NATIVE QUAILS

shoveler

pink-eared duck

Australian wood duck

Cape Barren goose

magpie goose

PRESENTING THE BILL
Duck and goose bills are
adapted for particular
ways of feeding. The
shoveler and the pink-
eared duck have broad
bills for dredging surface
water; the shorter bills
of the Australian wood
duck and the Cape
Barren goose are suited
to grazing; and the
hooked bill of the mag-
pie goose enables it to
dig out the roots of
water plants.

DUCKS, GEESE AND SWANS

Ducks, geese and swans, collectively known as waterfowl, usually live on or close to fresh or brackish water. They have webbed feet that act as paddles, and they spread these webs apart and push backwards to propel themselves through the water. As their feet move forward, the webs close to minimise resistance. The dense, waterproof feathers of waterfowl also equip them well for an aquatic existence. Waterfowl are members of the family Anatidae in the order Anseriformes.

Only 19 of the world's 150 or so species of waterfowl are found in Australia, where inland water is relatively scarce, but, several of these – the Cape Barren goose, the freckled duck, the magpie goose, the musk duck, the pink-eared duck and the Australian wood duck – live nowhere else in the world.

Australian waterfowl species have adapted to the unpredictability of this country's rainfall by developing an uncanny knowledge of the avail-ability of water, and often travel long distances to their feeding and breeding grounds.

Most waterfowl appear to stay with the same mate for several years, if not for life. The blue-billed duck, the musk duck and the freck-led duck are exceptions; the males of these species remain with the females for one season, or sometimes for only as long as it takes to mate.

At least one parent, and in some species both, protect the chicks until they can fly – usually after a couple of months. Most hatchlings can feed themselves within a day or two, and they then leave the nest. The magpie goose and the musk duck are highly unusual among the world's water-fowl; they collect or catch food for their young and then present it to them or drop it in front of them.

Domesticated ducks
Waterfowl were among the first animals to be farmed for their meat and eggs. The greylag goose, for example, was first domesticated 4500 years ago, although waterfowl were hunted much earlier than that.

Except for traditional hunting by Aborigines, hunting in Australia is

now largely a sporting activity and not a necessity of life. Duck shooting is now banned in Western Australia and New South Wales as a result of pressure from conservation groups.

Because of their trusting nature and attractive plumage, waterfowl have been kept for ornamental pur-poses for more than 2500 years.

New feathers for old
All birds moult at least once a year to replace worn feathers with new ones, but most waterfowl species moult twice – once to replace body feathers with breeding plumage, and again after the breeding season.

In the second moult all the flight feathers are shed together, leaving the birds flightless for a month or two. This is when waterfowl are most vulnerable to their predators, so they must either stay on the open water, out of reach of foxes and dingoes, or hide in the reeds. This second moult usually coincides with the time when the young birds are still flightless.

Bills of lading
One feature unique to waterfowl is their broad, flattish bill. Most of them sift water and mud through

their bills to obtain their diet of seeds or small aquatic animals. The tongue operates like a piston, draw-ing water up from the bill into the mouth. As the tongue moves down, it drives the water past rows of plates, called lamellae, along the edge of the bill, but the food is retained. The food is then brushed free and swallowed by the action of the bristly tongue and the lamellae.

The bills of some waterfowl species have become modified for specific activities. For example, the wide beak of the shoveler enables it to sift the water as it swims along. This adaptation has been taken to the extreme, with side flaps, by the pink-eared duck, which uses its extra-wide beak to feed on tiny animals. Grazing waterfowl, such as the Australian wood duck and the Cape Barren goose, have shorter beaks. The magpie goose uses the hook at the tip of its beak for pulling up the roots of aquatic plants.

BLUE-BILLED DUCK ◼
These compact little ducks, 40 cm long, have relatively short necks, making them look squat. The male has a bright blue bill, a black head and a deep chestnut body; the female is a much plainer brown.

Blue-billed ducks are rare, and are seldom seen in flocks of more than a few birds. They like rivers and deep lakes where there is tall dense vegetation, and spend much of their time diving or dabbling for food, which consists of insect larvae as well as seeds and plant material.

These ducks are very shy and when disturbed they tend to dive under water rather than fly away. This may be because they undergo two moults of flight feathers each year, during which time they are flightless and vulnerable. They nest in reedbeds, often pulling the stalks together overhead to form a canopy.
Scientific name: *Oxyura australis*

◼ BLUE-BILLED DUCK
The male blue-billed duck uses its tail as a rudder under water and fans it out on a vertical plane during courtship.

■ WHISTLING DUCKS
Plumed whistling ducks
are sometimes known as
grass whistling ducks
because they graze on
grasses on land rather
than feeding in or on
water, as most ducks do.

WHISTLING DUCKS ■

These ducks are uncharacteristically long-necked and long-legged for waterfowl, enabling them to walk around grasslands and particularly the margins of swamps. Their loud, distinctive, high-pitched whistles, which are uttered by both sexes and are often interspersed with twittering calls, account for their common name. They nest away from the water's edge in long grass, often under bushes, or sometimes in reeds at the edge of a swamp.

The plumed whistling duck *Dendrocygna eytoni*, 40–60 cm long, has pink bills and legs, and is pale brown with distinctive long feathers (plumes) on their flanks that stick up over their folded wings. During the nonbreeding dry season, they frequently congregate in flocks of thousands in northern Australia.

These ducks are sometimes called grass whistling ducks because they feed on grasses, and they are also known as tree ducks because they often perch in trees.

The wandering whistling duck *D. arcuata*, 55–60 cm long, is less widespread and more aquatic than the plumed whistling duck. Also known as the water whistling duck, it feeds mainly on water plants, although it often roosts on land, sometimes with plumed whistling ducks.

The spotted whistling duck, *D. guttata*, has been recorded breeding in western Cape York Peninsula.

Whistling ducks do not engage in elaborate mating behaviour, and casual observers seldom notice the mutual nibbling of paired birds. The females lay 6–15 creamy white eggs.

On their back, the ducklings of *D. eytoni* are brown while those of *D. arcuata* are blackish brown, with pale to whitish underparts, distinctive stripes across their cheeks and a line above their eyes. Very soon after hatching they take on the long-legged, upright appearance of adult whistling ducks.
Scientific name: *Dendrocygna* spp.

MAGPIE GOOSE ■

The magpie goose is unique to Australia and southern New Guinea, and has no close relatives elsewhere in the world. It seems to be a cross between a duck and a goose, and its feet match neither – the webs reach only halfway to its toes, rather than to the tips. Its scientific name, *Anseranas semipalmata*, means 'half-webbed goose-duck'.

■ MAGPIE GOOSE
The magpie goose's long legs enable it to make its way over dense, swampy vegetation – or mud when the swamps are drying out – in search of food.

This lanky black and white bird stands about 70 cm tall and has a distinctive bump on its head. Its hooked beak and long neck are useful for reaching into mud to feed on the roots and bulbs of aquatic plants. Nowadays it is closely associated with the Top End of Australia. Huge numbers of magpie geese breed on the extensive swamps in the north, taking advantage of the wet season.

This species was once found over most of eastern and south-eastern Australia, and is gradually re-establishing itself in these areas. Like many other Australian waterbirds, it has been affected by the extensive drainage of wetlands. In addition, its habit of eating grasses and pulling up roots has made it unpopular with farmers. Its liking for rice plants has resulted in many birds being shot or poisoned.

The magpie goose displays several behaviour patterns that are uncharacteristic of waterfowl. While most ducklings or goslings must feed themselves from the time of hatching, newly hatched magpie geese are fed by their parents, who drop titbits in front of their chicks. This feeding behaviour may last for up to six weeks. Another difference is that the magpie goose moults gradually.

The magpie goose also builds an unusual nest for a waterfowl. It consists of a pile of uprooted reeds, trampled flat, but the depression, which most waterfowl line with down, remains bare. A male magpie goose may have one, two or even three mates, all of which may lay their eggs in the same nest and take turns to incubate the eggs.
Scientific name: *Anseranas semipalmata*

FANCY FOOTWORK
The webs on the foot of a magpie goose reach only halfway down the toes and not to the tips as in other waterfowl.

DISTRIBUTION

■ BLUE-BILLED DUCK

■ WHISTLING DUCKS

■ MAGPIE GOOSE

DISTRIBUTION

■ AUSTRALIAN
WOOD DUCK

■ FRECKLED DUCK

■ BLACK SWAN

■ AUSTRALIAN
WOOD DUCK
Both Australian wood
duck parents care for the
young. Here a female is
brooding her ducklings,
spreading her wing to
keep them warm.

AUSTRALIAN WOOD DUCK ■

This widely known native duck is
found from the coast to remote
inland properties and wetlands. It is
the least aquatic of all the Australian
ducks, mostly grazing on grass and
herbs, but it takes to water for the
safety of its ducklings when they are
too small to fly, and when the adults
are moulting their flight feathers
and so are also flightless.

The male has grey plumage with
a freckled breast and a chocolate
brown head and upper neck. The
crest on the back of its head
accounts for this duck's other common name – the maned duck. Males
are 48 cm long; females are smaller,
drabber and brownish, with a white
line above and below their eyes.

Wood ducks pair for long periods,
possibly for life. They nest high up
in hollows of dead or living trees,
sometimes a kilometre or more from
water. The female coaxes the newly
hatched ducklings out of the nest by
flying repeatedly from the ground
to the nest and back, calling all the
way. She then leads her brood to
the nearest pond for safety.

Only the female incubates the
eggs, but both parents care for
the young. Until they fledge after
57 days, the young usually stay near
water, but will run into vegetation
for cover and sit tight if necessary.
Scientific name: *Chenonetta jubata*

FRECKLED DUCK

The freckled duck, dark grey or
brown with paler freckling, is
Australia's rarest duck. It is similar
in size to the Pacific black duck
(page 134) and resembles it from a
distance, but at close range it can be
seen that the freckled duck has a
small head crest and no eye stripe.

■ BLACK SWAN
Lakes must have a good surface area
for the large black swan to obtain
liftoff. A black swan taking to the air
reveals its spectacular white flight
feathers (above). Another feature of
this bird's dramatic colouring is a red
beak with a sparkling white tip (right).

Males have a somewhat darker head
than females, and during the breeding season the base of their bill
becomes bright red. When they are
flying, freckled ducks are without
the green-blue patch that marks the
flight feathers of Pacific black ducks.

The freckled duck differs from
other dabbling ducks in a number
of ways. The ducklings do not have
the normal patterned down but are
plain, like geese and swans. The
voice box of adults is more like that
of swans and geese, and their tra-
chea (windpipe) resembles that of
the magpie goose. Nor does the
freckled duck go through the typical
twice-yearly moult of other waterfowl; instead it undergoes one flightless period of three to four weeks
while moulting its flight feathers.

Freckled ducks mainly inhabit the
shallow water of freshwater lakes,
where they swim, moving their
heads from side to side, and feed on
small aquatic animals in the muddy
bottom. They usually build nests
among the branches of lignum or
other bushes or low trees, close to
the water surface, and sometimes
on old nests of other water birds.
Scientific name: *Stictonetta naevosa*

BLACK SWAN ■

Early explorers who reported the
existence of black swans were met
with scepticism until later reports
confirmed their stories. Black swans
are native to Australia, and are
found wherever there are lakes with

plenty of waterweed, except on
Cape York. The species has been
introduced in New Zealand, where
large flocks now occur.

With a wingspan of up to 2 metres
and a tip-to-tail length of up to
1.4 metres, this is Australia's largest
native waterfowl. Only the introduced mute swan (*Cygnus olor*), with
a wingspan of 2.4 metres, is bigger.

Black swans eat mainly waterweed, which grows in freshwater
lakes or lagoons near the coast or in
brackish inland lakes; inland freshwater lakes are generally too murky
for waterweed to grow. With their
long necks they can reach down to
depths of up to a metre. They also
graze on grasses around swampy
edges or on dry land near water,
and often occur in huge numbers
in coastal bays, such as the southern
parts of Botany Bay near Sydney.

When a lake starts to dry out, flocks
of several hundred black swans may
fly long distances in a V-formation.
They seem to prefer flying at night.
On water or land they look almost
totally black, but in flight their white
primaries and outer secondaries are

very striking. Their beak is bright red with a narrow white band across the top and a white tip. Some of the wing feathers close to their body are curled, making their back look frilly when their wings are folded. Cygnets are covered in pale grey down.

On coastal wetlands and smaller lakes and ponds near towns, single pairs build large nests of waterweed or reeds in shallow water or floating among aquatic vegetation. Flocks of several thousand descend on large inland lakes after heavy rain to feed and breed. They inhabit low islands in colonies of up to several hundred pairs, building nests just a beak's reach apart (about 1.5 metres). Nesting material may be scarce, and the swans collect any suitable materials that they can find near the nest site. The nest may be just a scrape in the ground lined with down.

Black swans usually breed from April to September, but may do so whenever conditions are favourable. Like most swans, they appear to mate for life. Courtship involves ritual calling, head-bobbing and neck-stretching, reinforcing the bond between the pair. Both sexes incubate the clutch of four to six eggs, marking each changeover of duty with an elaborate ceremony that further cements the relationship.
Scientific name: *Cygnus atratus*

PYGMY-GEESE

Although the stubby-billed pygmy-geese look superficially like geese, they are in fact small ducks that spend most of their time on lakes, ponds and dams.

The cotton pygmy-goose, *Nettapus coromandelianus*, is found in India and South-East Asia as well as in Australia, where it is now confined to north-eastern Queensland. The loss of wetlands and the spread of water hyacinth, which kills pond weed and aquatic grasses, probably account for its recent decline. The smaller green pygmy goose *N. pulchellus*, 30–36 cm long, occurs from Broome in Western Australia across the top of the continent to central Queensland. It feeds on waterlilies.

Pygmy-geese tend to mate for life and both birds are actively involved in selecting a nest site and caring for the young, although the female alone incubates the six to ten eggs. Nests are built in tree hollows, usually over or near water, and thickly lined with down. Both species breed during the wetter months from November to April, when males defend their mates and offspring by chasing other males away.

The male cotton pygmy-goose, about 35–38 cm long, has a white face, neck and underparts, freckled grey-brown flanks, a brown crown, and glossy green upper parts and breast band. The female is slightly smaller with duller plumage, no breast band, and a well-marked dark line through the eye.

The male green pygmy-goose has a green head, neck and upper parts, a whitish body closely barred with green and a large white cheek patch. The female is slightly smaller and duller, with no green on its neck.
Scientific name: *Nettapus* spp.

CAPE BARREN GOOSE

The native Cape Barren goose is a plump, stumpy-billed bird 75–100 cm long. It has grey plumage with rows of black spots on the wings, pink legs, black feet, and a small beak almost completely covered by a pale greenish-yellow waxy layer (cere).

Cape Barren geese nest only on the Bass Strait islands off Tasmania, each pair mating for life. Unusually for waterfowl, mating occurs on land. At the onset of the season, a male or female approaches a partner, and then one or both birds display

by promenading around each other, slowly bowing their heads. This courtship dance is called waltzing. The male utters a loud, trumpeting call but the female makes a pig-like grunt, which has earned the bird the alternative name of pig goose.

The male generally builds a nest of grass, plants or nearby materials on or near the ground in tussock grasses or among rocks or low bushes. He then takes on guard duty while the female lines the nest and maintains it, laying four to five creamy white eggs. After incubating for 34–37 days, the goslings hatch covered in striking black, white and grey patterned down. Both parents look after the young, brooding them nightly until they are about four weeks old. These geese guard their offspring fiercely, and will attack any animal that approaches.

Cape Barren geese spend most of their time grazing their grassy island homes. They rarely swim, but fly between the islands and the Tasmanian and mainland coasts in the nonbreeding season, sometimes in flocks of several hundred.
Scientific name: *Cereopsis novaehollandiae*

DISTRIBUTION

☐ PYGMY-GEESE

■ CAPE BARREN GOOSE

■ CAPE BARREN GOOSE According to some accounts, sealers and settlers had hunted this species virtually to extinction by early in the twentieth century. As recently as 1977, about a thousand Cape Barren geese were shot, but since then protection by wildlife agencies has increased numbers to around 17 000, which may be close to the population before European settlement.

SHELDUCKS ■

The Australian shelduck (*Tadorna tadornoides*), also called the mountain duck, occurs in two distinct populations, one in south-eastern Australia and the other in the south-west. The Radjah shelduck (*T. radjah*) is found from north-eastern Western Australia to the north of Queensland.

Both shelduck species have obvious white shoulder patches on their wings and glossy green patches on their flight feathers. Small portions of these wing patches are visible on their folded wings. At 60–70 cm long, the Australian shelduck is somewhat larger than the 50–55 cm Radjah shelduck.

The Australian shelduck is easy to identify by its black head, chestnut breast and lower neck, white neck band and dark brown body. The female also has a small white patch around each eye.

Females initiate mating with much head-dipping, water-thrashing and mock chasing, and unattached females often cause a stir by enticing males that have already mated.

Paired for life, both birds select a nest site in a tree hollow 2–20 metres high; the female incubates her 5–14 eggs in the down-lined grassy nest. The young are taken to water soon after hatching and are looked after by both parents.

Male and female Radjah shelducks look very much alike, with a pink bill and legs, a white head, neck, breast and belly, and a chestnut band across the breast (slightly narrower in the female) and down the back.

They build their nest in a hollow tree in or near water, lining it with down when they lay their eggs – usually between April and June, but the timing is influenced by the wet season. Pairs usually mate for life. The female incubates the eggs, but both sexes take care of the young.

■ SHELDUCK
The Australian shelduck is an adaptable feeder and often grazes on land. It is easily recognisable by its black head, chestnut breast and white neck band.

Shelducks are equally at home grazing on grasses and sedges at the water's edge and upending themselves in water to feed on molluscs, crustaceans, insect larvae and vegetation. They also sift the muddy ooze in quest of small animals in shallow water or on mudflats.
Scientific name: *Tadorna* spp.

MUSK DUCK ■

Early explorers named the unique Australian musk duck for its strong, musky smell and taste. These come from the male's preening gland, which produces an oil that the duck spreads liberally over its feathers.

At 66 cm long, musk ducks are quite large. Despite their unobtrusive dark brown plumage and their habit of floating on the surface of deep water far from shore, these ducks are easily recognised by their practice of swimming very low in the water, rather like a cormorant but with a short neck. Their long, stiff tail feathers usually lie fanned out flat on the water, except when the ducks are roosting at night.

During the mating season the male makes a loud plonking noise by smacking the surface of the water on either side of its body with its feet, and then utters a loud, shrill whistle. Males splash to attract females and also to advertise their territory and chase off encroaching males.

Males take no part in incubating or nurturing the ducklings, which peck at the base of their mother's bill to beg for food. Unusually for waterfowl, she often feeds them until they are quite large, even after they are capable of finding their own food.

Musk ducks feed by diving, and often stay under water for as much as a minute. They use their strong beak to catch water beetles, crayfish, water snails and freshwater mussels.

Musk ducks spend most of their time on the water, but walk or run when the need arises. They are rarely seen in flight, as they usually take to the air while it is dark. They shed their flight feathers twice a year.
Scientific name: *Biziura lobata*

PINK-EARED DUCK

The pink 'ears' that give this duck its common name are two barely visible small pink spots on either side of its head, but it is recognisable by the dark brown mask around its eyes and the zebra-like stripes along its body. It is 36–45 cm long.

This species is rare near the coast but occurs in large flocks on inland wetlands, where its distinctive chirruping call can be heard, especially when it is in flight.

■ MUSK DUCK
When it roosts at night, the musk duck sticks its tail feathers into the air in a vertical fan formation. Hanging beneath its beak, the 66 cm-long male musk duck has a large, pendulous sac that it inflates when courting. The smaller female has no sac.

During long dry periods, pink-eared ducks are forced to move to more permanent wetlands, including lakes and sewage treatment settling ponds. When the wetlands flood, however, these ducks are quick to take advantage of the growth of microscopic water plants and animals. At these times they nest in huge numbers, using every available tree hollow, stump, log or abandoned nest. Only the females incubate the six to eight eggs, but both parents care for the young.

On each side of their beak, pink-eared ducks have a flap that gives the bill a broad sweep. This enables the ducks to sift through water or through soft mud in search of their minute animal prey.
Scientific name: *Malacorhynchus membranaceus*

DISTINCTION OF BIRTH

Some birds require no parental care, but others need a lot of attention. Naked, helpless chicks, such as eagles, hatch from small eggs that contain little yolk, while active young, such as geese and cranes, come from larger, yolk-rich eggs. High in fats, the yolk provides the chick with food reserves. The magpie goose hatchling pictured above will remain in the nest for only a day before its parents lead it away to feed.

Chicks that are independent at birth keep a seventh to a third of the yolk in their gut after hatching, which provides them with nourishment until they can find their own food. Birds that leave the nest soon after hatching have eggs with a yolk content of 35–50 per cent; nest-bound chicks that are fed by their parents come from eggs with a yolk content of 15–20 per cent.

HARDHEAD

The hardhead is 45–60 cm long. It feeds mainly on the surface of water but it is also an accomplished diver.

Both the male and the female are brown with a white patch under the tail. The male has a whitish eye and a blue band across the top of its black bill. The female is paler, with dark brown eyes and a less marked band on the bill.

Hardheads usually live on large permanent swamps with plenty of reed beds or in woody swamps, but they are also found on lakes, coastal swamps and sewage farms. From August to December they make neat nests of reeds, sticks and sedges in a reed bed or in the branches of bushes standing in water. Flooding may also stimulate nesting. The female incubates the 9–12 eggs.
Scientific name: *Aythya australis*

TEALS

Teals are small ducks, 40–50 cm in length, and are commonly found in most types of wetlands. The grey teal (*Anas gracilis*) favours fresh water and the chestnut teal (*A. castanea*) prefers coastal habitats, but the species often occur together.

Male grey teal and the females of both species are brown to greyish brown with pale-edged feathers. The two species can be difficult to tell apart, but grey teal are generally somewhat greyer and paler about the neck and chin. The male chestnut teal has a glossy dark green head and a chestnut body with a white patch on the flanks.

Both teal species prefer to nest in the hollow limbs of trees close to water, but they sometimes nest on the ground, concealed in tall vegetation. They use little or no nesting material, but the female plucks

down from her breast to cover the eggs. The female lays and incubates 4–15 eggs, and both parents participate in caring for the young.
Scientific name: *Anas* spp.

GARGANEY

The garganey is a typical northern hemisphere duck. A vagrant in Australia, it breeds in Eurasia, migrating south in the nonbreeding season. It is occasionally seen on Australian lakes and ponds. It inhabits fresh water with plenty of vegetation.

The male garganey can be identified in its breeding plumage by the clear white stripe over its eye and down the side of its head, which contrasts with its dark crown and brown head.

Female garganeys resemble the females of many other duck species, but can be identified by a dark line through the eye. Females and nonbreeding males, both 37–41 cm long, look like smaller versions of the Pacific black duck (page 134).
Scientific name: *Anas querquedula*

■ HARDHEAD
The hardhead, also known as the white-eyed duck, dives to reach small animals and water plants that are beyond the reach of other ducks. It can swim as far as 40 metres under water.

■ TEALS
Brackish water and the salt water of coastal bays and estuaries are where teals are most commonly found, and they nest on the ground or in tree hollows. This pair of chestnut teal (*Anas castanea*) will remain together, caring for their brood, until the young birds can look after themselves.

■ MALLARDS
Mallards were brought into Australia in the late nineteenth century, and are now widespread in city parks. They have long been associated with humans as domestic or ornamental birds, and many kinds of domestic ducks have originated from their readiness to cross-breed.

DISTRIBUTION

■ SHOVELERS

■ PACIFIC BLACK DUCK

■ MALLARD

SHOVELERS

Shovelers are named for their dark, broad, spatula-like bill, edged with fine sieve plates. They use these to dredge surface waters and mud for small molluscs, aquatic insects and seeds, sometimes swimming in small groups, with one bird stirring up food for another following close by. When swimming, they look hunched and sit low in the water. Shovelers are 45–53 cm long.

The northern shoveler (*Anas cypeata*) is seen in Australia only rarely. The male has a bright green head, a white front and chestnut flanks with a white patch behind.

The male Australasian shoveler (*A. rhynchotis*) has a greyish head, chestnut sides, a white patch near the tail and a white crescent running down its face. Females of both species look similar and are hard to distinguish at a distance. At close range, the female northern shoveler has an orange bill and the female Australasian shoveler a dark bill.

Australasian shovelers usually nest hidden in tall grass close to water, but occasionally use a hollow tree stump. The male has little to do with incubating the eggs or caring for the young.

Although widespread in eastern and south-western Australia, the Australasian shoveler usually occurs only in small numbers, often with other ducks. The population seems to have dwindled in recent years.
Scientific name: *Anas* spp.

PACIFIC BLACK DUCK ■

Australia's native Pacific black duck, often known as the black duck, is widely distributed and is found on lakes, ponds, inland swamps and lagoons with abundant aquatic vegetation. A highly adaptable surface-feeding species, this bird is as much at home in a city park as it is in the outback.

The Pacific black duck is 50–60 cm long. It dabbles on the surface, occasionally upending itself to feed on aquatic plants or animals. Male and female black ducks are mainly brown with pale stripes above and below their eyes and iridescent green secondary wing feathers that are visible as a green patch on their folded wings. In flight, their green secondaries and white underwing feathers are distinctive.

Black ducks usually nest between June and December, but may do so at any time if there is flooding. They often choose tree hollows, but also nest on the ground among vegetation or in abandoned nests of other water birds. They use little or no nesting material, but the female places down around her eight to ten white eggs. After 26–28 days the young hatch. The female leads them from the nest almost immediately and stays with them until, after about 50–55 days, they can fend for themselves and fly.
Scientific name: *Anas superciliosa*

■ PACIFIC BLACK DUCKS
These ducks are found in a variety of watery habitats in Australia. The adults eat plants and animals but the ducklings feed almost entirely on aquatic insects.

OUSTING THE LOCALS?

Hybrids – the offspring of two different species – are rare in wild birds, but are more common in wildfowl than in other groups. Hybrids are usually infertile, but fertile young can be born if the parents are from similar species.

The introduced mallard and the Australian black duck produce fertile hybrids when they interbreed. The mallard male, being larger, can outcompete the male black duck and often mates with female black ducks. The young then dominate pure-bred black ducks.

Mallards have not yet spread very far into inland wetlands, but some conservationists think that mallards and their hybrids should be removed before they become a threat to black ducks.

MALLARD ■

Common in the wild throughout Europe, North America and Asia, in Australia the mallard is an introduced species.

Mallards can now be found in many urban parks, often in the company of Pacific black ducks, accepting handouts of bread from their human visitors. They also live on ponds and dams on rural properties, and there are wild populations in south-eastern New South Wales, Victoria and eastern South Australia.

Male mallards are 55–70 cm long and females are slightly smaller. The male has a yellow bill, a bright green head and a white collar. Its back and sides are grey-brown and its rump is black. It has a distinctive small glossy black curl on its tail.

The female mallard looks similar to the female black duck but does not have the distinctive pale stripe above and below its eyes.
Scientific name: *Anas platyrhynchos*

GREBES

Grebes are water birds that are especially well adapted to swimming under water, and dive for nearly all their food. Their feet are lobed – not webbed like ducks' feet – with flaps on either side of the toes. Their order name (Podicipediformes) and family name (Podicipedidae) come from the placement of their legs at the rear of their body, which makes them awkward on land but extremely adept under water.

Grebe nests are floating mats of vegetation, often very wet, in which the eggs lie just above the surface of the water. Both parents take turns at incubating the eggs.

The chicks are covered in short, dense down and have a well marked striped pattern that they keep for several months. They leave the nest not long after hatching and are cared for by both parents, often riding on a parent's back between its wings for the first three or four weeks of life.

Fish-eating species such as the great crested grebe consume some of their own feathers. Scientists believe that this unusual habit may help to form the pellets of undigested scales and bones that they regurgitate. Another theory is that feathers in the bird's stomach may reduce the build-up of gastric parasites.

These birds are reluctant to fly when disturbed, preferring to dive quickly under water. When surprised, they may patter across the surface of the water before diving out of sight. They have small, narrow wings, but can fly considerable distances between wetlands. They lack manoeuvrability in flight, so they tend to fly at night, when they are safest from birds of prey.

Grebes have no visible tails – their rear ends look like powder puffs. Their body feathers moult over a long period, but their flight feathers moult all at the same time, leaving them flightless for about three weeks.
Family: Podicipedidae

AUSTRALASIAN GREBE

The frequent trilling call of the little grebe is often the first thing that attracts attention to these small birds – 23–25 cm long – as they swim among aquatic vegetation or across open water. Their diet consists of small fishes, snails and various other aquatic animals.

These grebes nest in solitary pairs on large or small, relatively shallow bodies of water where there is ample floating waterweed. The parents use the waterweed to make a nest, which they attach to reeds.

They incubate the two to six eggs and take care of the young, sometimes carrying them on their backs for protection.

In the breeding season, both males and females have quite distinctive plumage, with a long narrow chestnut patch running from behind their eyes down the side of their neck and a striking small yellow patch at the base of their bill. When little grebes are not breeding they are often quite difficult to distinguish from hoary-headed grebes, with which they may occur in mixed flocks.
Scientific name: *Tachybaptus novaehollandiae*

HOARY-HEADED GREBE

Hoary-headed grebes are about 29–30 cm long. At a distance they resemble little grebes, but at closer range the streaked appearance of the adult hoary-headed grebe is quite obvious. This nomadic species is confined largely to Australia, although a few birds have recently taken up residence in New Zealand.

This grebe is considerably more gregarious than the little grebe, and may be seen in large numbers on the same lake during the nonbreeding

AUSTRALASIAN GREBE
The male and the female Australasian grebe cooperate to build their floating nest, which they make from waterweed and attach to a few reeds to prevent it from drifting with the current.

season. It may be that the birds find safety in numbers as they undergo simultaneous moulting of their wing feathers. Quite often hoary-headed grebes build their floating nesting platforms within a metre of each other in groups of several hundred.
Scientific name: *Poliocephalus poliocephalus*

GREAT CRESTED GREBE

This bird is quite distinctive when seen swimming. Its erect neck and prominent crest and the frills on either side of its head differentiate it from all other Australian water birds. The pure white front of its neck and cheeks contrasts with its black crest and dark grey-brown back, sides and wings. At 46–51 cm long, this is the largest of the Australian grebes. The females are a little smaller than the males, but otherwise look very similar.

The elaborate courtship ritual of the great crested grebe has long been a source of fascination for ornithologists. The display begins with head-shaking and erect crests. The male then dives, surfaces with a piece of weed and swims towards the female. The two birds then swim away from each other, dive, and emerge facing each other, both holding the weed. This is then followed by the 'penguin dance', in which both birds hold themselves high and, with breasts touching, paddle water vigorously.

Great crested grebes are usually found in relatively clear water. They like deeper water than other Australian species, perhaps because their main food source is small fishes. In Australia the great crested grebe is restricted to the eastern states and two areas in Western Australia, but it occurs throughout Eurasia and much of Africa.
Scientific name: *Podiceps cristatus*

POWER DIVE
As the grebe pushes its foot back against the water, the lobes of its toes flare out to form a paddle. When the grebe pulls its foot forward, the lobes fold into a narrow blade, thereby reducing energy expenditure and drag.

DISTRIBUTION

AUSTRALASIAN GREBE

HOARY-HEADED GREBE

GREAT CRESTED GREBE

135

PENGUINS

Penguins are well adapted to life at sea. Their wings, which they no longer need for flight, have evolved into flippers for rapid underwater swimming. Their bones are more solid than those of other birds and this, together with a layer of blubber, gives them the neutral buoyancy that prevents them from sinking too deep or floating on the surface.

Their streamlined bodies minimise drag as they swim, and their short feet and legs, set well back on their bodies, act as rudders. It is this placement of their feet and legs that gives penguins their waddling gait on land. Penguins belong to the family Spheniscidae in the order Sphenisciformes.

■ LITTLE PENGUIN
This little penguin chick nestling in its burrow is in the final stages of its juvenile plumage. Little penguins, often called fairy penguins, are the smallest of all penguins, and they are the only penguin species to breed in mainland Australia.

Penguins live on small fishes, crustaceans and squids, so they need to be strong divers. The heavier the bird, the longer it can stay under and the deeper it can dive.

Penguins live only in the southern hemisphere but occupy habitats from high Antarctic sea-ice through subantarctic islands to the equatorial Galapagos Islands. They normally breed in colonies; in the breeding season the Antarctic and subantarctic species form groups of a million birds or more. In warmer latitudes, breeding birds form looser colonies.

Generally, penguins nest on beaches or rocky headlands, except for the royal penguin (*Euayptes schlegeli*) and the macaroni penguin (*E. chrysolophus*), which may breed more than a kilometre inland. Most penguins make nests out of bones and stones, but those in warmer climates sometimes dig burrows in the sand. King penguins (*Aptenodytes patagonicus*) and emperor penguins (*A. forsteri*) do not build nests but keep eggs and chicks safe and warm on their feet, under a flap of abdominal skin.

There are about 17 penguin species, ranging from 1 kg to 40 kg in weight. Only the little penguin breeds in Australia, but Australia's Antarctic territories are breeding grounds for five species. Vagrant species visit Australian shores, usually arriving in a weakened state, spending only a few days ashore.

The most common vagrants come from New Zealand. The fiordland penguin (*Eudyptes pachyrhynchus*), which breeds on New Zealand's South Island and surrounding

■ ROCKHOPPER PENGUIN
The small rockhopper penguin (*Eudyptes chrysocome*) is found on islands of the Southern Ocean and sometimes strays into Australian waters

islands, has been recorded here many times. The Snares penguin (*E. robustus*) and the erect-crested penguin (*E. sclateri*), which breed on islands south of New Zealand, have also been seen. Penguins that breed on Macquarie Island sometimes stray onto southern Australian beaches, and some Antarctic species have visited Australia's shores.

The long-distance record goes to a Magellanic penguin (*Spheniscus magellanicus*) from South America, found at Phillip Island in 1976.

LITTLE PENGUIN ■

Little penguins, sometimes known as fairy penguins, gather at the edge of the surf at dusk before waddling in procession across the sand to the burrows where they roost. At dawn they make the return journey.

Growing to about 40 cm long and weighing only 1 kg, they are a uniform blue-grey above and white below. They swim in the waters around the southern half of Australia, from northern New South Wales to Perth in Western Australia. Unlike many other penguin species, little penguins come ashore, and they can

be seen along the southern Australian coast throughout the year.

Little penguins nest under dense vegetation or rocks, or dig burrows in loose sand with their feet. Colonies vary greatly in size, from only one or two pairs to around 15 000 pairs. Most breeding colonies form on offshore islands, probably to minimise predation from foxes and cats. Depending on the location, females lay their eggs between August and September, and in some years pairs raise a further one, or even two, clutches when the first chicks have fledged. There are usually two eggs in a clutch, and they are incubated by both parents for about 35 days. Although both eggs generally hatch, parents usually cannot bring back enough food for both and generally only one hatchling survives. Until the chick fledges at 42 days it is fed regurgitated food by its parents, one of which is always on guard. Breeding is usually over by late February, when the adults start their annual moult. Young penguins do not breed until they are three or four years old.
Scientific name: *Eudyptula minor*

DISTRIBUTION

■ LITTLE PENGUIN

Polar personalities

Most of us will never be lucky enough to see them in their natural habitat, but penguins are the endearing inhabitants of Australia's subantarctic territories.

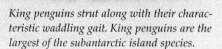

Macquarie Island lies in the Southern Ocean about 1500 km south-east of Tasmania. Until the late 1800s the island was regularly visited by seal hunters, but when seals became scarce the sealers turned their attention to penguins, boiling them down in large cast iron pots for their oil. The island was declared a wildlife sanctuary in 1933, and is one of four bases maintained by the Australian National Antarctic Research Expeditions. All of the Macquarie island subantarctic penguins are occasionally found on beaches in southern Australia.

Heard Island is 4000 km south-west of Fremantle, Western Australia, and south of the Antarctic Polar Front – a current that produces a concentration of nutrients and ensures a ready supply of food for the island's millions of penguins.

The camera catches a pair of king penguins in an affectionate moment of their courtship. Half a million king penguins breed annually on Macquarie Island.

Five species of penguin breed on the islands: king penguins (*Aptenodytes patagonicus*), gentoo penguins (*Pygoscelis papua*), royal penguins (*Eudyptes schlegeli*), rockhopper penguins (*E. chrysocome*) and macaroni penguins (*E. chrysolophus*) – but royals breed only on Macquarie Island, where they are endemic, and macaronis only on Heard Island.

King penguins are slate grey above and white below and have distinctive bright yellow patches on either side of their neck. All the other species have black upper parts and white fronts, and each has species-specific markings.

Sharing living space

Each penguin species has a slightly different breeding pattern, so these two islands can sustain very large numbers of breeding birds. Macaroni penguins breed in large colonies on steeply sloping hillsides, while rockhoppers prefer rocky headlands; these two species come ashore only in summer, when they breed and moult. Macaronis lay two eggs in early to mid November, though they usually discard the

King penguins strut along with their characteristic waddling gait. King penguins are the largest of the subantarctic island species.

smaller first egg. The eggs hatch after about 35 days and the young fledge 65 days later, in February. Rockhoppers have a similar breeding timetable, but often attempt to rear both young.

King penguins breed on the beaches, taking more than 12 months to rear their chicks, so chicks with downy coats are present on these islands all year round. The chicks grow very little in the colder months, however, because the parents have to forage much further afield during winter and return to feed their single young much less frequently than in the summer. Gentoo penguins also breed on the beaches, but because they do not travel as far to feed, they feed their chicks much more regularly – usually at least once a day – and parents can often rear two chicks in a season.

Macquarie Island is a rich breeding ground for rockhopper penguins, with about a million birds breeding there each year.

SEA BIRDS

Sea birds are oceanic and offshore birds that eat marine animals – fishes, and squids and other invertebrates. The group includes the tube-nosed sea birds of the order Procellariiformes – petrels and shearwaters, albatrosses and storm-petrels – and the pelican group of the order Pelecaniformes – tropicbirds, gannets and boobies, darters, cormorants, pelicans and frigatebirds. Some of these birds, such as the pelican and certain cormorants, have adapted to coastal and inland aquatic environments, and the darter is solely a freshwater bird.

strong, flexible wrist bones for mobility

long, narrow wings for lift and glide

strong bill with hooked tip for catching fish

webbed feet for swimming and for use as air brakes when landing

BIRD OF THE OCEANS
A typical sea bird, the royal albatross is adapted to a life spent largely offshore, returning to land only to breed.

DISTRIBUTION

GOULD'S PETREL

All the tube-nosed sea birds have horny, tubular coverings over their nasal openings. They spend most of their lives plying the oceans, returning to land to breed. Food is often hard to come by, and many sea bird species can go for some time without nourishment, flying thousands of kilometres between feeding and breeding grounds.

All sea birds are long-lived, taking several years to hone their flying skills and become fit and strong enough to breed. Breeding pairs tend to bond for life, raising a single chick each year and caring for it for months until it can fly and fend for itself.

How sea birds navigate the oceans is a mystery. Some experts suggest that they use celestial navigation; others believe that they respond to the earth's magnetic fields.

Sea birds preen their waterproof feathers with oil from a gland at the base of their tail. They also have glands near their eyes that remove salt from their bodies.

A HIGH-DIVER'S NOSE
The nasal openings of some sea bird species, such as the southern giant-petrel, are encased in a horny tube to prevent water being forced into them when the bird dives.

PETRELS AND SHEARWATERS

Petrels and shearwaters are easily identified by their unusual tube-noses, which are fused together at the top of their bill. The bill is strongly hooked and the upper half has extremely sharp edges that are ideal for grasping and cutting through slippery fishes and squids.

Petrels are robust birds and use their short, stubby bills to capture prey. They surface-dip or plunge-dive, often at night when squids – their favourite food – rise to the surface. Shearwaters generally feed underwater. They are shaped for

pursuit of their main prey – fishes – with a long, thin bill and neck, a streamlined body, sleek feathers, and webbed feet that are situated far back on their body.

Most shearwater and petrel species nest in burrows, but giant-petrels nest on the ground.
Family: Procellariidae

GOULD'S PETREL ■

Gould's petrel is Australia's rarest endemic sea bird. It breeds only on the slopes of Cabbage Tree Island, off the coast of central New South Wales. It is distinguished from other petrels by its black head and contrasting white chin, and by the black diagonal stripe on its underwing.

Adults come ashore in October to nest in rock crevices and under the fallen fronds of the cabbage tree palm. The female lays a single egg in late November or early December. Chicks hatch in January, and fledge

in April. Adults return to their nests after dark to feed their young with squids and small fishes, and depart before dawn. Gould's petrels are believed to feed in the Tasman Sea, but very few have been seen there.

Gould's petrels grow to 30 cm long, but their wingspan is more than 70 cm; they are able to glide effortlessly over the ocean but have difficulty flying through forest, so they land at their breeding ground by crashing headlong through the canopy. They generally leave by launching themselves from the tops of the palm trees, which they climb by using their bill and claws to grip the textured trunk.

While they are ashore, Gould's petrels sometimes become trapped by the sticky fruits of the bird-lime tree. Brooding adults and their young also risk being taken as prey by pied currawongs. Recent conservation measures to remove bird-lime trees from the island and to control the number of currawongs has reduced these threats, and the Gould's petrel population is now recovering from past declines.
Scientific name: *Pterodroma leucoptera*

■ GOULD'S PETREL
The only place Gould's petrels breed is on Cabbage Tree Island, just off the mouth of Port Stephens on the central coast of New South Wales.

PROVIDENCE PETREL

The providence petrel, also known as the brown-headed petrel, is typical of the gadfly petrels of the genus *Pterodroma*. These birds swoop and soar on the air currents above the ocean. They inhabit more temperate waters than many other petrels and shearwaters and are found in the south-western Pacific Ocean, mainly between Brisbane and Bass Strait. Gadfly petrels frequent waters over 200 metres deep, where they often feed on squids brought to the surface at night on current upwellings.

These birds are 40 cm long and have a 95–100 cm wingspan. They are large and solidly built, with a dark brown head and a brown body, and the plumage on their back and upper wings is tipped with frosty grey. Their hooked bill is black, short and stout, with a squat tube nose. Like most petrels, this species lays a single white egg in a chamber lined with vegetation at the end of a metre-long tunnel. Both parents incubate the egg for seven weeks and then feed the chick for four months. In the summer, the breeding grounds fall silent as the birds go to sea.

The providence petrel used to breed on Norfolk and Lord Howe islands. In 1790 the convicts and crew of the *Sirius* were shipwrecked on Norfolk Island. Facing famine, they ate more than 170 000 of these birds in three months. This, together with the introduction of pigs and goats, which eroded the soil so that the burrows collapsed, and rats, which eat eggs and chicks, destroyed the island's breeding population. Today, this petrel breeds from March to November on one island off Norfolk Island and on Lord Howe Island in the forest floor of Mount Lidgbird. There are now over 20 000 birds but the petrel is still vulnerable.
Scientific name: *Pterodroma solandri*

PROCELLARIA PETRELS

All species in this group are confined to the southern hemisphere and live in Australian seas. All nest on sub-antarctic islands or on the offshore islands of New Zealand.

Procellaria petrels are 46–56 cm long, with a 115–136 cm wingspan. Of the four species, three are dark brown to black with pale, horn-coloured bills, so they are barely distinguishable in the field. The grey petrel, however, is grey above and white below, with dark underwings and a pale green bill.

Also known as the shoemaker, the white-chinned petrel (*Procellaria aequinoctialis*) is abundant and widespread in the Southern Ocean but rare around the coast of Australia. The grey petrel (*P. cinerea*) is sometimes spotted around the southern coast. The two other species, the rare black petrel (*P. parkinsoni*) and the Westland petrel (*P. westlandica*) breed only in New Zealand.
Scientific name: *Procellaria* spp.

GIANT-PETREL

The northern giant-petrel has a wingspan of nearly 2 metres. Giant petrels take living animals, such as birds, from the surface and scavenge on dead ones.

PROVIDENCE PETREL

This petrel acquired its common name when it provided the entire diet of the convicts and crew of the *Sirius*, shipwrecked on Norfolk Island in 1790.

GIANT-PETRELS

Giant-petrels, or fulmars, generally inhabit cold waters in high latitudes, now and then straying into warmer waters. These tube-nosed sea birds are 87 cm long, with wingspans of nearly 2 metres. They spend almost their entire life feeding at sea and are at risk from long-line fishing.

The two giant-petrel species common in Australian waters are hard to tell apart, except at close quarters. Both are generally brown, although 10 per cent of southern giant-petrels (*Macronectes giganteus*) are white, with some dark feathers giving them a spotted appearance. They have a green bill tip and a dark iris, whereas the northern giant-petrel (*M. halli*) has a red bill tip and a pale iris.

Both northern and southern giant-petrels nest at Caroline Cove on Australia's subantarctic Macquarie Island, often among tussock grasses. Sealers called giant-petrels stinkers because the chicks regurgitate a foul-smelling oil when disturbed.
Scientific name: *Macronectes* spp.

COMMON DIVING-PETREL

These petrels, which occur only in the southern hemisphere, breed in burrows among tussock grasses or in rocks crevices on subantarctic islands throughout the Southern Ocean.

Plump birds 20–25 cm long, with a 35 cm wingspan, they are black above and white below, with a short, rounded tail and wings. They fly close to the water, dashing through the waves looking for small fishes and crustaceans. Their legs are far back on their body to assist them when diving for prey. On emerging, they scurry across the surface and

PROVIDENCE PETREL

PROCELLARIA PETRELS

GIANT-PETRELS

COMMON DIVING-PETREL

COMMON DIVING-PETREL

Below their bill, diving-petrels have a pouch that they can expand and use for storing food.

■ PRION
Small grey and white petrels, all four prion species look very similar. Pictured here is the broad-billed prion, *Pachyptila vittata*, so named for its extremely wide bill.

into the air with whirring wings. Common diving-petrels often rest in large, densely packed groups called rafts, particularly off their breeding grounds before dark, when they return to land; raft formation may be a strategy for avoiding marine enemies. From below, their white underparts merge with the sky, camouflaging them from underwater predators such as seals and sharks. On moonlit nights, they rarely come ashore for fear of being taken by gulls, skuas or giant-petrels.

The common diving-petrel breeds on subantarctic islands and the offshore islands of New Zealand, and also on islands in Bass Strait and southern Tasmania, where it is common. Records of this species along the south-eastern coast are usually of birds swept off course by storms.
Scientific name: *Pelecanoides urinatrix*

■ SHORT-TAILED SHEARWATER
Commonly known as the muttonbird, the short-tailed shearwater dives to depths of up to 10 metres in order to catch fishes to feed its chicks.

PRIONS ■

Prions are small grey and white petrels, 25–30 cm long with wingspans of 56–59 cm, that inhabit the cold Southern Ocean. Their other common name – whalebirds – may refer to the fine, comb-like bristles on their beaks, with which they filter animal plankton and small crustaceans from seawater, as baleen whales do. Alternatively, they may be called whalebirds because large numbers are often seen in the company of whales and dolphins.

All four prion species are bluish grey above and white below, with a dark open M-pattern on their upper wings and dark tail bands. The best way to tell them apart is by bill width: the broad-billed prion (*Pachyptila vittata*) has a bill about 25 mm wide, while the thin-billed prion's bill (*P. belcheri*) is only 8–10 mm wide.

Prions are sometimes seen from headlands and are often washed ashore after winter storms, particularly in southern Australia. The fairy prion (*P. turtur*) and the Antarctic prion (*P. desolata*) are known to nest in Australia, the fairy prion on islands off the Victorian and Tasmanian coasts and the Antarctic prion on Macquarie and Heard islands.
Scientific name: *Pachyptila* spp.

SHORT-TAILED SHEARWATER ■

The short-tailed shearwater is also known as the muttonbird. It is brown with silver underwings, and is 41–43 cm long. It breeds only in Australia on offshore islands of mainland south-eastern Australia, especially in Tasmania and on the islands of Bass Strait. During the breeding season – between October

┌ LONG-LINE FISHING ┐

Long-line fishing lines have fishhooks attached to a line of up to 100 kilometres, played out behind the fishing boat. Before the hooks sink, surface-feeding sea birds such as albatross and shearwaters snatch them and get dragged underwater to drown. Thousands of ocean-going boats set hundreds of millions of baited hooks each year.

Long-line fishing is now threatening many species with extinction, including 16 out of 21 albatross species. These are large, long-lived birds with low reproductive rates and low natural death rates. Southern bluefin tuna long-line fishing may account for a yearly mortality of 2–3 per cent of adults and 14–16 per cent of immature wandering albatross (*Diomedea exulans*).

The world population of the southern giant petrel (*Macronectes giganteus*) has declined from 38 000 to 31 000 pairs in ten years. Between 1997 and 1998, an estimated 2000–4000 were killed in southern oceans. These populations cannot withstand this level of mortality. Seemingly small changes to survival of adults can have catastrophic consequences, especially when added to other hazards, including nesting habitat destruction and ingestion of floating plastic.

and April – an estimated 23 million short-tailed shearwaters nest here. In autumn, dense flocks leave Australian coasts for the high latitudes of the northern hemisphere.

Short-tailed shearwaters are most often seen close to when storms sweep them onto beaches. On the coast, thousands of them can be seen returning to land just after dusk each day to feed their chicks in burrows beneath tussock grasslands. They regurgitate food for their single chick for the first three months.

The breeding cycle of short-tailed shearwaters is very precisely timed and synchronised: most of them return to their colonies between 20 and 25 September, and 61–71 per cent of the eggs are laid between 24 and 27 November.

This species is the only wild Australian bird that is legally harvested. The industry is centred on the Furneaux Islands in Bass Strait, where each year about 400 000 chicks are pulled from their burrows. The chick meat is salted or canned and the down is used as stuffing for sleeping bags and quilts.
Scientific name: *Puffinus tenuirostris*

DISTRIBUTION

■ PRIONS

■ SHORT-TAILED SHEARWATER

ALBATROSSES

Albatrosses are among the largest of all flying birds. The 14 species that are currently recognised mainly live in the southern hemisphere; nine are recorded from Australian seas. Albatrosses are seen from headlands in Australia south of latitude 30°S.

The wandering albatross (*Diomedea exulans*) and the royal albatross (*D. epomophora*), with wingspans of 3.2 metres, are sometimes known as great albatrosses. The smaller albatross species, commonly known in Australia and New Zealand as mollymawks or mollyhawks, have wingspans of 1.8–2 metres.

Most albatrosses are black and white, with long narrow wings for sustained gliding, short tails, and webbed feet that they use for swimming and as air brakes when they land. These birds have difficulty taking off from flat, low surfaces, and must run flapping into the wind to become airborne. The upperwings of all adult albatrosses have dark markings; this plumage extends across the back in the mollymawks, but is broken by a white back in the royal and wandering albatrosses. Their tube-noses are small and differ from those of petrels and shearwaters in not being fused together. They use their strongly hooked bill to hold the fishes and squids that are their main sources of food.

Three mollymawks are the most abundant of the albatrosses found in Australian waters: the black-browed albatross (*D. melanophrys*), which breeds annually on Macquarie Island; the shy or white-capped albatross (*D. cauta*), which breeds annually on islands off Tasmania;

and the yellow-nosed albatross (*D. chlororynchos*), which breeds annually on the Crozet Archipelago in the southern Indian Ocean.

Two species of sooty albatross also occur in Australian seas: the sooty albatross (*Phoebetria fusca*) and the light-mantled sooty albatross (*P. palpebrata*). Both breed every two years on Macquarie Island.

Some albatrosses take a long time to find a mate – up to 12 years for royal and wandering albatrosses – but they then pair for life.

Juveniles gather in associations known as gams to practise their courtship dances: calling, clapping their bills, pointing at the sky, and dancing opposite each other with outspread wings and upturned tails.

Mature males display at the nest site to attract a mate and females then lay a single egg. Males and females share the two-month incubation period and feed the chicks for up to eight months. Albatrosses return to the same nest for every breeding season.

The wandering albatross (*Diomedea exulans*) weighs up to 11 kg and its wingspan exceeds 3 metres. They are expert navigators and use little energy to travel large distances at great speed. In Australia, they are most often seen in winter along the southern coast, particularly between latitudes 30°S and 50°S. Here the wind blows almost constantly from west to east, circling Antarctica.

Wandering albatrosses breed every other year. They spend a year plying the Southern Ocean for food; then, in November, the males return to their breeding sites on subantarctic islands. Females arrive in December and lay their eggs in January. The pair spends 11 months incubating and feeding the chick. In Australian waters, this bird is known to nest only on Macquarie Island, where the breeding population is small: in 1996 only seven pairs raised their chicks.

These birds may live as long as 100 years, but the species is under threat from long-line fishing (see opposite).
Family: Diomedeidae

DISTRIBUTION

ALBATROSSES

GENTLE GIANTS
Wandering albatrosses – the gentle giants of the bird world – are shown here with black-browed albatrosses off the coast of New South Wales.

SURFING THE WIND
Albatrosses and other sea birds glide in great loops 20–30 metres above the waves. At this height the slowing effect of the sea surface on the wind is negligible and the wind speed increases.

MEET A MOLLYMAWK
The smaller albatross species, such as the black-browed albatross, are sometimes known as mollymawks.

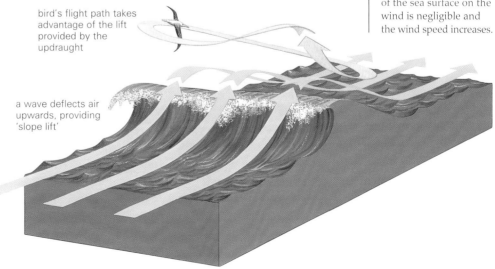

bird's flight path takes advantage of the lift provided by the updraught

a wave deflects air upwards, providing 'slope lift'

DISTRIBUTION

STORM-PETRELS

STORM-PETRELS

The smallest storm-petrels weigh less than 20 grams and, at 18–20 cm long with a wingspan of 32 cm, are the smallest of all sea birds. They are generally black and white or brown and grey. These birds resemble petrels but have short, sometimes forked or squared-off tails, shorter wings and long black legs that dangle beneath them as they fly. Storm-petrels look fragile, but are hardy birds that forage over very deep water, plucking fish eggs, animal plankton and marine larvae from the surface of the sea as they patter or bounce over the waves.

Storm-petrels typically breed in burrows that they excavate in soft soil under vegetation or in cracks and crevices amongst rocks and boulders on the sandy islands off southern Australia. All species lay one very large white egg. Skuas and gulls are major predators of adult and chick storm-petrels, frequently taking adults in flight as they return to or depart from their breeding

colonies on moonlit nights. This is probably why storm-petrels return to their breeding colonies after dark, usually before the moon rises, or after it has set, fluttering to land rather like giant moths.

Several species of storm-petrel are found in Australian waters. Of these, the most common and widespread breeding species is the white-faced storm-petrel (*Pelagodroma marina*).

Other species found in Australian seas include the white-bellied storm-petrel (*Fregetta grallaria*), which breeds on Lord Howe Island; the black-bellied storm-petrel (*F. tropica*), which breeds on subantarctic islands; Wilson's storm-petrel (*Oceanites oceanicus*), which breeds in Antarctica and on subantarctic islands, including Heard Island; and the grey-backed storm-petrel (*O. nereis*), which breeds on subantarctic islands and off New Zealand.
Family: Oceanitidae

SMALL BUT HARDY
Storm-petrels are the tiniest of the sea birds. The white-faced storm-petrel, *Pelagodroma marina*, is the species most frequently seen in Australian waters.

DISTRIBUTION

TROPICBIRDS

TROPICBIRDS

Tropicbirds inhabit tropical and subtropical seas all around the world. Adults are easily identified by the long slender tail feathers that trail behind them like streamers.

Also known as bosun-birds, they are white with black markings, and have strong, pointed bills. Their weak, webbed feet make them ungainly on land. They range from 95 cm to 104 cm long, including their tail feathers.

Tropicbirds spend their entire lives at sea except during the breeding season. Largely aerial, they wheel 15 metres or so above the ocean and seldom rest on the water. They are thought to feed mainly during the night on flyingfishes and squids, capturing their prey by plunge-diving. Like gannets and boobies (pages 143–4), they have a cushion of air cells beneath the skin at the front of their bodies that absorbs the impact of diving.

Of the three species of tropicbird, two are recorded from Australian seas. Neither of them is common, but in the right place they can be seen from headlands and boats. Although they mainly occur in northern Australia, they have been observed off the coast of all mainland states except South Australia.

SPECTACULAR TAIL FEATHERS
The two central tail feathers of the red-tailed tropicbird are a brilliant red and trail like streamers. This bird dives on its prey from up to 14 metres above the surface or snatches it from the water.

Cape Byron and Danger Point in northern New South Wales and Cape Leeuwin on the south-western coast of Western Australia are both good places to look for them.

The red-tailed tropicbird (*Phaethon rubricauda*) is a spectacular species. An adult in fresh plumage has a rosy pink flush to its feathers, and the two long central feathers of its pointed tail are bright red, as is its bill. In eastern Australia this species breeds on small coral islands of the Great Barrier Reef. Lord Howe Island, off the coast of New South Wales, is home to the largest breeding population in the South Pacific Ocean. In November and December these birds can be seen performing striking aerial courtship displays, circling the nesting area. Along the west coast, the species nests as far south as Rottnest Island and Cape Naturaliste, laying a single egg in an unlined depression among rocks.

The white-tailed tropicbird (*P. lepturus*) is slightly smaller than the red-tailed tropicbird and has a bright yellow bill and white tail streamers. It is a regular but rare visitor to the Coral Sea, occasional vagrants being blown further south, especially after cyclones.
Family: Phaethontidae

GANNETS AND BOOBIES

Gannets and boobies are conspicuous birds, very similar to one another in body shape, with long, pointed wings and tails and large, strong, conical bills. Their beak meets their head to form a distinctive facial mask that surrounds their round, beady eyes. The colour of the mask, bill and webbed feet distinguishes one species from another. While gannets are found in cold and temperate waters, rarely venturing north of the Tropic of Capricorn in Australian seas, boobies are subtropical and tropical.

Gannets and boobies often wheel in large flocks, spreading out over a large area of ocean to search for shoals of fishes. Their flight consists of a few wingflaps followed by a long glide. Once they locate their prey, the birds plunge-dive into the sea from about 20 metres above the surface. They have keen eyesight and streamlined bodies, and are able to target fish with precision, falling upon them like an arrow and then bobbing back up to the surface. When one bird dives, its companions soon arrive to share the spoils. All boobies are very partial to flyingfishes.

Air sacs under their skin cushion the bodies of these large birds against the impact of their dives, and they have dispensed with external nasal openings to prevent water shooting up their nostrils.

Gannets and boobies are gregarious when breeding, often gathering in crowded, smelly colonies that resound with the noise of courting, greeting and fighting. All species incubate their eggs by spreading their webbed feet over them.

Four booby species are recorded from Australasian seas, two of which are easily seen from land – the brown booby and the masked booby. Being subtropical and tropical, boobies breed all year, forming loose colonies of several pairs, often with eggs and chicks at different stages of development. Males select the nest site and advertise for a mate by sky-pointing.
Family: Sulidae

GANNETS ■

Gannets are strong fliers that are able to move against the wind with little wing-flapping. They plunge-dive for fishes and also take squids. These birds are silent when hunting but vociferous when on the ground.

Gannets collect in breeding colonies that can consist of thousands of birds. They nest on offshore islands and isolated headlands, and sometimes on structures such as channel markers. Their nest is a low mound of debris and droppings. Competition for nesting material is fierce, and much theft goes on. Most gannets lay their single white eggs in October, and the chicks have grown feathers by late April or early May.

Gannets do not reach sexual maturity for six or seven years. Before growing adult plumage they go through a series of moults: juveniles are usually a mottled brown.

Young gannets spend several years at sea before returning to their birthplace to breed. They may visit this colony several times before establishing a nest site or securing a mate, but once a pair has formed it generally lasts for life. Pairs renew their bond each year with courtship

rituals that involve mutual preening and billing, and remain together until the chick fledges.

Two gannet species are known in Australian waters. The Australasian gannet (*Morus serrator*) has a yellow head, a black tail tip and black-edged wings. It is 84–91 cm long and has a wingspan of 1.7–1.8 metres. It is common and widespread along Australia's southern coasts, from Townsville in Queensland to Shark Bay in Western Australia. The similar Cape gannet (*M. capensis*) breeds in South Africa and Namibia and is an accidental visitor to Australian seas.
Scientific name: *Morus* spp.

BROWN BOOBY ■

The brown booby is the most commonly seen species on the tropical mainland and is a frequent visitor to the waterfront at Cairns. It attains a length of 71–76 cm and a wingspan of 1.4 metres. Adults look impeccably groomed. Their white belly and underwings contrast sharply with the chocolate brown of their upper body, throat and neck, and their feet and facial mask may be yellow, blue or green. Immature birds are dull brown above with a dull brown head and a dark tail, and are mottled brown, grey and white below.

This species builds its nests either in sandy clearings among bushes on islands or perched on cliffs.
Scientific name: *Sula leucogaster*

■ GANNETS
Summer breeders, Australasian gannets collect in noisy colonies consisting of thousands of birds. They build their nests about a metre apart, just out of pecking reach of their neighbours.

■ BROWN BOOBIES
The first brown booby chick to hatch – usually from two eggs, but sometimes from three – is likely to be the only one to survive: its superior size and strength enable it to grab the largest share of the food supplied by the parents.

DISTRIBUTION

AUSTRALASIAN GANNET

■ CAPE GANNET
■ BROWN BOOBY

DISTRIBUTION

■ MASKED BOOBY

■ RED-FOOTED BOOBY

■ **RED-FOOTED BOOBY**
Islands on the Great
Barrier Reef and in the
Coral Sea provide the
red-footed booby with
suitable nesting habitat.
This sea bird also roosts
in trees and bushes.

MASKED BOOBY ■

The masked booby prefers to live
offshore, breeding on the sandy
islands of north-eastern and north-
western Australia, including Lord
Howe Island. As nesting sites, these
birds favour patches of open ground
on headlands and islands, from
which they can take off easily into
the wind. The masked booby lays
two bluish white eggs about six
days apart, but only the first hatchling is likely to reach adulthood
because its size enables it to take all
the food its parents provide.

With its white plumage, black
flight and tail feathers and the feath-
erless black mask around its eyes,
the base of its bill and its throat, the
masked booby looks very like the
Australasian gannet (page 143). It
grows to 76–86 cm long and has a
wingspan of 1.8 metres. It is the
heaviest of the boobies, and searches
for flyingfishes and squids farther
south than other booby species.
Scientific name: *Sula dactylatra*

RED-FOOTED BOOBY ■

The red-footed booby grows from
66 cm to 79 cm long and has a
wingspan of 1.4 metres. It is usually
seen only from boats and is easily
confused with other boobies because

■ MASKED BOOBY
Boobies are the gannets of the tropics.
The masked booby breeds throughout
the year in clearings on sandy islands.

its plumage varies from white to
mottled brown to dusky brown or
grey. However, its bluish bill and
pink to red feet are distinctive.

The red-footed booby nests on the
ground or in shrubs, often with several species of frigatebird (page 147).
The species squabble over food and
sticks for nest-building and chase
one another across the sky. At the
nest site both the male and female
red-footed booby make harsh, repetitive 'karr-ucks' and loud crackling
sounds. The female produces one
white egg. In the hot tropical sun,
the bird on incubation duty sometimes stands in the nest beside the
egg to shade it, rather than keeping
the egg under its large webbed feet.

These boobies supplement their
diet of squids and fishes with crustaceans. Unlike other boobies, they
may dive for food at night as well as
during the day. They are sometimes
led astray by lights, and have been
observed landing on ships' decks
and in waterfront gardens.
Scientific name: *Sula sula*

ABBOTT'S BOOBY

At 79 cm long, this slender black and
white booby is relatively large. It is
the rarest booby in Australian seas
and is classed as endangered. In
1989, the total breeding population
was estimated at 1900 pairs. Its sea
distribution is little recorded,
although it is rarely seen far from its
only known breeding grounds on
Christmas Island in the Indian Ocean.

Abbott's booby is sometimes called
the forest booby because – unusually
for a sea bird – it nests in rainforest.

Its nest is a substantial structure of
sticks and twigs, often cradled in the
living leaves of its nesting-tree.

The trees used by Abbott's boobies
grow on a phosphate deposit that is
now being mined. Since the forest
does not regenerate after mining, nest
sites are being lost. This, together
with a low reproduction rate and a
slow breeding cycle, is causing the
species' decline. These birds usually
breed only once every two years. It
has been estimated that it takes each
pair 9.5 years to rear two young, and
that if 60 per cent of fledglings die
before they breed, it takes 28.8 years
for each pair to replace themselves.
Scientific name: *Papasula abbotti*

TOSS THE FEATHER

By throwing feathers, sticks and
small pieces of pumice into the
air, young boobies like these brown
booby chicks develop skills that
they will need in later life for fishing and nest building.

Booby parents can be away from
the nest for long periods fishing,
and these tossing games may also
help the chicks stave off boredom.

DARTERS

There are four species of darter worldwide. One of them, the darter (*Anhinga melanogaster*) is widespread throughout mainland Australia, especially in tropical and subtropical regions, but avoids the arid inland. It inhabits freshwater lakes and rivers and brackish estuaries. It is quite common to come across these birds roosting on logs with their wings and tails outstretched.

At first sight the darter looks like a cormorant, but its long, needle-sharp bill and flexible, snake-like neck are distinctive. Its hunting tactics are different too. Both cormorants and darters are underwater hunters, but cormorants pursue their prey, whereas darters are stealthy stalkers and, with their highly articulated neck drawn back into a S-shape, stab their prey with lightning speed.

Darters are opportunistic feeders, taking anything from small aquatic insects to frogs and freshwater turtles, but they prefer fishes. Under water, they lure fishes into the shadow of their spread wings and tail and spear their prey with a slightly opened bill so they can hold it firmly until it reaches the surface. There they manipulate it or toss it in the air so as to swallow it head first.

Darters often swim with only their long neck and head above the surface, earning them the name of snake bird. Their glossy black and silver streaked plumage is not water-resistant, unlike that of most water birds. This lack of waterproofing reduces the bird's buoyancy and enables it to slip into the water unnoticed by its prey. Because of its water-absorbent feathers, the darter must leave the water and spread its wings to dry before it can fly. Its broad wings allow it to soar on thermal air currents, and its flap-and-glide flight is easily recognised.

Darters build substantial nests of sticks and twigs, often low on a limb over water, frequently lining the nests with fresh eucalypt leaves. Females lay three to five pale blue eggs.
Family: Anhingidae

WATER-RESISTANT PLUMAGE
The darter's feathers are absorbent, enabling it to slip smoothly beneath the water without alerting its prey.

DISTRIBUTION

■ DARTER

CORMORANTS

Cormorants are sometimes called shags. Five species occur in Australia. They are black or pied, medium to large aquatic birds with a longish neck and a longish bill that is hooked at the tip. A transparent membrane protects their eyes while they are under water. They inhabit rivers, estuaries and coastal waters, but seldom venture far out to sea.

Well-adapted to life in water, cormorants feed mainly on fishes, which they capture by underwater pursuit. Their large webbed feet, set well back on their body, propel them through the water and their long, stiff tail acts as a rudder. Once a fish is captured, the cormorant returns to the surface to swallow it. The bird juggles the fish into position to avoid damage from any spiny fins, and then swallows it head first.

As with darters, the plumage of cormorants is not fully waterproof. This permeability enables the birds to sink below the surface, but before flying again they must haul themselves from the water and spread their wings out to dry.

Cormorants usually occur in flocks or small parties. When fishing, some species form a organised group, encircling shoals of fishes and driving them into shallow water. They nest in colonies, either with other water birds, other cormorant species, or as a single species. Each year they use the same site, laying two to five eggs in nests in trees or on the ground. Both parents incubate the eggs with their webbed feet and care for the young, which are born naked.
Family: Phalacrocoracidae

LITTLE PIED CORMORANT ■

This highly adaptable species, which is 58–63 cm long with a wingspan of 84–92 cm, is sometimes called the little cormorant or little shag. It is widespread and common throughout Australia, and is often seen around farm dams and on river banks. The little pied cormorant eats fishes, frogs, crustaceans and water snails. It is the smallest of the pied cormorants, and can be identified by its relatively short yellow bill.

These birds form loose breeding colonies of a few to several hundred pairs. Nests are substantial twig structures built in trees or on the ground by both males and females.
Scientific name: *Phalacrocorax melanoleucos*

DISTRIBUTION

■ LITTLE PIED
CORMORANT

■ LITTLE PIED
CORMORANT
Cormorants spend much of their time on perches spreading their wings out to dry and oiling their feathers with secretions from preen glands on their rump.

DISTRIBUTION

■ BLACK-FACED
CORMORANT

■ PIED CORMORANT

■ LITTLE BLACK
CORMORANT

■ GREAT CORMORANT

BLACK-FACED CORMORANT

The black-faced cormorant, also known as the white-breasted cormorant, is endemic to the southern coasts of Australia, where it is widespread. Unlike most cormorants occurring in Australia, it is totally marine. At 61–69 cm long and with a wingspan of 93–102 cm, the black-faced cormorant is similar in size to the little pied cormorant but can be distinguished from it by its black bill.

Black-faced cormorants are gregarious, often forming large flocks. Breeding colonies, too, are sometimes large, and are usually situated on offshore islands. Nests are substantial structures of seaweed and other debris, situated on rock ledges just above the high-tide mark.
Scientific name: Phalacrocorax fuscescens

■ LITTLE BLACK CORMORANT
This sleek black cormorant is common in Australia and can be recognised by its small size and its fine grey bill.

PIED CORMORANT

Found only in Australia and New Zealand, the pied cormorant is 66–81 cm long and has a 110–130 cm wingspan. It can be identified by its large size and its yellow facial skin.

The pied cormorant feeds mainly on small fishes and crustaceans. Except in the dry centre, this bird is common and widespread throughout the mainland, especially on coastal estuaries, wetlands and rivers. It is also found along rivers and lakes far from the coasts, and in times of flood large numbers breed on islands in inland lakes.
Scientific name: Phalacrocorax varius

LITTLE BLACK CORMORANT ■

Common and widespread, the little black cormorant is small – 58–63 cm long with a wingspan of 95–105 cm – and has glossy black plumage and a purplish grey bill. It inhabits both fresh and salt water, preferring freshwater lakes and swamps when breeding. It is a gregarious bird, often occurring in very large flocks.

When feeding, flocks of little black cormorants form lines, driving fishes before them. Birds at the back of the line fly to the front of the school of fishes to block its escape. Once trapped, the fish panic and the water 'boils' with activity, attracting more birds to the melee.

These cormorants breed in colonies, often in paperbark trees in inland swamps, and frequently along with other water bird species. Nests are large twig structures, sometimes lined with fresh eucalypt leaves.
Scientific name: Phalacrocorax sulcirostris

GREAT CORMORANT

At a length of 90 cm and with a wingspan of 1.3–1.5 metres, this cormorant is the largest member of its family. It is found worldwide and is common in both fresh and salt water environments in Australia. Often occurring in large flocks, it feeds on fishes, crustaceans and turtles.

Great cormorants often breed in colonies in trees standing in water, usually along with other water bird species. Each year the same nests are used, with a new stick layer added, and nests can grow to 2 metres thick.
Scientific name: Phalacrocorax carbo

AUSTRALIAN PELICAN

DISTRIBUTION

■ AUSTRALIAN PELICAN

Very few people would fail to recognise a pelican. Of the seven species found throughout the world, only the Australian pelican, *Pelecanus conspicillatus*, is found here.

These huge black and white birds, sporting long pink bills with suspended pouches, weigh up to 8.2 kg and have a body length of 1.2 metres and a wingspan of 3.4 metres. Australia's largest flying bird, the Australian pelican is widespread and common, inhabiting large bodies of fresh or salt water.

A FORMIDABLE BILL
After driving fishes into the shallows, the pelican scoops them into its huge bill pouch. The bird then drains the water away and swallows the fishes.

Pelicans are quick to exploit any resource; if they are fed regularly by humans, they become extremely tame. They are skilled fishers that forage by day and night, alone and in groups, mainly on fishes. They capture prey by sitting and waiting, or by paddling stealthily through shallow water, powered by their huge webbed feet, with their head held low to scoop fishes into their enormous expandable bill pouch.

Pelicans often preen and roost on exposed mudbanks and islands, where in hot weather they flutter the thin skin of their pouch in order to keep cool. When in groups, pelicans fly in a loose V-shaped formation or in a line. Their large, broad wings enable them to soar

gracefully and effortlessly in circles on thermal currents, and they have been recorded at altitudes as high as 3000 metres. Despite their size, pelicans are excellent fliers, capable of sustained long-distance migrations and able to exercise enormous control and precision both in the air and on water. When they land, they glide along the surface of the water before lowering their legs and skiing to a gentle stop.

■ AUSTRALIAN PELICAN
On coming in to land, a pelican tilts its body back a little and spreads its wings so that they act as air brakes.

Pelicans are gregarious and form flocks that may consist of hundreds or even thousands of birds. Breeding colonies, too, are often very large, and are usually in remote places such as islands in lakes and swamps. Pelicans breed throughout the year,

although in inland areas the breeding season is influenced by water levels and the availability of food.

During the breeding season, the bills and pouches of both male and female pelicans change colour dramatically. The lower part of the pouch becomes bright salmon pink, while the throat region turns bright yellow. Areas at the top and base of the bill change to a vivid cobalt blue and a black diagonal stripe stretches from the base of the pouch.

These handsome birds show off in courtship displays on land and water and in the air. Fluttering their pouches, they strut, swim in circles and make short flights. Females locate a suitable nest site and as they excavate a scrape in the ground with their bill and feet, they are mated, sometimes by more than one male. Nests are often lined with vegetation, feathers or bones. The parents take turns to incubate the clutch of one to three eggs, one sitting, the other fishing.

The young are born naked and pink, but soon learn to wrestle food from their parents' gullet. Chicks can waddle within two weeks and gather together in creches. Twelve weeks after hatching they are able to fly and catch food for themselves.
Family: Pelecanidae

GAPING AGGRESSION
When it is being threatening, a pelican thrusts its great bill forward, pouch bulging, and snaps it open and shut.

FRIGATEBIRDS

Frigatebirds are large aerobatic birds that inhabit most tropical seas around the world and they are found in subtropical and tropical coastal Australia. They feed mainly on flyingfishes, which they snatch from the surface of the sea with their long hooked beak. The frigatebird's plumage is not waterproof – if the bird accidentally finds itself in the water, it must become airborne immediately or risk drowning.

Also known also as pirates of the sky, sea hawks or men-o'-war, frigatebirds harass terns, gulls and boobies, forcing them to disgorge and drop food when they are returning to their nests to feed their chicks. With lightning speed, the frigatebird catches the falling meal before it hits the water.

These large birds (86–120 cm long) have deeply forked tails and angular, sharply pointed wings that span up to 2.3 metres. Both males and females are glossy black and brown,

with the females having white on the chest. On their throat males have a small red pouch that they inflate during the breeding season.

Frigatebirds are supreme in the air, but have very short legs and move

awkwardly on the ground. They generally land on low bushes, trees or other launching pads, where they build flimsy nests of sticks and thin twigs. They nest every second year on remote islands in colonies, each female producing a single large egg.

The least or lesser frigatebird (*Fregata ariel*), which breeds on islands off northern Australia, including ones in the Coral Sea, is the species most frequently seen in Australian waters. The great frigatebird (*F. minor*) also breeds on Coral Sea islands, while the rare Christmas frigatebird (*F. andrewsi*) breeds only on Christmas Island and is vagrant to the mainland.
Family: Fregatidae

ALL PUFFED UP
To attract females during the breeding season, the male great frigatebird (*Fregata minor*) occupies its nest site and inflates a patch of red skin on its throat into a huge pouch.

DISTRIBUTION

■ FRIGATEBIRDS

HERONS, IBISES AND STORKS

The large, long-necked, heavy-billed birds in the six families that comprise the order Ciconiiformes live in wetlands where they wade and forage. Their feet, which are covered with fine scales, have three long unwebbed forward toes and one long toe pointing backwards. Various members of the heron and ibis and families occur in Australia, plus one member of the stork family.

TAKING THE PLUNGE
Long-legged waders, herons, ibises and storks are skilful hunters, stalking the shallows and then plunging their spear-like bills into the water to grasp or impale prey. Illustrated here is a white-necked heron brandishing its prey.

HERONS AND BITTERNS

With their long legs, bills and necks, these common inhabitants of Australia's coastal and inland waterways are readily recognisable as they stalk and feed in wetlands, shallow waters, wet pastures and grasslands. In flight they are just as distinctive, though not always as elegant, with legs trailing behind them and necks folded back in an S-shape against their bodies.

The family comprises 64 species worldwide. Fifteen are found in Australia, including one, the white-necked heron (*Ardea pacifica*), that lives only in Australia.

Herons and bitterns often hunt for prey in muddy habitats, cleaning their feathers with a serrated nail on their middle toe. They dress their plumage with a talc-like material produced by the constantly fraying ends of feathers known as powder-down feathers, which grow in tufts around their body.

Herons are gregarious, and some gather to nest and breed in large, raucous and seemingly chaotic colonies. Their calls are often harsh croaks or guttural growls. The rare great-billed heron (*A. sumatrana*) of northern coastal Australia is said to roar like an angry bull. Attaining a length of 1.5 metres, this is Australia's largest heron. The smallest is the northern coastline's pied heron (*A. picata*), which grows to about 48 cm long. Most of the 11 heron species found in Australia develop decorative breeding plumes.

Bitterns are shy, reclusive birds that live deep among marsh grasses, reeds and rushes, where their drab plumage provides almost perfect camouflage. When disturbed or threatened, they stand like statues, with straightened necks and bills pointing skywards. At times they sway gently in this pose, like reeds in the wind. There are 12 bittern species altogether, three of which are commonly found in Australia.

Typically, breeding pairs of both herons and bitterns build nests, incubate their eggs and feed their young. Many species of heron are known to protect their young from sun and rain by stretching their wings over them in the nest.

The names egret and heron have no scientific significance, but it is common usage to call the white members of this family egrets and species with mixed plumage herons.
Family: Ardeidae

LITTLE EGRET
At breeding time two ribbon-like plumes sprout from the back of the little egret's head, with many more appearing on their back and breast. When not breeding, however, little egrets are white all over and look like the great egrets and the intermediate egrets (opposite page), except that they are smaller – about 56 cm long – and less common. They frequent both inland and coastal wetlands.

Little egrets build stick nests in trees and breed in colonies when food is plentiful, often in spring and summer, usually in association with other water birds. Females lay three or four eggs. Groups of these birds puddle around in shallow water to flush out their prey of small fishes, crustaceans and frogs.
Scientific name: *Egretta garzetta*

EASTERN REEF EGRET ■
This is a common species around the coastline of mainland Australia and its offshore islands but is rarely found inland or in Tasmania. Eastern reef herons live mostly on fishes and marine invertebrates.

There are two forms of eastern reef egret. The more common form in temperate areas, sometimes called the blue heron or blue reef heron, has grey plumage, with a slate grey bill. The other form, which is white with a yellow bill, becomes more prevalent towards the tropics. Adult eastern reef egrets reach a maximum of about 65 cm long.

■ **EASTERN REEF EGRET**
These egrets hunt by stealth, both by day and at night, in clear and often still waters. At times they can be seen crouching on rocks or coral growths before lunging at a passing fish.

They congregate in loose nesting colonies, usually between September and January, although breeding can occur all year. They build flat nests of sticks in trees or shrubs, on rocky ledges, and even on the ground. The female lays two to five eggs.

When breeding, eastern reef egrets develop long plumes on their necks and backs. Interbreeding occurs between the two forms, and both light and dark hatchlings are often seen in the same nest. Mixed pairs occasionally produce pied offspring.
Scientific name: *Egretta sacra*

WHITE-FACED HERON

White-faced herons usually hunt in the shallow waters of mudflats, inland lakes and swamps, estuaries and coastal wetlands. They are not fussy eaters, and also stalk frogs, rodents, insects, small reptiles and even baby birds in wet pastures or grasslands. They thrive during plagues of mice and grasshoppers.

Sometimes known as the matuka, white-fronted heron or blue crane, this is the most common heron in Australia. It may be seen feeding on its own, in pairs or in small flocks. It is thought not to migrate, although it does travel in search of food.

When fully grown, these birds are about 68 cm in length. The white plumage on their face and throat contrasts starkly with the mostly grey-blue feathers of the rest of their body. Their bill is black, straight and stout and their long legs are yellow.

When they breed – which can take place at any time of year, depending on the availability of food – long plumes grow from around their neck, grey on the back and cinnamon-coloured on the breast. Their

▨ WHITE-FACED HERON
In inland swamps and coastal wetlands, white-faced herons can often be seen puddling around with their feet to dislodge their aquatic prey.

nests are loose platforms of twigs and sticks built in trees that are often some distance from water. The female usually lays four eggs.
Scientific name: *Egretta novaehollandiae*

WHITE-NECKED HERON

This species, also known as the Pacific heron, is largely restricted to mainland Australia, although vagrants are occasionally reported from Tasmania, New Zealand and southern New Guinea. Population explosions occur after major floods.

White-necked herons are stately birds, reaching lengths of about 90 cm and wingspans of up to 1.6 metres. Body plumage is mostly grey-black, contrasting with a white head, neck and chest. Their bill, legs and feet are black, and two parallel lines of black dots run the length of their neck. When breeding, they grow long maroon neck feathers.

They prefer shallow, inland freshwater habitats, where they stalk crustaceans, frogs and insects in wet grasslands and around waterholes. They often perch in trees. Only rarely are they seen near salt water.

The species is mostly solitary, although several birds can sometimes be seen feeding together. They are nomadic in their search for food, but are not migratory. They form small, loose colonies during breeding, and often make their simple stick nests in trees overhanging water. The female usually lays four eggs.
Scientific name: *Ardea pacifica*

GREAT EGRET AND INTERMEDIATE EGRET ▨
When they are not breeding, these species resemble each other; the great egret (*Ardea alba*) is larger than the intermediate egret (*A. intermedia*), but both have white plumage. At breeding time, however, both sexes produce spectacular white filamentous breeding plumes known as aigrettes, and the differences between breeding plumages are important for species identification. Aigrettes were once the height of fashion in women's hats, so these birds were hunted extensively before bans were introduced.

With necks longer than their bodies, great egrets are elegant birds that grow to around a metre long. Their long breeding plumes occur only on their back and extend beyond their tail. Intermediate egrets are smaller (up to 62 cm long), and their breeding plumes grow on their breast as well as their back.

These birds tend to breed when there is plenty of food – usually in spring and summer. They breed in colonies, often with other water birds. Intermediate egrets forage in groups, poking about in shallow water to disturb their prey of fishes, crustaceans and frogs, but great egrets are solitary feeders that wait quietly before snatching their food.

These two species can be found both inland and on the coast. Their nests are usually platforms of sticks in trees, although great egrets will nest in reed beds at ground level. The females of both species usually lay three or four eggs.
Scientific name: *Ardea* spp.

DISTRIBUTION

▨ LITTLE EGRET

▨ EASTERN REEF EGRET

▨ WHITE-FACED HERON
▨ WHITE-NECKED HERON

▨ GREAT EGRET AND INTERMEDIATE EGRET

▨ INTERMEDIATE EGRET
At breeding time both sexes of this species grow lacy plumes on their back and breast. The male and the female share in incubating the eggs, displaying their plumes when changing shifts at the nest.

149

DISTRIBUTION

CATTLE EGRET

NANKEEN NIGHT HERON

BLACK BITTERN

AUSTRALASIAN BITTERN

CATTLE EGRET

Cattle egrets once occurred naturally only in Africa and Asia. They were introduced into Australia in 1933 in an effort to control cattle ticks in the Kimberley region. Around the same time, however, the species began spreading unaided worldwide, and cattle egrets are now widespread not only in Africa and Eurasia but in the Americas as well. The cattle egret's Australian distribution has expanded rapidly since the 1940s, but whether this stemmed from migrations from Asia or the earlier human introduction is unclear.

Cattle egrets form small groups, feeding on insects disturbed by grazing stock. Sometimes they even perch on the heads and backs of cattle, feeding on skin parasites.

Like many other egrets, cattle egrets breed when food is plentiful, nesting in trees in colonies with other water birds. The female usually lays three or four eggs.

Cattle egrets are normally white with yellow bills, legs and feet, but at breeding time the plumage on their neck, throat and back, and on the top of their head, becomes tinged with orange-buff, their legs darken and their bill turns orange-red, only the tip staying yellow. Their bills and necks are proportionately shorter than those of most other Australian herons, and they reach about 53 cm in length.
Scientific name: *Ardea ibis*

NANKEEN NIGHT HERON

Of the nine species of night heron found worldwide, only the nankeen night heron occurs in Australia. By day these nocturnal birds roost hidden in leafy trees, often in large colonies by the water. At dusk they fly slowly and silently to nearby hunting grounds, where they prey on small aquatic animals, insects and sometimes rodents. Their guttural quacks can often be heard around swamps at night.

Nankeen night herons grow to about 60 cm long. Their necks and legs are shorter than those of most herons and their bills are stouter, giving them a bulky appearance. Their plumage is chestnut on the back and cream on the belly. Their heads are crowned in blue-black, and two long white plumes extend from the back of their neck.

Nankeen night herons frequent the edges of swamps, rivers, lagoons and mangroves throughout Australia. In the tropics they breed during the summer wet season, but in the south they breed in spring. On treeless islands they nest on the ground, but they normally nest in trees, up to 5 metres above ground. Females usually lay two or three eggs. Population explosions occur during years of heavy flooding.
Scientific name: *Nycticorax caledonicus*

BLACK BITTERN

Less shy than other Australian bitterns, at times black bitterns may even call or display from a rock or tree stump. This is the bittern species most likely to be seen in the open, although it is still largely reclusive.

The black bittern, sometimes known as the yellow-necked or mangrove bittern, is not thought to be migratory. It is found in coastal areas in all states except Tasmania, Victoria and South Australia, and it prefers to forage in low, dense vegetation next to creeks, rivers, marshes and mangroves. It is sometimes even found near water in rainforests.

Black bitterns are mostly nocturnal, roosting in trees during the day. At night they hunt alone or in pairs for crustaceans, frogs and fishes. Breeding occurs from September to January in loose colonies, and nests are built in trees over water. The female lays up to five eggs.

Adults reach about 60 cm in length. In males, most of the plumage is blue-black; females are more brownish. The throats and necks of both sexes have white stripes, and the sides of the neck are yellow-buff.
Scientific name: *Ixobrychus flavocollis*

■ AUSTRALASIAN BITTERN
The forlorn calls of the Australasian bittern may have inspired the bunyip myths of Australian folklore.

AUSTRALASIAN BITTERN

Also known as the Australian brown bittern, the Australasian bittern is an extremely shy bird, rarely seen but frequently heard. Its loud call, reminiscent of a foghorn or a bellowing cow, often booms eerily at night across the swamps and marshes of Tasmania and south-eastern and south-western mainland Australia.

With males growing a metre tall, and females only slightly smaller, these are large birds – the biggest of Australia's bitterns. However, their plumage of mottled brown and buff with black streaks perfectly camouflages them in their habitat of dense reed beds bordering wetlands around fresh or brackish water. Occasionally they roost on tree branches near or overhanging water.

When disturbed, they adopt the characteristic, statue-like bittern stance, neck extended and bill pointing skyward. If flushed they fly a short distance, legs trailing and neck bent into their body, before dropping down into thick vegetation.

Australasian bitterns are mostly nocturnal, territorial, solitary birds that prey on small birds and mammals, frogs, fishes, insects and snails. They are thought to be nomadic, moving about at night between waterholes in search of food.

They breed from October to January in nests of reeds, hidden in dense vegetation. Females usually lay six eggs. Breeding pairs prefer solitude, but small groups of nests can sometimes be found.
Scientific name: *Botaurus poiciloptilus*

■ CATTLE EGRETS
Cattle egret breeding colonies can be large and raucous. Their nests, built of sticks lined with twigs, are well made compared with those of other herons.

IBISES AND SPOONBILLS

Ibises and spoonbills are more closely related than the different shapes of their bills might suggest. The ibis has a long bill that is slender and curves downward, ending in a point. In contrast, a spoonbill's bill – long, stout, straight and widened at the tip like a flat spoon or a spatula – is unique and makes these birds instantly recognisable.

Ibises and spoonbills, however, share many features. They all have some bare skin on their faces or heads, and sometimes on their necks. They have no voice boxes but can grunt, albeit only feebly at times, or croak, and spoonbills also clap their bills. Ibises and spoonbills are extremely gregarious, and large numbers often congregate and make a surprising racket. They form huge flocks that fly in formation and sometimes soar at great heights. All fly with their long necks extended and their legs trailing behind.

Ibises and spoonbills inhabit the world's tropical and temperate regions, usually living near fresh water. The members of this family are medium to large birds reaching 50–90 cm long. Twenty-six ibis species occur worldwide. Three are found in Australia, including one endemic species, the straw-necked ibis (*Threskiornis spinicollis*). Ritual bowing is an integral part of courting and nesting displays by ibises, and mutual preening is common within breeding pairs.

There are six species of spoonbill, two of which occur in Australia. The yellow-billed spoonbill (*Platalea flavipes*) is endemic.
Family: Threskiornithidae

AUSTRALIAN WHITE IBIS

These birds collect together in enormous numbers. Flocks of more than ten thousand have been recorded from Victoria, and they nest, alongside other wetland birds, in colonies that can reach huge proportions in areas prone to flooding.

Australian white ibises forage along the edges of swamps, streams and lakes and in nearby grasslands. A common sight on irrigated pastures and sporting ovals and in urban parks, they may tolerate the approach of humans and can become quite tame. They prefer fresh water but are sometimes seen around brackish and salt water.

They often feed by moving their bill from side to side through

AUSTRALIAN WHITE IBISES
These birds are common in city parks and on sports ovals, and they often show an interest in people's picnics.

shallow water, probing for prey such as crustaceans, aquatic insects, snails, fishes, frogs, and even snakes.

Adults grow to about 70 cm long. Their head and the upper half of their neck is bald and black with pink bands on the back of the head. There are naked scarlet patches under their wings and on each side of their breast. White plumage covers much of the rest of their bodies, but the tips of their wings are black

FARMER'S FRIENDS

In Australia, flocks of white and straw-necked ibises frequently forage for grasshoppers and other leaf-eating insects among crops such as lucerne. Each bird may consume as much as 25 per cent of its own body weight in grasshoppers alone every day, so farmers welcome the presence of these birds on their properties and often refer to them as 'farmer's friends'.

with a dull green sheen, and some other flight feathers are the same greenish black. Their bills are black and their legs are pinkish above the knee and purplish brown below.

Australian white ibises roost in trees, but breeding pairs usually build their nest close to the ground on stick platforms, often lined with water plants. They form breeding colonies with other ibis and spoonbill species. Breeding sites are chosen by flocks of males, who then establish territories and take up display positions on branches, under which they trample out future nest sites. They become noisily aggressive towards each other, snapping their bills and showing off their bare patches of scarlet skin from display perches. When interested females approach, males nod their heads ceremonially in low, deep bows.

The female lays two to five eggs, and both parents undertake the incubation and feeding of the chicks. The chicks leave the nest after three weeks, but it is another two weeks before they are able to fly.
Scientific name: *Threskiornis molucca*

STRAW-NECKED IBIS

This is Australia's most common ibis, and is one of the country's most readily recognised birds. There are occasional reports of the species from southern parts of New Guinea, but otherwise it is found only in Australia.

Adults reach about 70 cm in length. Straw-necked ibises look rather like vultures, with bare, black heads and upper necks and throats.

DISTRIBUTION

AUSTRALIAN WHITE IBIS

STRAW-NECKED IBIS

FORKS AND SPOONS
Ibises and spoonbills can be differentiated by their bills. An ibis's slender bill curves downward to a point, whereas a spoonbill's is straight and widened at the tip, rather like a flat spoon.

■ GLOSSY IBIS
From a distance the glossy ibis looks black, but in fact its body plumage is a dark reddish brown and its wings have a metallic, iridescent sheen.

Their common name stems from the stiff, yellow, straw-like feathers that extend from the front of their neck down to their upper breast. The plumage on their lower breast, belly and tail is white, and the plumage on the rest of their body is black with a metallic bronze or green sheen. Their bill and lower legs are black and their upper legs are red.

Straw-necked ibises feed in pairs or in flocks, which can become so large that they are deafeningly noisy, even though the birds have no voice boxes. They gather around swamps, streams and lakes and on pastoral lands throughout the Australian mainland, but rarely in Tasmania. They prey on frogs, snakes, insects and molluscs and plagues of grasshoppers and locusts (see box, 'Farmer's friends', page 151).

Large flocks of straw-necked ibises seek out suitable nesting locations and always breed in colonies, some of which contain up to 200 000 individuals. When these birds are courting, red patches of skin develop on either side of their

breast but fade once breeding pairs have formed. A pair bow to each other and reinforce their bond with mutual preening before establishing a nesting territory, driving unpaired neighbouring birds away by pecking at them and raising the straw-like feathers on their neck.

The pair build a nest of sticks and trampled plants, in which the female lays up to five eggs. Both male and female incubate the eggs and feed the young for up to two months.
Scientific name: *Threskiornis spinicollis*

GLOSSY IBIS ■

This species might appear to be merely a dull black, but seen close up its plumage is striking. The feathers that cover much of its body are almost maroon in colour, and on its wings they have an iridescent green sheen. The skin on the bird's face is blue-green, its bill is greenish brown and its legs are black.

Growing to just over 50 cm long, this is the smallest ibis in Australia. Although it has a relatively wide distribution in the country's east and north-west, it is not particularly common anywhere else.

Glossy ibises prefer shallow inland freshwater habitats, including swamps, lagoons and wet grass-lands. Like other ibises, they probe water and mud with their bills in search of aquatic prey such as frogs, molluscs, crustaceans and insects. They also eat rice seeds and peck insects off leaves. Sometimes they follow ploughs on farmlands, eating the insects as they are unearthed.

Glossy ibises are gregarious birds that usually feed in flocks and breed in small groups of their own species,

always, it is believed, amid larger colonies of straw-necked ibises.

Ceremonial displays and bowing between breeding pairs occur, as in other ibis species. The female lays up to six eggs, which are incubated by both parents. Within a month, the young can feed themselves and fly.
Scientific name: *Plegadis falcinellus*

YELLOW-BILLED SPOONBILL ■

Sometimes known as the yellow-legged spoonbill, this species is endemic to mainland Australia and is the larger and more common of the two spoonbills found here.

Yellow-billed spoonbills can reach about 90 cm long, with the bill, which is longer in males, accounting for almost a quarter of that length. Their plumage is white, except for black tips on some flight feathers. Their bill, legs and feet are yellow. A thin black line borders their facial skin, which is tinged lilac blue in adults. Long breeding plumes grow from the lower front of their neck and extend down over their breast.

Yellow-billed spoonbills can breed at any time of the year, depending on conditions, but they are most likely to do so after heavy rainfall. Aggression between males during breeding is very strong; with wings and bills open, they jump up and down and push at each other with their feet. They nest on their own or in loose colonies, often with other water bird species, building nests of trampled vegetation and sticks in trees and shrubs near or in water. The four or so white eggs are incubated by both sexes. Hatchlings stay in the nest for four weeks and are fed by regurgitation.

These birds are highly nomadic, and are a common sight wading through coastal and inland swamps and dams and along the edges of rivers, lifting their long legs slowly and deliberately, with heads down and partly open bills moving rhythmically from side to side through shallow water and sediments.

Their live mainly on water insects, but they also eat crustaceans, fishes and molluscs – in fact they grasp at anything that touches the tip of their 'spoon', sifting food through tooth-like knobs at the end of their bill. They feed by both day and night.
Scientific name: *Platalea flavipes*

■ YELLOW-BILLED SPOONBILLS
This pair of yellow-billed spoonbills are at their nest. The spiny white feathers that are visible on their necks are their breeding plumage.

DISTRIBUTION

■ GLOSSY IBIS

■ YELLOW-BILLED SPOONBILL

■ ROYAL SPOONBILL

ROYAL SPOONBILL

White all over with black legs and bills, these are striking birds. Their facial skin is black, with small red orange patches around their dark red eyes and on their forehead. They are about 75 cm long. During the breeding season they grow ornamental plumes, about 15 cm long, from the nape of the neck. Nesting pairs raise these in fanned crowns as a sign of aggression towards other birds that approach during this time.

Royal spoonbills are found in both saltwater and freshwater wetlands throughout mainland Australia, but they are rarely seen in Tasmania. They live mainly on fishes, although they also eat crustaceans, which they crush between large knobs at the base of their bill. They capture their prey by swaying their bill from side to side through shallow water and sediments, grasping small animals

in the 'spoon' at the end of their bill and forcing them down their throat by flicking their head upward.

The courtship rituals of both of Australia's spoonbill species are similar. A female waiting on a branch of a tree near a nesting site initially flaps her wings and opens her bill, as if in aggression. She follows this with pecks towards her suitor, and then both birds bob their heads up and down as the male nears and tries to nibble the female's bill. The pair is formed when he succeeds. The two birds then mate and construct a nest together. The female lays up to four eggs, and both parents incubate and feed the young.
Scientific name: *Platalea regia*

■ ROYAL SPOONBILLS
When they are breeding, royal spoonbills grow long plumes from their head and the nape of their neck.

STORKS

The stork family contains 17 species, represented in most temperate and tropical parts of the world. Storks usually have black and white plumage, long, brightly coloured legs and long, stout bills, which they stretch out when they fly. The white stork (*Ciconia ciconia*), of Eurasia, is the best known stork species, but it does not occur in Australia.

White storks undertake long annual migrations in large flocks to winter in Africa. They mate for life and build massive, permanent, untidy nests in tall trees and on chimneys and church spires. A pair often returns to the same nest year after year to breed, and the offspring sometimes take over the site when the parents die. In many parts of Europe people believe that white storks are good omens, and they frequently protect the nests in order to encourage the birds to return.
Family: Ciconiidae

BLACK-NECKED STORK

Australia's only stork, it is also known as the jabiru and the policeman-bird. Attaining lengths of over 1.2 metres and wingspans of 2.2 metres, black-necked storks are bigger than white storks and are among Australia's largest birds.

The black-necked stork has glossy green-black plumage on its head, neck and tail and in a broad band across its wings. The rest of its body is white. Its bill is black and about

30 cm long – much heavier than that of the white stork and more akin to that of the South American jabiru, after which this Australian stork is often named. Its legs are up to 60 cm long and red. The female's eyes are yellow and the male's are black.

The black-necked stork's distribution extends across the northern coastline and down to south-eastern New South Wales, but it prefers tropical and warm temperate wetland habitats and is rarely seen around the southern end of its range. It is also found in New Guinea, South-East Asia and India.

Black-necked storks usually frequent estuaries and inland and coastal rivers, creeks and lagoons. They feed mainly on fishes, but their diet also includes crustaceans, frogs, insects, rodents, reptiles and carrion. They usually stalk their prey quietly, and then run and jump along in great strides for a short distance to catch it. Normally they hunt alone, but now and then they can be seen in pairs or small family parties.

These birds build stick nests lined with grass and bark in trees, sometimes as much as 25 metres above ground, between March and June in the north and August and April in

■ BLACK-NECKED STORK
The black-necked stork is commonly seen in tropical and warm temperate wetlands. It is one of Australia's largest birds and the country's only stork.

the south. Both males and females build and repair nests, incubate the two to four eggs and provide food for the offspring. In hot weather, parents regurgitate water over the eggs and nestlings to cool them down. These storks are thought to be mute, but they make noises at the nest by clapping their bills.

Black-necked storks are nomadic but not migratory. Their flight looks ponderous and they seem to struggle to become airborne, needing a series of running jumps to take off, but once launched they can soar hundreds of metres above ground.
Scientific name: *Ephippiorhynchus asiaticus*

DISTRIBUTION

■ BLACK-NECKED STORK

slots reduce drag and increase stability

AERIAL HUNTER
The wedge-tailed eagle's long, broad wings provide maximum lift on updraughts and agility near ground level.

EAGLE EYES
Raptors' eyeballs have two fields of extremely acute vision, called foveas. The sideways-directed foveas (red) scan large areas separately, and the forward-directed foveas (green) focus on prey together.

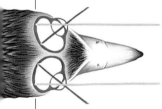

LOCKED CLAWS
As a raptor's claw closes, a tendon attached to the claw locks it into position by catching on corrugations inside the tendon sheath.

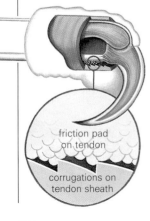

friction pad on tendon

corrugations on tendon sheath

RAPTORS

Raptors are birds of prey that have short, hooked bills, intense eyes and powerful clawed feet. The female is usually larger than the male. They belong to two families: the Accipitridae, which contains the hawks and eagles, and the Falconidae, which contains the falcons.

All raptors except the letter-winged kite hunt during the day. Some feed mainly on insects and others consume carrion, but most Australian species eat vertebrates – often introduced rats, mice, rabbits and birds. Some also eat plague locusts. The name of their order is Falconiformes.

Raptors have extremely keen eyesight – about twice as acute as that of humans. Their eyes are very large and are set slightly further forward than those of most birds. This gives them binocular vision – an essential attribute for judging distances.

Their eyes are also extremely sensitive to movement, and their high visual resolution enables them to distinguish even motionless animals from their surroundings. Once they spot their prey, they can rapidly adjust the lenses in their eyes to focus on the creature as it moves among obstacles. The presence of a raptor is often betrayed by alarm calls from other birds.

Nesting and nurturing

Most hawks and eagles build stick nests in trees, while falcons lay on a cliff ledge, in a tree hollow, or in an abandoned eagle nest. Before mating, which occurs on the nest or a nearby perch, the male performs aerobatics and presents food or nesting materials to females in midair to show off his prowess and hunting ability. Clutches range from five or six eggs for small hawks to one or two for large eagles.

The eggs hatch within a month in small species and within six weeks in large ones. The young of the smaller species spend about a month in the nest before flying, while those of large eagles take up to three months to leave the nest.

The female incubates the eggs and cares for the chicks, and the male provides food until the young are large enough to be left and the female can hunt again.

Deadly talons

Raptors living in open country hover in the air searching for their prey, while those living in wooded country perch in foliage ready to pounce.

Hawks and eagles clutch their prey strongly in their feet, crushing it and driving their talons through the vital organs. Falcons strike their victim a heavy blow with their feet or grasp it with their feet and bite through the vertebrae at the base of its skull.

Once they have secured their victim, raptors anchor it to a perch with their feet and then pluck and shred it with their beak. The indigestible remains, such as bones, fur and feathers, are later regurgitated as a pellet, or casting. Scientists often use these castings to analyse what the raptor has eaten.

Aerodynamic engineering

Raptors have broad wings in order to maximise their lift in thermal updraughts and provide agility near the ground. Their wing tip feathers separate like fingers to increase stability and reduce stalling speed, permitting a slow, searching flight.

KILLING ONLY TO EAT
This peregrine falcon is about to start feeding on a pigeon it has just caught. Raptors store any surplus food, retrieving and consuming it later.

Hawks that live in forested regions and give rapid chase have short wings for precision flying between tree trunks and for rapid acceleration in attack. Those that soar in the open have long wings for gliding. Smaller hovering kites (which are hawks) have more pointed wings to give them a buoyant, flapping flight. Falcons have long pointed wings for swift aerial pursuit.

A tail increases drag when flying, but it is invaluable for steering and braking, so species that need good manoeuvrability in the air or in dense cover have long tails, while those that fly swiftly or have little need for tight manoeuvres generally have short tails.

HAWKS AND EAGLES

In Australia, hawks and eagles range in size from the collared sparrowhawk – the male of which is about as big as a dove – to the wedge-tailed eagle, which is about the size of a turkey. They are mostly shades of grey and brown, often with highlights of white, reddish brown or black, and many have brightly coloured eyes and feet; the cere (the waxy membrane at the base of the upper beak) is also usually brightly coloured.

Hawks, the small and medium-sized members of this family, have bare, scaly legs. Eagles are larger and their legs are fully feathered to the base of their toes, except for sea-eagles, which have bare legs.

Hawks and eagles occupy all kinds of habitats on dry land as well as around fresh and inshore coastal waters. Some live only in forested areas, but many are widespread, even living in cities. They are most frequently seen in flight, often circling high in the sky, but some hide in trees and rarely fly high.

Of about 220 hawk and eagle species in the world, there are 18 in Australia, all of them native. Five of these birds – the black-shouldered kite, the letter-winged kite, the square-tailed kite, the black-breasted buzzard and the red goshawk – are unique to Australia.
Family: Accipitridae

OSPREY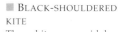

Large brown and white hawks, about 60 cm long with a wingspan of about 160 cm, ospreys are fish-eaters. They live right around the Australian coastline, but they are much more common in the north than in the south.

The osprey circles and hovers over inshore waters and estuaries or perches on tall, dead trees, scouring the water for signs of movement. When it catches sight of potential prey it plummets into the water feet first, often disappearing below the surface before rising into the air with its catch. It also hunts upriver, and in wet years it will occasionally move some distance inland over rivers or freshwater lakes.

It builds a huge stick nest in a tall dead or partly dead tree, or sometimes on artificial structures such as electricity transmission poles. The female lays two to four eggs from late autumn to early spring.
Scientific name: *Pandion haliaetus*

PACIFIC BAZA

The Pacific baza, sometimes known as the crested hawk, is blue-grey with a vividly banded belly, boldly barred underwings, brilliant yellow eyes and a distinctive black crest. It has a wingspan of about 100 cm and grows to about 40 cm in length.

This species is found in northern and eastern Australia from the Kimberley region in Western Australia to around Sydney. It lives in forests and woodlands, including well wooded towns and cities. Its diet consists of insects and tree frogs, as well as fruits such as small rainforest figs. It is a quiet, well camouflaged bird that can easily be overlooked, but it may sometimes draw attention to itself with its two-note whistling call, or by the patter of insect fragments being dropped from the trees above.

The Pacific baza builds its flimsy stick nest high in the canopy of a living tree, laying two or three eggs between September and January.
Scientific name: *Aviceda subcristata*

BLACK-SHOULDERED KITE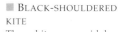

This is a small, grey and white, gull-like hawk with a wingspan of about 90 cm and a body about 35 cm long. It lives in open and lightly wooded

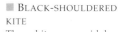 OSPREYS
Ospreys add to their seaside nests each year, using sticks and seaweed. The birds perch and nest in tall, dead trees, which are becoming scarce.

country across most of Australia, though it is rare in the driest parts of the mainland and in Tasmania.

The black-shouldered kite eats rodents, particularly the introduced house mouse. When hunting, it flies with quick wingbeats and long glides on gracefully upcurved wings. Stopping to hover suspended in one position, it flutters its wings, lowering its yellow feet and peering down. When it sights a mouse it gradually flutters down within range and, then, at the last moment, pounces with its wings held high above its back and catches its prey in its talons.

Once caught, the mouse is carried to a high perch and swallowed

 BLACK-SHOULDERED KITE
These kites prey widely on the house mouse, an introduced species, and in mouse plague years the kites may rear two broods of young.

DISTRIBUTION

OSPREY

PACIFIC BAZA

BLACK-SHOULDERED KITE

Uniquely among the raptors, the letter-winged kite is a nocturnal hunter. During the day it roosts in leafy trees, sometimes nestling in groups.

DISTRIBUTION

■ LETTER-WINGED KITE

■ BLACK KITE

■ HARRIERS

■ WHISTLING KITE

whole, a feat that is made possible by the kite's wide gape. As well as hunting from the air, this kite perches aloft searching the ground for signs of prey, and it can often be seen on roadside powerlines and utility poles.

Black-shouldered kites may breed at any time of the year, though generally in autumn and spring, laying three to five eggs. During mouse plagues, they congregate to nest, and each pair may rear two broods of young within a year.
Scientific name: *Elanus axillaris*

LETTER-WINGED KITE ■
The letter-winged kite is a rare hawk of far inland Australia. It resembles the black-shouldered kite in size and appearance, except for its underwing pattern – a solid black line from the body to the bend of the wing that resembles a broken letter M or W when seen from below.

More subtle differences include its owl-like eyes and its softer plumage. These features reflect the fact that, like the owl, this kite hunts at night – the only raptor to do so.

Though an inland bird, the letter-winged kite appears in more settled and coastal districts in times of drought. It also appears in farmland during mouse plagues. By day, it roosts in well foliaged trees, and by night it systematically circles an area and hovers over open ground. Its feeding and breeding habits resemble those of the black-shouldered kite (page 155), but during rodent plagues it breeds even more prolifically and continuously.
Scientific name: *Elanus scriptus*

BLACK KITE
The black kite is a gregarious, rather shabby hawk – brown rather than black – that hangs around the more unsavoury aspects of civilisation, such as rubbish dumps and abattoirs. It is about 50 cm long with a wingspan of about 130 cm, and can be recognised by its long, forked tail. It soars effortlessly to great heights, sometimes in spiralling columns of hundreds or thousands of birds.

It occurs over most of inland and northern Australia in most habitats, but especially over farmland, pasture and human settlements. It is most abundant in the tropics, where it is the ultimate scavenger, investigating anything edible. It patrols fires, ready to pounce on animals flushed out or caught by the flames.

It eats mammals, birds, reptiles, amphibians, fishes, invertebrates, carrion and offal. Remarkably, it has learnt to bait fishes to the surface with scraps of food, and to turn road-killed cane toads over and open them from the belly to avoid the poison glands.

The black kite builds a stick nest in a tree which it lines with soft

materials, cattle dung and rubbish. The female lays a clutch of one to four eggs between February and October in the tropics, or between July and November in the south.
Scientific name: *Milvus migrans*

HARRIERS ■
These slender, long-winged, long-tailed hawks float on raised wings and have long legs for reaching deep into thick cover. Harriers eat small mammals, birds, reptiles, amphibians, fishes, insects and carrion.

Australia has two harrier species. The spotted harrier (*Circus assimilis*) inhabits the croplands and grassy plains of inland and northern Australia, while the swamp harrier (*C. approximans*) lives in the wetlands and moist farmlands of the south and in coastal areas. The ranges of the two species overlap to some degree.

The swamp harrier – the more common of the two – has brown plumage, becoming paler and greyer with age, and a distinctive white patch on its rump. Spotted harrier adults are blue-grey and reddish brown spotted with white; younger birds are ginger and brown. Both species have a wingspan of about 130 cm and a body about 55 cm long.

Swamp harriers nest on the ground or on water, where they build a platform of sticks and vegetation among long grass, shrubs or reeds. Spotted harriers nest in trees. Harriers usually lay three or four eggs in spring, but spotted harriers also lay in autumn and winter.
Scientific name: *Circus* spp.

WHISTLING KITE
The whistling kite is an untidy looking, dusty-brown hawk that floats lazily through the air on down-curved wings. It is 55 cm long with a wingspan of 135 cm and a long, rounded tail. Its most notable feature is a loud, whistling call – a rapid, upward-moving, chattering sound preceded or followed by a long downward note – a characteristic sound of coastlines, wetlands and tropical woodlands in Australia.

This kite is found throughout Australia – though rarely in Tasmania – and is most abundant in the tropics. In the south it has declined in farmland, where it now

■ HARRIERS
The spotted harrier, the less common of the two Australian harrier species, lives mainly on the dry inland plains. It builds its stick nest in a tree or a bush, lining it with green leaves.

■ COLLARED SPARROWHAWK
This female juvenile collared sparrow-hawk is feeding on a recent catch. These birds hunt in woodland, darting swiftly from among the foliage to snatch birds on the wing.

occurs mainly near water. In the northern half of Australia, from Shark Bay in Western Australia round to the central coast of New South Wales, it shares the coast with the Brahminy kite (this page).

The whistling kite eats mammals, bird, reptiles, fishes, insects, crustaceans, carrion and offal, commonly by scavenging along the tide line. It also scoops live fishes from the water in a shallow dive, breaking the surface with its feet.

It breeds throughout the dry season in the tropics, and usually in late winter and spring in the south, although it will also breed in the autumn. It builds its nest of sticks in a tall living or dead tree, and lays one to four eggs – most often two.
Scientific name: *Haliastur sphenurus*

BRAHMINY KITE ■

This spectacular chestnut and white maritime hawk has a short tail, a wingspan of 120 cm and a body about 50 cm long. Similar in its feeding habits to the whistling kite (opposite page), it soars effortlessly on coastal breezes looking for food.

It nests during the dry season in the tropics, where it is common, and in late winter to spring in subtropical regions. It builds a platform of sticks and flotsam, which it lines with leaves and other soft material – including human rubbish – in a mangrove or other coastal tree, or on a human-built structure.
Scientific name: *Haliastur indus*

BROWN GOSHAWK

This is a wary hawk with short wings, a long tail and long legs. The female has a wingspan of 90 cm and is about 50 cm long, while the male has a wingspan of 75 cm and is about 40 cm long. Adults are slate grey on top and a finely barred reddish brown on white underneath. Young birds are brown above and heavily streaked and barred brown on white below. Both adults and young have yellow legs and eyes.

This hawk is common throughout Australia, in forest and woodland and in well wooded towns. It usually flies rapidly with several quick, deep flaps and then a long glide, although it also soars in spirals.

It perches, camouflaged among the foliage, until it spots its prey of birds, mammals, reptiles, insects or carrion. It then dashes or glides out to snatch it unawares, or after a short chase.

The brown goshawk builds a stick nest, lined with leaves, in the crown of a tree. In spring the female lays two to four eggs.
Scientific name: *Accipiter fasciatus*

COLLARED SPARROWHAWK ■

The collared sparrowhawk is a smaller version of the brown goshawk (this page), with spindlier legs and longer toes. The female has a wingspan of 75 cm and is 35 cm long, and the male has a wingspan of 60 cm and is 30 cm long.

The collared sparrowhawk is more specialised for catching small birds than its larger relation, although it also sometimes eats small mammals, lizards and insects. It conceals itself in the cover of leafy branches or flies through the trees, and then flashes out to snatch a bird in midair or from a perch. It is found throughout Australia in forest and woodland, and in well-wooded areas in cities and towns, but is less common than the brown goshawk. The breeding habits of these two birds are similar.
Scientific name: *Accipiter cirrhocephalus*

GREY GOSHAWK

The grey goshawk occurs in two forms: it can be either pale grey on top and white underneath, or pure white. Both forms have red eyes and an orange-yellow cere (the waxy membrane at the base of the upper beak) and legs. Females have a wingspan of about a metre and are about 50 cm long; males have a span of 75 cm and are around 40 cm long.

This species is found in rainforest and wet eucalypt forest on the coastal fringe from the Kimberley region across northern Australia and down to southern Victoria and Tasmania. Both forms exist throughout the range, except in Tasmania, where only the white form occurs.

The grey goshawk's feeding, nesting and breeding habits are similar to those of the brown goshawk (this page), except that in the tropics its laying season starts in May.
Scientific name: *Accipiter novaehollandiae*

DISTRIBUTION

■ BRAHMINY KITE

■ BROWN GOSHAWK

■ COLLARED SPARROWHAWK

■ GREY GOSHAWK

■ BRAHMINY KITE
Found along the mangrove-lined fringes of coastal bays and inlets, mainly in the tropics, the Brahminy kite soars in low circles looking for food. It is a scavenger, feeding largely on fishes and other marine creatures cast up by the tide.

DISTRIBUTION

■ RED GOSHAWK

■ SQUARE-TAILED KITE

■ WHITE-BELLIED
SEA-EAGLE

RED GOSHAWK ■

The red goshawk is the rarest of all Australia's raptors. Once it was found across the whole of northern Australia from the Kimberley region to Cape York and as far south as Sydney, but it is now endangered in southern Queensland and almost extinct in New South Wales. It is also becoming rare in the eastern parts of Queensland, but its numbers have not fallen noticeably in far northern Australia (although it was never common in this region).

It lives in coastal and near-coastal open forest, particularly alongside rivers. Its decline in numbers is the result of habitat clearance, especially of trees growing along river banks.

This powerful goshawk is reddish brown, mottled on its back and wings and streaked underneath. It has bold dark bands under its wings and tail and sturdy yellow legs and feet. Females have a wingspan of 130 cm and are about 60 cm long, while males have a wingspan of 115 cm and are around 50 cm long.

The red goshawk's diet consists mostly of birds, but it also feeds on mammals, reptiles and large insects. It conceals itself among tree foliage, darting out to chase and seize birds as they fly nearby. It also flies slowly through the treetops or soars into the sky and then dives at its prey from a height.

It builds a stick nest in a tall tree, generally not far from water. The female lays one or two eggs. Laying takes place during the dry season in the tropics and during the spring in eastern parts of Australia.
Scientific name: Erythrotriorchis radiatus

■ RED GOSHAWK
The rare red goshawk usually builds its nest high in a tree fork close to water. Established pairs are thought to use the same nest year after year.

SQUARE-TAILED KITE

The square-tailed kite is a rare hawk that leads a solitary life in open forest and woodland. It is brown and reddish brown, and the adults have a distinctive white face. It has a wingspan of about 140 cm and is about 50 cm long.

When in flight it can be identified by its long, square or slightly forked tail and the long, upswept 'fingers' at the ends of its wings.

The square-tailed kite is found over most of the Australian mainland, except in the driest central regions. It is frequently confused with other hawks and may be more common than has hitherto been realised in the coastal forests of the south-east. It is now being spotted in the wooded hinterland of many cities on the eastern seaboard. It eats lizards and insects as well as small birds, their eggs and young, which it plucks from foliage while gliding slowly among the treetops. It builds a stick nest in a living tree and lays two to three eggs in spring.
Scientific name: Lophoictinia isura

WHITE-BELLIED SEA-EAGLE ■

The white-bellied sea-eagle soars majestically on its long, broad, upcurved wings over estuaries and inshore waters, and over inland rivers and lakes. Adults are grey and white, growing to about 80 cm long with a wingspan of about 2 metres. Young sea-eagles, which are often confused with ospreys (page 155), are brown and have a pale tail.

There are sea-eagles all around the Australian coastline. They are still quite common around coastal cities, but are becoming less so as their nest sites are disturbed by urban development and the removal of tall trees.

They eat mammals, birds, reptiles, fishes, carrion and tideline offal. Live prey includes rabbits, flying foxes, water birds and sea birds, spiny or poisonous fishes, and sea snakes. To catch their prey, they descend in a shallow glide to scoop food from the surface without entering the water. They also rob other fishing birds, including ospreys, of their catch by chasing them and forcing them to drop their booty.

The white-bellied sea-eagle builds a huge stick nest lined with leaves, grass and seaweed, usually in the fork of a tree in forest or woodland but sometimes on a cliff or islet. The female lays one to three dull white eggs – usually two – between May and August in the north and between June and September (in rare cases in November) in the south.
Scientific name: Haliaeetus leucogaster

■ WHITE-BELLIED
SEA-EAGLE
Hunting from a perch or in flight, the sea-eagle glides down over the water to scoop up its fishy prey or catches creatures such as sea snakes and water birds on land.

WEDGE-TAILED EAGLE ■

At a metre long and with a wingspan of up to 2.3 metres, the wedge-tailed eagle is dark in colour with a long, wedge-shaped tail. It can often be seen soaring on upcurved wings at great heights. The young are paler than the adults, with golden or tawny highlights.

It is common throughout mainland Australia, avoiding only the most settled areas. It is rare in Tasmania, where it is endangered by forest clearance. It eats mammals, birds, reptiles and carrion. Eagles search for prey by low circling, by waiting on a lookout perch, or by soaring high. Once they spot their prey they attack in a swift glide or dive. Pairs or groups of eagles join forces to attack large prey, such as wallabies.

At breeding time, pairs of eagles circle high over their territories in a display of ownership, which culminates in a series of undulating dives with folded wings. The male may dive at the female, who rolls over in flight to present her claws. The same manoeuvre is used by intruding eagles when they are attacked by territory owners, but in this case it is defensive. Two raptors locking claws and tumbling in the sky indicates fights between rivals rather than courtship manoeuvres by mates.

Wedge-tailed eagles build a huge stick nest, lined with green leaves, in a tree or sometimes on a cliff or rocky islet or some other inaccessible place. The male presents nesting material to the female and passes food to her, sometimes in flight.

Females lay one or two eggs, occasionally three, between April and September or – exceptionally – as early as January or February in the tropical north.

Scientific name: *Aquila audax*

LITTLE EAGLE

The little eagle is Australia's smallest eagle, and one of the smallest in the world: the adult has a wingspan of about 120 cm and grows to about 50 cm long. It is a common but inconspicuous and often overlooked eagle of wooded areas throughout mainland Australia, even living on the outer fringes of cities.

It is either pale underneath with thin black streaks, or wholly brown. Apart from its smaller size, it can be distinguished from the wedge-tailed eagle by its shorter, square-tipped tail, the lack of reddish brown colour on its back and wings, and the small black crest on its nape. It is often confused with the whistling kite (page 157), but it is stockier, with a

shorter tail and flatter wings. It soars at great heights, almost invisible to the naked eye, but reveals itself by loud, two- or three-note whistling calls. Displaying males perform a series of steep, undulating dives.

The little eagle eats mammals, birds, reptiles, and occasionally insects and carrion. In southern agricultural areas it prefers rabbits, but it also catches birds such as magpies and crows. It searches for prey from a lookout perch, by flying from tree to tree, or by soaring and scanning

UP ABOVE THE WORLD SO HIGH

Hawks, eagles and falcons spend much of their waking life in the air, searching for prey. Often all that can be discerned of these birds is their silhouette. However, each major group has a characteristic wing shape, which an observer can use to identify these magnificent birds while they are on the wing.

wedge-tailed eagle

brown falcon

swamp harrier

black kite

brown goshawk

the scene below. When it spots prey, it descends in stages before a final gliding or diving attack to seize it on the ground. More rarely, it dives at birds in the treetops.

Little eagles build stick nests lined with green leaves in trees. They lay one or two eggs in the dry season in the north of Australia or during spring in the south.

Scientific name: *Hieraaetus morphnoides*

BLACK-BREASTED BUZZARD

The black-breasted buzzard is one of only a few birds in the world known to use tools. To broach the eggs of large, ground-nesting birds, such as emus, it either breaks the shells with blows from its bill or, from a standing position on the ground, hurls stones at the eggs using its bill. As well as eggs, it eats mammals, birds, lizards and carrion, sometimes robbing the nests of other raptors.

This hawk is large, with a wingspan of about 150 cm and a body about 55 cm long. It is short-tailed with a black and reddish brown body and a white patch under each wing. It lives in inland and northern Australia, most commonly in the tropics. It is found in woodlands and open plains, gliding rapidly at low levels or soaring high in wide arcs. It has a distinctive, hoarse, yelping call.

The buzzard's nest is a platform of sticks lined with leaves, in a dead or partly dead tree. In spring the female lays one or two eggs, occasionally three. At times, breeding units consist of a female and two males, the second male perhaps acting as a helper in the harsh desert environment.

Scientific name: *Hamirostra melanosternon*

■ WEDGE-TAILED EAGLE

The wedge-tailed eagle is Australia's largest bird of prey and is one of the most powerful raptors in the world.

DISTRIBUTION

■ WEDGE-TAILED EAGLE

■ LITTLE EAGLE

■ BLACK-BREASTED BUZZARD

■ BROWN FALCON
■ NANKEEN KESTREL

■ BLACK FALCON

■ PEREGRINE FALCON
■ AUSTRALIAN HOBBY

■ GREY FALCON

■ BROWN FALCONS
These two immature brown falcons are competing for a share of the kill. Brown falcons are birds of open grassy woodland and have adapted well to living in agricultural areas.

FALCONS

Falcons are sleek birds with long, pointed, backswept wings; they are the fastest fliers of all the raptors. Their soft, dark eyes are surrounded by a prominent ring of yellow or pale skin, and their dark head markings can be anything from a full black 'helmet' to a wispy moustache-like mask.

Another distinguishing feature of these birds is their toothed bill for biting through the neck of their prey. For this purpose, falcons have a 'tooth' on each side of the cutting edge of their beak, close to the tip, which fits into a corresponding notch in their lower jaw.

Falcons come in various shades of grey or brown, often with streaked or barred underparts. They are small to medium-sized, ranging from the nankeen kestrel, which is about the size of a dove, to the female peregrine and the black falcon, which are as big as the smallest eagle species.

Of the 35 falcon species that occur throughout the world, Australia has six, all of which are native, and two of which – the black falcon and grey falcon – are found only in Australia.

Falcons are found in all habitats in Australia. They are most commonly seen in flight, even among high-rise buildings in cities, either streaking across the sky or circling lazily, spending much of their time on the lookout for prey.

The presence of these birds is generally announced by urgent alarm calls from other birds looking nervously towards the sky.
Family: Falconidae

BROWN FALCON ■
A great advantage for this falcon in its Australian habitat is its long legs with their heavy armour of coarse scales that protect it from snakebite – a unique feature among Australian falcons. Also unusual is its slow flight, relative to other falcons; only one other falcon, the nankeen kestrel, shares this characteristic.

About 45 cm long with a wingspan of about a metre, the brown falcon is a plain, plump-looking falcon. It is variable in colour, from a pale form like the nankeen kestrel to a dark form like the black falcon. However, even the darkest examples have pale underwings with prominent barring.

Often seen perching on roadside posts, poles and wires or hovering over paddocks, the brown falcon is common in open country throughout mainland Australia and Tasmania. It is frequently seen on inland plains and tropical savannas, gathering in flocks at bushfires to catch fleeing or trapped animals. It eats mammals, birds, reptiles, amphibians, insects

■ NANKEEN KESTREL
An inhabitant of farming country, this kestrel can often be seen hovering over paddocks on the lookout for prey.

and carrion, searching for food mainly by waiting on a lookout perch and then gliding to the ground. It chases insects on foot, robs other raptors, and follows large animals and farm machinery for prey they might flush out.

The brown falcon uses old stick nests of crows or other raptors, usually in a tree. It lays two or three eggs, occasionally up to five, in the dry season in the tropics or during spring in the south.
Scientific name: *Falco berigora*

NANKEEN KESTREL ■
The nankeen kestrel is a small falcon that is commonly seen perching on roadside posts, poles and wires or hovering over paddocks searching for small prey on the ground. At about 30 cm long and with a wingspan of about 70 cm, it is the smallest Australian falcon. It is reddish brown on top and cream below with reddish brown streaks. Males have a grey head and tail.

The nankeen kestrel resembles the black-shouldered kite but is more slender; when hovering it has a more horizontal posture and shows a black band near the tip of the tail. Like the brown falcon, it is a slow flier compared with other falcons.

This falcon is common in open and lightly wooded country throughout mainland Australia but is rare in Tasmania. It lives in farmland and also in towns and cities, where it may roost on buildings. It eats mostly insects, such as crickets and grasshoppers, as well as mice, small birds up to sparrow size, and small lizards. It hunts on the wing or from a lookout perch. To attack, it dives to the ground with its wings closed.

When spring comes it lays its eggs almost anywhere that is inaccessible to ground predators – usually in tree hollows, but sometimes in old stick nests of other birds or ledges in sink-holes, mine-shafts, cliffs, machinery or city buildings.
Scientific name: *Falco cenchroides*

BLACK FALCON

The black falcon is actually a dark sooty brown in colour. It is often confused with the brown falcon (opposite page), but it is more powerful and square-shouldered with short legs and dark underwings.

It is a sleek, fast falcon, about 50 cm long with a wingspan of about 110 cm, usually seen circling lazily or chasing and harassing other birds. It sometimes perches on posts or dead treetops, but – unlike the brown falcon – never on wires.

It lives on the lightly wooded plains of inland Australia and is not common. It appears near the coast only as a refugee from drought. It eats mammals, birds, insects and carrion, often appearing at bushfires to catch fleeing prey. It follows farm machinery, shooters, stock and other raptors, such as harriers, in the hope of discovering injured or disturbed prey. It also robs other raptors.

The black falcon takes over an old stick nest in the top of a live or dead tree, or very occasionally on a power pole. It lays three or four, sometimes five, eggs between autumn and spring – usually in spring.
Scientific name: *Falco subniger*

PEREGRINE FALCON

In the days when falconry provided food for humans, the peregrine's hunting prowess made it the ultimate falconer's bird. Today falconry is banned in Australia, and the peregrine is reviled and illegally persecuted by pigeon-fanciers.

The male peregrine falcon is about 40 cm long with a wingspan of 80 cm, while the female is about 50 cm long with a wingspan of a metre. The peregrine falcon is stockier than the

Australian hobby, with a full black 'helmet' and a larger beak and feet. Its underparts are cream with fine horizontal black bars. Young peregrines are browner and streaked.

The peregrine is found worldwide. It is fairly common throughout Australia, around cliffs, in wetland habitats and even in cities. It eats birds – mostly pigeons, parrots and starlings, but also ducks and other large birds. It attacks flying prey in a spectacular dive, known as a stoop, at speeds that have been measured at 140 kilometres an hour; this makes it the fastest bird on Earth, even discounting the exaggerated speeds that have often been claimed.

The peregrine nests on cliff ledges, in tree hollows, in old nests of raptors and crows, and on the ledges of city buildings. In spring it lays three, four or occasionally five eggs.
Scientific name: *Falco peregrinus*

AUSTRALIAN HOBBY ▦

This falcon has a wingspan of about 75 cm and is about 30 cm long. It is slate grey on top with a partial black 'helmet' and a pale collar. Its forehead and throat are pale and it is reddish brown underneath.

The hobby is common throughout mainland Australia, though rare in Tasmania. It lives in open and lightly wooded country, including farmland, and is frequently seen in towns and cities, where it chases sparrows, starlings and various other introduced species. It also preys on bats and insects, such as beetles, in flight. It commonly hunts around dusk, and sometimes after dark with the help of street lighting. It has sometimes been accused of killing racing pigeons, but it is too small to be a threat to pigeons.

The hobby takes over an unused stick nest of other species of bird high in a tree or on a power pylon. In spring it lays between two and four eggs – most often three.
Scientific name: *Falco longipennis*

GREY FALCON

About 40 cm long with a wingspan of about 90 cm, this is Australia's rarest falcon. It is a soft grey on top and the palest grey underneath, with black wing tips and a bright orange yellow cere (the waxy membrane at the base of the upper beak), eye rings and feet.

▦ PEREGRINE FALCON
Contrary to popular belief, the peregrine falcon was not introduced into Australia but has been here for thousands of years.

▦ AUSTRALIAN HOBBY
This small falcon often hunts at nightfall and sometimes by artificial light, and is able to catch bats in flight.

It has longer wings and shorter legs than the grey goshawk (page 157). The young are darker grey on top, with pale facial skin and feet.

The grey falcon does not hover, but is a very fast chaser of birds such as parrots. It lives far inland and in the drier parts of northern Australia, mostly in woodland alongside rivers, although it also ranges out into the plains. It appears in coastal areas only when avoiding drought. It has left the agricultural parts of southern Australia, possibly because of the loss of prey or nest sites.

When nesting, it takes over an old stick nest high in a living tree close to water. The female lays two to four eggs in late winter or spring.
Scientific name: *Falco hypoleucos*

FALLING PREY TO PESTICIDES

Pesticide use affects all living things, but the raptors are most vulnerable, since eating contaminated prey concentrates these substances. The raptors most affected are the bird-eaters, such as falcons, and the fish-eaters, such as ospreys.

DDT is a powerful insecticide, once extensively used worldwide but now banned in many countries. It affects the shell gland in birds, causing eggs to break easily when laid. In Europe and North America the peregrine falcon population fell dramatically in the 1960s as a result of DDT use, and recovered only following reintroduction programs involving captive-bred peregrines. In 1987 DDT use was banned in Australia and the peregrine population is building up again.

brolga

sarus crane

CRANES AND THEIR RELATIVES

Members of the order Gruiformes are ground-feeding birds that generally have long necks, long bills, and long legs for walking and wading. They vary greatly in size and form, ranging from the large-bodied bustards of the plains to dumpy little button-quails that hide among grass tussocks. Representatives of five of the twelve families occur in Australia.

WHICH CRANE IS WHICH?

The sarus crane is often mistaken for a brolga, but the sarus crane has more red on its head, extending down its neck. It also has grey chin feathers, whereas black, hair-like feathers grow on the brolga's slightly pendulous chin.

DISTRIBUTION

■ BROLGA

■ SARUS CRANE

CRANES

Cranes are large, long-legged, long-necked birds of elegant carriage, often with a bustle of wing feathers covering their tail. They perform impressive dancing displays, in which they bow gracefully to one another, leap vertically and sidestep. Cranes have loud honking calls and fly with shallow wingbeats and heads and legs extended.

Males and females look alike, although females are smaller. Unlike herons, cranes do not grow special plumes in the breeding season. They feed in fresh or saltwater wetlands or pastures on insects, invertebrates, small animals and vegetation.

Fifteen crane species occur throughout the world, and four of these are endangered. Two species are found in Australia.
Family: Gruidae

BROLGA ■
Long thought to be Australia's only crane, the brolga is found across the north and in smaller numbers down the eastern half of the continent to Bass Strait. This well-known bird is sometimes called the native companion or Australian crane. It stands up to 1.4 metres tall and is grey all over, except for a bare scarlet patch across its face, the back of its head and the nape of its neck. It also has a tuft of dark feathers under its chin, dark wing tips in flight, and dark legs. The chicks are grey with paler patches until they gradually attain adult head colouring.

Brolgas congregate in pairs or groups in open swamps or pastoral regions. Monogamous pairs together build raised platform nests of grass and sticks, and the female usually lays two eggs. Both the female and the male incubate the eggs and share in the brooding and guarding of the young for up to 11 months. As well

as animal matter, they eat green plant material, seeds and tubers. Bulkuru sedge is a favourite food.

As swamps dry up in northern Australia's dry season, large flocks of brolgas gather in the permanent wetlands of Kakadu, Cape York, the Atherton Tableland and Townsville Common. Their meeting ritual is famous. One brolga flies down to a group of standing brolgas, bounces lightly as it lands, and then bows, wings outstretched, to its mate, who bounces and bows in return. Soon all the birds in the in the flock are lifting their feet, bowing their necks and spreading their wings in the celebrated brolga ceremonial dance.
Scientific name: *Grus rubicunda*

■ BROLGA
Brolgas breed in shallow swamplands, building nests of dry grass or sedge. Both sexes incubate the eggs.

SARUS CRANE
Until 1966 it was believed that the brolga was Australia's only crane, but then groups of sarus cranes began to be observed on the edge of the Gulf of Carpentaria, on the Atherton Tableland and around the Ord River region. These cranes have always been found in northern India and South-East Asia.

The sarus crane differs from the brolga only in having the red head marking extending further down the neck, a grey-feathered receding chin, and a slightly paler bustle. Its chicks are brownish. Like the offspring of all cranes, the chicks are able to run and swim soon after hatching but are fed by the adults for some time.

The resemblance between sarus cranes and brolgas is so marked that a group of birds that look like brolgas may well include sarus cranes.
Scientific name: *Grus antigone*

RAILS

As well as the rails, this group includes crakes, swamphens and coots. Rails feed on or near water and shelter in reed beds or in long grasses along the banks. Their distinctive flick of the tail is probably a means of communication. Each species has a distinguishing call, with some calling only during the breeding season, and many rails are more likely to be heard than seen.

Most rail species are about the size of a bantam hen, though some are as small as sparrows and others are as big as a large domestic fowl. Some are more slender than others – perhaps to make it easier to move through reeds and sedges.

Rails have short wings and tails, solid legs, and feet with long toes. Most of the smaller rail species are splotched, spotted or barred, which makes them difficult to see in the vegetation that many of them favour. They eat invertebrates, small vertebrates and plants.

Concealed nests

Rails lay three to ten speckled eggs on platforms of vegetation, which they build on land or anchor above water. Most keep their nests hidden, though the coot's floating nest is not always concealed. The chicks are darker than their parents, and in some species look quite different.

Because rail chicks hatch already covered in down, they are able to leave the nest soon after hatching and can both run and swim, but not yet fly. Although chicks are able to peck within a few days, they also beg for food and are looked after by both parents, being brooded in the nest to maintain their body heat.

Reclusive rails

Of the 126 rail species worldwide, 17 occur in Australia, but many of these are very shy birds, not often seen by humans. Others are rare, or are specialised in small areas.

Among those least often seen are the small crakes with short bills, such as the Australian spotted crake (*Porzana fluminea*) and Baillon's crake (*P. pusilla*). Both species are barred on the abdomen and striped and white-spotted above, but the spotted crake, which is 19–21 cm long, is brownish green with a dark underside, while Baillon's crake is 15–16 cm long and paler and more orange. Also rarely seen is the spotless crake (*P. tabuensis*), which

is slate grey and grows to about 17–20 cm long. All three species are found in the reed beds and rushes of creeks and damp claypans. The white-browed crake (*P. cinerea*), brown with white streaks above the eyes and 18 cm long, is also secretive – except in Cairns, where it can be seen scurrying across lily pads in park ponds.

The red-necked crake (*Rallina tricolor*) lives only in rainforest on the east of Cape York. It grows to about 28 cm long and is olive brown with a chestnut head, neck and throat.

The chestnut rail (*Eulabeornis castaneoventris*), 43–52 cm long with a grey head merging into olive grey along its back, lives on crabs. At low tide it emerges from mangroves onto mud flats in creeks around Darwin and along the northern coast.

RAIL WAYS
Some of the larger rails have very specialised habitats and distributions; for example, the red-necked crake (*Rallina tricolor*), pictured above, lives only on the eastern side of Cape York.

■ **BUFF-BANDED RAIL**
Of all the rails in Australia, the buff-banded rail is the one most likely to be seen. It lives on swamp fringes.

Wandering water birds

Like most water birds, rails are nomadic. Each species has a specific habitat, and they move around as rain and evaporation make successive areas suitable. To the casual observer, rails appear to be flightless because they walk as they feed and, when disturbed, run – rather than fly – into cover. The larger ones sometimes patter along a water surface flapping their wings, and occasionally one of the bigger species will lift off with its big toes trailing and then drop back to the water after a short flight. However, at night these birds do fly; some migrate long distances, but others only ever make short flights.
Family: Rallidae

BUFF-BANDED RAIL ■

These rails live in vegetation along the edges of swamps and paperbark woodlands and eat small insects and aquatic life. They are often active at dusk, especially during the summer, scurrying from the undergrowth to peck in nearby grass.

Also known as banded rails, these medium-sized, slender birds are 28–33 cm long, with white eyebrows on a chestnut face. They are brownish orange with a splotched back, barring underneath, and a bright orange band across the chest. The chicks are black. They live in coastal areas of Australia, as well as in Indonesia and New Guinea. They are generally nomadic, and at times migrate across Torres Strait.
Scientific name: *Gallirallus philippensis*

DISTRIBUTION

■ PURPLE SWAMPHEN

■ DUSKY MOORHEN

■ **PURPLE SWAMPHEN**
Visitors to city parks are likely to recognise the purple swamphen. It can often be seen grazing on lawns, flicking its stubby tail continuously to show its white undertail.

PURPLE SWAMPHEN ■

In every country where it lives this bird is known by a different name. It ranges – from southern Europe across Africa to South-East Asia, where it is called the purple gallinule, and as far as New Zealand, where it is known as the pukeko. In Australia, it occurs almost everywhere except in the western and central deserts.

This large rail grows to 44–48 cm long and is black and indigo blue except in Western Australia, where it is a paler blue. It has a red bill and a red shield on its forehead, and looks like a heavily built, long-legged domestic fowl. It has a short tail that flicks up to reveal a white patch beneath. Its chicks are covered in dark down and have a whitish bill.

It sometimes enters the water to feed, but more often it eats aquatic rhizomes in reeds and bulrushes along the edge, or grazes on clover, shoots, fruits and a little animal matter in swamps and paddocks. Where it has settled in public parks it can become very bold, venturing close to picnickers. It makes easily identifiable harsh screeching noises.

Breeding groups, which consist of two to seven males, one or two females and some helpers, are very gregarious and practise polygamy, polyandry, incest and homosexuality within these groupings.

Purple swamphens breed in spring, two to three months after rain. All members of the group help to build a nesting platform, as well as extra roosting and brooding platforms, by pulling down and trampling vegetation. All share brooding and parental duties, although the dominant male broods overnight.
Scientific name: Porphyrio porphyrio

■ DUSKY MOORHEN
This rail feeds its young for about nine weeks. Adults within a breeding group share in caring for the young.

LORD HOWE WOODHEN

The Lord Howe woodhen lives only on this small volcanic island, 600 kilometres off the east coast of New South Wales. When this bird was discovered by Europeans in 1788 it was common all over the island, but by 1973 only 20 birds remained, living high on Mount Lidgbird. This decline was due to the birds having been taken for food by sailors and whalers, to human disturbance of its habitat, and to the introduction of pigs, cats, dogs, goats and rats onto the island.

In 1980 a captive breeding and release program, which was funded by the National Parks and Wildlife Foundation, was combined with a policy of cat control and pig elimination. By 1990 the wild population of Lord Howe woodhens had increased to over 200 individuals. As each pair needs a territory to forage in, the birds have now spread back down from Mount Lidgbird to the settled lowlands, and today the loud clapping, talking or whistling of tourists along many tracks on the island will sometimes bring these inquisitive birds foraging around their feet.

Lord Howe woodhens are 32–42 cm long, with a short tail and a long, slightly curved bill. Both sexes are olive and chestnut brown and barred under the wings and tail. They are flightless – their ancestors were probably fliers that lost the need to migrate because adequate food and water were available on the island. They are related to the weka of New Zealand.

These rails inhabit all sorts of vegetation except rainforest, including settled lowland areas. They feed on worms, insect larvae and crustaceans, turning over soil and ground litter with their bill rather than their feet.

They have a breeding territory of about 3 hectares, and a mating pair shares this area and all breeding duties. Sooty black chicks leave the nest after hatching, and are minded and fed by both parents. Sometimes young from a previous brood are cared for with the new offspring, though chicks more than five months old are not tolerated in the territory.

The Lord Howe woodhen's call is a piercing whistle, often made in duet or with a thumping note that is heard only at close range.
Scientific name: Gallirallus sylvestris

DUSKY MOORHEN ■

The dusky moorhen is one of the more easily seen members of the rail family. It is medium-sized, about 38 cm long, and similar in shape to the swamphen. It is a dusky slate grey with patches of white on each side under its tail. Its bill is red with a yellow tip and it has a bright red shield on its forehead. Young or nonbreeding birds are paler with a greenish shield, and chicks are dark with a red bill, a bluish crown and whitish tips on their facial down.

These rails always seem busy as they swim around the margins of water among vegetation, especially duckweed. They swim with a fore-and-aft rocking action, their low, flat back curving gently up to the tail tip. Common in eastern, south-eastern and far south-western Australia, they are often sedentary in a particular area, though some populations are nomadic. They are particularly fond of town lakes and waterways with

overgrown banks. They can be mistaken in the water for ducklings, but their loud 'krek' call and other shrill notes make them easily recognisable.

Dusky moorhens live in groups of between two and seven. During the breeding season, which begins in September, they share breeding duties and defend territories.
Scientific name: *Gallinula tenebrosa*

TASMANIAN NATIVE-HEN ■

As its name implies, this rail is found only in Tasmania. It often grazes in family groups in pasture, tussock grass and cereal crops near creek beds with well-vegetated edges. Also called a narkie or water-hen, it is quite common within its range, which is expanding slightly as more land is being cleared.

This species is a much dumpier bird than the black-tailed native-hen (this page), but has a similar erect black tail and general outline. Solidly built and 43–45 cm long, it is olive brown and slate grey with a thick yellow-green bill extending to a very small shield on its forehead. It has red eyes, a black abdomen and a white patch on its flanks. Chicks are born covered in black down that gradually pales as they grow.

These rails live and breed in bands of between two and seven, with females breeding with more than one male a season. The group nest is a saucer-shaped hollow among tussocks or undergrowth. Adults feed mainly on plants, but the young are fed insects until they are two weeks old. The young leave the parental territory after a year, travelling as far afield as 10 kilometres.

The Tasmanian native-hen is an active and aggressive bird that moves its tail in jerks. It mainly utters low-pitched grunts but may also make a saw-like rasping noise. Its alarm call is a loud scream.

While it did not survive the arrival of the dingo on mainland Australia, in Tasmania, it seems to be coping well with the presence of cats and Tasmanian devils. However, its habit of grazing on pasture and cereal crops has made farmers consider it a pest, and it is not a protected bird.
Scientific name: *Gallinula mortierii*

BLACK-TAILED NATIVE-HEN

The erect black tail of this rail resembles that of a bantam rooster. Seen from a distance, this 30–38 cm-long bird looks almost black. In fact, it has an olive green and slate grey back with a darker underside and a set of white splashes along its flanks. It has deep pink legs, orange eyes and a green shield and bill. Its chicks are green and black.

These nomadic birds can be absent from an area for years, then suddenly arrive in thousands after rain, disappearing some weeks later. They feed on insects, seeds and shoots, foraging as the water recedes around the edges of claypans and temporary lakes. They like the seeds of lignum plants and are also found in lignum swamps and along creek edges.

They occur almost everywhere in mainland Australia except in the wet tropics and the wet eastern seaboard areas. A flock of black-tailed native-hens can be a striking sight, surging like a tide across a drying lake, swimming in waves across a flood-plain channel, or slipping in what seems an endless single file between the bushes of a lignum swamp.

Also known as black-tailed water-hens and native bantams, these are generally gregarious birds. They breed in pairs in small groups and lay their speckled eggs in a platform nest. Although not as vocal as some other rails, they have a repetitive yapping alarm call and a quiet cackle.
Scientific name: *Gallinula ventralis*

EURASIAN COOT ■

The Eurasian coot – the coot species that lives in Australia – is also found in New Guinea, South-East Asia, India, North Africa and Europe.

It is 38 cm long and slate grey, though it looks black. Its bill and the shield on its forehead are white. It has a row of flaps running along both sides of its toes. On open water it is easily confused with the dusky moorhen, but its back is more convex. Chicks have a cream bill and are covered in dark down except for

their spiky head plumage, tipped with orange red. They moult gradually to the coloration of the adults.

Coots congregate on open water in large flocks, pecking and diving for water plants, or graze beside ponds, lakes and rivers. They are highly nomadic and occasionally fly during the day if disturbed. In some seasons almost every pond, dam and lake in a town can be filled with coots – and then a few weeks later it may be difficult to find a single bird. But although coots are so mobile their overall distribution remains constant.

Flocks of coots on open water make contact calls of single 'kyok' sounds. They can also screech and make harsh grating noises.
Scientific name: *Fulica atra*

■ EURASIAN COOT
The Eurasian coot's nest is a clump of twigs and waterweeds, often with an approach ramp of nesting material.

■ TASMANIAN NATIVE-HEN
When danger threatens, this almost flightless rail either runs away or swims – sometimes it even clambers up sloping tree trunks.

DISTRIBUTION

■ TASMANIAN NATIVE-HEN
■ BLACK-TAILED NATIVE-HEN

EURASIAN COOT

DISTRIBUTION

Australian bustard

Australian bustard

Australian bustards are sometimes known as plains turkeys or wild turkeys. They are large, stately, brown birds that carry their head tilted upwards on a longish, thick neck, giving them a somewhat aloof appearance. They look like heavy cranes or small emus, and have thick legs with small front toes and no hind toe. They occur in Australia and southern New Guinea living in open grassy country with scattered bushes and trees. The brown male stands about a metre tall on greenish cream legs and has a black crown and a black streak behind its eyes. It has a white neck with very fine black barring, which can be seen only at close range, and a dark band across its breast. Its belly is white to grey. The female is a little smaller and less heavily marked.

Australian bustards are nomadic and omnivorous. They amble around foraging in single-sex groups, and then fly off to new areas that are rich in fresh food after rain has fallen. They eat vegetable matter, small vertebrates and insects, particularly grasshoppers. They can survive for long periods without drinking. Like cranes, they fly with their neck and legs extended. Despite their heavy appearance they are powerful fliers, though slow.

Males have an elaborate mating display. They come together in groups during the breeding season, which occurs after rain has fallen. Each male extends his throat sac so that it looks like a huge white feather boa hanging from beneath his chin almost to the ground. He steps from foot to foot to set his throat swaying, raises his tail over his back and fans it out to display extensive white patches, and lowers his wings. Rocking from side to side, he makes a booming, roaring noise.

■ FULL-DRESS COURTSHIP
To attract females during the mating season, the male Australian bustard inflates his foreneck so that its long feathers fan out like a feather boa, hanging down in front of his long legs.

The eggs are light green and brown, blotched with darker shades. Females lay their eggs – usually only one, but sometimes as many as three – on the ground, generally among low shrubs or tussocks of grass. They then feed and protect the chicks, without any assistance from the male, until fledging or even longer. Apart from the loud noise that the males make at breeding time, Australian bustards are usually silent, although they do utter an occasional croak.

The Australian bustard was once common and widespread, and was found on grassy plains, scrublands and in low woodlands everywhere except in the very wettest parts. Between 1860 and 1935, however, shooting severely reduced its numbers and range, as the only birds that could breed successfully were those in monsoon areas, which shooters were unable to reach in the wet season. Its numbers have also been reduced by habitat destruction and being preyed upon by foxes. In 1935 it became a protected species, and this, coupled with a change of attitude in some areas, has seen it slowly moving back into New South Wales and other southern regions, although it is still not common.

When approached on foot, the Australian bustard either runs away or crouches down in the grass with its bill and tail raised so as to conceal its outline. It can be approached very closely in a car, and its tolerance of motor vehicles, combined with its local name of wild turkey, means that it is still at risk from some sections of the community.
Family: Otididae;
Scientific name: *Ardeotis australis*

Button-quails

Button-quails are small, dumpy ground-dwellers. They resemble true quails but are unlike them in that the female button-quail is larger and more brightly coloured than the male and dominates the courtship ritual, producing booming calls with her specialised vocal organs. Female button-quails often mate with several males in the one season.

The drab, mottled colouring of the button-quails provides camouflage for their life among the grass and leaf litter, while their short, stout legs and three forward-pointing toes are adapted for walking and running. They usually feed during the day and make migratory flights at night, when they are sometimes disoriented by bright lights and collide with buildings and windows. They occur throughout Australia in grassland and crops, grassy woodland and open forest, heath and scrub, and one species – the black-breasted button-quail – lives in rainforest. Although common in their range, button-quails are not easy to see, since when approached they either freeze and then creep furtively away through cover, or suddenly burst into whirring flight from almost underfoot. They display caution with a peculiar rocking gait, creeping slowly forwards and stopping periodically in mid step to rock their body back and forth.

Signs of the presence of button-quails are their booming calls or the characteristic circular feeding scrapes that they make in the leaf litter as they search for insects and seeds. They make these scrapes by pivoting on one foot while scratching with the other, the bird turning a half or full circle before changing feet and reversing direction. Button-quails also eat green shoots and small berries, and swallow sand or grit to help grind up their food.

In the Australian tropics the button-quail's breeding season is determined by the rainfall, while in southern Australia it breeds from spring to autumn. The three small species – the little button-quail, the red-chested button-quail and the red-backed button-quail – lay their eggs at almost any time of year, although it is usually in spring in southern Australia.

Button-quails live singly, in pairs or in small groups, but breeding females are solitary and defend their territory against other females. They make their mating calls with their windpipe, which is long and swollen at its base, and inflate their enlarged oesophagus with air like a tiny balloon in order to resonate the calls. Once a female has attracted a male to the area, she booms again to entice him to join her in constructing a nest, sometimes offering him various morsels of food. Button-quails can sometimes be heard at night making their booming noises.

The pair make a flimsy grass nest in a scrape on the ground among grass. These nests are often hidden beneath or inside grass tussocks, or under a bush, a log or a fallen branch, and are sometimes hooded or domed. The incubating adult is virtually invisible, and is very cautious when entering or leaving the nest, which has a separate side entrance for this purpose. The male normally incubates the eggs, though in the early stages the female sometimes takes turns. The three or four, sometimes five, well-camouflaged eggs take two weeks to hatch.

Normally the female promptly attracts another male and presents him, in turn, with a clutch of eggs to incubate. She repeats this with a succession of males, enabling her to produce up to seven clutches in a season at fortnightly intervals.

The downy chicks are striped for camouflage. They are able to feed themselves within a few days, and can fly within two weeks. The male looks after the chicks, normally without any assistance from the female. He feeds them for up to two weeks by calling them to take food from the tip of his beak, and he also broods them and shepherds them about. When danger threatens he gives a soft warning call and the chicks scatter and lie motionless with their eyes closed. He also defends them by feigning injury in an attempt to lure a potential predator away from them, or by charging at an intruder with his feathers puffed out.

The young grow very rapidly. They are independent in a month, fully feathered within six weeks and fully grown within two months, so that the male is ready to become an incubator again within two months. The young acquire their adult plumage and are able to breed in three to five months.
Family: Turnicidae

RED-CHESTED BUTTON-QUAIL

The red-chested button-quail grows to about 15 cm long and is grey on top and rust coloured underneath. It is probably quite common in good seasons, although it is not often seen. Like the little button-quail, it has a stout bill for pecking up its staple diet of seeds. It also eats green shoots and insects.

This button-quail has declined in the southern parts of its range, where native grasslands have been taken over for agriculture and are now used for grazing and crops.
Scientific name: *Turnix pyrrhothorax*

RED-BACKED BUTTON-QUAIL

The red-backed button-quail of Australia's northern and eastern coastal fringe is a dark species, similar in size to the little button-quail. It has a yellow bill that is more slender than that of the red-chested and the little button-quail, and it is more insectivorous, eating seeds and insects in roughly equal quantities. It is common in the rank, moist grasslands of the tropics but has declined in the southernmost part of its range, where its habitat has been destroyed.
Scientific name: *Turnix maculosa*

LITTLE BUTTON-QUAIL

At about 14 cm long, this is one of the smallest button-quails. Reddish brown above and white underneath, it is stout-billed and eats mostly seeds, including fallen grain; it also eats green shoots and insects.

The little button-quail is common in the fields, grassy woodlands and plains of most of Australia, and shares much of northern and eastern Australia with the red-chested button-quail, which is a similar size. Both species have declined in the southern parts of their range.
Scientific name: *Turnix velox*

DOMINANT FEMALE
The female button-quail dominates courtship and defends territory. She attracts a male with her booming call and will sometimes entice him by offering him titbits of food. The male incubates the eggs and raises the young.

LITTLE BUTTON-QUAIL
The little button-quail builds its nest at the base of a grass clump, often forming a grass canopy over the top.

DISTRIBUTION

RED-CHESTED BUTTON-QUAIL

RED-BACKED BUTTON-QUAIL

LITTLE BUTTON-QUAIL

PAINTED BUTTON-QUAIL ■

The painted button-quail, at about 20 cm long, is one of the largest button-quails. It is grey and rufous, with a slender bill and red eyes. It occurs in eastern and south-western Australia, and also in Tasmania, though it is rare there. It is common in the northern part of its range but declining in the south. It lives in grassy woodland and open forest, particularly where there is abundant leaf litter, and also in heath and scrub.

The painted button-quail is more insectivorous than most button-quails, but also eats seeds, green shoots and berries. The female lays her three or four eggs – sometimes five – between spring and autumn in the south, and in the north at any time when grass, litter cover, seeds and insects are abundant.

Scientific name: *Turnix varia*

BLACK-BREASTED BUTTON-QUAIL ■

The black-breasted button-quail is the only button-quail that is found in rainforest. It grows to about 20 cm long and is a mottled fawn-brown in colour. The female has black foreparts spangled white, while the male is duller and mostly brown so that it looks like the male painted button-quail, but it lacks the rufous colouring and having white eyes rather than red. The black-breasted button-quail lives in rainforest and lantana thickets in coastal areas of

■ BLACK-BREASTED BUTTON-QUAIL
The female black-breasted button-quail attracts males to her territory with a rapidly repeated booming call.

■ PAINTED BUTTON-QUAIL
These button-quails live in woodland. They clear circular scrapes with their feet in the leaf litter in search of food.

southern Queensland, and also in extreme northern New South Wales. This species is quite vulnerable to extinction because its populations are declining in these small fragments of habitat.

The black-breasted button-quail eats mostly insects, which it uncovers in the litter of the forest floor. It sometimes spreads its wings over a freshly made scrape, possibly to delay the retreat of exposed prey. The female lays three or four eggs between spring and autumn.

Scientific name: *Turnix melanogaster*

PLAINS-WANDERER

This small, ground-dwelling bird resembles a button-quail except that it is more slender and has longer legs. It has a hind toe like the true quails but the female is larger and brighter than the male, having a black and white speckled collar and a rufous patch on her breast. It is she that utters the booming courtship call. The male is the incubator, caring for the eggs and chicks while the female mates with another male, which she subsequently leaves with a further clutch of eggs to incubate.

The plains-wanderer is the sole member of its family, and is unique to Australia. It is not related to the button-quails but to shorebirds or waders, most closely to the seed-snipes (family Thinocoridae) of South America. This relationship is not as unlikely as it sounds, since Australia was once joined to South America as part of the southern supercontinent of Gondwana.

Once living in the extensive grasslands of southern inland Australia, the plains-wanderer is now rare and threatened. Its decline is due mainly to the heavy grazing of domestic stock and the conversion of its native short, open grasslands to tall, dense crops and improved pasture.

By banding these birds, scientists have shown that when the plains-wanderer is displaced from an area it does not return. When birds are forced to disperse they probably perish. The plains-wanderer is now found mainly on the plains of the Riverina district of New South Wales and in south-western Queensland. Its mottled grey-brown colouring provides superb camouflage as it makes it way through the short grass, holding its body close to the ground. From time to time it stands on tiptoe, scanning the landscape beyond the taller wisps of grass for predators.

The plains-wanderer eats seeds and insects. It nests on the ground, making a shallow grass-lined scrape in the shelter of a tussock. In spring, plains-wanderers lay between two and five well-camouflaged eggs, which take three weeks to hatch. They may lay a second clutch in summer if rain falls. In Queensland they lay their eggs in autumn and early winter. The young are independent in about two months.

As well as being threatened by overgrazing, cultivation and fires, plains-wanderers are eaten by foxes and are sometimes poisoned by spraying to destroy locusts. They can be protected by fenced reserves covering as little as 50–100 hectares on the least productive parts of inland grazing properties. Such reserves offer hope for the plains-wanderer's survival.

Family: Pedionomidae;
Scientific name: *Pedionomus torquatus*

WADERS AND SHOREBIRDS

Waders and shorebirds (suborder Charadrii) constitute about 10 per cent of Australia's bird species, most of them small to medium-sized birds living in wetlands and along the coasts, beaches, reefs and tidal mud flats of the seashore. Some, such as the sandpipers, have long legs and a long beak for probing in the mud; others, such as the plovers, are short, plump birds with long legs and a comparatively short bill.

Of this group of birds, it is mainly the plovers and dotterels that nest and breed in Australia; most other waders and shorebirds that are seen in Australia are migratory, spending the northern summer in the northern hemisphere, where they breed, and migrating south before the onset of the northern winter.

When they arrive in Australia these birds may still be in partial breeding plumage, but they soon don their less colourful nonbreeding plumage for most of the southern summer.

When they are not breeding, most waders congregate in large groups, but at breeding time they disperse and become highly territorial. Before leaving for their breeding grounds, waders gain weight and moult into their rich chestnut coloured breeding plumage. A few migratory wader species remain in Australia for their first year or two.

LIVING BY THE SEA
The pied oystercatcher (*Haematopus longirostris*) is found right around the Australian coastline. It opens shellfish either by hammering them on the side or by stabbing its bill between the shell valves, depending on the method it learned from watching its parents.

PAINTED SNIPE

Native to Australia, the painted snipe is one of two species in its family and is the only one found in this country. Superficially it resembles the snipe, but it is probably more closely related to the rail family.

AN EXPANDING BIRD
When a painted snipe is threatened, it fans out its wings and tail, making its body appear much larger than it is. The bird accompanies this display with a snake-like hissing.

The painted snipe is less agile than the true snipe and flies more slowly and rather clumsily, with its legs dangling down. Its bill is long, slender and slightly down-curving at the tip, adapted to probing in soft mud. Around its large eyes, which are set well forward to provide binocular vision, is a pronounced pale eye ring and streak. Its wings are a glossy olive green, broad and rather short. There is conspicuous yellow spotting on its flight feathers and tail. A white bar at the side of its breast extends in a conspicuous V-shape across its back.

Painted snipes are found in south-eastern and eastern mainland Australia and Tasmania in and near freshwater swamps and shallow lagoons, especially where there is a considerable amount of dense vegetation. They feed mostly during the morning and evening on molluscs, earthworms, crustaceans, seeds and various insects, especially grasshoppers and crickets.

These birds appear to be nomadic within Australia, but little is known about their movements as they are extremely secretive and difficult to observe. They are commonly active at night, spending much of the day hiding in swamp vegetation. If disturbed by accident they freeze.

The breeding season for the painted snipe varies depending on weather conditions and the availability of food. In southern Australia they breed in shallow freshwater wetlands between August and February, but in northern Queensland breeding occurs during March and April.

The female painted snipe, which has a chestnut-bronze head, breast and neck, is the bigger and more conspicuous bird, at about 30 cm long; the male is about 24 cm long. It is she who establishes the breeding territory, and generally initiates courtship with flight displays and booming calls. Mated pairs tend to remain together only until the eggs have been laid, and the male then incubates the eggs and raises the young alone. Females frequently mate with a number of males in the course of a season, laying several clutches of eggs.

Outside the breeding season, painted snipes tend to move about either alone or in small groups, and they are commonly found in flooded areas.
Family: Rostratulidae;
Scientific name: *Rostratula benghalensis*

PAINTED SNIPE

SNIPES AND THEIR RELATIVES

Members of this family of waders make remarkably long annual migratory flights to the southern hemisphere, most travelling from high-latitude breeding grounds in the northern hemisphere.

Of the 88 species in this family worldwide, about 30 per cent are regular visitors to Australia. Many are dull coloured, well-camouflaged birds, but in the breeding season their plumage is often brighter with more reddish brown or black. Within this family, bill size and shape vary, some birds having long, sensitive bills with flexible tips to grasp prey from beneath the surface. Females are usually a little larger than males and often have longer bills.
Family: Scolopacidae

BILLS AT WORK
The various groups of waders do not compete for the same types of food. Curlews and godwits use their long bills to find deep-burrowing creatures such as lugworms. Greenshanks and oystercatchers can reach shellfish that burrow less deeply, while knots and sanderlings feed on creatures such as sandhoppers and crabs near the surface.

GODWITS ■
Three godwit species are regular visitors to Australia. Black-tailed godwits (*Limosa limosa*) and bar-tailed godwits (*L. lapponica*) are very common, while Hudsonian godwits (*L. haemastica*), which are 37–42 cm long, are usually strays that have been blown off their normal course.

Godwits arrive in early August and leave for their breeding grounds in early April. They feed during the day at the tide line, on mud flats or estuaries, probing the mud to extract bivalves and marine worms. They roost at night in large flocks on sites close to their feeding grounds, preferably near fresh water.

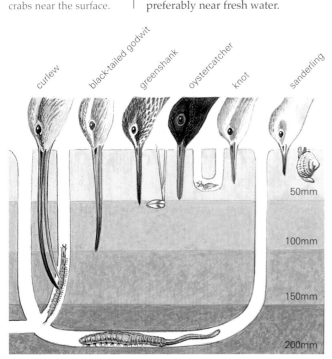

curlew black-tailed godwit greenshank oystercatcher knot sanderling

50mm
100mm
150mm
200mm

Black-tailed godwits are long-legged, long-billed waders with rather short heads and long necks. They grow to about 40–44 cm long, with males being smaller than females and having shorter bills. In their nonbreeding plumage they are a uniform grey-brown, but in flight they display a conspicuous white wing bar, a white rump and a black band at the end of their tail.

Large numbers of black-tailed godwits arrive from northern Asia and gather in northern Australia, particularly on the coast of Arnhem Land and the Gulf of Carpentaria, though some settle on the eastern and south-eastern coast and inland. They remain in separate flocks on muddy estuaries, where they feed often with their heads completely immersed. They embark on their northward migration in March or early April.

Bar-tailed godwits breed further north than black-tailed godwits. Those wintering in Western Australia migrate along the Chinese coast and up into northern central Siberia to breed, whereas south-eastern populations breed in Alaska. Up to 100 000 bar-tailed godwits arrive annually in Roebuck Bay and Eighty Mile Beach in Western Australia.

In their nonbreeding plumage, bar-tailed godwits, which grow to about 37–39 cm, are generally mottled grey-brown with white underparts and black, relatively short legs. Their tails are brown and usually barred, and their bills curve slightly upwards and have a pinkish base. The breeding plumage of the male is a rich chestnut red.
Scientific name: *Limosa* spp.

■ GODWIT
The black-tailed godwit (*Limosa limosa*) often immerses its head completely when pulling its prey from the mud. These birds breed in Eurasia.

SNIPES
Snipes are small to medium-sized waders, extremely well camouflaged and with long, straight bills. When disturbed they crouch on the ground or take off with a rasping cry. Three species visit Australia, but none breeds here. All are brownish black with streaks of brown or buff on their upper parts, and pale buff to white underneath. Their flanks are finely barred with dark brown.

They live in freshwater swamps, in wetlands, near sewage farms, on the borders of reservoirs and dams, and sometimes on coastal salt marshes. Snipes are nocturnal, usually roosting during the day in the swamps then moving out to wet meadows to feed at night. Occasionally during the day they feed in near-liquid mud.

Latham's snipe (*Gallinago hardwickii*) breeds on the grasslands and cultivated areas of Hokkaido and Honshu Islands in Japan, in the southern Kurile Islands, and on the Russian island of Sakhalin. Around July to August, these 27–33 cm-long birds migrate to Australia. They settle mainly along the eastern coastal strip, particularly from the Richmond River in New South Wales down to Tasmania, where they are common. They feed in brackish or freshwater swamps, probing the mud for seeds, snails, earthworms, beetles and other invertebrates. In February they leave for their breeding grounds.

Swinhoe's snipes, or forest snipes (*G. megala*), which are 27–29 cm long, breed in the forested regions and tundras of central and eastern Siberia. During the Siberian winter they mostly migrate to southern China, Borneo and the Malay Peninsula, but are sometimes seen as far south as northern Western Australia and the Northern Territory.

The slightly smaller pin-tailed snipe (*G. stenura*), 25–27 cm long, breeds in eastern Siberia and Mongolia and spends the northern winter mainly on the Malay Peninsula and on the islands of Sumatra. Small numbers visit northern Australia and the Pilbara region of Western Australia.

Scientific name: *Gallinago* spp.

CURLEWS AND WHIMBRELS

Curlews and whimbrels are medium-sized to large waders, with brown mottled plumage, a long, down-curving bill and a characteristic call. The sexes look alike, except that the female is larger than the male and has a longer bill. All but the little curlew congregate at high tide at roosting sites such as sandy spits, rocky outcrops and salt marshes, and even in mangroves. At low tide they often forage in large flocks on the mud and sand flats, probing for crabs and other invertebrates. They are wary birds.

The eastern curlew (*Numenius madagascariensis*) is the largest of the curlews, with a body length of 60–66 cm and a strongly down-curving bill more than half the length of its body. It uses this long

bill to pluck ghost shrimps from deep, sandy burrows. Like many waders, however, it is an opportunistic feeder and has an armoury of prey-capturing methods. It finds shrimp burrows by sight, but it can also forage in poor light in submerged eelgrass beds, waving its open bill to detect crabs by touch.

Generally visiting Australia from August to late March, this curlew may find a partner for life in its sub-arctic breeding grounds. In Australia it settles mainly on the east coast, where it resides in estuaries, mangrove swamps and along seashores. The call of the eastern curlew, often heard at night, is a clear, two-note whistle and an occasional yodel.

Eastern curlew numbers have significantly declined in recent years. Whether the cause is local or whether it arises during their migration through parts of Asia is not yet known.

At 40–45 cm long, the whimbrel (*N. phaeopus*) is smaller than the eastern curlew and has a much shorter bill, a white triangular rump and distinctive eyebrow and lateral crown stripes. It breeds in Siberia and frequently roosts and feeds among eastern curlews along the east coast of Australia as well as along the west coast.

The little curlew (*N. minutus*), growing to 28–31 cm long, is a smaller version of the whimbrel. It has a shorter and more down-curved bill than any of its relatives. At the end of the dry season it arrives in large flocks from its breeding grounds in the Arctic Circle, settling on the blacksoil

floodplains and grasslands of the northern parts of Australia. It forages in the cool of the early morning and late afternoon, usually devouring seeds and insects. During the heat of the day enormous flocks gather around freshwater pools; more than 100 000 birds have been observed at Fogg Dam, near Darwin.

At the onset of the wet season little curlews disperse inland, where their movements are influenced by local weather conditions. They start to migrate northward in early April, and by the end of April most have left Australia.

Scientific name: *Numenius* spp.

COMMON GREENSHANK

The common greenshank is a 30–35 cm-long grey sandpiper with a slightly upturned bill and greenish legs. Its underparts are white and its chest is strongly flecked with brownish black. On the ground it is sometimes confused with the smaller and more fine-billed marsh sandpiper (page 172), but it is easily distinguished in flight by a white rump extending in a V up its back and by its 'tchu-tchu-tchu' flight call.

Common greenshanks prefer salt marshes and intertidal mud flats. They feed mainly on aquatic invertebrates, though they also eat tadpoles, frogs and small fishes. They occur in large flocks at Eighty Mile Beach in north-west Western Australia and in the Gulf of Carpentaria in Queensland. They are also seen in substantial numbers in the southern parts of Australia and in the shallow freshwater swamps of the inland.

Scientific name: *Tringa nebularia*

■ CURLEW
The largest wader to visit Australian shores, the eastern curlew (*Numenius madagascariensis*) breeds in Siberia and Mongolia. It is often active at night, when its call can be heard.

■ GREENSHANK
The greenshank wades in the shallows or forages on mud flats. It is generally gregarious but tends to be quite solitary when feeding.

DISTRIBUTION

GODWITS

SNIPES

CURLEWS AND WHIMBRELS

COMMON GREENSHANK

WOOD SANDPIPER

MARSH SANDPIPER AND LESSER YELLOWLEGS

COMMON SANDPIPER

TEREK SANDPIPER

TATTLERS

TEREK SANDPIPER
A small, pale sandpiper, this species can be easily distinguished from other waders by its orange-yellow legs and slightly upturned bill.

WOOD SANDPIPER

This sandpiper is a regular migrant to Australia in comparatively small numbers, with the greatest concentrations occurring in the Kimberley in Western Australia. It prefers flooded grassy meadows and shallow swamps, where it forages for insects and their larvae, worms, molluscs and crustaceans.

It is similar in appearance to the common sandpiper, but lacks the white wing bar and, at 19–23 cm, is slightly bigger. Its olive brown upper parts are distinctly spotted with white, and in flight its white rump is conspicuous. Its legs are usually dull green and its bill is about as long as its head, which bears well-marked white eyebrows.

Wood sandpipers are generally solitary or found in small groups. Uniquely among waders, they occasionally use the old nests of other tree-nesting birds.
Scientific name: *Tringa glareola*

MARSH SANDPIPER AND LESSER YELLOWLEGS

The marsh sandpiper (*Tringa stagnatillis*) is similar in appearance to the greenshank (page 171) but a bit smaller – hence its other common name, the little greenshank. It grows to about 22 cm long, and has a finer bill than the greenshank.

Marsh sandpipers occur in large numbers on the extensive intertidal mud flats of northern Australia, often along with greenshanks. They feed chiefly on aquatic insects, crustaceans and molluscs, sometimes sweeping their bill from side to side in the water when feeding.

A similar species is the rarely recorded lesser yellowlegs (*T. flavipes*), which is slightly larger and has a shorter, stouter bill and longer wings.
Scientific name: *Tringa* spp.

WOOD SANDPIPER
Only small numbers of wood sandpipers are seen in Australia each year. They are found in freshwater wetlands, where they feed mainly on insects.

COMMON SANDPIPER

In flight the white bar on the common sandpiper's wing is distinctive, as is its characteristic flight of rapid flickering wingbeats alternating with momentary glides. While it is feeding, it constantly bobs its body and tail, and when it takes off it calls with a three-note, high-pitched 'tsee-tsee-tsee' whistle.

This 19–21 cm-long sandpiper is sandy brown above and on the sides of the chest with a white wing bar. Its underparts are white and it has a shortish, dark brown bill with a paler base, dull green legs and prominent white eye rings and eyebrows.

Common sandpipers occur along most of the Australian coastline, especially in the Northern Territory and north-western Queensland. They are found on estuaries, dams, rivers, streams, lakes and sewage ponds. These birds are usually solitary, but they sometimes roost in small flocks. They forage for their food by running and pecking at the surface, and by probing in mud for insects, molluscs, crustaceans and the young of some fish species.
Scientific name: *Actitis hypoleucos*

TEREK SANDPIPER

Looking like a smallish grey-brown *Tringa* sandpiper, but with rather stubby legs and a long, slightly upturned bill, the Terek sandpiper inhabits the estuaries, mangrove swamps, tidal mud flats, coastal lagoons and coral reefs of north-western Western Australia, the Northern Territory and the east coast of Australia. From August to March it is a regular visitor, but in early April it departs for its breeding grounds in northern Russia. Brown on top with orange-yellow legs and white underparts, it grows to 22–24 cm long.

Terek sandpipers feed on tidal mud flats and around mangroves on small crabs, beetles, water bugs and crustaceans. They characteristically dash forward in a crouched posture with head lowered, frequently changing direction. They also probe the mud with their long bills for other crustaceans, insects and molluscs.

They usually roost communally when the tide is high, often in the company of other waders, such as eastern curlews, whimbrels and grey-tailed tattlers.
Scientific name: *Xenus cinereus*

TATTLERS

There are two tattlers that visit Australia in the nonbreeding season – the grey-tailed tattler (*Heteroscelus brevipes*), sometimes called the Siberian tattler or grey-rumped sandpiper, and the wandering tattler (*H. incanus*), also known as the American tattler. These two species look very similar, with brownish grey upper parts, white underparts, a grey breast and a long, blackish bill. The grey-tailed tattler is 25 cm long; the wandering tattler, at 27 cm long, is slightly larger.

Outside the breeding season these two species can be distinguished from one another only by their individual calls and their habitat preferences. The grey-tailed tattler likes the sandy and muddy shores of beaches and estuaries around most of Australia's coastline, but it appears in the greatest concentrations in the Broome to Port Hedland area of Western Australia, and the Gulf of Carpentaria and Moreton Bay in Queensland, where it feeds on crustaceans and other intertidal invertebrates. The wandering tattler inhabits rocky coastal areas with coral reefs, probably only along the north-eastern coast, and particularly the Great Barrier Reef. Crabs, molluscs and worms are its staple diet.
Scientific name: *Heteroscelus* spp.

KNOTS

These birds probably take their common name from their soft 'knut knut' calls. They arrive in Australia towards the end of August and migrate north to the Arctic Circle again during March and April.

There are two knot species: the red knot (*Calidris canutus*), sometimes known as the lesser knot or the common knot, and the great knot (*C. tenuirostris*). Both are common and widespread in Australia, particularly in the Broome to Port Hedland area of Western Australia and in the Gulf of Carpentaria in Queensland, where flocks of up to 200 000 red knots and over 250 000 great knots have been recorded.

Even during the breeding season considerable numbers of knots spend the northern summer in Australia. They are generally found with other waders, particularly godwits and sandpipers, feeding in the sand and on mud flats, where they probe rapidly for gastropods and crustaceans. They sometimes submerge much of their head.

The red knot is 23–25 cm long, has a short bill and is rather dumpy in appearance. Both sexes look alike – mainly cinnamon brown in their breeding plumage, and grey with a pale barred rump and uniformly grey tail when they are not breeding.

At 26–28 cm long, the great knot is a little larger than the red knot, has longer legs and a longer bill. Its rump is also whiter, and in breeding plumage it has blackish brown spotting on a white breast. Its nonbreeding colours are similar to those of the red knot.
Scientific name: *Calidris* spp.

■ KNOTS
Red knots feed together in compact flocks. When flying, members of the flock twist and wheel in synchrony.

SHARP-TAILED SANDPIPER ■

These sandpipers are sometimes called Siberian pectoral sandpipers, because they breed in Siberia and closely resemble pectoral sandpipers (this page), a few of which also pass the northern winter in Australasia.

The sharp-tailed sandpiper is 17–22 cm long, with scaly brown upper parts and olive green or ochre yellow legs, a buff breast streaked with brown, and a chestnut crown. Its bill is quite short, usually greenish brown, and slightly downcurved.

Australia provides the main winter feeding grounds for these birds. Most are found in the Broome to Port Hedland area of Western Australia or on the wetlands of Victoria, south-western New South Wales and eastern Australia, but they also occur inland in large numbers during floods. They appear to leave southern Australia early in the year, moving north to fatten up before flying northwards in April. In February and March they occur in their thousands on the tidal wetlands of the Gulf Country in Queensland.
Scientific name: *Calidris acuminata*

PECTORAL SANDPIPER

Most birds of this species migrate to South America for the southern summer, but small numbers reach Australia before returning to Siberia and Alaska to breed.

The pectoral sandpiper is very similar in appearance to the sharp-tailed sandpiper (this page), though it is slightly larger, at 19–24 cm, and does not have the chestnut crown. It also differs in that the fine brown streaking on its breast terminates abruptly at its white belly, rather than petering out gradually, as it does on the sharp-tailed sandpiper. It has a yellow base on its bill, which is otherwise the same shape and colour as that of the sharp-tailed sandpiper. The diet of both birds is also similar.
Scientific name: *Calidris melanotos*

SANDERLING

Sanderlings are by far the tamest of the small waders, and they are also the whitest. In their nonbreeding plumage these 20–21 cm-long, straight-billed birds are pale grey, almost white, except for a grey mantle, dark wing tips, black legs and a characteristic black patch on the shoulder of their wings. In breeding plumage, their head and upper parts are rust coloured.

Sanderlings prefer sandy beaches, where they snap up insects and other small invertebrates in the sand while running along the tidal edge following the receding waves. The largest numbers of these birds occur in south-eastern Australia and in the Broome area of Western Australia.

Two similar species are observed from time to time in Australia and can be quite easily confused with the sanderling: the white-rumped sandpiper (*C. fuscicollis*) and Baird's sandpiper (*C. bairdii*).
Scientific name: *Calidris alba*

■ SHARP-TAILED SANDPIPER
Concentrations of thousands of these birds have been reported from coastal areas in Victoria and South Australia. They choose places that offer them grass and other plants among which to hide.

DISTRIBUTION

■ KNOTS

■ SHARP-TAILED SANDPIPER

■ PECTORAL SANDPIPER

■ SANDERLING

DISTRIBUTION

■ STINTS

■ CURLEW SANDPIPER

■ BROAD-BILLED
SANDPIPER

■ RUFF

■ RUDDY TURNSTONE

STINTS ■
Stints are the smallest of the sand-pipers and are characterised by short bills, short legs and dumpy bodies. Feeding mostly by day, they energetically pick over mud flats – mostly between the tidelines – and on swampy edges, saltmarshes and lake margins, looking for small invertebrates. They roost on sandy beaches and spits.

The red-necked stint (*Calidris ruficollis*) is the most common, numerous and widespread small migratory wader in Australia. Apart from its small size – it grows to only 13–16 cm long – it is hard to distinguish from other stints except in the breeding season, when its neck, chest and facial plumage turns chestnut red. Large numbers of these birds congregate along the coast and on inland wetlands.

The long-toed stint (*C. subminuta*), with yellowish legs and plumage resembling that of the sharp-tailed sandpiper (page 173), is uncommon in Australia, though substantial

numbers have been seen at Lake Forrestdale near Perth, Western Australia. Another species that is rare in Australia is the little stint (*C. minuta*) This bird occurs in very small numbers, mostly in brackish swamps or estuaries.
Scientific name: *Calidris* spp.

CURLEW SANDPIPER ■
This medium-sized sandpiper is common in Australia. It is 18–23 cm long, and in nonbreeding plumage it is grey with a distinctive long, black, downward-curving bill, black legs, a white wing bar and white rump. In breeding plumage, its head and underparts are bright chestnut. It arrives in Australia in August and returns northwards to breed in March and April.

Curlew sandpipers inhabit intertidal mud flats, coastal and inland wetlands and sewage treatment plants. Large concentrations of these birds occur on the south-eastern coast and in Western Australia, especially at Eighty Mile Beach and

■ STINTS
The red-necked stint's ability to store surplus food as fat enables this small bird to migrate vast distances.

at the Port Hedland saltworks. They feed on marine worms, molluscs, insects and crustaceans.

Two similar sandpipers – the dunlin (*C. alpina*) and the stilt sandpiper (*Micropalama himantopus*) – occasionally visit Australia.
Scientific name: *Calidris ferruginea*

BROAD-BILLED SANDPIPER
The broad-billed sandpiper looks like the sanderling (page 173) and is often mistaken for it, though it is a little smaller, at 16–18 cm. It has double white eyebrows and its bill curves slightly downward at the tip.

It is a common migrant to northern Australia, with large concentrations occurring in some areas of Port Hedland, Western Australia, and the Gulf of Carpentaria, Queensland. It is similar in its habits to the curlew sandpiper (this page).
Scientific name: *Limicola falcinellus*

RUFF
From September to April the ruff is a regular visitor to Australia, but in very small numbers and in widely scattered locations. It gathers on muddy freshwater swamps, estuaries or sewage farms and mainly forages for worms, crustaceans, spiders and insects.

In their nonbreeding plumage both males and females have dark brown feathers edged with buff on their back, and a rather uniform greyish brown breast. At about 20 cm long, the female is much smaller than the male, which is about 32 cm long.

■ CURLEW SANDPIPER
The curlew sandpiper breeds in the high Arctic tundra, flying south to Australian shores during August.

Ruffs breed in northern Eurasia, from Scandinavia to far north-eastern Siberia. At breeding time males develop plumes on the crown and sides of their head; they can erect these plumes to form a sort of neck ruff, and this feature probably accounts for their common name.

Their genus name, *Philomachus*, is derived from Greek and means 'battle-loving', and their species name, *pugnax*, is Latin for 'pugnacious'.
Scientific name: *Philomachus pugnax*

RUDDY TURNSTONE ◼

The turnstone gets its name from its habit of turning over stones and other debris in its never-ending search for food. It is a marine wader, usually frequenting rocky shores, but it is sometimes also found in grassy paddocks and estuaries and along sandy or muddy shores, especially where there are mussels and cockles living. Turnstones are opportunistic feeders, commonly taking fly larvae, sandhoppers, gastropods and barnacles, but they also feed on eggs, meat from carcasses, and even bread.

When it is not breeding, this dumpy 22–24 cm-long wader has a brownish back and breast band, a black and white harlequin facial pattern, short orange legs and a short, wedge-shaped bill. During the breeding season its back and wing coverts turn chestnut orange. In flight it reveals a broad white wing stripe, a white rump and a white tail.

The ruddy turnstone occurs on most Australian coasts and is widespread and common on the islands of the Great Barrier Reef, and on Lord Howe and Norfolk Islands.

These birds seem to have two separate routes into Australia, some of them entering north-western Australia from Asia and the others flying across the Pacific Ocean into eastern Australia. They begin to arrive in September and return northwards in March and April.
Scientific name: *Arenarea interpres*

RUFF PLAY

Once in their breeding finery, male ruffs gather at display grounds, known as leks. A lek is a slightly raised stretch of ground, perhaps 20 metres square, that the males occupy to establish territories and attract females. Within a group of male ruffs there are usually two types: resident males, which defend a territory they occupy almost continuously; and marginal males, which have no territory but stay at the lek's edge.

Displays among males consist of ritualised aggression, including the raising of head plumes and neck ruffs, running and wing flapping, and sometimes overt threats and fights. Within the lek, most top-ranking residents hold a territory approximately 30–50 cm across. Rarely do they lose this, and these birds are the most successful in acquiring a mate.

Females visit the lek for short periods. When they arrive, the resident males squat motionless. The female chooses the first male that moves, touching him gently on the ruff and inviting mating by crouching down. After mating, the female leaves and begins the task of constructing a nest and rearing a brood.

◼ RUDDY TURNSTONE
As their name suggests, turnstones are continually turning over stones and seaweed with their broad, strong bills in search of small crustaceans and sandhoppers taking cover beneath.

PHALAROPES

Unlike most waders, phalaropes spend much of their lives at sea, where they often swim in large flocks feeding on krill. All three species of this family visit Australia, though it is not their main summer habitat. While the red-necked phalarope (*Phalaropus lobatus*), which is only 18–19 cm long, is an annual visitor, the 20–22 cm grey phalarope (*P. fulicaria*) and the 22–24 cm Wilson's phalarope (*Steganopus tricolor*) are stragglers that have strayed from the main migration.

Phalaropes are excellent swimmers and each of their toes is lobed to aid in swimming. When they are floating in the shallow water of wetlands or estuaries, they spin as they feed, probably to stir up food particles, which they then pick from the surface with their needle-like bills.

Compared with other waders, they have a small head, a long neck and a wide body. In Australia these birds are usually seen in their pale grey and white nonbreeding plumage.
Family: Phalaropodidae

A SWIMMING WADER
Phalaropes are the only truly aquatic waders. The grey phalarope (*Phalaropus fulicaria*) spends much of its life at sea, far from its Arctic breeding grounds.

DISTRIBUTION

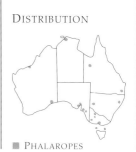

◼ PHALAROPES

175

DISTRIBUTION

■ COMB-CRESTED JACANA

COMB-CRESTED JACANA

Jacanas, or lotus birds, are a small family of highly specialised waders with long legs, extraordinarily long toes and long, straight claws. These elongated toes enable jacanas to walk about on waterlily pads and other water weeds. They need a good supply of aquatic vegetation to obtain their staple diet of insects and seeds and to build their nests.

Of the seven species worldwide, only the comb-crested jacana

(*Irediparra gallinacea*) lives in Australia, where it usually frequents swamps and lagoons in eastern and northern parts of the country, and less commonly in the south. It is a black and white bird with yellow tinges on its face and lower throat and a reddish pink comb on its forehead. At 24–27 cm long, the females are larger than the 20–21 cm males.

The comb-crested jacana breeds during the wetter times of year,

females usually mating with several males. Males build floating nests from aquatic plants and females usually lay three or four eggs in a nest. The eggs are golden and look as if black syrup has been drizzled over them, giving them superb camouflage. Each male incubates his eggs for four weeks. When danger threatens, he conceals the nest and eggs by treading the nest down so that it sinks and the eggs are touching the water. Although the chicks can run and swim as soon as they have dried off after hatching, the male cares for them for two or three weeks. If the chicks sense danger, they may climb under their father's wings and be ferried to safety.

Comb-crested jacanas are usually sedentary and are weak fliers, but they are capable of long-distance movements if their wetland homes dry out, forcing them to go in search of new territory.
Family: Jacanidae

WALKING ON WATER
The long-legged, long-toed comb-crested jacana is sometimes called the lilytrotter because it picks its way delicately across lily pads. Another name for this species is the Jesus Christ bird, because from a distance it can appear to be walking on water.

STONE-CURLEWS

DISTRIBUTION

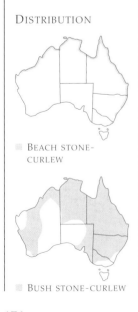

■ BEACH STONE-CURLEW

■ BUSH STONE-CURLEW

Stone-curlews, or thick-knees as they are also known, are terrestrial and coastal waders with large heads, large, staring eyes, robust bills and quite long, strong legs with thick knees. Males are slightly bigger than females and have longer legs, but their plumage is identical.

Like plovers, they move in short runs and stops. They can run fast but are reluctant to fly. They often stand motionless with their head drawn into their shoulders and, when threatened, run away in a crouched position.

These birds usually breed in spring in the south and during the wet season in the north, and they probably pair for life. During the breeding season both males and females dance and call mournfully. Females lay two or three eggs in a scrape on the ground. Both parents incubate the eggs and care for the

chicks. Of the nine species of stone-curlew that occur worldwide, only two live in Australia.

Australian stone-curlews are sedentary and, when not breeding, are gregarious. For most of the day they shelter in shaded areas and are generally silent. From dusk to dawn they feed on insects, crabs, small reptiles and mammals, and sometimes vegetable matter. At night, especially by moonlight, they often call with an eerie wailing sound.
Family: Burhinidae

BEACH STONE-CURLEW
A large wader, the beach stone-curlew is 54–56 cm long with striking black, white and olive brown patterning on its wings and head and a substantial black bill, which is sometimes yellow at the base. Its underparts are a sandy grey, grading to a white belly. A broad black band

runs through its eyes and curves down the sides of its neck, and its eyebrows and throat are white. Its wings have dark brown shoulders and distinctive white wing bars. It has greenish yellow legs.

Beach stone-curlews are found on reefs near islands and sandy beaches with extensive mangrove-backed sand flats. During the day they usually rest on shaded foreshores or among mangrove trees, emerging at night to forage on the tidal sand and mud flats, where they feed on crabs and various other marine invertebrates. Their call is a squeaky whistling cry.

They breed from October to January. Females lay one or two eggs into a scrape on the sand or shingle beneath a shrub just above the high-tide mark. Little is known about their parenting habits.
Scientific name: Esacus neglectus

BUSH STONE-CURLEW

The bush stone-curlew, also known as the bush thick-knee, is widespread throughout the lightly timbered open woodland, forest and coastal plains of Australia. In northern Queensland it has adapted well to urbanisation and breeds freely in parklands, near golf courses and cemeteries, and sometimes even in bushy gardens. Grey and brown, with some black and white patterning, these birds are remarkably well camouflaged in their habitat.

Outside the breeding season these large waders, which are 54–59 cm long, may form small flocks and wander over large areas in search of food but, with the advent of the breeding season, they become territorial and form breeding pairs. At this time the birds call throughout the night, sometimes in chorus, with a series of mournful whistles and screams, rising in pitch and ending with several staccato notes.

Breeding generally takes place in spring, but may occur at any time from June to December. The nest is usually on the ground and the clutch consists of two or three eggs, which take 23 days to incubate. The young remain with the parents for up to five months. When the chicks are young the parents will attack an intruder with outstretched wings, often growling and hissing.

Scientific name: *Burhinus grallarius*

BUSH STONE-CURLEW
Stone-curlews live, feed and nest on the ground, which makes them vulnerable to being preyed on by foxes and feral cats. When threatened, the bush stone-curlew stands still, or stretches itself out close to the ground.

OYSTERCATCHERS

The long, straight bill of the oystercatcher is adapted for opening bivalve shells, chiselling and prising limpets and gastropods from rocks and dismembering crustaceans. These waders also eat marine worms, insect larvae and other invertebrates. Each bird is a specialist, feeding on a particular food and opening shells with its bill either by hammering them until they break open or swiftly stabbing through the shell-closing muscle and then prising the two halves apart. Individuals use either one or the other method – never both.

Oystercatchers are one of the few waders to feed their offspring, and in doing so they pass on their dietary preferences and foraging techniques to them – which is extremely important, since their feeding habits are so specialised.

During the breeding season, oystercatchers are territorial and nest in solitary pairs. Although copulation often takes place without any preliminaries, courting pairs engage in an exaggerated form of display flight, known as butterfly flight. In the early stages of courtship communal 'piping' ceremonies, in which birds make high-pitched piping notes, play a part in the display.

Oystercatchers probably remain paired for life. Unlike most waders, when they are not breeding they live in loosely knit family groups, which may join up with other groups to form large flocks.

There are 21 oystercatcher species throughout the world, two of which are endemic to Australia.

Family: Haematopodidae

PIED OYSTERCATCHER

Pied oystercatchers are noisy black and white birds, about 42–45 cm long, with sturdy pink or orange-red legs, an elongated reddish bill and conspicuous red eye rings. Both sexes are alike in plumage, but the females are slightly larger than the males. In flight their white wing bar is conspicuous.

These birds are found all around the Australian coast on beaches and sand dunes, especially in areas with extensive intertidal mud flats. They are most abundant in Victoria, South Australia and Tasmania.

Pied oystercatchers are extremely sedentary, and individuals usually establish their breeding territory within a few kilometres of their birthplace. Most adults do not breed until they are six years old.

Scientific name: *Haematopus longirostris*

SOOTY OYSTERCATCHER
Its sooty black plumage, red bill and pink legs make this oystercatcher immediately recognisable.

SOOTY OYSTERCATCHER

The sooty oystercatcher, also called the black oystercatcher, is found along the coast, usually within 50 metres of the shoreline. It is 40–52 cm long, and looks like the pied oystercatcher, except that its plumage is completely black. It usually feeds and roosts on rocky platforms and generally breeds on offshore islands.

Sooty oystercatchers do not reach maturity until they are as much as three or four years old. After fledging, juveniles remain with their parents for up to nine months and then disperse to other areas.

Scientific name: *Haematopus fuliginosus*

DISTRIBUTION

PIED OYSTERCATCHER

SOOTY OYSTER-CATCHER

177

DISTRIBUTION

■ BLACK-WINGED STILT

■ RED-NECKED AVOCET

■ BANDED STILT

■ BLACK-WINGED STILT
Stilts have extremely long legs. They wade through shallow water, like this black-winged stilt, pecking at scraps of food on the surface, or just below.

STILTS AND AVOCETS

Seven species of stilt and avocet are found worldwide; three live in Australia, and two of these – the banded stilt and the red-necked avocet – live nowhere else. They are fairly large black and white waders with webbed feet and slender bills, necks and legs. Stilts have straight bills while those of avocets are upcurved. The sexes resemble one another, except that males are generally larger and the female avocet's bill tends to be shorter than the male's and more curved.

Outside the breeding season these gregarious waders often form flocks of thousands, and they breed in loose colonies. The Australian species are nomadic, and may move considerable distances in response to periods of drought or rain.
Family: Recurvirostridae

BLACK-WINGED STILT ■
The black-winged stilt, sometimes called the white-headed stilt or pied stilt, is an elegant, easily identifiable species with a black and white body, long reddish pink legs and a slender long black bill. It grows to about 33–37 cm long. In flight its legs trail behind its tail. It is quite common in wetlands on the mainland, but it reaches Tasmania only as a vagrant.

In Australia black-winged stilts generally breed from early August to April – depending on rainfall – in shallow, open freshwater wetlands. Males and females together build a platform nest of dry waterweed lined with vegetation, usually on a small island in shallow water.

Birds pair for the season, and sometimes for several. Both parents incubate two to four eggs for about 25 days. When the nest or the young are threatened, black-winged stilts may feign injury to distract a predator, and colony members may yap in chorus or perform aerobatics to repel the intruder. After hatching, chicks are able to leave the nest immediately, but they remain with the parents for another month.

Once the breeding season is over these stilts tend to flock. In the coastal wetlands of the Northern Territory and Queensland, numbers rise dramatically during this time. Those from inland areas disperse to coastal salt marshes and estuaries.
Scientific name: *Himantopus himantopus*

RED-NECKED AVOCET ■
The red-necked avocet is restricted to Australia. It is fairly common in wetlands, gathering in large flocks in the nonbreeding season in coastal areas and on flooded salt lakes. Up to 95 000 birds have been seen at Lake Eyre in South Australia. During droughts they usually move to coastal wetlands and swamps.

The red-necked avocet is black and white, 40–48 cm long, with a chestnut neck and head and long, slender, greyish blue legs that project beyond its tail when it flies. It has a slender, black, upcurved bill, which it sweeps from side to side to capture the larvae of insects and crustaceans that swim in the water or become stuck in the mud. Avocets also feed in deeper water, where they swim and up-end themselves like ducks.

Avocets breed mainly beside shallow water. Their nests are a scrape in the ground lined with vegetation. They breed within two weeks of heavy rain but, as conditions are variable, breeding may occur only at intervals of many years.
Scientific name: *Recurvirostra novaehollandiae*

BANDED STILT
This stilt is endemic to Australia. It breeds when inland salt lakes fill and the brine shrimps on which the young stilts are fed are plentiful. This happens only sporadically.

Banded stilts living on the coast seem to know when there is rain in their breeding habitat, and gather en masse to migrate inland. About two weeks after the rain has begun, they are incubating their eggs. They breed in colonies of thousands of birds: 20 000 nests were once recorded at Lake Ballard in Western Australia.

■ RED-NECKED AVOCET
After rain, this avocet makes its nest on bare ground – a scrape lined with plant matter. This bird's upturned bill distinguishes it from its relatives, the stilts.

In its nonbreeding plumage, the banded stilt, which is 35–43 cm long, is similar in appearance to the black-winged stilt, except that it has no black on its head, nape or back. In its breeding plumage, it has a broad chestnut band on its breast.
Scientific name: *Cladorhynchus leucocephalus*

THE WONDERS OF MIGRATION

Of the five million shorebirds that migrate from Alaskan and Siberian breeding grounds each year, some two million fly to Australia. Most stay from August to April, settling on the coast of Arnhem Land and the Gulf of Carpentaria, the north-western coast between Port Hedland and Broome, or the south-eastern coast.

Some of these birds fly amazing distances without feeding. Curlew sandpipers, for instance, fly as far as 3600 kilometres nonstop from the Malay Peninsula to north-western Australia.

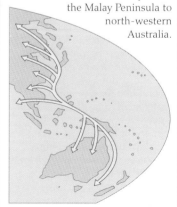

PLOVERS, DOTTERELS AND LAPWINGS

Members of this large family of small to medium-sized waders are mostly terrestrial waders inhabiting open areas. They generally have compact bodies, big eyes and relatively short bills, sometimes ending in a thick tip. Their markings are often bold. In most species the sexes look alike.

They are mainly surface feeders, typically foraging with a run-pause-peck action, sometimes vibrating one foot against the ground to disturb prey. Plovers and dotterels live on marine worms, molluscs, insects and crustaceans, but also take maggots from carcasses. In inland areas, lapwings feed mainly on insects.

There are about 40 plover and dotterel species worldwide, 14 of which live in or visit Australia. Most occur in the tropical regions and are sedentary, but some travel long distances, both within Australia and overseas. Of the 24 lapwing species worldwide, two are endemic to Australia.
Family: Charadriidae

BLACK-FRONTED DOTTEREL

The black-fronted dotterel is endemic to Australia. It is small, at 16–18 cm, with long wings and a short tail. Its crown and upper parts are brown with dark and pale streaks and it has a chestnut shoulder patch. Across its white face and undercarriage it has two broad black bands, one passing through its eyes and across its forehead and the other across its breast. It has a red, black-tipped bill, pinkish legs and coral eye rings. During its buoyant, butterfly-like flight it shows a prominent white wing stripe.

This is a common and widespread species in Australia, found near wetlands, lakes and dams but rare along the seashore. It is usually sedentary, but during droughts it moves to more permanent wetlands near the coasts.

Black-fronted dotterels usually occur singly or in pairs, but in winter loose flocks of up to 100 individuals may gather to feed on molluscs, crustaceans, flies, ants and sometimes seeds. They often vibrate one foot in the mud to stir up the little creatures on which they feed.

Black-fronted dotterels usually breed in Australia from September to February, but sometimes later. The female lays three or four eggs. Both sexes share in building a nest and incubating and tending the young. If disturbed at the nest, they

■ BLACK-FRONTED DOTTEREL
The female black-fronted dotterel lays her eggs in a shallow scrape, often on the open ground, not far from water.

use a range of tricks, including distraction displays and feigned wing injury, to lure the intruder away.
Scientific name: *Elseyornis melanops*

PACIFIC GOLDEN PLOVER

The Pacific golden plover is a dumpy bird 23–26 cm long. In its nonbreeding plumage it has a golden brown speckled back with paler underparts. It is a strong flier and can migrate long distances without stopping. From its Arctic breeding grounds, it travels to north-eastern Africa, southern Asia and Australasia.

These birds arrive in Australia in August, and are mostly found on the east coast from southern Queensland to Tasmania. They are quite common in coastal wetlands, and on the cays of the Great Barrier Reef. They fly north in March, by which time most have acquired their gold and black breeding plumage.
Scientific name: *Pluvialis fulva*

GREY PLOVER

The grey plover, or black-bellied plover, has one of the widest wintering ranges of any wader and is a strong migratory flier. It breeds in the Arctic tundra from north-western Russia to eastern Canada.

It is a regular migrant to Australia, where it is found almost exclusively on coastal mud flats between the tide levels, roosting at high tide on sandy beaches and spits. It is quite common on the northern, western and southern coasts.

The grey plover is easily confused with the Pacific golden plover (this page) but, at 27–31 cm, it is slightly larger. It is also greyer, and has a bigger head and larger eyes. During the breeding season, it has striking black, white and grey plumage.
Scientific name: *Pluvialis squatarola*

HOODED PLOVER ■

This wader is 19–23 cm long, and is black, brown and grey above and white below, with pinkish legs, a black hood and throat with a white collar, red eye rings and a black-tipped red bill. In the south-east it occurs on beaches. In south-western Australia it also frequents inland and coastal salt lakes.

In the winter in south-eastern Australia, these birds gather in small groups in the salt and freshwater lakes behind the dunes. In Western Australia, flocks of up to several hundred birds sometimes fly inland to saltpans and temporary lakes.

Hooded plovers usually nest on beaches above the high-tide mark or in sand dunes, often among pied

■ BLACK-FRONTED DOTTEREL

■ PACIFIC GOLDEN PLOVER

■ GREY PLOVER

■ HOODED PLOVER

■ HOODED PLOVER
The rare hooded plover nests on a beach. When disturbed, it leaves the nest, returning only when the danger is past, so that the eggs or chicks are left vulnerable to predators such as ravens or gulls.

■ RED-CAPPED PLOVER
If disturbed at its nest, the red-capped plover adopts various tactics to lure the intruder away. Sometimes it spreads both wings and drags them along the ground, feigning injury.

DISTRIBUTION

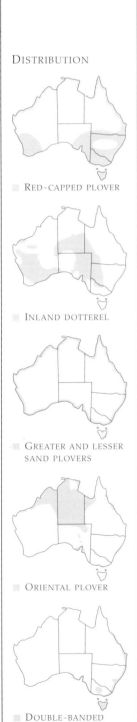

■ RED-CAPPED PLOVER

■ INLAND DOTTEREL

■ GREATER AND LESSER SAND PLOVERS

■ ORIENTAL PLOVER

■ DOUBLE-BANDED PLOVER

oystercatchers. The oystercatchers provide a useful distraction, chasing would-be predators away.

The hooded plover is endemic to Australia, but scientists estimate that there are only about 1800 of the species left. Its strongholds are Tasmania, southern Victoria and south-western Australia. In New South Wales it is listed as vulnerable and rare. It is unfortunate that the hooded plover's breeding season – August to February – coincides with the time when holiday-makers are liable to disrupt nesting.
Scientific name: *Thinornis rubricollis*

RED-CAPPED PLOVER ■
The red-capped plover is a small endemic species that breeds through-out coastal and most of southern inland Australia. It is common along seashores, beaches and estuaries, and large numbers occur inland when salt lakes flood. Although it seldom makes long-distance migra-tions, flocks may move to the coast when the inland dries out and then return to breed when conditions improve. This bird may also breed in various other habitats, from sandy beaches and salt marshes to the shorelines of wetlands and dams.

The red-capped plover is 14–16 cm long and brownish in colour. The male has a rufous crown and nape and a white breast, forehead and eyebrows. Its bill and feet are black. The female has very little rufous about its head and its beak and its legs are paler than the male's.
Scientific name: *Charadrius ruficapillus*

INLAND DOTTEREL ■
The inland, or Australian, dotterel is endemic to mainland Australia but does not occur in Tasmania. It is 19–23 cm long, with a buff back, a chestnut belly, a black band through its eyes and over its head and a Y-shaped black collar on its chest.

This species often congregates, far from water, in small flocks in open

country – usually in the arid and semi-arid southern half of the continent. It appears to feed on succulent plants during the day and on insects at night.

It may breed at any time, mainly in response to rain, and in favourable conditions may raise two broods in a year. The female lays three or four eggs in a shallow scrape in the ground ringed with pebbles. Both the parents incubate the eggs for 25–28 days and care for the young.
Scientific name: *Charadrius australis*

GREATER AND LESSER SAND PLOVERS
Two other migrants to Australian coasts are the greater sand plover (*Charadrius leschenaultii*), found mainly on the west coast, and the lesser sand plover (*C. mongolus*), which predominates in the east.

The two species are similar, except that the greater sand plover is paler and has a longer bill and legs. In their nonbreeding plumage they have grey-brown upper parts and white underparts, while in breeding plumage they have a bright chestnut and black head and breast. At

■ INLAND DOTTEREL
The distinctive Y-shaped black collar on the inland dotterel's breast makes this bird easy to identify. This is a gregarious, nomadic species.

22–25 cm, the greater sand plover is slightly larger than the lesser sand plover, which is 18–21 cm long.
Scientific name: *Charadrius* spp.

ORIENTAL PLOVER
Oriental plovers breed in Mongolia and northern China and arrive on the northern coasts of Australia in September, leaving between February and April. Up to 30 000 birds have been recorded in the Broome to Port Hedland area of Western Australia, and smaller numbers in the North-ern Territory. They feed on insects at night on open grasslands and recently burnt woodlands.

They look like the greater sand plover (this page) and are the same size, but have longer legs. Breeding colours are also slightly different, the male having a black line between its chestnut breast and white belly. The female lacks this line and its throat is pale buff rather than white.
Scientific name: *Charadrius veredus*

DOUBLE-BANDED PLOVER
This is the only Australian migrant plover that does not come from the northern hemisphere. It migrates from New Zealand, arriving in Australia between February and April and departing in July and August. It is a common coastal plover, especially in south-eastern Australia, and it returns to the same wintering sites year after year.

In nonbreeding plumage this bird resembles the lesser sand plover (this page) except for its finer bill and slightly smaller legs. Males are larger than females and they start their moult into breeding plumage much earlier, usually in May. Both develop two breast bands across their white underparts – the upper one blackish and the lower one brownish – but the male's upper band is broader than the female's and his lower one is chestnut brown rather than the orange-brown of the female.
Scientific name: *Charadrius bicinctus*

RED-KNEED DOTTEREL

Australia's endemic red-kneed dotterel is aquatic in its feeding and breeding habits, and sometimes swims. It lives in freshwater wetlands throughout Australia, feeding in mud, sand or shallow water. It flushes out aquatic invertebrates by stirring the mud or water with one foot, then pecking its prey from the surface. A gregarious species, it occurs in loose flocks of up to 3000, but is often seen singly or in pairs.

It is 17–19 cm long and has greenish brown upper parts and white underparts, a blackish cap extending down to form a broad breast band, and long reddish legs. Its back, upper wing coverts and central tail feathers are white, and in flight it is the only plover to show white on the trailing edges of its inner flight feathers. Its fairly long, thin bill is pinkish red with a black tip.

Between August and January the female lays usually four eggs in a depression in the ground, which is lined with vegetation and may be quite large. Both sexes share in territorial defence, incubation and care of the young. When danger threatens the parents utter an alarm call and the young may swim away.
Scientific name: *Erythrogonys cinctus*

LAPWINGS

Lapwings are large black and white waders. During the breeding season they are aggressive, defending their territory against their own kind and attacking any predator that comes close to their nest. Nests are a scrape on the ground, usually lined with vegetation. The female lays between two and four eggs that are incubated by both parents. The young can fly within three to four weeks.

Lapwings usually breed in open habitat in solitary pairs or loose groups. When not breeding they are

■ LAPWING
Yellow facial wattles give the masked plover its name. It is common in open grasslands and often calls noisily.

gregarious, often moving in flocks to coastal areas. There are two lapwing species in Australia.

The masked plover (*Vanellus miles*) is 30–37 cm long and has a black crown and yellow facial wattles. It is common in open grassy regions and calls loudly when alarmed. It is also known as the spur-winged plover because it has a yellow spur on each wing. The northern subspecies has a larger wattle and less black on its neck and shoulders than the southern form. The masked plover generally breeds between May and July and pairs stay together for life. They are sedentary, but nonbreeding flocks form between August and November.

The banded plover (*V. tricolor*), found only in Australia, prefers the drier open southern regions, though it also occurs in grassy coastal districts. It is 25–29 cm long. It has a black crown, a white throat and underparts, white eye stripes and a black breast band extending up each side of its neck to its face. It has yellow eyes and a pale yellow, black-tipped bill, above which is a small red wattle. It breeds in winter and spring and after rain. This species is probably nomadic, moving on when conditions become too dry or flooded.
Scientific name: *Vanellus* spp.

PRATINCOLES

Pratincoles are short-legged waders, though they can run fast if necessary. They inhabit flat open places such as flood plains, river deltas, treeless pastures and ploughed fields, often near water. Their long wings and deeply forked tails equip them for fast, graceful flight. Most feed on insects, often at dawn and dusk, by aerial hawking.

They tend to nest in colonies, the male and female both incubating the two or three eggs for about 18 days. Unusually among waders, they feed their offspring by regurgitating food onto the ground for the first few weeks of the chicks' life, until they can feed themselves. The chicks are able to fly after about four weeks.

Two species occur in Australia. The Australian pratincole (*Stiltia isabella*) is more of a ground-dweller than many pratincoles and has longer legs, and its tail is square rather than forked. It is 19–24 cm long and has a sandy rufous head, neck, upper parts and breast, grading to cream on the chin and throat and to dark brown on the lower breast and belly.

Its underwings are black and its short, down-curving bill is red at the base and black at the tip.

These pratincoles live in the interior, where they do not seek shade in the heat of the day but pant and drink water often. Outside the breeding season they may form loose flocks of hundreds or even thousands.

They breed on the blacksoil plains of north-western New South Wales and south-western Queensland. They lay usually two eggs on bare ground, sometimes surrounding them with pebbles or rabbit droppings. Both parents incubate the eggs for 21 days and then guard the chicks. Chicks may use a burrow, usually a rabbit burrow, as a shelter when danger threatens. In the wet season the Australian pratincole migrates to Indonesia and New Guinea for three or four months.

POUNCING ON PREY
Unlike most members of this family, the Australian pratincole (*Stiltia isabella*) relies very much on its long legs for capturing its prey.

The oriental pratincole (*Glareola maldivarum*) is slightly larger and plumper than the Australian species and has a forked tail. Its colouring is similar except for fawn underwings. It breeds in central and southern Asia but is common in northern Australia during November and December. Flocks of several thousands gather – particularly before storms, when they perform aerobatic displays.
Family: Glareolidae

GULLS AND TERNS

Skuas, jaegers and noddies, as well as gulls and terns, belong to this group. Gulls and terns, in particular, are common throughout the world. This is a family of predominantly coastal birds that have white, grey and black plumage, long, generally pointed wings, and webbed feet for swimming. The larger skuas and jaegers also bear strong, hooked claws. All birds in this group belong to the order Charadriiformes.

Both gulls and terns are gregarious birds, often roosting in large flocks and breeding in huge, noisy colonies on offshore islands along the coast or on isolated inland lakes.

There are about 45 gull species, three of which are resident in Australia. Of the world's 42 tern species, 14 breed in the Australian region. Other gull and tern species occasionally visit Australian waters.

Gulls are robust birds with broad, pointed wings and a short, squarish tail. Adults are usually grey or black above and white below, with legs and large, hooked bills of red, black or yellow, and the two sexes are similar in appearance. Young birds are mottled grey or brown. Many gull species do not grow adult plumage for several years.

Gulls have strong legs that are adapted for both walking and swimming. Their diet includes fishes, crustaceans, offal and food scraps discarded by humans. Gulls breed in colonies, building nests from materials such as seaweeds, grasses and sticks, or making a shallow scrape in the ground.

Terns are slender and less robust than gulls, with comparatively weak legs and a slim, straight bill. They have a distinctively forked tail and long, slender, pointed wings.

Terns dive onto small fishes or pluck them from the surface of the water, and they also feed on insects that they snatch from the air. Some tern species that live inland feed almost exclusively on small land-dwelling vertebrates. Unlike gulls, terns seldom scavenge for food, and they are not as aggressive or as adaptable as gulls.

With the exception of noddies, terns rarely rest on water. Most terns' nests are bare or only sparsely lined.

Two tropical terns that breed on Lord Howe and Norfolk islands build no nests at all. The white tern (*Gygis alba*) lays her single egg in the notch or curve of a tree, and the grey ternlet (*Procelsterna cerulea*) lays one egg in a rock crevice. Stragglers of these two species are occasionally seen in eastern Australian waters.
Family: Laridae

SKUAS ■

Skuas are found worldwide. They have hooked bills and are aggressive, formidable hunters that prey on small sea birds, especially prions and storm-petrels, which they often harass to disgorge their food. They patrol the nesting colonies of sea birds, stealing unguarded eggs and chicks, and also eat a wide variety of fishes, squids and carrion.

SEA SWALLOWS
Terns are often called sea swallows because of their forked tail and slender, pointed wings. The largest species is the Caspian tern, *Sterna caspia*.

Two species, the southern skua (*Catharacta antarctica*) and the South Polar skua (*C. maccormicki*) occur regularly in Australian waters. A third species, the great skua (*C. skua*) breeds on subantarctic islands, and has been recorded as a vagrant.

All skuas are powerful, robust birds, 53–65 cm long, with broad wings and wedge-shaped tails. They are generally dark brown, but the South Polar skua undergoes an intermediate phase of light plumage.

Skuas pair for life. The southern skua and the South Polar skua breed in Antarctica and on subantarctic islands. Here they nest in loose colonies, each pair defending its breeding site against intruders, including other skuas. Their nest is little more than a scrape in the ground. The female lays two olive brown blotched eggs, but only one chick usually survives.

After breeding, skuas disperse, and many immature birds travel to the warmer coastal waters of southern Australia and New Zealand, attracted to fishing trawlers where scraps and offal are thrown overboard while the catch is being hauled in and cleaned.
Scientific name: *Catharacta* spp.

JAEGERS

Jaegers come to the southern hemisphere during their nonbreeding season. The Arctic jaeger (*Stercorarius parasiticus*), the pomarine jaeger (*S. pomarinus*) and the long-tailed jaeger (*S. longicaudus*) all migrate from their breeding grounds in the Arctic Circle and are usually present in Australian waters from around September to April.

DISTRIBUTION

■ SKUAS

■ JAEGERS

■ PACIFIC GULL

■ KELP GULL

■ SILVER GULL

■ SKUAS
During the breeding season, the great skua (*Catharacta skua*) defends its nest sites vigorously against intruders, particularly those of its own species.

Jaegers are slightly smaller than skuas, ranging in length from 41 cm to 51 cm. They are grey-brown above and mainly white below. All species have light, dark and intermediate colour phases. Adults jaegers sport elongated central tail feathers. Arctic jaegers have pointed ones, pomarine jaegers have rounded and twisted ones, and the tail feathers of the long-tailed jaeger are very long indeed.

Jaegers have long wings and are fast, agile fliers. They obtain much of their food by harassing other birds and often work in pairs, chasing gulls or other small sea birds until they disgorge any food they are carrying. The jaegers then catch the food as it falls. These powerful birds also take small birds, such as storm-petrels, on the wing, and steal the eggs and chicks of other sea birds. At their breeding grounds in the Arctic Circle, they feed on lemmings.

Jaegers pair for life. They do not nest in colonies. Nests are just a scrape in the ground, lined with grasses or lichen. The female lays three or four eggs, and both birds feed the chicks and defend their territory vigorously against intruders.
Scientific name: *Stercorarius* spp.

PACIFIC GULL

The only gull species endemic to Australia, the Pacific gull is common around Tasmania and the southern coastal mainland. Pacific gulls grow to about 63 cm long, making them one of the largest gulls in the world.

These gulls are usually seen singly or in pairs. Breeding pairs nest well away from each other and defend their territory vigorously until the young have fledged.

Juveniles have drab grey and brown feathers and take four years to acquire mature plumage. Adults are white with black wings and back and a black tail band that distinguishes them from the smaller kelp gull. Their yellow bill is tipped with red and their legs are yellow.

These gulls feed largely on fishes, shellfish and molluscs, which they split open by dropping them from a height onto a rocky surface. They pilfer eggs and young from other sea birds and scavenge offal and fragments of human food.
Scientific name: *Larus pacificus*

■ SILVER GULLS
Adaptable, quarrelsome scavengers, these gulls are found all around the coast. They are particularly drawn to the easy pickings from garbage bins alongside city beaches.

KELP GULL ■

The kelp gull is extremely common in New Zealand, but it was not officially recorded in Australia until the early 1940s. Since then it has become firmly established as a breeding species and is expanding its range rapidly.

It is similar in appearance to the endemic Pacific gull (this page) – indeed, juveniles of the two species are virtually indistinguishable from each other. At 58 cm long, however, the kelp gull is slightly smaller than the Pacific gull, and adults have a completely white tail and only a small red spot on the lower bill that fades in the nonbreeding season.

Kelp gulls form loose nesting colonies in the breeding season and also roost and feed in flocks. They eat mainly fishes and crustaceans, but they also survive by scavenging and stealing.
Scientific name: *Larus dominicanus*

SILVER GULL ■

The ubiquitous silver gull is perhaps the most familiar sea bird in Australia. Adults reach 40–43 cm in length, and their plumage is white with pale grey upperparts and black wing tips studded with white 'windows'. Their eye ring, bill and legs are deep red. Immature birds have mottled grey and brown upperparts. They do not acquire their adult plumage, with its striking red trimmings, until their second or third year.

Like many other gull species around the world, this quarrelsome native bird is extremely adaptable and is quick to exploit any available food source. It has become an omnivorous scavenger, visiting beaches, city parks and dumps to

feed on almost anything. It is this resourcefulness that has made the silver gull so abundant that it is regarded as a pest in many towns and cities; but away from human habitation, these birds forage more traditionally on fishes, crustaceans and other small marine animals. They live in coastal regions, and also venture inland along rivers and inhabit large lakes and marshes.

Silver gulls are gregarious and often form large flocks where there is a abundance of food or a convenient roosting site. They nest in colonies varying in size from only a few pairs to many thousands of birds.

The largest silver gull colony in New South Wales is on the Five Islands Nature Reserve off the Wollongong coast: over 50 000 pairs nest there annually. They build a saucer-shaped nest on the ground and line it with whatever is available, including rubbish. The female lays one to three eggs and both parents incubate and feed the young, which fledge at about four weeks.
Scientific name: *Larus novaehollandiae*

■ KELP GULL
The kelp gull looks like the Pacific gull, but it is slightly smaller and its tail is completely white.

salt gland

DRINKING SEA WATER
Sea birds such as the kelp gull have glands above their eyes that remove salt from their bloodstream, so that they can drink sea water and survive.

DISTRIBUTION

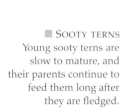

SOOTY TERNS
Young sooty terns are slow to mature, and their parents continue to feed them long after they are fledged.

LITTLE TERN

The little tern, with a body length of 25 cm, is Australia's smallest tern. This migratory shorebird, with a worldwide distribution, is a seasonal visitor along the northern and eastern coastlines of Australia. A small population breeds along the east coast in summer, and a larger population visits Australia but breeds in the northern hemisphere.

Little terns nest in small colonies on sandy beaches in shallow depressions in the sand, usually just above the high-water mark. Many sites have been destroyed by development or disturbed by beach users and off-road vehicles. Furthermore, foxes, cats, dogs and gulls often pilfer the little tern's eggs and chicks. These depredations reduced the Australian breeding population dramatically, but protective measures have recently improved breeding success.

In October, little terns engage in spectacular courtship flights above island habitats created solely for them. Spiralling in unison, they utter their high piping calls, and throughout summer they plunge headlong into shallow, sheltered water catching small fishes for their young.
Scientific name: *Sterna albifrons*

SOOTY TERN AND BRIDLED TERN

The sooty tern (*Sterna fuscata*) is 46 cm long with solid black upperparts, white underparts and a forked tail. It breeds in large, noisy colonies on islands off Australia's northern coasts. The female lays a single egg in a scrape in the ground. These terns do not breed until they are least four years old; often they are six to eight years old before raising young.

Little is known about these terns once they leave their breeding colonies. It is thought that they disperse widely through tropical

LITTLE TERN
Breeding little terns can be distinguished by their bright yellow bill; nonbreeding birds have a black bill.

and subtropical waters, spending months at a time at sea. They are partly nocturnal, often foraging at night, skimming the water surface for fishes, octopuses and plankton.

The bridled tern (*S. anaethetus*) is similar in appearance to the sooty tern but paler and brown above. It ranges over much the same area as the sooty tern and breeds in colonies on islands off northern Australia.
Scientific name: *Sterna* spp.

CASPIAN TERN

The Caspian tern has a large red bill and a shaggy black cap. This large tern, 53 cm long, is widespread and abundant throughout Asia, Africa, Europe, North America and New Zealand, as well as Australia. It lives beside both fresh and salt water, and in Australia is common around the coast and on inland rivers and lakes.

Caspian terns are not as gregarious as other terns and usually live singly or in pairs, although they do sometimes form small nesting colonies. They are largely fish-eaters, capturing small fishes by plunge-diving from a height of about 15 metres.
Scientific name: *Sterna caspia*

ROSEATE TERN

The roseate tern breeds on offshore islands around the western, northern and north-eastern coasts and is present in Australian waters all year. It ranges in size from 33 cm to 38 cm, and has a very pronounced forked tail and long white tail-streamers.

When in breeding plumage, the bird's underparts turn a faint pink and its black legs and bill turn red. Roseate terns breed in colonies. They make nests in the sand, which they sometimes line with vegetation.
Scientific name: *Sterna dougallii*

WHITE-FRONTED TERN

White-fronted terns nest in large colonies in New Zealand and on islands in Bass Strait. They disperse after breeding, and many visit the south-eastern coast of Australia.

The white-fronted tern is 35–43 cm long, with grey upperparts, white underparts, a black bill and legs, a forked tail, and a black cap that recedes outside the breeding season. It looks like the roseate tern (this page) but is common where roseate terns are seldom seen. It feeds by plunge-diving for small fishes.
Scientific name: *Sterna striata*

COMMON TERN

The common tern, 32–38 cm long, is abundant in the northern hemisphere. In Australia it is a nonbreeding migrant to the coastal northern and north-eastern mainland between October and March. These visitors are likely to have come from Siberia or northern China.

Nonbreeding adults and immature birds resemble the roseate tern, but the outer tail feathers of the common tern are darker. The common tern feeds in both marine and freshwater habitats, and has been seen taking insects from cultivated fields.
Scientific name: *Sterna hirundo*

GULL-BILLED TERN

The gull-billed tern reaches 35–43 cm in length, and is so called because of its large black bill and gull-like flight. It is found on every continent in the world and occurs throughout Australia, although it is not generally common.

These terns are migratory, travelling to inland lakes and marshes to breed in loose colonies. After the breeding season, which is influenced by weather conditions, populations disperse northwards in winter or southwards in summer. Small groups may be seen around salt or brackish waters near the coast; others may fly as far as New Guinea or Indonesia.

Unlike most terns, gull-billed terns never dive. Instead, they pluck fishes from the water surface while in flight, search for insects on the wing, or prey on terrestrial vertebrates such as small lizards and mice.
Scientific name: *Sterna nilotica*

CRESTED TERN

The crested tern is the most common and widespread of all Australian terns. It is a graceful bird, 46–49 cm long, with a long forked tail, long wings, a black cap and a yellow bill.

Crested terns are gregarious and nest in colonies on offshore islands. These colonies range in size from less than 20 pairs to thousands. They are noisy places, with birds announcing their comings and goings or defending their nest sites.

The crested tern's courtship flight is spectacular. Pairs fly in a mirror image of each other, wing tip to wing tip, with great speed and grace, often spiralling high into the air.

Crested terns are frequently seen on the margins of coastal estuaries and beach fronts, often in the company of silver gulls and other terns.
Scientific name: *Sterna bergii*

CRESTED TERNS

These terns first breed when they are two years old, following an elaborate, spiralling courtship flight.

ARCTIC TERN

This uncommon vagrant spends most of its life flying, covering about 32 000 kilometres a year. Its slender body, narrow, pointed wings and forked tail equip it for sustained flight. It breeds in the Arctic, but as soon as its chicks can fend for themselves it flies south and spends the northern winter in Antarctica and around subantarctic islands. It is rarely seen in Australian waters.
Scientific name: *Sterna paradisaea*

NODDIES

Noddies are tropical and subtropical terns that are widespread and common throughout the world's oceans. The common or brown noddy (*Anous stolidus*), the black noddy (*A. minutus*) and the lesser noddy (*A. tenuirostris*) inhabit Australian waters. These species range from 30 cm to 45 cm long. All three have dark brown, grey or black plumage and pale caps.

Noddies breed in large colonies on islands and coral cays, building their stick and seaweed nests in shrubs or on the ground. The female lays one egg, which is incubated by both parents. Noddies are so reluctant to abandon incubation that they can easily be caught by hand.

Noddies never dive for food; they prefer to seize their prey – fishes, sea jellies and large planktonic organisms – from the water surface.
Scientific name: *Anous* spp.

WHISKERED TERN AND WHITE-WINGED BLACK TERN

The whiskered tern (*Chlidonias hybridus*) is rarely seen on the coast but is found throughout most of mainland Australia. It is seen in Tasmania only as a vagrant. This gregarious bird lives in groups and nests in vegetation on inland lakes and in swamps, occasionally entering estuaries and inlets. Unlike most terns, it lines its nest with grasses.

The whiskered tern is about 24 cm long, with pale grey upperparts, and a short, slightly forked tail. In the breeding season it has a distinctive black cap, grey underparts and bright red legs and bill. At other times, its black cap is smaller and streaked with white, its underparts are white, and its legs and bill are black. These terns live almost entirely on insects and small vertebrates.

The white-winged black tern (*C. leucopterus*) is a nonbreeding migrant to bodies of fresh water around the northern coast. It has similar habits to the whiskered tern.
Scientific names: *Chlidonias* spp.

□ GULL-BILLED TERN
■ CRESTED TERN

▨ ARCTIC TERN

■ NODDIES
▨ WHISKERED TERN

▨ WHITE-WINGED BLACK TERN

■ NODDY
The common noddy (*Anous stolidus*) is the most widespread of the noddies. Common noddies are good swimmers, and large groups, called rafts, frequently rest or roost on the water. When a distant flock takes to the air it looks like a cloud of smoke.

PIGEONS AND DOVES

Pigeons and doves are plump land birds that have close, downy plumage. They eat seeds and fruits. They are a large, diverse group of birds that are found throughout the world except in the Arctic and Antarctic regions. Many of the 310 worldwide species occur in the tropics. Australia has 22 native species and three that are introduced.

There is little difference between pigeons and doves – the larger species are generally called pigeons while the smaller ones are called doves. Apart from the colourful tropical species, these birds are usually grey and brown. They belong to the sole extant family in the order Columbiformes.

■ LAUGHING TURTLEDOVE
A native of the Middle East, Africa, India and Russia, this dove was deliberately introduced into Western Australia in the nineteenth century. It is now quite common in the south-west corner of Western Australia.

Pigeons are characteristically plump, with a short neck and tail and a small head, although a few, such as the brown cuckoo-dove, are comparatively long and slender with long tails. They range in weight from 2.3 kg (the goura pigeon of New Guinea) to 30 grams (the Australian diamond dove). They vary widely in colouring, from dull brown and grey to brilliant green and purple, and some have iridescent plumage.

Most species feed on fruits or seeds or both, as well as the occasional invertebrate. Some are known as fruit-pigeons or fruit-doves because they process fruits without destroying the seeds, so that they are important dispersers of rainforest seeds (see box, 'Sowing the seed', page 191). Unlike many other birds, which can take only small amounts of water before having to raise their heads to swallow, pigeons are able to drink continuously.

Courtship and chick care
Most pigeons put on displays for courtship or defence. When they are courting, it is usually the male that displays. He faces the female, spreads his wings and tail slightly, then bows repeatedly, often cooing softly at the bottom of the bow. Many species also perform courtship flight displays. The male bird flies

up from a perch and, at the highest point, spreads his wings and tail and glides back down to the starting point. Pigeons in flight make a distinctive sound, clapping their rather stiff flight feathers together.

Many pigeon species breed at any time, particularly those living in the harsh inland, where they are dependent on weather conditions. Others breed between late winter and summer. Pigeon nests are usually flimsy platforms of twigs, and some species use the nests of other birds, if available. Depending on the habits of the species, nests may be placed on the ground, in the crown of a tree, on a cliff face or on a city building.

The usual clutch size is one or two cream or white eggs. When the young hatch they are blind and helpless and sparsely covered with down, but they develop quickly – in some ground-dwelling species that are at high risk from predators, lightly feathered chicks are able to flee the nest at two or three days old. Nevertheless, even when the chicks finally leave the nest their feathers are not fully developed and they must still be fed for some time.

Pigeons are unique in that both sexes produce food for their young. The crop, a pouch in the throat where food is stored before being digested, secretes highly nutritious

crop-milk, with which the adults feed their young. As the chicks grow, this is mixed with other foods.
Family: Columbidae

SPOTTED TURTLEDOVE ■
The introduced spotted turtledove occurs naturally from India to Indonesia, and entered Australia when specimens were deliberately released in Adelaide in 1881. It is now common around urban and rural areas on the east coast, and in Adelaide and Perth.

These birds may breed at any time of the year and often have two or three consecutive broods.
Scientific name: Streptopelia chinensis

LAUGHING TURTLEDOVE ■
Found throughout the Middle East, Africa, India and Russia, the laughing turtledove was brought to Western Australia in the 1860s. Its distribution spread following settlements along railway routes, and it is now common in gardens around the coast of Western Australian from Esperance on the southern coast to Geraldton on the western coast, and also around the inland town of Kalgoorlie.
Scientific name: Streptopelia senegalensis

ROCK DOVE
The introduced rock dove, or common street pigeon, is believed to have originated in the British Isles, the Mediterranean region and North Africa, and probably arrived in Australia with the First Fleet. Flocks were established in the Sydney region by the beginning of the nineteenth century, and the species is now in evidence almost everywhere there is human habitation.

In its natural environment, the rock dove nests in loose colonies on cliffs along the coast; nowadays, ledges on skyscrapers and all sorts of urban buildings have replaced coastal cliffs as nesting sites.
Scientific name: Columba livia

■ SPOTTED TURTLEDOVE
This introduced species is at home around towns and cities, where it eats mostly plant seeds and domestic animal feed.

A juvenile, pictured above with its parent, is mottled brown with only a few green feathers, but the adult's wings are a brilliant emerald green. At the right, an adult landing on its nest reveals its cinnamon underwings.

WHITE-HEADED PIGEON

Although it is predominantly a fruit-eating bird, the white-headed pigeon is not a typical fruit pigeon but a close relative of the rock dove (opposite page). It is 38–42 cm long, with a white or dirty white head and dark grey upperparts. In direct sunlight, its upperparts have a metallic green and purple sheen.

This pigeon is endemic to the east coast of Australia, inhabiting rainforest and wet eucalypt forest. It eats mainly fruits and berries, digesting whole fruits, including seeds.

Land clearance once threatened this species, but since the camphor laurel has become a popular shade and street tree the white-headed pigeon population has been making a recovery; these birds now also occur in agricultural areas and beside roads, where they often come down to the ground to forage on fallen fruits, seeds and grain.

White-headed pigeons are large but often difficult to see in dense habitat. When approached, they sit silently or leave the tree quietly, without the usual loud clapping of wings. They are more visible in open places, where they often perch on a conspicuous bare branch.

White-headed pigeons breed at any time of the year, but particularly between September and March. Their nest is a small twig platform. They usually nest in the forest understorey, although some nests have been found in open areas.
Scientific name: *Columba leucomela*

BROWN CUCKOO-DOVE

The brown cuckoo-dove, or brown pigeon, is a slender, plain brown bird, slightly paler below than above, with a long tail. It ranges from 38 cm to 44 cm long. Brown cuckoo-doves occur along the east

coast of Australia from Cape York to south of the Victorian border. They frequent forest edges, regrowth forest and other disturbed areas, but are never far from rainforest. Pairs or small parties can often be seen feeding on the edges of rainforest tracks. When disturbed they flutter only a short distance, unlike many other pigeons, which fly swiftly out of sight. They feed on the seeds of native and introduced plants, taking fallen fruits from the ground and fruits from trees, vines and shrubs. They balance with their tail when reaching for fruits on outer branches.

Because they prefer disturbed areas and feed on the fruits of introduced weeds, brown cuckoo-doves have fared well compared with rainforest pigeons, which have suffered from forest clearing.
Scientific name: *Macropygia amboinensis*

EMERALD DOVE ■

The emerald dove, also known as the green-winged pigeon, is widely distributed throughout India, southern Asia, the south-western Pacific and Australia. In Australia there are two populations of emerald doves, one in the Top End and the other on the east coast. These birds live in areas where there is dense cover and a relatively sparse ground layer

– for example, in rainforest, wet eucalypt forest and monsoon forest. They also inhabit disturbed areas such as the edges of scrubby creeks, forest remnants, lantana thickets and regrowth forest.

Mainly a ground-dwelling pigeon, the emerald dove takes most of its food from the forest floor but it roosts and nests in bushes and trees. It feeds on fallen seeds and fruits, and on those that it can pluck from low-growing plants. Occasionally these birds feed in trees, but they are not as acrobatic as the fruit-pigeons, and eat only fruits that are within easy reach of a sturdy perch.

This dove is small and plump, about 23–26 cm long, with a short tail. It is usually seen singly or in pairs. Juveniles are mottled brown in colour; adults are dusky brown with bright green wings that are cinnamon beneath.

Emerald doves are inconspicuous in dense forest, but they are quite common and easy to see around forest edges and tracks in the early morning or late in the afternoon. If startled, they quickly fly low into the cover of a bush. Emerald doves are skilful fliers and have no trouble negotiating dense vegetation to disappear rapidly.
Scientific name: *Chalcophaps indica*

■ COMMON
BRONZEWING
Despite having been a
popular bird for hunting
and eating during the
early days of European
settlement, the common
bronzewing is still found
in considerable numbers
throughout Australia.

COMMON BRONZEWING ■

The common or forest bronzewing is a plump pigeon that ranges from 30 cm to 35 cm in length. It is common and widespread throughout Australia, living in a variety of habitats, including eucalypt forest and woodland, mallee and heath.

These birds are large, but they are extremely well camouflaged. They have a brown to pinkish breast, a cream forehead and iridescent patches of bronze and green in their wings. Often their presence can be detected only by a low, resounding 'oom-oom-oom', repeated slowly over and over again. When they are approached, common bronzewings leave the ground with a noisy clapping of wings and fly swiftly to a safe perch in a tree, where they perch motionless, blending into the surroundings. They are perhaps most often seen when flushed from the sides of roads in country areas.

A largely terrestrial bird, the common bronzewing feeds mainly on the seeds of native and exotic grasses and acacias, which it collects from the ground. It also eats seeds from pastures and cereal crops. At harvest time these birds can be seen feasting on spilt grain beside silos and along roadsides.

This is one of the few native pigeons whose numbers have not suffered greatly from land clearance. Nesting traditionally required large tracts of native vegetation, but these pigeons have adapted well to the spread of agriculture, particularly in wheat-growing areas where some native vegetation remains.

Common bronzewings have also benefited from the building of dams, because they need to drink every day. Although sedentary, they will travel many kilometres to water during dry periods.

Scientific name: *Phaps chalcoptera*

BRUSH BRONZEWING

The brush bronzewing is found only in south-western and south-eastern Australia, including Tasmania and various islands, in areas with dense undergrowth, such as heathland, mallee and eucalypt forest. Many of these areas have been cleared for agriculture and urban development. As a result, the bronze brushwing's numbers have declined considerably since European settlement, though it is still common in areas where suitable habitat remains.

The bronze brushwing's range overlaps that of the very similar common bronzewing (this page). The brush bronzewing is a redder and slightly smaller bird, growing to 28–30 cm long. Where the two are found together, the brush bronzewing generally prefers the denser, moister habitats. Its call is slightly higher and less resonant than that of the common bronzewing.

■ CRESTED PIGEON
This bird of woodland and lightly timbered areas owes its name to its pointed crest of black feathers.

The brush bronzewing spends most of its time on the ground, where it forages for seeds. It is most active in the early morning and evening; in the heat of the day it rests in the shade.

Usually seen singly or in pairs, brush bronzewings are wary. When approached, they run quickly into dense vegetation and stand still, or fly a short distance before landing and running for cover.

Scientific name: *Phaps elegans*

FLOCK BRONZEWING

The flock bronzewing, or flock pigeon, is a large, plump, ground-dwelling pigeon that ranges from 28 cm to 31 cm long. It is reddish brown above and bluish grey beneath. Its distinctive facial markings of dull brown in the female and bold black and white in the male have earned it another common name – the harlequin bronzewing, or harlequin pigeon. Both male and female have a white forehead.

As its name suggests, this bird lives in large flocks that may contain thousands of individuals. It inhabits the arid grassy plains of northern and central Australia, and occurs in spinifex, saltbush and open mulga country. The flock bronzewing feeds on grass seeds, particularly those of Mitchell grass, and the Barkly Tableland supports most of today's population. Flocks are nomadic and disperse from the tableland to other regions, depending on conditions.

Flock bronzewings are vulnerable to habitat degradation, and their natural range has shrunk because large areas of land within it are now grazed by domestic and feral stock. They are most commonly seen as a dense cloud of birds, flying strongly and swiftly, with rapid wingbeats and a sound like heavy surf.

Scientific name: *Phaps histrionica*

CRESTED PIGEON ■

The familiar pigeon, with its finely pointed head crest of black feathers, is an unassuming presence in the parks and nature reserves of most Australian cities.

About 30–35 cm long, it has subtle grey plumage. Its wings are barred with black and adorned with iridescent green and purple patches. It has a red eye ring and dark pink legs. When they land, crested pigeons characteristically flick their tail briefly high above their body.

Crested pigeons are usually seen in pairs or in small groups of about six birds, but occasionally they gather in flocks of a hundred or more. When approached, they tend

DISTRIBUTION

■ COMMON
BRONZEWING

■ BRUSH BRONZEWING
■ FLOCK BRONZEWING

■ CRESTED PIGEON

to run rather than fly away, but when flushed out they fly with rapid, whistling wingbeats followed by a smooth glide on level wings. The whistle is generated by the shape of a single feather in each wing.

Crested pigeons feed on the ground on the seeds of native and introduced grasses and herbs, including those of Paterson's curse. They also eat green herbage and insects. They roost and nest in trees.

Crested pigeons thrive on farmlands where forest has been cleared and are prevalent in lightly timbered areas with a sparse understorey. They were once rare in coastal areas, but their range has now expanded to include most of mainland Australia.
Scientific name: *Ocyphaps lophotes*

SPINIFEX PIGEON

The spinifex pigeon, sometimes known as the plumed pigeon, is a small, orange-brown bird. It is 20–33 cm long and prettily marked with dark wing bars and a dark curved line over its breast. In flight it reveals the iridescent copper patches on its wings.

This pigeon can be identified by its long, pointed crest and its distinctive facial markings: a grey face with a bright red eye patch, highlighted by a black line above and a white one below extending to the chin. There are two distinct populations: one, with a rich reddish belly, lives to the west of the Kimberley; the other, with a white belly, is found to the east of the Kimberley.

Named for their most common habitat, these pigeons are often found in spinifex grassland, especially in areas where there are rocky ranges and outcrops. Well adapted to their arid environment, they are most active in the early morning and in the evening. In the heat of the day they rest in shallow scrapes in the shelter of a bush, grass tussock or rock. They feed on the ground on a wide variety of seeds from herbs, grasses and shrubs, and also glean the occasional insect.

Spinifex pigeons live in flocks, usually numbering six to ten birds but occasionally these groups swell to as many as 50 birds. The flocks are sedentary and, provided water is available, they occupy the same home range all year round.

Members travel within this range, feeding and drinking together. In the breeding season, the males become territorial and protective of their mate, and pairs spread out over the home range to nest.
Scientific name: *Geophaps plumifera*

 SPINIFEX PIGEON
Spinifex grassland is the preferred habitat of this small bird, which is also known as the plumed pigeon.

PARTRIDGE PIGEON AND SQUATTER PIGEON

The partridge pigeon (*Geophaps smithii*) and the squatter pigeon (*G. scripta*) are closely related. They are both plump, short-tailed birds, dull brown, with broad white stripes either side of the breast. Both inhabit woodland, open forest and savanna, but each lives in a different part of tropical Australia. The partridge pigeon lives in the northernmost part of the Northern Territory and the northern tip of Western Australia, while the squatter pigeon lives in coastal Queensland and northern New South Wales.

The partridge pigeon is 25–28 cm long, and is recognised by a bright red or yellow patch around its eyes. The squatter pigeon is slightly larger, at 27–32 cm long, with bold black and white facial markings, white breast stripes and a brown forehead. The squatter pigeon makes a low, musical 'coo-poop-poop' sound; the partridge pigeon utters a low-pitched coo as a single note.

Both species are ground-dwelling pigeons that feed on native and introduced grasses and herbs, and the occasional insect. They are often seen feeding or dust-bathing on dirt tracks or roads. Being well camouflaged, they generally become immobile at the first sign of danger – or, when seriously threatened, they walk or run as a group before being flushed into the air. They usually settle 10–20 metres away from the intruder, either alighting on a branch or descending to the ground, where they continue to run. Their flight pattern alternates between flapping and gliding. When they glide, their wings are curved downwards.
Scientific name: *Geophaps* spp.

ROCK PIGEONS

Both the white-quilled rock pigeon (*Petrophassa albipennis*) and the chestnut-quilled rock pigeon (*P. rufipennis*) have adapted to life among the rocks and boulders of the sandstone gorges and plateaus of far northern Australia, where they live on the seeds of grasses, herbs, trees and shrubs. They occasionally enter woodland to forage, but seldom venture more than a few hundred metres. If threatened, they run or fly back to their rocky shelters, where they are well camouflaged. During the day they shelter in small holes, caves or crevices where the temperature remains comparatively low.

Rock pigeons are wary and agile terrestrial birds. When disturbed, they run with ease across the broken rocky landscape to a high ledge. From here they flap-glide to another, usually lower, ledge and repeat the process if necessary, effectively evading flightless intruders.

Both species are large, dark brown birds that range in length from 28 cm to 32 cm; the chestnut-quilled rock pigeon is the slightly smaller of the two. In flight, the white or chestnut wing patches of both species are prominent, although in some areas the white-quilled rock-pigeon has little or no wing patch.
Scientific name: *Petrophassa* spp.

DIAMOND DOVE

The diamond dove is a small grey pigeon, 19–22 cm in length, with a red eye ring and small white spots ('diamonds') on its wings.

Occurring only in Australia, the diamond dove inhabits the lightly wooded plains and grasslands of arid and semi-arid regions. It is common, especially among mulga and spinifex, and its range has probably increased since European settlement because dams provide reliable water sources in areas that were previously too dry for it.

DISTRIBUTION

■ SPINIFEX PIGEON

■ PARTRIDGE PIGEON
■ SQUATTER PIGEON

■ WHITE-QUILLED ROCK PIGEON
■ CHESTNUT-QUILLED ROCK PIGEON

■ DIAMOND DOVE

■ DIAMOND DOVE
Its red eye ring and the sprinkling of 'diamonds' on its wings make this small, slender dove easy to recognise.

■ PEACEFUL DOVE
Because of its densely barred neck and upper breast, this bird is sometimes referred to as the zebra dove.

Diamond doves are usually found in loose flocks of 10–30 birds, but individuals, pairs and huge flocks are often seen feeding on the ground, foraging for the tiny seeds of grasses and herbs. On cool days they rest on the warm ground, and occasionally nest there, but they generally roost and nest in trees. When on the ground, they walk with a comical waddle, but they can also run surprisingly fast.

Because of the unpredictability of food and water in inland Australia, the diamond dove is extremely nomadic. These birds need to drink every day: in periods of drought flocks move away from dry areas, but following good rains they will move into desert regions where surface water is available.
Scientific name: *Geopelia cuneata*

PEACEFUL DOVE ■

The peaceful dove is a small greyish brown bird about 18–23 cm long. It has a white belly and a long tail and can be identified by its pale blue eye ring. Its neck and upper breast are strongly barred; these markings break up into the dark 'scallops' of its upper wing feathers.

This native pigeon is also found in New Guinea and South-East Asia. In Australia it inhabits eucalypt woodland and other grassy, lightly timbered areas, as well as rainforest edges near clearings. It has also adapted well to life in rural areas and in some northern towns, where small flocks are often flushed from roadsides. Peaceful doves are usually seen in pairs or small parties, but larger groups sometimes form outside the breeding season.

Peaceful doves are probably sedentary with some local movement in response to the availability of food.

■ WONGA PIGEON
Tall trees are used by wonga pigeons as nesting sites but these birds spend most of their time feeding on the ground.

They feed entirely from the ground on the seeds of both native and introduced grasses, sedges and herbs, but they prefer to roost and nest in trees.

Despite this dove's common name, males of the species are far from peaceful, particularly in the breeding season, when they engage in much cooing and bowing to warn other males away. Peaceful doves may nest at any time of the year, although breeding tends to peak during the wet season. Males and females cooperate in building a flimsy nest in a tree or shrub up to 8 metres from the ground.
Scientific name: *Geopelia striata*

BAR-SHOULDERED DOVE ■

The bar-shouldered dove is also sometimes known as the pandanus pigeon, the mangrove dove or the kookawook. It is a grey and brown pigeon, 27–30 cm long, and is darker above than below.

Like other members of its genus, it has a long tail, but it can be identified by its larger size and the metallic bronze plumage on its neck that is broadly scalloped with black. It has a distinctive 'kook-a-wook' call that distinguishes it from the similar sized introduced spotted turtledove (page 186). This native species also occurs in New Guinea.

In Australia, the bar-shouldered dove is found mainly in tropical and subtropical wet eucalypt forest, monsoon forest and mangroves where there is moist, dense vegetation, usually close to more open areas for foraging and never more than a short distance from water. In drier parts of the country it stays close to creekside vegetation or swampy areas. It is also common

■ BAR-SHOULDERED DOVE
This native species has adapted well to human settlement and frequently nests in suburban gardens.

in tropical towns, where it nests in urban parks and gardens among thick vegetation.

Bar-shouldered doves are usually seen singly or in pairs, but outside the breeding season they may also congregate in large groups of up to a hundred. They are active during the day, and feed mostly on the ground on the seeds of native and introduced grasses, shrubs and weeds.
Scientific name: *Geopelia humeralis*

WONGA PIGEON ■

The wonga pigeon is an elusive bird, often heard but less frequently seen along the east coast of Australia. It is endemic to Australia and seems to have no close relatives. Its size and palatability made it a sought-after delicacy for early settlers.

SOWING THE SEED

There is a special relationship between fruit-doves and many rainforest trees, such as the blue quandong, the rainforest lime and the common lilly pilly. The trees provide the doves with food and the birds disperse the trees' seeds.

In Australia, fruit-doves that do this are from the genera *Ptilinopus*, *Ducula* and *Lopholaimus*. These birds feed solely on fruits. Their guts digest the fruit flesh and the intact seeds pass out with their droppings and germinate.

Not all fruit-eating pigeons disperse seeds – some swallow grit to enable them to grind and digest fruit flesh and seeds in their gizzards.

blue quandong

rainforest lime

common lilly pilly

This large, bluish grey pigeon, 42–45 cm long, is distinguished from other species by the broad, white V on its chest and its white forehead. It is a shy, wary bird that inhabits areas with thick cover but a relatively clear understorey, such as rainforest, wet eucalypt forest, regrowth areas and brigalow scrub. It is predominantly a ground-dweller, fast and agile on its feet and seldom flying, although it roosts on a branch. It feeds on the seeds of both native and introduced plants, on fruits taken from the ground and from low bushes that can be reached from the ground, and also on invertebrates.

Except in the breeding season, the wonga pigeon is solitary and sparsely distributed throughout its range. Its utters a loud, resonant, monotonous hoot that usually betrays its presence, but this call is very difficult to trace. The pigeon does, however, venture into picnic areas and gardens that back onto bush if there is a steady food supply from picnickers or chicken sheds.

The wonga pigeon is unusual among pigeons in that the male puts on a bowing display only occasionally, as a sign of aggression, and never in courtship. Its courtship dance involves opening and closing its wings and tail while swinging its head rhythmically from side to side.
Scientific name: *Leucosarcia melanoleuca*

IMPERIAL PIGEONS

The duculas, or imperial pigeons, are closely related to the fruit-doves (this page and page 192). Two species live in Australia: the Torresian or pied imperial pigeon (*Ducula bicolor*), which migrates to coastal northern Australia, and the Christmas Island imperial pigeon (*D. whartoni*), which occurs solely on that island.

The Torresian imperial pigeon sports distinctive black and white plumage and is about 38–44 cm long. It is a regular breeding migrant to Australia, the bulk of the population arriving from New Guinea during July and August to form large colonies among mangroves and on offshore islands. Torresian imperial pigeons nest on islands and travel in flocks to feed on fruits and berries in wet eucalypt and lowland rainforest on the mainland.

Until 1960 these birds were hunted in their hundreds. They are now protected and the species is common, although some islands where they once bred have not been repopulated.

The Christmas Island imperial pigeon is dark grey and about 39 cm long. It occurs all over the island but prefers tall, moist rainforest, where it feeds on rainforest fruits and fruits from introduced shrubs that have invaded disturbed areas. Little is known of its habits, but its numbers have declined as a result of poaching and habitat clearance for mining, and it is now considered rare.

A national park has been established on the island, and poaching and rainforest clearing have now stopped, so it is hoped that there will be no further decline.
Scientific name: *Ducula* spp.

WOMPOO FRUIT-DOVE ■

This is the most spectacular of the Australian fruit-doves. Its back and upper wings are a vivid green, its throat and breast are purple and its abdomen and underwings are a brilliant yellow. It has a pale grey head with red eyes and a red and yellow bill. Within their range, these birds show a marked size difference: those in the south are 55 cm long, whereas those from Cape York are only 35 cm long.

These colourful pigeons are found in New Guinea and in eastern Australia from Cape York to northern New South Wales. They inhabit tropical and subtropical rainforest, where they are surprisingly difficult to see among the dense foliage. Their presence is usually first detected by a deep, resonant 'wom-POO' advertising call. When a wompoo fruit-dove is flushed from cover, an observer may hear a loud clapping of wings and glimpse a flash of bright yellow underwing as the bird makes its escape over the canopy.

Wompoo fruit-doves feed solely on fruits taken from trees, vines and shrubs. They are usually seen singly or in pairs, but larger numbers may sometimes congregate at a fruiting tree. They move around within their locality in response to the availability of food. Small flocks may be seen flying between patches of forest or out of the forest to an isolated fruiting tree, especially when fruit in the forest is scarce.

Wompoos rely on rainforests, so their range reflects the patchy distribution of coastal rainforest. These birds were once common south of Sydney in the Illawarra district, but they are now seldom seen south of Newcastle.
Scientific name: *Ptilinopus magnificus*

■ WOMPOO FRUIT-DOVE
A bird of the rainforest, this fruit-dove is now considered rare and vulnerable in New South Wales, largely because of land clearance and fragmentation of its habitat.

various fruiting trees, particularly wild figs. It announces its territory by making a loud, hooting call.

Superb, rose-crowned and banded fruit-doves regularly travel long distances in search of food, and will eat the fruits of a wide variety of trees, vines and shrubs.

Despite their bright colouring, these birds are not easy to see in the dim light among dense vegetation. They usually occur singly or in pairs, although larger numbers sometimes gather at particularly abundant food sources. They feed hanging upside down in order to reach fruits dangling from thin branches.
Scientific name: *Ptilinopus* spp.

TOPKNOT PIGEON ▦

The topknot pigeon, 40–46 cm in length, is unique to the east coast of Australia and appears to have no close relatives among pigeons. It is a large, grey, tree-dwelling bird with a banded tail. Its broad crest gives this pigeon's head a squarish appearance when seen from a distance.

The topknot pigeon is found in all types of rainforest and is almost wholly arboreal; only rarely does it descend to the ground in order to drink, since it gathers most of its water from foliage and feeds entirely on the fleshy fruits of trees and vines. In dry weather it drinks from streams, perching on a rock or hanging from a low branch.

Although the topknot pigeon is a large bird, it is quite acrobatic at times, hanging upside down on thin branches to feed from clumps

▦ SUPERB FRUIT-DOVE
The female *Ptilinopus superbus* is mainly green, with a small deep blue crown; the male has a larger purple crown and a reddish brown neck.

of fruit. It is highly nomadic and travels in flocks, covering considerable distances in order to feed on the fruits of a variety of forest trees. Some flocks appear to travel the full length of the Queensland coast. It has learnt to feed on the berries of the introduced camphor laurel, which has been planted as a shade tree, and will visit isolated trees in open agricultural areas.

In the past, flocks of topknot pigeons consisted of thousands of individuals but today flocks of 50 birds are more usual. Early settlers used to shoot these birds for the table, but the decline in their numbers is probably due more to the clearance of their rainforest habitat than to the depredations of nineteenth-century hunters.
Scientific name: *Lopholaimus antarcticus*

▦ ROSE-CROWNED
FRUIT-DOVE
This small fruit-dove, *Ptilinopus regina*, breeds throughout the northern wet season, laying a single egg.

DISTRIBUTION

▦ ROSE-CROWNED
FRUIT-DOVE

▦ SUPERB FRUIT-DOVE
▦ BANDED FRUIT-DOVE

▦ TOPKNOT PIGEON

OTHER FRUIT-DOVES ▦

The rose-crowned fruit-dove (*Ptilinopus regina*) and the superb fruit-dove (*P. superbus*) are small, plump, colourful birds that range from 22 cm to 24 cm long.

The rose-crowned fruit-dove has a yellow-lined, rose-coloured crown, a greyish blue head, throat and back and a yellow-orange abdomen, and is green above. The female is generally less colourful than the male.

The female superb fruit-dove is primarily green with a white underbelly, and the male has a dark purple crown, green cheeks and wings, and a reddish brown neck. His pale grey breast gives way to a broad dark blue band and a white belly.

In Australia both these fruit-doves inhabit dense, moist rainforest, mangroves, monsoon forests and wet eucalypt forest along the east coast. The rose-crowned fruit-dove also lives in the coastal region of the Northern Territory.

The banded fruit-dove (*P. cinctus*), at 33–35 cm long, is a somewhat larger bird, predominantly black, white and grey. In Australia it is restricted to small patches of rainforest growing in gullies among the sandstone escarpments of Arnhem Land, where it moves around in order to take full advantage of

▦ TOPKNOT PIGEON
Although it is quite a large bird, this pigeon moves with agility through the forest canopy and often hangs upside down to reach bunches of fruit.

PARROTS AND COCKATOOS

Parrots are descendants of an ancient line and have no close living relatives. Where they came from is hotly debated. Since they are mostly found in Africa, India, Australasia and South America, with the greatest number of species occurring in South America and Australasia, it seems almost certain that they originated on the ancient southern continent of Gondwana. Parrots belong to the Psittacidae family in the order Psittaciformes. Altogether there are 345 species; 44 of the 53 species found in Australia occur nowhere else in the world.

Probably the best known feature of parrots is their spectacular plumage. In most species the males are more brightly coloured than their mates, the eclectus parrot being a notable Australian exception. Some have colourful crests, which they use mainly as courtship adornments.

Apart from its striking plumage, the parrot's most conspicuous feature is its short, blunt bill, which has a downcurved upper section. The size of the bill and the length of the curve in each species is related to the type of food it eats. Some parrots have comparatively long bills that are perfect for extracting seeds from fruits; others have broader and stronger bills that are designed for cracking hard seeds.

Unlike most birds, which have three toes pointing forwards and one pointing back, parrots have two toes pointing forwards and two pointing back, so that they can use their feet almost like hands. They also use their bills to grasp firmly, and so, with specialised feet and bill, they can climb with great agility.

Parrots nest in concealed hollows, mostly in trees, although some ground-dwelling species use hollows in thick vegetation or among boulders. They usually lay their eggs, which are relatively small and always white, on consecutive days, and a normal clutch numbers two to four.

Many seed-eaters need to drink every day, often gathering at dusk in noisy flocks around watering places, and at these times they are vulnerable to falcons and eagles, as well as to reptiles such as goannas. Native cats, introduced cats and foxes also prey on ground-dwelling parrots.

The land of parrots

Australia has long been renowned for the number and variety of its parrots. In the late sixteenth century the German cartographer Mercator made a world map that included a land, somewhere near present-day Australia, that he named Terra Psittacorum – the Land of Parrots – and early settlers often referred to Australia as 'Parrot Land'.

Australian parrots have diversified into a wide range of species, from the giant cockatoos of the rainforests to nocturnal ground-dwelling parrots. Most Australian parrots inhabit woodlands and forests, but some species live in deserts, and there are even some that are found on beaches.

The majority of Australian species are nomadic to some degree, moving around to take advantage of feeding and breeding places.

Parrots in peril

Many Australian parrot species have adapted well to the changes brought about by European settlement, and are now a familiar and treasured feature of gardens, farms and parks.

Forest clearing has created grasslands where species such as galahs and red-rumped parrots thrive; these parrots travel along corridors of cleared land, spreading from one region to the next. As one example, the clearing of parts of the eastern slopes of the Great Dividing Range has enabled galahs and corellas to spread from inland regions to the east coast. But some other species did not fare so well when their environments were altered, and a number have disappeared. In northern New South Wales the clearing of large rainforest areas is probably responsible for the disappearance of the double-eyed fig-parrot, and the population of ground parrots declined when a great part of their habitat was destroyed by the draining of coastal swamps in South Australia.

Other impacts of agricultural activity have not been so straightforward: the superb parrot, for instance, benefited at first from the clearing of forested areas and the building of dams, but the loss of old trees is now creating a shortage of nest sites for these birds.

PARROT FEATURES
Parrots have colourful plumage and a strong, downcurved bill. Their feet have two toes pointing forwards and two back, so that the birds can use them rather like hands. Shown here is a male Australian ringneck.

ALL BILL AND CLAW
Hanging on tightly, western rosella (*Platycercus icterotis*) chicks wait for a parent to bring them a meal.

DISTRIBUTION

RED-TAILED
BLACK-COCKATOO

YELLOW-TAILED
BLACK-COCKATOO

SHORT-BILLED
BLACK-COCKATOO

LONG-BILLED
BLACK-COCKATOO

GLOSSY
BLACK-COCKATOO

RED-TAILED BLACK-COCKATOO ▪

In flight, with flocks sometimes numbering up to a hundred birds, these large, predominantly black cockatoos look like great squadrons of low-flying aircraft. In the air they maintain contact between flock members with frequent loud, metallic screeches. Their noise and their purposeful, conspicuous flight give these flocks a powerful presence.

Birds from different areas have subtle variations in colour and size, with the larger ones growing to about 60 cm long. Typically, the male is black with a blood red band in his tail and a large black crest that fans out in front of his face during courtship. Females are similar to males, except that their plumage is flecked with fine yellow markings.

Red-tailed black-cockatoos are endemic to Australia, living in wooded areas scattered across the west and north of the continent. They are widely distributed, but are most abundant in tropical Australia – for example in the northern forests of Arnhem Land.

They are nomadic birds that closely follow the flowering of bloodwood eucalypts and she-oaks, and the tiny seeds of these trees constitute the main part of their diet. In heavily timbered country they generally collect the seed

directly from the branches of the tree, but in more open country they are happy to forage on the ground.

These cockatoos nest in hollow branches, high in eucalypt trees. The female broods alone but the male helps to feed the nestling. Unlike many other parrots, this species rarely lays more than one egg.
Scientific name: *Calyptorhynchus banksii*

OTHER BLACK-COCKATOOS ▪

Four other large black-cockatoos are endemic to Australia. The yellow-tailed black-cockatoo (*Calyptorhynchus funereus*) and the short-billed black-cockatoo (*C. latirostris*) are both still relatively common, but there are conservation concerns for both the long-billed black-cockatoo (*C. baudinii*) and the glossy black-cockatoo (*C. lathami*). At 44–50 cm long, the glossy black-cockatoo is a little smaller than the other three species, which are about 50–70 cm long.

The mournful, discordant cries of a flock of yellow-tailed black-cockatoos is a distinctive sound in the woodlands of south-eastern

▪ RED-TAILED BLACK-COCKATOOS
In the forested regions of their range, these cockatoos can often be seen in family groups or parties of several families, their cries ringing over the treetops as they call to one another.

Australia. This species specialises in eating moth larvae, which it digs from inside the timber of living trees, tearing open the trunks or branches with its bill in order to extract the larvae. It supplements this diet with the seeds of banksias, she-oaks and hakeas, and with pine cones. The yellow-tailed black-cockatoo has yellow patches on its cheeks and on its tail.

Short-billed black-cockatoos are still relatively common in the drier forests of south-western Australia. Their diet comprises mainly seeds from banksias, grevilleas and hakeas, which they collect from trees or shrubs or forage from the ground. They look a little lighter in colour than yellow-tailed black-cockatoos, because their feathers are narrowly edged with white and they have white patches on their ears and tail.

The long-billed black-cockatoo is similar in colouring to the white-tailed black-cockatoo. It feeds mainly on tree seeds, particularly those of marri gums, extracting the seeds with its specially modified long bill, but it also eats wood-boring larvae. Long-billed black-cockatoo numbers are low, and a shortage of nest sites in mature trees is likely to contribute to future declines.

Glossy black-cockatoos feed exclusively on the cones of she-oaks. Unlike some of their noisy relatives, these birds are unobtrusive. Female

glossy black-cockatoos have red tails, patches of yellow on their head and neck and a flash of yellow on their tail. Males are similar, but lack the yellow colouring. Some populations of this cockatoo are decreasing as a result of the clearing of their preferred food trees.
Scientific name: *Calyptorhynchus* spp.

■ PALM COCKATOO
This cockatoo – a resident of the Cape York Peninsula – is wholly black apart from a patch of red skin beneath its eyes.

■ YELLOW-TAILED BLACK-COCKATOO
Banksia seeds are part of the diet of *Calyptorhynchus funereus*, but this bird particularly favours moth larvae, which it extracts from tree branches.

PALM COCKATOO ■

The palm cockatoo grows up to 64 cm long and weighs more than a kilogram. It is Australia's largest parrot, and is sometimes known as the great black cockatoo or the Goliath cockatoo.

This black parrot is a conspicuous bird, easily recognised by its massive bill, its untidy long crest and the naked crimson patch on its face. It is the only black-coloured cockatoo in Australia without a band of colour on its tail. It inhabits the rainforests and woodlands at the tip of Cape York Peninsula in north Queensland, and is common inside this very limited range. It is native to this part of Australia, but is also found – along with other larger and thinner related forms – throughout the lowland forests of New Guinea.

True to its name, the palm cockatoo feeds on palm and pandanus fruits. The large pandanus fruits are made up of many hard orange wedges that contain seeds. These tough, fibrous outer pods are no match for the palm cockatoo, however, with its massive bill and strong jaw muscles. With its foot it lifts a pandanus fruit to its bill, anchoring it with its hooked upper mandible. It then uses its sharp lower bill to tear the fruit open, revealing the seeds within, which it then devours. Palm cockatoos also feed on other seeds, nuts, berries and leaf buds, as well as a variety of insects and their larvae.

These cockatoos roost on dead or leafless branches at the tops of tall trees growing on the fringes of the rainforest. They leave their roost each morning for the trees where they feed. During the comparatively cool morning they forage for food, but in the heat of the afternoon they shelter in the shade of the rainforest before returning to their roost.

Despite their size, these cockatoos are surprisingly agile as they move around in the branches and among the foliage collecting food. Unlike many other large and slow-flying forest birds, palm cockatoos venture boldly onto the ground to feed on fallen fruits and other foods, and are well equipped to fend off possible ground predators, such as goannas.

Like most parrots, palm cockatoos are sociable birds, and are usually found in small groups of up to six individuals. These small parties often engage in a variety of playful antics, including mock attacks, while perched high on exposed branches. They are generally extremely noisy and utter regular loud whistles, screeches and wailings.

The breeding season begins just before the onset of the wet season. The birds make their nests inside shallow tree hollows, which they line with twigs that they have chewed into splinters. Large birds generally select high locations for their nests, especially if tall trees are available, but the entrance to the palm cockatoo's nest may be as little as 3 metres above ground level. The female lays a single white egg, which she incubates, and both parents take care of the chick.
Scientific name: *Probosciger aterrimus*

▭ PALM COCKATOO

BILL ADAPTATIONS

Australian black-cockatoos are members of the genus *Calyptorhynchus*. This name means 'hidden beak' – which is puzzling since these birds have very large, strong bills.

The shape of their bill is related to the type of food they eat. Yellow-tailed and white-tailed black-cockatoos have narrow bills with pointed, lengthened upper mandibles for prising seeds from deep woody fruits such as gumnuts and digging into timber to extract wood-boring insect larvae. The glossy black-cockatoo's staple diet is the tiny seeds of she-oak cones, which the parrots harvest by tearing the cones apart – a tough job that needs their bulbous bill with its broad lower mandible.

Red-tailed black-cockatoos have a wide, blunt bill, ideal for crushing hard nuts and seeds, but in order to obtain wood-boring insect larvae from trees, they must rip the timber rather than dig into it. The long, narrow upper mandible of the long-billed black-cockatoo enables this parrot to pull seeds out of the deep fruit of the marri eucalyptus.

male yellow-tailed black-cockatoo

female red-tailed black-cockatoo

female glossy black-cockatoo

DISTRIBUTION

■ GANG-GANG
COCKATOO

■ SULPHUR-CRESTED
COCKATOO

■ LONG-BILLED CORELLA
■ WESTERN CORELLA

■ LITTLE CORELLA

GANG-GANG COCKATOO ■

Gang-gangs are common winter visitors to many urban parks and gardens. In Canberra, flocks of up to 50 gang-gangs frequently gather in native and exotic trees and shrubs to feed quietly on a variety of seeds and fruits. The seeds of hawthorns and Roman cypresses seem to be particular favourites.

These friendly and sociable birds have a somewhat comical appearance, perhaps because of their short quirky head crest or because of the nonchalant way in which they watch the approach of a human observer.

They are 35 cm long, and the male's orange-red head and ashen grey plumage suffused with pink is unlike that of any other Australian parrot. The female's head is grey.

In the summer, gang-gang cockatoos make their home in the tall wet forests of the high mountain ranges of south-eastern mainland Australia. Here they gather in small family groups to breed in high tree hollows in the safety of the forest canopy.

In winter they form small flocks and venture down from the mountains and out into open country. Despite their heavy, laboured flight,

they can travel long distances in search of winter food.

One of the strangest bird calls to be heard in the Australian bush belongs to the gang-gang. It often calls on the wing, and its rasping sound has been likened to the sound of a cork being drawn from a wine bottle. Scientific name: *Callocephalon fimbriatum*

SULPHUR-CRESTED COCKATOO ■

The sulphur-crested cockatoo is a familiar sight over much of eastern and northern Australia. Growing to about 49 cm long, this large cockatoo is immediately distinguished by its white plumage and large yellow crest. In flight, a yellow wash under the wings is also visible. When folded, the crest of a sulphur-crested cockatoo is slightly upcurved; when the bird becomes excited it erects this crest in a crown. In southern Australia large noisy flocks are common, with groups of over a hundred birds often forming. In the north, smaller groups are the norm.

Sulphur-crested cockatoos prefer timbered country interspersed with open fields. Each flock of birds has a

■ SULPHUR-CRESTED COCKATOO
This parrot normally holds its forward-curving yellow crest closed but when excited it raises it in a broad crown.

permanent night roost in a group of tall trees, usually near a watercourse. Their early morning departure is a noisy affair and their return to the same roost in the evening is a repeat of the morning's performance, with individuals screeching and fighting as they jostle for the best perch.

The flock feeds in the surrounding open country on a wide variety of seeds, grains and insects. They use a sentinel system to warn of danger. While most are busy feeding, a few individuals remain on the alert in elevated positions on the edge of the flock. If they spot danger they give a harsh screech and the whole flock immediately reacts, flying either from the ground to trees or from one group of trees to the next. Sulphur-crested cockatoos use their powerful bills to dig up seed buried in the ground or to extract insects from timber, and large concentrations of birds can cause isolated but significant crop damage.

These cockatoos nest in hollows in the high branches or trunks of old or dead eucalypts. Females lay two or three eggs and both parents share in the incubation and rearing of the chicks. Sulphur-crested cockatoos probably mate for life. Scientific name: *Cacatua galerita*

CORELLAS

All corellas have the same basically white plumage with yellow-washed underparts and a prominent bare patch of blue skin around their eyes. All corella species grow to about 38 cm long. The long-billed corella (*Cacatua tenuirostris*) is distinguished from its relatives by its very long

■ GANG-GANG COCKATOO
The grey feathers of the gang-gang are fringed with white, giving it a scaly appearance. The male has a bright orange-red head, and the female's head is grey.

upper mandible, and by the prominent wash of orange on its upper breast and around its forehead. The western corella (*C. pastinator*) has only a small area of orange-red on its forehead, while the little corella (*C. sanguinea*) has no orange wash.

Corellas sometimes gather in feeding flocks of many hundreds of birds, eating fallen seed from the ground. Both long-billed and western corellas have a habit of digging up freshly planted wheat and other agricultural seed with their bills, and for this reason they are often unpopular with farmers. Females lay clutches of two or three eggs in a tree hollow high up in the canopy. Corellas seem to develop a strong attachment to their nest hollows, using the same one every breeding season for year after year.

Restricted to western Victoria and the south-eastern corner of South Australia, the long-billed corella is often seen feeding in pastures near watercourses. Because of illegal shooting and trapping for the cage-bird trade, this species is now rare in parts of its former range.

Western corellas are restricted to the open forests and woodlands of south-western Western Australia. For reasons that are still not clearly understood, their numbers have declined significantly since European settlement, and now they are unfortunately rare.

Inland Australia and the tropical north is the habitat of the little corella. Within their range, these corellas are very common, and they have benefited from the presence of stock water and crops. They travel in huge, noisy flocks, sometimes of more than a thousand birds, and

considering that they are so conspicuous in flight, they are surprisingly secretive at the nest.
Scientific name: *Cacatua* spp.

GALAH

This bird's common name comes from an Aboriginal word for the species. This parrot is one of the most abundant and familiar in Australia, and is found right across the continent wherever there are hollow trees, open country and water. The only habitat galahs do not penetrate is thick forests.

Agricultural clearing of areas that were once forested and the dam construction in arid parts of the continent have favoured the galah, as has the spread of grain crops. Since European settlement, populations have increased and the galah's range continues to expand.

Galahs roosting in tall trees are a familiar sight at dawn in inland Australia, their pink breasts glowing in the early morning sunlight. Reveille at these birds' roosting sites is a deafening affair, and in the evening noisy flocks return from their feeding forays screeching and wheeling around the trees before they settle for the night.

At around 35 cm long, both males and females have grey backs, white heads and rosy pink underparts. They are ground-feeders, pecking at grain, green shoots and seeds from both exotic weeds and native plants.

Galahs usually pair for life and nest in any month, depending on locality. Breeding adults with an established territory have a largely sedentary lifestyle. They usually nest near water in a hollow that they line with leaves. Both sexes share the

incubation and rearing of up to five young. Because they are such strong, fast fliers, breeding pairs may fly up to 10 kilometres from the nest site in search of food.

After they leave the nest at about two months old, young galahs are often left by their parents in 'creches' with youngsters from other nests. The young are dependent on their parents for about another two months, and then, when they become independent, they gather in large flocks and wander widely. They soon acquire the grey and pink coloration of the adult birds.
Scientific name: *Cacatua roseicapilla*

MAJOR MITCHELL'S COCKATOO

This parrot so impressed the explorer Sir Thomas Mitchell in 1835 that the bird was eventually named in his honour. The Major Mitchell's cockatoo is a delicate shade of pink and has a pronounced red and yellow head crest and white wings.

Sometimes known as pink cockatoos, Major Mitchell's cockatoos are distributed widely throughout arid Australia and are usually associated with timbered areas, where they are often seen perched in acacias or she-oaks. Their diet includes seeds from a wide range of grasses and other annuals, which they take from either branches or the ground. Unlike many other species of cockatoo, they are wary birds and will not allow humans to approach them.

The female lays about three eggs and both the male and the female share incubation duties. Youngsters spend about two months in the nest

■ GALAH
The spread of farming across Australia has suited the galah, with stock water provided in dry areas and plentiful supplies of grain.

DISTRIBUTION

■ GALAH

■ MAJOR MITCHELL'S COCKATOO

■ MAJOR MITCHELL'S COCKATOO
These are unusual parrots in that pairs establish a permanent breeding territory. They select a hole in a large tree and defend an area of many kilometres around against other cockatoos.

NESTING SECURITY
Using her beak, the female eclectus parrot hauls herself out of her nesting hollow. The nest of wood chips may be as deep as 7 metres inside a tree. A male is alighting at the entrance to the nest.

DISTRIBUTION

ECLECTUS PARROT AND RED-CHEEKED PARROT

COCKATIEL

RAINBOW LORIKEET

and then become independent members of an extended family group within the breeding territory. Populations of Major Mitchell's cockatoos appear to fluctuate. This has frequently been attributed to illegal trapping for the cage-bird trade, which has been a serious problem, but it is also possible that the fluctuation is a result of the birds' feeding preferences, which are not yet fully understood. Alternatively, it could be linked to rainfall in the remote parts of their range where they travel to breed.
Scientific name: *Cacatua leadbeateri*

ECLECTUS PARROT ■

In the bird world it is unusual for the female to be more brilliantly coloured than her mate, but this is the case with the female eclectus parrot. Her plumage is a brilliant red and blue, but the mainly green male is rather more sombre and has only patches of blue and red, chiefly on the tail and underwing. Both male and female are about 43 cm long and are quite thickset.

Just as unusual among parrots is the eclectus parrot's breeding behaviour. Eclectus parrots nest in small groups, rather than in pairs, with up to eight birds attending the nest and taking care of the young. These birds live in the remote rainforests of Cape York Peninsula, and they were not discovered by the scientific world until 1913. The rainforest canopy

■ ECLECTUS PARROTS
The female of this species is a vivid red with blue markings but her mate is mainly a less conspicuous green.

provides a variety of nuts and seeds, and the fruits of the pandanus are a particular favourite. Eclectus parrots travel and roost in noisy flocks.
Scientific name: *Eclectus roratus*

RED-CHEEKED PARROT

Red-cheeked parrots are common in rainforests and mangroves throughout the islands of Indonesia and New Guinea, but in Australia this species is confined to a relatively small area of rainforest on the tip of Cape York Peninsula.

These small, plump parrots are 22 cm long and are predominantly green. Males have a pronounced red face with a blue crown, while females have a brown face and crown. Red-cheeked parrots feed in small, noisy flocks high in the canopy, where they consume mostly seeds, nuts and fruits.
Scientific name: *Geoffroyus geoffroyi*

COCKATIEL

The cockatiel is endemic to the dry inland of Australia. Evenly spread across all habitats except thick forests, treeless deserts, and towns, this parrot makes an annual migration; in summer large numbers of birds head south, and then return north in winter.

Because cockatiels prefer to be near a reliable water supply, in times of drought some populations become nomadic, forming flocks of up to a hundred individuals. Agriculture has provided the cockatiel with new sources of water and seed, and so populations have expanded.

Predominantly grey in colour, cockatiels have a prominent yellow crest, an orange ear patch and a long pointed tail, and grow to about

■ RAINBOW LORIKEETS
The most widespread of the lorikeets, these birds are a common sight flashing colourfully overhead.

32 cm long. In flight their angular wings are highlighted with flashes of white. Despite their elegant shape, their closest relatives are the larger and heavier cockatoos.

Although these birds often call with a distinctive warbling cry when flying, they are usually quiet – and seemingly unafraid – when feeding. Acacia seeds and grass seeds, which they usually peck up from the ground, form the bulk of their diet.

When disturbed, cockatiels fly to safety in a nearby tree, returning to their original spot to feed once the danger has passed.
Scientific name: *Nymphicus hollandicus*

RAINBOW LORIKEET ■

The appropriately named rainbow lorikeet displays all the colours of the spectrum in its plumage. Its back and its upper wings are green, its head is violet blue and its bill and eyes are red. Its belly is dappled in blue, orange and yellow and its underwings are orange washed with yellow.

There are two different colour forms of this lorikeet in Australia, and other, related forms are found throughout lowland New Guinea and the islands of the South Pacific. In particular, the colour of the collar plumage on the nape of the rainbow lorikeet's neck varies with locality – it is red in northern Australia and green on the eastern seaboard.

Rainbow lorikeets are medium-sized parrots, growing up to 30 cm long, and are well known in coastal parts of eastern Australia, where they inhabit forests, heaths and even town gardens. However, they are more typically tropical birds, and are abundant and conspicuous in northern Australia.

Rainbow lorikeets mostly feed on pollen and nectar that they gather from flowering eucalypts and banksias, chattering shrilly among the blossoms as they eat. They have also developed a liking for cultivated fruits, especially apples and pears, and will readily eat foods offered by humans, but feeding them is inadvisable as they have delicate digestive systems and inappropriate foods can result in their developing nutritional deficiencies and becoming overweight.

They make daily feeding sorties to food sources, sometimes travelling more than 50 kilometres. They roost together in flocks of up to a hundred or more, regularly using the same safe night-roosting places – usually in tall trees, but sometimes in thick vegetation on islands.
Scientific name: *Trichoglossus haematodus*

SCALY-BREASTED LORIKEET

Common within their range, and often feeding in the company of rainbow lorikeets, scaly-breasted lorikeets are nomads of eastern Australia's coastal lowland forests and heathlands. They feed on pollen, flowers and fruits, and their movements follow the flowering seasons of eucalypts, banksias and grevilleas. They are very agile and can perform accomplished acrobatic feats to get at their food, including swinging upside down from the outermost branches of bushes.

Growing to about 23 cm long, the scaly-breasted lorikeet is generally green with a red bill and eyes. Its breast feathers are flecked with yellow, which creates a scaly effect and accounts for its common name. When this lorikeet takes to the air it reveals orange-red underwings.
Scientific name: *Trichoglossus chlorolepidotus*

VARIED LORIKEET

The varied lorikeet lives in forests and woodlands across tropical northern Australia. It is nomadic, and large flocks can suddenly appear in an area to feed on flowering trees and then disappear again.

Predominantly green and yellow, varied lorikeets are only 18 cm long and so are often difficult to observe clearly, especially when they are energetically feeding. They gather in groups to eat eucalypts, paperbarks and grevilleas, often swinging upside down to reach sprays of blossom or seed pods.
Scientific name: *Psitteuteles versicolor*

OTHER LORIKEETS

Three similar species of small, green lorikeet are found in the forests and woodlands of Australia's southern and eastern coasts. Although they have separate ranges, these overlap and the birds often form mixed flocks. In flight they form tight, fast-moving groups, their pointed wings giving them a dart-like appearance.

The purple-crowned lorikeet (*Glossopsitta porphyrocephala*) occurs across southern Australia, except on the Nullarbor Plain, and ranges as far west as Perth. This lorikeet has an orange head and ear patches, a pale blue breast and a purple crown. The musk lorikeet (*G. concinna*) is at home in both coastal and inland districts from Brisbane to Adelaide. It is identified by its prominent red ear patch. The little lorikeet (*G. pusilla*), which has a red face, lives along the eastern coast, ranging as far north as Cairns.

All three species are mainly green and small (15–22 cm long), and are

■ VARIED LORIKEET
This lorikeet of northern woodlands is easily identified at close quarters by its red crown and extremely prominent white eye ring.

fast fliers, so they are difficult to observe closely, and ornithologists often depend on the slight differences in calls in order to identify the three species. These calls also easily distinguish them from other similar small parrots. They build their nests in tree hollows, often very high up in the forest canopy, and they usually pair for life. Both parents share in the preparation of the nest and care of the young.

The favourite food of *Glossopsitta* lorikeets is eucalypt flowers, and they eat the fruit, pollen and nectar. They also visit flowering she-oaks, paperbarks and exotic plants. Large numbers of these lorikeets may roost together at night and then travel long distances during the day to concentrations of flowering trees.

Orchardists are not fond of these birds because of the damage they sometimes inflict on fruit trees.
Scientific name: *Glossopsitta* spp.

DISTRIBUTION

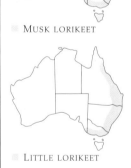

■ SCALY-BREASTED LORIKEET

■ VARIED LORIKEET
■ PURPLE-CROWNED LORIKEET

■ MUSK LORIKEET

■ LITTLE LORIKEET

■ SCALY-BREASTED LORIKEET
Sharp shrieks and endless chattering from the middle of a flowering tree are sure signs that a flock of scaly-breasted lorikeets is feeding among the foliage.

■ DOUBLE-EYED
FIG-PARROT
Part of this little parrot's
name comes from its
fondness for fig seeds.
The specimen illustrated
is emerging from a clump
of native figs on which it
has been feasting.

AUSTRALIAN KING PARROT ■

Inhabitants of the coastal and mountain forests of eastern Australia, king parrots usually feed on seeds in the canopy of native trees. They also eat exotic foods such as cotoneaster berries and acorns, which they often take from the ground.

They nest in the hollows of tall trees and, while the entrance is usually high up, the nest inside the tree is often close to ground level. Adults use their bills and both feet to grip the inside of the tree as they climb

■ AUSTRALIAN
KING PARROT
These parrots live in
coastal and mountain
eucalypt forests and are
rarely seen on the
ground. This male is
feeding on an acacia.

up and down. In the winter months, outside the breeding season, many king parrots disperse from native forests and visit farms, gardens and parks, sometimes in their hundreds.

The blue and green backs and brilliant scarlet undersides of the male king parrots, and the mainly green plumage of the females and immature birds, make these conspicuous and colourful flocks.

They vary considerably in size but are generally about 43 cm long. They have a distinctive, buoyant flight.
Scientific name: *Alisterus scapularis*

DOUBLE-EYED FIG-PARROT ■

At a mere 13 cm long, this is Australia's smallest parrot. It is bright green and has a plump, short-tailed body. Only the male has bright red ear patches.

There are eight different forms of the double-eyed fig-parrot, most of them living in New Guinea. In one of its many colour forms this parrot has a spot close to each eye, so that it seems to have four eyes; it is these markings that have given rise to its common name, but none of the Australian forms has this feature. The three Australian forms all belong to the same species, but they are sometimes given their own common names – Marshall's, McLeay's and Coxen's fig-parrots. Each form is restricted to small areas of rainforest on the east coast, ranging from Cape York to Grafton in northern New South Wales. In the past the Coxen's form was seen around the Border Ranges area of New South Wales and Queensland, but no one has recorded it for three decades. It may be extinct, since much of its rainforest habitat has been cleared.

The main food of fig-parrots is native fig seeds, which they extract with their large bills. Although noisy in flight, these birds are much less vocal when feeding. Because they are not easy to observe in the canopy of tall rainforest trees, they are among Australia's least-known parrots.
Scientific name: *Cyclopsitta diophthalma*

RED-WINGED PARROT

Red-winged parrots live in the woodlands of northern Australia, where they search in the trees for seeds and berries, usually coming to the ground only to drink. The male is mainly green with scarlet wing patches and a blue rump; the female is similar, but with duller red wings.

The red-winged parrot and the Australian king parrot have the same distinctive way of flying, and they share breeding and feeding traits. Accordingly, they used to be classified in the same genus. There are, however, considerable size differences, red-winged parrots generally reaching no more than 32 cm in length – although, as with the king parrot, sizes vary.
Scientific name: *Aprosmictus erythropterus*

REGENT PARROT

Regent parrots have slender bodies and very long slender tails. The males are golden, with a red bill, blackish blue features on the wings and tail and red wing patches. The female is greener and has a more sombre appearance.

Two populations of the regent parrot are known. One occurs throughout the Western Australian wheat belt, where numbers have fluctuated over the years. In the past this parrot probably benefited from forest clearance for wheat farming, but numbers appear to have declined in recent years.

In eastern Australia a population of more brilliantly coloured regent parrots is confined to a small area of open woodland along the Murray River around Mildura. This population has also declined seriously in recent years.

Regent parrots nest in tall eucalypts, especially near rivers. They lay their eggs at the bottom of a deep hollow, sometimes more than 5 metres down into the tree trunk. The female incubates the eggs and broods the chicks while the male brings her food. In the breeding season males often feed together. Regent parrots eat a variety of foods but are particularly fond of acacia and eucalypt seeds.
Scientific name: *Polytelis anthopeplus*

SUPERB PARROT

Male superb parrots are a deep emerald green with a brilliant yellow throat and head and a red collar beneath their throat; females are almost entirely green. Both sexes are about 40 cm in length and have long, slender bodies and tails. In the air, with their pointed, backward-sweeping wings, streamlined bodies and effortless flight, they have an arrow-like appearance.

The superb parrot lives only on the Riverina plains and timbered slopes of central New South Wales. It favours open woodlands and is found in trees along such rivers as the Murrumbidgee and the Lachlan.

These parrots are often quite tame when feeding on the ground and allow humans to approach closely. They feed on grass seeds and often pick up spilt grain from roadsides. At other times they feed on blossoms and fruits in the tree tops.

Populations of superb parrots appear to fluctuate considerably. Early this century numbers dropped because of trapping for the bird trade and the laying of poisoned grain to kill rabbits. When the rabbit problem lessened in the 1950s, the superb parrot appeared to make a comeback. However, in recent decades numbers have once more declined, due to the loss of mature nesting trees, and also possibly because of illegal bird trapping.
Scientific name: *Polytelis swainsonii*

PRINCESS PARROT

This rare parrot has subtle pastel pink, yellow, lilac and grey plumage. Sleek in appearance and alert in manner, it was named in honour of Princess Alexandra, later to be Queen consort to King Edward VII of England. The princess parrot grows to about 42 cm long and is slender with a long, pointed tail.

Only a few bird experts have ever seen this parrot in the wild, but – ironically – it is common in aviaries. In captivity it is tame and confident and breeds easily and regularly. In its natural habitat it is nomadic, appearing in an area for a short time and then leaving, sometimes for decades. It lives in the arid deserts of central Australia and apparently breeds very rarely.

On the few occasions when the princess parrot has been observed in its habitat, it has been in spinifex country, and spinifex seed seems to be an important part of its diet. Those who have seen this bird in the wild often comment on how unafraid it is of nearby humans.

When breeding, groups congregate along inland watercourses, where they nest in loose colonies. They lay their eggs in tree hollows, usually in river red gums, and up to ten nests have been recorded in a single large tree. Once breeding is over, the birds quickly disappear into the surrounding deserts.
Scientific name: *Polytelis alexandrae*

EASTERN ROSELLA

At the time of the early European settlers, this parrot was common around the village of Rose Hill near Sydney, and the birds became known as Rose Hillers. This was corrupted into 'rosella', which is now used to describe a group of similarly patterned Australian parrots.

The 30 cm-long eastern rosella has a scarlet head and throat, white face markings, a yellow belly and a blue

■ PRINCESS PARROT
An elusive nomad, this rare parrot lives in spinifex country in the arid interior. Observers say it is remarkably tame.

■ CRIMSON ROSELLA
This colour form occurs in moist forests south of Brisbane. There is also a yellow form and an orange 'Adelaide' form.

and green tail. The black feathers on its back are edged with yellow, creating a scalloped effect. Males are more richly coloured than females.

The eastern rosella lives on the eastern seaboard, where it prefers open country with a scattering of trees. It has benefited from the extensive clearing of forests for agriculture, and is also common in urban areas where there is open ground and a scattering of mature trees in which to nest. Frequently feeding on the ground, these rosellas eat various seeds, fruits and insects.

The female lays about five eggs in a hollow tree limb and incubates them for nearly three weeks, taking short daily breaks to feed herself. Once the young hatch, the male helps with the feeding. Youngsters leave the nest after a month.
Scientific name: *Platycercus eximius*

CRIMSON ROSELLA ■

A well-known and familiar species from the eastern states of Australia, the crimson rosella is 35 cm long and has three different colour forms. In the coastal and mountain forests from Brisbane south to Melbourne, it sports a dynamic blue and red plumage, while in the hills of South Australia – where it is known as the Adelaide rosella – it has a mottled orange appearance. In the Murray Valley, where it is known as the yellow rosella, it is almost completely blue and yellow. All three forms have a blue tail, wings and throat patch and a red forehead.

Although most at home in eucalypt forests, crimson rosellas are adaptable and are now also found in rural and

urban landscapes. In the parks and gardens of many towns and cities their loud, bell-like call is familiar. They feed on a wide range of native and exotic seeds and fruits, either on the ground or in shrubs or trees.

Breeding adults tend to stay together in established territories. Nonbreeding youngsters gather in flocks and become nomadic for their first few years. On the east coast these young rosellas are mainly bright emerald green, except for the same blue throat as the adults. As they mature, their red colouring develops patchily. Flocks of immature birds often include green, red and mottled individuals.

Scientific name: *Platycercus elegans*

EVOLUTION OF A SPECIES

Rosellas (*Platycercus* spp.) illustrate how new species can evolve. The crimson rosella (*P. elegans*) has three similar forms, all with blue cheeks: the crimson form lives on the east coast, the yellow form along the Murray Valley, and the orange form around Adelaide. These three forms look different, but they interbreed and therefore belong to the same species. However, the green rosella (*P. caledonicus*) of Tasmania, which once belonged to this species, has been geographically separated for thousands of years and has become a new species. Similarly the northern, eastern and pale-headed rosellas (*P. venustus, eximius* and *adscitus*) would once have been a single species.

crimson rosella
(*Platycercus elegans*),
yellow form

crimson rosella
(*Platycercus elegans*),
orange form

green rosella
(*Platycercus caledonicus*)

OTHER ROSELLAS

The green rosella (*Platycercus caledonicus*) occurs only in Tasmania, where it is both common and conspicuous. It is 35 cm long and has a green back and tail, a yellow belly and a blue throat and wings. Like the mainland crimson rosella, juveniles are largely green. In winter they band together in large flocks. Green rosellas live in forests, heathlands, farmland and gardens.

The pale-headed rosella (*P. adscitus*), which is less colourful than other rosellas, is 30 cm long and has a white or pale yellow head. It occurs in coastal Queensland, where it lives in most habitats, including forests on offshore islands, but avoids thick rainforests. Like other rosellas, this species is often noisy in the early morning and late afternoon.

The northern rosella (*P. venustus*) favours waterholes in hill country in northern Australia, from Broome to the Gulf of Carpentaria. It also lives in mangroves and paperbark forests. Unlike their southern counterparts, these birds rarely visit rural or urban areas, and are thus one of the least studied rosellas. They are 29 cm long, with a black head and white throat. Their backs are strongly patterned in black and yellow.

Restricted to the south-west corner of Western Australia, the western rosella (*P. icterotis*) is usually a forest-dweller, but now and then it ventures into farmland and orchards. At 28 cm long, it is the smallest of the rosellas and spends more time feeding in the tree tops than do other rosella species. It also differs from other rosellas in having a distinctive yellow throat patch.

Scientific name: *Platycercus* spp.

BLUE BONNET

This unusual parrot of the eastern inland has no close relatives. While it shares such characteristics as flight pattern and calls with grass parrots and rosellas, others features – such as its tiny vestigial crest and pointed flight feathers – are not found in any other parrot. Its name is misleading, since it does not really have a blue bonnet but rather a blue face patch.

There are four different colour forms of this species, all of which have a fawn back. The wing plumage varies in each but usually forms a pattern of red, blue and fawn. All have red and yellow bellies, but again the patterning varies with the form. They grow to 26–30 cm long.

Blue bonnets favour lightly timbered country, where they mostly feed on the ground, seeking safety when necessary in the branches of eucalypts, acacias and she-oaks. The availability of trees with suitable hollows limits breeding in some desert areas. Blue bonnets have particular seed preferences and tend to avoid grass seeds, concentrating instead on the fruits and seeds of saltbushes and mistletoes, which are usually plentiful.

Blue bonnets do not seem to be as reliant on an immediate supply of water as many other parrot species. Because of their feeding and drinking habits, they do not need to undertake long migratory or nomadic movements in search of food or water, and are usually sedentary. Only during particularly severe droughts are they forced to leave the driest regions.

Scientific name: *Northiella haematogaster*

NORTHERN ROSELLA
A hollow limb in a eucalypt near water is the ideal nesting site for *Platycercus venustus*, a parrot of northern Australia that is rarely seen in populated areas.

RED-CAPPED PARROT

Found only in a narrow strip of forest in the south-west corner of Western Australia, this parrot is a true forest specialist. It rarely moves away from the marri eucalypt, which is its principal food source.

The marri is a common forest eucalypt in the area, and grows to 40 metres high. Since these trees produce fruit prolifically all year round, red-capped parrots have a continuous food supply. The parrot's long hooked bill is well adapted to extracting seeds from inside the deep nuts of this eucalypt. Red-capped parrots share this special source of food with the much larger long-billed black-cockatoo, which also has a specially adapted bill.

Forestry practices adopted at the time of European settlement have increased the abundance of marri, and as a result the numbers of red-capped parrots have probably risen during the past hundred years.

The red-capped parrot is a thickset parrot 36 cm long. The male has an emerald green back, a dark purple chest, and a yellow face capped with a bright red crown. Females are mainly brown, and are quite dull when compared with their mates.

Adult red-capped parrots generally occur in pairs and are somewhat secretive and difficult to detect high up in the forest canopy where they feed and nest. Pairs rarely move far from their nesting territory. Juveniles, on the other hand, band together in small conspicuous flocks and tend to wander over large areas.

The flight of this parrot is undulating and swift, and when flying it usually gives a harsh, grating call, repeated several times.
Scientific name: *Purpureicephalus spurius*

AUSTRALIAN RINGNECK ▪
Australian ringnecks are large, sedentary parrots of the arid southern inland. Despite the irregular supply of food, this specialist of dry country is always able to find enough to eat. It feeds on a wide range of foods, including seeds, berries, fruits, blossoms, and insects and their larvae. It forages in trees and shrubs as well as on the ground, where it sometimes digs for food.

This largely green parrot, which grows 34–38 cm long, has many forms, each of which has a slightly different call. A few of the common names given to these various forms are the Port Lincoln parrot, the mallee ringneck, the twenty-eight parrot and the Cloncurry parrot.

All forms have a green breast and back and a distinct yellow collar. Most have a red band across the top of their bill, some have a yellow belly

▪ RED-CROWNED PARAKEET
One form of this parakeet lives on Norfolk Island, and owes its survival to conservation measures that were adopted in the 1980s.

and one has a prominent black head. They have a strong, graceful flight and generally give their whistling contact call when in the air.

Australian ringnecks are extremely timid and do not tolerate the close approach of humans, but among themselves they are sociable and usually occur in pairs or in small family parties. When a family party alights on a branch there is generally a boisterous display of social bonding that includes tail-fanning and body-shaking. Other parrots, such as rosellas, blue bonnets and red-rumped parrots, sometimes gather with ringnecks to feed or drink.
Scientific name: *Barnardius zonarius*

RED-CROWNED PARAKEET ▪
The red-crowned parakeet is found in New Caledonia, New Zealand and other islands in the Tasman region, including Norfolk Island. Each island has its unique form of red-crowned parakeet, though the Lord Howe Island form is now extinct.

Confined to the rainforests of Mount Pitt in the centre of the island, the 30 cm-long Norfolk Island form is the rarest and most threatened of the remaining red-crowned parakeets. It is a brilliant emerald green with a red head and eye, and has a loud, staccato call. In recent years disease, loss of nest sites and the killing of young birds by cats and introduced rats have been the main threats for the red-crowned parakeet.

The Norfolk Island form of this parakeet has been preserved from extinction by community and conservation agencies on the island – one of many unsung conservation success stories. In 1983, fewer than 20 individuals survived, out of a population that once numbered thousands. At that time some birds were captured in case of further losses in the wild; nest boxes were provided for the remaining wild birds; and cats, rats and exotic birds were removed from the parakeet's nesting areas. This remarkable effort has seen the population rebuild to over a hundred birds, and the number is still increasing.
Scientific name: *Cyanoramphus novaezelandiae*

▪ GREEN ROSELLA
PALE-HEADED ROSELLA

NORTHERN ROSELLA
▪ WESTERN ROSELLA

BLUE BONNET
▪ RED-CAPPED PARROT

AUSTRALIAN RINGNECK

▪ AUSTRALIAN RINGNECK
In some forms of ringneck the male has a scarlet frontal band. These birds live in the arid interior, never moving far from their birthplace.

■ MULGA PARROT
These parrots fly swiftly, generally close to the ground. Like most parrots, they fan their tails when they land.

Mulga parrots live in the scrublands and sandy plains of southern Australia, where drought conditions are the norm. Scientists know little of their habits, but they probably make their way about their range in response to irregular desert rainfall.

They are unobtrusive parrots. They are almost completely silent when feeding and they call softly to one another at other times. They are most frequently seen, usually in pairs or small family groups, when feeding on the ground in the shade of seed-bearing trees and shrubs.

Their normal diet most probably consists of grass seeds and the seeds of acacias and other shrubs.
Scientific name: *Psephotus varius*

GOLDEN-SHOULDERED PARROT

The golden-shouldered parrot from Cape York is one of the continent's most endangered birds. The beauty of this slender, elegant bird has contributed to its great rarity: specimens smuggled out of Australia into Europe and North America can be sold for enormous sums. Illegal trapping for the cage-bird trade has had a devastating impact on wild populations of these birds.

These parrots are found in grassy woodlands, where they spend much of their time on the ground feeding on the seeds of small grasses. In the heat of the day they rest in trees.

The development of cattle-grazing in the golden-shouldered parrot's habitat in the mid-twentieth century, and the farming practice of burning off in order to provide green shoots for livestock, have changed the nature of the tropical grasslands of Cape York and considerably reduced the availability of food for the parrots. This may have been another factor in this parrot's rapid decline in numbers over recent years.

Male golden-shouldered parrots are turquoise with golden wings, a black cap, and a red abdomen and undertail. Females are olive green. Both sexes grow to about 26 cm long. They nest in termite mounds, where the breeding pair dig a burrow up to half a metre long into the mound and then hollow out a large nesting chamber. They often use the same burrow for many years.

The female lays around five eggs during the dry season, from April to August, and incubates and broods the young alone. Sometimes, if there is plenty of food, a pair will rear two broods in a single season.
Scientific name: *Psephotus chrysopterygius*

SWIFT PARROT

Swift parrots breed in Tasmania during the summer and become elusive migrants on the Australian mainland in the winter.

The entire wild population of swift parrots, which consists of only about 5000 birds, nests in the eucalypt forests of Tasmania. After breeding, most of them leave for the coastal forests of the mainland, travelling as far west as Adelaide and occasionally as far north as Rockhampton in Queensland. Most of these annual long-distance migrations, especially those over Bass Strait, are made at night. Flocks move in tight, fast-moving and sometimes erratic formations, often in company with lorikeets. On the mainland, flocks of up to several hundred birds move from place to place, following the annual flowering of eucalypts.

The swift parrot looks like a lorikeet except that it is smaller, at only 24 cm long. Also unlike lorikeets, these parrots have flashes of bright red under their wings and a long tapering tail, though these characteristics can be seen only when the bird is flying. The swift parrot is predominantly green in colour, with a red face and red shoulder patches. Its blue forehead and yellow cheek markings are usually difficult to see when it is flying fast or feeding high in the forest canopy, but it is easy to distinguish from similarly coloured parrots because of its piping two-syllable call.
Scientific name: *Lathamus discolor*

MULGA PARROT ■

An inhabitant of mulga shrublands, the mulga parrot, also known as the many-coloured parrot, is a close relative of the red-rumped parrot (opposite page). Males are generally bright green with a golden flash on their wings and golden patches on their forehead and under their tail. Their belly is red, their wings are edged with dark blue, and they have a red spot on the back of their crown. Females are generally olive brown with red wing flashes. These parrots have long, blue-green tails that accentuate their slenderness. They grow to 27–31 cm long.

HOODED PARROT

The home of the hooded parrot is the open forest and grasslands of Arnhem Land in the Northern Territory. This parrot resembles the golden-shouldered parrot (opposite page) in shape, colour and breeding habits, and some believe that they are two forms of the same species.

At 27 cm long, the hooded parrot is slightly larger than the golden-shouldered parrot. It is turquoise, with a brown back, large yellow flashes on its wings and a red patch under its tail. Its main distinguishing feature, seen only in the male, is its black hood and face. Females are olive green. Hooded parrots have a harsh alarm call that is more pronounced than those of its relatives.

Although the hooded parrot is not as threatened as the golden-shouldered parrot, it has declined in numbers for similar reasons, and is probably still the target of illegal trapping for the cage-bird trade. It is particularly vulnerable when small flocks gather at the few remaining waterholes at the end of the dry season. Like the golden-shouldered parrot, it depends on an abundance of grass seed, especially when it is raising its young, so that changes in burning practices on grazing lands have dramatically reduced its numbers. Establishing fire patterns that are more suitable for these parrots – and for all seed-eating wildlife – is a challenge for wildlife managers.
Scientific name: *Psephotus dissimilis*

RED-RUMPED PARROT

The male red-rumped parrot has a bright red patch on its rump, which can most easily be seen in flight. Its plumage is mainly green with a bluish hue, and underneath it is generally yellow. The female is a dull olive green. Both males and females are about 27 cm long. The main call of this species is a rasping two-syllable whistle, but it also utters a harsh chatter.

These parrots normally live in the dry open woodlands of the south-eastern corner of Australia, close to supplies of fresh water. Their numbers seem to have increased as a consequence of forest clearing and the resulting new supplies of seed and water. They are now common on farmland, around homesteads, and even in urban parks. They may make minor seasonal movements, but most red-rumped parrots appear to be sedentary.

The favourite food of red-rumped parrots is grass seeds, but they also consume berries and vegetable

■ HOODED PARROT
These birds are found in the open eucalypt forests of Arnhem Land. Only the male has a black hood and face.

matter, including thistle leaves. To aid in digestion, they consume grit and sand to break up tough seeds in their muscular gizzards. They feed on the ground in pairs or small family parties, moving quickly and quietly as they forage. Flocks are trusting, even when on the ground, and allow humans to approach closely.

Pairs, often recognised by their mutual preening behaviour, remain together outside the nesting season.
Scientific name: *Psephotus haematonotus*

BOURKE'S PARROT

The male of this species is predominantly pastel pink and blue. Its underparts are mainly pink; the front edges of its wings, as well as most of its underwings, are blue; and it has a blue patch on its forehead. Its crown and back are a greyish brown. The female is less colourful and has no blue markings on its head. These parrots are about 21 cm long and have a fine, delicate appearance. They have a quiet disposition and are not easily alarmed.

They normally live in the mulga shrublands of the central and western inland. They are unobtrusive and can be present in considerable numbers yet go largely unnoticed. During the day they feed quietly in pairs or small flocks on the ground, or sit motionless in low shrubs. Their call is a soft twitter. Bourke's parrots appear to be active both day and night, and there are many records of birds heading for waterholes to drink late at night.

In most areas these parrots probably live mainly on acacia seed, which they take directly from trees or from the ground. In some regions their numbers may have declined because sheep and rabbits have depleted their food sources, or because cats have preyed on them. In other areas, however – particularly in Western Australia – the provision of water for stock, together with low rates of sheep stocking, may have lead to increases in their numbers.
Scientific name: *Neopsephotus bourkii*

■ RED-RUMPED PARROT
True to its name, the male of this eastern Australian species has a scarlet rump. The female is largely olive green in colour.

205

■ GRASS PARROT
Unlike most parrots, the rock parrot (*Neophema petrophila*) is found on offshore islands and coastal sand dunes. In windy weather it shelters behind rocks, but on still days it circles high in the sky.

DISTRIBUTION

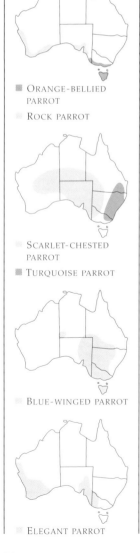

■ ORANGE-BELLIED PARROT

■ ROCK PARROT

■ SCARLET-CHESTED PARROT

■ TURQUOISE PARROT

■ BLUE-WINGED PARROT

■ ELEGANT PARROT

GRASS PARROTS ■

Six small species of ground-feeding parrot from the *Neophema* genus are found in Australia, all of them growing to about 20–22 cm long. Some species are difficult to tell apart in the field, especially when only the more sombre female or immature birds are visible.

The orange-bellied parrot (*Neophema chrysogaster*) is a seriously endangered species. Males have green backs, blue foreheads, blue-edged wings and yellow bellies with an indistinct orange belly pattern. Females are generally less colourful.

Fewer than 500 of these birds remain in the wild. Unlike most Australian bush birds, the orange-bellied parrot has a well-defined annual migration pattern. In summer it breeds in the isolated south-west wilderness of Tasmania, and then flies across Bass Strait to winter on the coastal flats of the south-eastern seaboard. Compared with the safety of their breeding haunts, their winter refuges are fraught with danger caused by intensive human activity. Urban centres, recreational activities and industrial development all threaten these birds.

Recently, measures such as control of feral animals, development of nature reserves and minimisation of human disturbance have been implemented to protect this species.

It seems incongruous to find a parrot moving about the seashore and sand dunes, yet that is where the rock parrot (*N. petrophila*) forages for food. Rock parrots feed on the seeds of small plants growing on the coastal dunes, rocky islands and salt marshes of southern and western Australia. They usually nest on islands in a protected site among boulders overhung with vegetation. Rock parrots are mainly olive brown above and yellow below, with blue wings and facial markings.

Despite its vivid colouring, the scarlet-chested parrot (*N. splendida*) is so docile that it often goes unnoticed; this may be partly why it is reported to be rare. The male scarlet-chested parrot's face is a brilliant, glossy blue, its chest is blood red and its belly is golden-yellow. Its green back is its most obvious feature when it feeds on the ground, and its blue wings are apparent only in flight. Females are similar in colouring, but lack the red chest.

Scarlet-chested parrots are residents of the arid shrublands of southern Australia. They usually remain in pairs or small flocks, but from time to time – and inexplicably – they form large flocks that move to the edges of their usual range.

Three other grass parrots – the turquoise parrot (*N. pulchella*), the blue-winged parrot (*N. chrysostoma*) and the elegant parrot (*N. elegans*) – are very difficult to tell apart. The males of all three species have dull green backs and yellow bellies. Turquoise parrots have a blue face, while the other two species have blue eyebrows and foreheads. The main difference between them is the colouring on the wings: turquoise parrots have a two-toned blue patch and a dull red patch on their wings; the elegant parrot's wings have no red on them and are edged in two-toned blue; and the wings of the blue-winged parrot are deep blue.

The turquoise parrot is the most common of these species in eastern Australia and only the elegant parrot occurs in Western Australia, but all three species sometimes occur together in parts of central and south-eastern Australia.
Scientific name: *Neophema* spp.

■ GRASS PARROTS
A male turquoise parrot (*Neophema pulchella*) feeds its young at the nest. This nomadic species inhabits the mountain ranges of eastern Australia.

■ BUDGERIGAR

■ NIGHT PARROT
■ GROUND PARROT

BUDGERIGAR ■

In the wild the budgerigar has only one colour form – green with fine dark stripes across its head and back, and a yellow face. The blue band on the top of the bill is darker in the male than the female. Both sexes grow to 18 cm long.

Budgerigars are nomadic, feeding on any small seeding plants and breeding whenever the irregular rains of the inland bring new plant growth. If conditions are favourable, a pair may have several broods in quick succession.

Budgerigars usually nest in colonies of hundreds of birds. Each pair claims a nest site in a small tree hollow, and the female lays around five eggs. The chicks remain in the nest for about five weeks before taking to the air, and they become independent within days.

Wild budgerigars are well known for their impressive coordinated flight displays involving twists and turns, performed especially at dusk as flocks prepare to roost. As the sun sets, these noisy, fast-wheeling birds drop into the thick foliage of the trees and settle down for the night.
Scientific name: *Melopsittacus undulatus*

NIGHT PARROT

Over the years many expeditions have been mounted to find this parrot. There have been only two confirmed sightings in the twentieth century – one in 1912 in the deserts of Western Australia, and one dead specimen in 1990, found beside a track in the arid Diamantina region of south-western Queensland. There have been unconfirmed sightings from northern South Australia, but until the 1990 find it was feared that the species might be extinct. Our knowledge of these parrots comes from nineteenth-century reports.

Night parrots are shy nocturnal birds that live in the deserts of central Australia, probably feeding mainly on spinifex seeds. They are well camouflaged and nomadic, and extremely difficult to find – as the scarcity of confirmed sightings amply shows. Like ground parrots, they conceal themselves during the day in the base of tussocks or even in burrows dug in the sand; when disturbed they break from cover, flying clumsily for a short distance before dropping to the ground and running into cover. It is very difficult to flush them a second time.

Night parrots reach a length of 25 cm and resemble ground parrots, except that they have no red patches. They are thickset and yellow-green with black mottled markings, and they whistle and croak as they fly.
Scientific name: *Geopsittacus occidentalis*

GROUND PARROT ■

Unlike almost all other parrots, this bird lives on the ground and is largely nocturnal. It lives in swampy heaths, where it roosts by day beneath tussocky vegetation. If disturbed it bursts from the undergrowth, flying low over the heath for 50 metres or so before crashing down out of sight in the undergrowth. It is rarely observed while on the ground.

As darkness falls, and just before dawn, ground parrots become very vocal, making the thin, whistling calls typical of many parrots.

■ BUDGERIGARS
The arid inland of Australia is the natural home of the world's most popular cage bird. Budgerigars in the wild are always the same vivid green.

Growing to about 30 cm long and with green plumage flecked with black streaks, ground parrots look like large budgerigars. They have a prominent red spot above their bill, and in flight their long, slender tail marked with yellow bars becomes obvious. They feed on heathland, where they rely on regular bushfires to maintain a balance of food plants.

Much of the ground parrot's eastern seaboard habitat has been destroyed by urban and industrial development. Fortunately this bird also occurs in large numbers in the remote west of Tasmania, where it is protected in large national parks.
Scientific name: *Pezoporus wallicus*

■ GROUND PARROT
Heathland flowers are the staple diet of the ground parrot. It once lived in swampy country along the coast from Brisbane to Adelaide, but many of their habitats were destroyed when these areas were drained and built over.

CUCKOOS

Of about 130 cuckoo species worldwide, 13 occur regularly in Australia. Twelve of these species lay their eggs in the nests of other species. The thirteenth, the pheasant coucal, is the sole Australian representative of its family, and is the only Australian cuckoo to incubate and rear its young.

Australian cuckoos range in size from the little bronze-cuckoo, at about 14 cm long, to the pheasant coucal at 75 cm long. Their plumage is mainly black, brown, grey and fawn, and most have dark bars across their underparts. All cuckoos have a slightly downcurved bill, and most are insect-eaters, though the channel-billed cuckoo and the koel are chiefly fruit-eaters and the coucal eats small animals. All cuckoos have a distinctive call, and this can be the best means of identification. They belong to the order Cuculiformes.

PARASITIC CUCKOOS

LARGE AND SMALL
Australian parasitic cuckoos range in size from Gould's bronze-cuckoo, about 14 cm long, to the channel-billed cuckoo, which can reach 65 cm in length.

ROOM FOR ONE ONLY
A cuckoo chick, barely hatched, heaves its host's egg out of the nest. The host bird is a robin.

Parasitic cuckoos lay their eggs in the nests of many host species, but each cuckoo species favours a few hosts that it regularly chooses. These are probably the species that are more ready to accept an alien egg – incubating it and rearing the young cuckoo as though it were their own – and so offer better survival odds for the cuckoo.

To escape detection, many cuckoos lay eggs similar to their host's eggs in pattern, colour, size and shape; others choose hosts that build enclosed nests and then lay dark, nondescript eggs in their dimly lit interiors, where the eggs are difficult to distinguish from the hosts' own.

By accepting the cuckoo's egg, the host bird jeopardises the lives of its own young. In some species, the young cuckoo's first task after it hatches is to eject the host's young from the nest; it balances the eggs or nestlings on the flattened area in the middle of its back and then levers them, one by one, up the side of the nest and over the edge.

Other cuckoo species lay eggs that have very short incubation times, so that the chicks hatch much earlier than the other eggs in the nest. This early hatching, coupled with a more brightly coloured gape, enables the young cuckoo to out-compete the other nestlings for food, so that they simply starve to death.

Young cuckoos are so demanding that the host birds continue to feed them well after they leave the nest; sometimes even birds that did not incubate the eggs will feed them.

Ten of the 12 species of parasitic cuckoo that live in Australia have been recorded breeding here. Of the other two species, the oriental cuckoo is known to breed in the northern hemisphere; but whether the chestnut-breasted cuckoo breeds in Australia or not is something of a mystery.
Family: Cuculidae

ORIENTAL CUCKOO

Common in most forest and woodland areas of northern and eastern Australia, especially from January to May, this species is also fairly common and widespread throughout Asia. It is found in Australia for most of the year, but does not appear to breed here.

The oriental cuckoo is 28–34 cm long, with grey upperparts that become darker on its wings and conspicuous black and white bars on its lower breast and belly. Its underwings, which are visible in flight, are also barred with black and white. Its feet and eye rings and the base of its bill are yellow. Immature birds have brown instead of black bars on their underparts, and are mainly a rufous brown above.

Although generally silent in Australia, this cuckoo has a very distinctive high-pitched 'pi-pi-pi-pi' call, followed by a series of three to five 'kup-kup-kup' sounds.
Scientific name: *Cuculus saturatus*

PALLID CUCKOO

The pallid cuckoo is the most common and widespread of the Australian cuckoos. Growing to a length of 28–34 cm, pallid cuckoos are easily identified by their predominantly grey plumage and broadly barred black and white undertail. Immature pallid cuckoos are mottled with brown and buff above, have a white spot on their nape, and are streaked with greyish brown and white below.

The pallid cuckoo inhabits open forests and areas of woodland, as well as cleared and cultivated open country, and is able to parasitise a wide range of other bird species, including yellow-faced honeyeaters, fuscous honeyeaters, willie wagtails, hooded robins and some species of woodswallow.

As is the case with other cuckoos, its call – a loud, ascending, whistling 'too-too-too', repeated several times – normally betrays its presence some time before it can actually be seen.
Scientific name: *Cuculus pallidus*

BRONZE-CUCKOOS

In addition to the breast bars that characterise many cuckoo species, four of the five bronze-cuckoos are distinguished by the metallic bronze or green plumage on their upper-parts. The exception is the black-eared cuckoo (*Chrysococcyx osculans*), which is grey above with a broad black eye stripe and only a faint metallic gloss. It is 19–21 cm long.

The immature Horsfield's bronze-cuckoo (*C. basalis*) is very similar to the black-eared cuckoo except that it has rufous coloration on its tail, but the adult of the species, 14–17 cm long, has the typical dull green metallic sheen on its upper parts. This species also has a longitudinal dash of rufous on either side of its tail, incomplete coppery bronze crossbars on its underparts, and white eyebrows. Both Horsfield's bronze-cuckoo and the black-eared cuckoo are widely distributed over much of Australia.

The little bronze-cuckoo (*C. minutillus*) is found only in the rainforests and open forests of the northern parts of Australia. It is 14–16 cm long, and can be distinguished from the very similar Horsfield's bronze-cuckoo by the narrow, incomplete bronze crossbars on its underparts, extending up its throat, and by its less pronounced white eyebrows. Gould's bronze-cuckoo (*C. russatus*), which lives only on the eastern side of Cape York Peninsula, is the same size as the little bronze-cuckoo but its upperparts are more bronze and it has a reddish coloration on its chest. The males of both the little bronze-cuckoo and Gould's bronze-cuckoo have red eye rings.

The shining bronze-cuckoo (*C. lucidus*) is 16–18 cm long and has white underparts with complete coppery bronze crossbars and a copper-coloured head. Young birds have grey-brown or greenish brown upperparts, with darker brown mottling on their face, and whitish underparts with some brown bars on their flanks. The shining bronze-cuckoo lives throughout eastern Australia and in south-western and northern Western Australia.

Bronze-cuckoos call with a combination of rising or falling whistles.
Scientific name: *Chrysococcyx* spp.

FAN-TAILED CUCKOOS

The fan-tailed cuckoo (*Cacomantis flabelliformis*), which favours open forests, woodlands and gardens with plenty of trees, is one of the more commonly seen members of the cuckoo family. Its mournful

BRONZE-CUCKOO
This shining bronze-cuckoo (*Chrysococcyx lucidus*) is displaying the breast bars that are common to many cuckoo species.

descending trill often draws attention to its presence. In Australia it ranges throughout the eastern part of the continent from Cape York in Queensland around to the Eyre Peninsula in South Australia, and also occurs in the south-western corner of Western Australia.

The adult bird is 24–28 cm long and has, as its name suggests, a fan-shaped tail. It has a dark, slate grey back and wings, pale rufous underparts and a boldly barred black and white undertail. Immature birds are predominantly brown above, with a red-brown edging to their feathers, and are paler underneath, with no markings. The striking yellow eye ring of the fan-tailed cuckoo is visible from a distance and distinguishes it from the related – though slightly smaller, at 20–24 cm long – brush cuckoo (*C. variolosus*), which inhabits open forests and denser woodlands throughout northern and eastern Australia. The brush cuckoo is paler and has grey eye rings. Both the fan-tailed cuckoo and the brush cuckoo visit New Guinea regularly.

The closely related chestnut-breasted cuckoo (*C. castaneiventris*) is 23–25 cm long, with dark chestnut underparts and less distinct barring on its undertail. It is restricted in Australia to the rainforests of Cape York Peninsula, but its range extends north to New Guinea, Sulawesi and the Aru Islands. There are no records of this cuckoo breeding in Australia.
Scientific name: *Cacomantis* spp.

COMMON KOEL

More often heard than seen, the common koel visits Australia from Indonesia and New Guinea each year to breed. Its arrival in late September or early October is heralded by the male's unusual call, a loud, repetitive 'ko-el', the second note being higher than the first, and each stanza increasing in pitch. This call may persist throughout the night and into the early hours of morning, and sometimes gives people sleepless nights. The female's call is a less distinct, repetitive 'wook-wook-wook'.

At 39–46 cm long, koels are large cuckoos. Adult males have striking deep blue-black plumage and bright red eyes, while adult females and younger birds are pale brown and finely barred with dark brown below, and darker brown and black on their upperparts. Adult females have conspicuous white spots on their back and wings, and immature birds are similar but have a broad black line above their eyes.

The koel lays a single egg in the nest of a figbird or a magpie-lark, or in that of a larger honeyeater, such as a friarbird. Once hatched, the koel chick forces the other eggs and hatchlings out of the nest.

When the chick leaves the nest it roosts in the outer branches of a tree, cheeping incessantly while its significantly smaller step-parents search desperately for enough food to satisfy the nagging youngster – a full-time job, as the young koel grows to nearly twice their size over the next four to six weeks. During March and early April, adult koels gradually make their way back to Asia, where they may breed again, this time parasitising various members of the crow family.
Scientific name: *Eudynamys scolopacea*

DISTRIBUTION

ORIENTAL CUCKOO

PALLID CUCKOO

BRONZE-CUCKOOS

FAN-TAILED CUCKOOS

COMMON KOEL

HUNGRY AS A HUNTER
The insatiable fledgling pallid cuckoo dwarfs its tireless foster-parent. Over 80 bird species play host to this cuckoo.

CHANNEL-BILLED CUCKOO ■

The channel-billed cuckoo looks nothing like any of the other Australian cuckoos. It grows to about 58–65 cm long and has a massive, gently downcurved bill. Its body is predominantly pale grey, becoming darker on the wings and tail, and its cere (the base of the upper bill), its eyes and the naked skin around its eyes are all red. In flight its long tail and wings give this bird a silhouette somewhat resembling a crucifix. Channel-billed cuckoos eat mainly figs and other native fruits, which is also unusual in the cuckoo family.

Between August and October these cuckoos migrate southward from Indonesia and New Guinea to tall, open forests in northern and eastern Australia. The females lay one or two eggs in the nests of larger birds, such as the collared sparrowhawk, the Australian magpie or the pied currawong. When laying her eggs the channel-billed cuckoo frequently damages the eggs that have already been laid in the nest, but if the host's own eggs do eventually hatch, the

young channel-billed cuckoo does not evict the chicks, as many cuckoos do. Instead, the parasitic chick starves out the other chicks by demanding all the food that the adult birds bring to the nest.

The call of the channel-billed cuckoo, a loud 'kawk' followed by a more rapid and weaker 'awk-awk-awk …', is as distinctive as the bird's

■ CHANNEL-BILLED CUCKOO
This is the largest parasitic cuckoo in the world. Unusually, it feeds on native figs and other fruits rather than insects.

appearance. These cuckoos call most often in flight, although they sometimes also call when perching.
Scientific name: *Scythrops novaehollandiae*

COUCALS

Coucals are mainly ground-dwellers. Unlike parasitic cuckoos, they incubate and raise their own young. Their nests are usually platforms of flattened grasses, often in a tussock, over which they pull the surrounding vegetation in order to form a dome, though occasionally they build their nest up to 2 metres above the ground in low, bushy trees.
Family: Centropodidae

PHEASANT COUCAL ■

The long, pheasant-like tail and short, rounded wings of this bird account for the common name for this sole Australian representative of the coucal family.

Outside the breeding season, the pheasant coucal's straw-coloured plumage, mottled with black and brown, provides good camouflage in the thick vegetation of northern and eastern Australia where it lives. In breeding plumage its head, neck and underparts become sooty black and its back, wings and tail rufous with black and buff barring. Coucals vary considerably in length – from 45 cm to 75 cm – partly because their tails tend to grow longer during the breeding season.

Pheasant coucals feed on terrestrial and aquatic animals such as lizards, frogs, small mammals and birds, and on insects, which they mostly catch on the ground. If startled from their refuge in the long grass, they will fly clumsily, usually for only a

■ PHEASANT COUCAL
These birds live mainly on the ground, sometimes clambering around in the bushes to collect nesting material.

CUCKOOS IN THEIR OWN NEST
Unlike all other Australian cuckoos, pheasant coucals raise their own young. These chicks are begging for food.

short distance, before dropping back into the dense vegetation. Their call is a distinctive 'oop-oop-oop-oop-oop …', dropping in pitch in the middle of the call and rising at the end. Both male and female pheasant coucals construct the nest, incubate the two to five eggs and then feed their young. The young leave the nest 15 days after hatching.
Scientific name: *Centropus phasianinus*

OWLS

These nocturnal birds of prey can see objects and movement in half the light needed for human vision, and they can also see well in daylight. Owls locate their prey by sound and then swoop silently, seizing their victim in their claws and biting its neck. They swallow their smaller prey whole and regurgitate the bones in pellets of fur and feathers.

Owls are not related to the diurnal birds of prey, the raptors (pages 154–61), but they share some of the raptors' hunting adaptations, such as a hooked beak and powerful feet with sharp claws. Their flight feathers have soft edges, so that their flight is virtually soundless.

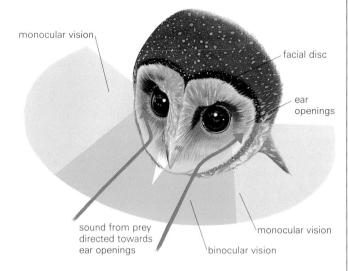

monocular vision

facial disc

ear openings

sound from prey directed towards ear openings

monocular vision

binocular vision

Australia has nine owl species, which fall into two groups: the masked owls – masked owl, sooty owl and lesser sooty owl, barn owl and grass owl; and the hawk-owls – powerful owl, barking owl, rufous owl and southern boobook.

Masked owls have prominent facial discs, edged with a ruff of stiff feathers. They are pale underneath, with moth-like plumage, and their calls are various screeches and screams. Hawk-owls are brown with indistinct facial discs, and their calls are commonly double hoots.

Owls appear singly, in pairs or in family groups. Except for the power-ful owl, the barking owl and the rufous owl, females are larger than males. Pairs normally bond for life in traditional nest hollows, and the female incubates the eggs while the male feeds her.

Males also offer titbits of food dur-ing courtship, and the male masked owl performs flight displays, the female joining him in chattering duets from a perch. The pair then mate in their nest hollow. Courting hawk-owls hoot in duet, and each preens the other's head before mat-ing on a branch.

Being nocturnal, owls are more often heard than seen. During the day, small birds sometimes reveal the presence of hawk-owls by diving and scolding at their tree roosts.
Order: Strigiformes

MASKED OWL ▪

The masked owl lives in forests and woodlands over much of Australia, except for the driest central regions.

▪ MASKED OWL
This owl detects its prey by sound as it scans the landscape from a perch. It swallows its smaller victims whole and tears larger ones into strips.

Its loud, harsh screech can be heard in wooded farmland and in the forested fringes of cities. By day it sleeps in hollows or roosts in thick foliage. On the Nullarbor Plain and similar places it lives in caves.

Its upperparts are brown and its underparts and facial disc vary from chestnut to white. It grows to about 40–50 cm long, and is particularly large and dark in Tasmania. Paler masked owls can be mistaken for barn owls, but the masked owl has thick legs that are feathered down to the base of its toes, and large feet.

This owl eats mammals, birds, reptiles and insects. In southern Australia, introduced mice, rats and rabbits form most of its diet. Females lay two or three eggs at any time

of year, although usually between autumn and spring. The eggs hatch in five weeks and the young stay in the nest for about ten weeks.
Scientific name: *Tyto novaehollandiae*

SOOTY OWLS
There are two sooty owl species. Both have large eyes and round faces bordered with dark feathers, and both have dark grey upperparts spotted with white, although the spotting on the lesser sooty owl (*Tyto multipunctata*) is more profuse.

At 40–45 cm long, the sooty owl (*T. tenebricosa*) is the larger of the two species. It has a grey face and a grey underside spotted with white. The lesser sooty owl (about 35 cm long) has a white face, and its white

SIGHT AND SOUND
Located at the front of their head, owls' eyes give them quite wide frontal binocular vision, and their heart-shaped facial disc directs sound towards their large ear openings. The hearing of masked owls, such as this lesser sooty owl, is so acute that they need little light to detect prey.

DISTRIBUTION

▪ MASKED OWL

▪ LESSER SOOTY OWL
□ SOOTY OWL

DISTRIBUTION

BARN OWL

GRASS OWL

POWERFUL OWL

■ GRASS OWLS
The almost naked legs of the rare grass owl are visible when the bird flies (left). Above, a chick peers from its nest at the end of a tunnel hidden by ground cover.

underparts are barred with grey. Sooty owls mostly eat possums, gliders and rats, which they catch in trees and on the ground.

The sooty owl is uncommon, but not as rare as some believe. It lives in rainforest and wet eucalypt forest between Brisbane and Melbourne; recent sightings have confirmed that there is also a population living in the Eungella area near Mackay in Queensland. The lesser sooty owl lives in rainforest around Cairns in far northern Queensland, and is common within its limited area.

These owls lay one or two eggs – usually two – in a tree hollow at any time of year, but generally in autumn or spring. The eggs hatch in about six weeks and the young remain in the nest for another three months.

The call of both sooty owl species is a descending whistle or scream – a spine-chilling sound at close range. By day they sleep in hollows, in dense gully vegetation, or in caves.
Scientific name: *Tyto* spp.

BARN OWL ■
Barn owls are about 35 cm long, a mottled pearl grey above and white underneath, with slim legs that are bare on the lower half and end in small feet. With their heart-shaped facial disc and asymmetrical ear

■ BARN OWL
Although common in open woodland in much of Australia, the barn owl is not often heard because it rarely calls.

openings, they can pinpoint sounds of scuttling prey in total darkness, their silent flight then enabling them to pounce without warning.

Common in open woodland and farmland over most of Australia, but rare in Tasmania, barn owls roost in tree hollows and caves and eat small mammals and birds, reptiles, frogs and insects. Introduced house mice and also rats form much of their diet.

The barn owl lays a clutch of three or four eggs in a tree hollow or other cavity whenever food is abundant, usually from autumn to spring. Breeding may be continuous, with clutches of up to seven eggs being produced during mouse plagues. The eggs take a month to hatch, and the young remain in the nest for seven to ten weeks.
Scientific name: *Tyto alba*

GRASS OWL ■
This rare owl lives in extensive areas of rank, swampy grasses in northern and inland Australia, including the canefields of the Queensland and

northern New South Wales coasts. It is seldom seen. It is easily confused with the barn owl, but the grass owl is a darker brown above and cream or fawn below. It is about 35 cm long and has long, slender, bare legs that trail behind its tail in flight. As well as a screech like that of the barn owl, it has a distinctive repeated chirruping call.

The grass owl eats mammals, birds and insects, mostly the native canefield rat, the native long-haired or plague rat and the introduced house mouse. It hunts in flight, stopping to hover, then dropping to reach deep into cover with its long legs. It lives on the ground, making nest chambers and tunnels, which are invisible from above, in tall, thick grass. The feathers on the lower parts of its legs are reduced to a few bristles.

The female usually lays a clutch of three or four eggs in autumn and winter, though when food is abundant she can also lay at other times, and may produce up to eight eggs in each clutch during rodent plagues. The eggs hatch in a month, and the young are able to fly within two months. Eggs and nestlings are extremely vulnerable to foxes, which may explain the rarity of this species.
Scientific name: *Tyto capensis*

POWERFUL OWL
At about 60 cm long – the size of a small eagle – this is Australia's largest owl. It eats birds, large insects and mammals, mostly possums and gliders that it takes from the trees, but also flying foxes and a variety of other animals, including rats, and sometimes even cats. It catches insects and some birds in flight. Powerful owls hunt within a large permanent home range of 800–1000 hectares.

Powerful owls are brown with relatively small heads and big yellow eyes. Their feathers are marked with

dark bars, fine on the upperparts and coarse and wavy underneath.

Endemic to Australia, the powerful owl lives in the eucalypt forests of south-eastern Australia, from near Rockhampton in Queensland to near Melbourne in Victoria, and inland as far as the western slopes of the Great Dividing Range. It is uncommon, though not as rare as was once believed. By day these owls sleep in dense vegetation in gullies, but at night they range out into urban bushland and sometimes into near-by gardens. Their distinctive call is a slow, loud, mournful 'woo-hoo'.

Powerful owls lay a clutch of one or two eggs – usually two – in a big tree hollow in late autumn or early winter. The eggs hatch in five to six weeks, and the young spend a further eight to nine weeks in the nest. Recently fledged young powerful owls have white down on their heads and underparts, marked by a few streaks and smudges.
Scientific name: *Ninox strenua*

BARKING OWL

This owl gets its name from its distinctive call – a quick double hoot, rather like the barking of a dog. Its repertoire also includes a quavering wail that sounds like a terrified woman screaming for help, and from this sound it gets several macabre folk names – the screaming woman owl and the murder bird.

The barking owl is a sturdy species, about 40 cm long, grey-brown above and white streaked with greyish brown on its underparts. It has large yellow eyes and dark yellow feet. It is found in the open forests, woodlands and paperbark swamps of northern, eastern and south-western Australia, where it roosts in trees during the day. It is common in the tropics but is now rare in more southern regions.

It feeds on large insects, birds up to magpie size, and mammals; in the south, rabbits form a major part of its diet, though it also takes and eats small possums, gliders and birds. In summer and autumn this owl consumes large quantities of insects, which it catches on the wing.

In late winter or spring, the barking owl lays a clutch of two or three eggs in a nest lined with wood chips or twigs. It builds its nest in a large tree hollow, or occasionally in a tree crotch, rock crevice or rabbit burrow.

The eggs hatch in five weeks, and the young spend a further five weeks in the nest before they start to fly – which they can manage while they are still downy. When they fly from

■ BARKING OWL
Named for its 'barking dog' call, this owl also has a high-pitched cry that sounds like a scream for help – hence its other common names, the screaming woman owl and the murder bird.

the nest they have the adult pattern of streaks on their breast, though they still have a fluffy collar.
Scientific name: *Ninox connivens*

RUFOUS OWL

The rufous owl is a rich reddish brown with fine cream-coloured bars, and has big yellow eyes. It is 50 cm long and lives in tropical lowlands, woodlands and paperbark swamps, sleeping by day in riverine rainforest and ranging at night into more open forest and woodland. It eats mammals, birds and large insects, mostly taking flying foxes, possums and gliders from the trees, but also catching many birds and a variety of smaller mammals on the ground as well as in the trees. Its call is a slow 'hoo-hoo', like that of the powerful owl, but softer and with less carrying power.

Females lay a clutch of one or two eggs – usually two – in a large tree hollow during winter or spring. The eggs take five to six weeks to hatch, and the young remain in the nest for a further six to eight weeks. Recently fledged young rufous owls are snow white on the head and underparts and have dark eye patches.

The rufous owl is not common in its range, which extends across northern Australia from the Kimberley region of Western Australia to Cape York Peninsula in Queensland and down the east

coast, where it overlaps with the range of the powerful owl. Because the calls of the rufous owl and the powerful owl sound so similar, the range of the rufous owl is not known for certain. It may occur as far south as Gladstone or it may extend even further south.
Scientific name: *Ninox rufa*

SOUTHERN BOOBOOK ■

This owl is common throughout mainland Australia, Tasmania and offshore islands, and its nightly two-note 'mopoke' or 'boobook' call is a familiar sound. It occurs in open forest, woodland, farmland, and even leafy suburbs. In areas lacking hollows or dense trees, it may roost in caves or derelict buildings.

On its upperparts the southern boobook is a rich brown, normally spotted with white; underneath, its white and brown colouring forms a splotched patterning. It has pale hazel eyes surrounded by dark patches, and white eyebrows. Its feet are small and pale. At only about 30 cm long, it is Australia's smallest owl.

When breeding, the southern boobook eats mostly small birds such as sparrows, and mammals such as mice; at other times insects are its main diet, and boobooks are sometimes seen chasing insects around streetlights. In spring, or occasionally in summer or autumn, the boobook lays a clutch of two or three eggs, sometimes four, in a tree hollow. The eggs hatch in a month, and the young spend a further five to six weeks in the nest. Recently fledged young have down on their heads and underneath, marked in a faint pattern like the adults' plumage. The young beg with a trilling, cricket-like call.
Scientific name: *Ninox novaeseelandiae*

DISTRIBUTION

■ BARKING OWL

■ RUFOUS OWL

■ SOUTHERN BOOBOOK

■ SOUTHERN BOOBOOK
Shown here landing at its nest, the southern boobook is the smallest and most abundant of Australia's owls. It is sometimes known as a mopoke, because of its two-note call.

Featherlight!

Some birds cannot fly, and a few fishes and mammals can. What marks birds out is not the power of flight but the possession of feathers.

The outer feathers of a bird are either body feathers, which give the body a streamlined shape and reduce drag in flight, or flight feathers on the wings and tail that are spread to provide efficient aerodynamic surfaces. There are also fluffy underfeathers, called down, that trap a layer of air next to the bird's skin to provide insulation. If the bird becomes cold, it fluffs up its feathers to increase this air layer.

Protection, primping and preening

Feathers are designed for more than flight. Their coloration and patterning can provide camouflage, which is very useful for females incubating eggs in an open nest. Many birds are dark above and lighter below to counteract the effects of their own shadow. Colours, patterns and forms are also important for species to recognise one another. Males often have bright plumage for courtship display, and some birds, such as the lyrebird, have splendid decorative plumes.

Feathers also provide waterproofing, and water birds reinforce this by preening themselves with a waxy oil, secreted from a gland at the base of the tail, that protects the bird against wetting and keeps its feathers flexible.

Barn swallows flying in formation show some of a bird's wing movements: the preparation for the downstroke, the downstroke itself, and the upstroke.

An Australian darter in flight illustrates how birds can use their tail feathers as a rudder when they fly.

Preening also helps to keep a bird's flight feathers in top condition. A typical feather has a central shaft, from which grows a series of barbs. From each barb grow hundreds of little barbules, each equipped with tiny hooks that lock into the barbules of the neighbouring barb so that the barbules mesh together like the teeth of a zip to create a smooth,

The slots at the tips of a wedge-tailed eagle's wing help the bird to ride the thermal currents.

light, flexible surface. These attachments easily come unstuck during the bird's normal activities, but the bird simply runs its beak along its feathers to preen itself and the barbules zip together again.

Replacing worn feathers

In time, feathers loosen in their follicles and are pushed out by new feathers growing underneath in a process called moulting. Since feathers provide both protection and mobility, moulting must occur in a way that does not compromise these functions, so most birds lose and replace their feathers gradually. Birds living in the same place all the time and those living in open habitats generally moult once a year, usually just after breeding, but long-distance migrants and water birds wear out their feathers more rapidly, and may moult twice a year.

A penguin's feathers grow more densely than those of other birds, and penguins must replace all their plumage in one moult. New feathers begin to form while the birds are still hunting at sea, which reduces the moulting period a bit, but they still need to come ashore for about 15 days to complete the process. During this time their waterproofing and insulation are significantly reduced, so that they cannot go to sea and therefore cannot feed. Replacing feathers takes a lot of energy and penguins lose about 39 per cent of their body weight when they moult, so moulting must take place when other energy-demanding activities such as breeding are completed, and when food is plentiful so that the birds can build up their reserves of body fat.

FROGMOUTHS AND NIGHTJARS

The order Caprimulgiformes contains three families – the frogmouths, the owlet nightjars and the nightjars. All are nocturnal, insect-catching birds with wide, gaping bills and large eyes for night vision. Like owls, they have binocular vision for pinpointing prey. Their plumage is dappled grey and brown for daytime camouflage and their feathers have soft edges for silent night flying. Sensitive bristles around their beak help them to detect and capture their prey.

SHOW OF AGGRESSION
These young tawny frogmouths are peeping out from the nest and showing their yellow throats to frighten off an enemy.

FROGMOUTHS

Frogmouths live in forests and woodlands. During the day they sit upright and motionless on branches or on the ground, head tilted up and eyes closed to slits. The tufts of bristly feathers around their broad, triangular beak help to break up their outline, and their plumage, which is finely streaked and mottled in grey, brown and reddish brown, resembles tree bark in the dappled forest light.

So perfect is their camouflage that a frogmouth roosting in a tree looks just like a broken branch. If this disguise is penetrated, however, it adopts a threatening pose, fluffing out its feathers, displaying its large orange eyes and opening its beak in a wide, frog-like gape to reveal a startling yellow throat.

At dusk frogmouths begin hunting for food. From a perch they watch the ground for insects, small frogs and lizards, planing down on them on their long, rounded wings.

All Australian frogmouth species are spring and summer breeders, pairs forming lifelong bonds and occupying the same small patch of forest throughout the year. The pair build their nest together, breaking twigs into small pieces and weaving them into a platform in the fork of a tree. They also share incubation.

Of the 14 frogmouth species, three are found in Australia; the others occur across South-East Asia, from India to the Philippines.
Family: Podargidae

■ TAWNY FROGMOUTHS
On their daytime perch, tawny frogmouths tip their heads up, raise their beaks and slit their eyes in an uncanny imitation of broken branches.

TAWNY FROGMOUTH ■
Tawny frogmouths are common throughout Australia wherever there are trees and space to hunt for food, though they are scarcer in dense rainforest and the sparse interior.

They are plump-bodied birds with light grey to dark grey plumage and large orange eyes. In the south-east they grow to about 50 cm long, and in the north and west they reach 40 cm long. Frogmouths are so well camouflaged that their humming 'ooom-ooom' call is often the only clue to their whereabouts. They resort to aggressive behaviour – feathers fluffed out and beak wide open – only when their camouflage is unsuccessful.

Tawny frogmouths lay up to four eggs, which hatch into downy chicks after a month. Parents share all the nesting duties, including incubation, brooding and feeding of the young. After the breeding season frogmouth families often perch side by side on the same branch during the day.
Scientific name: *Podargus strigoides*

DISTRIBUTION

■ TAWNY FROGMOUTH

DISTRIBUTION

■ MARBLED FROGMOUTH

■ PAPUAN FROGMOUTH

MARBLED FROGMOUTH

The marbled frogmouth, or plumed frogmouth, occurs in two widely separated east coast locations – the Cape York Peninsula and the coast between Gladstone in Queensland and Lismore in New South Wales. Because of the destruction of its habitat by farming activities, the southern population is under threat.

In the north, marbled frogmouths have an average body size of 40 cm, while in the south they are a little larger, at 46 cm long. They have the frogmouth's typical plumage, patterned like the bark of a tree in shades of chestnut, cream and brown. They call with a 'koor-lo' or 'caw-caw' sound.

During daylight hours marbled frogmouths roost alone in the tangled vine thickets of rainforests, disguised in their camouflaging plumage. After dark they use their huge, hooked bills to catch large insects, and sometimes frogs, from the forest floor. Both parents incubate the single egg, but very little is known about their breeding habits.
Scientific name: *Podargus ocellatus*

■ PAPUAN FROGMOUTH
The mottled plumage and complete immobility of the Papuan frogmouth provide good camouflage in its shady daytime roost in deep forest cover.

PAPUAN FROGMOUTH ■

This is Australia's largest frogmouth. Adults grow to almost 55 cm long – large enough to challenge the rainforest's nocturnal predators, such as the rufous owl. This they do with screams and threat displays.

Papuan frogmouths inhabit the remote tropical forests of Cape York Peninsula and Queensland's coastal ranges as far south as Townsville, but are even more common in Papua New Guinea. Their call is similar to that of the tawny frogmouth.

The plumage of the Papuan frogmouth is a mixture of black, brown, cream and rufous streaks and blotches. Pairs roost together, sometimes with that year's young, in the same or adjacent trees. At night they move into open forest, where they can more easily detect the large, ground-dwelling invertebrates, such as beetles and spiders, on which they feed. Sometimes they also take small frogs, lizards, birds and mammals. These frogmouths normally lay only one egg, and incubation is shared by the parents.
Scientific name: *Podargus papuensis*

DISTRIBUTION

■ AUSTRALIAN OWLET NIGHTJAR

■ AUSTRALIAN OWLET NIGHTJAR
Owlet nightjars have a characteristic two- or three-note 'chirr' call. They give voice at night as well as from their nest hollows during the day.

OWLET NIGHTJAR

The owlet nightjar's large, forward-facing eyes and round face give it an owlish appearance, though it is not closely related to the owl. Like its relatives the frogmouths and the nightjars, it has a wide mouth fringed with fine bristles, and its plumage gives it almost perfect camouflage. Owlet nightjars nest in hollows during the day and hunt, mainly for insects, at night. They live in the western Pacific region, and one species occurs in Australia.
Family: Aegothelidae

AUSTRALIAN OWLET NIGHTJAR ■

A dainty bird about 23 cm long, the Australian owlet nightjar has large eyes and finely stippled soft grey plumage, so that when it sits at the entrance to its hollow, it looks remarkably like a possum.

This species occurs in timbered areas all over Australia. By day it roosts in tree hollows and rocky crevices, and occasionally in abandoned farmhouses and tunnels in earth banks. If it senses danger, it bursts straight from its roost and flies to the safety of another hollow.

These birds are at their busiest around dawn and dusk, when they catch beetles, grasshoppers and other flying insects on the wing or glide from low perches to take ants and spiders on the ground. They sometimes even run along the ground pecking at prey.

A male and female pair share a territory but roost apart. They line a tree hollow with green leaves to prepare a nest, in which the female lays two to five glossy white eggs. The male and female then share the incubation of the eggs and the rearing of the chicks.
Scientific name: *Aegotheles cristatus*

NIGHTJARS

Streaky brown plumage provides almost perfect concealment for nightjars in trees or on the ground among the leaves and twigs where they roost in the day. They have a pigeon-sized body and a broad, wedge-shaped head that sits close to their body to create a smooth outline that is hard to detect among the rocks and dead leaves. At night on country roads, headlights sometimes catch the red eye-shine of a nightjar.

Between dusk and dawn, the nightjar feeds and drinks as it glides on its long, pointed wings and tail. Its mouth acts as a basket to engulf beetles, moths and flying insects, while the fine bristles of its wide-gaping bill detect the movement of half-caught prey. Nightjars collect water with a quick dip of their bill as they sweep low over the surface.

Nightjars occur widely throughout warm and tropical areas of the world, but Australia has only three species. Their common name relates to their jarring song or call, and their scientific family name comes from the Latin word *caprimulgus*, meaning goat-sucker: in ancient times goatherds who heard the nightjars call before dawn blamed them for any loss in milk production.
Family: Caprimulgidae

WHITE-THROATED NIGHTJAR

This is the largest of Australia's nightjars; adults are 32–37 cm long, the females larger than the males.

Both sexes are flecked and spotted with grey, fawn and black on their backs and have grey and black bands on their chests. When they puff themselves up in defence, white crescents on their throat expand into two startling 'eyes'. They are sometimes called night hawks or moth hawks because of their hawk-like shape.

These nightjars live in eucalypt forest between the Great Dividing Range and the coast from Cape York Peninsula southward to Melbourne. They breed in summer and lay a single speckled egg on the ground. Parents share incubation of the egg, which hatches after 24 days. The chick is able to fly a month after this.
Scientific name: *Eurostopodus mysticalis*

SPOTTED NIGHTJAR ■

In the mainland, the vast areas of dry, inland scrub and woodland west of the Great Dividing Range are home to the spotted nightjar.

Its fluffy plumage, patterned in black, rufous and cream, renders this 30 cm-long bird almost invisible when it roosts on the ground among the fallen leaves.

The large buff spots on the ends of the spotted nightjar's wings, from which it gets its common name, are revealed in flight and during defence displays. When a nest or a chick is threatened, the parents attempt to frighten the intruder by fanning out their tail and spreading their wings

STAYING ALIVE

Survival for night birds depends as much on avoiding predators during the day as on finding food at night. The owlet nightjar (above) hides in a tree hollow, but other birds in this group roost in the open.

Most of these birds have a wide head, making it difficult for predators to distinguish their head from their tail, and many have bristly feathers around their beak to break up their outline. Ground-dwellers have plumage that imitates ground litter, and the plumage of tree-perchers looks like bark or dappled shadows. By remaining perfectly still, these birds merge completely into their surroundings.

■ SPOTTED NIGHTJAR
The spotted nightjar nests in ground litter and lays a single green egg on a shady patch of bare ground.

forward along the ground to reveal rows of buff-coloured spots. At the same time they puff out their white throat and, with their mouth open, emit a warning hiss.

The parents share incubation, and probably brooding and feeding. A downy orange chick hatches after a month and can fly a month later.
Scientific name: *Eurostopodus argus*

LARGE-TAILED NIGHTJAR

Large-tailed nightjars inhabit the rainforest fringes along the coast of the Northern Territory and Queensland. Pairs live in small territories, which they advertise with a monotonous 'tock-tock', like an axe cutting wood; indeed, they are sometimes called axe birds or hammer birds. Another common name for this bird is the white-tailed nightjar, because of the white bars on its tail edges and its white wing patch.
Their wings are shorter and more rounded than those of other Australian nightjars, and the bristles along the edge of their beak are more distinct. At about 29 cm long, they are slightly smaller than other Australian nightjars, but they have similar markings – buff, grey and black. If threatened, they flap their wings and open their mouths wide.

After dark, large-tailed nightjars leave their roosts on the forest floor and fly to open ground to feed. Females lay two pink, spotted eggs among leaf litter in spring. Both parents share the 22-day incubation and care for the downy pink chicks.
Scientific name: *Caprimulgus macrurus*

DISTRIBUTION

WHITE-THROATED NIGHTJAR

SPOTTED NIGHTJAR

LARGE-TAILED NIGHTJAR

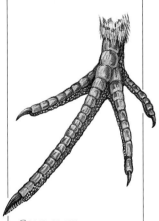

COMB CLAW
A feature of many nightjars is the comb-like claw on their long middle toe – a very useful tool for grooming or scratching.

SWIFTS

Superbly adapted to an aerial existence, swifts spend most of their time in the air, where they feed on insects and other invertebrates, scooping them up in their wide beaks. Their sleek bodies and long, curved wings permit them to manoeuvre with great precision, whether gliding or travelling at speed. Short hairs and a transparent membrane protect their eyes from debris as they dart through the air.

Some swift species land only to nest or roost, and a few species scarcely ever roost, remaining airborne for weeks or even months, sleeping in the air while they glide in circles. Because they spend so much time in the air, swifts have little use for their legs, which have consequently become reduced and weak.

NAKED IN THE NEST
White-rumped swiftlet chicks hatch after three weeks and the young fledge six to seven weeks later. This species often nests in caves and rocky overhangs that receive little or no light.

OPEN WIDE!
Birds that catch flying prey on the wing need a wide-opening beak, or gape. Shown here is the gape of a swift (bottom) compared with the larger gapes of a swallow (centre) and a nightjar (top).

Outside the breeding season, swifts are gregarious, occurring in large flocks where there is suitable prey; only a few species are solitary by nature. Most hunt early in the morning and late in the evening, but some species continue through the night, aided by their excellent night vision.

Some swiftlets nest and roost in dark caves, where they navigate using a system called echolocation. By emitting a series of rattles or clicks and analysing the returning echoes, they can calculate the distance of solid objects. As they approach the roost or nest site, they emit these clicks at a faster rate.

This echolocation system is not as sensitive as that of bats, and swiftlets probably use it solely for navigation, not for hunting. No one knows how the birds produce the clicks, though it is likely that they use either their tongue or their voice box (syrinx). They emit the clicks through their open mouths: swifts that do not use echolocation carry their nesting material in their mouths, but the uniform swiftlet uses its feet, leaving its mouth free for sonar navigation.

Because of their aerial lifestyle, little is known about the courtship and mating rituals of swifts, nor is there much scientific study of their breeding habits. What is known, however, is that the parents share nest building and incubation. Most species nest in colonies, pairs constructing nests in caves, crevices, tree hollows and even structures such as church towers and house roofs. Swifts' nests are made of cobwebs, moss and other plant material, usually bound together with saliva.

The edible-nest swiftlet (*Collocalia fuciphaga*), which lives in South-East Asia, makes its nest entirely of saliva, and these nests are harvested as the basis of the famous birds'-nest soup.

Despite their fondness for the air, swifts do sit on their eggs. Some incubate for as little as two minutes, others for as long as five hours, and they sometimes leave their nest unattended for hours. Of the swift species that visit Australia, only the white-rumped swiftlet breeds here.

Swifts look very much like martins and swallows, which are members of the songbird family Hirundinidae (pages 284–5). However, the two groups are not related; the likeness is an example of the process of convergent evolution, where unrelated groups of animals have developed similar features in response to life in similar environments.

■ WHITE-RUMPED SWIFTLET
Grey-brown with a black gloss on its wings, the white-rumped swiftlet is marked out from the other swiftlet species by its greyish white rump.

Of about 85 swift species worldwide, only six occur in Australia, and none of these is endemic.
Order: Apodiformes; Family: Apodidae

SWIFTLETS ■

Out of about 16 swiftlet species in the world, Australia has only three. They are smaller and more slender than other swifts, and look more like two species of Australian martins from the family Hirundinidae, with which they are often confused. They are virtually confined to forests and clearings of Cape York Peninsula, although the white-rumped swiftlet (*Collocalia spodiopygius*) has been recorded as far south as northern New South Wales.

The white-rumped swiftlet is the most abundant of Australia's three swiftlets. It is 9–11 cm long and is grey-brown with black on its wings. White-rumped swiftlets often form large, swarming flocks, feeding on flying insects and drifting spiders.

FORK-TAILED SWIFT
The migration of the fork-tailed swift is long and arduous, and dead birds are often washed up on beaches. These birds rarely alight on the ground in Australia.

They roost and nest in colonies, sometimes of several hundred birds. They breed between July and February, and at any one time an individual nest can contain eggs, new chicks or fledglings.

The glossy swiftlet (*C. esculenta*) and the uniform swiftlet (*C. vanikorensis*) are uncommon visitors to Australia. The glossy swiftlet is only 9–10 cm long. Its wings are slightly longer than its body, and it is identified by its glossy blue-black upperparts, grey-white breast and white abdomen. The uniform swiftlet is larger, at 10–12 cm long, and is grey-brown, becoming slightly paler on the throat and abdomen.
Scientific name: *Collocalia* spp.

WHITE-THROATED NEEDLETAIL

At 19–21 cm long, white-throated needletails are the largest of Australia's swifts. They are common summer migrants to northern and eastern Australia from their breeding grounds in Asia, arriving here around October. Most leave in May, though some remain until August. They rarely land in Australia, and drink simply by skimming the surface of the water.

White-throated needletails feed over a variety of habitats, taking flying insects that are swept high into the air on thermal currents. They often fly at considerable heights in flocks of several thousand birds. Although they are not the fastest bird species, they can fly

extremely fast, reaching speeds of up to 130 kilometres an hour.

These swifts mate in Asia, but often stage aerial courtship displays in Australia, groups of birds in a flock suddenly stopping to chase one another through the air or to dive vertically for 30 metres or so before swooping back to the flock.
Scientific name: *Hirundapus caudacutus*

HOUSE SWIFT

The house swift ranges throughout southern China westward into Africa and eastward into South-East Asia, but it is only a rare visitor to Australia's Top End; it was first recorded in 1979 in Darwin.

It is 13 cm long and grey in colour with a white rump and a square tail. Its long, tapering wings distinguish

WHITE-THROATED NEEDLETAIL
Against the bright sky, this swift looks black; in fact its plumage is grey-brown with a green gloss (right). It is sometimes known as the spine-tailed swift because the feathers of its short, square tail are tipped with spines (below).

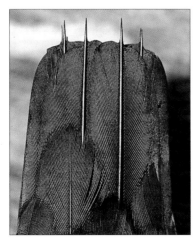

it from the similar-sized Australian martins. These birds breed throughout virtually their whole range, but they have not been recorded as breeding in Australia.
Scientific name: *Apus affinis*

FORK-TAILED SWIFT

Fork-tailed swifts breed in the northern hemisphere and migrate to Australia each year around October. They spend all day – and probably the night – on the wing, hunting, resting and even sleeping in the air. At night, rafts of sleeping fork-tailed swifts circle at great heights.

These swifts have warm black plumage and a white chin and throat. Their distinctive white rump is rarely seen in Australia, since these birds seldom alight here, but they are easily identified by their long, forked tail. They reach 16–20 cm long and resemble white-throated needletails; however, they have no white undertail and their flight is more buoyant and fluttering.

Though fork-tailed swifts occur all over Australia, including Tasmania and offshore islands, they usually remain in the west and are uncommon on the east coast. Most depart in late April and May for their northern breeding grounds, but some individuals stay behind for months, particularly in the north.
Scientific name: *Apus pacificus*

WHITE-RUMPED SWIFTLET

GLOSSY SWIFTLET

UNIFORM SWIFTLET

WHITE-THROATED NEEDLETAIL

HOUSE SWIFT

FORK-TAILED SWIFT

KINGFISHERS

Kingfishers, bee-eaters and rollers have large heads and stout bills. Their weak feet, on which some toes are fused together, easily wrap around a perch, but they cannot walk – they have to hop. Nearly all have green or blue in their plumage.

All kingfishers belong to the order Coraciiformes, which is represented in Australia by four families. River kingfishers mostly feed in water, whereas forest kingfishers are mainly ground-feeders. Rollers and bee-eaters, each represented in Australia by one species, are colourful insect-eating birds.

■ AZURE KINGFISHERS
When they have acquired their full adult plumage, these three young azure kingfishers will fly away to claim their own territory.

EXPERT FISHERS
Kingfishers were named for their fishing skill and their regal purple and blue plumage. The azure kingfisher sits motionless on its perch above the water until it spots its prey, and then dives with great accuracy to pick up its catch.

RIVER KINGFISHERS

These birds sometimes sit patiently for more than an hour waiting for prey. Perched quietly on branches over clear water, they stare intently down, flicking their tails. When a fish, aquatic insect, crab or yabby comes within range the kingfisher takes aim and launches itself into the water. It swims under water by flapping its wings, and then uses its long, dagger-like bill like a forceps to grab its prey rather than stab it.

When the kingfisher surfaces it flies back to its perch, where it slaps its catch against the perch to stun it and soften it for easier digestion. It then swallows its catch head first, and resumes its vigil.
Family: Alcedinidae

AZURE KINGFISHER ■
The plumage on the upper body of this bird, sometimes called the blue kingfisher, is electric blue. Its breast and belly are russet, its legs red and its eyes brown. It has white ear tufts and a patch of pale feathers in front of its eyes. Its long black bill takes up more than a quarter of its 19 cm body length.

The azure kingfisher occurs along the northern coast, from Broome in Western Australia to Cape York in Queensland, along the east coast of the mainland, and in Tasmania. In winter some southern azure kingfishers move northward into warmer regions. This migratory behaviour is marked by the injuries and deaths of birds in flight that collide with windows.

Although generally common within their range, azure kingfishers are shy, and most people's only glimpse of one is a brilliant blue flash by a quiet river bank. Pairs of adult birds occupy permanent territories along the forested edges of coastal creeks, rivers and mangroves, where they patrol the water's edge, zigzagging between a series of favourite fishing perches. The size of their territory may be anything from a couple of hundred metres to half a kilometre long.

In southern and eastern Australia, the azure kingfisher's breeding season starts in September and goes on until January, but in the north it is slightly later and is linked to the wet season. During courtship, males and females call with a clear, high-pitched, piping 'peee-peee'. The pair build a nest together in a river bank above the waterline. They use their bills and feet to excavate a tunnel

about a metre long, ending in a nest chamber where the female lays between four and seven eggs. The chicks hatch after three weeks of incubation, which the parents share.

Frantic activity follows as the parents dash back and forth delivering food to their hungry offspring. Fish bones and scales – remnants of their meals – litter the tunnel and chamber. After three to four weeks the young are well feathered and can make their first flight.
Scientific name: *Alcedo azurea*

LITTLE KINGFISHER
Even the common house sparrow is bigger than Australia's smallest kingfisher, which reaches a length of only about 12 cm and a weight of about 12 grams.

This tiny, jewel-like bird is royal blue on the head and back and white below. Its head and neck have white streaks like those of the azure kingfisher. It lives in the coastal monsoon forests of the Northern Territory, from close to the Western Australian border to Arnhem Land, and in Queensland from Cape York to Townsville. It also occurs in New Guinea, the Solomon Islands and the Molucca Islands in Indonesia.

The little kingfisher's nesting and fishing habits are similar to those of the azure kingfisher. Pairs occupy territories along the lush edges of mangroves, rivers and creeks, where they fish for small aquatic creatures. During the wet season they tunnel nests in rotten tree stumps or the banks of streams. Both sexes build the nest, and the female lays five or six glossy white eggs. Incubation is shared by both parents.
Scientific name: *Alcedo pusilla*

FOREST KINGFISHERS

This family is found only on the Australian mainland. Its eight species prey mostly on land animals, but two – the sacred kingfisher and the collared kingfisher – also eat fishes and small aquatic animals.

Forest kingfishers have broader, flatter beaks and longer tails than their river cousins, and all except the blue-winged kookaburra and the yellow-billed kingfisher have a dark band running through their eyes to the back of their neck.

These birds are patient hunters, perching on low branches to scan the ground for prey, which they grab with their beaks. They excavate their nests in termite mounds on the ground or in trees, in earthen river banks and in the hollows of trees.
Family: Halcyonidae

LAUGHING KOOKABURRA

The natural habitat of the laughing kookaburra – the open eucalypt forests of Australia's eastern and southern states – overlaps with major population centres, and this bird is a common visitor to suburban gardens. It has been introduced and established in Western Australia and Tasmania, and in New Zealand.

These birds may live for 20 years and tend to stay in the same area all their life, so individuals can become well known to local residents.

This is the largest of the kingfisher family, growing to about 47 cm long. Its lower back, rump and tail are russet brown barred with black, and its wings are brown with blue flecks. Its underparts are white and its white head is marked with a dark band running over its crown and through its eyes. Dominant males are flecked with light blue over their lower back and rump. Laughing kookaburras eat insects and small invertebrates; they also take frogs, reptiles, rodents and birds.

Laughing kookaburras occupy their territories all year, living in hierarchical family groups consisting of a dominant breeding pair and offspring raised over several breeding seasons. A family group loudly advertises its territory, especially early in the morning and at dusk, perched on telegraph poles or on the branches of trees. They call in unison, heads thrown back and tails flicking up and down.

In September they begin nesting, mostly in tree hollows or tree termite

LAUGHING KOOKABURRA
The raucous call of the laughing kookaburra rises to a barking 'kook-kook-kook' and ends in a cackling 'ha-ha-ha'.

nests. They breed in summer, females laying two to four white eggs. Older offspring help to defend the nest, share incubation and bring food to the mother bird and the newborn chicks. A month after hatching young kookaburras are ready to fly; the helper birds will protect them from predators.
Scientific name: *Dacelo novaeguineae*

BLUE-WINGED KOOKABURRA

Blue-winged kookaburras are about 40 cm long. The adult's head is finely streaked with brown, and it lacks the laughing kookaburra's dark stripe. Its wings are predominantly pale blue and its rump bright blue. Males have all-blue tail feathers, but those of the female are rufous with dark blue bars.

Other common names for the blue-winged kookaburra are the howling jackass and Leach's kookaburra. Its territorial call starts with the same soft growls and loud, hooting barks as that of the laughing kookaburra, but ends in a wild 'ow-ow-ow'.

These birds inhabit tropical paperbark and eucalypt woodlands from the Kimberley in Western Australia across the Northern Territory and southward to Brisbane. Those from the Pilbara region in the west differ from others of the species in having a white, unstreaked crown. Their feeding and breeding habits are like those of the laughing kookaburra, although in coastal habitats they also eat turtles, fishes and crayfish.

Groups of blue-winged kookaburras defend their territories, and members help with nesting duties.
Scientific name: *Dacelo leachii*

BUFF-BREASTED PARADISE KINGFISHER

This is the most spectacular of the Australian kingfishers. Rich blue above and coppery yellow below, it has two long white tail plumes, a bright red bill, red feet, and a black band running through its eyes and down to the nape of its neck. The juveniles are less colourful, without the long tail feathers and with a black bill. Adults are 29–36 cm long, including their tail plumes. They are difficult to see in their shady habitat in the rainforests of Queensland's northern coast, where they feed on insects, lizards, frogs and spiders.

Each year in October buff-breasted paradise kingfishers fly from New

DISTRIBUTION

AZURE KINGFISHER

LITTLE KINGFISHER

LAUGHING KOOKABURRA

BLUE-WINGED KOOKABURRA

BUFF-BREASTED PARADISE KINGFISHER

BUFF-BREASTED PARADISE KINGFISHER
This kingfisher is sometimes known as the white-tailed kingfisher or the long-tailed kingfisher, because of its slender, elegant tail, which may be as much as 25 cm long.

221

YELLOW-BILLED
KINGFISHER

COLLARED
KINGFISHER

RED-BACKED
KINGFISHER

FOREST KINGFISHER

SACRED KINGFISHER

Guinea to their breeding grounds in north Queensland, departing again the following March. They fly at night, all arriving within a few days, and congregate in lowland rainforest where large ground termite mounds provide nesting sites. While the males are establishing territories and courting, the forest rings with their repeated 'chop-chop' calls.

They peck out a tunnel and nesting chamber near the base of a termite mound, and the female lays three or four eggs. Both parents incubate the eggs, which hatch in a month, and spend a further frantic month collecting food for the chicks. By the end of the breeding season their tail plumes are often worn and faded by their trips up and down the tunnel.
Scientific name: *Tanysiptera sylvia*

YELLOW-BILLED KINGFISHER ◼

This kingfisher has a striking yellow bill and orange head, circled by a black line that is broad at the back and thinner between the eyes. Its wings and back are green and its tail is blue. The female has a black patch on her crown. Adults are 20 cm long.

In Australia this bird occurs only on the tip of Cape York Peninsula, where it is common on the edges of rainforest, gallery forest and mangroves that border woodland. It also occurs in neighbouring islands and in New Guinea. It is solitary except in the summer breeding season, when it forms loosely knit pairs and small family groups. It nests in hollows, usually drilled into termite mounds, and lays three or four eggs.

The yellow-billed kingfisher lives on insects, small lizards and worms. It is sometimes known as the sawbilled kingfisher because its yellow bill has a slightly serrated edge for digging and for gripping slippery prey such as worms.
Scientific name: *Syma torotoro*

COLLARED KINGFISHER
The collared kingfisher, which is sometimes called the mangrove kingfisher, inhabits the mangroves and mudflats of Australia's northern coasts, from Shark Bay in Western Australia around to north-eastern New South Wales.

A moderately large kingfisher, it grows to 28 cm long and is mostly green. It eats insects, reptiles and aquatic animals, such as worms, which it picks off the mudflats.

Collared kingfishers in the northern part of their range occupy the same area all year round, but those in more southerly regions leave their breeding grounds and fly north to New Guinea for the winter.
Scientific name: *Todiramphus chloris*

RED-BACKED KINGFISHER
The red-backed kingfisher inhabits Australia's dry inland regions of desert, mallee and mulga. It is nomadic right across the continent, except for the Cape York and south-eastern and south-western coasts. In dry winter months it may migrate northward or towards the west and north-east coasts.

Up to 24 cm long, it is is bluish green above and white below, with a

◼ YELLOW-BILLED KINGFISHERS
In the dappled light of the forest, the light and dark coloration of this kingfisher provides effective camouflage. The yellow-billed kingfisher is easier to detect by its whistle than by sight.

◼ FOREST KINGFISHER
The forest kingfisher excavates a nest cavity in a tree termite mound by gradually chipping out a hole with its beak.

green tail and a green-streaked head. It has a black streak through its eyes and rufous feathers on its rump.

Red-backed kingfishers are usually solitary, but pairs or small groups form in the breeding season. Nesting sites include termite mounds, banks of dry creek beds and tree hollows.
Scientific name: *Todiramphus pyrrhopygius*

FOREST KINGFISHER ◼
Forest kingfishers inhabit open woodlands, swamps, mangroves and gardens. They occur in Arnhem Land, in northern and eastern Queensland and down the east coast as far south as the Hunter Valley in New South Wales.

Also known as blue kingfishers, they have magnificent royal blue wings, head and tail that contrast with their white underparts. Males also have a broad white collar. Adults reach 22 cm in length.

Southern populations of forest kingfishers migrate to New Guinea in winter, but those in Arnhem Land are permanent residents. During the breeding season forest kingfishers lay four to six eggs in a nest cavity excavated in a tree termite mound, often laying two clutches in a season. Both parents incubate the eggs.
Scientific name: *Todiramphus macleayii*

SACRED KINGFISHER ■

This common kingfisher occurs all over Australia, except in the densest rainforests and inland deserts. Sometimes known as the tree kingfisher, it prefers wooded areas but also inhabits coastal and inland waterways. Its range includes Norfolk and Lord Howe Islands.

Adult sacred kingfishers are about 23 cm long, with turquoise plumage on their crown and back and the dark eye band common to most kingfisher species. Their chin and throat are white, grading to cinnamon-ochre on the chest and belly.

In winter most sacred kingfishers in the southern states migrate to northern Australia; some travel more than 2000 kilometres to reach Indonesia and New Guinea. In August they return to their breeding grounds, where they proclaim their territories with a loud 'kek-kek-kek'.

These solitary birds pair only when they breed. They prefer to nest in river banks or termite mounds, but they also excavate nests in trees. Females lay three to six eggs, which hatch in two to three weeks. The young can fly at four weeks.
Scientific name: *Todiramphus sanctus*

■ SACRED KINGFISHER
The most familiar of the Australian kingfishers, the sacred kingfisher spends its day watching for insects and lizards in leaf litter. Occasionally it dives into fresh or brackish water in pursuit of yabbies or fish.

ROLLERS

These colourful insect-eaters are named after their rolling courtship flights. They live alone or in pairs, defending their territories with great vigour. Rollers are widespread, ranging from Australasia to Europe and Africa, but only one species, the dollarbird, occurs in Australia.
Family: Coraciidae

DOLLARBIRD

This bird's name refers to the white coin-like patches on its wings, which are visible only in flight. Dollarbirds are often seen by roadsides, where utility poles provide ideal perches.

Dollarbirds are migrants, and those of the Australian region spend the winter in the islands around New Guinea. A loud 'chac-chac-chac' in the tropical forests and open woodlands of northern and eastern Australia heralds their arrival each spring. Dollarbirds also inhabit South-East Asia and India, where they are called broad-billed rollers.

The dollarbird's broad head and short neck sit on a body about 27 cm long. Adults have a red beak and paler legs, a blue-green body and a brown head. The male's plumage tends to be brighter than that of the

female. It often perches on a bare branch that serves both as a lookout and as a launching pad for catching prey and for courtship flight displays. With swoops and glides, the dollarbird catches flying insects on the wing.

In the breeding season these solitary birds gather and challenge each other in flying displays. Each male establishes a territory and courts a partner, and then the pair search for a nest hollow high in a tree, where the female lays up to four white eggs. Both parents incubate the eggs.
Scientific name: *Eurystomus orientalis*

DISTRIBUTION

■ DOLLARBIRD

BEE-EATERS

Bee-eaters are brightly coloured birds from tropical and temperate woodlands. They have slender bodies, curved beaks and long tail feathers. They are insectivorous, eating mainly bees and wasps. Some bee-eaters hunt on the wing, others by perching and diving like kingfishers, and some use both methods. They are sociable birds that flock to migrate and breed in colonies.

Bee-eaters are migratory birds that nest in hollows dug in banks. Of the two dozen species, the rainbow bee-eater is the only one that occurs in Australia; the rest live in Africa and from Eurasia to Indonesia.
Family: Meropidae

RAINBOW BEE-EATER ■

A slender bird about 26 cm long, the rainbow bee-eater has a green and blue back, coppery wings and a golden crown. It lives in woodlands over most of the country, migrating

■ RAINBOW BEE-EATERS
In typical bee-eater style, these birds are scanning the sky for their favourite foods – honeybees and wasps.

to northern Queensland and New Guinea in the winter and returning south in October to breed. These birds cross Torres Strait in large flocks; as many as 850 have been recorded flying over in an hour.

When flying or perching the rainbow bee-eater emits a characteristic 'prrp-prrp' call. It sweeps into the air in pursuit of prey and returns to its perch gripping the insect around the thorax. First dashing the bee's head against the perch, it rubs the bee's abdomen to remove its sting.

Rainbow bee-eaters are loosely dispersed in pairs or family groups, but when they are breeding they often gather at their nesting sites. They use their beaks and feet to excavate nest tunnels in sandy banks or flat ground. They breed in summer, and other family members help the parents with the incubation and the feeding of the chicks.
Scientific name: *Merops ornatus*

DISTRIBUTION

■ RAINBOW BEE-EATER

SONGBIRDS

The songbirds are members of a very large group of birds with complex voice boxes and songs so intricate that there can be vocal differences in a species across its distribution. These 'dialects' can be quite distinctive, and in some species individuals even develop their own unique repertoire.

Another feature common to these birds is the way they perch, and this is the origin of the name of their order, Passeriformes: *passer* is the Latin word for a sparrow, which is a typical member of the order. About 60 per cent of living birds – some 10 000 species – are from this order.

COMMUNICATING THROUGH SONG
Each bird species has a characteristic song by which it recognises other members of its kind, warns off other species and attracts mates. This is a pair of splendid fairy-wrens (*Malurus splendens*), an Australian member of one of the oldest songbird families in the world. The male (above) is in his full breeding plumage.

PERCHING SONGSTER
A bird's small lungs are augmented by a system of air sacs that drive compressed air across tightened membranes in the syrinx (voice box) so that they vibrate in song. The songbird's perching mechanism is also illustrated here. Songbirds have four toes, one of which points backward. When the bird alights, the tendons in its legs and feet flex, pulling the toes around the perch in a strong grip that needs no muscular exertion.

There are two major suborders of songbirds – the suboscines and the oscines. Suboscines appear to be more primitive birds with less well-developed voice boxes. They are restricted mainly to the southern continents, with South America supporting most species. Australia has only one suboscine family, the pittas. Oscines are sometimes referred to as true songbirds.

Ancient beginnings

For many years it was thought that songbirds originated in the northern hemisphere and only later spread to Australia and the rest of the southern hemisphere. Then, in the 1980s and 1990s, scientists developed highly sophisticated techniques for comparing and contrasting the genetic make-up of animals.

As a result of these developments, evidence is mounting that songbirds probably first appeared on the great southern supercontinent of Gondwana. This consisted of the present-day landmasses of South America, Africa, India, Australia and Antarctica before they began to break away from each other and drift apart millions of years ago.

The discovery in Australia, in the early 1990s, of the world's oldest known songbird fossil has added weight to the theory that the songbirds originated in, and radiated out from, the southern hemisphere. Australia is now widely thought to have some of the oldest songbird families in the world, including the lyrebirds, the scrub-birds, the treecreepers, the honeyeaters and the fairy-wrens.

Why birds sing

Birdsong is most noticeable in the early morning, and until the nineteenth century people believed that birds sang to welcome the new day. The name of the lark family, Alaudidae, literally means 'those that sing praises [to the Lord]'.

In 1868, an ornithologist called Bernard Altum hypothesised that birdsong was a signal of territorial ownership, and that the size of the birds' territories could be calculated from the distances between singing males. It is now accepted that birds use their songs both to ward off trespassing males and to attract females. Males patrol the borders of their territory, especially in the early morning and evening, and have favourite vantage points from which they sing.

Birds not only recognise the songs of their own species; they can also recognise the songs of individual birds. An attentive human listener, too, may pick up these differences: the detailed individual repertoires of lyrebirds and grey thrushes have been especially noted. By recognising the identity and position of their neighbours, birds can respond quickly if a neighbour shifts the boundary of its territory or is absent, or if a stranger arrives.

Females also sing. For example, mated pairs often take part in duets, and the song they produce can sound as if only one bird is singing. The song of the eastern whipbird, in which the female completes the male's song, is a classic example of this. Birds that perform in duet are usually found in dense vegetation and have strong bonds both to their mate and to their territory.

Perching mechanism

Songbirds are small to medium in size. Most are land-dwellers and feed on insects, fruit, seeds or nectar. The anatomy of their feet is a unifying feature between the species. All have three forward-pointing toes of equal length and one toe pointing backwards. When songbirds crouch, the structure of the tendons leading to the toes forces the foot to tighten its grip on a branch or a perch. This causes the toes to lock, and prevents the bird from falling off its perch when it is resting.

This locking mechanism is not restricted exclusively to songbirds, but it is certainly best developed in them, and the arrangement of the foot tendons and the presence of a large, opposable and very functional hind toe are features unique to songbirds. This is why songbirds are sometimes also called passerines, or perching birds.

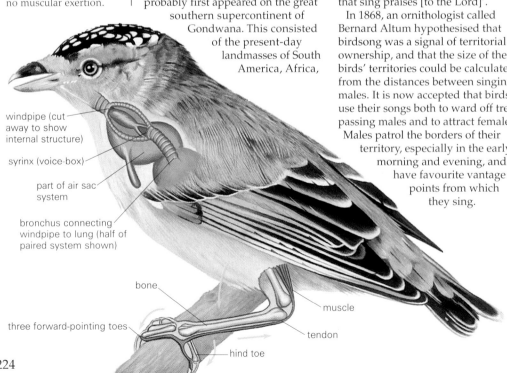

windpipe (cut away to show internal structure)

syrinx (voice-box)

part of air sac system

bronchus connecting windpipe to lung (half of paired system shown)

bone

three forward-pointing toes

muscle

tendon

hind toe

PITTAS

Pittas are shy birds, often living in remote habitats, but they are among the world's most brightly coloured creatures, and enthusiasts go to great lengths to glimpse one.

There are an estimated 23–31 living species in the very ancient Pittidae family. All are grouped in a single genus called *Pitta*. Pittas are ground-dwelling birds that favour tropical to warm temperate wet forests and scrubland. Most species are found in South-East Asia, although there are also some in Africa, India, southern China, southern Japan, the Solomon Islands, the Bismarck Archipelago, New Guinea and Australia.

When disturbed, pittas normally run along the ground, but they are reasonably strong fliers and will take to the wing when flushed. They also fly to branches up to 10 metres high to call and to roost. Flashes of white are visible under their wings during flight.

Anvil chorus

Pittas forage, sometimes noisily, through leaf litter in search of small invertebrates. They have plump, upright bodies, stout bills for tackling prey, short tails, and long legs with large, strong feet for scrabbling about in ground debris. Unusually for birds they have a sense of smell, which is believed to be part of their adaptation to life on the ground.

Many species, including noisy and red-bellied pittas, use small rocks or pieces of wood as anvils on which to smash open the shells of snails to obtain the soft bodies that form part of their diet. Birds may use the same rock over and over, polishing the surface with constant use, and small piles of broken shells can be found lying around nearby.

Rainsong

Pittas have distinctive, clear, whistling calls of two to four notes. The call of the rainbow pitta sounds like 'want-a-whip', and the noisy pitta's main call sounds like 'walk-to-work' or 'want-a-watch'. In some areas people believe that the persistent calling of these birds is a sign of forthcoming rain.

A skilled human whistler can entice these elusive birds from hiding by mimicking their calls. During the breeding season pittas are highly territorial, and they call more insistently as the season approaches.

Home-making

Pittas build dome-shaped nests of leaves, twigs and plant fibres, with a side entrance, on or near the ground. Some species, such as the noisy pitta, line their nests with moist animal dung; others use pieces of decayed wood or grass. The females lay up to four glossy white eggs,

strikingly marked with purplish black or brown spots and blotches. Both parents incubate the eggs and feed the young. Unlike the chicks of many ground-dwelling birds, which are self-sufficient and mobile shortly after birth, pitta hatchlings are helpless and need constant care for the first few weeks of life.

Australian pittas

Australia has three known resident pittas, of which the noisy pitta (*Pitta versicolor*) is the most familiar. Its distribution in Australia extends from Cape York Peninsula eastward to the central coast of New South Wales. There are two forms, one in the north of its range, the other in the south. The northern form migrates to New Guinea in winter.

The red-bellied or blue-breasted pitta (*P. erythrogaster*) migrates at the beginning of summer from New Guinea to breed on the northern tip of Cape York Peninsula.

The rainbow pitta (*P. iris*) lives exclusively in the rainforests, vine thickets and mangrove swamps of Australia. Its range extends across the northern end of the Northern Territory and along the northern coastline of Western Australia.

Noisy pittas grow to about 20 cm long; red-bellied pittas and rainbow pittas are a little smaller.
Family: Pittidae

NOISY PITTA

RED-BELLIED PITTA
RAINBOW PITTA

JEWELS OF THE FOREST
Pittas are sometimes called jewel-thrushes because of their vivid plumage. These secretive ground-dwellers live either in rainforest or monsoon vine forest. The noisy pitta (*Pitta versicolor*), pictured here, has the widest distribution of the three species found in Australia and is the best known.

DISTRIBUTION

■ SUPERB LYREBIRD

■ ALBERT'S LYREBIRD

LYREBIRDS

Lyrebirds are the largest songbirds in Australia. Because of their ground-dwelling habits and their large size, they have often been grouped with the pheasants or the Australian mound-builders (pages 126–7), but in fact they are quite different from these groups.

Lyrebirds have huge leg and thigh muscles, adapted to a life of running from danger; they can fly for a short distance, but it is a laborious and clumsy process for them, whereas pheasants have extremely large breast muscles to power their wings for escape with a rapid burst of flight and a long glide.

Lyrebirds build a typical nest, whereas mound-building birds incubate their eggs using the heat from a mound of decomposing vegetation.

Within the lyrebird family there are two species, both of which are found only in Australia – the superb lyrebird and Albert's lyrebird. Both are brown and up to a metre long, including the tail. Both have large feet for turning over the leaf litter in which they forage on the forest floor.

Lyrebirds evolved in isolation on the Australian continent, and they

■ SUPERB LYREBIRD
The outer tail feathers of the male superb lyrebird (above) are shaped like an ancient Greek lyre – a feature that gives the family its common name. The male builds a mound (right) that he uses as a stage on which to display.

are well adapted to the moist forest environments along the east coast. Fossil lyrebird specimens have been discovered in areas that are now quite arid, showing that in past geological ages, when conditions were wetter, lyrebirds were found over a much wider range.
Family: Menuridae

SUPERB LYREBIRD ■
Known in rural areas as the bush pheasant, the superb lyrebird is renowned for its spectacular appearance and ravishing song. Its display of its lyre-shaped tail feathers, which is known throughout Australia through the representation of a male bird on the 10 cent coin, is part of the mating ritual. The male bird builds a mound 1–2 metres across and 50 cm to 1 metre high to attract females and repel rivals. In autumn and early winter, the mound becomes his stage. In a stunning performance, he spreads and arches his 60 cm-long tail feathers forward over his body and slowly rotates on the spot, singing all the while.

Although superb lyrebirds are large and their song is loud, they are very wary and shy, and their display is difficult to observe in the wild.

The superb lyrebird has a plump body and a long, slim tail, with two long white central tail feathers in the male only. The bird appears to be all dark in the field, but in a good light its wings have a copperish tone. The male is 80–100 cm long and the female is somewhat smaller.

These birds live in the forests of eastern Australia, from sea level to the tree line at high altitudes, and extending west to the limit of forested habitat. They are native to moist eucalypt forests, but also occur in pine plantations and other places with tree cover and a moist understorey. Lyrebirds may also live in suburbs where shrubs are cultivated and pets are controlled, but they cannot survive where native vegetation has been cleared completely.

They scratch about in leaf litter for invertebrates, insect larvae and amphipods. Scrapes on the forest floor often indicate their presence.

Males and females establish separate territories. The female builds the nest unaided, placing it directly on the ground, in a cave or tree hollow, atop a stump or on a creek bank. It is a large, domed structure, lined with a variety of materials such as bark, ferns, small sticks and stringy roots, and a final layer of breast feathers. The female lays a single egg, which is camouflaged by a pattern of spots, blotches, and/or streaks in shades of grey, brown or reddish purple.
Scientific name: *Menura novaehollandiae*

AVIAN ARIAS

The two lyrebird species are remarkable songsters – as well as producing their own calls, they can faithfully mimic songs and other sounds. The superb lyrebird, pictured here, is most often heard, and has been known to imitate the calls of birds as different as the superb fairy-wren and the yellow-tailed black-cockatoo, although it usually mimics birds that share its habitat – the eastern whipbird, the grey shrike-thrush and the pilotbird are favourites. A patient listener may detect up to 15 different mimic calls in rapid succession.

In Victoria, a young lyrebird kept by a flute player learned the woodwind scales and some simple melodies. Lyrebirds have also been known to imitate barking dogs, steam trains, chainsaws, and even the sound of horses' hoofs on bitumen.

ALBERT'S LYREBIRD

Albert's lyrebird was named for Prince Albert, the Prince Consort of Queen Victoria. It has rusty brown plumage and is smaller than the superb lyrebird. The male attains a length of only 85 cm and also lacks the lyre-shaped outer tail feathers of the superb lyrebird. Instead, it has 14 dark, seemingly frayed, tail feathers. The central ribbon-like plumes of its tail extend beyond the others and curve inwards to cross at the tip.

The male Albert's lyrebird does not build a mound from which to call and display during the breeding season. Instead, he stamps down lianas and other plants to make a platform. Occasionally he may display from a fallen branch, a rock or a log. He displays by arching his tail over his back until he is almost covered and holding his wings low. He then prances, turning this way and that, singing and mimicking to advertise his territory. Both males and females mimic, but they also have several other distinctive calls, including rattling noises and a soft, ascending note that sounds disturbingly like a dingo howling.

Albert's lyrebird is confined to the very moist forests – usually dense subtropical rainforest – of northern New South Wales and extreme south-eastern Queensland. It is common within this limited range, but is secretive and seldom seen.
Scientific name: *Menura alberti*

ALBERT'S LYREBIRD
In winter, at the peak of the breeding season, the male Albert's lyrebird sings for up to four hours a day, sometimes fanning his tail at the same time.

SCRUB-BIRDS

Scrub-birds are related to lyrebirds and have a similar talent for song and mimicry. The two members of this entirely Australian family are very small – less than 20 cm long. It is unusual for birds so diminutive to utter such loud calls and songs. Both species occur in moist environments where there is an overstorey of trees or shrubs, and both are very difficult to observe in the field.

Scrub-birds build untidy dome-shaped nests on the ground with a side entrance and an interior lined with a delicate layer of wood pulp.

These birds live their entire lives close to the ground, and very seldom fly. They feed on invertebrates that they scratch from the forest floor with their powerful legs and feet, like lyrebirds. Sometimes they move beneath the leaf litter, which has earned them the bushman's nickname of mouse-bird.
Family: Atrichornithidae

RUFOUS SCRUB-BIRD

The rufous scrub-bird is found in the coolest and wettest forests of northern New South Wales, from Barrington Tops northward to south-eastern Queensland. Today it is known only from altitudes of more than 400 metres, but records indicate that these birds lived in the coastal lowlands until land clearing for agriculture and the dairy industry completely removed forests from most lowland sites. Recent investigations suggest that the rufous scrub-bird, although rare and difficult to observe, occurs widely across what is left of its range.

Rufous scrub-birds have been studied intensively in northern New South Wales. Males occupy territories that are about 200 metres across, where they sing loudly to attract females and drive away other males. If a recording of their song is played within a territory, the male runs in circles around the source of the sound; most circle clockwise, but a few move anticlockwise.

Scrub-birds are mainly brown with strong black barring on their back and sides. The rufous scrub-bird has reddish hues in its plumage, a white throat bordered with black and short, rounded wings.

The female rufous scrub-bird lays two eggs, and she alone incubates them and cares for the young. The young fledge relatively quickly, and leave the nest at two or three weeks.
Scientific name: *Atrichornis rufescens*

NOISY SCRUB-BIRD

The noisy scrub-bird is one of the rarest birds in Australia, although it is relatively common in the very small area of south-west Western Australia where it still occurs. For many years this little bird was thought to be extinct, but it was rediscovered in the 1960s at Two Peoples Bay. It lives in moist gullies in the steeply sloping country around the bay, frequently emerging into wet heathland. In the early 1960s, only about 40 noisy scrub-birds were found in the area, but there are now around four hundred.

The noisy scrub-bird is a darker brown than its rufous relative, but has the same short, rounded wings and black-bordered white throat.

The female noisy scrub-bird lays only one egg a year. Each female of this species must breed at least twice over its lifetime to maintain the population size, and three times if the scrub-bird population is to increase. This reproductive pattern of low clutch size and long periods between broods is common in species prone to extinction.
Scientific name: *Atrichornis clamosus*

RUFOUS SCRUB-BIRD
Scrub-birds are small relations of the lyrebirds and, like the lyrebirds, they have loud voices and are accomplished mimics. Both species are quite rare.

DISTRIBUTION

RUFOUS SCRUB-BIRD
NOISY SCRUB-BIRD

DISTRIBUTION

WHITE-THROATED TREECREEPER

RED-BROWED TREECREEPER

WHITE-BROWED TREECREEPER

BROWN TREECREEPER

RUFOUS TREECREEPER

BLACK-TAILED TREECREEPER

AUSTRALIAN TREECREEPERS

Australian treecreepers are medium-sized songbirds, 16–20 cm long, with a jaunty, upright stance. They have compact bodies, a thin but strong bill, and extremely large feet and claws. They use these claws like climbing spikes, hooking them into bark and hopping vertically up trunks and along the undersides of branches in apparent defiance of gravity.

Of the world's seven treecreeper species, six occur in Australia; the seventh is a New Guinean species. Australian treecreepers are generally brown with streaked patterns below. Except for the black-tailed treecreeper, all have distinctive eye stripes or eyebrows – usually a thick white line with rufous patches. Females are often marked in a rich rufous colour around the eyes and throat. Members of the group differ mainly in the darkness of their plumage – from near black to near red – and the colour, shape and extent of their eyebrows. All treecreepers reveal a pale wing stripe in flight.

Australian treecreepers were so named because they resemble the northern hemisphere treecreepers, which also climb trunks vertically. In fact, Australian treecreepers, called woodpeckers by bushmen, are more similar to the woodpeckers of the northern hemisphere, but there are no true woodpeckers in Australia. Like true woodpeckers, however, Australian treecreepers use their bills to probe beneath bark for insects, and both groups nest in holes in trees. True woodpeckers drill their own holes, but Australian treecreepers build a nest in a natural tree hollow, usually in a eucalypt.
Family: Climacteridae

WHITE-THROATED TREECREEPER ▪

The white-throated treecreeper is the most common and familiar species in this group. It is frequently seen in forests and woodlands around the eastern perimeter of Australia, extending inland along rivers and in wooded areas. Its series of loud, high whistles, falling in pitch towards the end, is one of the most common bird calls of eastern Australia.

There are two forms of white-throated treecreeper. A small northern form, 14 cm long, sometimes called the little treecreeper, occurs in Queensland from Cooktown to Mackay. It is usually found in rainforest, frequently at higher altitudes. The larger southerly form, 16–18 cm long, is found at all altitudes and occurs from the Snowy Mountains to lowland rainforest and out into the moister mallee woodlands in the west. Females have a rufous patch on the side of their neck.

White-throated treecreepers feed by hopping along or up a branch, searching for insects. Ants are a favourite food. Sometimes a treecreeper will track a trail of ants up a trunk, snapping up an ant with each upward hop. When it reaches the upper branches, the bird glides down in a spiral to the base of the tree to begin the process all over again.
Scientific name: Cormobates leucophaeus

OTHER AUSTRALIAN TREECREEPERS ▪

All treecreeper species except the white-throated treecreeper have helpers at the nest – that is, young birds from previous clutches help their parents to brood, feed and protect the new nestlings.

▪ WHITE-THROATED TREECREEPER
A treecreeper's large, strong feet and sharp claws enable it to climb vertically up tree trunks and even cling to the undersides of branches. It probes the bark with its bill for insect prey.

▪ RUFOUS TREECREEPER
The rufous treecreeper (*Climacteris rufa*) is the most richly coloured of the treecreepers. It builds its nest in a tree hollow or sometimes a hollow log.

The red-browed treecreeper (*Climacteris erythrops*), 13–15 cm long, requires native forest with a mixture of eucalypts for its habitat, and frequents the tall, moist forests of south-eastern Australia. Like the white-throated treecreeper it has a white throat, but its bright rufous eyebrow and chest markings, particularly in the female, make it an attractive and distinctive species.

The white-browed treecreeper (*C. affinis*), 14 cm long, and the brown treecreeper (*C. picumnus*), 16–18 cm long, favour dry habitats. The white-browed treecreeper lives in mallee and woodland in central Australia, avoiding treeless plains and deserts. The brown treecreeper populates similar habitats in the east, occasionally reaching the coast where dry conditions prevail. Both species spend much time on the ground pursuing insect prey in a series of bounds.

The rufous treecreeper (*C. rufa*), 15–17 cm long, frequents the south-western part of the continent, where it occurs in a wide variety of habitats. It is a red brown colour.

The black-tailed treecreeper (*C. melanura*), 17–20 cm long, is a bird of the far north and north-west. It has very dark plumage, and is the only treecreeper that does not have an eye stripe or eyebrow.
Scientific name: Climacteris spp.

FAIRY-WRENS, EMU-WRENS AND GRASSWRENS

Early settlers in Australia called these small songbirds wrens because they carry their tails upright, like the wrens of the northern hemisphere, when they perch or hop along the ground. The resemblance, however, is no more than superficial, and the two groups of birds are not closely related. The family evolved in the Australian region and, except for several fairy-wren species that are found in New Guinea, it is still restricted to Australia.

Fairy-wrens, emu-wrens and grasswrens are sedentary and tend to live in small parties. They are basically ground-feeders, foraging mainly for insects or, in the case of grasswrens, for seeds. They are all able to move very rapidly, and they dive for cover into low shrubs or rock formations when alarmed. Males assert their territorial claims by singing from the tops of shrubs or rocks, particularly during the breeding season. They usually hold their tail jauntily erect when they are courting or feeding but trail it behind when they fly or when they are trying to avoid detection.

Members of this family construct domed nests in grass or shrubs, often close to the ground. They make these structures of grass, bark strips and cobwebs, sometimes lining them with softer materials such as down or fur. All are 12–15 cm in length, half of which is tail. Females and young birds are predominantly a dull grey-brown with paler underparts, and are often so similar that species identification can be tricky.

Fairy-wrens are the most familiar members of the group. Not only are they are more widely distributed than the other species, but their shape – they look like a dainty ball of feathers with a long, slender tail – and the brilliant colouring of the males make them especially memorable. At least one fairy-wren species occurs in any one part of Australia, and in some regions there are as many as three.

The superb fairy-wren has been studied extensively, and much is known about its habits and the social structure of its groups. The lifestyles of other fairy-wrens, although not so well known, are believed to be essentially the same.

Emu-wrens and grasswrens are so secretive in their habits and are found in such isolated parts of Australia that most people are unaware of their existence.
Family: Maluridae

SUPERB FAIRY-WREN

Superb fairy-wrens are familiar residents of parks and suburban gardens throughout the south-east of Australia. They require open grassy areas where they can hop about and forage, and a variety of shrubs close by in which to hide and build their nests.

These wrens tolerate humans, and in some Melbourne parks will seek out picnickers, looking for scraps of cheese and breadcrumbs. Like many other small ground-feeding birds, their numbers have diminished in city environments, possibly as a result of cats preying on them or pesticides poisoning their food, and they have vanished from many suburban gardens where they were once quite common.

Male and female fairy-wrens are both about 14 cm long. The females are brown above and paler below. For their first few months the young birds resemble the females, but as the nesting season approaches, young males moult into a striking breeding plumage of electric blue and jet black, with only their brown wings and white belly remaining unchanged. If they can find a mate and establish a territory, these males breed in their first year, but at the end of summer they moult back into nonbreeding plumage, retaining a

bluish coloration only in their tail. Older males retain their breeding plumage throughout the year.

Superb fairy-wrens start nesting in spring and may continue until midsummer. The female lays three to four eggs at one-day intervals. After laying the last egg, she incubates the clutch, and the eggs hatch about 14 days later. When the hatchlings begin to demand food, the father participates in parental duties for the first time; one or more family helpers also assist in protecting and feeding the new chicks.

The young remain in the nest for about 12 days, although they may leave prematurely if disturbed. Their powers of flight are weak for some time and they are vulnerable to predators, so the protection of their parents and helper birds is very important for their survival.
Scientific name: *Malurus cyaneus*

DIVERSIONARY TACTICS
Fairy-wrens have developed a display known as a rodent run to distract potential predators from young birds. The adult drops to the ground and lowers its head and tail, so that it looks like a mouse. It then scampers away, hoping the intruder is in pursuit.

■ SUPERB FAIRY-WREN
Widely known as blue wrens, these little birds are a common sight flitting about in parks and gardens throughout south-eastern Australia.

DISTRIBUTION

■ SUPERB FAIRY-WREN

DISTRIBUTION

VARIEGATED
FAIRY-WREN

LOVELY FAIRY-WREN
RED-WINGED
FAIRY-WREN
BLUE-BREASTED
FAIRY-WREN

PURPLE-CROWNED
FAIRY-WREN

WHITE-WINGED
FAIRY-WREN

CHESTNUT-SHOULDERED FAIRY-WRENS ■

Four very similar fairy-wren species are sometimes collectively known as chestnut-shouldered fairy-wrens because all the males in breeding plumage have a rich chestnut patch on each shoulder. Together, they are distributed over most of mainland Australia except for southern Victoria, but their territories seldom overlap. Their similar appearances and separate distributions suggest that these species evolved from a single stock and that each became regionalised.

In Queensland and New South Wales, variegated fairy-wrens (*Malurus lamberti*) often share districts with superb fairy-wrens (page 229). The two species are occasionally seen together, but variegated fairy-wrens prefer undisturbed native vegetation with a fairly dense understorey. In eastern Australia they are common in heathland, and in spring the black breast and electric blue cap, mantle and tail of the males are a spectacular sight among the wildflowers.

The lovely fairy-wren (*M. amabilis*) occurs around Cape York Peninsula and southward to Cairns. It frequents the margins of rainforests and often forages in trees. Females differ from other fairy-wren hens in having a pale blue head and back. The red-winged fairy-wren (*M. elegans*) lives mainly in rank vegetation around freshwater lakes and streams in the extreme south-western corner of mainland Australia. The fourth species, the blue-breasted fairy-wren

■ PURPLE-CROWNED FAIRY-WRENS
The male of this species has a purple cap edged with black and his mate has chestnut patches on her cheeks.

■ CHESTNUT-SHOULDERED FAIRY-WREN
The variegated fairy-wren (*Malurus lamberti*) is the most widespread of the fairy-wrens. A male is pictured here.

(*M. pulcherrimus*) occurs in two isolated populations, one in Western Australia and one in South Australia, separated by the Nullarbor Plain. Scientific name: *Malurus* spp.

PURPLE-CROWNED FAIRY-WREN ■

The crown of the male purple-crowned fairy-wren is magenta with black edging and a black dash, but this species is otherwise not brightly coloured. Females have a broad red-brown patch on each side of the face.

These fairy-wrens live in dense vegetation, favouring pandanus thickets or canegrass and paperbark stands alongside rivers. They inhabit a few isolated and remote areas in far northern Australia. The population around the Gulf of Carpentaria seems to be reasonably secure, but in the Kimberley their habitat has been so severely trampled by buffalo and cattle over the past hundred years that there are fears for their survival. Scientific name: *Malurus coronatus*

WHITE-WINGED FAIRY-WREN ■

At rest, the male white-winged fairy-wren is electric blue with white shoulders. In flight, its white feathers become more prominent and the bird looks like a silvery butterfly. Females are paler and greyer than other fairy-wrens and have pale blue tails.

■ WHITE-WINGED FAIRY-WREN
Mainly a bird of the dry interior, this fairy-wren breeds after substantial rain. Mainland males have a cobalt blue body but one island race is black-bodied.

White-winged fairy-wrens inhabit shrublands in the most arid parts of Australia, particularly saltbush country, where they are often one of the more abundant birds. They forage mostly in the outer leaves of shrubs, sometimes dropping to the ground to search for seeds and insects. The black and white wrens on Dirk Hartog and Barrow islands, off the coast of Western Australia, used to be regarded as a separate species, but they are actually forms of the white-winged fairy-wren. Scientific name: *Malurus leucopterus*

RED-BACKED FAIRY-WREN ▣

These birds are found around the northern edge of Australia, from the Kimberley in Western Australia to about Port Stephens in New South Wales, living in rank grassland and tussocks. The female is brown above and buff below, but the breeding male's black and red plumage is unusual for a fairy-wren. When the male displays, he extends his red feathers across his wings, making him look even ruddier.

After breeding, these fairy-wrens gather in loose flocks of 20 or 30 birds. Since most males apparently moult into nonbreeding plumage, these flocks often consist of brown birds.
Scientific name: *Malurus melanocephalus*

SPLENDID FAIRY-WREN ▣

The splendid fairy-wren replaces the superb fairy-wren (page 229) in the interior of the eastern mainland states and across the continent to the south-west corner. In the more arid parts of its range the splendid fairy-wren frequents low mallee, mulga woodland and nearby shrubs. These wrens have not adapted well to urban sprawl and are seldom found in gardens and parks.

The breeding plumage of the male splendid fairy-wren is an intense blue and black; the female is grey brown with dull white underparts.
Scientific name: *Malurus splendens*

EMU-WRENS

Emu-wrens live only in Australia. They get their name from their tails, which consist of six feathers similar to emus' feathers in that they lack the hooks that usually hold the barbs of feathers together. But there the similarity to these big birds ends, for these wrens are no more than 18 cm long, and three-fifths of that is tail.

The southern emu-wren (*Stipiturus malachurus*) is the most widespread of the three emu-wren species currently known. It inhabits heaths and vegetated sand plains around the southern half of Australia, including Tasmania. Its body is round and brown, with dark streaks on the wings and back. Males have pale powder blue throats and breasts.

When white settlement began, in 1788, these birds were abundant around Sydney Harbour, and a picture of one, painted by an unknown convict artist in 1791, is held in the Mitchell Library in Sydney. Since then, they have suffered from habitat destruction and have such feeble powers of flight that they are easily caught by cats and dogs. However,

they are plentiful in the swampy heathlands of several coastal national parks, where their future should remain reasonably secure.

White settlers had occupied Australia for more than a hundred years before discovering the rufous-crowned emu-wren (*S. ruficeps*), which occupies remote desert spinifex country in central and Western Australia. Similar to the

▣ SPLENDID FAIRY-WREN
Unlike its eastern counterpart, the superb fairy-wren, the splendid fairy-wren avoids human settlements.

southern emu-wren but smaller, this species is 12–13 cm long and weighs only 5 grams. It is probably the lightest of all Australian birds.

The third species, the elusive mallee emu-wren (*S. mallee*), is restricted to mallee with an understorey of spinifex in north-western Victoria and nearby parts of South Australia. It is sometimes regarded as a form of rufous-crowned emu-wren; the two species are so alike that where their distributions overlap only an expert can distinguish between them.
Scientific name: *Stipiturus* spp.

▣ RED-BACKED FAIRY-WREN
These fairy-wrens live in grassland, where they hop along the ground in the early morning and at the end of the day, searching for insects.

DISTRIBUTION

▣ RED-BACKED FAIRY-WREN

▣ SPLENDID FAIRY-WREN

▣ SOUTHERN EMU-WREN

▣ RUFOUS-CROWNED EMU-WREN

▣ MALLEE EMU-WREN

DISTRIBUTION

■ STRIATED GRASSWREN
■ EYREAN GRASSWREN

□ THICK-BILLED
GRASSWREN
■ WHITE-THROATED
GRASSWREN
■ BLACK GRASSWREN

□ DUSKY GRASSWREN
■ GREY GRASSWREN
■ CARPENTARIAN
GRASSWREN

GRASSWRENS ■

Grasswrens are endemic to the Australian mainland and are among the rarest and most elusive of all Australia's birds. It is very easy to understand why so little has been published about them: they frequent shrublands and rocky outcrops in some of the country's most arid regions, several species living in places that are so remote and have such a harsh climate that few people have ever visited them. Six of the eight species of grasswren that are currently known range over quite limited areas – some of them are restricted to a single river system.

Grasswrens are 14–22 cm long and have a longish tail, which they generally carry upright. They feed on insects and seeds, gathered for the most part from the ground. Their agility and somewhat furtive habits make them extremely difficult to see and they often appear to be drab brown or grey. However, they actually have quite bold patterning with streaks of black and white, particularly around their head and back. Some species have conspicuous areas of rufous or black.

The striated grasswren (*Amytornis striatus*), the most widely distributed of the grasswren group, has been recorded from most of the mainland but is not abundant anywhere. It prefers spinifex, generally mixed with mallee. Land clearing for grazing and agriculture has reduced its numbers and is now seriously threatening its survival, particularly in the eastern parts of its range.

The only other grasswren that is at all widespread is the thick-billed grasswren (*A. textilis*). This species has a fragmented distribution on saltbush plains from the west coast across to into New South Wales, where it has not been recorded for many years and has probably died out. This species, the first grasswren to be described scientifically, was sighted at Shark Bay in 1818 by French naturalists on the *Uranie*.

The next grasswren species to be discovered by Europeans was the Eyrean grasswren, *A. goyderi* (see box, 'The lost grasswren'). This bird is restricted to a small area in the north-eastern corner of South Australia. It has a very stout bill, giving it a somewhat finch-like appearance. This characteristic probably indicates that it has a high proportion of seed in its diet.

By the close of the nineteenth century the majority of Australia's birds had been recorded, but only the three grasswrens named above had been encountered. The dusky grasswren (*A. purnelli*) is now known to inhabit spinifex on rocky hills and gorges in central Australia; its range overlaps that of the thick-billed grasswren, and the two species are difficult to tell apart.

The most recently discovered of these species is the grey grasswren (*A. barbatus*), which was first named in 1967. It lives in dense clumps of lignum, canegrass and saltbush on the floodplains where the Bulloo River flows from Queensland into New South Wales, and also in north-eastern South Australia.

Grasswrens of the arid interior do not breed at a particular time of year but nest after heavy rains have fallen. The three tropical species, however, nest during the wet season. These tropical grasswrens are large, boldly marked birds that frequent rocky

THE LOST GRASSWREN

The Eyrean grasswren (*Amytornis goyderi*) was discovered in 1874 when six specimens were collected near Lake Eyre. Two were sent to the bird artist, John Gould, one went to the Australian Museum in Sydney, and the others disappeared.

Later searches failed to find any more of these birds. In 1961, however, some birdwatchers retraced the path of the 1874 expedition and managed to find some birds and photograph a nest containing young. Eventually, in 1980, a group of Eyrean grasswrens was captured.

It is now known that, although they are usually rare, Eyrean grasswrens can increase their numbers rapidly in a good season. After substantial rains, they are one of the commonest birds in parts of the Simpson Desert where thickets of canegrass grow on sandhills.

outcrops across the Top End. The most easterly representative of the genus is the Carpentarian grasswren (*A. dorotheae*), which is restricted to a small region just inland of the south-western corner of the Gulf of Carpentaria. The Arnhem Land escarpment in the Northern Territory is home to the white-throated grasswren (*A. woodwardi*) and much of the population is safely within the boundaries of Kakadu National Park. The black grasswren (*A. housei*) inhabits the sandstone outcrops and ravines of the north-west Kimberley, the most inaccessible region of the three. So remote is it that this grasswren's eggs have yet to be discovered by scientists.
Scientific name: *Amytornis* spp.

■ GRASSWRENS
Carpentarian grasswrens (*Amytornis dorotheae*) live in a tiny area in the Northern Territory. They move about their rocky habitat in pairs or parties of four or five.

PARDALOTES, SCRUBWRENS AND THORNBILLS

Pardalotes, scrubwrens and thorn-bills have no obvious linking characteristics. They can be brightly coloured or drab, fine-billed or stout-billed, long-tailed or short-tailed. They dwell in rainforest or desert, feeding on the ground or in the outer leaves of tall trees, or anywhere in between. Despite this, genetic research suggests that their ancestors split off from each other relatively recently, and that all these birds belong to the same large family.

The most recent classification puts them in 15 genera, six of which have only one species. Gerygones are the most widespread genus, with representatives from South-East Asia through to New Zealand and a few Pacific islands. Scrubwrens, one thornbill and relatives of the fern-wren also inhabit New Guinea, but the others live only in Australia.
Family: Pardalotidae

PARDALOTES

Pardalotes occur nowhere else in the world. They are dumpy birds, 9–11 cm long, with short tails and short, blunt bills. The four species currently recognised are black, brown or olive green above and pale brown, grey or lemon below. Many species have a prominent eyebrow, and some are marked with red and yellow on the rump. Although quite common in most areas of Australia, including suburban gardens, these birds usually go unnoticed because they spend most of their time in the canopy of trees, usually eucalypts.

Pardalotes move around in pairs or family parties but after breeding may congregate in large flocks. They feed mainly on small insects gleaned from outer foliage. In many places their staple diet is the sweet shells produced by the leaf-sucking insects known as lerps (see page 535).

All species build a domed or cup-shaped nest of shredded bark, sometimes lined with dry grass and placed in a tree hollow or an earthen tunnel. The female lays three to five white eggs and pairs share parental duties.

Spotted pardalotes (*Pardalotus punctatus*) are found over south-east and south-west Australia. Their main call, consisting of three high-pitched notes, is a familiar bush sound. The male spotted pardalote is the most colourful of all pardalotes. Its dark

upper parts are dotted with white spots and it has a yellow throat and a red or yellow rump. Females are much duller. Spotted pardalotes nest in late winter. They dig a tunnel in an earthen bank, often in a road cutting or dry creek bank, and build their nest in a chamber at the end. Pardalotes have been known to nest in hanging baskets or in a heap of soil awaiting a gardener's attention.

The striated pardalote (*P. striatus*) inhabits most of Australia. It lacks the spots and rump colour of the spotted pardalote and has a white stripe with a red or yellow spot on each wing. It nests in a tree hollow or earthen tunnel during the warmer months.

The red-browed pardalote (*P. rubricatus*) is found in most of northern Australia, including the arid interior, and its range overlaps with that of the striated pardalote. Its red eyebrow and its five- or six-note call help to identify the red-browed pardalote. It nests in tunnels in spring, or, in arid regions, after rain, and prefers shrubby eucalypt woodland, leaving taller timber to the striated pardalote.

The forty-spotted pardalote (*P. quadragintus*) is rare and endangered. Its wings and tail are spotted with white but it has no distinct head markings. These birds live only in Tasmania, where they were once widespread. Today, only eight small populations survive near Hobart, probably numbering fewer than 3400 birds. They nest in holes in trees, rarely in tunnels, and often line their nests with feathers.
Scientific name: *Pardalotus* spp.

■ PARDALOTE
Pardalote is Greek for spotted, and most of these birds are marked with white spots or streaks. This is a male spotted pardalote (*Pardalotus punctatus*).

BRISTLEBIRDS

Bristlebirds live in heaths and swamps around coastal southern mainland Australia. The bristles at the corner of their mouth probably help them make their way through tangled vegetation. All three species have suffered from the spread of settlement, and have disappeared from areas they once inhabited.

Bristlebirds are 18–27 cm long and brownish, with long tails, strong legs and short, rounded wings. They forage on or near the ground for insects, seeds and berries. When alarmed they run rather than fly.

The western bristlebird (*Dasyornis longirostris*) lives in a very small area of Western Australia around the Fitzgerald River National Park and Two Peoples Bay, where efforts are being made to ensure its survival.

NESTING UNDERGROUND
Some pardalote species, such as the spotted pardalote, build their nest at the end of an underground tunnel.

DISTRIBUTION

- ROCK WARBLER
- FERNWREN

- LARGE-BILLED SCRUBWREN

- ATHERTON SCRUBWREN

- WHITE-BROWED SCRUBWREN

- YELLOW-THROATED SCRUBWREN
- TROPICAL SCRUBWREN
- TASMANIAN SCRUBWREN

■ SCRUBWRENS
The white-browed scrubwren (*Sericornis frontalis*) is the most widely distributed species in this genus. It builds its domed nest near the ground in dense undergrowth.

The future of the rufous bristlebird (*D. broadbenti*) seems to be reasonably secure. It ranges from close to Melbourne to the mouth of the Murray River, and has been recorded from sand dunes and gardens.

The eastern bristlebird (*D. brachypterus*) used to occur in pockets from the Queensland border to eastern Victoria, but has not been reported north of Sydney for many years. It is quite common at the Barren Grounds Nature Reserve, New South Wales, which provides secure habitat for bristlebirds, ground parrots and other important species.
Scientific name: *Dasyornis* spp.

ROCK WARBLER ■

Rock warblers live on the sandstone outcrops that dominate much of the Sydney landscape. They move over boulders and cliff faces searching for small insects in crevices. Now and then they forage on the ground, but seldom in trees or shrubs. Their range is restricted to areas within about 250 kilometres of Sydney.

Each pair occupies a fairly large territory, so they are never abundant. Since white settlement, the species has disappeared from many settled areas. However, these birds still live in many national parks and around the shores of Sydney Harbour.

In August, these birds build a football-sized nest of grass and shredded bark, which they hang from a cave ceiling. As sandstone caves are not always available, limestone caves, culverts and mine tunnels are also used. One pair nests regularly in the sandstone cellar of a Sydney winery.
Scientific name: *Origma solitaria*

FERNWREN

The little-known fernwren is confined to upland rainforests in and near the Atherton Tableland in Queensland. It resembles the scrubwren in behaviour, appearance and size but has a black crescent across

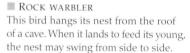

its upper breast, and its structure is distinct enough for it to be placed in a genus of its own. It appears to be almost entirely terrestrial, and feeds on the forest floor, searching in the leaf litter for small invertebrates.
Scientific name: *Oreoscopus gutturalis*

SCRUBWRENS ■

Scrubwrens are small, dumpy birds, 11–14 cm long. They are restricted to Australasia, and six species are currently recognised in Australia.

The large-billed scrubwren (*Sericornis magnirostris*) ranges from Cooktown in Queensland to the Dandenong Ranges in Victoria. It is olive brown with no distinct markings, making it difficult to identify, although its long, slightly upturned bill is helpful. Instead of building its own nest, this bird often takes over the used nest of its close relative, the yellow-throated scrubwren.

In north Queensland the closely related and very similar-looking

■ ROCK WARBLER
This bird hangs its nest from the roof of a cave. When it lands to feed its young, the nest may swing from side to side.

Atherton scrubwren (*S. keri*) is restricted to upland rainforests. It feeds mostly on the ground, whereas the large-billed scrubwren forages among stems, branches and vines.

The white-browed scrubwren (*S. frontalis*) inhabits dense undergrowth, including coastal dunes and heathlands. Although it prefers to keep under cover, it is an inquisitive bird – a patient observer can easily coax it into the open.

The yellow-throated scrubwren (*S. citreogularis*) is common in rainforests from south-eastern Queensland to southern New South Wales, with one population on the Atherton Tableland in Queensland. It often shares its habitat with the large-billed scrubwren. Males have bright yellow throats contrasting with glossy black faces; females are much duller. Like most scrubwrens, the yellow-throated scrubwren eats mainly insects, but also includes seeds in its diet. Its nest, suspended from a branch often over a creek, is a huge bundle of rootlets and bark that looks like flood debris.

The tropical scrubwren (*S. beccarii*) lives near the tip of Cape York Peninsula and ranges north into New Guinea. It is very similar in appearance and behaviour to the large-billed scrubwren and the Atherton scrubwren, but it can be distinguished by its pale eyebrows and the white in its wings.

The Tasmanian scrubwren (*S. humilis*), a larger and darker version of the white-browed scrub-wren, is restricted to Tasmania and some islands in Bass Strait.
Scientific name: *Sericornis* spp.

SCRUBTIT

The diminutive scrubtit, 11 cm long, is found only in Tasmania, where it inhabits dense, wet fern gullies and rainforests. The name of its genus –*Acanthornis* – reflects the inability of ornithologists to decide whether it belongs with the scrubwrens (genus *Sericornis*) or the thornbills (genus *Acanthiza*). It has been seen foraging on tree trunks like a treecreeper.
Scientific name: *Acanthornis magnus*

HEATHWRENS

Heathwrens are small, shy, brown birds endemic to Australia. They forage on the ground under shrubs for small insects and seeds. There are two species, both about 13 cm long, brown above, and paler below with bold dark streaks. Both have a chestnut rump and a white eyebrow.

Heathwrens are fine songsters and accomplished mimics. They sing, with tail cocked, during winter and early spring, from a vantage point in a shrub for half an hour at a time.

The chestnut-rumped heathwren (*Hylacola pyrrhopygia*) inhabits heaths and woodlands with well developed undergrowth in the south-eastern corner of mainland Australia, usually well away from settled areas. It is not well known because of its fairly remote location and retiring habits.

The shy heathwren (*H. cauta*) is found across southern Australia in dense understorey within or near mallee. It can be distinguished from the chestnut-rumped heathwren by a prominent white spot on each wing.
Scientific name: *Hylacola* spp.

FIELD WRENS

Field wrens are closely related to heathwrens. They are about the same size (12–14 cm long) and look similar, but field wrens have dark streaks on their breast and a brown back. Like heathwrens, field wrens are skilled songsters and mimics.

Both field wren species inhabit low vegetation in parts of southern and western Australia. However, they are not common anywhere, and are difficult to observe because of their reluctance to fly and their habit of foraging on the ground for insects and seeds. Males sometimes perch on a shrub and, with tail cocked, utter a melodious territorial song.

■ SPECKLED WARBLER
The speckled warbler can be picked out from the heathwrens and field wrens by the white streaks on its crown.

The rufous field wren (*Calamanthus campestris*) inhabits arid saltbush and dry shrublands in southern Western Australia and South Australia.

The striated field wren (*C. fuliginosus*), which is slightly larger and more streaked, prefers a damper habitat of tussock grass and swampy heathland. It lives in southern Victoria and Tasmania, but is also sparsely distributed on the south coast of New South Wales.
Scientific name: *Calamanthus* spp.

SPECKLED WARBLER ■

The speckled warbler, about 12 cm long, is greyish above with a cream breast and dark streaks above and below. It has white streaks on its crown. It inhabits the understorey of dry woodlands, where it feeds on the ground on insects and seeds, often with thornbills or whitefaces.

Speckled warblers range over the tablelands and slopes of the Great Dividing Range southward from central Queensland, but are not often seen near the coast. They utter a pleasant sustained song, frequently interspersed with mimicry of other birds. On the ground they build a substantial domed nest of dry grass and bark with a long, spout-like entrance. The female lays three to four chocolate brown to red eggs.
Scientific name: *Chthonicola sagittata*

WEEBILL

At 8–9 cm long, weebills are the shortest of all Australian birds. They frequent eucalypt woodlands throughout the mainland, spending most of their time in the tree canopy. Here they capture small insects, sometimes hovering to glean prey from the outer leaves and even chasing flying insects. Brownish green

■ FIELD WREN
The rufous field wren (*Calamanthus campestris*) forages for insects and seeds in arid scrub country, hopping over the ground with its tail cocked. It is sometimes found on the coast and on gibber plains.

DISTRIBUTION

- ■ PILOTBIRD
- ■ REDTHROAT
- ■ LARGE-BILLED GERYGONE

- ■ BROWN GERYGONE
- ■ DUSKY GERYGONE
- ■ GREEN-BACKED GERYGONE

- ■ WESTERN GERYGONE

- ■ FAIRY GERYGONE

- ■ WHITE-THROATED GERYGONE

- ■ MANGROVE GERYGONE

above and yellow beneath, weebills resemble pardalotes (page 233) both in appearance and foraging behaviour, and they often move around in mixed flocks with other small birds.

Weebills have a clear, high-pitched song with a rising inflection and a similar but less distinct contact call that is often repeated. Their call and a short stout bill distinguishes these birds from thornbills and gerygones. Scientific name: *Smicrornis brevirostris*

PILOTBIRD ■

Pilotbirds are rufous brown, ground-dwelling birds, about 17 cm long, with a faint scaly pattern on their underparts. They are generally similar to rock warblers (page 234), but their tails are not black, and they occupy very different habitats. Pilotbirds live in dense forests, usually next to creekbeds with thick undergrowth, from the Blue Mountains southwards to the Dandenong Ranges near Melbourne.

Pilotbirds often forage in the company of superb lyrebirds (page 226). They capture worms and small insects exposed by the vigorous scratching of their larger companion, a habit that accounts for their name. Pilotbirds utter a variety of sounds, but their main territorial call is a piercing four-note 'guinea-a-week'. Scientific name: *Pycnoptilus floccosus*

■ PILOTBIRD
After they have fledged, young pilot-birds hide at first on the forest floor, and then they begin to roam around and feed with their parents.

REDTHROAT

The redthroat occurs throughout a wide area of mallee, mulga and salt-bush country in the more arid parts of central and western Australia, but it is not common anywhere. It is a plain grey-brown bird, 12 cm long, with white between its eyes and bill; males have a chestnut red patch on their throat.

Redthroats feed on the ground on beetles, ants and other insects and seeds. Both males and females sing melodiously from a prominent perch, interspersing their song with mimicry of other bird calls.

The female lays three to four dark brown eggs in a domed nest made of bark, twigs and grass in a low shrub. Scientific name: *Pyrrholaemus brunneus*

GERYGONES ■

Gerygones are found from South-East Asia to New Zealand, but the Australian mainland is home to most species – eight in all. Like thornbills, they are brownish above, pale cream or yellow below and 10–12 cm long. Most species have a pale eyebrow or white spot on the forehead and white patterns in the tail. Gerygones forage for insects in the outer foliage of trees, where they would be easily overlooked but for their clear, melodious calls.

Gerygones build elegant nests that they hang from the outer stems of trees and vines. There is a side entrance, sheltered by an awning, and a hanging tail-piece. Some tropical species frequently build close to a wasps' nest, apparently to provide protection from predators.

The large-billed gerygone (*Gerygone magnirostris*) of the Northern Territory and Queensland coast is an inhabitant of mangroves.

The brown gerygone (*G. mouki*) is common in moist forest gullies from Cairns in Queensland to eastern Victoria. These birds do not have the clear, tuneful song that characterises others in this group, but their foraging is accompanied by frequent insect-like contact calls that sound like 'which-is-it, which-is-it?'

The dusky gerygone (*G. tenebrosa*) of the north-west coast is another inhabitant of mangrove swamps, whereas the green-backed gerygone

■ GERYGONES
Fairy gerygones (*Gerygone palpebrosa*) are found in Queensland rainforests. This female is feeding her fledgling.

(*G. chloronotis*) lives in drier territory in the Top End and the Kimberley district in the far north-west.

The western gerygone (*G. fusca*) is the only member of this group to favour south-western Australia and the dry interior. It is plain brown, and identification depends on eye colour and the extent of white in its tail and above its eyes.

The fairy gerygone (*G. palpebrosa*) is the only member of this group in which the male differs from the female; each has lemon yellow underparts, but the male has a brown throat. Fairy gerygones are common in the rainforests and vine thickets of northern Queensland.

White-throated gerygones (*G. olivacea*) are the best known members of the genus. These fairly common migratory birds inhabit the open woodlands of northern and eastern Australia from the Kimberley in the north-west to Victoria. In September, they arrive at their breeding grounds. The territorial song is a gradually descending cadence of pure notes that lasts about four seconds.

The mangrove gerygone (*G. levigaster*) inhabits mangrove forests across the northern coast from Broome in Western Australia into New South Wales. This bird has a clear, sustained song.

Two gerygone species were once endemic to Lord Howe and Norfolk islands. The Lord Howe gerygone (*G. insularis*) was abundant on the island until 1918, when rats swam ashore from a wrecked ship, but has not been recorded since 1936. The Norfolk Island gerygone (*G. modesta*) still survives. Scientific name: *Gerygone* spp.

WHITEFACES

Whitefaces are endemic to mainland Australia. They are similar in size and appearance to thornbills and are often seen feeding on seeds and insects in mixed flocks with some of the terrestrial thornbills. The three whiteface species all have a whitish stripe across their forehead.

The southern whiteface (*Aphelocephala leucopsis*) is widely distributed over the southern part of the continent. This bird frequents grasslands and is particularly common on sheep stations, where it often nests in old buildings or hollow fence posts. Nearer to the coast, southern whitefaces have not fared so well; like many small ground-feeding birds, they have become scarce or disappeared from many suburban habitats, perhaps because of pesticides or predation by cats.

The banded whiteface (*A. nigricincta*) ranges over a large area of arid shrubland and spinifex in central Australia, but is not common anywhere. It usually occurs in small parties, often with thornbills or chats, and is believed to be able to survive without any surface water.

The remaining member of the genus, the chestnut-breasted whiteface (*A. pectoralis*), is one of the least known birds in Australia. Not only is it rare, but it is restricted to a very limited area in one of the most remote and inhospitable parts of South Australia. Its nest and eggs were unknown until 1968. In recent years it has been observed and photographed by a number of birdwatchers in saltbush and gibber plains near Leigh Creek.

Scientific name: *Aphelocephala* spp.

THORNBILLS

Thornbills, which are currently classified into 12 species, are restricted to Australia except for one species that is also found in New Guinea. They are absent from the far north of the continent but elsewhere most districts have several species. They range from 9 cm to 11 cm in length and have slender bills.

Thornbills eat mostly insects, and occasionally seeds. Their habitat preferences are diverse; some species are adapted to foraging in the forest canopy, others keep to the shrub layer or the ground. They make nests of dried grass and bark strips in the leaves of a tree or shrub or concealed inside a tree hollow.

The yellow-rumped thornbill (*Acanthiza chrysorrhoa*) is probably the best known thornbill. It is brightly coloured, widely distributed across the southern half of the continent and a ground-feeder. It has a pleasant, tinkling song and builds a remarkable two-storey nest consisting of a domed main chamber with a cup-shaped structure on top.

The buff-rumped thornbill (*A. reguloides*), rather similar in appearance and habits to the yellow-rumped thornbill, occurs in the woodlands of eastern Australia. It nests inside a tree hollow or between a tree trunk and a piece of peeling bark – a trait which led to its old name of barktit.

The chestnut-rumped thornbill (*A. uropygialis*) inhabits the dry woodlands of western and central Australia, nesting inside a tree hollow or fence post. The slaty-backed thornbill (*A. robustirostris*) is another arid country thornbill, but occurs more in shrublands. The slender-billed thornbill (*A. iredalei*) inhabits semi-arid saltbush and saltmarshes.

Most thornbills are distributed over a wide area; the inland thornbill (*A. apicalis*) is one of the most widespread, favouring a huge area of central and western Australia. There is a great deal of regional variation, so that in the past the inland thornbill has been split into a number of species; on the other hand, it has often been lumped in with the brown thornbill (*A. pusilla*), which has a very similar call and is one of the most common thornbills in south-eastern Australia. The brown thornbill is a bird of dense undergrowth, although it frequently ventures into the lower branches of nearby trees.

The yellow thornbill (*A. nana*) and the striated thornbill (*A. lineata*) are two common thornbills of the south-eastern mainland; both are birds of the canopy and outer foliage with rather similar contact calls. Striated thornbills usually search for food in eucalypt trees, while yellow thornbills commonly frequent wattles, casuarinas and paperbarks.

The remaining thornbills are unusual for this group in being restricted to small areas of Australia. The mountain thornbill (*A. katherina*) occurs only in high altitude rainforest in north Queensland, where it feeds in the top of the canopy and is difficult to observe. The western thornbill (*A. inornata*), perhaps the plainest of the group, is confined to the south-western corner, where it is fairly plentiful around Perth.

The Tasmanian thornbill (*A. ewingii*) is restricted to Tasmania and some Bass Strait islands. It resembles the brown thornbill so closely that identification is a problem, but the two species do not interbreed. Generally, brown thornbills occupy the drier areas, leaving the wetter forests to the Tasmanian thornbills.

Scientific name: *Acanthiza* spp.

THORNBILL

The nest of the striated thornbill (*Acanthiza lineata*) is a neat oval dome of interwoven bark strips and grasses with a round entrance near the top.

DISTRIBUTION

SOUTHERN WHITEFACE

BANDED WHITEFACE

CHESTNUT-BREASTED WHITEFACE

THORNBILLS

237

HONEYEATERS

Of 173 species of honeyeater in the world, 66 live in Australia. The family probably evolved on the supercontinent of Gondwana, and honeyeaters today are important birds in the Australian environment. They help to pollinate and cross-fertilise plants, and also to reduce insect pests.

These birds are widespread and common throughout Australia; they are found in every habitat where nectar is plentiful, coming into cities and towns to feed in native gardens and parks. Five to ten species may share a single area.

Some species are now seriously endangered by human activities, such as land clearance and logging, that have destroyed their habitats. Feral animals and domestic pets have also taken their toll. People can help to improve the situation by planting local native trees to restore honeyeaters' natural environment.

Food for gods – and honeyeaters

Honeyeaters are so named because they feed on the honey-like fluid called nectar that collects in the cups of flowers. This nectar is generally available throughout the year, providing these birds with a constant supply of energy-rich food to fuel their very active metabolism.

Honeyeaters have a longish, downward-curving bill that is able to probe deeply into flowers, and a specially adapted muscular tongue with numerous fibrous hairs at the end that acts like a sponge to soak up the nectar. The lapping action of the tongue is extremely fast – up to as many as ten licks a second. The birds also use this brush-tipped tongue to reach into cracks in bark when searching for another favourite food – honeydew – the secretions of plant-sucking insects that combine with the sugary substance that oozes from leaves.

Some honeyeater species have evolved particular adaptations or techniques for reaching nectar. Spinebills have an especially long and slender bill that enables them to reach to the bottom of long tubular flowers, such as the mountain devil, and the white-plumed honeyeater takes a cunning short cut by piercing the side of a flower with its sharp, pointed bill in order to feed on the nectar at the base.

Honeyeaters supplement their diet with a variety of other foods such as fruits and insects in order to procure the protein and vitamins that they need to remain healthy. When these birds feast on fruits, they inevitably spread seeds to new areas. One species, the regent honeyeater, concentrates on the nectar and fruit of mistletoe plants. Honeyeaters take insects from trees and eat the shells of lerps – parasitic insects of native trees that produce sugary protective shells – and often strip the lerps themselves from leaves.

Honeyeaters may be migratory, nomadic or sedentary. Certain species feed from only one or two types of trees, and these birds travel around the country following the seasonal flowering patterns of their chosen food. Some honeyeaters migrate from Australia's alpine and subalpine regions to avoid the cold winters, while others remain in a particular area for as long as their food supply remains constant. They usually feed on the various tree species within their range as they come into flower during the year.

Plumage and plainsong

In general, honeyeaters' coloration varies from dull green to brown, but there are often distinctive patches of white or yellow on their face or neck, or both, that are useful for identifying species. A few species, such as the scarlet honeyeater, are brightly coloured.

The calls of honeyeaters vary within and between species from a simple single whistle to complex songs, and the birds use these calls

BRUSHING UP NECTAR
The hairs at the end of a honeyeater's tongue enable the bird to gather nectar – a sugary fluid – from inside flowers. Shown here is a white-plumed honeyeater (*Lichenostomus penicillatus*).

SIPPING ON SWEETNESS
A noisy miner (*Manorina melanocephala*) demonstrates the characteristic feeding behaviour of honeyeaters, deftly sipping nectar from the bases of flowers.

A BLOSSOM BANQUET
Perching on a waratah, a New Holland honeyeater (*Phylidonyris novaehollandiae*), which is found in southern Australia, shows how tiny these birds are.

to communicate or to beg, or as signals of alarm or distress. These birds are quite territorial and defend their range aggressively against other species. Some – for example noisy miners – mimic the calls of larger members of the family to frighten off bigger birds that they are unable to drive away by fighting.

Breeding seasons for honeyeaters vary depending on the availability of nectar and honeydew. The males of some species perform elaborate mating flights in order to attract females, and long-term partnerships are common. The pair construct a cup-shaped nest, made from twigs and strips of bark bound together by cobwebs, in the fork of a branch in shrubs or trees. Some honeyeaters suspend their nests among eucalypt foliage. They line the nest with pieces of animal fur, feathers and soft plant material.

The one to four eggs are incubated for two weeks, sometimes by the female and sometimes by both parents. Both birds share the feeding duties. During the two weeks that they spend in the nest, honeyeater nestlings sometimes receive extra food from nonbreeding pairs.
Family: Meliphagidae

WATTLEBIRDS

Wattlebirds, together with friarbirds, are the largest honeyeater species in Australia. They are named for the fleshy lobes, called wattles, that hang from the sides of their throat, although these are not present in the little wattlebird. All three species have grey-brown plumage with pale streaks, and all are loud and aggressive. Their nests are untidy cups of twigs lined with grass or stringy bark fibres, generally supported in forks of trees or large shrubs.
Scientific name: *Anthochaera* spp.

LITTLE WATTLEBIRD

At a length of 26–30 cm, the smallest of the wattlebirds is still larger than most other honeyeaters. The little wattlebird has a similar distribution to that of the red wattlebird but also occurs in Tasmania. It is found mainly in heaths, particularly those where banksias are common. It is one of the first heathland birds to begin calling, often starting half an hour before daylight and making loud sounds variously described as 'kwock-a-wock', 'chock' and 'yekop, yekop, yekop'.

■ RED WATTLEBIRD
Named for the red lobes of skin on its cheeks, this bird is widespread in the eucalypt forests of southern Australia and is often seen feeding in gardens.

The little wattlebird is smaller than other wattlebird species and – although it is called a wattlebird – does not have the characteristic wattles on its cheeks. It has a darker, more even coloration, with more prominent silvery streaking, and it has rufous patches on its wings that are visible when it flies.

The little wattlebird's diet is very similar to that of the other wattlebirds, the nectar from banksias being of paramount importance. This bird nests most often in the shrub layer and very occasionally in grass tussocks. It lays from one to three eggs.
Scientific name: *Anthochaera chrysoptera*

RED WATTLEBIRD ■

Red wattlebirds were hunted as game birds in the nineteenth and early twentieth centuries, but they are now protected. At 33–36 cm long, they are the largest honeyeater species on the mainland. They occur in eastern, southern and south-western Australia, but not in Tasmania. They inhabit mainly eucalypt forests and woodlands but are also found in parks and gardens.

This bird's main features are its size and long tail, its red wattles, its lemon yellow belly and the white edges at the tips of its wings and tail feathers. Its call resembles a harsh cough.

Red wattlebirds feed mainly on nectar, honeydew, lerps and insects, but also eat fruits and seeds. They are generally common and are often abundant at rich food sources.

Although red wattlebirds usually nest from July to December, they nest throughout the year when conditions are good. The female lays two to three eggs. They usually breed only once a year, but in favourable conditions may raise a second brood.
Scientific name: *Anthochaera carunculata*

YELLOW WATTLEBIRD

The yellow wattlebird is the largest honeyeater, at 37–47 cm long. It is found only in Tasmania and is distinguished by its large, dark eyes and its long, droopy, yellow wattles. Its loud call sounds like a cough.

This bird's habitat, diet and breeding habits are similar to those of the red wattlebird. It, too, was a popular game bird. Shooting was banned in 1972, but the species is not protected. The main threat to its survival now is the clearing of mature forests.
Scientific name: *Anthochaera paradoxa*

DISTRIBUTION

LITTLE WATTLEBIRD

RED WATTLEBIRD
■ YELLOW WATTLEBIRD

■ LITTLE WATTLEBIRD
This wattlebird's nest is a cup of twigs and plant fragments, lined with grass or feathers and built in the branches of a shrub. The female lays up to three eggs, but more commonly two.

DISTRIBUTION

■ HELMETED FRIARBIRD

□ SILVER-CROWNED FRIARBIRD

□ NOISY FRIARBIRD

□ LITTLE FRIARBIRD

WITH KNOBS ON
A dark, mainly bald head characterises the friarbirds, and all species except the little friarbird have a knob on the top of their bill.

FRIARBIRDS

Friarbirds are a group of four large honeyeaters that are characterised by a dark, mostly bald head and a frill of grey feathers around the neck that has been likened to a friar's tonsure. These birds have a substantial bill for catching large insects and reaching deeply into nectar-laden native flowers. A prominent knob on the top of their bill appears to be purely ornamental. The feathers on their nape and around their neck are pale and silvery, and stand out in contrast with the duller brownish grey plumage that covers the rest of their body.

Friarbirds are social and quarrelsome, often gathering in loose groups at abundantly flowering trees to feed. Birds chase others away from their feeding branches and call with raucous cackling and gurgling sounds.

These honeyeaters build open cupshaped nests that they place in a tree fork or suspend by the rim from branches among thick foliage.
Scientific name: *Philemon* spp.

HELMETED FRIARBIRD
The helmeted friarbird is 32–35 cm long. It is found in northern Australia, generally at the edges of rainforest but also in eucalypt forests and woodlands, as well as in mangroves and urban parks and gardens. It feeds in the upper levels of trees on nectar, fruits, insects and spiders. These birds breed once or twice a year, from August to September or from December to January. The female generally lays a clutch of two to four eggs.

The helmeted friarbird stands out from other friarbirds because of the less prominent and more rounded

knob on its bill and the line of greybrown silvery feathers between the nape of its neck and the knob.
Scientific name: *Philemon buceroides*

SILVER-CROWNED FRIARBIRD
As its name implies, the feathers on the head of the silver-crowned friarbird are silvery and more noticeable than those of the helmeted friarbird. The knob on this friarbird's head is also more prominent.

This bird, 27–32 cm long, lives in northern Australia and is found in eucalypt and paperbark forests and woodland, scrubland and urban gardens. It generally lays two eggs a year at any time between September and December. It snatches insects from around flowering trees, and also eats fruits and seeds.
Scientific name: *Philemon argenticeps*

NOISY FRIARBIRD
The noisy friarbird is 31–35 cm long, and can be distinguished by the absence of feathers on its head and the prominent knob on top of its bill. It is found in the eastern quarter of Australia, mostly in eucalypt forests and woodlands, but also in parks, gardens and orchards. Its diet consists of nectar, lerps, honeydew, fruits, seeds and insects – sometimes as large as cicadas – that it swallows whole. It also takes eggs and nestlings from other birds.

Numbers fluctuate considerably. Populations increase in size and the birds become especially noisy when eucalypts are in flower. Noisy friarbirds nest once or twice a season from November to January. Females usually lay two to three eggs.

■ LITTLE FRIARBIRD
This is the smallest of the friarbirds. It feeds on small pockets of flowering eucalypts and melaleucas, often hanging upside down to reach the blossoms.

Breeding in this species is closely tied to the emergence of cicadas in the summer; these then become an important item of diet for the dependent juvenile birds.

In the southern half of its range, the noisy friarbird is generally a regular altitude migrant, moving down onto the western slopes and the coastal plain from the mountains during winter, when food becomes scarce. Whether the same birds always go in the same direction is not known, but it has been observed that poor flowering on the slopes results in a paucity of birds, whereas in seasons when the trees flower prolifically the birds are often abundant. It would therefore appear that they are partly nomadic.
Scientific name: *Philemon corniculatus*

LITTLE FRIARBIRD ■
The little friarbird is 25–29 cm long and is found in eastern and northern Australia in habitats similar to those of other friarbird species but more open. The little friarbird breeds once or twice a year, from June or July until November or December. The female lays two to three eggs, and sometimes even four.

This friarbird is the only one in the group without a knob on its bill. The area of feathers covering the top of the head is larger than in the other friarbirds, and it has bluish grey bare patches on the sides of its face.
Scientific name: *Philemon citreogularis*

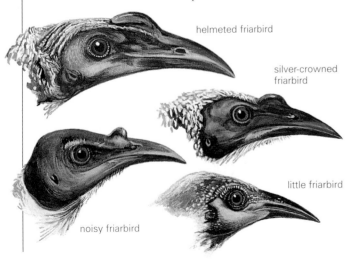

helmeted friarbird

silver-crowned friarbird

little friarbird

noisy friarbird

OTHER HONEYEATERS

BLUE-FACED HONEYEATER

The blue-faced honeyeater is found mainly in open forests, woodlands, and timber along watercourses, but also visits orchards, and banana and sugarcane plantations. It lives in northern and eastern Australia, but not in the south-eastern corner of the continent. This large honeyeater, 30–32 cm long, has a golden-olive back and a black head with a white band around the nape. Its underparts are white, except for a black area extending down its throat and forming a bib. Its most distinctive feature is the bare skin around its eyes, which is bright blue in adults and green or yellow-green in juveniles.

Blue-faced honeyeaters occur singly, in pairs and in small flocks. They feed on insects, fruits and nectar, and call with a loud, quickly ascending 'kwip' whistle, which they repeat at regular intervals. The female lays two eggs, usually between July and January, in a large bulky cup made of bark strips and supported in an upright tree fork.
Scientific name: *Entomyzon cyanotis*

SPINY-CHEEKED HONEYEATER

The plain cinnamon throat and upper breast plumage of the spiny-cheeked honeyeater distinguishes it from other honeyeater species. It also has a blue iris and a bright pink bill with a black tip.

■ SPINY-CHEEKED HONEYEATER
This bird can be identified by its black-tipped pink bill. It is widely distributed in woodland and scrubby arid country.

The spiny-cheeked honeyeater is found throughout most of Australia, except east of the Great Dividing Range, in Tasmania, in the south-west corner and the far north. It lives in eucalypt woodland, arid scrubland and heath and looks very like the wattlebirds, but, at 22–26 cm long, is slightly smaller than the little wattlebird. Spiny-cheeked honeyeaters feed on insects, fruits, nectar, honeydew and lerps, and also eat small reptiles and nestlings.

These birds nest from July to December and after rain in arid parts of the country. They make a thin-walled cup nest of grass and fine, long leaves and suspend it from a horizontal or sloping branch among thick foliage. The female lays two eggs, sometimes three.
Scientific name: *Acanthagenys rufogularis*

BELL MINER

The loud, bell-like, chiming call of the bell miner is well known to those who live east of the Great Dividing Range, from Gympie in the north to Melbourne in the south, but the bird itself is difficult to see. This medium-sized honeyeater, 19 cm long, is dark olive green with yellow-orange legs and bill. It has a small patch of orange-red bare skin behind and below its eyes.

Bell miners live in the canopy in patches of tall forest with a dense shrub layer. They are sedentary and form small colonies that occupy fairly stable territories, which they defend aggressively against most other species of bird, from pardalotes to currawongs.

They feed for the most part on the sugary white coverings secreted by tiny sap-sucking insects known as lerps. Because the insects remain and the bell miners prevent other lerp-eating birds from entering their territory, the trees can suffer damage to their foliage. If this damage becomes pronounced the miner colony moves away and does not return for several years. Bell miners also consume other insects and spiders, and sometimes nectar.

The bell miner's nest is a fragile, thin-walled cup made of twigs, grasses and leaves bound together with cobwebs and sometimes lined with downy seeds. It is suspended by its rim in the thin fork of a shrub or sapling. Birds nest once or twice a year, from April to September in the north and from June to December in the south. The female lays two eggs, or sometimes three.
Scientific name: *Manorina melanophrys*

■ BELL MINER
Sometimes called bellbirds, these forest-dwelling honeyeaters are known for their haunting, bell-like call.

BLACK-EARED MINER

The black-eared miner is 25 cm long and similar in appearance to the yellow-throated miner (page 242), but without the pale rump. Restricted to mallee near the Murray River where New South Wales, Victoria and South Australia meet, this secretive species is endangered. Clearing of its habitat has brought it into closer contact with the yellow-throated miner, and the two species may interbreed.
Scientific name: *Manorina melanotis*

NOISY MINER

The familiar native noisy miner forms territorial groups of 6–30 birds. It inhabits the coastal strip of eastern and south-eastern Australia inland to the western slopes of the Great Dividing Range, living mainly in open forest. The partial clearing of forest and the removal of most of the shrub layer for grazing or housing

DISTRIBUTION

BLUE-FACED HONEYEATER

SPINY-CHEEKED HONEYEATER

BELL MINER
■ BLACK-EARED MINER

NOISY MINER

■ BLUE-FACED HONEYEATER
This honeyeater is loudly chasing an intruder away from a food source.

■ SCARLET
HONEYEATER
A bottlebrush flower is
providing nectar for this
jewel-like honeyeater.
This is a male; the
female of this species is
brown with a faint wash
of red on her chin.

DISTRIBUTION

■ YELLOW-THROATED
MINER

■ WHITE-EARED
HONEYEATER

■ YELLOW-FACED
HONEYEATER

■ SCARLET HONEYEATER
■ PIED HONEYEATER

■ BLACK HONEYEATER

has created ideal habitats for these
birds, and their numbers are increasing. They nest once or twice a year
and females lay two to three eggs.

Noisy miners are 24–28 cm long
and are grey all over, except for a
black forehead and cheeks. Their
feet, their bill and a patch of bare skin
behind their eyes are bright yellow.

These birds feed on insects, nectar
and fruits. They are very aggressive,
and often keep all other smaller
birds out of their territory. Group
members launch coordinated
assaults on rivals, and their calls are
extremely loud. Their alarm call, in
particular, which they use to alert
the group, even warns other bird
species of danger. Noisy miners
direct their highest, most piercing
calls at intruders flying overhead.
Scientific name: *Manorina melanocephala*

YELLOW-THROATED MINER
The yellow-throated miner is also
known as the white-rumped miner,
because of the off-white rump that
sets it apart from other grey miners.
It resembles the noisy miner in
behaviour and size (25–28 cm long),
but can be distinguished from the
noisy miner by the yellow wash on
its neck feathers and the absence of
black feathers on its forehead.

The yellow-throated miner is
found in the drier open woodlands
and scrublands of the interior, and
has a wide distribution across most
of mainland Australia, but it does
not occur in the south-east, in Tasmania or in Cape York Peninsula.
Scientific name: *Manorina flavigula*

WHITE-EARED HONEYEATER
The white-eared honeyeater is
common in the forests, woodlands,
mallee and heaths of south-eastern
and south-western Australia, but it
is not found in Tasmania. It is about
20 cm long with olive wings and tail,
a dark grey crown, a black face, and
a prominent white ear patch.

White-eared honeyeaters are mostly
seen singly or in pairs. They feed on
insects, spiders, berries and nectar.
These birds are aggressive for their
size and call with a ringing 'chock-
chock' that can be quite loud.

White-eared honeyeaters breed
from July to December. They build
their cup nests suspended in a low
shrub or tussock of grass, and have
been known to land on human
observers to take hair or cloth fibres
to use as lining material. The female
lays two or three eggs.
Scientific name: *Meliphaga leucotis*

YELLOW-FACED HONEYEATER
The yellow-faced honeyeater is a
strongly migratory species. It lives
in the wetter forests of the east coast
of Australia, and each autumn large
numbers move north along the
Great Dividing Range into eastern
Queensland. It is a medium-sized
honeyeater that grows to 11–17 cm
long. The overall greyish brown
colour of the yellow-faced honeyeater is broken by a streak of yellow
beneath its eyes that runs from its
bill to its ears. It feeds on berries,
insects and nectar.
Scientific name: *Meliphaga chrysops*

SCARLET HONEYEATER ■
The male scarlet honeyeater is bright
red over its head, back and chest,
and black elsewhere. The female is
brown with dull white underparts
and a trace of scarlet on its chin. This
small bird reaches a length of only
10–11 cm, including its bill.

The scarlet honeyeater lives in wet
forests along the east coast from Iron
Range in Queensland to Melbourne.
It is a resident in the north of its
range, nomadic in the centre, and
migratory in the south. It feeds
mainly on insects and nectar, which
become scarce in the south in winter,
accounting for the bird's absence.
Scientific name: *Myzomela sanguinolenta*

PIED HONEYEATER AND BLACK HONEYEATER
The pied honeyeater (*Certhionyx
variegatus*) and the black honeyeater
(*C. niger*) are nomadic birds of scrublands and woodlands in the dry
interior. They use their long, downcurved bills to feed on insects and
nectar, invading areas after rain when
flowers bloom and insects proliferate.

The black honeyeater, at a length
of 9–12 cm, is the smaller of the two
species. Females are dull brown on
their head and upperparts and dull
white with darker blotches underneath; males have black upperparts
and white undersides.

The pied honeyeater is 14–18 cm
long. Males and females resemble
male and female black honeyeaters,
except that males have a white patch
on their wings and both sexes have a
small sky blue wattle under the eye.
Scientific name: *Certhionyx* spp.

YELLOW-THROATED HONEYEATER

The diet and nesting behaviour of the yellow-throated honeyeater are similar to those of the white-eared honeyeater, but the yellow-throated honeyeater sometimes builds a nest as high as 10 metres above ground. It forages, mainly for insects, on tree trunks and large tree limbs, and utters a resonant 'tonk-tonk-tonk', 'chooka-wok' and 'pick-em-up'. This bird has also been seen taking hair and clothing fibres from humans to use as nesting material.

The yellow-throated honeyeater lives only in Tasmania and on the islands of Bass Strait, and is the only member of its genus to breed in Tasmania. It inhabits forests, woodlands and heath, but is also found in gardens, parks and orchards. This bird is similar in size and patterning to the white-eared honeyeater, except that its ear patch is cream in colour and much less distinct, and it has a bright yellow throat.

Scientific name: *Meliphaga flavicollis*

YELLOW-TUFTED HONEYEATER

The yellow-tufted honeyeater mainly inhabits the forests of south-eastern Australia, particularly those with a dense shrub understorey. It is also found in woodlands, mallee, acacia shrubland and heath. It lives in sedentary colonies of 10–100 individuals. The bird is 20–22 cm long with olive green to olive brown upperparts, a black face mask bordered with yellow below and a yellow ear tuft. Its crown is also bright yellow, while its throat and breast are dull yellow with bright yellow flecks. Its call is a harsh whistle or churring sound.

Yellow-tufted honeyeaters feed mainly on insects taken from foliage in the canopy or tucked into the crevices of bark, but they also take nectar and fruits, and will feed in the dense shrub layer beneath the canopy. Nests are often close to the ground in thickets. The form known as the helmeted honeyeater (subspecies *cassidix*), found only near Yellingbo, east of Melbourne, is considered at risk from forest clearing and competition from bell miners.

Scientific name: *Lichenostomus melanops*

SINGING HONEYEATER

This honeyeater is 17–22 cm long. It is greyish brown above and darker on the wings and tail, which are edged with yellow. Below, it is a lighter grey. Its most conspicuous feature is a black band through its eyes.

This bird is widespread, and is found everywhere on the mainland west of the Great Dividing Range, except in Cape York, Arnhem Land and the south-east corner of Victoria. Its habitats include mangroves, woodlands, heathlands, mallee, and mulga and spinifex scrub. It is absent only from dense forests.

Most people would not describe this bird's loud 'sheek', 'terrik-terrik' calls as singing, but it does utter melodious calls at dawn. It is very aggressive towards smaller bird species, particularly honeyeaters. It sometimes augments its typical honeyeater diet with the eggs of zebra finches and double-barred finches.

Scientific name: *Lichenostomus virescens*

REGENT HONEYEATER

Regent honeyeater numbers have declined greatly in recent decades. Once recorded in flocks of thousands, with a range extending from the Lofty Ranges in South Australia through to south-eastern Queensland, the estimated total population of regent honeyeaters is now a mere thousand, and the bird is an endangered species.

It is confined mostly to scattered regions on the western slopes of the Great Dividing Range but sometimes occurs on the eastern slopes down to the coast in parts of New South Wales and Victoria. Clearing and habitat fragmentation may account for its loss from most of its former range.

The regent honeyeater is 20–23 cm long and is mostly black with body feathers edged with cream or yellow. Its wing and tail feathers have broad golden-yellow edges. The pinkish warty skin around its eyes earned it the name warty-faced honeyeater.

This honeyeater is difficult to monitor because it is highly nomadic. It lives in forests and woodlands and eats honeydew, lerps, fruits and insects, but mainly lives on nectar from white box, yellow box, mugga ironbark, Blakely's red gum and river oak on the western slopes, and swamp mahogany on the coast. It also feeds on the nectar and berries of mistletoes growing on these trees, which may be an important food source when little else is available.

■ YELLOW-TUFTED HONEYEATER
These sociable honeyeaters often nest in colonies. Youngsters are sometimes fed by helpers as well as the parents.

■ SINGING HONEYEATER
This bird is feeding by hovering beneath a rose mallee blossom. The singing honeyeater is an important pollinator of this endangered eucalypt.

DISTRIBUTION

■ YELLOW-THROATED HONEYEATER
■ YELLOW-TUFTED HONEYEATER

■ SINGING HONEYEATER

■ REGENT HONEYEATER

DISTRIBUTION

■ WHITE-PLUMED
HONEYEATER

■ WHITE NAPED
HONEYEATER

■ BROWN HONEYEATER

■ PAINTED HONEYEATER

Fortunately, many sites for this species are inside nature reserves. However, where important sites are on private land, the bird remains at risk. Landcare groups and local landholders are working together to preserve the bird's remaining habitat and to plant its preferred tree species.

Taronga Zoo has a captive breeding program. Much has already been learned about the species, and if the program is successful it will be possible to introduce captive-bred regent honeyeaters into the wild, should it become necessary.
Scientific name: *Xanthomyza phrygia*

WHITE-PLUMED HONEYEATER

This bird is named for the white plume with a black upper margin over its ear. The white-plumed honeyeater is 15–17 cm long, with an overall olive grey plumage, and a yellow-olive head, wings and tail.

White-plumed honeyeaters often appear in parks and gardens but their preferred habitat is open forest, woodland, timbered watercourses and, less commonly, tall eucalypts far from water. The species ranges over much of mainland Australia, but is not found in the far north or the south-west. It has adapted to urban life, probably because of its preference for open habitats, and feeds in introduced trees and shrubs.

It eats insects, spiders and berries, and has developed a clever technique for cutting holes in the base of long tubular flowers to reach nectar.

■ WHITE-NAPED HONEYEATER
The white band across the back of its neck clearly identifies this species. This individual is busy taking a bath.

■ BROWN HONEYEATER
A lively bird that lives in a wide variety of habitats, from mangroves to heath, this honeyeater utters a repeated penetrating, musical call.

White-plumed honeyeaters utter a clear, pleasant 'chick-o-wee' call, and have a loud, piping alarm call that is often taken up by other members of the species, as well as other honeyeaters. This alarm call warns many nearby birds of the approach of potential predators.

Pairs of birds weave grasses, bark strips – and even horsehair when available – into cup-shaped nests that they suspend in small trees or shrubs. The nest is usually between 2 metres and 5 metres above the ground, and sometimes hangs over water. The female lays two to three eggs between July and December.
Scientific name: *Lichenostomus penicillatus*

WHITE-NAPED HONEYEATER ■

The 13 cm-long white-naped honeyeater has white underparts and an olive green upper body and wings. It also has a black cap on its head and a white band on its nape. Other honeyeaters share these features, but the combination of a white throat and the orange-red crescent patch of bare skin over the eye distinguishes the white-naped honeyeater from other black-capped honeyeaters. Its call is also very distinctive, and its presence is often detected by its lisping 'sherp-sherp-sherp'.

White-naped honeyeaters inhabit south-eastern Australia from Cooktown through to St Vincent Gulf, but are not found in Tasmania. They also live in south-western Australia. They are mainly found in forests, particularly those with smooth-barked eucalypts, as well as woodlands and heath, and will move into nearby gardens. They forage for food among foliage, searching for insects, spiders, nectar, fruits and berries. Larvae and adult lerps are especially important in this honeyeater's diet.

Nesting occurs from July to December. The female lays two to three eggs in a cup-shaped nest suspended in the outer foliage of a eucalypt, usually 2–6 metres above the ground. Up to 12 adult birds have been recorded feeding one brood of chicks in the nest.

Thousands of white-naped honeyeaters move north along the Great Dividing Range in autumn and then make their way south in the spring. It is not yet known where they go, but they are certainly absent from the Snowy Mountains during the cold winter weather.
Scientific name: *Melithreptus lunatus*

BROWN HONEYEATER ■

The brown honeyeater occupies a wide range in mainland Australia, as well as islands to the north near southern New Guinea. It avoids the very dry interior and is absent from most of the south-east. It lives in a wide range of habitats, including mangroves, forests, woodlands, heaths and gardens, where it feeds on insects and nectar.

This bird is 13–15 cm long, and is dull brown with yellowish wing and tail feathers. Its bill is noticeably longer and more down-curved than that of other honeyeaters of similar size. It has an indistinct yellowish and silvery white spot behind each eye and its gape is yellow, although it turns black during the breeding season. Its song is loud and sweet.

Between July and January the female lays two eggs in a small, deep, cup-shaped nest of shredded bark and grasses suspended in the fork of a shrub, usually 1–2 metres above the ground.
Scientific name: *Lichmera indistincta*

PAINTED HONEYEATER

The distinctive call of the painted honeyeater is described as 'georgie-georgie-georgie'– hence its other common name, Georgie. It reaches 16 cm long, black above with yellow patches in the wings and tail feathers, and white below with black flecks on the sides of its breast and belly. Its bill is bright pink.

The painted honeyeater lives in forest and woodland in the eastern half of mainland Australia, but usually remains in areas to the west of the Great Dividing Range. It is a summer-breeding migrant in the south of its range and is an irregular winter visitor to the far inland and northern Queensland. The female lays two eggs between October and December in a nest suspended among drooping foliage, generally 5–15 metres from the ground in a eucalypt, but sometimes in a low shrub. The painted honeyeater feeds mostly on the fruits of mistletoe, but it has also been recorded taking nectar, insects and fruits from other native shrubs.

Scientific name: *Grantiella picta*

YELLOW-WINGED HONEYEATERS

All five species in this genus are similar in appearance and size. The crescent honeyeater (*Phylidonyris pyrrhoptera*), the New Holland honeyeater (*P. novaehollandiae*), the white-cheeked honeyeater (*P. nigra*), and the white-fronted honeyeater (*P. albifrons*) all have black upperparts and white underparts flecked or marked with black, and their heads have white markings. Their yellow wing patch and yellow outer tail feathers are the most conspicuous feature of the group. The tawny-crowned honeyeater (*P. melanops*) has much paler markings and is olive brown, instead of black, with a tawny crown and a white eyebrow and throat.

The crescent honeyeater is distinguished by broad dark bands that begin near its shoulders and extend across its breast but do not meet at the centre of its breast. The New Holland and white-cheeked honeyeaters are alike except that the New Holland species has a much smaller white ear patch and its iris is white rather than dark. The white-fronted honeyeater is distinguished

COME INTO THE GARDEN

Honeyeaters are easy to attract to gardens, and a selection of local grevilleas, banksias and eucalypts can be planted that will provide nectar all year round.

Honeyeaters feed on insects, fruits, nectar and honeydew. The latter foods provide energy, whereas insects and spiders provide protein for nestlings. Honeyeaters also need shelter and water. A bird bath should be about a metre above ground and a safe distance from cover to protect birds from cats. These are young western spinebills (*Acanthorhynchus superciliosus*).

from the rest of this group by the prominent area of white feathers between its bill and its eyes and the small red spot behind each eye.

Members of this group forage more or less in the same way and on the same types of food. They take nectar, honeydew and insects. Their breeding patterns are also very similar. There are differences, however, in the preferred habitats of each

species, and it is this that probably minimises competition among them. The crescent honeyeater is confined to the extreme south-east, including Tasmania, where it prefers wet forests, alpine woodlands and coastal heath. The New Holland and white-cheeked honeyeaters occupy very similar habitats, mainly heath and woodland, and their ranges overlap in the south-west and on part of the east coast. Only the New Holland honeyeater occurs in the south-east and Tasmania; the white-cheeked honeyeater appears further north on the eastern coast. Where their ranges overlap, the New Holland honeyeater prefers the shrub layer in forest and woodland, while the white-cheeked honeyeater is confined more to heathland.

The white-fronted honeyeater is widespread over much of Australia, except for the wetter coastal areas in the north, east and south-west. It prefers arid shrubland to woodland. The tawny-crowned honeyeater has range similar to that of the New Holland honeyeater, but is confined to low alpine and coastal heath, where it is often found in recently burnt areas less used by New Holland honeyeaters.

Scientific names: *Phylidonyris* spp.

RUFOUS-THROATED HONEYEATER

This honeyeater is found along timbered watercourses and adjoining woodland, as well as in the mangroves of northern Australia, from Broome in Western Australia to Noosa Heads in Queensland. It also ventures into gardens and street trees in coastal towns. This species is uncommon east of the Great Dividing Range. It is 13–14 cm long.

The mature bird's head and back are grey-brown and its underparts are a dull white, but its wing feathers are edged with yellow and its throat and chin are rufous. Immatures have a white throat. These honeyeaters eat insects, taken from the ground and over water, as well as fruits and nectar. They build a small, purse-shaped nest of grass, bark and plant fibres suspended at the end of a branch 1–7 metres above ground, usually near or overhanging water. Nesting occurs from September to April and females lay two to three eggs.

Scientific name: *Conopophila rufogularis*

■ YELLOW-WINGED HONEYEATER
The crescent honeyeater (*Phylidonyris pyrrhoptera*) is found only in south-eastern Australia. The female builds the nest but both parents feed the young.

■ CRESCENT HONEYEATER

■ NEW HOLLAND HONEYEATER

■ WHITE-CHEEKED HONEYEATER

■ WHITE-FRONTED HONEYEATER

■ TAWNY-CROWNED HONEYEATER

■ RUFOUS-THROATED HONEYEATER

■ SPINEBILL
A male western spinebill visits a kangaroo paw plant. Western spinebills are important pollinators of the various members of this plant family.

DISTRIBUTION

■ EASTERN SPINEBILL
■ WESTERN SPINEBILL

■ RED-HEADED
HONEYEATER

■ LEWIN'S HONEYEATER

SPINEBILLS ■

There are two spinebill species, the eastern spinebill (*Acanthorhynchus tenuirostris*) and the western spinebill (*A. superciliosus*). They are best distinguished from other honeyeaters by their long, thin, down-curved bill, which is proportionally longer than the bill of other honeyeater species. These birds, about 15 cm long, were once thought to be sunbirds (page 283), but the structure of their tongue places them in the honeyeater family. A feature that distinguishes them from other honeyeaters is their ability to hover for short periods at long tubular flowers when taking nectar.

The eastern spinebill lives in wet forests, woodlands and heaths in coastal eastern and south-eastern Australia, and can also be common in gardens. It has a black bill and a black cap that runs down its breast, bordering a white throat with a central rufous and black patch. Its lower breast and belly are rufous and its back and tail are a dull reddish brown. The white patch on its outer tail feathers is obvious in flight.

When this bird flies, its wings make a 'frrup-frrup' sound as it darts in and out of cover seeking nectar, insects and spiders. Its clear, high-pitched staccato call is also distinctive. Its nest is a cup suspended 2–10 metres above the ground in the fork of a shrub or tree.

■ LEWIN'S HONEYEATER
A Lewin's honeyeater perches on a tree root over water. This species has a repeated staccato machine-gun-like call.

The western spinebill lives in the undergrowth of forests and woodlands, as well as in heath and scrub. It has not adapted to gardens as readily as its eastern counterpart, but its call and nesting behaviour are similar. It also resembles the eastern species, except for a broad, bright rufous collar that extends to its throat and has a white and black border on the lower edge.
Scientific name: *Acanthorhynchus* spp.

RED-HEADED
HONEYEATER ■

The red-headed honeyeater occurs in coastal north-western and northern Australia, and on islands off the northern coast of Australia, from Derby in Western Australia to Cape York Peninsula in Queensland. It lives along watercourses in mangroves and swampy woodlands.

It feeds on insects and nectar and nests from March to September, after the wet season. Red-headed honeyeaters suspend their tiny, cup-like nests among the foliage in the tops of the tallest mangroves. The females lay two eggs.

This honeyeater is 11–13 cm long and resembles the scarlet honeyeater (page 242), but in the male only the head, the lower back and the rump are red; the breast is a sooty brown, fading to grey-brown lower down. The female is dull brown with a red wash on its forehead and throat.
Scientific name: *Myzomela erythrocephala*

LEWIN'S HONEYEATER ■

Mainly a rainforest bird, Lewin's honeyeater also occurs in nearby more open habitat and in undergrowth near clearings. It is found on the wetter east coast of the mainland, from Cooktown to Melbourne. It is

seldom found below an altitude of 600 metres in the north of its range, but lives at all altitudes in the south of its range.

This medium-sized honeyeater is 20–22 cm long; the female is slightly smaller than the male. It is a dark olive green, with a creamy yellow line running from its bill to its eyes and a creamy yellow crescent over its ears. Native fruits form most of its diet, but it also feeds on insects and nectar. These honeyeaters can be bold and have been known to enter houses. They are very aggressive towards other honeyeaters.

Nesting occurs between August and January. Females lay two eggs, sometimes three. The nest is made of bark, grass and leaves, bound together by cobwebs and suspended in the fork of a shrub or tree.
Scientific name: *Meliphaga lewinii*

■ RED-HEADED HONEYEATER
The male of this tropical species has a bright red head and rump; the grey-brown female is less easy to see.

CHATS

All five chat species are endemic to Australia. They walk or run rather than hop, and feed on or close to the ground, taking mainly insects and seeds from dense, low shrubbery interspersed with bare patches. Like honeyeaters, they have brush-tipped tongues for lapping up nectar. They have a strong, bouncy flight and their call is generally a metallic 'tang'. They usually appear in small parties or family groups, and when they are not breeding they form small, highly nomadic flocks, sometimes of mixed species.

Chats are 9–13 cm long. Their heads and bodies are brightly coloured, the males particularly so. They have black bills and legs and white-tipped brown tails.

Most chat species inhabit arid regions, breeding in colonies after rain has fallen. They construct cup-shaped nests of twigs and grasses in low shrubs or grass tussocks or on the ground. During the breeding season, adults may feign a broken wing to lure predators away from their nests. Some chats cope with very cold weather in arid areas by entering a state of torpor or dormancy.
Family: Ephthianuridae

CRIMSON CHAT ■

The crimson chat is found over much of mainland Australia, apart from the east and north coasts. It mainly inhabits arid shrublands. Its movements fluctuate from year to year, perhaps because it depends on water. It feeds on insects and sometimes nectar.

The male has a crimson cap, breast and lower back, and a white throat. Dark brown bands run from its bill through its eyes and onto its back. The female is paler, with a crimson wash on its upper breast and lower back. Immature crimson chats resemble females.
Scientific name: *Ephthianura tricolor*

ORANGE CHAT

Orange chats inhabit much the same range as crimson chats, but their movements fluctuate less. They live mainly in acacia scrubland, spinifex and tussock grassland, particularly near salt lakes, inland swamps and clay pans.

These birds feed on the ground on insects. The male is orange with a black throat, brown wings and brown flecks on its back, and the female is yellowish brown.
Scientific name: *Ephthianura aurifrons*

■ CRIMSON CHAT
Arid shrublands are the main habitat of this chat, and it especially favours acacias growing near salt lakes. Pictured here is a male feeding its young.

YELLOW CHAT

The rare yellow chat is found among the long grasses and rushes of remote coastal and inland swamps. It also lives in vegetation around inland bores. Its distribution is very fragmented, with isolated populations over the northern half of Australia. The male is a vivid yellow with a black breast band and grey-brown upper back, wings and tail. The female is a duller yellow and does not have a breast band. Yellow chats feed on insects, mainly flies.
Scientific name: *Ephthianura crocea*

WHITE-FRONTED CHAT ■

The white-fronted chat is an inhabitant of the southern half of Australia, including Tasmania. It prefers low vegetation in coastal areas and on saltbush plains. The male has a white face bordered by a black band running across its white breast and around the back of its head. Its wings and tail are black, and its back and shoulders are grey. The female is grey above and white below, and has a less distinct dark band across its breast only.
Scientific name: *Ephthianura albifrons*

■ WHITE-FRONTED CHAT
Ground-dwelling insects form the staple diet of these chats, which inhabit salty coastal and inland areas.

GIBBERBIRD

The gibberbird is the least colourful of the chats. Males are a sandy brown with a yellow face, breast and flanks. Females are browner above and paler below. These birds tend to roam in pairs rather than family parties.

Gibberbirds inhabit the stony plains – the gibber plains – of central Australia and are one of the few bird species that can live all year in this hot, dry environment. They scour the ground for insects, perching on rocks for a better view. Gibberbirds breed when insects are plentiful.
Scientific name: *Ashbyia lovensis*

■ CRIMSON CHAT

■ ORANGE CHAT

■ YELLOW CHAT
■ WHITE-FRONTED CHAT

■ GIBBERBIRD

AUSTRALIAN ROBINS

■ JACKY WINTERS
This robin is a common sight in open woodland, fluttering from a perch to catch insects in the air, from leaves or from the ground. It often hovers low over its prey before diving.

DISTRIBUTION

■ JACKY WINTER

■ SCARLET ROBIN

When English colonists arrived in Australia, they came across a group of small, plump, upright birds, with large heads and reddish orange breasts, which swooped on their food from raised perches. They called these birds robins because they looked and behaved rather like the European robin, *Erithacus rubecula*, of the flycatcher family Muscicapidae. However, recent studies have revealed that the two groups are not closely related.

The breasts of Australian robins are variously coloured from red, orange or yellow to black, grey or white. In most species the sexes look alike, but in some the males are more brightly coloured than the females.

Australian robins eat mainly insects and other small invertebrates. The triangular shape of their beak is characteristic of insectivorous birds, and the sensory bristles around their mouth are well developed. Most robins catch their prey by pouncing on it, but a few species are more aerial and feed on insects caught on the wing. Others are largely terrestrial.

■ SCARLET ROBIN
The female builds the nest and incubates the eggs. When the chicks are newly hatched her brightly coloured mate passes her food for herself and the young robins.

Australian robins are not particularly strong or brilliant singers – their songs are simple and frequently monotonous – but their voices are pleasant and they make a musical contribution to the chorus of bird-song wherever they live.

All Australian robins construct cup-shaped nests, which vary from flattened saucers to large, coarsely built structures. The female lays two to four eggs. The role of the sexes in breeding is still uncertain in some species. In others, however, females are known to build the nest and incubate the eggs. The male feeds his mate as she sits on the nest, and both parents feed the hatchlings. The normal incubation period is just over two weeks; after a further two weeks the nestlings are fledged. Most robins live no more than a few years, but some hardy individuals survive for more than ten years.

There are about 40 species in this family, of which 21 live in Australia. A few of the Australian robins also occur outside this country. Robins are found throughout the Australian mainland and in Tasmania. They are primarily birds of woodland and forest, and consequently eastern Australia has the most species.
Family: Petroicidae

JACKY WINTER ■

The Jacky Winter has a broader range of feeding behaviours than most robins. It often drops on its prey from an elevated perch, but it may also hover in the air and then pounce. This habit of searching for food from the air while rapidly beating its wings and spreading its tail earned the Jacky Winter its early nickname, the fascinating bird: it was thought that its hovering mesmerised, or fascinated, its prey.

This brown bird is 13 cm long and has white panels on the tail, best seen during flight. Another common name, the brown flycatcher, comes from its way of darting from a branch to grab a flying insect and returning to its perch to eat it. After landing, it wags its tail from side to side.

Jacky Winters are bold and trusting, and will follow larger animals, including humans, to snatch insects flushed out by their passage. They live in open forest and woodland, and avoid thick forests. Away from denser habitation, they frequent gardens, and their liking for fence lines along paddocks earns them yet another nickname – post sitter. Their whistled 'peter-peter-peter' is most often heard in the early morning.

The female builds a flat, open cup nest, which is one of the smallest nests of any Australian bird, both absolutely and in proportion to the size of the bird. The nestlings are heavily spotted, unlike the streaked young of most other robins.
Scientific name: *Microeca fascinans*

SCARLET ROBIN ■

Male and female scarlet robins differ greatly in appearance. The male, with his red breast and boldly contrasting black head and upperparts, white wing stripe and prominent forehead, is Australia's version of the robin redbreast, but the brown female, with only a light wash of pink across her breast, can easily be confused with related species.

Europeans first discovered scarlet robins on Norfolk Island, where specimens are 11 cm long – considerably smaller than the mainland birds, at 13 cm long. This species has the widest distribution of any robin; it occurs on Pacific islands as far east as Samoa, as well as in Australia.

In Australia, the scarlet robin avoids dense trees, preferring eucalypt forest and woodland with an open understorey. On the lookout for small invertebrates, it perches on a branch or rock and then pounces to the ground to capture its prey. It seems particularly attracted to areas that have been recently burnt, and males feeding among blackened vegetation are a striking sight.

A fearless bird, the scarlet robin usually chooses a conspicuous perch from which to sing. Males are particularly obvious as they assert their territorial claims. From their vantage point they give a persistent trilling whistle, rendered as 'weecheedalee-dalee.' This species characteristically flicks its wings when perching.

During courtship the female droops and flutters her wings while the male feeds her. The nest is a delicate open cup of bark strips, bound with cobwebs and decorated with lichen. Nestlings are a warm brown in colour with fine, pale streaks.
Scientific name: *Petroica multicolor*

OTHER RED-BREASTED ROBINS

Like the scarlet robin, Australia's other red-breasted robins differ markedly between the sexes. The brown females of the various species are difficult to tell apart, but the bright males are easily identified.

The orange underparts of the male flame robin (*Petroica phoenicea*), 14 cm long, and the red crown and breast of the male red-capped robin (*P. goodenovii*), 11 cm long, clearly indicate the source of these birds' common names.

Flame robins are noted for their annual movements (see box, 'A roving robin'), while the red-capped robin inhabits drier wooded country and areas of grassland throughout much of the continent.

The male rose robin (*P. rosea*), 11 cm long, and the male pink robin (*P. rodinogaster*), 12 cm long, both have pink breasts, but the back and throat of the rose robin are grey with a brown tinge, while those of the pink robin are a sooty black. The rose robin occupies rainforest and wet eucalypt forest. The pink robin is found in temperate rainforest, particularly densely forested, ferny

A ROVING ROBIN

Most of the Australian robin species live permanently in a given area, making only local trips. The flame robin (*Petroica phoenicea*) is an exception. In summer, this species inhabits forests along the Great Dividing Range and in nearby foothills and coastal areas. It is also common in Tasmania.

In winter, however, food is scarce in the highlands, so in autumn these birds move into open country at lower altitudes. Many fly north, some to south-eastern Queensland. Flame robins from Tasmania cross Bass Strait to join mainland birds migrating northwards.

gullies. This species is noted for its uncharacteristic food-catching techniques – it flits about the outer canopy, catching insects from the leaves and in the air. Both rose and pink robins move into more open country as winter approaches.
Scientific name: *Petroica* spp.

PALE-YELLOW ROBIN

The pale-yellow robin is one of Australia's lesser known yellow-breasted robins. Compared with its brighter relative, the eastern yellow robin (page 250), it has a more subdued plumage and, at 13 cm long, is smaller. It is also a shyer bird, with a more limited and fragmented distribution. It has a preference for lowland rainforest.

Despite these differences, pale-yellow and eastern yellow robins have many habits in common. One of the most obvious is their way of perching motionless on the side of a tree trunk or a vine to view their surroundings. The pale-yellow robin seems to have a particular affinity for the thorny lawyer cane vine, or 'wait-a-while'. It frequently attaches its nest to this vine and uses the leaves in nest construction.
Scientific name: *Tregellasia capito*

HOODED ROBIN

The hooded robin is also known as the pied robin or the black and white robin. Surprisingly for such a strikingly patterned bird, a male hooded robin sitting quietly can pass unnoticed, but when it flies or drops down to capture prey, the black and white flash of its strongly contrasting wing and tail stripes quickly attracts attention. The sexes are both 16 cm long, but are quite different in appearance. The female lacks the male's bold coloration, though it still shows faint evidence of the wing and tail patterns.

This species, one of the most widespread of the robins, inhabits most of mainland Australia, except for the north-east. It prefers dry, open forests and woodlands with sparse understoreys. It is not a highly vocal bird, but it begins to sing very early in the morning and may carry on well into the night.
Scientific name: *Melanodryas cucullata*

DISTRIBUTION

FLAME ROBIN

RED-CAPPED ROBIN

ROSE ROBIN

PINK ROBIN
PALE-YELLOW ROBIN

HOODED ROBIN

RED-CAPPED ROBIN
A bright red forehead characterises the male red-capped robin (*Petroica goodenovii*). He advertises his territory by trilling repeatedly from a low perch.

Perhaps the best known of the Australian robins, the eastern yellow robin was one of the first local birds to be named by Europeans – in fact, it was independently named twice in 1790. It is widespread throughout eastern Australia, and occurs in a wide range of habitats: rainforest, eucalypt forest and woodland, dry mallee scrub, and parks and gardens.

Eastern yellow robins may come quite close to picnickers in search of an easy meal. Despite such proximity, they may escape notice, clinging to the side of a trunk or vine and silently surveying their environment. They often forage quite close to gardeners, waiting for insects turned up during digging.

Eastern yellow robins are 15 cm long. The bright colour of their underparts give them their name, as well as some nicknames, such as yellow bob. Those that live in open habitats have olive rumps, whereas those inhabiting rainforests have bright yellow ones, which are more visible in the shade.

The eastern yellow robin is one of the first birds to start singing in the morning – the name of its genus, *Eopsaltria*, means 'dawn harpist'. It is also one of the last to fall silent at night. Its calls range from a bell-like piping through a persistent 'chop-chop' to harsh scolding.

Its eggs are an attractive blue-green with reddish spots. Several adult birds may help the parents to look after the nestlings.
Scientific name: *Eopsaltria australis*

■ EASTERN
YELLOW ROBIN
While the female is sitting on the nest and brooding the eggs, the male brings her food.

DISTRIBUTION

■ SOUTHERN SCRUB
ROBIN
■ NORTHERN SCRUB
ROBIN

■ EASTERN YELLOW
ROBIN

■ GREY-HEADED ROBIN

SCRUB ROBINS

The southern scrub robin (*Drymodes brunneopygia*) and the northern scrub robin (*D. superciliaris*) were long thought to belong to the thrush family. Their shape and some of their mannerisms – running, hopping and pausing to look around – are certainly very similar to those of northern hemisphere thrushes, but it is now known that these birds are actually large terrestrial robins.

The two species are similar in many respects. Both are 22–23 cm long and sombrely coloured, with a black streak through the eyes, two white wing bars, a long, white-tipped tail and long legs. The northern scrub robin is a pale cream, whereas the southern bird is a darker, duskier brown.

Scrub robins carry their long tails erect, raising and lowering them and sometimes fanning them as they make their way about. Their tails are almost as long as their bodies. Both species are shy and are initially quite difficult to see, but they are also inquisitive and will eventually emerge from cover to investigate a patient observer.

Like thrushes, scrub robins spend a great deal of their time hopping around on the ground, searching for insects and other small invertebrates by flicking through the leaf litter with their bill. They call with thin, drawn-out whistles, either from the protection of dense scrub or from a raised and rather exposed perch.

The role of the sexes and most of the breeding biology of scrub robins is unknown, but they have been observed building nests at the base of shrubs or a short way up a tree trunk. The female lays a single egg.

The main difference between the two species is their choice of habitat. The southern scrub robin, which is found only in Australia, inhabits arid scrubland, especially mallee and broombush; in some areas, clearing of this vegetation has threatened the bird's survival.

The northern scrub robin, which is less well known than its southern relative, occurs in lowland rainforest in New Guinea, and until fairly recently inhabited two areas of lowland rainforest in northern Australia. In one of these areas – the northern tip of the Cape York Peninsula – the species is common, but unfortunately the population from the Roper River in the Northern Territory appears to have become extinct early this century.
Scientific name: *Drymodes* spp.

■ GREY-HEADED ROBIN
This grey-headed robin is putting the final touches to its nest, a cup woven from fine twigs and fibres and partly covered with lichen or moss.

GREY-HEADED ROBIN ■

Grey-headed robins are exclusive to the Atherton Tableland in Queensland, and even here they are limited to rainforest at altitudes of more than 200 metres. They also live in the mountain forests of New Guinea.

Within its small Australian range, this robin is common. It is frequently seen along forest edges, and visits picnic areas searching for handouts. Its call, a long whistle followed by three shorter, lower notes, is a common if somewhat monotonous sound of the Atherton rainforests.

At 17 cm long, the grey-headed robin is one of the largest robins, and has proportionately long legs. Males and females are similar in appearance. This species will be affected by the impact of global warming; a temperature increase of just 3.5°C will significantly reduce its habitat and cause its extinction.
Scientific name: *Heteromyias albispecularis*

LOGRUNNERS

Logrunners are a distinctively Australian family of ground-dwelling songbirds. There are two species in the family. The smaller, the southern logrunner (*Orthonyx temminckii*), is about 20 cm long. It occurs on the east coast, from Maryborough in Queensland to the Illawarra district in southern New South Wales, and – rather surprisingly – in the highlands of New Guinea. The second species, the chowchilla (*O. spaldingii*), is 28 cm long and is restricted to the Atherton Tableland in Queensland.

Both these birds are rainforest residents. Within these habitats they generally keep to the forest floor. Invertebrates are the mainstay of their diet, but both species have also been seen feeding on berries.

Logrunners are difficult to observe in the poor light on the rainforest floor, as their predominantly brown and grey patterned plumage provides effective camouflage against predators. The sexes are easily identified because the females have a chestnut throat. In both species, the wings have broad dusky bars.

Chowchillas are a solid brownish black on top and white below; the skin around their eyes is a bluish white. The southern logrunner has more rufous upperparts, which are mottled with black, and a grey face. The male's white underparts are bordered on each side by black.

The tail is a distinctive feature of the logrunner family, being tipped with exposed spines that are extensions of each tail feather's shaft; the southern logrunner is sometimes called the spine-tailed logrunner. The bird presses its tail on the ground for support while it scratches around on the forest floor.

Revealing their presence

Adult southern logrunners and chowchillas normally move around in pairs, often accompanied by offspring from previous seasons and occasionally forming larger groups. When they are agitated they often hide by quickly throwing leaf litter and soil over themselves.

The birds themselves are hard to see, but they leave telltale cleared patches through the ground litter on the rainforest floor because they throw the ground litter aside as they hop or run over the ground. Unlike most ground-feeding birds, which kick their legs backwards in order to scratch forest litter away, these birds kick vigorously sideways to rake away leaves and other debris. This enables them to see the entire disturbed area and to collect more insects than they would if they swept the litter behind them.

They can also be traced by their calls. Early in the morning and late in the afternoon they announce their presence with loud contact calls that carry for considerable distances through the still rainforest. These are usually bubbly sounds with occasional short, sharp 'weet-weets'. If disturbed, the birds produce a series of loud shrieking notes, though these quickly fade into the surrounding vegetation. Male and female chowchillas often gather morning and evening into groups of birds calling and displaying to maintain territories.

Nests and eggs

Nesting takes place in the cooler months, from April to September. Both species build a bulky nest of fibrous roots and fern fronds, lined with some feathers, under an overhang or against a tree buttress on the forest floor. Southern logrunners lay two eggs, chowchillas only one. The eggs are pure white; this is unusual for ground-nesting birds, which normally produce eggs that are patterned and coloured in order to blend into the surrounding vegetation. Logrunners' eggs become naturally stained by the decomposition of the nest lining.

Shrinking territories

Ancestral logrunners once populated a much larger range of Australasia; their fossils, dating back 15 million years, have been found in southern and northern Australia far from present rainforest regions. Climatic changes reduced the distribution of rainforest and the range of the logrunners. The presence of the southern species in the highlands of New Guinea is an example of this retraction and broken distribution.

The southern logrunner was found on the Illawarra escarpment in the early 1820s. Specimens were first seen in the rainforest at Hat Hill, now known as Mount Kembla. While rural development, mining activity and urban sprawl have encroached on their domain, their numbers, although reduced, persist. Their range now falls within areas covered by rainforest protection legislation.

The chowchilla's habitat is protected, since most of it falls within a World Heritage site.
Family: Orthonychidae

DISTRIBUTION

SOUTHERN
LOGRUNNER
■ CHOWCHILLA

LIFE ON THE
FOREST FLOOR
Logrunners are rainforest birds that seldom fly. Here a female southern logrunner (*Orthonyx temminckii*) is feeding her chicks in their nest on the forest floor.

DISTRIBUTION

GREY-CROWNED
BABBLER

WHITE-BROWED
BABBLER

HALL'S BABBLER

CHESTNUT-CROWNED
BABBLER

**GREY-CROWNED
BABBLER**
Babblers' large, domed
twig nests have a small
entrance tunnel.

BABBLERS

There are four babbler species
in Australia, three of which live
nowhere else in the world; the
fourth also occurs in New Guinea.
Babblers prefer dry conditions and
are commonly found on the ground
and in the trees of dry woodland,
farmland and shrubland. They are
usually sedentary within a limited
home range.

Babblers are gregarious birds,
living in family groups of up to
twelve. These groups, consisting of
adults and young from previous
nestings, are often referred to as
happy families or happy Jacks.

Babblers are 18–29 cm long, and
have a long tail that they often hold
slightly raised and fanned. The broad
white tip of their tail and their white
throat and eyebrows contrast with
the grey or dark brown coloration
of the rest of their body.

All Australian babblers have a
longish, downward-curving beak,
its scimitar shape emphasised by a
broad eye stripe of dark plumage
outlined by a broad white eyebrow.

Babblers are sometimes called
chatterers; both common names
describe their bubbly chatter. Family
members often form noisy gatherings. Constantly on the alert, they
move as a tight group, flying one
after the other with a low, long,
bouncing flight. Together they
methodically scour branches and
the ground under bark, leaves and
fallen limbs for insects.

The large stick nests of Australian
babblers are a familiar feature of the
inland. Resembling large bottles
with side entrances, they are built of
woven twigs and sticks, lined with
grass and feathers, and normally

■ WHITE-BROWED BABBLER
Babblers are sociable birds that live in
family groups. They search the ground
and branches for insects and seeds, all
the while clucking softly to each other.

placed in the outer extremities of
trees. Family groups use old nests
as communal roosting shelters, and
blue-faced honeyeaters (page 241)
often commandeer babbler nests, as
do several other species.

Babblers' eggs are greyish with a
pattern of thin dark lines. The eggs
are incubated and the nestlings fed
over a period of six weeks. Offspring
from previous nestings often help
their parents to rear the new brood.
Family: Pomatostomidae

GREY-CROWNED
BABBLER ■
At 20–29 cm long, the grey-crowned
babbler is the largest and most conspicuous of the babblers. It is easiest
to identify by its grey head, which
is bordered by a broad white eye
stripe. The underparts of northern
birds are heavily washed by a rusty
colour, but southern birds are light
grey beneath. Like other babblers,
these birds form noisy flocks that
probe for food both in trees and
on the ground.

Grey-crowned babblers occur
in New Guinea, across northern
Australia extending south to the
Pilbara in Western Australia, down
to Alice Springs in central Australia,
and throughout the eastern states.
Populations in the south-east may
be decreasing as a result of the disturbance of their habitats.

This species is sedentary and maintains communal territories. Nests are
occupied by pairs or family groups.
Scientific name: *Pomatostomus temporalis*

WHITE-BROWED
BABBLER ■
The white-browed babbler is similar
in appearance to the grey-crowned
babbler, but is smaller (18–21 cm
long) with a smaller eye stripe and
darker grey-brown plumage with
a dirty white abdominal area.

This species ranges throughout
southern Australia and north to the
Tropic of Capricorn, but avoids the
wetter east coast. Although they are
normally sedentary, these birds
show nomadic characteristics after
breeding. In most other behaviour,
the white-browed babbler resembles
the grey-crowned babbler.
Scientific name. *Pomatostomus
superciliosus*

HALL'S BABBLER
Hall's babbler lives in the mulga
shrublands of south-western
Queensland and north-western
New South Wales. These birds were
unknown to science until 1964,
when it was discovered that they
differed from the closely related and
very similar-looking white-browed
babbler. Hall's babblers also have a
broad white eyebrow, but their main
plumage is considerably darker and
only their throat is white.

Hall's babbler is 20–22 cm long.
It can be identified by the distinct
demarcation between its white
throat and upper breast and its dark
brown lower breast. It is sedentary
and noisy, and feeds on invertebrates in ground litter and on tree
branches and trunks. Hall's babbler
is similar to other Australian babblers
in habits and breeding behaviour,
except that it is less timid.
Scientific name: *Pomatostomus halli*

CHESTNUT-CROWNED
BABBLER
As its common name suggests, the
chestnut or ruddy colour of the
chestnut-crowned babbler's crown
distinguishes it from other babbler
species babbler. It is 21–23 cm long
and is found in inland woodlands of
mallee, native pine and she-oak; it
also occurs in stands of tall saltbush
and other shrubs.

The chestnut-crowned babbler
is widely distributed throughout
much of the Darling and Cooper
river systems of western New
South Wales and Queensland, as
well as in the shrublands of South
Australia and Victoria.
Scientific name: *Pomatostomus ruficeps*

WHIPBIRDS, WEDGEBILLS AND QUAIL-THRUSHES

This family of birds can be divided into two groups. The whipbirds and the wedgebills are both arboreal and terrestrial, and often hold their broad tails fanned out in display. Quail-thrushes, on the other hand, are generally terrestrial birds, and they rarely fan their tails. Whipbirds and wedgebills lay eggs that are basically bluish in colour, whereas quail-thrushes' eggs are predominantly off-white.

All members of this family have distinctive calls, which they use to maintain contact with each other while they are feeding or to deter intruders when they are asserting ownership of a nesting territory. Sometimes these are in call-and-answer form, with one bird, usually the male, calling, and the second, usually the female, responding.
Family: Cinclosomatidae

☐ EASTERN WHIPBIRD
☒ WESTERN WHIPBIRD

CHIRRUPING WEDGEBILL

CHIMING WEDGEBILL

WHIPBIRDS ☒

Australian whipbirds belong to an ancient group of birds that are found nowhere else in the world. It is likely that the two extant species occupied a much wider range in the past and that their distributions overlapped.

Both species have small, erect crests and broad tails, which they often fan. The eastern whipbird (*Psophodes olivaceus*), 30 cm long, is the larger of the two, and its plumage is mainly a dark olive green. The smaller western whipbird (*P. nigrogularis*), 25 cm long, is much paler and has a slightly rusty coloration. Both species have white cheek stripes, a black throat, and white-tipped tail feathers. All immature whipbirds are rusty in colour and lack the distinctive white cheek stripe of the adults.

Whipbirds are sedentary, moving about only locally. Eastern whipbirds occupy rainforest, open forest and vegetation bordering watercourses from Cooktown in Queensland southward to Melbourne. They frequently move into drier areas to feed. The western whipbird is confined to two distinct populations in drier heath and mallee; one lives in south-west Western Australia, while the other is found in Victoria and the south-eastern corner of

South Australia, including Kangaroo Island. Whipbirds usually forage in pairs, looking for insects in low shrubbery or on the ground.

Eastern whipbirds are secretive and their loud call often issues from thick undergrowth before the bird is visible. The loud whipcrack note of the male eastern whipbird is generally completed by the softer, lower 'choo' of a second bird, usually its mate or another family member. Male western whipbirds utter repetitive grating calls that are followed by a shorter response from the female.

In late winter or spring, males and females embark on chasing and calling flights. They build a flattened bowl-shaped nest of twigs, vines and tendrils in low, dense undergrowth. The female lays two blue eggs, marked at their broadest point with a series of fine black scrawls and dots. These eggs take three weeks to hatch. Both parents feed the chicks for about two weeks.
Scientific name: *Psophodes* spp.

WEDGEBILLS ☒

Wedgebills are dry-country relatives of whipbirds. At 19–21 cm long they are slightly smaller than whipbirds, but they resemble them in shape and, like them, they fan their tail when displaying. They have small crests and white-tipped tails, but they are paler than whipbirds, with a uniform sandy brown colour on top and a lighter underside.

☒ WHIPBIRDS
The whipcrack calls of the eastern whipbird are a common sound in wet forests. Both sexes feed the chicks.

These are ground- and tree-dwelling insectivorous birds. There are two species – the chirruping wedgebill (*Psophodes cristatus*) and the chiming wedgebill (*P. occidentalis*).

The ranges of both species adjoin and they overlap a little. Chirruping wedgebills inhabit areas of low shrubs and heath in north-eastern South Australia, south-western Queensland and western New South Wales. Chiming wedgebills range through similar habitats from central Western Australian coastal areas to south-western Queensland.

Wedgebills breed in autumn or spring, and the female lays two to three eggs in a bowl-shaped nest.
Scientific name: *Psophodes* spp.

☒ WEDGEBILLS
The chirruping wedgebill (*Psophodes cristatus*), pictured here, is similar to the chiming wedgebill (*P. occidentalis*) in appearance. The best way to tell the species apart is by their calls. Chiming wedgebills often call in unison, whereas chirruping wedgebills have a call-and-answer pattern.

DISTRIBUTION

■ CINNAMON
QUAIL-THRUSH
■ SPOTTED
QUAIL-THRUSH

■ CHESTNUT
QUAIL-THRUSH

■ CHESTNUT-BREASTED
QUAIL-THRUSH

■ CINNAMON QUAIL-THRUSH

This quail-thrush lives in semidesert scrub. There are two races, one living on the Nullarbor Plain and the other in the stony gibber plains of eastern central Australia.

QUAIL-THRUSHES

Of the five species of quail-thrushes recognised worldwide, four are found exclusively in Australia and one in New Guinea. All except the spotted quail-thrush are restricted to the dry interior of Australia. In shape, size and behaviour they are like thrushes, but they behave like elusive quails when flushed from leaf litter or thickets. Although they are largely ground-dwellers, quail-thrushes will fly to low perches when they are advertising or defending a nesting territory.

Quail-thrushes are shy, and are camouflaged by their bold grey, olive green, black, chestnut and white markings. All Australian species have white eyebrows and a white neck patch or cheek stripe. They move around in pairs or small family groups, and appear to have a permanent territory. Within this large range they fossick through leaf litter for invertebrates, keeping in touch all the while with soft, high-pitched lisping whistles. Calls vary little from species to species.

They make their nests in shallow depressions beside fallen branches, under grass tussocks or at the base of small shrubs or trees. Females build the cup-shaped nest from twigs, lining it with finer sticks, grasses and occasionally feathers. They lay two off-white to buff coloured eggs, peppered with dots of grey, brown and sometimes a faint lavender. Incubation periods are unknown, but parents feed their nestlings for two or three weeks.

Quail-thrushes bluff to distract predators from their young. If threatened, a sitting bird leaves the nest, uttering a variety of high notes

■ CHESTNUT QUAIL-THRUSH
A male chestnut quail-thrush perches on a dry branch. Quail-thrushes are ground-dwelling birds, but occasionally perch to declare their territorial rights.

and hisses. Often the bird fans its tail slightly to exhibit the white edging, and droops its outstretched wings to feign injury.

Their first downy feathers of young quail-thrushes are a dark slate in colour. Later, feathers with rufous or chestnut edges grow on their upper body, head, wings and tail. This edging gradually gives way to the adult colour and pattern.
Scientific name: *Cinclosoma* spp.

CINNAMON QUAIL-THRUSH ■

The male of this species is a dull cinnamon brown with a broad white band on its black breast; the female is similar but grey beneath. Both sexes are 18–21 cm long.

These quail-thrushes occur in two isolated populations – one across the Nullarbor Plain, the other in central Australia extending east into western Queensland and north-western New South Wales. There has also been a report of this bird as far north as McKinlay in north-west Queensland.
Scientific name: *Cinclosoma cinnamomeum*

SPOTTED QUAIL-THRUSH

The spotted quail-thrush, the largest species at 28 cm long, lives in the forests of eastern Australia and in south-eastern South Australia, and is the only one that inhabits Tasmania. The small black spots on the bird's underside and above are responsible for its name; this and its pink legs distinguish it from other species.

Spotted quail-thrushes forage for insects, small vertebrates and seeds on the floor of eucalypt forests.
Scientific name: *Cinclosoma punctatum*

CHESTNUT QUAIL-THRUSH ■

Chestnut quail-thrushes occur in a wide belt from Western Australia east through the lower Northern Territory and south to western Victoria and western New South Wales. Their rich chestnut and black plumage blends well with their umber-toned environment.

Although it is about the same size as the spotted quail-thrush and the female's breast is a similar colour, the chestnut quail-thrush has no spots. The male has a chestnut back and a black throat and upper breast. The female is generally greyer.
Scientific name: *Cinclosoma castanotus*

CHESTNUT-BREASTED QUAIL-THRUSH

Slightly larger than the cinnamon quail-thrush, the male chestnut-breasted quail-thrush can be distinguished by its chestnut breast band; the female is pale below.

Like the cinnamon quail-thrush, this species has two populations. Western birds occur near Shark Bay in Western Australia eastward to the south-west of the Northern Territory, inhabiting dry open places and often rocky shrubland desert.

Eastern chestnut-breasted quail-thrushes are found in similar habitats from northern central New South Wales into the Queensland interior. They may also frequent more timbered country, and are often seen on rocky hills or plateaus.
Scientific name: *Cinclosoma castaneothorax*

SITTELLAS

There are only two members of this family of small tree-dwelling birds in the world. The varied sittella (*Daphoenositta chrysoptera*) occurs in Australia and New Guinea; the other species, the black sittella (*D. miranda*), is found only in New Guinea.

The varied sittella has five distinct colour forms. These five forms were once thought to be separate species, but all forms have the same behavioural characteristics and where their ranges overlap they readily interbreed, so they are now classified as the same species.

This little bird is about 12 cm long, with a short tail, short legs with powerful feet and a slender, slightly upturned yellow and black bill. All forms have a grey to dark brown back and wings and white or dark grey undersides with or without dark streaks. Their crowns can be white,

USING AVAILABLE RESOURCES
A female varied sittella broods on her inconspicuous nest, built in a tree fork, of bark bound together with cobwebs.

black or grey. The form seen in Sydney has orange wing patches that are especially obvious in flight; others have white wing patches.

Varied sittellas have a fluttering flight, and when flying or feeding they call with a rapid 'chip-chip-chip'. They forage for food in small groups of three or more, in which males generally outnumber females, clinging to bark and hopping along the branches. They use their slightly upturned bill to dig insects from beneath loose bark.

Varied sittellas live in wooded areas over most of the Australian mainland and breed in all but the coldest months. The female incubates up to three eggs for about three weeks, and the nestlings are then fed by both parents and by other flock members for a further three weeks.
Family: Neosittidae

WHISTLERS AND SHRIKE-THRUSHES

Most members of this family are skilled and exuberant singers. Many have strong bills, often with bristles growing near their mouth, either to sense prey or to funnel food towards their bill. They are leisurely feeders, generally obtaining their food from the surface of bark and leaves or off the ground. They eat mostly insects and other invertebrates, augmented with a little fruit.

They are mainly tree-dwellers. Some migrate, but most are sedentary. Most species breed between September and January, but some have slightly longer or shorter breeding seasons. The white-breasted whistler and the grey whistler sometimes breed all year round. Of around 40 species worldwide, 14 are found in Australia.

Two members of this family – the crested shrike-tit and the crested bellbird – are endemic to Australia. Both are distinctive in appearance and unusual in behaviour.

The most numerous and widespread Australian group in this family – the whistlers – range from the coastal rainforests to the dry desert scrubs of the interior. They are noted for their strong, whistling songs, often delivered in long, high-pitched bursts. Sometimes called thickheads because of their large-headed appearance, whistlers can

be brightly coloured, and there are often pronounced differences between the sexes.

The eight whistler species in Australia spend most of their time in trees, where they methodically search the branches and leaves for invertebrates and sometimes snatch prey from foliage as they fly. A few species descend to the ground to pluck invertebrates from the surface.

The four shrike-thrush species are larger and drabber than whistlers. Their robust, hooked bills are designed for subduing live prey, and large species sometimes take nestlings, small reptiles and frogs from trees or the ground. Their songs, which are shorter and richer than those of the whistlers, can be heard from a considerable distance. The calls of all species in this group have a quality that identifies them as shrike-thrushes, but each species has a distinctive song.

Male shrike-thrushes and whistlers are especially vocal in the breeding season, when they strongly defend their territories. They build open, cup-shaped nests – whistlers usually in foliage, shrike-thrushes in forks near trunks or in cavities or cracks. Females lay two to four eggs. Both sexes build the nest, incubate the eggs and feed the young.
Family: Pachycephalidae

CRESTED SHRIKE-TIT ▪

Crested shrike-tits are 16–19 cm long with green or yellow shoulders, bright yellow underparts and grey wings. They have a pronounced crest and bold black and white stripes on their head. The sexes are similar in appearance except for the throat, which is black in males and dark olive green in females.

Mainland Australia has three distinct populations, one in the east, one in the north and one in the west. Western birds have white, rather than yellow, bellies. Crested shrike-tits are widespread in the east but they do not occur in large numbers, and in the north and west they are considered rare.

One of the first clues to this bird's presence is the sound of breaking bark as it searches for food. It has a strong bill, flattened from side to side, which it wedges between a piece of bark and the trunk of a tree, rotating its body around its bill until it has prised the bark loose to reveal the insects hiding underneath.

The shrike-tit favours eucalypt forests and woodlands, particularly those where the trees have stringy bark. This bird also picks insects off leaves while swinging acrobatically from twigs at the end of branches, and cracks open seed capsules with its beak to get at the kernels.

▪ CRESTED SHRIKE-TIT
The powerful bill of the crested shrike-tit prises the bark from trees and rips apart rotting wood in search of spiders, beetles and other insects. Pictured here is a male of the eastern population.

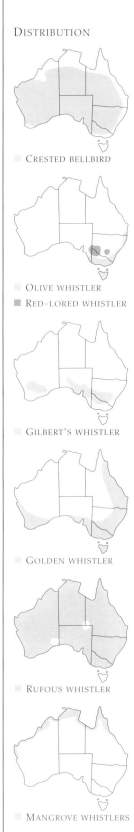
Crested shrike-tits have a long, high, piping whistle and a chatter or chuckle call that sounds rather like 'knock-at-the-door'. These birds call as they forage in pairs or small family parties and swoop strongly among the canopy of eucalypt forests and woodland.
Scientific name: Falcunculus frontatus

CRESTED BELLBIRD ■

The intriguing voice of the elusive crested bellbird has been likened to a cowbell, with two slow notes followed by three faster ones. The crested bellbird's Aboriginal name, panpanpanella, reflects this cadence, as does its early European name, dick-dick-the-devil.

Male birds generally choose to sing from an exposed perch on a dead branch, often at the top of a tree, and their song is one of the characteristic sounds of the drier parts of Australia and one of the most arresting.

The crested bellbird is 22 cm long, and both sexes have brown upper-parts and a white abdomen. The male has a black crest that often rises when the bird is singing, and a broad black breast band that extends through its eyes from the crest. Its throat and forehead are white and its eyes are orange. The female resembles a grey shrike-thrush except for her reddish brown eyes and small black crest.

This bird is found in dry wooded country or arid scrub throughout most of the continent; it avoids the far north and the humid eastern and extreme south-western regions. It is solitary for the most part, except during the breeding season, and when not calling to advertise its territory it is unobtrusive. It feeds on insects, particularly caterpillars, that it plucks from branches and leaves, and it occasionally hops about foraging on the ground.
Scientific name: Oreoica gutturalis

■ CRESTED BELLBIRD
The male crested bellbird's song seems to change direction as the bird adjusts the volume while turning its head.

OLIVE WHISTLER ■

Despite its drab appearance and rather languid behaviour, this large whistler is a fine singer. The territorial song of both northern and southern populations is a pleasant 'cho-cho-cho'. Southern birds also utter a loud, sweet, ringing 'tu-we-tchow', which has a sharp, crack-like cadence; in northern birds this is replaced by a sad 'peee-pooo'.

With a preference for dense, wet vegetation such as tea tree thickets and beech forests, the olive whistler is a shy, reclusive bird. Measuring about 21 cm long, it is dark olive green to brown above with an ochre breast and belly and a white throat flecked with black. Normally solitary, it feeds on the ground in the leaf litter and understorey.

Common in Tasmania, which is the stronghold of the species, on the mainland the olive whistler is confined to the south-eastern corner and the southern and central eastern highlands, with numbers decreasing towards the north of its range. Over much of its range it frequents highland regions, and in the Snowy Mountains it occurs at altitudes above 500 metres in summer, moving down the slopes in winter.
Scientific name: Pachycephala olivacea

RED-LORED WHISTLER

The red-lored whistler has one of the most restricted ranges of any Australian bird. It occurs only in and around the Ninety Mile and Big Deserts area on the border of Victoria and South Australia, with scattered outliers in southern central parts of New South Wales. Within this distribution the red-lored whistler is further confined to areas of mallee and native broom.

Although it appears safe in most of its range, it is now almost extinct in New South Wales, where it has suffered greatly from the clearance of mallee for agricultural purposes.

Basically a brownish bird, the red-lored whistler is 20–22 cm long with a reddish belly, face and lore (the space between the eyes and the bill). It is more often active on the ground than most whistlers, and is shy and elusive for much of the year.

During the breeding season the male, at other times normally silent, becomes vocal, uttering a series of resonant whistles and repeated notes that may swell into an explosion of song. Its nest is a substantial cup of bark and twigs placed in a low tree fork or dense shrub within 2 metres of the ground.
Scientific name: Pachycephala rufogularis

GILBERT'S WHISTLER

It took several years of debate before scientists came to the conclusion that Gilbert's whistler and the red-lored whistler are two different species. They differ primarily in the colour of the lores. In Gilbert's whistler this area between the eye and the bill is black in the male and uniformly grey in the female, while in the red-lored whistler it is red.

The mallee habitat of Gilbert's whistler overlaps that of the red-lored whistler, but its distribution is more extensive and includes other dry woodlands from inland south-western Australia to the southern inland areas of New South Wales. Gilbert's whistler is not common, but the species is more secure than its red-lored relative.

Gilbert's whistlers are generally reclusive birds, but during breeding they become bolder and more vocal. Their song, which is very similar to that of the red-lored whistler, is often the first hint of their presence.
Scientific name: Pachycephala inornata

■ OLIVE WHISTLER
An impressive songster, the male olive whistler has a wide repertoire of calls during the breeding season. There are many regional variations in his song.

GOLDEN WHISTLER ■

Both male and female golden whistlers sing vivaciously in order to establish their territories, and immature family members sometimes join the chorus. This whistler's most familiar song is a persistent, loud 'tchee-tchee-tchee-tchee' ending with a crack-like 'tu-wit'. There are various other vocalisations in this bird's repertoire, and these are sometimes accompanied by a rocking back-and-forth motion.

Golden whistlers grow to about 16 cm long. In Australia the adult male has a bright yellow belly, a black head and breast band, a white throat, and an olive green back and wings, but the female is a subdued shade of grey or brown. The young males, even when they are sexually mature, resemble females until they acquire their adult plumage at three years old. The nestlings are covered in brick red feathers.

Found in coastal and near-coastal regions of Australia from north-eastern Queensland around the southern coastline to Shark Bay in Western Australia, the golden whistler is very adaptable in its choice of habitat; it occurs in rainforest, eucalypt forest and woodland and drier inland scrub, in pine plantations, and even in parks and suburban gardens – anywhere, in fact, where the foliage is dense enough to form a relatively unbroken canopy.

The golden whistler also occurs on islands throughout the South Pacific. In each locality it shows variations in its plumage, and ornithologists have named over 70 populations. Its throat may be white or yellow, its back black or green, and it may or may not have the breast band and collar. The female's plumage may be like the male's, or the adult male plumage may be absent. Golden whistlers on Lord Howe Island resemble those of the Australian mainland, whereas on Norfolk Island both sexes have the brown 'hen' plumage.

Golden whistlers are inquisitive birds and can easily be attracted by an observer making loud kissing and 'pssing' noises. It lives on insects, and berries in season.
Scientific name: *Pachycephala pectoralis*

RUFOUS WHISTLER

The calls of these persistent and animated singers are often lengthy, and males and females sometimes sing in duet. Another of their common names is thunderbird, because they react to sudden loud noises, such as thunder or the backfiring of a car,

with a rapid series of 'pee-pee-pee' notes, sometimes repeated as many as 40 times. Another well-known call is an explosive 'ee-CHONG', in which the first note is drawn out.

The male rufous whistler has the same white throat and black breast band as the golden whistler, but its underparts are a light rufous and its back, wings and head are grey. Females and young birds are more subtly coloured, but can be distinguished from the golden whistler by the thin dark streaks on their throat and breast. The rufous whistler shows little change in plumage across its distributions.

Occurring virtually all over mainland Australia, rufous whistlers prefer more open wooded country than their golden cousin, although the two species are found together in some localities. Depending on their range, rufous whistlers may be migratory, nomadic or sedentary. Birds in the south-east migrate north in autumn, but elsewhere the pattern of movement is less clear.

This species feeds on insects, supplemented by berries in season. It is a trusting bird, and will approach humans imitating its voice.
Scientific name: *Pachycephala rufiventris*

MANGROVE WHISTLERS ■

Three whistler species are found among the mangroves of northern Australia. Both the mangrove golden whistler (*Pachycephala melanura*) and the white-breasted whistler (*P. lanioides*) live almost exclusively in mangroves; the grey whistler (*P. simplex*) also occurs in the rainforests and the eucalypt and paperbark forests beyond.

Male and female mangrove golden whistlers look very like male and female golden whistlers, and forage among the leaves in the same way.

The male white-breasted whistler has a white throat, a grey back and wings, and a distinctive black and chestnut breast band, the black extending over its head and the chestnut over its collar. The female is predominantly grey to brown – darker on the upperparts and paler beneath – with cream to light grey on its throat and grey streaks on its breast. White-breasted whistlers are one of the largest whistler species, growing to about 20 cm long. They hunt among the undergrowth in mangroves, taking insects from the leaves and small crabs from the mud at low tide.

■ GOLDEN WHISTLERS
These common and inquisitive birds nest readily in parks and gardens. Both parents feed the chicks: here, a male brings the hungry youngsters a snack.

■ MANGROVE WHISTLER
At low tide the white-breasted whistler (*Pachycephala lanioides*) hunts from a perch in the mangroves, using the slight hook on its bill to pick up crabs.

DISTRIBUTION

■ GREY SHRIKE-THRUSH

■ LITTLE SHRIKE-THRUSH

■ SANDSTONE SHRIKE-THRUSH
■ BOWER'S SHRIKE-THRUSH

At 14–15 cm long, the grey whistler is the smallest of the whistlers. Both sexes are a drab olive green, grey and brown. They sing incessantly as they glean small insects from the foliage in the middle to upper layers of the forest canopy.

Scientific name: *Pachycephala* spp.

GREY SHRIKE-THRUSH ■

Sometimes called the harmonious thrush, this bird is often considered the most melodious in this family, its rich, clear notes carrying up to half a kilometre. Its song – variations on the cadence 'pip-pip-pip-HO-EE' – is a striking example of how vocal differences can exist between birds of the same species: the general cadence and intonation is the same throughout this bird's distribution, but there are distinct local differences; even within a district, individual birds create their own repertoire by incorporating small variations into the local song. These personalised songs are distinctive enough for a skilled listener to be able to recognise individual birds.

The grey shrike-thrush is about 24 cm long, and is the most common and widespread of Australia's shrike-thrushes. It occurs throughout the mainland, Tasmania and southern New Guinea in rainforests, eucalypt forests and woodlands,

heaths and dry inland scrub, shunning only the most barren desert country. It forages methodically on trunks, branches and fallen timber, and on the ground. Possibly the most carnivorous songbird of its size, this shrike-thrush takes not only invertebrates but lizards, frogs, mice, eggs and nestlings.

The plumage of the grey shrike-thrush varies from region to region. It is grey in the east, brown in the north, and grey with buff underparts in western areas. This species' disposition also changes according to region. Western birds are generally shy and have not adapted well to the presence of humans, whereas those in the east are bolder – and can sometimes become extremely bold around homesteads, accepting handouts and building their nests on front porches. More commonly, however, they nest in tree hollows, crevices or forks or on tree stumps.

Grey shrike-thrushes are sedentary, and pairs usually mate for life.

Scientific name: *Colluricincla harmonica*

OTHER SHRIKE-THRUSHES ■

Australia's other three shrike-thrush species are more restricted than the grey shrike-thrush in both their distribution and their habitat.

The smallest of the group, at 17–19 cm long, is the little shrike-thrush (*Colluricincla megarhyncha*), which occurs along the northern and eastern coasts of Australia. Eastern birds are rufous with pale bills,

■ GREY SHRIKE-THRUSH
Common and widespread in open forests and woodlands, these birds feed on a wide variety of insects, lizards, eggs and nestlings.

■ BOWER'S SHRIKE-THRUSH
A shrike-thrush perches on its nest of leaves and bark, which it builds among vines or in a small tree in the upland rainforest of north-eastern Queensland.

while northern species have black bills and much paler plumage. They also differ in habitat preference, the eastern birds occupying mainly rainforest and the northern mainly mangroves. This species also occurs throughout lowland New Guinea, where many other plumage variations occur.

The sandstone shrike-thrush (*C. woodwardi*) is a ground-dwelling bird that is found among rugged sandstone gorges and escarpments from the Kimberley in Western Australia eastward through the Barkly Tableland to the Queensland border. At about 26 cm long, it is roughly the same size as the grey shrike-thrush but more chestnut in colour. It is also rather more timid, and is less easy to approach.

It traverses its rugged habitat quickly and easily in a manner that few pursuers can follow. Usually occurring singly or in pairs, sandstone shrike-thrushes build their nests at the onset of the rainy season on ledges and in crevices. When they sing from the tops of rocky outcrops, the sound often echoes from adjacent cliff faces.

The most restricted species of shrike-thrush is Bower's shrike-thrush (*C. boweri*). This species has a grey back and a heavy black bill, and is about 20 cm long. It is found at altitudes of 400 metres and over in the Atherton Tableland, where it occurs in areas of rainforest and nearby clearings.

Scientific name: *Colluricincla* spp.

MONARCHS AND FLYCATCHERS

Members of this group are active, insect-eating birds, most either catching prey on the wing or gleaning it from the leaves and bark of trees. They generally have a hooked, triangular, blue-grey bill that is often flattened and is usually surrounded by bristles designed to guide prey into its open waiting bill.
Family: Dicruridae

MONARCHS ■

These lively songbirds live in wet forests, especially rainforests, and feed mainly by gleaning insects from bark and leaves. Adults have black face masks. In most species pairs share the construction of the nest – a deep cup of woven grass, moss or small roots that sits in a tree fork.

One parent incubates the two to three eggs while the other feeds its mate. In the breeding season they sing vigorously and become very territorial, dive-bombing birds as large as hawks to defend their nests.

Probably the most familiar species is the black-faced monarch (*Monarcha melanopsis*), which is 16–19 cm long with bluish grey upperparts, wings, tail and upper breast, an orange belly and a black face and throat. It is arboreal, living mostly in rainforests or wet eucalypt forests bordering watercourses. It inhabits a broad coastal strip from Cape York in Queensland to about Melbourne. Some populations, especially in the Atherton Tableland, are sedentary, but most are highly migratory, wintering in northern Queensland and New Guinea and migrating south in August and September. The male calls mainly from October to January, when the birds are breeding, with a whistling 'why-yew-which-yew', the first two notes short, the third longer and rising in pitch, and the fourth short and falling. Unusually in this genus, the female builds the nest alone.

Two similar but less familiar monarchs share part of the black-faced monarch's range. The spectacled monarch (*M. trivirgatus*) occurs from northern Queensland south to about Sydney. Slightly smaller than the black-faced monarch, its black face markings extend through its eyes to its ears, and its orange underparts reach the sides of its throat. Its belly is white and its tail black, fringed with white. The rare black-winged monarch (*M. frater*), a summer migrant to northern Cape York

■ MONARCH
This black-faced monarch (*Monarcha melanopsis*), a songbird of rainforests and wet eucalypt forests, is busily nesting in north-eastern Queensland.

Peninsula, looks like the black-faced monarch except for its black wings and tail. It is about 19 cm long.

The white-eared monarch (*M. leucotis*) gets its name from its distinguishing feature, a white tuft behind its ears. Growing to 14 cm long, this bird is most common in the treetops of northern Queensland but may occur as far south as the Tweed River in northern New South Wales.
Scientific name: *Monarcha* spp.

OTHER MONARCHS

In Australia there are two species of these small black and white birds with bare blue skin around their eyes. Males have frills on their napes, which they raise during territorial and courting displays. They feed by flitting up tree trunks and probing loose bark to flush out invertebrates.

The pied monarch (*Arses kaupi*) lives in wet forests from Cooktown to Townsville. The frilled monarch (*A. telescophthalmus*) occurs in rainforests and open forests in north-eastern Cape York Peninsula.

These two species are very alike, but the pied monarch can be distinguished from the frilled monarch by its black breast band.
Scientific name: *Arses* spp.

YELLOW-BREASTED BOATBILL

This bird uses its large bill to hawk or glean invertebrates from rainforest foliage. It is 11–12 cm long and has a yellow breast and belly, and a yellow crescent above its eyes. Its olive green to black upperparts are broken by white tail patches and it has a white throat. It feeds in the upper canopy, but its loud whistling call, uttered by both sexes when birds are breeding from September to February, betrays its presence.
Scientific name: *Machaerirhynchus flaviventer*

DISTRIBUTION

■ MONARCHS

■ YELLOW-BREASTED BOATBILL

UP IN A SWING
The frilled monarch (*Arses telescophthalmus*) suspends its frail nest between the branches of a tree fork.

259

DISTRIBUTION

■ FLYCATCHERS

■ SPANGLED DRONGO

■ MAGPIE-LARK

■ SHINING FLYCATCHER
The jet black male shining flycatcher (*Myiagra alecto*) sits on the nest while his more colourful mate does the hard work.

FLYCATCHERS ■

These acrobatic hawkers of insects and spiders have semi-erectile crests and attract attention with their croaks, scolds and trills. Of the five species in Australia, all except the restless flycatcher (*Myiagra inquieta*) show plumage differences between the sexes. This is especially noticeable in the shining flycatcher (*M. alecto*); the male of this species is entirely black, while the female has white underparts and a chestnut back, wings and tail; only her head and nape are black. Shining flycatchers are 17–18 cm long and live in the mangroves of northern and north-eastern Australia, where they eat insects, molluscs and crabs. Their 'toowhit-too-toowhit' call can be heard all year.

The male satin flycatcher (*M. cyanoleuca*) has a blue-black head, breast and upperparts and white underparts, while the female has grey-brown wings and tail, a greyish blue back, cheeks and crown, a rusty orange throat, and a white breast and underparts. Satin flycatchers are about 17 cm long.

The female leaden flycatcher (*M. rubecula*) is similar, except that her tail is edged with paler brown, and her crown is lighter. Male leaden flycatchers have a glossy leaden grey head, throat, breast and upperparts and a white belly. Leaden flycatchers are about 15 cm long.

The broad-billed flycatcher (*M. ruficollis*) has a slightly broader bill and more intense coloration than

■ LEADEN FLYCATCHER
The rufous throat of this leaden flycatcher (*Myiagra rubecula*) shows that it is a female; the male has a leaden grey head, wings and upperparts.

the satin flycatcher and the leaden flycatcher, and normally has some white in its tail. It is 16 cm long.

The leaden flycatcher occurs in the north and east of mainland Australia in eucalypt forests, woodlands and mangroves; the satin flycatcher lives in eastern coastal Australia, including Tasmania, and favours wet eucalypt forests. Both the leaden and the satin flycatcher are migratory, moving north in autumn and flying south to breed in spring. The broad-billed flycatcher is sedentary and lives in mangroves and riverine vegetation in northern coastal Australia.

The restless flycatcher is found in northern Australia, with the exception of Cape York Peninsula, in the eastern half of the mainland and in the south-west. It prefers open habitats such as riverine woodland and forest fringes. It resembles a willie wagtail in that both males and females have white underparts and black upperparts, but its white chin and lack of white eyebrows are distinguishing features. Its call is raspy and it has a habit of hovering before pouncing on invertebrates.

There are two forms, the smaller, about 18 cm long, living in the north, and the larger, about 21 cm long, in the east and south-west.
Scientific name: *Myiagra* spp.

SPANGLED DRONGO

The spangled drongo is Australia's only member of this largely tropical genus. During the winter, spangled drongos in the northern parts of

Western Australia and the Northern Territory migrate to Indonesia, while the eastern Australian birds migrate to New Guinea. Some, however, stay in Australia and others may head south, occasionally even turning up in Tasmania. They prefer the fringes of wet forests, but may also frequent mangroves, woodlands and gardens.

The spangled drongo, which grows to 28–33 cm long, is glossy black with indistinct blue-green spangles on its head, neck and breast and a green sheen to its wings and tail. It has red eyes, a slightly hooked black bill and a long, flared, forked tail. The bristles around its bill funnel prey into its mouth. Common in its range, it is a noisy bird that hunts by perching on branches, pursuing passing insects with agility. It also takes insects from foliage and under bark, and eats fruit and nectar.

Between September and March males make aerial displays, swooping down with arched wings and cocked tails from 15 metres or more in the air. Breeding pairs nest 10–20 metres up in dense foliage, guarding their territory vigorously, and the female lays three to five eggs.

The calls of the spangled drongo range from cacklings to twangings and mimicry of other birds.
Scientific name: *Dicrurus bracteatus*

MAGPIE-LARK

The magpie-lark is a large ground-dwelling flycatcher. It is common in most of mainland Australia but is a rare vagrant to Tasmania. It is found on flat ground near water, where it plucks insects and small vertebrates from the surface or the air. It also eats seeds.

About 26–30 cm long, and with black and white plumage, magpie-larks walk with their head bobbing.

Males have white eyebrows and a black face, while females have a white face. They are quite aggressive and can hold their own with large birds such as Australian magpies, with whom they vie for resources, and even hawks, which they frequently mob. Their shrill, staccato call has earned them their other common name, peewee.

Magpie-larks are also sometimes known as mudlarks because of their mud nests. During breeding, which is normally between August and December but may be at any time, males and females gather mud from beside watercourses and build bowl-shaped nests, lined with grasses and feathers, on horizontal branches up to 20 metres above ground. Females lay three to five eggs, and both parents incubate the eggs and feed the young. Magpie-larks defend their nests valiantly, and it is thought that willie wagtails often nest close by to take advantage of their protection.
Scientific name: *Grallina cyanoleuca*

FANTAILS

In Australia there are five species of these small flycatchers. Using fine grasses and cobwebs, fantails weave cup-shaped nests with long tails of material dangling from the base, usually on horizontal branches about 10 metres above the ground. Both sexes incubate the three or so eggs for a fortnight, and the nestlings are fledged after another 14 days.

The grey fantail (*Rhipidura fuliginosa*), which occurs in wooded areas throughout Australia, is the most common species. Just 14–17 cm long and dark grey with a broad grey-black band separating its throat and breast, it chases small insects, sometimes fluttering though the air like a leaf. It is inquisitive and is attracted by humans making 'kissing' noises. Some populations are sedentary, some migratory and others nomadic.

The slightly smaller mangrove grey fantail (*R. phasiana*), which is found on the north-west and north coasts, resembles the grey fantail but has a smaller and paler band on its throat.

The rufous fantail (*R. rufifrons*) lives in northern and eastern Australia in the understorey of rainforests, dense eucalypt forests and mangroves, where it mostly gleans and occasionally hawks. It is 15–18 cm long, with brown upperparts becoming rufous on the rump and tail, a rufous forehead and a mottled black and white throat and upper breast. Its chestnut rump is visible when it fans its tail. In the south of its range it is migratory, but in the north it is more

FEATHERING THEIR NESTS

Willie wagtails' nests are neatly woven cups made of grasses covered with cobwebs and lined with soft grasses, hair or fur. These birds sometimes reuse nests from a previous year or dismantle old ones to recycle the materials.

Willie wagtails often plunder live animals to acquire the lining materials for their nests. The willie wagtail pictured here is gathering hair from a horse's mane.

sedentary. Like the grey fantail, it is trusting and inquisitive and responds to encouraging noises from humans.

The northern fantail (*R. rufiventris*) is 16–18 cm long and is darker than the grey fantail. Compared with other fantails, this species is quiet and seldom fans its tail. It is sedentary and inhabits woodlands, rainforest fringes and swamps across the northern coast of Australia.

The willie wagtail (*R. leucophrys*), or the black and white fantail, is

probably the best known of the fantails. Its upperparts and throat are black, its underparts and eyebrows white. Its song, often heard at night, sounds like 'sweet-pretty-creature'. It also scolds and chatters. It constantly wags its tail from side to side as it hawks and gleans for invertebrates. At 19–22 cm long, it is the largest of the fantails and the most terrestrial. These birds live in quite open country, where they forage on the ground or from low perches, sometimes on an animal's rump. They often follow animals, waiting to snatch disturbed insects.

Willie wagtails occur throughout the mainland and – less commonly – in northern Tasmania. Mainly sedentary or locally nomadic, they tend to be solitary or to occur in pairs, but winter flocks may form, often mixed with species such as grey fantails. When breeding, they defend their territory against even large predators, circling their attacker's head in a figure of eight pattern uttering an aggressive 'ricka-ticka-ticka-tick'. They defend their territory against other wagtails, enlarging their eyebrows in threat. Defeat is signalled by reducing the eyebrows and retreating.

They usually breed between August and February but will nest whenever conditions are favourable, raising up to four clutches of about three eggs a season. Both parents incubate the eggs. The young stay with their parents until the next clutch hatches and are then driven away. Willie wagtails are tame around humans, and will feed and nest near houses.
Scientific name: *Rhipidura* spp.

GREY FANTAIL

MANGROVE GREY FANTAIL

RUFOUS FANTAIL

NORTHERN FANTAIL

WILLIE WAGTAIL

FANTAIL
A perching rufous fantail (*Rhipidura rufifrons*) shows why these small flycatchers are called fantails – it is because of the way they splay their tail feathers as they swivel on a branch or swoop through the air feeding on small insects.

DISTRIBUTION

BLACK-FACED
CUCKOO-SHRIKE

GROUND CUCKOO-
SHRIKE

■ BLACK-FACED
CUCKOO-SHRIKE
This cuckoo-shrike
builds such a small nest
that in time the growing
nestlings find them-
selves sitting on the nest
rather than inside it. In
windy weather they are
sometimes blown out.

CUCKOO-SHRIKES

Cuckoo-shrikes are in fact related to
neither cuckoos nor shrikes, though
their black, white and grey coloration
and barring are like those of cuckoos
and their short, powerful bills are
like those of shrikes – a family not
found in Australia.

Of around 70 cuckoo-shrike
species throughout Australia, New
Guinea, Asia and Africa, only seven
live in Australia. The five members
of the genus *Coracina* are sleek,
slender birds, mainly grey with
some barring on the underparts;
except for the cicadabird, both sexes
look alike. Males and females of the
other two species, from the genus
Lalage, differ in their colouring.

All cuckoo-shrikes except the aptly
named ground cuckoo-shrike are
arboreal, most favouring forest
fringes and open woodlands. Their
flight is undulating, and many have
the curious habit of shuffling their
wings when alighting on a perch,
probably in order to realign their
flight feathers. They are mainly
insectivorous, gleaning food from
foliage or seizing it in the air, but
most supplement their diet with
fruits and seeds; only the yellow-
faced cuckoo-shrike feeds almost
entirely on fruits. Their nests are
shallow cups of fine twigs, leaves,
bark and cobwebs, which they build
in a tree fork, usually up to 20 metres
above the ground. Sometimes they
take over the nests of other species;
they particularly favour the bowl-
shaped mud-nest of the magpie-lark.
Family: Campephagidae

■ GROUND CUCKOO-SHRIKES
These ground cuckoo-shrikes are
defending their nest. These birds live
mainly on the ground, but if they are
harassed they may fly into a tree.

BLACK-FACED
CUCKOO-SHRIKE ■
The black-faced cuckoo-shrike's
call is a soft churring or warbling
'cree-arck'. The most common and
widespread member of this family, it
occurs throughout the mainland and
Tasmania. It is easily recognised by
its size (32–34 cm), its black mask
and its mainly grey plumage.

This bird inhabits most wooded
areas except rainforests; it is common in suburban areas, where it
perches on open branches or power
lines. It shuffles its wings when it
lands, and so is sometimes called
the shufflewing. It catches insects
among foliage or on the ground,
and also eats fruits and seeds.

These birds breed from August to
February, although rainfall in arid
areas may impose irregular seasons.
Pairs return to the same territories
year after year. Both partners build
the nest – a cup in a tree fork – and
care for the young. Outside the
breeding season they flock in large
groups of up to a hundred birds.
Populations can be sedentary, partly
nomadic or migratory.
Scientific name: *Coracina
novaehollandiae*

GROUND
CUCKOO-SHRIKE ■
The ground cuckoo-shrike is the
only nonarboreal cuckoo-shrike. It
is endemic to Australia and is wide-

spread in the interior, though not
common. A slender bird growing to
37–39 cm long, it is light grey with
fine black bars on its underparts and
rump. It has a black tail and wings
and bright yellow eyes. Its normal
gait is a brisk walk, head nodding
back and forth like a pigeon's, but
it can run fast on its long legs.

The ground cuckoo-shrike prefers
dry, open country, such as grassland
with scattered trees and rocky
outcrops. Constantly on the move,
parties of two to six birds search the
ground for grasshoppers and other
invertebrates, individuals now and
then leaping into the air to seize
flying prey as it passes or is flushed
from beneath the bird's feet. While
on the ground they seldom allow
close approach. When disturbed
they normally fly a short distance
and then land again, but they sometimes take refuge in a nearby tree.

Their most common call is a loud,
piping 'key-lick, key-lick', often
accompanied by a metallic 'queel',
generally uttered in flight.

These cuckoo-shrikes generally
breed in response to climatic conditions, commonly between August
and December. Although they are
mainly terrestrial, they build their
nests of twigs, grasses and cobwebs
in the horizontal fork of branches,
usually near the ground but sometimes as much as 25 metres above.
Both male and female build the nest
and care for the young, sometimes
helped by other family members.
In favourable conditions a pair may
rear more than one brood in the
course of a season.
Scientific name: *Coracina maxima*

BARRED CUCKOO-SHRIKE

The yellow-eyed cuckoo-shrike, or barred cuckoo-shrike, is confined to the east coast of Australia from Cape York Peninsula to the Manning River in New South Wales, and also occurs in New Guinea, the Moluccas and the Solomon Islands. Growing to 24–27 cm long, adults are dark grey above with dark grey barring on their white lower breast, belly and under-tail, and have lemon yellow eyes.

Unlike other group members, this cuckoo-shrike lives in rainforest and feeds mostly on fruits; insects form only a small part of its diet. Northern birds are mainly sedentary, while southern ones are nomadic, flying in pairs or flocks between fruiting trees.
Scientific name: *Coracina lineata*

WHITE-BELLIED CUCKOO-SHRIKE

Also known as the little cuckoo-shrike, this rather sedentary bird occupies most types of wooded habitats, including mangroves, plantations and gardens. It occurs across northern Australia and through the eastern regions to the South Australian border. It is also found in New Guinea and the Solomon Islands.

The white-bellied cuckoo-shrike, 26–28 cm long, is similar in its habits to the black-faced cuckoo-shrike (opposite page) but tends to be more solitary. It has several colour forms, all with grey upperparts. The most common form, which looks rather like a young black-faced cuckoo-shrike, has a light grey breast, dark grey wings and a black mask extending only as far as its eyes.

A less common plumage, which is found in south-eastern popula-tions, is a dusky black head and upper breast with irregular black barring on the lower breast.
Scientific name: *Coracina papuensis*

CICADABIRD

This small, active cuckoo-shrike lives in dense areas of moist forests, swamps and mangroves in northern Australia, and also along the east coast from Cape York Peninsula to Victoria. Both males and females have a whistling, cheeping call, but southern males also have a buzzing 'kree-kree-kree' call, usually repeated several times, which is remarkably similar to the sound of a cicada. These large insects form a major part of the cicadabird's diet when they are plentiful; at other times the birds eat an assortment of large insects and larvae, and some fruits.

Cicadabirds are difficult to observe, since they live high in the tree tops. They are also extremely wary of humans; the male generally emits its call from one perch and then quickly flies to another one, leaving the baf-fled observer studying the wrong spot. The bird's size – it is only 23–27 cm long – and its coloration also help to conceal it.

Males are a dark blue-grey and black with dark brown eyes, black bills and grey-black legs and feet. Females have brownish upperparts with cream eyebrows, pale buff underparts with conspicuous black bars, and a grey bill, legs and feet.

Cicadabirds in the northern and western populations are slightly smaller than those in the south.
Scientific name: *Coracina tenuirostris*

WHITE-WINGED TRILLER ■

The white-winged triller has a beautiful trilling song. Only 16–19 cm long, it occupies lightly timbered areas throughout the Australian mainland and irregularly in north-ern Tasmania. Many white-winged trillers migrate north to the tropics for winter and return south to breed. Some northern populations remain in the far north and breed there.

Adult male white-winged trillers are unique among cuckoo-shrikes in having two plumages a year. In the breeding season, between September and February, their upperparts are black and white, their rumps grey and their underparts white. When not breeding, their wings, tail and rump retain this coloring but the rest of their upperparts are brown, like the female's year-round plumage.
Scientific name: *Lalage sueurii*

■ VARIED TRILLER
As they move through foliage looking for insects or small fruits, these trillers make churring contact calls. Trillers are named for their melodious trilling call.

VARIED TRILLER ■

Varied trillers are found in the densely vegetated coastal areas of northern and eastern Australia. They search for insects under leaves and on branches, and occasionally hawk to catch flying insects. They also eat small fruits, swallowing them whole.

The male resembles the breeding male white-winged triller, with glossy black upperparts and white underparts barred with rufous, but it has white eyebrows and black eye stripes and is light orange beneath the tail. The female has brown upperparts, creamy buff eyebrows, and creamy buff underparts with fine brown-black barring. Varied trillers grow to about 18–21 cm long.
Scientific name: *Lalage leucomela*

■ BARRED CUCKOO-SHRIKE

■ WHITE-BELLIED CUCKOO-SHRIKE

■ CICADABIRD

■ WHITE-WINGED TRILLER

■ VARIED TRILLER

■ WHITE-WINGED TRILLERS
A female white-winged triller stands sentinel over her nest and her open-mouthed offspring.

DISTRIBUTION

■ OLIVE-BACKED ORIOLE

■ YELLOW ORIOLE

■ FIGBIRD

■ **OLIVE-BACKED ORIOLE**
These orioles live high in the tree tops and so are seldom seen, but their rolling 'ori-ori-ole, ori-ori-ole' song bubbles through the canopy.

ORIOLES AND FIGBIRDS

Of the 25 species of this family distributed across Australia, Eurasia and Africa, three occur in Australia: two orioles and the endemic figbird.

Orioles have slender, slightly downcurved bills that are often red, and red eyes. They live in the tree tops and make swift, undulating flights above the canopy on long, tapered wings. They travel singly or in pairs, feeding on fruits, insects and larvae, and are known for their melodious, bubbling calls. Typically, female orioles build cup-shaped nests from grasses and strips of bark. These hang among foliage between two branches, suspended by the rim. Females lay two to five eggs and incubate them while the males feed them at the nest. The young emerge from the egg naked and helpless, and both parents help to rear them.

Figbirds are distinguished from typical orioles by the bare patch of skin around their eyes and their stout black bill. They generally travel in flocks and feed mainly on fruits; they are particularly fond of figs. Unlike orioles, both figbird parents participate in building the nest but, like the orioles, both rear the young.
Family: Oriolidae

OLIVE-BACKED ORIOLE ■
This bird lives in northern and eastern Australia and is common throughout its range. It occupies a wide variety of habitats, including rainforest, eucalypt woodland, mallee, orchards, and parks and gardens. In winter, birds from eastern Australia migrate northward in order to breed, some travelling as far as New Guinea, and then return in August. They have a melodious song and are excellent mimics. As many as 27 mimic calls have been recorded – including the song of the common koel, which regularly parasitises their nests.

Olive-backed orioles are 25–28 cm long. They are predominantly olive green, with dark streaks becoming thicker on their breast and abdomen. Their eyes are red and the red bill is a little duller in females. They normally occur singly or in pairs, but in autumn and winter they occasionally form small, casual parties.

These birds glean insects from the upper leaves and branches in eucalypt woodland and open forest, and occasionally take passing insects on the wing. They also feed on the fruits and berries of native flora, including mistletoe. They gorge on easy pickings in parks, gardens and fruit orchards, much to the annoyance of the owners, but they can also earn favour by gathering in large numbers at caterpillar infestations and have been known, on occasions, to save entire crops.
Scientific name: *Oriolus sagittatus*

■ FIGBIRD
Native figs form an important part of this bird's diet. Flocks may descend on an isolated tree and gorge themselves until it is virtually stripped of its fruit.

YELLOW ORIOLE
The yellow oriole is less well known than the olive-backed oriole. It is found in far northern Australia and New Guinea, living in a variety of habitats but preferring denser, moister areas than its close relative.

The yellow oriole is about the same size as the olive-backed oriole but is a greenish mustard yellow in colour. It feeds on both fruits and insects. It is sedentary, singing from time to time during the day in order to mark its territory.
Scientific name: *Oriolus flavocinctus*

FIGBIRD ■
Figbirds live in noisy flocks of 20–50 individuals; even larger flocks may gather at a rich food source.

They are robust birds that reach 27–29 cm in length. Males have olive green backs and glossy black heads. The bare skin around their eyes is pink to buff. Their underparts are bright yellow in the north and grey in the south; the two forms meet around Townsville, where males sport combinations of yellow and olive grey underparts. Females are olive brown above and white beneath, heavily streaked with brown. The bare skin around their eyes is grey.

Figbirds occur in coastal northern and eastern Australia in a variety of habitats, from rainforests, eucalypt woodlands and mangroves to orchards. Mainly fruit-eaters, they often hang upside down to feed. They also eat the occasional insect.
Scientific name: *Sphecotheres viridis*

WOODSWALLOWS, MAGPIES, CURRAWONGS AND BUTCHERBIRDS

DUSKY
WOODSWALLOW

WHITE-BROWED
WOODSWALLOW

MASKED
WOODSWALLOW

LITTLE
WOODSWALLOW

Magpies, currawongs and butcher-birds do not look anything like woodswallows, but the four groups have been considered members of the same Australasian family since the 1980s, when DNA testing and the recognition that the four groups shared unique skull features revealed their genetic similarities.

Woodswallows are stout, small to medium-sized birds with short coni-cal grey bills. They often fly very high, and are the only songbirds that habitually soar. Their plumage is generally subdued – mainly grey and brown with black and white markings – and they usually call with soft squeaks and chirrups, though most also mimic other birds.

They mainly catch and eat insects on the wing, but they occasionally feed on the ground when insects are abundant there. Like the tongues of bee-eaters (page 223), woodswal-lows' tongues are especially adapted to take nectar from blossoms.

Uniquely among songbirds, woodswallows lack preen glands; instead, they have powder down, produced by special feathers on their belly. These feathers grow con-tinuously, the tips breaking down into a fine, water-resistant powder that the birds distribute through their feathers when they preen.

Woodswallows are gregarious and roost in clusters – usually at night, when a few birds to several hundred cram into a sheltered spot such as a tree crotch. It has been suggested that this is to keep warm, but these birds cluster even on the hottest days in the interior of Australia.

They nest in loose colonies, build-ing their flimsy, cup-shaped nests from twigs and grasses in shrubs or on stumps or fence posts. A third, unrelated bird sometimes helps the parents to rear the young.

There are ten woodswallow species worldwide; all occur in Australia, and four are endemic.

Butcherbirds, currawongs and magpies are large, robust birds, with powerful bills and plumage that is all-black, black and white, or black and grey. They are found all over Australia, from rainforests to semi-arid regions, and in populated areas. Their loud, melodious calls are a familiar sound in the bush. Several species have benefited

from European settlement and the ensuing land clearing, as tall trees and an open understorey provide the perfect foraging habitat. All are insect-eaters, and some also consume fruits and seeds. All species will eat carrion when other foods are scarce.
Family: Artamidae

DUSKY WOODSWALLOW

Sometimes called the bee bird, the endemic dusky woodswallow is considered a nuisance by bee-keepers as bees streaming to and from a hive provide easy pickings for them.

Dusky woodswallows are 17–18 cm long. Both sexes are predominantly a smoky brown. They live mainly in open woodland and rural and semi-rural areas, but also in fairly dense eucalypt forest, where they frequent watercourses and natural clearings. They occur around coastal eastern and southern Australia, including Tasmania, and are common through-out their range. Some south-eastern populations migrate north as far as central Queensland in autumn, returning south in spring to breed.

They usually live in groups of 10–30 birds, although in winter two to three hundred birds can cram into sheltered tree forks or hollows or cling to a tree trunk.
Scientific name: *Artamus cyanopterus*

WHITE-BROWED WOODSWALLOW AND MASKED WOODSWALLOW

These two species are widespread over most of the mainland except for the far north and the south-west, and are vagrant in Tasmania. They are almost identical in their habits,

and where their ranges overlap the two species often associate, frequently in mixed flocks, and sometimes inter-breed. The proportion of each species in a flock varies, the white-browed species dominating in the east and the masked species in the west.

The white-browed woodswallow (*Artamus superciliosus*) is 19–21 cm long. It is perhaps the most colourful of the woodswallows, its rich chest-nut breast and conspicuous white eyebrows contrasting vividly with its predominantly grey upperparts. At 17–19 cm long, the masked woodswallow (*A. personatus*) is slightly smaller, and is pale grey to cream below and dark grey above. Males have a distinctive black mask. In both species females tend to be much duller than males.

These birds travel vast distances in large flocks. In the breeding season flocks descend on an area where insects abound and conditions are right. Within days, the birds form loose colonies, build nests and lay their eggs. Because these birds are nomadic, breeding colonies rarely visit the same site in consecutive years.
Scientific name: *Artamus* spp.

LITTLE WOODSWALLOW

At 12–14 cm long, this is the smallest of the woodswallows. It is dark brown above and below, with dark grey wings and a black rump, and it looks rather like a martin or a swallow as it hawks through the open woodlands, grasslands and gorges of northern and inland Australia.

Little woodswallows are largely sedentary, except in the rolling grassy woodlands of the east, where they are nomadic. Unlike other wood-swallows, the little woodswallow sometimes nests in rock crevices.
Scientific name: *Artamus minor*

■ DUSKY WOOD-SWALLOW
Woodswallows tend to build their nests in exposed positions, such as on the top of a fence post or a broken stump.

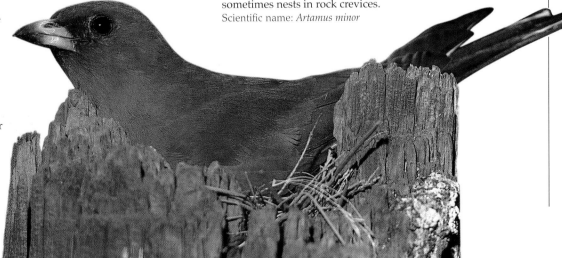

■ WHITE-BREASTED
WOODSWALLOW
These sociable birds
frequently form large
flocks, and between
feeding times they often
huddle together in neat
rows along a branch,
preening each other.

DISTRIBUTION

■ WHITE-BREASTED
WOODSWALLOW

■ BLACK-FACED
WOODSWALLOW

■ AUSTRALIAN MAGPIE

WHITE-BREASTED WOODSWALLOW ■

The white-breasted woodswallow is 17–18 cm long, with blue-grey upperparts and throat and a white breast and belly. It is the only Australian woodswallow species that does not have a white-tipped tail. It inhabits tropical woodlands and mangroves throughout the north-eastern half of the continent, its range also extending inland along timbered watercourses and reaching as far as the coastal mangroves of northern Western Australia.

Outside Australia this species is considered sedentary, but in Australia populations in the south of the range are strongly migratory. White-breasted woodswallows often form flocks of up to 200 birds, and huddle together between bouts of feeding as well as at night.
Scientific name: *Artamus leucorynchus*

BLACK-FACED WOODSWALLOW ■

These birds live in open or lightly timbered country throughout mainland Australia, except in the coastal south-eastern regions. They are also found in New Guinea and Timor.

Black-faced woodswallows are 18–20 cm long and grey, except for their black chin and lore (the space between the eyes and the bill) and their white-tipped black tail.

The species is sedentary, keeping to the same foraging area all year. It breeds rapidly in dry areas in response to rainfall.
Scientific name: *Artamus cinereus*

■ BLACK-FACED
WOODSWALLOW
In the Simpson Desert in
the Northern Territory, a
disintegrating fence post
provides a nest site for this
black-faced woodswallow.

AUSTRALIAN MAGPIE ■

The Australian magpie is among the best known of Australian birds. Its tuneful carolling can usually be heard from just about any back door in the country, and the bird even has more than one football team named after it.

Magpies occur throughout Australia except in arid deserts and dense rainforests. There are five different geographical forms; all are boldly marked in black and white, but the five forms have different amounts of white on their back.

Where forms overlap, they readily interbreed. Magpies reach 34–44 cm long, though the Tasmanian form is slightly smaller than the others. Their organ-like fluting song contrasts markedly with the loud caws and shrieks that they also utter. They also mimic the songs of other birds.

These birds eat a variety of invertebrates, including the larvae of scarab beetles, which can cause extensive damage to lawns. They feed mainly from the ground, using their strong

■ AUSTRALIAN MAGPIE
This bird's common name comes from its superficial resemblance to the European magpie, a form of crow, but the two species are not related.

pointed bills to probe the soil and turn up small sticks, stones or cow pats in search of insects. When conditions are hard they sometimes feed on seeds and carrion. Groups of magpies may form a line in order to patrol open areas, methodically searching for food.

Magpies live in small groups of 4–24 birds that occupy a territory throughout the year, with all members actively involved in defending it. Groups repeatedly breed successfully only in territories that provide enough trees for roosting and nesting and ample foraging space. Picnic areas surrounded by forest land are ideal.

Magpies nest from August to October, the female building the nest – a large untidy basket that she lines with fine grasses, feathers and wool. She usually constructs the nest from small sticks but will use anything she can find, including wire or plastic cable.

Adults vigorously defend their nests, eggs and young from potential intruders, swooping and diving on anything that approaches, from humans to cats, dogs and other birds. For several months after they have left the nest the young follow any nearby adult, cawing and begging persistently for food.
Scientific name:
Gymnorhina tibicen

CURRAWONGS

There are three species of currawong, all of them endemic to Australia. They are large, dark birds with strong, pointed bills and yellow eyes. They have a distinctive, powerful, undulating flight. They eat almost anything, using their bill to probe under tree bark, to pluck fruits and insects from the canopy, or to scavenge amid human refuse. They also rob the nests of other birds, taking both eggs and nestlings.

Currawongs construct bulky nests from long sticks woven together which they line with fine grasses. They nest in solitary pairs, but roam in large flocks after breeding. Unlike butcherbirds and magpies, currawongs are quiet near their nest.

The pied currawong (*Strepera graculina*) is the most common currawong species, occurring throughout mainland eastern Australia. It breeds in forests along the Great Dividing Range, descending to coastal regions at the end of the breeding season in noisy flocks of a hundred or more. This species is mainly black with large white wing and tail patches, and is about 46 cm long.

The black currawong (*S. fuliginosa*) is 46–48 cm long, and has smaller white wing patches and less white on its tail. It lives only in Tasmania, where it occurs in rainforest, eucalypt forest, heathland and gardens.

The grey currawong (*S. versicolor*) lives in the southern mainland and Tasmania in coastal heath, mallee, and eucalypt forest and woodland. It is 45–50 cm long, and varies from brownish grey to almost black. Grey currawongs remain in the same area all year. In Tasmania small flocks may form in the nonbreeding season.
Scientific name: *Strepera* spp.

 CURRAWONG
A pied currawong (*Strepera graculina*) bathes in a pool. This species has increased in numbers recently, perhaps because introduced fruits and berries are supplementing its winter food.

BUTCHERBIRDS

Butcherbirds are medium-sized birds with sturdy bills that end in a prominent hook. They mostly hunt by pouncing on prey from a vantage point, taking anything from large insects to small birds, reptiles and mammals. They carry larger victims back to a perch; here, because their feet are not strong enough to grasp large prey, they impale the carcass on a stick or wedge it in a tree fork, and then tear at it. They also leave food secured in this way to eat later.

Butcherbirds live singly, in pairs or in small family parties. Their song consists mainly of piping whistles and caws. They build untidy, cup-like nests in the fork of a tree or bush. Nesting birds are aggressive towards intruders, be they furred, feathered or human, and dive-bomb like magpies. Offspring often stay with their parents and help raise the next brood.

There are four species of this Australasian bird. The pied butcherbird (*Cracticus nigrogularis*) and the grey butcherbird (*C. torquatus*) are endemic to Australia and occur throughout most of the mainland; the grey butcherbird also occurs in Tasmania. Both these species live in a variety of habitats from eucalypt forest to farmland.

The pied butcherbird has a loud, fluting song, and males and females often perform in duet. It is 32–33 cm long, with conspicuous black and white plumage. At 24–30 cm long, the grey butcherbird is slightly smaller than its pied relative. It has grey to black upperparts broken by a white collar at the back of its neck, and white to grey-white underparts.

The two other species, the black-backed butcherbird (*C. mentalis*) and the black butcherbird (*C. quoyi*) have limited ranges in Australia; both also occur in New Guinea.

The black-backed butcherbird has a black head and face, a black and white back and wings and white shoulders and rump. It is only about 25 cm long, and is restricted to Cape York Peninsula. The black butcherbird occurs only in coastal northern and far north-eastern Australia, where it frequents mangroves and rainforest. Adults are wholly black and, at 42–44 cm long, are the largest of the butcherbirds. They are seldom seen, though their melodious call is frequently heard.
Scientific name: *Cracticus* spp.

■ BUTCHERBIRDS
Grey butcherbirds (*Cracticus torquatus*) are unafraid around humans, but it is not wise to feed them as they often use clothes lines as territorial perches and store food scraps amid the washing.

DISTRIBUTION

PIED CURRAWONG
■ BLACK CURRAWONG

GREY CURRAWONG

PIED BUTCHERBIRD

GREY BUTCHERBIRD
■ BLACK-BACKED BUTCHERBIRD

BLACK BUTCHERBIRD

■ VICTORIA'S RIFLEBIRD
■ MAGNIFICENT
   RIFLEBIRD
■ PARADISE RIFLEBIRD

■ TRUMPET MANUCODE

MAKING A SONG
AND DANCE

A male Victoria's riflebird attracts a female by fluffing out his feathers, spreading his wings and uttering a loud, rasping call. The two face each other and sway, breasts almost touching, raising and stretching out their wings more and more rapidly. Finally, the male embraces the female with his wings, and the pair is ready to mate.

BIRDS OF PARADISE

Birds of paradise, or riflebirds, are arboreal and live in the rainforests and woodlands of New Guinea, the Moluccas and Australia. Most of the 43 species are restricted to New Guinea, but Victoria's riflebird and the paradise riflebird are endemic to Australia, and the ranges of the magnificent riflebird and the trumpet manucode extend into Australia.

All four Australian representatives of this family are confined to rainforests and the wet eucalypt forests along the eastern coast, and although most male birds of paradise are brightly coloured and ornamented with flowing plumes, these species are relatively subdued. However, all perform the courtship displays for which this family is famous.

In their habits, the three Australian species of riflebird from the genus *Ptiloris* are fairly typical birds of paradise. The male in his fine plumage dedicates himself to a life of mating, posing strenuously to impress as many mates as possible, while the less flamboyant female builds the nest, incubates the eggs and cares for the young, seemingly alone. She builds her nest of loosely woven vine tendrils, stems, rootlets – and the odd snake skin – in the dense foliage of a tree, and lays one or two eggs.

The breeding season is generally from October to February. Little is known about incubation or fledging, except that the young seem to take three to seven years to attain adult plumage. Males are mostly territorial, females and young mainly itinerant.

Riflebirds have short, square tails, and long, downcurved bills. They walk up the trunks of rainforest and neighbouring eucalypt forest

■ VICTORIA'S RIFLEBIRD
When displaying, the male perches on a stump, curves his wings above his body and tilts his head back, swaying and pivoting backwards and forwards.

trees, probing the bark with their bills in quest of insects. They also pluck fruits from trees. They usually forage for insects alone, but pairs or small groups may gather at fruiting trees, sometimes along with other fruit-eating bird species.

These birds are mostly sedentary, but there is some winter movement into adjacent forest areas.

Australia's three riflebird species are similar in appearance; however, their ranges are completely separate, so there is no risk of mistaking one species for either of the others.

Unlike most other birds of paradise, trumpet manucodes breed in monogamous pairs and the two sexes have similar plumage. They are mainly fruit-eaters, and their bills are shorter and stouter than those of riflebirds.
Family: Paradisaeidae

VICTORIA'S RIFLEBIRD ■
Named after Queen Victoria, these birds of paradise are endemic to the rainforests and adjacent woodlands of southern Cape York Peninsula. As well as insects, they eat fruits from the trees, some of which they peel by holding the fruit with one foot and removing the skin with their bill.

At 23–25 cm long, these are the smallest of the Australian riflebirds. The female is predominantly brown above with pale eyebrows and has paler buff underparts faintly barred with brown. The male is an overall black, subtly shot with an iridescent purple sheen that becomes more blue-green on the head and more bronze on the lower breast. His throat is a velvety black with a metallic green and blue triangular patch in the centre.

When the male begins to display, he erects the feathers of his throat and sides to accentuate the bright colours of his plumage in the shafts of sunlight that pierce the dimness of the rainforest. He curves his rounded wings above his body and tilts his head back to expose his chin and throat to the light, and then moves from side to side in a fashion that looks almost mechanical.

The female is attracted to the male's display post by his raspy 'yaars' call, which becomes softer and more tuneful during the display. The pair then face each other closely, and each bird raises and extends its wings forward alternately in an increasingly rapid rhythm. Finally the male embraces the female with both wings, and copulation follows.
Scientific name: *Ptiloris victoriae*

MAGNIFICENT RIFLEBIRD

Magnificent riflebirds live in the northernmost tip of Cape York Peninsula and in New Guinea. In the silence of the rainforest, their loud whistling 'weee-o' calls often betray their presence as they search in ones or twos for invertebrates, fruits and seeds. They grow to about 28–33 cm long, with males being larger than females.

Like the other two Australian riflebirds, the male has iridescent black plumage, but the metallic greens, purples and blues extend further down his breast than they do in the other two species. The female bird is grey-brown above, and her underparts are a paler cream-buff with regular fine black barring.

The male's favoured display perch is generally a sunlit branch high in the canopy. He does not vocalise during courtship but stands erect and rapidly opens and shuts his wings, making a loud rustling sound. Sometimes he walks in a circle with his wings outstretched. When a female arrives he stands with his tail cocked and wings and head back to display his magnificent throat and breast.
Scientific name: *Ptiloris magnificus*

PARADISE RIFLEBIRD

This is the only bird of paradise to occur south of the Tropic of Capricorn. It inhabits the subtropical and temperate rainforests straddling the border between Queensland and New South Wales, from the Bunya Mountains in the north to Dungog in the south. Paradise riflebirds – nearly always females or immature birds – are occasionally spotted in wet eucalypt forests.

The loud, explosive 'yaass-a-yaass-aass' call of the paradise rifle bird is uttered by both sexes, but especially by the male in the breeding season. The male attracts mates by calling from an exposed perch high in the canopy and then curving his wings up and tilting his head in the typical riflebird display posture. He then sways his body in a circular motion, so that the iridescent throat colours catch the light, and claps his wings together so loudly that the noise can be heard 60 metres away. When a female approaches, the male encircles her with outstretched wings and claps the tips together repeatedly as he dances backwards and forwards and around her.

Paradise riflebirds are 27–29 cm long. Males have the usual glossy black plumage; females are predominantly olive brown, with reddish brown wings and buff-cream underparts scalloped with darker brown.

Paradise riflebirds are common in their range but generally difficult to find; their calls or the loud rustling of their wing feathers as they fly from tree to tree are the best indicators of their presence. At times they feed in association with other fruit-eating species such as bowerbirds.
Scientific name: *Ptiloris paradiseus*

TRUMPET MANUCODE

The call of the male of this species booms out across the lowland rainforests of Cape York Peninsula in a single, trumpet-like note. This sound is produced by an extended windpipe coiled between the bird's skin and its chest muscles.

The trumpet manucode is 27–32 cm long. Both sexes are black with a greenish blue iridescent sheen to their feathers, and both have bright red eyes. On their nape and neck and behind their eyes they have hair-like plumes, which grow longer in the male. Their tails are long and rounded. They feed mainly on rainforest fruits – particularly figs – although they also glean insects from the foliage.

These birds are most conspicuous during the breeding season, which extends from October to February. Males are territorial, advertising from high perches with a single loud trumpet call and occasionally with loud croaks. Courtship begins with the male chasing the female. From time to time both birds land on high perches where they face each other, the male crouching with feathers fluffed out and wings outspread, his trumpeting call answered by the soft chirping of the female.

There are records of the trumpet manucode migrating north, probably to New Guinea, but the remoteness of the bird's rainforest habitat makes close study of its habits difficult.
Scientific name: *Manucodia keraudrenii*

■ TRUMPET MANUCODE
Unlike riflebirds, these birds are monogamous. Both sexes build the nest, incubate the two eggs and rear the young.

■ MAGNIFICENT RIFLEBIRD
The male has a striking metallic blue-green triangle on his chin and upper breast and wispy plumes along his flanks.

DISTRIBUTION

AUSTRALIAN RAVEN

LITTLE RAVEN

FOREST RAVEN
LITTLE CROW

TORRESIAN CROW

AUSTRALIAN RAVEN
A dead rabbit in the snow provides a feast. These ravens like to eat carrion, hiding leftovers for later consumption.

RAVENS AND CROWS

There are five Australian species of these big, glossy black birds, all except the Torresian crow unique to Australia. Ravens are larger than crows, and generally have longer hackles on their throat. The bases of their head and neck feathers are grey, while on the crow they are white, but this can be detected only when the birds are preening or when the wind ruffles their feathers. All adults in this family have white eyes and the young have brown. The cawing call of each species is subtly different in pitch, tone and tempo.

Crows and ravens are adaptable birds that live in most habitats, including ones created by humans, and most can be found in cities. They eat anything from invertebrates and small vertebrates to grains, fruits, carrion, offal and human refuse, though most have a preference for certain types of food.

Intelligent and normally wary, they are bold around cities, picnic areas and national parks, where they tamely accept food from humans. Crows and ravens are reviled for feeding on lamb carcasses, but none can kill a healthy lamb – they feed on those that are already sick or dead. It is only the largest species, such as the Australian raven and the forest raven, that can feed efficiently on a carcass, and even they find it hard to penetrate hide, and normally start at soft spots like the eyes.

These birds are monogamous and bond for life, the pair building a large stick nest in a tree or on a structure such as a windmill platform or a utility pylon. The female incubates the clutch of four or five eggs for three weeks, during which time her mate feeds her. The young remain in the nest for four to six weeks, depending on the size of the species, and both parents feed them.

Most breed in the spring, though nomadic species are most likely to breed after rain and the Torresian crow may breed at any time.
Family: Corvidae

AUSTRALIAN RAVEN

This is a large bird, about 50 cm long, with long hackles on its throat and a slow, wailing cry with a dying fall – as if the bird is being strangled. It often calls from a high lookout perch, holding its body horizontally and fanning out its hackles as it gives voice. It is a common and widespread sedentary species in southern and eastern Australia.

Mated pairs defend a territory about a kilometre square. After the young leave the nest, their parents go on feeding them for some weeks, and they remain in their parents' territory for several months.

Australian ravens prefer to eat carrion, hiding excess food in crevices or burying it for later.
Scientific name: *Corvus coronoides*

LITTLE RAVEN

The little raven lives in the temperate farmland and alpine areas of south-eastern Australia. It is about 49 cm long and has a rapid, guttural 'barking' call, each note accompanied by a flicking of the wings.

Little ravens are nomadic. They travel in large flocks and stop only to breed in loose colonies in low trees.
Scientific name: *Corvus mellori*

LITTLE CROW
Little crows are tame and are often seen in outback towns. This one is picking at the carcass of a dead rabbit.

FOREST RAVEN

At about 53 cm long, the forest raven is the largest Australian member of this family. It has a deep voice that resounds through the forest, a short tail and a massive beak. It is sedentary and occurs along the coast of Victoria and the extreme south-eastern coast of South Australia. There is also an isolated population on the New England tablelands and the north coast of New South Wales. It is the only member of this family that lives in Tasmania and the only species to occur in dense forest.
Scientific name: *Corvus tasmanicus*

LITTLE CROW

At about 46 cm long, this is the smallest Australian species. It is a nomad of the arid inland but sometimes makes summer migrations to the coast in south-western Australia. It nests in loose colonies in low trees and forms large flocks that soar and swoop in formation. It has a monotonous, hoarse, 'quacking' voice.
Scientific name: *Corvus bennetti*

TORRESIAN CROW

This crow occurs in the northern two-thirds of Australia, where it lives a sedentary life near coastal waters and inland creeks and rivers. Abundant in farmland, it devours more grain than most crow species. It is about 50 cm long and has two calls: a rapid honking and a long, harsh cawing. On the coast it gathers in large flocks, particularly at communal roosts. It also occurs in New Guinea.
Scientific name: *Corvus orru*

MUD-NESTERS

The white-winged chough and the apostlebird are the only two members of this noisy, gregarious Australian family. Although they do not look alike, they share many of the same habits. Both species are terrestrial, for example, and feed in small or large flocks. Both construct intricate mud-nests, breed in colonies and live in close-knit family groups – usually consisting of a dominant male, two or three breeding females and the offspring from preceding seasons. These offspring may not reach sexual maturity until they are four years old, and until then they stay with their parents, helping to build the nest and incubate and feed the new chicks. Both species may produce up to three broods a season.

Choughs and apostlebirds are weak fliers, taking to the air only for short distances, even when alarmed; in trees they prefer to hop from one perch to the next. They trot along the ground on their strong legs with the rolling gait of a drunken sailor.
Family: Corcoracidae

WHITE-WINGED CHOUGH ▪

These predominantly black birds bob their tails up and down and jerk their heads back and forth as they rake the ground for insects and their larvae, snails, spiders, millipedes and occasional seeds. With their large, downcurved bills they also probe in soft mud for earthworms.

They normally stay in harmonious family groups of about seven birds, which mutter softly to one another as they forage. Only at the approach of danger do they churr and scream as they take to the air, flapping their wings and then gliding to cover.

During winter, they often gather in large groups to take advantage of plentiful food supplies, spreading out in methodical working parties. Although choughs maintain permanent feeding territories of up to a thousand hectares, they usually occupy only a small area at a time.

White-winged choughs occur throughout most of eastern and south-eastern mainland Australia except northern Queensland. About 43–47 cm long, they look rather like crows but can be easily identified by their curved beak and red iris, and by their large white wing patches, which become visible in flight. They prefer wetter areas of open forests and woodlands, where they can find

▪ WHITE-WINGED CHOUGHS
The young of this species leave the nest some time before they can fly, making them easy prey for foxes and feral cats. These fledglings are begging a wing-waving adult for food.

plenty of leaf litter to fossick in and mud to build their nests with.

Choughs breed from August to December, families constructing chunky, pudding-sized bowls of mud and fibre within 15 metres of the ground. If mud is scarce they sometimes use cattle or emu dung. They build their nests on horizontal branches in several layers, leaving each layer to dry before adding another. Nests may take several months to finish if there is either not enough rain or too much. Choughs breed in colonies, and it is not unusual to see rows of nests ranged along a branch like pots on a shelf.

Females lay three to five eggs, sometimes up to ten, which take about 19 days to incubate. Young birds leave the nest before they can fly, and at night they clamber up a sloping tree trunk to shelter and to sleep. Only after about two months can they fly strongly, and they still need much help in foraging. Many of the young die in their first year.
Scientific name: *Corcorax melanorhamphos*

APOSTLEBIRD ▪

Apostlebirds are grey-brown, about 29–32 cm long, with short, conical bills. Females have brown eyes and males have grey. They inhabit drier forests and woodlands of the eastern half of Australia, associating with

white-winged choughs where their ranges overlap. Apostlebirds forage on the ground in family groups for seeds and other vegetable matter, and occasionally for insects. They often remove parasites from their body by lying on the ground and flapping dust over themselves.

Apostlebirds' territories are smaller than those of the choughs, usually about 10–15 hectares, but large winter gatherings are still typical.

Groups are noisy, their voices a mixture of grating notes that may be uttered at any time, especially if the group is alarmed. They breed from August to February. Their nests are like those of the choughs, but are smaller and incorporate more grass. Sometimes more than one female lays in a nest and up to eight eggs may fill it, but space restricts the number of surviving nestlings to about four.
Scientific name: *Struthidea cinerea*

▪ WHITE-WINGED CHOUGH

▪ APOSTLEBIRD

▪ APOSTLEBIRD
Gregarious creatures, apostlebirds were so named because people thought that they always came in groups of twelve. In fact, their clans generally consist of between eight and 20 individuals.

DISTRIBUTION

■ GOLDEN BOWERBIRD
■ REGENT BOWERBIRD

■ SATIN BOWERBIRD

■ FAWN-BREASTED
BOWERBIRD
■ SPOTTED BOWERBIRD
■ WESTERN BOWERBIRD

■ GREAT BOWERBIRD

■ GOLDEN BOWERBIRD
This bowerbird incorporates a perch in his bower, from which he displays to attract females. He tends his bower throughout the year, constantly tidying it and adding to it.

BOWERBIRDS

Most male bowerbirds take no part in raising their young. During the mating season, all their energy is expended in the construction of intricate, modified nests – bowers – and elaborate courtship displays in order to woo passing females.

Once mating is over, females of most species work alone to build their nests and incubate and raise their young. Meanwhile, males, who are generally polygamous, return to courting females. Male catbirds are the exception: they normally mate with only one female in a season, and they do not build bowers.

Different groups of bowerbirds build different types of bowers. Some are quite simple; others are huge structures that the birds work on and use season after season. The males usually decorate their bowers with ornaments such as leaves, flowers and shells; sometimes they even use material commandeered from their human neighbours.

Bowerbirds are also not above a little pilfering from their own kind. Some, such as the satin bowerbird, are fond of taking objects from other birds' bowers, often destroying the walls to use the material in their own constructions.

Having completed their work, males attract females to the vicinity with their long, exuberant songs. Most are also expert mimics, copying the mechanical noises of machinery as well as the calls of other birds. Females, attracted by the singing, inspect both the male and the bower, but they will mate only if they are impressed with what they see.

Most bowerbirds live in forests, but the dry-country bowerbirds are more common in the arid interior of the Australian mainland.

Most of these birds are sedentary, though some travel within a confined area during winter to form large feeding flocks. They eat a combination of fruits, flowers, leaves, nectar and occasionally insects.

In general, females build their saucer-shaped nests from plant stems, rootlets and twigs, and line them with finer material. They lay one to three eggs – usually two – which hatch in about three weeks.

There are 19 bowerbird species worldwide. Two – the spotted catbird and the fawn-breasted bowerbird – occur in New Guinea and Australia, eight are endemic to Australia and nine to New Guinea.
Family: Ptilonorhynchidae

■ REGENT BOWERBIRD
The male regent bowerbird decorates his bower with snail shells, leaves, berries and yellow flowers, and uses his bill to paint the walls with yellow vegetable matter mixed with saliva.

GOLDEN BOWERBIRD ■

This is the smallest of the Australian bowerbirds, yet it builds the largest bower – a massive maypole construction (see box, 'Just a love nest', opposite page). It lives in the rainforests of northern Queensland, almost always in country that is 700 metres or more above sea level.

Golden bowerbirds grow to about 25 cm long. The males have golden yellow underparts and an olive brown back and wings; the females are olive brown above and dusky grey beneath, with indistinct markings on their throat and breast. Both sexes have yellow irises, the female's less bright than the male's, and both are accomplished mimics, imitating the calls of shrike-thrushes and currawongs, and even the screech of the sulphur-crested cockatoo.

The female builds her nest in the crevice or fork of a tree trunk. The one or two eggs hatch after about three weeks, and the young birds leave the nest about three weeks later.
Scientific name: *Prionodura newtoniana*

REGENT BOWERBIRD ■

After building and decorating his bower, the regent bowerbird displays his brilliant black and gold plumage to attract females. Once he has a female's attention, he struts around her holding an ornament in his bill while bobbing his head, bowing and flapping his wings, and even occasionally turning somersaults.

Males have rich golden-yellow plumage on their forehead, crown and neck. Their underparts and the rest of their back are glossy black, as are their wings except for a broad golden band. Their beaks and eyes are yellow, accentuated by black markings on the sides of their face. Females and young birds are mainly brown with a black crown patch and heavily mottled back and underparts. Adults grow to about 28 cm long.

Regent bowerbirds live throughout the rainforests and nearby eucalypt forests of southern Queensland and northern New South Wales. They are quite rare except in a few areas where food plants such as inkweed, coral berry and lantana are plentiful. They live mainly on native fruits, but will take cultivated fruits and berries from gardens and orchards. They also eat insects and spiders.

Although silent for the most part, they sometimes chatter and utter subdued metallic 'tiarr' sounds.
Scientific name: *Sericulus chrysocephalus*

SATIN BOWERBIRD ■

The male satin bowerbird is perhaps the best known of all Australian bowerbirds, and probably the best documented. This fame is due to his passion for collecting mainly blue items with which to decorate his avenue-type bower.

Satin bowerbirds live in rainforests, wet eucalypt forests and woodlands in eastern Australia. Females and young males are generally olive green above, becoming buff-white below with dark scalloping. Young males do not begin to acquire adult plumage until their fifth year, attaining full adult plumage only when they are seven. Males younger than seven and females are called 'green' birds and generally live in flocks, but mature males tend to be solitary, though they may join flocks outside the breeding season, which runs from September to February.

Both mature and immature males build bowers and display to females. They usually build their bowers on the ground and maintain them meticulously, collecting colourful objects from the forest and nearby houses. Blue pegs, straws and bottle tops are among their favourite stolen items, and from woodlands and forests they collect blue parrot feathers, flowers and brown snail shells. They paint the walls of their bower with a mixture of masticated vegetable matter and saliva.

When a female arrives, the male embarks on a ritualised display of exaggerated movements. He struts

and bows, holds his wings outstretched and quivering, usually while carrying an object in his bill, and makes buzzing and rattling calls interspersed with recitals of mimicry.

If the female is suitably impressed, she moves into the bower avenue to copulate. She builds a loose nest of sticks in a tree or bush up to 35 metres above the ground and incubates her two or three eggs for about three weeks. She feeds the young for a further three weeks before they leave the nest.
Scientific name: *Ptilonorhynchus violaceus*

DRY-COUNTRY BOWERBIRDS

Most Australian bowerbirds are wet-forest dwellers, but four species prefer drier areas. Males and females of this genus are similar in appearance, and are less colourful than their rainforest relatives. Males of all these species except the fawn-breasted bowerbird (*Chlamydera cerviniventris*) have a lilac patch on their nape, which is fully visible only when the bird is displaying. At other times this patch is partly or wholly concealed. In the female it is smaller or absent altogether.

The objects these birds collect to decorate their avenue-type bowers are also generally less colourful than those of the rainforest species. Mostly white, pale green or grey-brown, ornaments include bones, shells, glass, berries, leaves and stones, as well as items such as nails and pegs pilfered from nearby human habitations.

These birds are accomplished mimics, regularly copying the calls of a variety of other birds as well as noises of human origin such as squeaking gates, wood chopping,

■ SATIN BOWERBIRD
The male of this species ornaments his avenue-type bower with bright blue and violet-coloured objects to highlight his gleaming blue-black plumage and violet eyes.

JUST A LOVE NEST

Bowerbirds make four basic types of bower, the simplest being the stage bower. The bird clears part of the forest floor and decorates it with fresh leaves paler than the surroundings. This type is typical of the tooth-billed bowerbird.

Most common among Australian bowerbirds is the avenue bower. Males build two walls of woven sticks and grass stems, forming an avenue up to half a metre long. The bird clears the ground at each end and decorates it with ornaments. Some species place the ornaments inside the avenue, and some also paint the walls with a mixture of masticated berries and saliva.

The male golden bowerbird builds a maypole bower. He finds two small trees about a metre apart with a branch between them, which he later uses as a display perch. He then piles twigs up both uprights and decorates them with moss, green and white flowers, and fruits. The same bower is used year after year, and it can grow to over 3 metres tall.

In New Guinea, Archbold's bowerbird (*Archboldia papuensis*) builds a mat bower, placing dry ferns on the ground and then decorating them with dead beetles, snail shells and blue fruits.

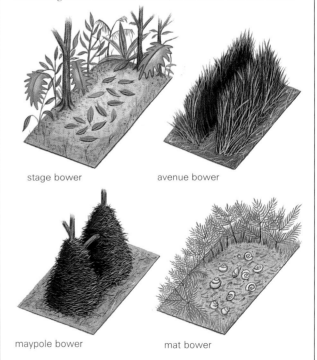

stage bower · avenue bower · maypole bower · mat bower

DISTRIBUTION

■ TOOTH-BILLED
BOWERBIRD

■ GREEN CATBIRD
■ SPOTTED CATBIRD

■ TOOTH-BILLED
BOWERBIRD
This photograph of an
immature tooth-billed
bowerbird shows the
species' notched upper
bill and serrated lower
bill. The bird uses the
notches and serrations
like teeth to tear up
stems and tough leaves.

cracking stockwhips and various
items of farm machinery. Although
these calls are given throughout the
year, they are more common during
the breeding season.

The fawn-breasted bowerbird is
confined to the drier rainforest
fringes, eucalypt woodlands and
mangroves of northern Cape York
Peninsula but it is also found in
New Guinea. It is 25–30 cm long,
and is mainly grey-brown with a
distinctive orange-buff abdomen
and chest. This bowerbird often
builds its bower on a raised platform
of sticks, which is sometimes more
than half a metre high.

The spotted bowerbird (*C. maculata*)
lives in a variety of dry woodland
areas throughout eastern Australia
and decorates its bower with white
and pale green objects, such as seeds,
bones, pebbles and snail shells, and
objects pilfered from houses. It is
28–31 cm long and predominantly
dark brown to buff with bold reddish buff spots.

The western bowerbird (*C. guttata*),
which was long considered to be
merely a form of the spotted bowerbird, is now recognised as a distinct
species. It lives in dense vegetation
and along tree-studded watercourses
in South Australia, Western Australia and the Northern Territory. At
24–28 cm long, it is smaller than the
spotted bowerbird, and is also darker
and more richly coloured. It has a
dark chestnut to buff spot on each
feather on its back, nape and head.

The great bowerbird (*C. nuchalis*),
which lives throughout the northern
part of Australia, is superficially
similar to the spotted bowerbird
and the western bowerbird, but is
larger – 32–35 cm long – and does
not have their distinctive spotting.

The spotted bowerbird, the western
bowerbird and the great bowerbird
build their bowers in shady areas

under vegetation and usually in the
vicinity of water, though sometimes
quite a distance away in drier areas.

For these species, the breeding
season coincides with the onset of
heavy rains that cause the sprouting
of young shoots and a consequent
abundance of the insects that feed
on them. These insects then become
an important source of food for the
bowerbird chicks.
Scientific name: *Chlamydera* spp.

TOOTH-BILLED
BOWERBIRD ■

Males and females of this species
have similarly coloured plumage –
predominantly olive brown above
and buff-white below with brown
streaks. They are 26–28 cm long, and
are found only in a small area of
northern Queensland.

This bird's common name comes
from the notches at the front of its
upper beak, which match a series
of tooth-like serrations on its lower
beak. It uses this adaptation to saw
through the stems of large green
leaves, and then uses the leaves to
decorate its stage-type bower.

The notched bill is also extremely
useful during the winter months,
when fruits are generally hard to
come by. At these times the tough
leaves of rainforest trees become the
bowerbird's staple diet, and it uses
its bill to tear them up.
Scientific name: *Scenopoeetes dentirostris*

CATBIRDS ■

There are two Australian members
of the genus *Ailuroedus* – a name
meaning 'cat-voiced', from two
Greek words.

The green catbird (*A. crassirostris*)
occurs in the subtropical and
temperate rainforests of southern

■ CATBIRD
Both sexes of the green catbird
(*Ailuroedus crassirostris*), a subtropical
and temperate rainforest species, utter
a loud, wailing, cat-like territorial cry.

Queensland and New South Wales,
and is a regular visitor to nearby
gardens. It has a cat-like 'ee-ow' call
that rises in volume and pitch in the
middle and then falls at the end. It is
predominantly green with numerous white spots on its underparts.

The spotted or black-eared catbird
(*A. melanotis*) occurs further north
but occupies similar habitats to the
green catbird. It is also mostly green
but is paler on the crown and has
black ear patches. Its back is covered
with buff spots and there are white
streaks and spots on its breast. It
has a long, mewing 'wa-a-a-a-a-a'
call that fluctuates in pitch. In both
catbird species male and female
plumage is similar.

Unlike other bowerbirds, male
catbirds mate with only one female
in a season. Females are probably
attracted to their mate by his singing,
but – despite thousands of hours of
research and field observations – it
is still not known what kind of
courtship is conducted. It is almost
certain, however, that the males do
not build bowers.

Female catbirds, like females of
other bowerbird species, build the
nest and incubate the eggs, and
males defend the territory and help
to feed the hatchlings during the
three weeks they remain in the nest.

Catbirds feed predominantly on
fruits – particularly figs – and a
variety of vegetable matter, such
as buds, shoots, flowers and seeds.
They also eat some insects.
Scientific name: *Ailuroedus* spp.

LARKS

Larks are a worldwide family of ground-feeding birds that sing as they fly. They are found in open grasslands, including cultivated paddocks and salt marshes, where they feed on seeds and invertebrates taken from among the grasses. It is rather surprising that Australia, with its large tracts of open country, has only two lark species – and one of them was introduced from Europe.

Larks live largely in treeless areas, so they must advertise their breeding territory from the air, and have developed extended 'song flights' for this purpose. A breeding male rises steeply into the sky, twittering loudly as he ascends. He reaches such a height that, while still clearly audible, he is barely visible. On reaching the flight's zenith, he continues to sing while hanging in the air, seemingly suspended. His call tails off during his rapid descent.

The duration and intensity of the lark's song varies with individuals. Several singing males may have territories very close to one another, and together they fill the sky with their loud melodies.

Since these elaborate songs are their main way of courting females, male larks have no need of bright plumage. Both sexes of all species are pale buff below and streaky shades of brownish earth colours above, providing excellent camouflage in their grassy surroundings. They reveal their white outer feathers only during territorial displays, when they fan their tails and raise their short, semi-erectile crests.

Family: Alaudidae

SINGING BUSHLARK

Singing bushlarks are widespread nomads in Australia, absent only from the central deserts, Tasmania, and the south-west of Western Australia. They also occur throughout South-East Asia and New Guinea. When they are breeding, their song is quite noticeable, as is their way of alighting on fence posts, but at other times they may be difficult to find. Bushlarks are gregarious and mainly insectivorous, often gathering in small, loosely knit groups to feed.

Singing bushlarks reach 15 cm long. They resemble house sparrows (page 277) in colour, but have distinctive buff eyebrows. There are many colour forms. Birds from the south-east, speckled black, grey and white, are darkest. By contrast, birds from the northern interior are an almost uniform cinnamon colour. The short, sparrow-like bill of the singing bushlark is distinct from the long, pointed bill of the larger European skylark (this page) and Richard's pipit (page 276). Singing bushlarks also have a shorter tail.

These birds prefer open grassy areas, but also inhabit countryside with scattered shrubs and trees. Flushed from cover, they fly a short distance just above the vegetation before dropping back to the ground. This activity is often accompanied by a series of short twitters.

The female singing bushlark builds a cup-shaped, sometimes domed, nest, often under a grass tussock.

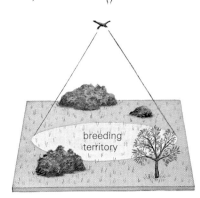

THE LARK'S ON THE WING
To advertise his breeding territory, a male lark rises almost vertically into the sky, warbling loudly, and then hovers high above the ground, a mere speck, singing all the while.

Between September and January, she lays her eggs, usually three. Both parents incubate the eggs for about two weeks, and feed the chicks for another two weeks after hatching.
Scientific name: *Mirafra javanica*

EUROPEAN SKYLARK ▪

European skylarks are native to Europe and Asia; they were brought into Australia and New Zealand in the 1850s, and are now found in Tasmania, south-eastern South Australia, Victoria and New South Wales. They are insectivorous and mainly sedentary, but move about locally in search of food in winter.

These birds are seen singly or in pairs, but they tend to travel in small groups. When disturbed, they rise twittering from the ground and move to safety with an undulating flight. They can often be seen in areas of short grass, and on sports fields in country towns.

The European skylark is 19 cm long, and has long legs and toes with elongated claws. It resembles Richard's pipit (page 276), but can be distinguished by its short erectile crest. Another difference is that it does not bob its tail like the pipit.

The cup-shaped nests of European skylarks are often found underneath grass tussocks between September and January. The female broods her three or so eggs for about two weeks, and both parents care for the nestlings for a further two weeks.
Scientific name: *Alauda arvensis*

▪ EUROPEAN SKYLARK
Male European skylarks usually sing in flight, but sometimes they give voice from an exposed position at ground level or on a perch.

■ RICHARD'S PIPIT
During the breeding
season, males sing from
perches and make song
flights, trilling as they
ascend, then dropping
some distance to fly
upwards again, gaining
in altitude each time.

PIPITS AND WAGTAILS

Pipits and wagtails are distributed throughout the world in grassland or open country, but Richard's pipit is the only member of the family that is native to Australia, although other vagrant pipits have been observed. The five wagtail species recorded on the mainland are irregular summer migrants.

All six species are terrestrial feeders. They are seen either foraging on grassy areas, or flying low over vegetation, uttering low 'chip, chip' calls. Pipits and wagtails run rapidly across flat ground for a few seconds before stopping and bobbing their tail up and down with head held high. This bobbing action is a family trait.

Although these birds have more distinct facial markings, the general colouring and patterning of pipits are reminiscent of larks. Wagtails in nonbreeding plumage are quite difficult to identify, but they have a more streamlined body. Both wagtails and pipits have long legs and tails and slender bills for picking up small seeds and insects.
Family: Motacillidae

RICHARD'S PIPIT ■

Richard's pipit has body plumage similar to that of the European skylark (page 275) but, at about 18 cm long, the pipit is somewhat shorter. Other subtle differences in appearance include the pipit's almost pure white eyebrows and cheek stripes that are narrowly bordered with black on the lower edges. Richard's pipit's dark breast streaks are also more prominent than those of the European skylark. The pipit has slightly longer legs and less obviously white outer tail feathers, and its almost constant tail bobbing is quite different from the movement of a skylark.

Richard's pipits are widespread and reasonably common throughout Australia in all but forested areas. Unlike skylarks, pipits do not have a strong song repertoire. Their melodies are simpler and shorter, but carry well over the open country in which they live.

Males sing continuously when they are engaged in territorial or courtship flight displays. They rise into the air, then drop a considerable distance before once more climbing and again dropping, each time gaining greater altitude. They also trill from perches on posts, logs or rocks.

Between August and January, the female builds a cup-shaped grass nest, usually beneath a tussock. She incubates two to four eggs that, like the eggs of other ground-nesting species, have a pale base with fine pale brown splotches and speckles to help conceal them.

After two weeks, the young hatch out. They remain in the nest for an additional two weeks, and both parents care for them.
Scientific name: *Anthus novaeseelandiae*

RED-THROATED PIPIT

Thought to be a rare vagrant from Asia, this species has recently been recorded from north-western Australia. Although this bird can be easily distinguished from Richard's pipit during the breeding season by the rich rufous plumage on its throat, it occurs in Australia only in its nonbreeding plumage.
Scientific name: *Anthus cervinus*

WAGTAILS

Five wagtails, all about 19 cm long, are known to occur in Australia. They have long, streamlined body profiles, and the outermost feathers of their long, thin tails are edged with white. Most have distinct white or yellow eyebrows. Wagtails breed in the northern hemisphere and arrive in Australia in their duller, nonbreeding plumage, so a knowledge of their facial, wing and tail patterns is essential for identification of the different species.

Of the five species, the yellow wagtail (*Motacilla flava*) is the most regular visitor to Australia. It is generally grey or black above with white-streaked wings, a black or white throat, and a yellow breast and rump. Its migratory movements are unconfirmed, but it seems to be an annual visitor from Asia. It is regularly reported from the Kimberley in Western Australia and from north-eastern Queensland, and there have been recent sightings in the Northern Territory, New South Wales, Rottnest Island in Western Australia and around Adelaide.

The remaining four species are rare summer migrants. The grey wagtail (*M. cinerea*) has been observed in the Northern Territory and Queensland; the white wagtail (*M. alba*) has been recorded in coastal areas of Western Australia and Victoria; and the yellow-headed wagtail, or citrine wagtail (*M. citreola*), has been seen in New South Wales, the Northern Territory and South Australia. The black-backed wagtail (*M. lugens*) is very like the white wagtail, in both colour and pattern. This species has been seen only near Derby in Western Australia and – once – on Fraser Island off the coast of southern Queensland, where its identity caused much puzzlement until it moulted into its breeding plumage and revealed a back that was distinctly black rather than dark grey.
Scientific name: *Motacilla* spp.

SPARROWS AND GRASSFINCHES

Recent research into the relationships between the numerous 'finch' groups has placed sparrows and grassfinches in the same family, the Passeridae. All members of this family have short, conical bills, well adapted for feeding on hard grass seeds and able to grasp the insects that, for many species, are a major part of the chicks' diet.

Sparrows were introduced into Australia, as well as many other places in the world, and two species are now resident here. All sparrows build loose, untidy, spherical nests in the crevices of trees, in small bushes, or in the roof spaces and wall crevices of buildings. Sparrows may be found singly, in pairs, or in small flocks, but they are generally considered fairly solitary and often pair for life. With a breeding cycle that can last throughout the year, several broods may be raised.

Grassfinches are widespread throughout Australasia, Africa and the southern regions of Asia. Some 20 species are found in Australia, 18 occurring naturally and two introduced. Most have colourful plumage and are highly social, with large flocks often moving around together looking for fallen or half-ripe grass seeds and water.

Grassfinches form strong pair bonds and, like sparrows, may well stay together for life. Both parents usually build the nest in bushy trees or among tall grasses, though in some species the male supplies the materials while the female undertakes the construction. The nest is usually a loose sphere of interwoven grasses with a front or side entrance tunnel. Both parents incubate the clutch of three to nine eggs and care for the young after hatching.
Family: Passeridae

HOUSE SPARROW

The house sparrow has become common and familiar in most parts of the eastern half of Australia where there is human habitation. The house sparrow is 14–16 cm long, and can be identified by its streaked brown and buff upperparts and paler uniform buff-grey underparts. The male has a conspicuous grey crown and a black face and throat. The female has a pale buff eye stripe. House sparrows utter a variety of chirping calls, typically a 'cheerrup' sound.
Scientific name: *Passer domesticus*

A GOOD IDEA AT THE TIME

House sparrows were brought to Australia from Britain between 1863 and 1870, and soon became widespread in most urban areas.

Although their introduction was welcomed by many people, these birds quickly became a major pest of fruit crops, and soon the government of the day was offering a reward for dead sparrows and their eggs. Today, the species is so well established in the east that extermination is impossible. So far, however, house sparrows have not colonised Western Australia: every specimen seen there is destroyed.

TREE SPARROW

The little-known tree sparrow is often confused with the house sparrow (this page). In Australia it inhabits southern New South Wales and south-eastern Victoria. It is quite scattered but relatively common within its restricted range. The species is thought to have been introduced into Victoria during the latter half of the nineteenth century.

Both males and females superficially resemble the male house sparrow, except for a distinct black ear patch and a chestnut brown rather than grey crown. At 13–14 cm long, the tree sparrow is the smaller of the two species, and where the ranges of the two species overlap tree sparrows are less competitive for food. Their call is like that of the house sparrow but higher pitched.
Scientific name: *Passer montanus*

ZEBRA FINCH

The zebra finch, or chestnut-eared finch, is easily identified by its generally grey plumage, brown wings, and black and white barred tail. The male has chestnut cheeks and fine black and white barring on its throat. Both sexes are 10–12 cm long and have a characteristic black 'tear drop' below their eyes and an orange bill.

This species is widespread across the Australian mainland, apart from Cape York Peninsula and some coastal areas. It is most common in dry, wooded grasslands near watercourses. These birds need to drink regularly, and dams and water tanks have increased their range. In flocks of a hundred or more, they feed on grass seeds and insects. When disturbed, they rise into the air uttering a distinctive nasal 'tiah', which they may repeat several times.

Zebra finches are the most numerous and widest ranging of Australian grassfinches, although their numbers have fallen in parts of Queensland, due to competition from nutmeg mannikins (page 281).

(page 281)

DISTRIBUTION

■ HOUSE SPARROW

■ TREE SPARROW

■ ZEBRA FINCH

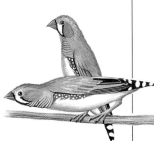

■ ZEBRA FINCHES
A male perched bolt upright is indicating hostility combined with a readiness to flee; if he adopts a horizontal posture, he is ready to attack (above). Zebra finches are extremely social and form flocks of 50–100 birds in the non-breeding season (left).

Zebra finches pair for life. They generally breed from October to April, but the time may vary with rainfall. Although the nest site is selected by the female and she constructs the loose, dome-shaped nest in a bush, the male gathers almost all the nesting material. Nests have been reported in hollows in the ground, although such locations are uncommon. Both birds care for the eggs and the young. The chicks hatch after two weeks and leave the nest after a further three.
Scientific name: *Taeniopygia guttata*

■ DOUBLE-BARRED FINCHES
Black rings around their white faces make these sociable birds look rather like little owls.

DOUBLE-BARRED FINCH ■
The double-barred finch is 11–12 cm long. It has a striking white face and cheeks, bordered with a sharp black line running through the throat, and a white breast, also bordered with black; the black lines are narrower in the female. It is mainly brown above with conspicuous fine white spotting on its otherwise black wings, and its bill is bluish grey.

The double-barred finch occurs in a broad coastal and inland band across northern and eastern Australia, where it inhabits grasslands, fringes of woodlands and parks and gardens near permanent watercourses. Like the zebra finch, this finch needs to drink regularly. It feeds on the ground on herb and grass seeds and some insects.

There are two distinct subspecies within the double-barred finch's range. The birds found in the northwest have a black rump, whereas those in the east have a white rump. The two subspecies overlap at the Gulf of Carpentaria and readily interbreed in the region.

DISTRIBUTION

■ DOUBLE-BARRED FINCH

■ CRIMSON FINCH

■ STAR FINCH
■ PLUM-HEADED FINCH

■ CRIMSON FINCH
These brilliantly coloured finches are found in the grasses around creeks and swamps in northern Australia. A male is pictured here.

Double-barred finches are highly social. Forming groups of up to 30, these relatively quiet birds preen one another and communicate through their soft 'tat' contact call.

The double-barred finch utters its soft notes more often in the breeding season. Pairs bond for life, and both birds care for the young. Using material gathered by the male, the female constructs the nest – a loose sphere of interwoven grass stems, with a side entrance tunnel – usually placed in a small tree or bush up to 4 metres from the ground. The female sometimes lays her eggs in the disused nests of other birds.
Scientific name: *Taeniopygia bichenovii*

CRIMSON FINCH, STAR FINCH AND PLUM-HEADED FINCH ■
The crimson finch (*Neochmia phaeton*) has unmistakable crimson, grey and brown plumage and a long, tapering tail. It is 12–14 cm long and inhabits tall grasslands near permanent water in northern and north-eastern Australia. It is generally seen alone, in pairs or small groups. Unlike most grassfinches, the crimson finch is not very social, and individuals are often aggressive. Its loud, repetitive 'chee-chee-chee-chee-chee' call is audible from some distance away.

The star finch (*N. ruficauda*) is also easily recognised. It is 11–12 cm long, with an olive green back and wings, a pale green breast marked with white spots, a yellow belly, and a red face and bill. It is found in the north and north-west of Australia, with isolated populations on the western and eastern coasts of Cape York Peninsula. It prefers tall, damp grasslands near water. It eats mainly seeds, pecking them up from the

■ STAR FINCH
Its bright red head and bill and the white 'stars' on its pale green breast make this finch easy to identify.

ground or plucking them from grass heads. Its nest, a ball of grass stems, is generally placed in a grass tussock or in a bush or tree within 5 metres of the ground. The male gathers nesting material and both sexes build the nest.

DNA research has recently placed the plum-headed finch (*N. modesta*) of eastern Australia in this genus. This bird, 10–12 cm long, is brown above with some white spotting. Its white underparts are barred with dark brown and it has a dark plum-coloured forehead. These finches inhabit tree-studded grasslands and reed beds near permanent water. When they are not breeding they move nomadically in flocks, but from August to March birds pair up to build a horizontally flattened flask-shaped nest of grasses and leaves among tussock blades – one of the smallest of all Australian grassfinch nests.
Scientific name: *Neochmia* spp.

RED-BROWED FINCH

The red-browed finch is sometimes called the red-browed firetail, but it does not belong to the same genus as the firetails (page 281). It is 10–12 cm long, and is easily identified by its bright red eyebrows. Its upperparts are olive green and its underparts are grey. Its bill is red, with a broad black wedge on the upper and lower mandibles. Young birds lack the red eyebrows and have a completely black bill.

The endemic red-browed finch is found in a variety of habitats, from open forest, grasslands and urban parks and gardens to agricultural areas, seldom far from water. Its range extends throughout eastern Australia, and near Perth there is a population descended from aviary stock. Due to its wide habitat tolerance and varied diet, which includes seeds, herbs, fruits and insects, this is one of the most familiar grassfinches in eastern Australia. The birds draw attention to themselves when feeding in tall grasses by their high-pitched, repetitive 'seeee' calls.

The red-browed finch forms medium to large flocks outside the breeding season, and maintains small family groups during the rest of the year. September to November are the commonest breeding months in the southern parts of its range; northerners breed slightly later.

The birds build a bulky flask-shaped nest of interwoven grasses with a front entrance tunnel leading to a chamber. They sometimes make a second, false entrance tunnel and chamber to deceive predators. They place this structure in a short, spiky tree or bush, generally 2–3 metres above the ground, and several pairs may nest close to each other. The female lays six to eight white eggs in the real chamber, which is lined with soft grasses or feathers.
Scientific name: *Neochmia temporalis*

PAINTED FINCH

The painted finch, also known as the painted firetail, inhabits the rocky, spinifex country of Australia's inland and central west. It is never far from permanent water; unlike most arid land species, which drink using a sucking technique, painted finches drink by scooping the liquid into their long, pointed bill and tilting their head backwards. They also use their long bill to take grass seeds from the ground and from narrow nooks and crannies.

These birds are 10–12 cm long, and can be easily recognised by the heavy white spotting on their black

underparts and by their red rump, black tail and chestnut-brown upperparts. The male has a large, bright red facial patch that extends past his eyes and to his upper throat.

Painted finches form loose sedentary flocks of about 20–30 birds throughout the year. Although they are common in suitable habitats, populations are thinly scattered throughout their range.
Scientific name: *Emblema pictum*

■ PAINTED FINCH
This finch is reputed to have the loudest call of all the Australian grassfinches: a harsh 'check-did-did-dit'.

LONG-TAILED FINCH, BLACK-THROATED FINCH AND MASKED FINCH

These three species form the genus *Poephila*, and they are all endemic to northern and north-eastern Australia. The long-tailed finch (*P. acuticauda*) and the black-throated finch (*P. cincta*) are similar in coloration, and they also share many traits, such as bill

wiping and head bobbing. Both have a blue-grey head and nape, a black throat, pale brown upperparts that are lighter below, and a white patch at the base of a black tail. The black-throated finch is 10–12 cm long; the long-tailed finch's tail is longer and thread-like at its tip, making the bird 13–15 cm long. Its bill is yellow or orange-red, depending on its location, whereas the black-throated finch's bill is black.

The third member of the genus, the masked finch (*P. personata*) is 11–13 cm long and is without the blue-grey coloration on its head and nape. Its upperparts are generally reddish brown, its underparts pale buff. Its conspicuous black face mask and robust yellow bill are identifying features.

These finches can be found in lightly timbered country with a dense grassy understorey, usually near water. Here they breed in loose colonies, with nests up to 50 metres apart. Female black-throated and long-tailed finches construct dome-shaped nests from material gathered by the males. The male and female masked finch collect material and construct their nest together, sometimes placing it on the ground or in a low grass tussock. All three species form social groups to bathe, drink and preen each other.

Each species has a melodious song that is commonly heard during the breeding season. Differences between the contact calls of all three species are discernible: the masked finch emits a whistling 'twet-twet', the long-tailed finch gives a loud 'twerrr' and the black-throated finch utters a more husky 'teeweet'.
Scientific name: *Poephila* spp.

■ RED-BROWED FINCH
Seldom far from water, these little birds are common along the east coast of Australia in grassy areas interspersed with dense vegetation.

DISTRIBUTION

■ RED-BROWED FINCH

■ PAINTED FINCH

■ LONG-TAILED FINCH
■ BLACK-THROATED FINCH

■ MASKED FINCH

DISTRIBUTION

☐ GOULDIAN FINCH
■ BLUE-FACED PARROT-FINCH

making up about three-quarters of the population and red the remainder. Yellow-faced birds are rare; their colouring results from lack of pigmentation in red-faced birds.

Outside the breeding season these birds are partly migratory, moving in quite large flocks to areas closer to the coast. They return inland to breed at the beginning of the rainy season. When they are not breeding, Gouldian finches feed for the most part on ripe or half-ripe grass seeds, but during the breeding season their diet consists almost entirely of insects. Like most other grassfinches, Gouldian finches need to drink several times a day. They are mostly silent, although they may utter a high-pitched whistling 'ssitt' from time to time.

This is the only species of grassfinch to nest exclusively in tree hollows or holes in termite mounds. It breeds in small, loosely knit social colonies from January to April, and several pairs of birds may share a single hollow. Land clearance, fire and the flooding of certain areas for dams have contributed to the loss of available nesting sites and the consequent withdrawal of the species from as much as half of its original range. The female lays four to eight white eggs directly on the bare floor of the hollow, and both sexes share incubation duties and care of the young birds.

GOULDIAN FINCH ■
This most brightly coloured of all grassfinches occupies the grassy woodlands and mangrove fringes of Australia's north. It grows to a length of 11–13 cm and has a green back, a yellow belly, a purple breast and a red or black head. There are also occasional yellow-headed individuals. The colours of its facial mask vary, but the differences do not denote male, female and young birds; they are simply plumage variations, with black-faced birds

The species was discovered by John Gilbert but was first described by the ornithologist John Gould, who named it after his wife, Elizabeth.

Trapping for the bird trade (it was legal until the mid-1980s), loss of habitat, predators, fire and the susceptibility of this species to parasitic mites have placed this finch on the list of endangered species.
Scientific name: *Erythrura gouldiae*

BLUE-FACED PARROT-FINCH ■
Apart from its blue face, the blue-faced parrot-finch is mainly grass green. It is 11–13 cm long. It has been recorded in various habitats and at most altitudes in Australia, but it seems to favour open grassland areas in dense coastal rainforests at altitudes of 1000–2000 metres. Its range in Australia is somewhat uncertain. The relatively few records from south-eastern Cape York Peninsula suggest that the Australian population of blue-faced parrot-finches is quite small, but its cryptic coloration and rapid flight make it easy to miss.

Blue-faced parrot-finches are also found in New Guinea, Sulawesi and the Solomon Islands, and there is continuing debate about whether the Australian birds are survivors of a once common indigenous population or part of a group that has only recently colonised Australia.
Scientific name: *Erythrura trichroa*

MANNIKINS

Three mannikin species occur naturally in Australia and two more have been introduced. They are typically thickset finches, 10–12 cm long, with stout, powerful bills that are usually greyish blue in adult birds. Except for the native pictorella mannikin, which prefers open acacia and spinifex country, mannikins inhabit tall, often rank grasslands along roadsides, river banks and swamplands.

The pictorella mannikin (*Lonchura pectoralis*) is found only in northern Australia, where it mixes with flocks of yellow-rumped and chestnut-breasted mannikins. Its upperparts are grey-brown, its underparts are mostly purple-buff, and its chest is heavily mottled with white and black. The male's black face is bordered by pale purple-buff crescents running from just above its eyes to the base of its throat. Females' faces are more brown. Pictorella mannikins are endemic to Australia. They live mostly in arid areas with scattered trees and in spinifex grasslands. Here they feed on grass seeds, either collected from the ground or taken from ripening plants, and a few insects. During long dry spells, birds tend to move towards the coast, returning inland at the onset of the wet season in order to breed, usually between January to April.

The native chestnut-breasted mannikin (*L. castaneothorax*) occurs throughout northern and eastern Australia, as well as New Guinea, and has been introduced into a number of other countries, including New Caledonia. It is instantly identified by its broad chestnut breast band, bordered below with black, and its black face and throat, and grey crown. Its belly is white and its upperparts rich chestnut. This species is found in tall grasslands and reed beds, especially along the fringes of swamps and rivers. Its numbers have increased since the construction of artificial waterways, and it has become a minor pest of grain crops.

In the north, the chestnut-breasted mannikin mixes readily with the endemic yellow-rumped mannikin (*L. flaviprymna*). The latter species is identifiable by its straw-coloured rump and tail, cream head and dark chestnut back and wings. Its breast and belly are fawn-buff and its undertail coverts are black. In their huge mixed flocks, chestnut-breasted mannikins easily outnumber yellow-rumped mannikins. Close social bonds are apparent between the two species and they readily interbreed.

The chestnut-breasted mannikin also mixes, and sometimes interbreeds, with the nutmeg mannikin (*L. punctulata*), which was accidentally introduced in about 1937 and is now common and widespread in eastern Australia and increasing rapidly in numbers. It has become a threat to native birds, since it competes for a wide variety of foods, breeds all year and tolerates human disturbance. It is 11–12 cm long and has a chestnut brown throat and upperparts. Its underparts are white, with heavy dark brown scalloping. Its mustard-coloured rump and tail move up and down and its wings flick rapidly as it runs along the ground or perches. Nutmeg mannikins form quite large flocks.

The black-headed mannikin (*L. malacca*) was unsuccessfully introduced. The pale-headed munia (*L. pallida*) is a vagrant to north Western Australia.
Scientific name: *Lonchura* spp.

 FIRETAIL
The black areas on the underparts of the diamond firetail (*Stagonopleura guttata*) are marked with white 'diamonds'.

 MANNIKINS
Chestnut-breasted mannikins (*Lonchura castaneothorax*) are social birds, often forming large flocks.

FIRETAILS

The hallmark of a firetail is its red rump. Ranging in length from 10 cm to 13 cm, all firetails of this genus have black face masks, red bills and red or blue rings around their eyes, and all roost at night in unlined domed structures.

The diamond firetail (*Stagonopleura guttata*) has black and white underparts – the black spotted with white – a grey head and brown upperparts. It lives in grassy woodlands near watercourses in south-eastern Australia, where it feeds on the ground on seeds and a few insects. It breeds in small colonies between August and January and forms larger flocks at other times. Its range once extended to the Atherton Tableland in Queensland, but numbers have dropped as a result of habitat clearance and it is now vulnerable throughout its reduced range.

The beautiful firetail (*S. bella*) lives in the coastal swamps, open forests and grasslands of south-eastern Australia. It is the only endemic grassfinch in Tasmania, where it is more common than on the mainland. It is grey-brown with black and white barring and a pale blue eye ring. It is among Australia's rarest grassfinches, due to habitat loss and predation by introduced animals such as cats.

The red-eared firetail (*S. oculata*) is like the beautiful firetail except that its black belly is spotted with white and it has a red eye flash. This rare bird lives in the forests of south-western Australia, where agriculture and mining have shrunk its habitat.
Scientific name: *Stagonopleura* spp.

DISTRIBUTION

PICTORELLA MANNIKIN

CHESTNUT-BREASTED MANNIKIN

YELLOW-RUMPED MANNIKIN

NUTMEG MANNIKIN

DIAMOND FIRETAIL

BEAUTIFUL FIRETAIL
RED-EARED FIRETAIL

DISTRIBUTION

GOLDFINCH

GREENFINCH

TRUE FINCHES

Several of the so-called true finch species were introduced into many countries in the mid to late nineteenth century. Two species became established in Australia – the goldfinch and the greenfinch.

Goldfinches and greenfinches pair first, and then select a nest site and establish a territory around it. The female incubates the eggs while the male brings food for her at the nest.

These birds forage in flocks for seeds, supplementing this diet with some insects obtained from both inside and outside their territory. The young are fed infrequently because the adult birds must travel quite far afield to gather food. The parents carry food to the nest in their crop and regurgitate it into the mouths of their nestlings.

Two other members of this family – the redpoll and the chaffinch – were introduced into New Zealand during the nineteenth century. They have not succeeded in gaining a foothold in Australia, but some vagrants from both species have been observed on Lord Howe Island.
Family: Fringillidae

GOLDFINCH

This species inhabits orchards, pine plantations, agricultural areas, and urban parks and gardens in south-eastern Australia and parts of the south-west. It is 12–14 cm long, and has buff and white upperparts, black and gold wings, white and buff underparts and a bright red face – though this feature is muted in the female and absent in young birds.

Occasionally flocks of 500 or more birds gather, but goldfinches are

■ GREENFINCH
The introduced greenfinch demolishes whole fruits by tearing at them with its strong bill to get at the seeds.

generally seen in groups of up to a dozen, called charms. They feed mainly on seeds and a few insects.
Scientific name: *Carduelis carduelis*

GREENFINCH ■

This thickset bird is 14–16 cm long, and has overall olive green plumage with bright yellow patches on the wings and tail. It is found in south-eastern areas of Australia, including Tasmania. It favours wooded areas such as urban parks and gardens, orchards and plantations of exotic trees, where it feeds on seeds.

Greenfinches are gregarious, and large numbers gather to feed and roost at night. Flocks often mix with goldfinches and sparrows outside the breeding season, which runs from October to January.
Scientific name: *Carduelis chloris*

REDPOLL

These birds form large flocks in the winter, but they do not mix readily with other finch species. They are 11–13 cm long with streaky brown and white plumage; males have a crimson crown and a pink breast and rump, but this coloration is less vivid or absent altogether in females. Redpolls belong to the same subgroup as the locally established greenfinches and goldfinches, and they mate, breed and feed their young in the same way.
Scientific name: *Carduelis flammea*

CHAFFINCH

Only male chaffinches have been sighted in Australia. They are brown above, with black and white wings, a pink breast and a slate blue head and nape. Females are more uniformly brown but have the same white wing bar. Both sexes are 14–16 cm long.

Unlike the other three introduced finch species, the male chaffinch establishes a comparatively large breeding territory before singing to attract a mate. The female incubates the eggs, but – again unlike other introduced finches – she obtains her own food while she broods. Finally, the parents often feed the nestlings on insects as well as seeds.
Scientific name: *Fringilla coelebs*

DISTRIBUTION

YELLOW-BELLIED SUNBIRD

SUNBIRDS

The sunbird family is a group that extends from Africa and the Middle East to Asia and the south-western Pacific. Sunbirds are generally small with long, curved bills, short legs and brightly coloured, iridescent plumage. The yellow-bellied sunbird (*Nectarinia jugularis*) is the only species that occurs in Australia. It is also found in New Guinea and in various nearby Pacific islands.

In Australia, the yellow-bellied sunbird's range is restricted to Cape York Peninsula and a coastal strip southward to Maryborough. There

have also been recent sightings on the north coast of New South Wales.

With its long, slender, downcurved bill, which is perfectly adapted for taking nectar and insects from flowers, this bird is a familiar sight as it hovers at food sources in tropical towns. Both sexes are 12 cm long, with bright yellow abdomens and light olive backs, and the iridescent blue throat and upper breast of the male distinguishes this species from all others. The iridescent colouring of the male and its hovering action have convinced quite a number of

observers that they are looking at a hummingbird.

When they are displaying or defending their territories, sunbirds make delicate, high-pitched trilling calls. At other times they utter short, high-pitched notes.

These birds seem to be attracted to human settlement; they are not at all timid in the presence of humans, sometimes even nesting and hunting insects inside buildings. As well as urban environments, the yellow-bellied sunbird frequents mangroves and the fringes of rainforests and orchards, and may be nomadic between these habitats. Sunbirds seem to be constantly on the move, never staying long in any one place.

In spring and summer males form loose groups that compete for the attention of females. They engage in flight displays, accompanied with much chasing and loud singing from exposed perches. Groups of five or six males can also sometimes be seen sitting quietly together.

The female uses bark strips, plant fibre, dead leaves and cobwebs to form a ball-shaped nest, which she suspends from the branch of a tree (or sometimes under the eaves or on the verandah of a building) by a long tether, with an equally long 'tail' hanging from the base. The side entrance to the nest is hooded. She normally lays two buff-coloured eggs finely dotted with pale grey and brown. Within about four weeks she has incubated the eggs and taken the main part in feeding the nestlings to fledging stage. Sunbird pairs remain together after nesting, often accompanied by their offspring.
Family: Nectariniidae

TROPICAL ACROBAT
Hovering on outspread wings, this female yellow-bellied sunbird (*Nectarinia jugularis*) is about to pluck an insect from the bark of a tree.

FLOWERPECKERS

Several members of the family known as flowerpeckers are widely distributed across the Asian and south-western Pacific region, but there is only one small flowerpecker species in Australia – the mistletoe-bird (*Dicaeum hirundinaceum*). It occurs over most of the mainland, though it is not found in Tasmania, and it also lives in Indonesia.

These tiny birds, 9–11 cm long, have short, broad bills, pointed at the end. They are difficult to see because they live among the foliage of trees and shrubs. Sometimes their high-pitched calls are audible as they flit overhead between their feeding areas.

The male has an iridescent blue-black back and wings, a scarlet throat, upper breast and undertail, and a grey undercarriage marked down the centre by a broad black stripe. Despite its resplendent plumage it blends with its surroundings, since many mistletoe flowers are red. Females are pale grey with a black tail and a pinkish undertail.

Mistletoebirds are mostly fruit-eaters that specialise in the fruits of mistletoes – parasitic plants that grow on other plants. They also eat other fruits and occasional insects. They are generally found alone or in pairs, inhabiting almost any area where mistletoes grow; this may be rainforest, wet or dry eucalypt forest, woodland, or even semi-arid deserts where watercourses support trees and shrubs. They are nomadic, visiting mistletoe-infested timber during the fruiting season. The mistletoebird and its principal food source are inextricably linked: a bird swallows the fruit whole and within a short time expels the sticky seed, which sticks to a branch and grows into a new parasitic plant.

During courtship the male tries to attract a mate with elaborate displays of wing flicking and tail fanning accompanied by intensive singing, which may include mimicry. The female suspends her nest from foliage at any height. She incubates her three white eggs, but both parents feed the nestlings for about four to five weeks.
Family: Dicaeidae

MISTLETOEBIRD

LIVING IN MISTLETOE COUNTRY
The nest of the mistletoebird (*Dicaeum hirundinaceum*) is built of vegetable matter and cobwebs and suspended from outer foliage. Here a male is feeding a chick on a mistletoe berry.

SWALLOWS AND MARTINS

Four of the 74 species in this family are native to Australia, but only one of them is considered endemic; the other three also occur elsewhere in the south-western Pacific. Two other species are regular summer visitors to Australia.

Swallows and martins feed principally on insects, which they catch in flight. Their long, pointed wings and streamlined bodies are perfectly adapted for graceful, swift pursuit and their short, broad bills are ideal for rapidly capturing prey.

Swallows and martins are social birds, often feeding and roosting together in apparently amicable groups. They keep in touch with each other by making short chipping contact calls. During the breeding season, males utter high-pitched soft twitterings from perches. Australia's native species generally breed in southern Australia. The fairy martin, however, has been known to breed in tropical Australia.

Most swallows and martins are migratory, but some of them are nomadic. None resides in one spot year after year. At the approach of cold weather, large numbers in the southern part of the continent assemble in trees or on power lines to migrate northward. From time to time some of them fly as far as New Guinea, but there are always a few birds that spend the winter months in the colder regions.
Family: Hirundinidae

A TELLING TAIL
The best way to tell a swallow from a martin is to look at the bird's tail: a swallow's tail (top) is long and forked, while that of a martin (bottom) is generally short and somewhat square.

■ WELCOME SWALLOW
Widespread throughout Australia, this swallow can often be seen darting over waterways, hawking for insects.

WHITE-BACKED SWALLOW ■

White-backed swallows are endemic to Australia. At 15 cm long they are the smallest Australian swallow. They have black and white plumage and a distinctive swallow shape.

They live mostly in open vegetated areas in the interior, but often venture towards the coast. They build tunnels in creek banks for roosting and nesting. The female lays up to six white eggs in a grass-lined chamber at the end of the tunnel and incubates them for up to 18 days. The young remain in the chamber for a similar period.

Scientific name: *Cheramoeca leucosternus*

RED-RUMPED SWALLOW

There have been recent sightings of Asian red-rumped swallows in the grasslands of north-eastern Queensland. At 18 cm long, they are the largest swallows in Australia.

This species is distinguished from other Australian swallows by its rust-coloured rump, its streaked body and pale eyebrows, and by a throat that is white rather than rusty.
Scientific name: *Hirundo daurica*

WELCOME SWALLOW ■

Of the Australian swallows, the best known is the native welcome swallow. Measuring 15 cm long, it has glossy blue-black wings and back, a whitish abdomen, and a rust red forehead, throat and upper breast. Its forked tail is tipped with white.

This bird is found throughout most of Australia, though greater numbers occur in the south, where they gather in flocks of several hundred. They inhabit all but densely forested and arid inland areas and are often seen making split-second manoeuvres as they travel at high speed over water, catching insects. Unlike other bird species, swallows seldom alight to drink. Instead, they scoop mouthfuls from the water's surface while in flight. Bathing birds skim the surface and dip into the water to dampen their feathers. Away from water, swallows sometimes circle around animals moving through grass to collect the insects that fly up.

In humid weather, welcome swallows may rise high in the sky in pursuit of insect swarms swept up by hot air currents. In winter, birds from Tasmania, Victoria and South Australia migrate northward, while those in New South Wales and Queensland move around in response to the availability of food. Living in urban areas has affected their migration patterns, since the warmth that is generated can make migration unnecessary.

Traditionally, these birds nest on open cave walls or along cliffs, but horizontal bridge beams and concrete tunnel walls also make ideal nesting and roosting sites. Barns, garages and other outbuildings are also popular locations.

■ WHITE-BACKED SWALLOW
This species builds tunnels in the banks of creeks or cuttings, where it roosts and nests. Sometimes 30 or more swallows gather in a single tunnel.

DISTRIBUTION

■ WHITE-BACKED SWALLOW
■ RED-RUMPED SWALLOW

■ WELCOME SWALLOW

Welcome swallows breed from August to December. During this time, males chase females and serenade them on the wing. Birds collect mud from local mud-holes and plaster together a compact, cup-like nest against a wall. As the mud dries, the birds line the interior thickly with grass and feathers, and then the female usually lays four white eggs, dotted with brown and lavender.

Incubation and fledging take about four weeks, but even after the young birds have left the nest they often sit nearby. The fledglings can be distinguished from their parents by their shorter tails, slightly duller plumage and yellow gapes.

Scientific name: *Hirundo neoxena*

BARN SWALLOW ■

This is the swallow species commonly seen in Europe and Asia, and each summer some members of the Asian population visit Australia during their nonbreeding season. Small to large flocks may be seen throughout open areas and towns across northern Australia from the Kimberley district in Western Australia to north-eastern Queensland, but in the southern states they usually appear individually and only in scattered locations.

The barn swallow is 17 cm long, and a black band between its rust-coloured head and its whitish abdomen distinguishes it from the welcome swallow.

Scientific name: *Hirundo rustica*

TREE MARTIN

Although the tree martin is common and widespread in Australia, it is often either overlooked or wrongly identified, probably because of its plain coloration and plumage. At 13 cm long, it is smaller than any of Australia's swallows but the same size as the fairy martin (this page).

Like all martins, it has a short, squarish tail. Its back, wings and head are dark brown to glossy black, its throat is dirty white and its breast pure white. Its rump is a buff colour, and is less distinct than that of the fairy martin. It also lacks the fairy martin's rufous head, having only a smudge of rust above its beak.

As their name implies, tree martins are mostly found around timbered areas – open forests, vegetation-lined waterways, and woodlands. They feed above the canopy on flying insects, often in small groups. Such gatherings are usually noisy, with birds uttering the soft, twittering notes typical of most martins.

As winter approaches, most of those living in the southern half of the continent migrate to northern Australia and the eastern Indonesian islands, although some always remain behind. The birds migrate in small flocks, feeding as they fly.

Unlike other Australian swallows and martins, tree martins nest in tree hollows. They may also select built structures, provided there is some sort of tunnel. The birds form a nest chamber at the end of the tunnel and line it with feathers and fine grasses. Nesting occurs between July and January and the female lays three to five eggs. Incubation and care of the nestlings lasts for four to five weeks. Both sexes feed the young.

Scientific name: *Hirundo nigricans*

FAIRY MARTIN ■

The native fairy martin is similar to the tree martin and the two species share behavioural characteristics. Fairy martins, however, more often frequent open grassland areas and are also seen in urban areas.

This species occurs in most Australian states but only irregularly in Tasmania. It avoids the western deserts and northern Cape York Peninsula. In autumn southern populations move north, while those in the north remain largely where they are. In spring, most birds fly south to breed, and individuals sometimes winter in the south of their range.

These birds build a bottle-shaped mud-nest with a narrow entrance. Sometimes the eaves of buildings are completely lined with nests and the birds often refurbish old ones. They also nest under bridges and culverts and on cliff overhangs.

Scientific name: *Hirundo ariel*

■ FAIRY MARTINS
A nesting colony of fairy martins may consist of several hundred mud-nests, all tightly clustered together.

■ BARN SWALLOW
This swallow is gathering nesting material. The nest is a cup of dried mud and plant fibre placed against a building or in a cave.

DISTRIBUTION

■ BARN SWALLOW

■ TREE MARTIN

■ FAIRY MARTIN

285

DISTRIBUTION

■ CLAMOROUS
REED-WARBLER

■ ORIENTAL
REED-WARBLER

■ LITTLE GRASSBIRD

■ TAWNY GRASSBIRD

WARBLERS

Warblers are part of a group of birds that are common throughout Europe and Asia. Of the 339 species known worldwide, nine are native to Australia. They may be migratory, sedentary or nomadic, and they inhabit reed beds, swamps or open grasslands, where they snatch insects from the surface of vegetation. They have long, pointed tails and their streaky plumage provides camouflage for living among aquatic plants or tall grasses. They are rarely found in well timbered areas.

Males and females are generally alike in their breeding plumage, but the males of the various species are subtly different. The eyebrow markings in each species are distinctive. Male reed-warblers, grassbirds and spinifexbirds call from among reeds and grasses, while cisticolas and songlarks make song flights similar to those of the larks.
Family: Sylviidae

CLAMOROUS
REED-WARBLER ■

The melodic spring song of male clamorous reed-warblers ensures that they are more often heard than seen. This loud repertoire, often delivered from the top of a tall

■ GRASSBIRDS
Thick reed beds and aquatic grasses are the habitat of the little grassbird (*Megalurus gramineus*).

reed spike, is their declaration of territorial ownership and their way of summoning females. At the height of the breeding season, they sing well into the night.

These birds are about 16 cm long, pale buff or lemon below and brown above, with pale eyebrows. This plumage makes them hard to spot among the reeds, but they can sometimes be enticed into the open by high-pitched sounds.

In late winter or spring clamorous reed-warblers migrate south in twos and threes from northern Australia and New Guinea. They are found over much of Australia wherever there are reed beds. They rarely venture beyond this dense vegetation, but they do occasionally feed among the leaves of tall eucalypts.

Between September and February pairs build their nests in the shelter of the reeds. The female usually lays three eggs. She incubates these for about two weeks, and both parents feed the nestlings for another two or three weeks. In autumn most birds migrate north, but a few young birds always remain through the winter.
Scientific name: *Acrocephalus stentoreus*

ORIENTAL REED-WARBLER

This reed-warbler is much rarer in Australia than the clamorous reed-warbler. The two species are alike in plumage, habits and song, but the

■ CLAMOROUS REED-WARBLERS
Among the reeds, a pair of warblers are weaving their nest of reeds and grasses lined with feathers or bulrush seeds.

oriental reed-warbler seems to be slightly larger. It usually lives in east Asia and has been observed only recently as a nonbreeding migrant to the northern tip of Australia.
Scientific name: *Acrocephalus orientalis*

GRASSBIRDS ■

Two grassbirds are known to inhabit Australia: the little grassbird (*Megalurus gramineus*) and the tawny grassbird (*M. timoriensis*). Both are heavily streaked above, but the tawny grassbird, 19 cm long, is larger and has a rufous crown. It occurs across the tropical north, from the Kimberley in Western Australia to Cape York Peninsula in Queensland, and down the east coast to southern New South Wales. It also occurs in New Guinea, the Philippines and Indonesia. Tawny grassbirds come and go with no clear seasonal pattern. They live in tall grasses in dry and swampy areas, and make clicking calls.

Found mainly in southern Australia, and also in the southwest of Western Australia, the little grassbird moves seasonally, probably in response to vegetation dying off in winter. It is sometimes seen at bores in central and northern Australia. These birds grow to 14 cm long and are darker than tawny grassbirds.

The little grassbird's call consists of three notes, high-pitched or low. An observer can attract a grassbird by careful mimicry.

Between August and April both species weave reeds or grasses into cup-shaped nests. The tawny grassbird builds inside a grass tussock. The little grassbird suspends its nest among reeds. Both lay three eggs on average. Incubation and fledging take a total of four or five weeks.
Scientific name: *Megalurus* spp.

SPINIFEXBIRD ■

In plumage the spinifexbird resembles the clamorous reed-warbler (opposite page). It frequents the spinifex-covered hillsides and stony plains that cross dry tropical Australia, broadly following the Tropic of Capricorn from the Pilbara in Western Australia into western Queensland. This arid habitat encompasses the Hamersley and Macdonnell ranges and the Great Sandy, Gibson and Simpson Deserts.

The spinifexbird defends its small territory by singing from the tops of spinifex clumps. It moves with agility, taking prey from leaves and crevices. It usually forages alone but in the breeding season pairs can be seen flying low. The male's song sounds like parts of the male reed-warbler's.

This bird is 15–16 cm long, brown above and buff below with a faintly rufous crown. Its tail pumps up and down in flight, and is often cocked when the bird is perched.

Between August and November the female builds a cupped grassy nest in a spinifex clump, lined with soft plant fibres and feathers. She lays two eggs. Incubation and care of the young have yet to be studied.
Scientific name: *Eremiornis carteri*

■ SPINIFEXBIRD
Unlike other warblers, this bird occurs in desert country. It lives among spiky spinifex clumps and associated grasses.

CISTICOLAS ■

In Africa and Asia cisticolas are common, but there are only two species in Australia. The relatively widespread golden-headed cisticola (*Cisticola exilis*) occurs from the Pilbara in Western Australia eastward to the east coast and round to south-eastern South Australia, but the rarer zitting cisticola (*C. juncidis*) is restricted to coastal areas of the Northern Territory and Queensland.

Cisticolas build domed nests, hiding them by stitching living leaves

into the outer walls with cobwebs. Golden-headed cisticolas mostly live among freshwater reeds, but zitting cisticolas prefer estuarine vegetation.

Where the species overlap, females and nonbreeding males are hard to tell apart. All birds are 10 cm long, with pale breasts and abdomens and cinnamon wings and backs streaked with brown. From September to March, male golden-headed cisticolas have a bright golden crown, but the crowns of male zitting cisticolas do not change. In summer, both species have shorter tails.

Male cisticolas display in summer. They rise high in the sky and seem to hang suspended, fluttering and singing. Then they drop back into the grass and begin again. They also often perch on a bush, tail cocked, and sing. The female lays up to three eggs. Within four weeks they have hatched and the nestlings are fledged.
Scientific name: *Cisticola* spp.

SONGLARKS ■

Uniquely Australian, the two songlark species are found over much of Australia but do not occur in Tasmania. Both species have a loud, metallic song. Each spring they migrate from northern to southern Australia. Between August and February the female builds a grassy cupped nest on the ground, usually beneath a grass tussock, and lays up to four eggs. Details of incubation and fledging are unknown. In the autumn, all generations move north.

The rufous songlark (*Cincloramphus mathewsi*) resembles the European

■ CISTICOLA
Cisticolas are grass-dwellers that feed on insects. Pictured here is a golden-headed cisticola (*Cisticola exilis*).

■ SONGLARK
The brown songlark (*Cincloramphus cruralis*) lives in the vast inland plains. It can sometimes be seen singing on a conspicuous perch, from which it launches itself upward in song flight.

skylark (page 275) and, at 17–19 cm long, is about the same size, but these brown birds can be identified in flight by their rufous rump. Breeding males have black bills and females and juveniles have brown bills. Rufous songlarks live in timbered country. Males sing their territorial song from exposed perches, frequently fluttering to the ground with wings upswept in a shallow V-shape.

Brown songlarks (*C. cruralis*) inhabit the treeless inland plains. In song flight, they hold their wings in a deep V. The female brown songlark resembles the rufous songlark but lacks the rufous rump, while the male is chocolate brown and more rounded than the rufous songlark. In no other songbird is there such a size disparity between the sexes: males are 25 cm long, but females are only 19 cm long.
Scientific name: *Cincloramphus* spp.

skylark (page 275)

■ SPINIFEX BIRD

■ GOLDEN-HEADED CISTICOLA

■ ZITTING CISTICOLA

■ RUFOUS SONGLARK

■ BROWN SONGLARK

287

Home, sweet home

A bird's nest may be anything from a scrape in the ground to a mound of earth, a tree hollow, a platform of sticks or a woven nest suspended from a tree fork.

Whatever the level of architectural sophistication, a bird's nest must provide an environment where the eggs can be safely incubated, and where, first the eggs and then the young birds can be protected from their many predators.

But nests and nest sites vary enormously, depending on the lifestyle of the bird concerned. One determining factor in the type of nest is the state of development of the newborn chicks: precocial chicks – those that are well developed when they hatch – do not need much parental care and protection, and some birds that give birth to precocial chicks do not bother to build elaborate nests. But chicks that are born helpless – altricial chicks – need the protection of a hidden or inaccessible nest while their parents are engaged in the demanding task of finding food.

The malleefowl's version of a nest is a mound of rotting vegetation covered with sand. While the eggs are incubating, the parent bird spends much time and energy checking the internal temperature of the mound and adjusting it if necessary by building up or thinning the sand layer. But once the chicks hatch, they are left completely to their own devices.

Wading birds, quails, chickens, grebes and rails are born almost independent and can follow their parents within hours. Gulls and terns are born covered with down and with open eyes; they can walk immediately, but they remain in the nest and are fed by their parents. Newly hatched herons, falcons and owls cannot leave the nest and are entirely dependent on their parents. Owls are born with their eyes closed, like the most helpless hatchlings of all, the songbirds, which have little or no downy covering.

Protecting the family

Birds that do build nests often ensure the safety of their growing brood by concealment. Many mainland birds rely on this technique, building hidden nests

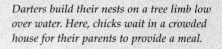

Darters build their nests on a tree limb low over water. Here, chicks wait in a crowded house for their parents to provide a meal.

in tall trees, thick bushes or hollow tree trunks. In another form of concealment, birds' eggs are often speckled or mottled for camouflage, but those laid in tree hollows, away from the beady eyes of predators, are usually white.

Isolation is another way of protecting the eggs and the young birds: grebes build floating nests that are out of reach of most predators, and sea birds breed on islands for the same reason.

Building materials

Birds weave nests from leaves, twigs, moss, grasses, seaweeds, cobwebs, wool, hair, fur, feathers – in short, virtually anything that the ingenious builder can fashion into a secure, well insulated, relatively safe structure.

Birds have been quick to exploit man-made structures and materials. As any city-dweller knows, pigeons long ago abandoned their natural homes on cliffs and took up residence on the ledges of high-rise buildings. Welcome swallows build cup-shaped mud nests under roof eaves, and eagles sometimes build their untidy stick nests on utility poles.

Birds that weave nests will readily incorporate scraps of fabric and plastic into their nests, and blue drinking straws are a favourite nest decoration for the satin bowerbird, who attracts a mate by ornamenting the approach to his bower with a motley but colour-coordinated collection of blue objects.

Above, eagles nest in overland telegraph poles on the Nullarbor Plain; tall trees are their natural nesting sites, but any elevated structure will do. At the right, a mistletoebird swings in its elaborate purse nest.

WHITE-EYES

White-eyes are a widespread group of small birds found in Africa, Asia, many South Pacific islands and Australia. Of around 80 species known worldwide, only seven have been recorded in Australia, and several of these are island species. They have all spread here from Asia. These birds are strictly tree-dwellers, and are common and familiar wherever foliage is dense enough to keep them well hidden, even in city gardens and parks. Despite their small size, white-eyes have a reputation for spreading themselves far and wide. Several species undertake annual migrations, and in the past 200 years the silvereye has established colonies in New Zealand and on islands such as Norfolk and Lord Howe.

White-eyes earned their name from the white or silver ring of fine feathers surrounding their eyes. This feature makes them easy to identify as a group, but distinctions between most species are subtle. All are about 13–14 cm long, and most have grey to green upperparts, light grey breasts and bellies, and green heads; some have yellow throats or tan flanks. Their dark bill is pointed and slightly downcurved – ideally shaped for pecking at tiny aphids, a favourite food. White-eyes also eat other insects and fruits, and some orchardists consider them pests, but their value as insect controllers probably outweighs the damage they do. They have brush-tipped tongues like those of honeyeaters (page 238) for mopping up nectar from flowers.

Like many small songbirds, white-eyes move around and feed in pairs

■ YELLOW WHITE-EYE
The most brilliantly coloured member of its family, this white-eye lives mainly among tropical mangroves.

during the breeding season and in small groups of 4–60 birds during winter. Their flocking behaviour offers them some protection against predators. Maintaining contact is an important factor in keeping the group together, and these sociable birds constantly utter high-pitched 'zee-oo' calls, especially while feeding. They also excel at mimicry, and often practise their singing in a soft voice known as their whisper song.

White-eyes build small cupped nests of fine twigs and grasses, bound with cobwebs and suspended from the outer branches of bushes and shrubs. The female lays up to three eggs, which are shaded a pale blue-green and occasionally finely dotted with lilac or brown at the larger end. Incubation and fledging take about three weeks.
Family: Zosteropidae

YELLOW WHITE-EYE ■
The green of the yellow white-eye's upper plumage is brighter than in other white-eyes, and its throat, breast and belly are lemon to bright yellow. These birds usually occur in family parties of up to six. They are not known to migrate, but they do move around in search of food.

These birds are generally confined to mangrove areas and nearby settlements from Shark Bay in Western Australia north and east to the western side of Cape York Peninsula in Queensland. One isolated population has settled around the mouth of the Burdekin River in Queensland.
Scientific name: *Zosterops luteus*

SILVEREYE ■
The best known of the Australian white-eyes, this bird has a distinctive silvery white ring of fine feathers around its eyes. It is especially common in south-eastern Australia, but may be found from Cape York Peninsula south to Tasmania and west into Western Australia to about Shark Bay. Silvereyes inhabit forests, woodlands and heaths, including those of subalpine regions, and also live in city gardens. They are mainly insectivorous but also consume large amounts of fruit and nectar.

This species appears in several regional colour forms. All have grey to olive green upperparts, a pale grey breast and belly, a lemon to yellow throat and a green head. But southern birds tend to have tan or chestnut-coloured flanks; western birds have green, not grey backs; north-eastern birds are slightly paler with brighter yellow beneath their tails; and birds from the Capricorn Islands, off Gladstone in Queensland, are slightly larger with more green on their heads.

In the south of their range, silvereyes migrate north each autumn, returning south in late winter. Banding has shown that Tasmanian populations cross Bass Strait in large numbers to winter on the mainland. They often migrate at night, and can be heard calling as they fly overhead. By spring, winter flocks have disbanded. Pairs establish nesting territories, which they defend strongly with strident warblings.
Scientific name: *Zosterops lateralis*

■ SILVEREYE
Orchardists complain that white-eyes eat their fruit, but the birds probably do more good than harm in that they keep insect pest numbers down. This silvereye is eating a persimmon.

DISTRIBUTION

■ YELLOW WHITE-EYE

■ SILVEREYE

■ ISLAND WHITE-EYE
This little bird, the Christmas Island white-eye (*Zosterops natalis*), is one of three little-studied white-eye species that occur only on tropical islands.

ISLAND WHITE-EYES ■

These three *Zosterops* species are the least studied of Australian white-eyes, probably because they are all confined to tropical islands.

The Christmas Island white-eye (*Z. natalis*) is found only on that island and on the Cocos-Keeling group of islands in the Indian Ocean. Apart from its location, the only feature distinguishing this species from the silvereyes is an obvious black streak from beneath its eyes to above its bill. The behavioural and nesting activities of this species are similar to those of the silvereye, but nothing is known of its migrational movements.

The pale white-eye (*Z. citrinellus*) looks rather like a bleached version of the silvereye. Its lower breast and belly are whitish, its throat is lemon yellow, and its back is pale olive green to yellow. The exact distribution of this species is uncertain, but in Australia it is restricted to islands in Torres Strait and along the northern Barrier Reef. Records of sightings south of Cooktown are yet to be confirmed. Very occasionally the pale white-eye is known to 'island-hop'. Small flocks hop around in low bushes and shrubs, feeding on insects and some berries.

The slender-billed white-eye (*Z. tenuirostris*) is found only on Norfolk Island. Its plumage and behaviour resemble those of the silvereye, with which it has had to share the island's shrubs and fruit trees since silvereyes began colonising the island. The longer, somewhat narrower bill of the slender-billed white-eye is the sole feature by which the two species can be told apart.
Scientific name: *Zosterops* spp.

THRUSHES

DISTRIBUTION

■ BASSIAN THRUSH

■ RUSSET-TAILED THRUSH

■ SONG THRUSH

■ EUROPEAN BLACKBIRD

Many people regard thrushes as the most melodious of all songbirds. Genetic studies have shown that these birds are part of a huge family of flycatchers, of which there are hundreds of species, but unlike flycatchers, which are aerial feeders, thrushes feed on the ground.

There are five representatives of this family in Australia. Two native species, the Bassian thrush and the russet-tailed thrush, inhabit eastern Australia. Two others, the European blackbird and the song thrush, were introduced from Europe in the nineteenth century and are now found in south-eastern Australia. Today the fifth species, the island thrush, lives only on Christmas Island (see box, 'Populate or perish', opposite page).

Thrushes are medium-sized birds with a distinctive way of feeding – they flick through leaf litter with their legs and bills, and then stand back to see what insects and other invertebrates they have uncovered. Another method of feeding they employ is to stomp heavily on the ground and then, with head held sideways, to listen for underground noises or detect movements that may indicate the presence of some sort of edible creature. Thrushes also eat a small quantity of seeds.

Although thrushes are ground-feeders, they roost and nest above ground. The limbs or outer branches of trees or the crevices of trunks form suitable sites for their bulky, cup-shaped nests of twigs and mosses. The female is the main nest builder. She incubates three to four eggs, which vary in colour from the finely scrawled or spotted grey-brown eggs of native thrushes to the blue-green semi-gloss patina of song thrushes' and blackbirds' eggs.

Males sing loudly during courtship to attract females, and throughout the breeding period to protect their territories. Each Australian species has a distinctive song. The best time to hear their calls is in the early morning from late winter to early summer.
Family: Muscicapidae

NATIVE THRUSHES ■

Only recently have the Bassian thrush (*Zoothera lunulata*) and the russet-tailed thrush (*Z. heinei*) been recognised as two distinct species.

Both are common natives of Australia. Usually found either singly or in pairs, these thrushes are probably sedentary. They are quiet, unobtrusive birds that scour

■ NATIVE THRUSHES
The plumage of the russet-tailed thrush (*Zoothera heinei*) camouflages it well in its rainforest habitat.

■ EUROPEAN BLACKBIRD
A male European blackbird feeds its voracious chicks. These birds can often be seen hopping across lawns in search of insects and earthworms.

the leaf litter of cool, wet native forests, looking for their preferred diet of snails, insects, worms and fallen fruits. When alarmed, they stand quite still, the soft brown of their plumage blending perfectly with the forest floor.

The best way of distinguishing the two species from each other is by their song. The song of the Bassian thrush is a tuneful crescendo of musical whistles and trills, while that of the russet-tailed thrush is a series of long, noisy double whistles.

The Bassian thrush is found throughout the wet eucalypt forests and rainforests of south-eastern Queensland, eastern New South Wales, Victoria, Tasmania and south-eastern South Australia. There is also an isolated population of rather more robust Bassian thrushes on the Atherton Tableland in north Queensland. Bassian thrushes grow to 26 cm long. The feathers of their dark brown back and wings, buff throat and dirty white breast and belly are edged with a darker shade, giving the bird's whole plumage a somewhat scalloped effect.

The little known russet-tailed thrush is 24 cm long, and is very similar to the Bassian thrush in general coloration. This species is found only in the rainforests of southern Queensland and northern New South Wales, and an isolated population inhabits the rainforests of the Clarke Range, not far from Mackay. The bird's upperparts are a little paler than those of the Bassian thrush, and its tail is shorter and russet-coloured.
Scientific name: *Zoothera* spp.

SONG THRUSH
The song thrush was introduced to south-eastern mainland Australia and Tasmania from England in l857. Several attempts to establish the bird failed, and today song thrushes can be seen and heard only in a confined area around Melbourne, where populations are currently stable. Song thrushes seem unable to adapt to the rigours of life in native bushland, and are generally found in parklands or gardens, where they feed quietly on the ground. They have an ingenious method of extracting the soft bodies of snails by tapping their shells against stones to break them open.

Song thrushes have brownish plumage, darker above and pale below, and their pale breast is heavily marked with dark streaks. Both sexes look the same. These birds are most often seen singly, although pairs are more common during the breeding season, which is from late winter to midsummer. Like blackbirds, they build a coarse-ly constructed cup-shaped nest and have similar nesting behaviour. The female lays three to five eggs.
Scientific name: *Turdus philomelos*

EUROPEAN BLACKBIRD ■
European blackbirds were imported from England in the middle of the nineteenth century, and their release into New South Wales, Victoria, Tasmania and South Australia has been very successful. They have adapted well to leafy gardens with lawns in Canberra, Melbourne and Adelaide, and throughout Tasmania. Populations have spread and shifted with new areas of settlement.

Blackbirds are most commonly seen in town and city gardens and parks but, unlike their cousins the song thrushes, they have also suc-ceeded in invading native bushland.

They are sedentary and normally occur in pairs. The sexes are easy to tell apart: females are a uniform soft dark brown, while males are black with a bright yellow eye ring and bill. Juveniles resemble adult females.

Females lay three to five eggs, and both parents share the two-week incubation and the feeding of the young, which takes a further two weeks. Adolescent birds sometimes stay with their parents for several months before leaving to establish their own territories.

The breeding season begins in late winter with males advertising their domains by almost constant singing. The blackbird's voice is very melodi-ous and carries for some distance. Singing males can be found perched in small, thickly leaved bushes or on the prominent outer branches of tall trees. If the birds are disturbed, they utter loud alarm calls before quickly flying or hopping away.
Scientific name: *Turdus merula*

POPULATE OR PERISH

Island populations of birds are particularly prone to extinction, and the smaller the island the more vulnerable its species. Small populations are at risk from natural causes such as cyclones because they have nowhere to fly. Another problem is the supply of breeding partners: if the population becomes too small, inbreeding may reduce the birds' fitness for survival.

The impact of human activities can be disastrous. In 1918, for example, the ship *Makambo* sank off Lord Howe Island and rats swam ashore. Rats eat birds' eggs and nestlings, and with-in five years the populations of five species – the island thrush (*Turdus poliocephalus*), the Tasman starling (*Aplonis fusca*), the robust white-eye (*Zosterops strenuus*), the Lord Howe Island warbler (*Gerygone insularis*) and the Lord Howe Island fantail (*Rhipidura cervina*) – had fallen drastically. Meanwhile two introduced species, the European blackbird and the song thrush, colonised the island, precluding recolonisation by members of the usurped species from elsewhere in the region. By 1938 all five original species were extinct on the island.

On Norfolk Island the clearing of land for agriculture and feeding competition from the introduced European blackbird have resulted in the probable extinction of the once abundant island thrush, pictured above. The only remaining Australian population of island thrushes is on Christmas Island.

DISTRIBUTION

■ RED-WHISKERED
  BULBUL

BULBULS

Bulbuls are naturally distributed across Asia and Africa. Two species have been introduced into Australia, but only one has become established.

In their native homes, these songbirds, which are 12–23 cm long, are common in and around forest edges. They are mostly tropical birds that utter clear, melodious whistles or noisy burbles and babblings. Some species, particularly those of the genus *Pycnonotus*, live in sparsely wooded areas and are often seen around human habitations. They tend to be bold and inquisitive.

Males and females have similar plumage. Shades of olive green, brown and grey generally predominate, but some species have patches, spots or stripes of bright yellow or red, and some – including Australia's introduced red-whiskered bulbul – have attractive crests. Bulbuls have short, rounded wings, little feet, short legs, a long tail, and a straight bill with a notch at the end and bristles near the gape.

Bulbuls have variable feeding habits: some are insect-eaters, some are fruit-eaters, and some consume both plant and animal material.
Family: Pycnonotidae

RED-WHISKERED BULBUL ■

The introduced red-whiskered bulbul is brown and white. It is about 23 cm long with a black head, nape and crest, and its white throat and cheeks are divided by a thin line of black feathers. Its red undertail and the 'whisker' of red behind its eyes are distinctive, although juveniles do not have red whiskers.

■ RED-WHISKERED BULBUL
The native habitat of this bird ranges from the Indian subcontinent to south China. In Australia, it lives near humans as it feeds mainly on introduced plants and the insects that accompany them.

To succeed in a new environment, an introduced species must be able to subsist on a wide variety of foods. The red-whiskered bulbul eats fruits from native figs and orchards and berries from various introduced plants. It also takes advantage of Australia's nectar-rich vegetation and preys on flying insects.

In Australia, the red-whiskered bulbul is found mainly in suburban areas; this is because in the bush it encounters strong competition from native birds such as honeyeaters. It rarely stays still for long, and is usually seen singly or in pairs, chirping its 'kink-a-ju' from power lines and other lookouts.

Red-whiskered bulbuls breed from August to March. The male and female interweave twigs and bind them with cobwebs to form a nest – preferably in dense vegetation, but many nests are exposed and the young are often dislodged during storms or become the victims of predators such as pied currawongs. Both sexes incubate the two to four eggs and feed their young.

Today the red-whiskered bulbul is common in Sydney, and most towns along the New South Wales coast have bulbuls in their gardens. Melbourne has a colony centred around the city's Botanic Gardens. Where the Melbourne bulbuls came from is a mystery, but in 1948 a pair were seen in the suburb of Toorak. Possibly they were aviary escapees.
Scientific name: *Pycnonotus jocosus*

STARLINGS

This large and varied family of birds consists of over 100 species in 27 genera. Starlings are small to medium-sized stocky birds. Most of them are insect-eaters and ground-feeders, though some have become urban scavengers and others are tree-dwellers that live largely on forest fruits. Australia has one native and two introduced species.

Starlings are gregarious, most of them roosting communally and some nesting in colonies. The young hatch blind and helpless and in need of constant parental care, but even so starlings often succeed in raising more than one brood in the course of a season – hence the family's power of survival.

Worldwide, several species of starling are threatened, one is endangered and four have become extinct, including the Tasman starling of Lord Howe and Norfolk Islands (see box, 'Populate or perish', page 291). This bird was once considered an orchard pest, but relentless persecution by humans combined with the introduction of rats killed the species: the last reported sighting of a Tasman starling was in 1923.
Family: Sturnidae

■ COMMON MYNA
This starling will eat almost anything, and is commonly seen scavenging in city streets and suburban gardens.

METALLIC STARLING

The metallic starling is Australia's only extant native starling. Adults are 21–24 cm long, with red eyes and black plumage iridescent with green and purple. The young are dull brown above and white with bold brown streaks below.

Most metallic starlings are summer migrants from New Guinea, though some remain year-round. In August or September they arrive in large, noisy flocks on the north-eastern coast of Australia to breed.

Like most starlings, this species is gregarious. It roosts communally and breeds in large colonies, from which comes a cacophony of wheezy chatters and sounds of the young begging for food. Branches, nests and droppings accumulate under the tree, mites abound and snakes search for fallen eggs and nestlings.

This bird feeds largely on rainforest fruits, although it sometimes raids orchards. It is clumsy, knocking as much to the ground as it consumes.
Scientific name: *Aplonis metallica*

COMMON MYNA

Usually seen foraging in small groups, common mynas thrive on insects, fruits and human refuse. They roost communally and several thousand may gather at night. Gradually, as the breeding season approaches, pairs leave the roost in search of a tree hollow.

These mynas are chocolate brown with black heads, a bright yellow bill and legs and white wing patches that are prominent when they fly. They are stocky, scavenging ground-feeders that grow to 26 cm long.

They pair for life and challenge native birds for nesting sites. They also nest in the eaves of houses or in any other nook or cranny. When the young fledge they often leave a legacy of mites, which do not survive long away from their host but can cause irritation to humans.

Native to South-East Asia, the common myna was introduced into Australia in Melbourne in 1862. A little later it was released into the Queensland canefields in the hope that it would control insect pests. It quickly became established – but not as a pest controller. It is now common in most urban areas on the east and south-east coasts of the mainland, and is continuing to spread.
Scientific name: *Acridotheres tristis*

COMMON STARLINGS
The speckled appearance of these starlings comes from white tips on their feathers, which disappear with wear.

COMMON STARLING

This species was originally confined to the northern hemisphere, but introductions by humans and its own adaptability have ensured its worldwide distribution.

Common starlings were first brought to Melbourne in the 1850s; other releases followed, and these birds are now found in all the eastern states and are a serious pest of seed and fruit crops. The starling patrol – shooters who kill any starlings seen near the border of South Australia and Western Australia – has so far prevented these birds from making their way westward across the Nullarbor Plain.

The common starling reaches 21 cm in length. Young birds are brown, but adults have iridescent black plumage with large white tips on their new feathers; these tips are gradually lost with wear, and by the breeding season the birds have become completely black.

These starlings roost communally at night, favouring palms, bushy trees and the eaves of buildings. Their droppings can be a serious hazard to human health, causing such respiratory diseases as histoplasmosis. During the breeding season flocks break up and form loose breeding colonies. They like to nest in tree hollows, but any crack or crevice will suffice. They compete with native species for nesting sites, sometimes forcibly evicting them. They raise as many as three broods in a season.
Scientific name: *Sturnus vulgaris*

METALLIC STARLINGS
Unlike most members of this family, Australia's only surviving native starling weaves a hanging nest. It breeds in colonies of several hundred nests to a tree.

DISTRIBUTION

METALLIC STARLING

COMMON MYNA

COMMON STARLING

REPTILES

AROUND 310 MILLION YEARS AGO, THE FIRST reptiles evolved, some 50 million years after amphibians successfully invaded the land. Another 50 million years later, they dominated the world's terrestrial environments. This domination continued for the next 140 million years, during which reptiles evolved not only giant land forms such as the dinosaurs, but flying forms (from which today's birds evolved) and large, marine, dolphin-shaped predators. However, this diversity eventually declined, with many kinds becoming extinct about 65 million years ago.

There were once as many as 16 major groups of reptiles; now there are just four: crocodiles and alligators, tortoises and turtles, snakes and lizards, and the primitive group Rhynchocephalia, which contains only two surviving species – New Zealand's lizard-like tuataras (*Sphenodon* spp.). Today there are roughly 6000 reptile species worldwide, of which 95 per cent are snakes and lizards. Australia has around 860 native reptile species, including about 630 lizard species, 190 snake species, almost 35 turtle species and two crocodile species.

SLIDING AND SLITHERING
The largest reptile group, the snakes and lizards, have elongated bodies and move across the ground with a muscular side-to-side undulation. Snakes have no legs at all; most lizard species do have legs, though in some species the legs are rudimentary.

Reptiles do not have a single characteristic body form. Each of the modern groups diverged on its own evolutionary path very early after the emergence of the first reptiles and adapted over hundreds of millions of years to particular modes of life, departing dramatically from the earliest reptilian body plan.

The ability of reptiles to exploit terrestrial environments more effectively than their amphibian predecessors hinged largely on two factors: the evolution of the land egg – a shelled egg that could be laid on land without drying out – and the development of efficient mechanisms for conserving water inside the body.

Other evolutionary factors that contributed to the terrestrial success of the reptiles were the possession of a skeleton and muscles suited to moving a body through air, which is a far less dense and supportive medium than water, and the development of lungs and an efficient respiratory system for extracting oxygen from air.

The land egg
The early stages of growth of all animals, including humans, must take place in a watery environment. For the amphibians – immediate predecessors of the reptiles – this meant

dependence on water in order to reproduce so that they were unable to roam far on land.

But with the development of an egg with a protective shell, reptiles were freed from this dependency on proximity to water. A shelled egg – an amniotic egg in scientific terminology – provides a compact, self-contained watery environment that can be laid on land without drying out and requires only a heat source for the embryo within to develop.

Self-contained survival kit
Land eggs do not merely protect embryos from desiccation; they allow them to develop within for longer than amphibians by providing them with food, oxygen, waste disposal and protection from predators and pathogens until they hatch as small, fully-formed, self-sufficient versions of their parents.

A reptile embryo is encased in a small fluid enclosure – its own little 'pond' – by a membrane called the amnion. The amnion is connected to a food source, the yolk, from which the developing reptile extracts nutrients through a system of blood vessels.

A second membrane, the allantois, surrounds the amnion and the yolk sac and collects waste

products from the embryo. The allantois performs the functions of a lung, transferring oxygen to the embryo and expelling carbon dioxide in the other direction.

Around the allantois is a third membrane, the chorion (initially continuous with the amnion), which is rich in blood vessels that absorb oxygen entering the egg from the external environment. The contents of the chorion are cushioned in albumen (egg white), which is a reservoir of water and proteins.

This entire elaborate structure is supported, protected and contained within the calcified shell, which is relatively waterproof but permeable to gases. In most reptiles the shell is soft and leathery, but in some species it can be hardened with extra calcium.

Birds' eggs have a similar structure to reptiles' eggs but, unlike birds, very few reptiles tend their eggs after they are laid; instead, most provide the heat necessary for development of the embryo by burying their eggs in sand or soil. All crocodiles and turtles and most lizards and snakes lay eggs, though there are some lizards and snakes that retain the eggs inside their bodies and give birth to live young.

Because the protective shell is formed just before the egg is laid, reptiles had to develop a means of internal fertilisation. For this purpose the males of all modern reptile species except the tuatara have evolved penises (one in turtles and crocodiles, two in lizards and snakes) to deliver sperm into the female's body before the shell and membranes form around the egg.

Water conservation

Another factor that allowed reptiles to conquer the land was the development of strategies for conserving water. A reptile's skin is dry and horny and its outer layers are waterproofed by a protein called keratin that limits water loss. Over time this process of keratinisation kills the outermost skin cells, and lizards and snakes periodically moult to shed this outer layer as it is replaced by new cells from beneath. Their tough, scaly outer skin also protects them from injury. Unlike fish scales, the scales of reptiles are derived from the inner skin layers. They have colour-bearing cells that provide many reptiles with the ability to change the shade or intensity of their colour patterns.

In some lizards and snakes, nasal salt glands help to reduce water loss by excreting excess salt so that the amount of water that needs to be excreted as urine is reduced.

Lizards and snakes also conserve water by excreting waste products as near-solid urine composed of uric acid crystals.

An amazing opal

Modern reptiles are descended from the same ancestral reptile group as the dinosaurs. One of the most exciting fossil finds in Australia was the discovery in 1988 of the opalised fossil of a pliosaur – a marine reptile that lived 110–120 million years ago – in Coober Pedy, South Australia. Inside the skeleton were gastroliths – stones for grinding food in the stomach – and the vertebrae of some fish, the pliosaur's last meal. The fossil, an almost complete skeleton, was nicknamed Eric.

In 1993, Eric came up for sale. Scientists feared that Australia might lose this precious find to an overseas buyer, but over 25 000 people donated money to buy Eric for Australia.

When he is not on tour, Eric can be seen at the Australian Museum in Sydney.

SALT BALANCE
The drops of moisture on this saltwater crocodile's tongue are the salty fluid exuded by the salt glands, which get rid of the excess salt that is absorbed from the animal's environment and its diet. At the back of the mouth, a fleshy flap rises to block the gullet so that the crocodile can go on breathing while almost under water.

ARMOUR PLATING
In turtles, the scales that characterise reptiles have evolved into the shiny patina that covers the protective shell.

CROCODILES

CROCODILE FETUS
Baby crocodiles puncture the membrane and shell of their eggs with an egg tooth called a caruncle, which is a hard, sharp outgrowth of the skin at the tip of their snout.

Crocodiles (order Crocodilia) roamed Earth at the same time as the dinosaurs, and they have remained relatively unchanged for over 200 million years. Well adapted to an amphibious life, crocodiles can hold their breath under water for up to an hour. They swim rapidly by means of their powerful tails, and on land they move very quickly over short distances. They can propel themselves at great speed down sloping river banks into the water.

FRESHIE
Easily recognised by its long, narrow snout, the freshwater species *Crocodylus johnstoni* is smaller and lighter than the saltwater crocodile.

Raised nostrils allow crocodiles to float with just their nostrils and eyes above the water, their huge bulk concealed from their prey.

Crocodiles have quick reactions and highly developed senses of smell, sight and hearing – ideal for their predatory way of life. They can even detect changes in pressure through the sensory pits around their snout. Their sharp, replaceable teeth are designed to hold prey; the powerful jaws of saltwater crocodiles are strong enough to crush the skull of a pig.

Crocodiles hunt for food at night, usually along the water's edge, and eat whatever they can catch, including mussels, crabs, fishes, snakes, lizards, turtles, birds and flying foxes. Saltwater crocodiles also take larger mammals, including the occasional human, and dead animals. They tend to crush large food items before swallowing them. Like dinosaurs, they have stones in their stomachs, called gastroliths, which grind up their food.

Crocodiles lay their eggs in moist holes or damp mounds at the edge of waterways. The sex of the hatchlings depends on the temperature at which the eggs are incubated. Despite their predatory ways, female crocodiles are gentle with their young.

Of the 23 crocodile species found in equatorial countries, there are two species found in Australia – the saltwater or estuarine crocodile and the freshwater or Johnston's crocodile. Both are found in northern Australia, where they live in creeks, billabongs and swamps and, in the case of the saltwater crocodile, in the sea.

Australian crocodiles – especially the saltwater crocodile – were so intensively hunted for their skins, it was feared that they might become extinct. They were protected in the 1960s and 1970s in the hope of halting their decline, and both species have since recovered dramatically. Today when large crocodiles pose a threat to humans they are captured and moved away. Some are taken to crocodile farms, and raised for their leather and meat.

SALTIE
The largest living reptile, the Australian saltwater crocodile *Crocodylus porosus,* has a shorter, broader snout than the freshwater crocodile. It also has heavier 'armour-plating' and powerful snapping jaws. Despite its name, it is commonly found in freshwater habitats throughout northern Australia, but it can survive in the ocean.

FRESHWATER CROCODILE ▪

The freshwater crocodile, or freshie, lives in the rivers, swamps and billabongs of northern Australia. This species occurs nowhere else in the world. Growing to a maximum length of around 3 metres, the freshwater crocodile is smaller than the saltwater crocodile, or saltie, and its snout is narrower. Unlike the saltwater crocodile it is considered harmless to humans; nevertheless, it is not advisable to dangle your hands over the side of a boat on the rivers of northern Australia.

Freshies mate at the beginning of the dry season (about June), after which females excavate a hole 6–30 cm deep in moist gravel or sand, where they lay 4–21 eggs. The nest site is then left unattended, and many of the eggs succumb to predators, flooding, overheating or suffocation before hatching occurs two to three months later. At this time the female returns to her nest and digs out the calling hatchlings. Sometimes she carries the hatchlings to the water in her mouth.

The females guard the hatchlings from predators such as large fishes, water pythons, sand goannas, turtles and sea eagles. Later, the young crocodiles shelter in tall vegetation and under fallen trees.

During the dry season, as billabongs dry up, adult freshies often congregate in large numbers and sometimes travel long distances over land to reach larger waterholes. During this time they eat very little and do not grow, but they compensate for the shortfall during the more plentiful wet season. Freshwater crocodiles feed on insects, fishes, frogs, lizards and birds.

Scientific name: Crocodylus johnstoni

▪ FRESHWATER CROCODILE
Shown here basking in shallow waters, the freshie is rarely a threat to humans, although females defend their nests aggressively.

SALTWATER OR ESTUARINE CROCODILE ▪

Saltwater crocodiles, or salties, are the largest crocodiles in the world. Specimens up to 9 metres long have been reported, but they rarely reach more than 5 metres. They are ferocious predators, moving stealthily and attacking with alarming speed. They launch themselves upward with their strong tail and snap their gaping jaws shut on their prey, which they take into deep water to drown in a 'death roll'.

Saltwater crocodiles can be found in the sea, but usually live in estuaries or freshwater swamps. They may inhabit coastal flood plains and rivers and even billabongs a long way inland, especially during the breeding season.

Salties breed in the wet season. They lay 30–70 eggs, usually at night, in a nest mound that the female builds out of plants, mud and soil. The female defends her nest for about three months until the eggs hatch. As the hatchlings struggle to escape from their shells, the mother excavates the nest and may roll the eggs gently around in her mouth to assist hatching. She then transports the fully formed hatchlings in the protection of her mouth down to the water's edge, where they swim immediately. The mother nurses her brood for several months before they begin fending for themselves.

Scientific name: Crocodylus porosus

DISTRIBUTION

FRESHWATER CROCODILE

SALTWATER CROCODILE

▪ SALTWATER CROCODILE
The huge, ferocious jaws of the saltie snap shut around its fish dinner.

carapace

large front flipper

tail

back flipper

scutes

tail

webbed feet

carapace

scaly skin

claws

TURTLE TRAITS
Sea turtles and fresh-water turtles share some characteristics: both have a two-part shell – the upper part is the carapace and the lower part is the plastron – and both have enlarged scales called scutes. However, there are some physical differences between the two groups: the sea turtle (top) has front and back paddle-like flippers, while the smaller fresh-water turtle (bottom) has legs and webbed and clawed feet.

TURTLES

Turtles (order Chelonia) have been on Earth with very little change for over 200 million years. Today there are about 260 species worldwide, 35 of which are found in Australia.

They are divided into two groups, based on how they retract their heads: the cryptodira withdraw their heads straight back and the pleurodira fold them sideways. In Australia the pig-nosed turtle and sea turtles represent the cryptodira and freshwater turtles represent the pleurodira.

Turtles are found in a wide variety of habitats, including deserts, rivers, estuaries and oceans. Like all reptiles, they obtain body heat from their surroundings. Their main feature is their protective shell, made up of the carapace on top and the plastron on the bottom, the two parts connected at the sides by a 'bridge' that is part of the plastron.

Most turtles eat both plant and animal material, but some species are entirely carnivorous or entirely herbivorous. They range in length from about 10 cm to more than 2 metres. Determining their sex can be difficult, but males generally have longer tails than females. All turtles lay eggs, usually in the ground near water. They leave their nests unattended, and the hatchlings must fend for themselves from the time they hatch. Turtles are often very slow-growing and may not reach maturity for decades. Some live for over a hundred years.

SEA TURTLES

Sea turtles use their large front flippers to 'fly' through the water and their smaller hind flippers to steer. Although sea turtles spend most of their life at sea – only the females coming to land to lay their eggs – they have lungs and must come to the surface to gulp air at least every half hour. They take several decades to reach maturity, and adults range from about 70 cm to over 2 metres in length. The largest sea turtle, the leatherback, weighs 300–500 kg. Except for the flatback, which is restricted to the Australian continental shelf, sea turtles are found in temperate and tropical waters all over the world.

Most sea turtles are carnivorous and spend much of their time searching for encrusting animals such as sponges, corals, crustaceans and shellfish, or for floating prey such as sea jellies. After migrating from their feeding grounds to the area around their nesting beaches, they mate under water, a single female mating with several males.

After mating, the male returns to his feeding grounds while the female remains near the nesting beach until she is ready to lay her eggs. Nesting usually takes place after dark. The female turtle chooses a nest site on the beach above high tide and uses all four flippers to excavate a large depression, called a body pit. Then she uses her hind flippers to dig a pear-shaped egg chamber, normally about 40–70 cm below the surface. She lays her eggs in the chamber and covers the site with sand before returning to the sea. A female sea turtle nests several times in a season, and when it is over it is normally three to six years before she returns to nest again.

It takes about two months for the eggs to hatch. The sex of the hatchlings is determined by the temperature in the nest, so it is not unusual to find that all the hatchlings from one nest are the same sex. Under cover of darkness, the hatchlings leave the nest, rush to the water and swim out to sea. Only one in several thousand survives the 20 years or so it takes to reach sexual maturity.

Once they are swimming in the ocean, hatchlings of all species are dispersed by oceanic currents – except for the flatback, which remains in Australian waters. Young turtles ride these currents for several years feeding on animal plankton. Only the leatherback turtle remains in the deep oceans. The others, when they are about 30–40 cm long, select feeding grounds in shallower waters and choose one, to which they remain tied for life. When they reach maturity they make numerous journeys – every few years – between their feeding ground and their nesting beach, probably following the same route each time.

Families: Cheloniidae, Dermochelyidae

LAYING EGGS IN THE SAND
The female sea turtle lays 50–150 white eggs the size of ping-pong balls in a chamber she has dug on the beach.

LOGGERHEAD TURTLE

This turtle has a large head, a red-dish brown carapace and a yellow underside. Adults have an average shell length of nearly a metre and weigh about 100 kg. They feed on shellfish and crustaceans.

Loggerheads are found throughout the year all around Australia except along the southern coastline, though they are more abundant in warm temperate waters. They inhabit coral reefs and shallow bays, and nest on islands or on the mainland in the region of the Tropic of Capricorn on both eastern and western coasts. Mon Repos beach near Bundaberg in Queensland provides the best opportunity to see hatchlings and nesting females.

The number of females nesting along Australia's eastern coast has halved during the last decade. A large number of loggerheads are believed to have drowned in prawn-trawling nets used in Australian waters. Overseas, special nets that allow turtles to escape have reduced the number of sea turtle drownings, and it is hoped these nets will be introduced into all Australian states.
Scientific name: *Caretta caretta*

HAWKSBILL TURTLE

Hawksbills are common in the waters of northern Australia and are often found feeding among coral and rocky reefs as far south as Shark Bay in Western Australia and Moreton Bay in Queensland.

They are usually olive green or brown with brown or black

HAWKSBILL TURTLE
The beak-like upper jaw of the hawksbill turtle gives it its common name. With this 'beak' it picks off and prises out encrusting animals – for example, sponges and soft corals – and marine plants such as algae.

markings and have cream coloured undersides. Adults have an average shell length of 80 cm and weigh about 50 kg. They have thick, over-lapping scutes, or shields, on their carapace and an upper jaw that looks like a bird's beak. Hawksbill turtles nest mainly on the islands in the northern Great Barrier Reef and Torres Strait, although some nest in the Northern Territory and Western Australia.

The thick scutes of the hawksbill's carapace are known as tortoiseshell and are used to make ornaments.

The hunting of these creatures for their tortoiseshell has led to a world-wide decline in their population.
Scientific name: *Eretmochelys imbricata*

LEATHERBACK TURTLE

Also known as the leathery or luth turtle, the leatherback is the largest of the sea turtles, with an average adult shell length of 1.5 metres and a weight of about 400 kg. It has notched jaws for gripping sea jellies and other soft prey. It is easily distinguished from other turtles by its immense size and ridged, tapering shell. The shell is black with small, light-coloured spots and the carapace has a tough, leathery skin.

The leatherback's feeding grounds are mainly in the deep ocean waters of temperate seas. Solitary adults often dive hundreds of metres for food, their size and insulating layer

■ LOGGERHEAD TURTLE
The loggerhead turtle has powerful jaws and crushing plates that can break open particularly large clam shells.

301

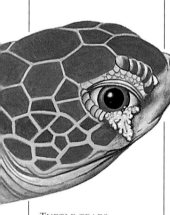

TURTLE TEARS
Sea turtles excrete their excess salt as a concentrated brine by special lachrymal (tear) glands around their eyes. When the females come out of the sea to lay their eggs, this often makes them appear to be crying.

of fat helping them to cope with extreme cold at such depths. Their breeding sites, however, are always in tropical zones and, like other sea turtles, they remain tied to these sites throughout their life.

Leatherbacks are most often found in southern temperate waters on the coast from southern Queensland to Victoria and off the coast of south-west Western Australia. They rarely nest in Australia, but favour tropical beaches in Irian Jaya, Mexico and Costa Rica, where they bury their eggs almost a metre deep.

Egg harvesting has led to a dramatic decline in leatherback turtle numbers, and there is growing concern about the increasing number that are dying as a result of eating plastic bags – presumably mistaking them for sea jellies.
Scientific name: *Dermochelys coriacea*

OLIVE RIDLEY

At specific times in the cycle of the moon, and particularly on windy nights with a pounding surf, thousands of female olive ridley turtles come onto land to lay their eggs. These gatherings, called arribadas in Spanish, last one or two days, but are becoming rare events because of the harvesting of the turtles and their eggs. Only scattered nestings occur in Australia, in the Northern Territory and the Gulf of Carpentaria.

The olive ridley, or Pacific ridley, is the smallest sea turtle found in Australia. The adult's average shell length is 70 cm and it weighs about 40 kg. It has powerful jaws and large crushing plates in and around its mouth, enabling it to feed on crabs and shellfish. Grey or olive grey with a yellow underside, it occurs in tropical Australian waters from the border between Western Australia and the Northern Territory to Townsville on the east coast.

Elsewhere in the world, ridleys are heavily exploited for their leather. Hunting them or taking their eggs for food and accidental drownings in commercial fishing nets have further reduced their numbers.
Scientific name: *Lepidochelys olivacea*

FLATBACK TURTLE ■

The flatback turtle lives almost exclusively in Australian waters, and its distribution is restricted largely to the continental shelf. It has a grey or grey-green to olive shell with upturned lateral edges and a skin-like texture. The flatback feeds on soft corals and sea pens in shallow inshore waters and bays of northern Australia, as far south as the Tropic of Capricorn. It is not found around the Great Barrier Reef, probably because sharp corals could damage its delicate, fleshy shell.

Adult flatbacks have an average shell length of 90 cm and weigh

■ GREEN TURTLE
A female green turtle may mate with a series of males and then store sperm for use later in the breeding season.

■ FLATBACK TURTLE
The female flatback, *Natator depressus*, returns to the sea after laying her eggs on the nesting beach.

about 80 kg. They nest on continental islands and on the mainland coast in certain areas of northern Australia. Unlike other sea turtles, hatchlings are not dispersed by oceanic currents and so remain in the waters off the Australian coast. Because they do not encounter the turtle hunters of Australia's neighbouring countries, they are probably the least threatened of the Australian sea turtles – despite drownings in commercial fishing nets.
Scientific name: *Natator depressus*

GREEN TURTLE ■

The green turtle gets its name from the colour of its fat rather than its carapace, which is usually a mixture of brown, black and olive green. Adults have an average shell length of just over a metre; they weigh about 130 kg and their head is small in comparison to their body.

Young green turtles are carnivorous but adults are herbivorous, feeding on seaweeds and seagrasses. They are the most abundant of the sea turtles in Australia and are often seen along the tropical coasts and on the Great Barrier Reef. They nest on islands off north Western Australia, in the Gulf of Carpentaria and at the northern and southern edges of the Great Barrier Reef.

Both the eggs and the meat of the green turtle are eaten, and it is the only sea turtle to have been commercially exploited in Australia. The green turtle is now protected in Australian waters, but it is still hunted in neighbouring countries.
Scientific name: *Chelonia mydas*

FRESHWATER TURTLES

All Australian freshwater turtles except one – the pig-nosed turtle – belong to the family Chelidae. They live in water, leaving it only to bask, migrate and nest, and to aestivate or hibernate – though some turtles even hibernate in water.

Chelid turtles are found only in Australia, Papua New Guinea and South America, with most living only in Australia. Some have long necks and others have short necks, but all are characterised by the way they retract their necks sideways beneath the rim of their shell for protection. Instead of flippers, chelids have legs with webbed feet and claws, which helps them to swim fast. The pig-nosed turtle (family Carettochelydidae) is unique among Australian freshwater turtles, with flippers like those of sea turtles.

The nesting season varies with species and location, but nearly all Australian freshwater turtles nest by excavating a hole in the earth with their back legs. They dig down to where the earth is moist and deposit 3–30 eggs in the hole before covering it over. Some females come out of the water only a metre or so to lay their eggs. Others travel up to a kilometre from water, heading for high ground away from flooding.

The choice of nest site is critical, as the unguarded eggs are vulnerable to land predators with an acute sense of smell, such as goannas, foxes and water rats. Baby turtles hatch underground after 7–11 weeks, and then scramble to the surface and rush to the nearest water.

The northern long-necked turtle (*Chelodina rugosa*), which inhabits the rivers and billabongs of lowland areas in northern Australia, is unique in its ability to nest and lay eggs under water.
Families: Chelidae, Carettochelydidae

SAW-SHELLED TURTLE
The extent of this turtle's distribution is not known and it is often mistaken for a species of short-necked river turtle (page 304), which inhabit the same waterways over much of their range. However, the saw-like serrations on its shell and the presence on its neck of numerous prominent tubercles – similar to warts – distinguish the saw-shelled turtle.

The saw-shelled turtle is often referred to as a 'snapper' because it is thought to be aggressive. This is not the case, however. If left alone

this turtle is shy and placid, though when it is handled it can bite quite severely in its own defence.
Scientific name: *Elseya latisternum*

SNAKE-NECKED TURTLE
Sometimes called stinker because it releases a strong-smelling liquid from its anal glands the first few times it is handled, this turtle is also known as the eastern snake-necked turtle or the long-necked turtle. There are large populations throughout New South Wales and Victoria, and some in south to mid-Queensland.

Snake-necked turtles feed on aquatic invertebrates, tadpoles and small fishes. They will travel up to two kilometres overland to reach waterholes containing food or search for places to hibernate or nest. They can often be found sleeping under fallen trees, having moved uphill to avoid flooding. They have been known to hibernate in groups at the bottom of waterholes, extracting oxygen from the water through the skin of their body orifices.

An adult grows to about 26 cm long. Its carapace is fawn to black and its plastron the colour of bone, often stained brown by the tannin from rotting vegetable matter in the

water. The individual shields of the plastron are sometimes edged in black – a feature that helps to distinguish this turtle from other species.

Mating at the end of spring and well into summer, these turtles lay an average of 16 eggs in holes in the banks of billabongs and streams.
Scientific name: *Chelodina longicollis*

BROAD-SHELLED TURTLE
This turtle has the largest shell (up to 48 cm long) of any Australian freshwater turtle. Its carapace varies in colour from light brown in the Murray and Darling River basins to dark in south-eastern Queensland. There is also a dark-coloured population living in the lakes on Fraser Island off the Queensland coast.

The broad-shelled turtle has a long, thick neck and a wedge-shaped head that is well adapted for fossicking for prawns and yabbies. Sometimes it buries itself in the sediment of rivers to ambush prey.

These turtles are rarely seen in large numbers. During hot weather they may be seen basking on tree stumps in the water. Unfortunately, like other turtles, they often drown in fish traps and nets.
Scientific name: *Chelodina expansa*

SAW-SHELLED TURTLE
As well as saw-like serrations on its carapace, from which it takes its common name, the saw-shelled turtle has a large, hard scale or shield on the top of its head and extending down its head on both sides. No other group of turtles in Australia has this shield.

DISTRIBUTION

SAW-SHELLED TURTLE

COMMON SNAKE-NECKED TURTLE

BROAD-SHELLED TURTLE

DISTRIBUTION

■ WESTERN SWAMP
TORTOISE
■ SHORT-NECKED
RIVER TURTLES

■ MARY RIVER TURTLE
■ FITZROY TURTLE
■ PIG-NOSED TURTLE

■ OBLONG TURTLE

■ SHORT-NECKED
RIVER TURTLE
This 'boofheaded' river
turtle was photographed
in the Thomson River,
Queensland.

WESTERN SWAMP TORTOISE ■

Fossil records from the gulf country of Queensland indicate that the western swamp tortoise was once quite widespread, but it is now found only in two nature reserves in the south of Western Australia. In one of these reserves the turtles have been reintroduced to replace extinct populations. By 1987 land reclamation, swamp drainage, and introduced predators had reduced the number of turtles in the wild to about fifty. Captive breeding programs had been attempted before, but it was not until 1988 that scientists were successful. Today the population exceeds a hundred individuals and captive-bred turtles are being released into the wild.

The Aborigines of the region call this turtle yakkinn. From head to tail, yakkinn grows to about 16 cm. By the time it reaches 12 cm, the male's tail is much longer than the female's, making it easy to tell the sexes apart. During the colder, wetter months this turtle feeds on live aquatic food in a race to build up body fat before the harsh summer months. As the shallow swamp waters evaporate, the turtles leave the water and seek refuge among grass and leaf litter or in holes – either natural holes or ones they have dug themselves. Here they remain without feeding throughout the summer, facing the dangers of both the elements and predators. In early summer, before they leave the swamps, females come ashore and lay up to five eggs in a nest.
Scientific name: *Pseudemydura umbrina*

■ WESTERN SWAMP TORTOISE
When the rains refill the swamps, the swamp tortoise hatchling leaves its nesting site to find water.

SHORT-NECKED RIVER TURTLES ■

Short-necked turtles of the genus *Emydura* are among the most abundant and conspicuous freshwater turtles in eastern and northern Australia. They are normally only 15–20 cm long, though some individuals reach 35 cm.

Most short-necked river turtles are nondescript, apart from some yellow or cream facial stripes – though the northern red-faced turtle (*Emydura victoriae*), which occurs in all the major drainages west of Darwin to the Fitzroy River of Western Australia, has a red band along the neck. However, in the Jardine River on the tip of Cape York, there is a population of Australia's colourful painted turtle (*Emydura subglobosa*), which has a yellow stripe from the snout to the ear and another along the upper jaw. A scarlet stripe runs from the corner of the mouth down the throat, and the underside of the shell and limbs are suffused with scarlet. The northern yellow-faced turtle, which does not yet have a scientific name, occurs in the coastal rivers bordering the Gulf of Carpentaria.

There are three closely related species found in south-eastern and eastern Australia: the Murray turtle (*Emydura macquarii*) throughout the Murray–Darling drainage, the Brisbane River short-neck (*Emydura signata*) in all but two coastal drainage basins between Sydney and Brisbane, and Krefft's river turtle (*Emydura krefftii*) in the coastal drainage basins north of Brisbane to Princess Charlotte Bay in Queensland. Scientists are debating whether these are separate species or one species with a variety of forms.

Short-necked turtles owe much of their success as a species to broad and opportunistic feeding habits. Young turtles are carnivorous, primarily relying on aquatic insect larvae for sustenance. As they grow, they become omnivorous and then adopt a herbivorous diet of fresh aquatic shoots found in the sand or mud. Animal foods include freshwater sponges, caddisfly larvae, midge larvae and pupae, dragonfly nymphs, crayfish, shrimps and freshwater snails. Smaller turtles feed on insects that fall on the water.

These turtles are familiar to us because of their tendency to bask. They climb from the water and rest on logs and exposed rocks, often in large numbers. They lie with their limbs and short neck extended, soaking up the sunshine, and it is thought that the consequent rise in their body temperature helps them to digest plant matter.
Scientific name: *Emydura* spp.

MARY RIVER TURTLE

During the 1970s this unusual species was known as the 'pet shop turtle' because of the vast number of hatchlings sold through the pet trade. Little was known about their natural habitat or about adults of the species until the discovery in 1990 of their only known natural waterway, the Mary River in Queensland.

The adult male grows to 40 cm or longer and the female is slightly smaller, making this Australia's largest short-necked turtle. Its carapace is dark and the plastron light. It has exceptionally long, fleshy projections, called barbels, under the chin. This species is recognised as a new genus of freshwater turtle because of the length and thickness of the tail and bone structure in adult males.

The Mary River turtle is considered vulnerable because its habitat is limited to one short river.
Scientific name: *Elusor macrurus*

FITZROY TURTLE

It may be the Fitzroy turtle's specialised diet of weed, sponges and insect larvae that has saved it from traps loaded with conventional meat baits. Although common, this turtle is rarely spotted because it does not appear to bask and is rarely seen near the surface of the water, as it extracts most of its oxygen through gill-like structures inside its tail vent (cloaca). It pumps water through the cloaca at the rate of 15–60 times a minute.

Restricted to the extensive drainage basins of the Fitzroy and Dawson Rivers in Queensland, this freshwater turtle is medium to dark brown, short-necked, and grows to about 26 cm in length. While most Australian short-necked turtles have a smooth carapace, in this species the carapace features a series of rough parallel ridges.
Scientific name: *Rheodytes leukops*

PIG-NOSED TURTLE ■

The pig-nosed turtle is Australia's most unusual turtle, and the only one belonging to the family Carettochelydidae. It is found in the freshwater and estuarine reaches of rivers in northern Australia and southern New Guinea. Other names for this turtle are the Fly River turtle, the pitted-shelled turtle and its Aboriginal name, warradjan.

Unlike other Australian freshwater turtles, the pig-nosed turtle is large – over 50 cm long and up to 22 kg in weight – and withdraws its head straight back into the shell instead of to the side. Its flippers resemble those of sea turtles, rather than the limbs of freshwater species, and it lacks the horny scutes that overlie the bony shells of most turtles.

Although a fast swimmer, this pig-nosed turtle is essentially a bottom-dwelling species, spending much of its time in and around logs and undercut banks and feeding mainly at night. It lives in the clear, shallow waters of the Daly River in the Northern Territory and the permanent billabongs of the Alligator River region in Kakadu National Park. It is omnivorous, feeding on leaves, fruits and flowers that fall on the water, and especially favouring figs, bush apples and pandanus fruits. Other foods include aquatic insect larvae, shrimps and yabbies, freshwater shellfish, fishes and mammals (flying foxes as carrion are a favourite), algae and ribbonweed.

Paintings of pig-nosed turtles are found among the rock art of Kakadu National Park and neighbouring Arnhem Land. Some of these are thousands of years old.
Scientific name: *Carettochelys insculpta*

OBLONG TURTLE

The most noticeable feature of this turtle is its long, thick neck. When extended, as it usually is when out of the water, the neck nearly doubles the turtle's overall length. Juvenile oblong turtles are pear-shaped, but as they grow the carapace becomes oblong when viewed from above. The carapace is black to dark fawn, and grows to more than 30 cm in length. The narrow plastron is bone-coloured, though it is often darkened by tannin from vegetation.

Oblong turtles are restricted to south-western Western Australia,

SLEEPING UNTIL IT'S ALL OVER

Most turtles spend part of their lives in a dormant state to conserve energy in very hot or cold conditions. During the winter turtles hibernate, either in or out of water, going into a deep sleep in which their metabolic rate slows down.

Aestivation is like hibernation but involves a lighter sleep. It occurs initially during hot dry weather, but the period of torpor may extend for a number of seasons in adverse conditions. As bodies of water evaporate, becoming too low or too warm, turtles seek a damp place where they can maintain their body fluid levels until conditions improve. Aestivation is more dangerous for turtles than hibernation because during their dormancy they are vulnerable to both aquatic and land predators, which remain active in the summer.

and although they are found in rivers such as the Swan, larger populations are found in lagoons and lakes. They are also common in parkland waters in suburban Perth. They often accept meat thrown into the water, but under natural conditions they eat live aquatic food.

Nesting occurs from September to January, often within a metre of the water, though they can nest as far as 500 metres away – sometimes in gardens. As oblong turtles are often forced to cross roads on their pilgrimage to nesting sites, traffic signs have been erected to warn motorists.
Scientific name: *Chelodina oblonga*

■ PIG-NOSED TURTLE
The nostrils of *Carettochelys insculpta* open at the end of a prominent fleshy proboscis that looks like a pig's snout.

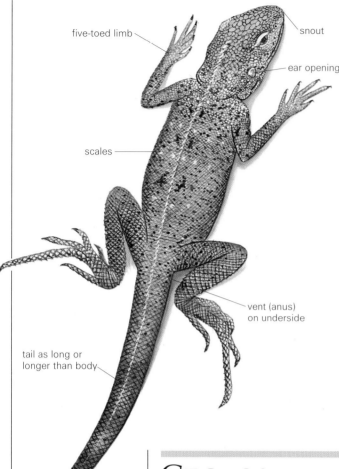

five-toed limb

snout

ear opening

scales

vent (anus)
on underside

tail as long or
longer than body

**LIZARD
CHARACTERISTICS**
Certain characteristics
distinguish a lizard.
Every member of the
suborder Sauria has
limbs, a tail as long or
longer than its body
(snout-to-vent) length
and a small external ear-
opening behind the eye.

■ CHAMELEON GECKO
The chameleon gecko's
original carrot-shaped
tail is black with striking
white bands around it.

LIZARDS

There are five lizard families in Australia – geckos, snake
lizards, dragons, goannas and skinks – all belonging to the
suborder Sauria. With the exception of the Galapagos Island
iguanas, lizards are found only on land or in fresh water.
While most lizards have limbs, in snake lizards and some
skinks these are so vestigial that they are not noticeable,
and these lizards can be mistaken for snakes.

Like all reptiles, lizards seek warmth from their outside
environment to activate them. Most lay eggs, but some bear
live young. Like many other reptiles female lizards do not
care for their young, which must be self-reliant from birth.

The tail of a lizard, which begins at
the vent (anus), is usually at least as
long as the body. Many lizards are
able to lose all or part of their tail
during fights or to distract predators. The tail often drops off at
special fracture sites and may continue to writhe after it has left the
body. This extraordinary behaviour
causes the lizard no pain and the

tail, to a large extent, grows back,
although the vertebrae of the original tail are not replaced. Instead, the
new growth consists of cartilage,
which is not as flexible.

Most lizards have five toes on their
legs and most feature an external
ear-opening some way behind the
eye. Only goannas have forked
tongues like those of snakes.

GECKOS

All Australian geckos are nocturnal,
hiding by day in burrows, under
rocks and logs, or beneath loose
bark. A few, such as the spiny-tailed
geckos (*Strophurus* spp.) bask in the
sun on sheltered branches.

Geckos with padded feet seem to
defy gravity as they scuttle along
smooth surfaces. They can do this
because microscopic bristles under
each pad catch on irregularities in

the surface. The gecko lifts the front
of each toe and disengages the bristles before taking the next step.

Australia has more than a hundred
gecko species. While most live in
deserts and the tropics, they are distributed throughout the continent
except in the cool, moist south-east
and Tasmania. Some are rarely seen
because of their retiring lifestyles
and remote locations.

All geckos eat insects and other
small invertebrates, and some lick
the sap from tree trunks or the juice
of sweet soft fruits. In Australia all
geckos are egg-layers, laying a
clutch of two eggs – occasionally one
– in burrows or sheltered crevices.
Some lay annually and others lay all
year round. Some lay soft-shelled
eggs and others hard-shelled, which
is one of the features that scientists
use to distinguish the two groups of
Australian geckos. It is not known
how long geckos live.
Family: Gekkonidae

CHAMELEON GECKO
This unusual-looking lizard has
large, liquid-black, forward-directed
eyes and long limbs. It is rich brown
with a black streak through the eyes
and a pale smudge on the snout.

Original tails are quite rare in
adults, and regrown ones are
mottled in sombre brown and black.
The chameleon gecko cannot change
colour but, like a chameleon, it is
flattened from side to side with a
raised ridge along the spine. Its
total length is about 20 cm.

This gecko lives in the tropical
rainforests of northern Queensland.

Most of its habitat is protected by the World Heritage listing of the Wet Tropics. By day it hides under leaf litter, emerging in the evening to eat insects and spiders. Its tail is fragile and easily discarded. Once severed, it wriggles with an apparent life of its own. This is common among lizards, but the chameleon gecko goes further – the broken tail distracts predators by producing loud squeaking noises, and the gecko makes its escape. The high incidence of breakage (about three-quarters of adults have regrown tails) may be due as much to disputes between geckos themselves as to predators such as snakes and marsupials.
Scientific name: *Carphodactylus laevis*

CLAWLESS GECKO ▫

This is Australia's smallest gecko, with a body length of only 39 mm and a tail, round in cross-section, about as long again. As its common name suggests, it is unique among geckos in having no claws. Its eyes are golden and very small.

This species is patchily distributed in the western half of Australia. In the south-west of its range, where it is found in areas with stony soils, it shelters by day under rock slabs, in leaf litter and sedge tussocks. This form is usually grey-brown with pale spots and darker stripes on the back. The tail is browner than the back. In the desert and tropical parts of its range, the clawless gecko is deeper brown, with a pattern of dark brown stripes on its back.

The clawless gecko is active on the ground at night and probably feeds entirely on small insects and spiders. Females lay two eggs in a clutch between late spring and early summer but, as yet, no one knows where the eggs are laid in the wild.
Scientific name: *Crenadactylus ocellatus*

RING-TAILED GECKO ▣

This is Australia's longest gecko, 23 cm in total length and 13 cm in body length. It is one of the most decorative, boldly marked with broad, sharply contrasting bands of pale fawn and dark purple to brown. On the long, slender, tapering tail are rings of black and white. Minute granular scales, mixed with rows of larger stud-like scales, cover the velvety skin. The head is large

■ CLAWLESS GECKO
The broad, flattened toe tips of the clawless gecko terminate in a pair of very large scales. The last bone in each toe is forked.

and flat, the limbs long and the toes, which have no adhesive pads, are slender, birdlike and well clawed.

Ring-tailed geckos live in Australia, New Guinea and the Solomon Islands. In Australia, they are confined to the rainforests and dry rock outcrops, cliffs and caves of the eastern part of Cape York Peninsula and the Atherton Tableland. Within their range, they are extremely common in some areas. At night the sight of large numbers of these spectacular geckos clinging to rock faces, their eyes glowing orange-red in the spotlight, is an unforgettable experience. Around Cooktown, ring-tails commonly live in buildings, where they pursue insects and smaller geckos.

Surprisingly little is known about the ring-tailed gecko. It lays two brittle-shelled eggs per clutch and is believed to breed in the wet season.
Scientific name: *Cyrtodactylus louisiadensis*

■ RING-TAILED GECKO
This stripy gecko is swift and agile and leaps nimbly between rocks or branches, aided by its clawed feet and slender tail. At other times it holds its tail in an elegant upward curve.

DISTRIBUTION

- BLACK MOUNTAIN GECKO
- HOUSE GECKO
- MARBLED GECKO

- BYNOE'S GECKO

- DTELLAS

- MOURNING GECKO

BLACK MOUNTAIN GECKO ■

Few Australian reptiles have such restricted and specialised distributions as the Black Mountain gecko, which is confined to the boulder-strewn slopes of a small mountain range near Cooktown in far north Queensland. This distinctive habitat is also the only place where the skink *Carlia scirtetis* and the microhylid frog *Cophixalus saxatilis* live.

The Black Mountain gecko is a very slender lizard with a flat head, large protruding eyes and long, thin legs and toes. Its body is grey with broad, irregular, purplish brown bands. Its whip-like tail is strikingly ringed in black and white. It has a total length of 11 cm and is one of Australia's swiftest geckos, darting nimbly over exposed rock faces and leaping easily between boulders. It lays two brittle-shelled eggs, probably depositing them deep in humid cavities under boulders.

Scientific name: *Nactus galgajuga*

HOUSE GECKO

This swift, nimble gecko is a familiar sight in tropical households around the world. Probably introduced into Australia with shipped cargo, it is confined to northern towns and cities, where its ubiquitous 'chuck … chuck … chuck' call can be heard both day and night.

The house gecko grows to 13 cm in length, and is easily identified by the rows of small spines along its tail. In daylight it is grey with dark mottling, but it fades to a pale flesh pink at night.

The microscopic bristles under its toes allow the house gecko to run

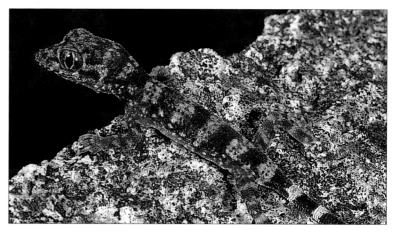

■ BLACK MOUNTAIN GECKO
The dark colours and broken pattern of this gecko perfectly match the mottled textures of the rocks it inhabits.

with ease over walls, ceilings and even windows. The nightly spectacle of geckos gathering around lights to hunt and devour their insect prey and pursue their mates can provide hours of entertainment.

Scientific name: *Hemidactylus frenatus*

MARBLED GECKOS

Marbled geckos are rather soft, velvety lizards with small scales. They are usually patterned with black or dark brown marbling or cross-bars on a paler grey or brown background. The lower surface is generally pale. The females lay two soft-shelled eggs, often in communal nesting sites in tree or rock crevices, but more often in moist soil under or between large rocks.

The southern marbled gecko (*Christinus marmoratus*) is found across much of southern Australia

living under tree bark in forests and woodlands or in rock crevices. It feeds on insects and spiders and averages 13 cm in total length.

Weighing up to six or seven times more than its southern relative, the oceanic marbled gecko (*C. guentheri*) can grow to a total of about 18 cm long. This gecko is found only on Lord Howe and Norfolk islands. It lives under bark or in the hollows of small, shrubby trees and in the crevices of large rock outcrops or boulder slopes. It normally eats insects, but has been seen feeding on nectar from Norfolk Island hibiscuses – it has even been known to tear open paper bags of sugar to feed on the contents!

Introduced rats have virtually wiped out the oceanic marbled gecko on the main islands of Lord Howe and Norfolk, but it is still common on many of the smaller islands of these groups.

Scientific name: *Christinus* spp.

BYNOE'S GECKO ■

This is the most widespread lizard in Australia, and perhaps the most abundant. It grows to about 10 cm long and is extremely variable in colour – usually black or brown to orange with either prominent bands or dark and pale spots arranged in rows or randomly scattered.

Bynoe's gecko is found all over Australia except in the coolest and dampest parts of the south-east and south-west. Since it lacks pads on its toes, it rarely climbs, preferring to live under logs and rocks, in abandoned burrows and beneath rubbish. Stacks of rusty sheets of iron could be home to 20 or 30 Bynoe's geckos. At night they emerge to hunt insects in open areas, streaking for

■ BYNOE'S GECKO
This widespread, common gecko has prickly rows of raised scales that stud its fine, granular skin.

cover if disturbed. This gecko lays two brittle-shelled eggs, which are sometimes laid in communal caches of a hundred or more.

Several all-female populations in central and Western Australia reproduce nonsexually (see box, 'The redundant sex', this page). These populations live alongside those with both sexes, and sometimes overlap with them.
Scientific name: *Heteronotia binoei*

DTELLAS ▦

These small, smooth geckos are widespread throughout South-East Asia and the Pacific. Australia has at least 16 species, and there may be several others yet to be named.

Dtellas (pronounced 'detellas') mainly inhabit deserts, tropical woodlands and rock outcrops. They all have well-developed circular pads on all five toes and a prominent curved claw on four of them.

In many parts of Australia dtellas are common in houses, hiding in cracks and behind wall-hangings during the day and emerging each evening to catch insects attracted to the lights. Often they compete for resources with the introduced house gecko (opposite page). Outside the human environment, dtellas live under the loose bark of standing or fallen trees and in rock crevices. Females lay one or two hard-shelled eggs under rocks or in decomposing mulch in hollow timber. They often deposit egg clutches communally.

The variegated dtella (*Gehyra variegata*), which reaches a total length of 12.5 cm, is the most widespread and abundant dtella species; large numbers are found under sheets of iron and rubbish over vast tracts of western and inland Australia. This gecko is grey to brown, with black wavy lines often mixed with pale spots.

The Top End dtella (*G. australis*) is common in homes in northern Australia. Reaching a total length of 14.5 cm, by day it is grey with faint darker or paler markings, but at night its colour and patterning fade to almost pure white. In some populated areas it has been largely driven out by the house gecko, although it remains successful on surrounding trees and rock outcrops – habitats that are rarely invaded by its introduced competitor.

Australia's largest dtella, the crocodile-faced dtella (*G. xenopus*) is named for its flat head, large eyes and long, upturned snout. This gecko, 18.5 cm long, is brown with bands of circular cream spots. It has been found only in the Kimberley

region of far north-western Australia, living in massive sandstone cliffs, caves and deep crevices.

The smallest species, the dwarf dtella (*G. minuta*) is 9.5 cm long in total. This blunt-faced dtella is reddish brown with alternating bands of black and cream spots. It lives in rock outcrops along the south-western edge of the Barkly Tableland in central Northern Territory. Its range is limited, but within that range it is extremely common.

A rather unusual species, the Pilbara dtella (*G. pilbara*), lives in 'galleries' inside the giant termite mounds that dominate many of the arid landscapes of central and north-western Australia. In this dark, humidity-controlled environment it grows fat on a limitless supply of termites. Mounds occupied by geckos are easily recognised by the liberal quantities of droppings splashed across their surfaces. The Pilbara dtella is about 10 cm long and pinkish brown with faint, irregular dark bands.
Scientific name: *Gehyra* spp.

MOURNING GECKO

The sombre coloration of this gecko – grey with a series of W-shaped dark lines across its back – probably accounts for its common name. Its tail, slightly flattened and edged with a fine, scaly fringe, can be coiled when the gecko is at rest. It reaches 11 cm in total length.

Mourning geckos are widespread from Indonesia to the Pacific islands. In Australia they live on northern Cape York and islands in Torres Strait. They have also been introduced in Cairns and nearby towns, probably among cargo. Excellent climbers, they hide in buildings and among palm fronds and coconut

husks. At night they emerge from their hideouts to hunt small insects.

All Australian mourning geckos are females and reproduce nonsexually (see box below). They lay one or two soft, sticky eggs on vertical surfaces, to which the eggs adhere as they dry and harden.
Scientific name: *Lepidodactylus lugubris*

▦ DTELLA
Like most *Gehyra* species, the variegated dtella is a good climber, although it is equally at home on the ground.

THE REDUNDANT SEX

For most animals, two partners – a male and female – are required to reproduce, with each providing half the complement of chromosomes needed to make a whole offspring. But a few lizards have bypassed this method of reproduction, and for them males are redundant. They lay unfertilised eggs containing the full quota of chromosomes and produce female clones of themselves. This is called parthenogenesis.

This form of reproduction allows species to occupy new habitats. It also benefits castaways washed ashore on remote islands. The islands of the Pacific are home to parthenogenetic populations of pelagic geckos (*Nactus pelagicus*) and mourning geckos (*Lepidodactylus lugubris*, right). One individual – that is, a single egg – can establish a new population. There is no need to find a partner, and new populations grow twice as fast as bisexual ones since all their members reproduce.

The disadvantage of this type of reproduction is that it reduces the opportunity to adapt to changing conditions, so that the natural selection process upon which evolution depends is less effective. Out of more than eight hundred gecko species, six occur as all-female populations. This small number suggests that they may not be around for long. Sexual reproduction seems to offer a better opportunity for long-term survival.

■ BEADED GECKO
By day the beaded gecko
is reddish on top with a
pale, jagged stripe along
the middle of its back
and pale spots along its
sides. By night, when
the gecko is active, the
red colour fades to a
pale pink. Its species
name, *damaeum*, refers
to this coloration, which
resembles that of *Dama
dama*, the fallow deer.

DISTRIBUTION

BEADED GECKO

KNOB-TAILED GECKOS

LEAF-TAILED GECKOS

VELVET GECKOS

BEADED GECKO ■

This ground-dwelling species is common in the dry interior of south-eastern Australia. It lives mostly in sandy mallee and spinifex country. During the day it shelters under objects on the ground and in cracks and holes in the earth, including the burrows of insects and other lizards. It is a small, slender gecko, with a body up to 6 cm long and a tail, round in cross-section, as long again.

The beaded gecko is closely related to the ground geckos (page 314) and is sometimes put in the same genus but, while the flat scales at the tip of ground geckos' toes are rounded and smooth near the base, the undersides of the beaded gecko's toes bear minute spiny scales. These scales may be adaptations to sandy soil.

This gecko probably eats insects and spiders. When fighting, males produce a chirping call. Females lay clutches of two eggs.

Scientific name: *Lucasium damaeum*

KNOB-TAILED GECKOS ■

Knob-tailed geckos are often mistaken for baby lizards because of their plump bodies, long limbs and large heads. Some have fat, heart-shaped tails; others have tails shrunk to almost nothing, but the tails of all species end in a fleshy ball of which the purpose is unknown. They do not have sticky pads on their toes.

Nine species occur in Australia, some in the driest parts of the continent. They shelter in burrows that they excavate in sandy soil, in the abandoned holes of other animals,

■ KNOB-TAILED GECKO
The smooth knob-tailed gecko, *Neph-rurus levis*, inflates its body and arch its back in a typically defensive posture.

or under rocks. They feed on insects, spiders, scorpions and sometimes smaller geckos, stalking their prey until they are close enough to lunge.

When threatened, knob-tails raise their bodies and sway. Waving their tail from side to side, they lunge forward, uttering a loud bark.

The prickly knob-tailed gecko (*Nephrurus asper*) has a large, box-shaped head and rosettes of spines all over its body. It is 13 cm long, its tail – a small blob with a ball on the end – contributing about 1.5 cm to the total length. Over most of its range of central and northern Queensland, this gecko is brown with cream spots, but on Cape York Peninsula it can be vividly banded in light and dark. It favours dry, stony country with open woodlands, and shelters by day under rocks and logs. In some parts of Cape York it inhabits sandy heaths. When foraging at night it often flicks a veneer of dust over itself as camouflage.

The smooth knob-tailed gecko (*N. laevissimus*) has large, dark eyes and smooth, pink skin. It is patterned with two or three black bands across the head, neck and shoulders and a black stripe over each hip. The black tail has white spots. From snout to tail it is about 11 cm long. This gecko lives in the spinifex sand dunes of central and western Australia. It digs burrows under spinifex clumps, where it rests by day, protected from the searing heat. At night it hunts in open spaces on sand that a few hours before would have been hot enough to kill it.

Australia's heaviest gecko is the centralian knob-tailed gecko (*N. amyae*). It weighs 65 grams and its body is 13.5 cm long. Two Queensland leaf-tails – *Saltuarius cornutus* and *S. salebrosus* – have longer bodies (14.5 cm and 14 cm respectively), but at 57 grams neither can match the centralian knob-tail's weight. Found only in the stony hills and ranges of central Australia, this species is common around Alice Springs.

Scientific name: *Nephrurus* spp.

PHYLLURUS LEAF-TAILED GECKOS ▨

The rough texture and broad, flat tails of these geckos camouflage them by virtually eliminating telltale shadows. Five species live in rainforests and rock outcrops from Sydney to mid-eastern Queensland.

Leaf-tails lack the toe pads of many other geckos, but their long, clawed digits give them a grip on rough surfaces. By day they hide in rock crevices, on cave walls and in tree hollows, squeezing their flat heads and bodies into narrow spaces. At night they sit in the open.

Most adults have regenerated tails, probably as a result of disputes with other geckos. When harassed, they arch their backs, wave their tails and utter loud, wheezing barks.

The ringed thin-tailed gecko (*Phyllurus caudiannulatus*) is the only leaf-tail with a cylindrical tail. Its original tail has white rings, but when regenerated it is plain brown streaked with black. This gecko is 9.5 cm in body length and 14.5 cm in total length. It is confined to the Bulburin State Forest on the Dawes and Many Peaks ranges of mid-eastern Queensland. In this small area it is common and lives on tree trunks. It is also found under loose bark and old sheets of iron. Hatchlings have been found under logs.

The broad-tailed gecko (*P. platurus*) is a rough-skinned gecko and is coloured and patterned like the sandstone where it lives – the central coast and ranges of New South Wales. It is larger than most geckos in this area, growing to 17 cm long. It occupies crevices and wind-blown caves, and the sheltered brickwork of houses. An ideal site is usually festooned with its droppings and shed skins. Females often lay their two eggs a year communally.
Scientific name: *Phyllurus* spp.

VELVET GECKOS ▨

Rarely more than 17 cm long, these geckos are covered with tiny scales that give the skin a velvety texture. Their tails store fat for times when food is scarce. The tail is about the same length as the head and body.

Most velvet geckos prefer rocky habitats. They dart among crevices at night hunting for insects and spiders. Large species also take smaller geckos, including their own kind. The flattened body of the velvet gecko enables it to retreat into narrow gaps when hungry predators such as snakes or owls appear. Some species live around houses; others

▨ LEAF-TAILED GECKO
The mottled pattern of its skin renders this *Phyllurus* gecko virtually invisible against the tree trunks where it rests.

prefer large trees, hiding during the day in hollows or beneath bark.

Male velvet geckos are territorial, defending their chosen site with surprising aggression. Elaborate backarching and tail-waving warn off trespassing males. A male may mate with several females in the spring.

Some subtropical species lay eggs several times over summer, but those in the far north may breed year round. The 13 velvet gecko species occur throughout Australia except in the far south-east.

The marbled velvet gecko (*Oedura marmorata*) is the most widespread velvet gecko species, inhabiting rocky and woodland areas over most of Australia except the far south and east. It reaches 18 cm long.

The fringe-toed velvet gecko (*O. filicipoda*) is particularly well adapted to life in the sandstone cliffs and caves of the Kimberley region of Western Australia. Fringes of skin on its toes grip rock faces, and it also uses its tail to grip. This is the largest of the velvet geckos, sometimes growing to more than 18 cm long. Its brown body is flecked with yellow, and its tail is banded with black and white and spotted with yellow.

The northern spotted velvet gecko (*O. coggeri*) is irregularly marked with dark-centred light spots on a greenish-brown background. In some lizards these spots join to form broad bands. A common species on the eastern Cape York Peninsula, it reaches 11 cm in length. Like all Australian geckos, females produce two eggs at a time, which they deposit in humid crevices or under logs or rocks. The eggs hatch after two to three months.

The reticulated velvet gecko (*O. reticulata*) is the only velvet gecko found in south-western Australia. It lives on smooth-barked eucalypt trees. This small, grey-brown gecko rarely grows larger than 13 cm long. Its life expectancy is about 15 years. Males are ready to breed when they are three years old; females take a further year.
Scientific name: *Oedura* spp.

COPING
WITHOUT EYELIDS
Some geckos have no movable eyelids, so they use their tongues to lick their eyes clean and free from dust. This behaviour is unique to geckos and snake lizards.

▨ VELVET GECKO
Adult marbled velvet geckos are a faded version of their youth. The juveniles are strikingly coloured with contrasting bands of black or dark purple along its body length, alternating with cream or yellow.

CLIMBING UPSIDE DOWN WITH SAFETY

Some geckos need a strong grip for their potentially dangerous climbs along smooth vertical and overhead surfaces, such as tree trunks and cave roofs. They owe their sure-footedness to enlarged, modified scales under each of their toes. Arranged in two broad rows, these scales are surfaced with hundreds of microscopic hooks, which form adhesive pads like velcro. Dtellas such as *Gehyra robusta*, below, are remarkable climbers, but the pad-tail gecko, which has matching adhesive pads on its tail, is the supreme acrobat.

■ BEAKED GECKO
With its beak-like snout and attractive pale-spotted back, the beaked gecko is easy to spot in its desert habitat.

PAD-TAIL GECKOS ■

Pad-tail geckos are relatively large and powerful. They have big heads with protruding eyes, moderately slim bodies and long limbs. They have a body length of about 12 cm and a tail that is about as long again. Adhesive pads under expanded toes and a slender, grasping tail allow them to climb despite their size. They live in remote parts of northern Australia, in trees or on rocks. They are active nocturnal hunters, preying on invertebrates and small vertebrates, including smaller geckos. Usually only two species are recognised, although one of these has two forms, which some experts consider to be separate species.

The Cape York pad-tail gecko (*Pseudothecadactylus australis*) is a Queensland species found in northern and north-eastern Cape York Peninsula and in the islands of Torres Strait. It grows to a body length of about 12 cm and is light brown, patterned with dark-edged pale splashes and dark, irregular lines. It is a tree-dweller, sheltering in hollow trunks and limbs during the day and emerging at night to forage among branches.

The giant cave gecko (*P. lindneri*) occurs among the ravines and valleys of the rugged sandstone escarpment of western Arnhem Land in the Northern Territory. It has a body length of 10 cm

and is pale to purplish brown, with irregular pale bands and splashes. Its original tail bears distinct dark brown and pale yellow rings. A rock-dweller, it is particularly active on humid evenings during the monsoonal wet season, when it hunts in caves and on rocks. Occasionally it is found on boulders and trees adjoining the escarpment. During the day it shelters in rock crevices and caves.

The Kimberley pad-tail gecko (*P. cavaticus*) is similar to the giant cave gecko in size, appearance and habits and is usually regarded as a subspecies. Found in the northern ranges of the Kimberley region of Western Australia, it differs from the giant cave gecko only in its more distinct body pattern and its scales.
Scientific name: *Pseudothecadactylus* spp.

BEAKED GECKO ■

The beaked gecko is common and widely distributed in the semi-arid and arid regions of Australia. This sole representative of the genus is small, slender and long-bodied. It

has a moderately long tail, shortish limbs and simple, clawed toes. It has large, protruding eyes and is distinguished by its short snout. Growing to a total length of about 9.5 cm, the beaked gecko is red to reddish brown with dark, irregular lines and pale splashes on its back.

It occasionally preys on small spiders and insects, but its main diet is termites. Being a ground-dweller, it probably buries its eggs, but this has yet to be confirmed.

These geckos are particularly common on sandy soil in spinifex grasslands. They normally shelter in small burrows but sometimes make use of shallow depressions under rocks or other ground litter. They show a marked preference for disused spider burrows, emerging from these at sunset and seldom straying far from the burrow entrance, even when foraging for food. They are active hunters and search for termites in the open spaces between clumps of vegetation. It is not unusual to find them in the company of other gecko species – some of which, such as the knob-tailed geckos, prey on beaked geckos.
Scientific name: *Rhynchoedura ornata*

DISTRIBUTION

■ PAD-TAIL GECKOS

■ BEAKED GECKO
■ LEAF-TAILED GECKOS

■ THICK-TAILED GECKO

■ PAD-TAIL GECKO
The vocal Cape York pad-tail gecko often calls during the day if something disturbs it.

SALTUARIUS LEAF-TAILED GECKOS ◼

This group's common name, which it shares with the genus *Phyllurus* (page 311), comes from its broad, flattened, often leaf-shaped tail. This tail breaks up the outline of the body and confuses predators hunting for the more typical lizard shape. The tail can be discarded if the gecko is threatened, although – unlike the tail of most other lizards – it breaks off only at the base. The body, head and original tail are elaborately decorated with numerous small, blunt spines, called tubercules. These are never present on the regrown tail, which is smooth and soft and conspicuously different from the body in both colour and pattern.

Leaf-tailed geckos spend daylight hours hidden inside humid tree hollows or deep rock crevices. They become active at dusk, when they move with a slow, deliberate crawl to a favoured vantage point. They remain motionless for hours, waiting to catch a passing insect or spider with a lunge of the head, either forward or to the side. By the early hours of the morning, most have returned to their retreats.

In late spring females lay one or two soft-shelled eggs, up to 28 mm in length, and bury them in moist soil or leaf litter so that they do not dry out. Left to develop unattended, minute replicas of the adults hatch after three months' incubation and disperse to fend for themselves, catching their own prey within a few days of hatching.

Leaf-tailed geckos occur only in the rainforests and major rock formations of the east coast of Australia, from Cape York southward to central New South Wales.

The northern leaf-tailed gecko (*Saltuarius cornutus*) is reputed to be Australia's largest gecko, reaching up to 30 cm in total length with hatchlings measuring about 7.5 cm long. It inhabits areas of tropical rainforest in north-eastern Queensland, but despite its size it is rarely seen because of its camouflage pattern and nocturnal habits.

There are two species of southern leaf-tailed geckos. One, *S. swaini*, inhabits the spectacular granite belt of northern New South Wales and southern Queensland, emerging at night from deep within giant boulders to forage on open rock faces. These geckos often live at high altitudes where temperatures can drop to – 9°C. At such temperatures the geckos remain dormant in their rock shelters, but they are clearly

well adapted to the cold because they have been observed active at temperatures as low as 10.5°C. The other, *S. wyberba*, occurs in the rainforests of south-eastern Queensland and north-eastern New South Wales, particularly on buttressed trunks of large rainforest trees or in the roots and hollows of mature strangler figs.

The rough-throated leaf-tailed gecko (*S. salebrosus*) is so called because even its throat has tubercules on it – this helps to distinguish it from other leaf-tailed geckos. It mainly inhabits rocks, particularly the large sandstone outcrops and tablelands of central Queensland. In some areas large numbers can be found at night regularly spaced 1–2 metres above the ground along vertical rock faces, all with their heads pointing downwards as they wait to pounce on unwary insects.
Scientific name: *Saltuarius* spp.

THICK-TAILED GECKO ◼

The more common of the two species in its genus, the thick-tailed gecko, or barking gecko, is common in southern Australia. It lives mostly in dry woodlands in rocky areas, particularly limestone and granite – though it is also found in the interior on red sand plains with spinifex and mallee. It also occurs on many islands along the southern and western coasts. By day it shelters under rocks and logs and in the burrows of mammals and other lizards. At night it hunts for insects and spiders and even other smaller lizards.

It has a body length of up to 10.5 cm, a big head with large eyes, and long limbs with slender toes ending in small claws. Its tail, which

is carrot-shaped, is very narrow where it joins the body. Further along it swells out before tapering to a narrow point. This gecko is very closely related to the knob-tailed geckos (*Nephrurus* spp.; page 310) but has no knob at the tip of its tail.

When disturbed the thick-tailed gecko raises its body and sways its raised tail from side to side. If further harassed, it barks and may lunge forward to bite. During winter several individuals sometimes share the shelter of a rock crevice.
Scientific name: *Underwoodisaurus milii*

◼ THICK-TAILED GECKO
The tapering tail of the thick-tailed gecko is about two-thirds the length of its body.

◼ LEAF-TAILED GECKO
A *Saltuarius* leaf-tailed gecko blends in perfectly with the weathered rock faces of its habitat.

DISTRIBUTION

GROUND GECKOS

SPINY-TAILED AND
STRIPED GECKOS

THEREBY HANGS A TAIL
The tails of *Diplodactylus*
geckos vary widely from
species to species. Some,
like the ground gecko
D. pulcher, have slender
tapering tails; others,
such as the burrow-
plug, *D. conspicillatus*,
have swollen tails.
Striped geckos have
stripes on their tails as
well as their bodies, and
spiny-tailed geckos are
distinguished by two or
more rows of spines on
their tails.

slender tail

swollen tail

striped tail

spiny tail

GROUND GECKOS ■

Unique to Australia, the genus
Diplodactylus contains two groups of
species that differ in appearance and
habits. In one group are the ground
geckos and in the other, the spiny-
tailed and striped geckos, sometimes
put in a distinct genus, *Strophurus.*

Ground geckos live exclusively on
the ground and during the day shelter under solid objects, in earth
cracks and burrows. With body
lengths up to about 6.5 cm, ground
geckos are relatively small. The tail,
which is shorter than the body, is
either round in cross-section and
evenly tapered, or swollen and
turnip-shaped. The pattern on the
back is usually pink to brown,
although some ground geckos are
grey. The belly is usually pure white.

Ground geckos are found in most
parts of mainland Australia, apart
from the extreme south-east. There
are about 20 species, the majority
found in the arid parts of Western
Australia. One widespread and common species in arid Australia is the
pale-snouted ground gecko (*D. sten-
odactylus*). This is one of the species
with a slender tail. It is active at
night in a range of habitats, including sand dunes and sand plains, at
the base of rocky hills and between
mulga and spinifex clumps.

Another of the slender-tailed
species is the pretty or fine-faced
ground gecko (*D. pulcher*) of south-
western Australia. This species lives
on harder soils and in woodland or
mulga scrub. It has a more pointed
snout than most ground geckos.

Several species are found along the
west coast of Western Australia. The
most widespread, the ornate stone
gecko (*D. ornatus*), inhabits coastal
dunes and sand plains and is found
from Jurien north to Exmouth.

The most widespread and abundant of the swollen-tailed ground
geckos is the fat-tailed or burrow-
plug gecko (*D. conspicillatus*). This
small-eyed species has a broad tail
about half the length of its body. It
shelters by day in spider burrows,
entering headfirst and plugging the
entrance with its tail to block predators. Like many ground geckos, it
feeds mostly on termites.
Scientific name: *Diplodactylus* spp.

SPINY-TAILED AND STRIPED GECKOS ■

The second group of geckos in the
genus *Diplodactylus* are the spiny-
tailed and striped geckos, of which
there are about 16 Australian species.

They share a unique feature –
their tail contains glands

that secrete a sticky substance it can
squirt up to 30 cm. When the gecko
is distressed, it wipes or squirts this
gum over a potential predator. The
gum is not toxic, but it may be irritating to the eyes and is foul-tasting.

This group, especially the striped
geckos, are usually longer and more
slender than ground geckos. The
largest species – the northern spiny-
tailed gecko (*D. ciliaris*) – can reach
9 cm in body length. Both can climb
– striped geckos in spinifex clumps
and sedges, spiny-tailed geckos in
bushes and trees. Many have either
a dark blue or orange mouth, and
usually a grey or patterned belly.

These geckos are usually greyish
and have two or more rows of soft
spines or low tubercles along the
tail, and sometimes on the back and
over the eyes. The apparent function

■ SPINY-TAILED GECKO
The flamboyant golden-tailed gecko,
D. taenicauda, has a vivid golden stripe
along its tail but lacks tail spines.

■ GROUND GECKO
Most ground geckos are distinguished
by a pale marking, such as a zigzag
stripe, along the centre of their back.

of these harmless spines is to break
up the outline of the gecko so that
it is quite difficult to see when it
is perching. The most vivid of the
spiny-tailed geckos is the golden-
tailed gecko (*D. taenicauda*) found
in the brigalow country of south-
eastern Queensland.

Five species of striped geckos
are found in the spinifex deserts
of northern Australia. One of these,
the robust striped gecko (*D. michael-
seni*), ranges further south to around
Shark Bay in Western Australia.

The jewelled gecko (*D. elderi*)
has features of both groups. It is
similar in body shape and size to the
ground geckos but, like the striped
geckos, it lives in spinifex clumps.
It also protects itself by squirting a
sticky substance from its tail.
Scientific name: *Diplodactylus* spp.

SNAKE LIZARDS

These lizards look very much like snakes, having no front legs at all and hind legs reduced to small flaps that are usually held flat on either side of the body and are hardly noticeable. Snake lizards are related not to snakes but to geckos.

Snake lizards can be distinguished from snakes by their long tails that can be voluntarily broken off – like those of most geckos and skinks – and by their flat, fleshy tongues, which they often use to lick the clear scale covering their eyes, as geckos do. The scales on their belly are in two rows, whereas snakes have a single broad row. Most snake lizards have an ear-opening, which snakes lack, and they share with geckos an ability to emit a squeaking noise.

Snake lizards are also called pygopods or flap-footed lizards. They are long and slender with large overlapping scales on their bodies. They are a small group of about 35 species found only in Australia and New Guinea. They inhabit most of mainland Australia except for the coldest parts of the south-east, and at least one species is found in every capital city. The largest species have body lengths of up to 31 cm, but because of their long tails they can be more than 75 cm in total length. However, most species are much smaller. The females grow larger than the males.

Some snake lizards are active by day, others by night. While several species have specific diets, most feed on a variety of small insects and spiders. Female snake lizards lay two soft-shelled eggs in a clutch in spring or early summer.

Because they look like snakes, many snake lizards are killed by mistake, but these lizards are not venomous or harmful in any way – most will not even attempt to bite.
Family: Pygopodidae

JAVELIN LEGLESS LIZARD ▨

When disturbed, this very alert, fast-moving reptile leaps and flicks itself through the air with such amazing speed that a spectator may doubt it was there at all. The javelin legless lizard is smooth-scaled, slender and very long-tailed, reaching a maximum of about 54 cm in total length. It has a long, pointed snout, prominent eyes, visible ear-openings and large hindlimb flaps. Its lips are white, contrasting markedly with

▨ JAVELIN LEGLESS LIZARD
Found on beaches and on trees growing in sandy soil, the sleek legless lizard, *Aclys concinna,* has a distinctive broad, dark stripe running along the centre of its back.

its greyish brown body and tail. It has pale flanks and its belly scales are whitish grey, each one with a dark spot at its centre.

The javelin legless lizard is active in the daytime and is found along a narrow coastal strip of Western Australia. Two geographically separated populations are recognised. The southern individuals grow to less than 50 cm long and can be found from Perth northward almost to Geraldton. The northern population occurs in the Shark Bay region and individuals are larger.

This lizard inhabits the dense vegetation of coastal dunes and banksia or eucalypt woodlands growing in sandy soil. It hunts and basks on the ground and in shrubs and tussocks. Spiders are its preferred food, but it also eats vegetable matter.

Scientists did not know about the javelin lizard until l962, when one was found in a backyard in the Perth suburb of Sorrento. Although it has been seen often since then, little is known about it except that the female lays two eggs in January.
Scientific name: *Aclys concinna*

WORM LIZARDS

There are ten species of worm lizards. All are very small and

slender with large, regularly arranged scales on the head. Compared with other snake lizards, they have a relatively long body – up to 14 cm – and a short tail that is only about two-thirds to three-quarters as long as the body.

Worm lizards feed exclusively on ants and are commonly found inside ant nests and ant tunnels under rocks. As their common name suggests, they spend most of their life underground, although they do move along the surface between ant nests. They are found in southern Australia from the southern table-lands of New South Wales to the south-west coast of Western Australia, but most species are found only in Western Australia. Usually dull in colour, many have a pink tail, and one – the striped worm lizard (*Aprasia striolata*) – has a pattern of well-developed dark stripes on a pale background in the eastern part of its distribution, which includes the Adelaide region.

Several worm lizard species are found only in very small areas. One such species, the pink-tailed or granite worm lizard (*Aprasia parapulchella*), is found in a small area of New South Wales, from Canberra to Bathurst and West Wyalong, and it appears to prefer native grasslands with granite outcrops. Although much of this area is now agricultural land, the pink-tailed worm lizard remains locally common, especially in the Australian Capital Territory.
Scientific name: *Aprasia* spp.

▨ JAVELIN LEGLESS LIZARD

▨ WORM LIZARDS

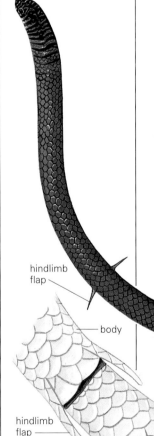

hindlimb flap

body

hindlimb flap

tail

BODY MEETS TAIL
The hindlimbs of a snake lizard are reduced to tiny flaps on either side of the body. Just below the flaps, the tail can be voluntarily broken off.

■ BRIGALOW SCALYFOOT
Usually found in woodland debris, the sleek Brigalow scalyfoot, *Paradelma orientalis*, has been known to climb rough-scaled wattle trees to lick their sap.

■ BURTON'S
SNAKE LIZARD
Often mistaken for a snake, Burton's legless lizard waits motionless on the upper branches of a plant, presumably for unwary geckos.

BRIGALOW SCALYFOOT ■

This snake lizard can be readily identified by its coloration, highly polished milky sheen and relatively large hindlimb flaps. Its 16 cm-long body is grey with a black band across the neck, contrasting with the cream to pale yellowish brown on top of its head. It reaches 40 cm in total length.

By day the brigalow scalyfoot hides under rocks, logs, sheets of fallen bark and in dense grass tussocks, emerging at night to feed. Scientists are unsure of its precise diet, but it probably eats insects – although it may also be partial to soft-bodied spiders.

When provoked, the brigalow scalyfoot raises its head and forebody and flicks its tongue. This behaviour closely resembles that of an alarmed venomous snake – surely an effective way of deterring small predators. However, the ear-openings, hindlimb flaps and thick, fleshy tongue display the hallmarks of a harmless lizard.

The brigalow scalyfoot is found in the mid-east and south-eastern interior of Queensland, mainly in dry forest dominated by eucalypts and wattles, including brigalow. This fertile land is ideal for crops and grazing, and vast tracts have been cleared. Because of this loss of habitat, the brigalow scalyfoot is now officially listed as vulnerable. Fortunately, it remains common and protected in several of the large national parks.
Scientific name: *Paradelma orientalis*

BURTON'S SNAKE LIZARD ■

A striking feature of this lizard is its long, wedge-shaped head, which is unique among Australian reptiles. Its basic colour varies from grey, cream, yellow and red to deep brown. Some have no patterning; others have stripes and spots.

It is a robust species, with prominent ear-openings and small hindlimb flaps. It is one of the largest snake lizards, growing to 75 cm in total length. Its tail is at least as long as its body and breaks off easily.

Burton's snake lizard, unlike other snake lizards, feeds exclusively on other reptiles – geckos, small snakes, and particularly skinks. It lies in wait under cover and wriggles its tail to attract passers by. The inquisitive prey inspects the wriggling tail more closely, and once the prey is within range the snake lizard strikes with lightning speed. The jewelled gecko (page 314), which lives alongside Burton's snake lizard in spinifex clumps without becoming its dinner, protects itself by exuding a sticky substance from the spines of its tail.

Although active by day, Burton's snake lizard is most likely to be seen moving about in the early evening. In more arid regions it is active at night. Widely distributed in mainland Australia, it is found in most habitats except rainforests, high-altitude regions and extremely arid areas. It often lays its eggs communally, and up to 20 eggs have been found in a single location.
Scientific name: *Lialis burtonis*

DELMAS

There are 16 delma species, and they are found over most of mainland Australia, apart from the extreme south-east. They generally live in woodlands, heathlands and deserts, although several species – such as the long-snouted delma (*Delma nasuta*) of northern Australia – are commonly found inside tussocks of spinifex in desert regions. Still other species shelter in leaf litter or grass tussocks in paddocks. Delmas feed on insects and lay two eggs in spring or early summer.

Delmas have a short body and very long tail. The largest species reach a body length of 15 cm, but the tail can be up to four times as long as the body. When disturbed, delmas use their tail to spring off the ground in an attempt to escape. This defensive behaviour has given rise to stories of 'spinifex snakes' that attack from spinifex clumps; however, all delmas are harmless. Like other snake lizards, if handled they twist their body and tail violently to free themselves, and they readily break off almost their entire tail to distract a predator.

Two delma species are threatened by development around large cities. The striped delma (*D. impar*) is found only in native grasslands on volcanic soils in south-eastern Australia, including the Melbourne and Canberra areas. This snake lizard is now very rare because of changes to grasslands caused by grazing, fire and suburban development. The collared delma (*D. torquata*) is a small species found only in a few small patches of woodland on rocky slopes around Brisbane.
Scientific name: *Delma* spp.

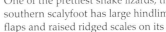

BRONZEBACK

A bronzeback specimen was collected in 1897 at Charlotte Waters Telegraph Station in the Northern Territory but the species was lost to scientists until 1978, when two herpetologists found ten in a few hours at Abminga, near the southern border of the Northern Territory. Since then it has been reported in three more locations.

The bronze-coloured back of this lizard is very striking, and it has a rather narrow, pointed snout and a blunt tail. It reaches a total length of up to 26 cm, of which the tail constitutes up to 60 per cent. It lives in the litter beneath gidgee and mulga trees along the temporary watercourses of northern South Australia and adjacent areas of the Northern Territory. Beneath this litter is a loose, loamy soil and beneath that a deep, cracking clay, into which the bronzeback escapes when it is threatened. The bronzeback 'swims' through the soil and leaf litter, feeding on insects such as cockroaches and moth larvae, and on small spiders. Little is known about its

■ KEELED LEGLESS LIZARD
Slithering and sliding along the ground and below it, the keeled legless lizard forages on sand plains.

reproductive behaviour, but it is assumed that, like other snake lizards, it is an egg-layer.
Scientific name: *Ophidiocephalus taeniatus*

SOUTHERN OR COMMON SCALYFOOT ■

The colour of this attractive snake lizard is extremely variable, ranging from pale grey with three rows of prominent, white-edged black blotches, to reddish brown with little or no patterning. Its body length is 23 cm, and it can be as much as a metre long if its tail is intact.

The southern or common scalyfoot puts on an impressive display when provoked, raising its head, flickering its tongue and mock-striking like a small venomous snake. If grasped, it struggles violently and rotates its body rapidly. Its tail breaks off very easily, so scalyfoots with complete original tails are uncommon.

Southern scalyfoots can often be seen by day crossing tracks or basking on top of dense, low vegetation. In hot weather they are active at night. When fleeing among low plants, they look sinuous and snake-like, but on bare, open ground they move with a rapid series of leaps. Spiders are the main ingredient of their diet, although they also like to

■ SOUTHERN SCALYFOOT
One of the prettiest snake lizards, the southern scalyfoot has large hindlimb flaps and raised ridged scales on its back and sides, giving it a rough feel.

eat insects and small soft fruits. Southern scalyfoots are mostly found across southern Australia, but isolated populations occur as far north as Cape York. The most vividly patterned scalyfoots live mainly in the western heathlands of Western Australia, while plain-coloured ones are often associated with mallee country and eucalypt forests with a thick ground cover of tussocks. Females often lay communally, and up to 76 eggs have been found at a single site.
Scientific name: *Pygopus lepidopodus*

KEELED LEGLESS LIZARD ■

The keeled legless lizard, sometimes called the slender slider, differs from all other snake lizards in having two raised ridges, called keels, on each scale. It is very slender and long-tailed and reaches a maximum of about 40 cm in total length. It has a pointed snout, tiny ear-openings and small hindlimb flaps.

The lips and throat of this elegant lizard are yellow, contrasting with its generally greyish brown body. The sides of its head are dark grey to almost black. A broad, pale stripe extends along its back, and there are many more faint, narrow lines along its length. The scales on its belly are whitish, mottled in places with greyish brown.

The keeled legless lizard occurs along the coast of Western Australia. Until recently it was believed that there were two distinct populations of these lizards – one stretching southward from Eneabba to Mandurah and the other northward from Kalbarri to Shark Bay – but the species has now been found to be common near Geraldton, suggesting that its distribution is unbroken from Mandurah to Shark Bay.

The keeled legless lizard inhabits sandy plains where banksias or spinifex grow. Its camouflage protects it from predators, including cats and foxes, so large numbers persist in small pockets of suburban bush. It feeds on the body juices of spiders and soft larval insects, as well as the nectar from flowers.

The keeled legless lizard mates in spring and deposits two eggs about six weeks later, probably in soil beneath leaf litter, logs or rock.
Scientific name: *Pletholax gracilis*

DISTRIBUTION

■ BRIGALOW SCALYFOOT

■ BURTON'S SNAKE LIZARD

■ DELMAS

■ BRONZEBACK
■ SOUTHERN OR COMMON SCALYFOOT

■ KEELED LEGLESS LIZARD

DRAGON LIZARDS

There is an Asian genus of lizards called *Draco* that glides using skin folds extending from the sides of its body. These folds are like the wings of mythological dragons, and have earned the entire family the name dragon. Some members, with their projecting tubercles and spines and long tails, are even more evocative of miniature mythological dragons.

Dragon lizards have a unique arrangement of teeth, illustrated below left. The only other animal in which this arrangement exists is the New Zealand tuatara, which is not a lizard but its nearest living relative – a survivor from a group that was common a hundred million years ago. The similar dentition of dragons and this relic from long ago suggests that dragons are the most primitive of the surviving lizards.

Dragon lizards have obvious ear-openings and a short, fleshy tongue that is commonly used in capturing prey. Their scales have a microscopic honeycomb structure that gives them a rough texture. They all have eyelids, large eyes and acute eyesight. Their tails are not designed to break off at specific fracture points, unlike those of geckos and skinks, but some of the more slender dragons have a very long, thin tail that is easily damaged, so it is rare to find an adult with a complete tail. The tails regrow to replace some – but not all – of their lost length.

All Australian dragons lay soft-shelled eggs – from two in small species to as many as 35 in bearded dragons. They usually lay their eggs

JAWS
What distinguishes dragon lizards from all other Australian lizards is their teeth. The cheek teeth, which are shaped like flattened triangles, are permanent, while at the front of each jaw are several longer, conical teeth that regularly regrow. These front teeth grasp the lizard's prey in much the same way as the canine teeth of dogs.

■ JACKY LIZARD
Fond of foraging on the ground, the jacky lizard is semi-arboreal and is often seen perching on banksia cones.

in shallow burrows in soil, although forest dragons lay theirs in leaf litter.

Most Australian dragons live in dry areas and are active during the day. The greatest number of species in one area occurs in the south of central Western Australia, where a variety of soil types and vegetations provide many different environments. Many species are also found in the seasonally dry north, but only water dragons and two species of forest dragon are found in wet environments. Most are ground-dwellers, though some live in trees.

Almost all dragons are capable of scampering quickly to cover. Most of them rely on camouflage to avoid predators. If they are detected, they may confront their attacker with a display of mock aggression.
Family: Agamidae

JACKY LIZARD ■
The jacky lizard was the first dragon lizard to be described from Australia. It is common along the coast and ranges of south-eastern Australia, and is found even in

suburban nature reserves of Sydney and Melbourne. While bushwalking in these areas, it is not unusual to come across the relatively large, grey shape of a jacky lizard disappearing quickly and noisily into the undergrowth. It spends much of its time on the ground in open forests and heathlands.

Jacky lizards grow to a body length of 11 cm and an overall length of about 30 cm, including their long, tapering tails. They are well camouflaged by a light and dark greyish colour pattern, their uneven scales breaking up their outline and reducing reflected light that might signal their position. To avoid detection this lizard stays stock-still, quietly resuming its activity when the danger is over. If caught by a predator, the jacky lizard opens its mouth wide to reveal a bright yellow lining. Often the predator is so startled that it lets the lizard go.

Like most dragons, jacky lizards are ambush predators, remaining still for most of the time until they dash forward – up to one or two body lengths – to seize their prey, mainly grasshoppers and ants.

Males display from elevated positions in spring, when they turn dark grey to black, and their throat and chest become shiny black. They drop from their perches to capture food or to mate with passing females. In November females lay five or six eggs, which hatch in late February.
Scientific name: *Amphibolurus muricatus*

GRAVEL DRAGON
This small, robust lizard is the sole member of its genus. Only four specimens are known to science, three from south of Halls Creek in north-eastern Western Australia, and one from near Wave Hill Station in the Northern Territory.

Gravel dragons are ground-dwellers and live in arid, rocky areas, where they usually shelter under spinifex hummocks. They reach a total length of about 9.5 cm, and have thickset bodies, relatively short limbs and a tail markedly shorter than their body. They are dull reddish in colour and have an irregular pattern of small, raised knobs on their back. An identification feature unique to the gravel dragon is a spiky fringe of pointed scales on its upper lip.
Scientific name: *Cryptagama aurita*

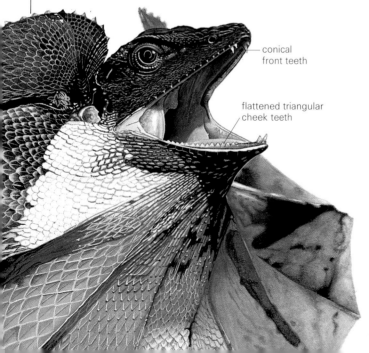

conical front teeth

flattened triangular cheek teeth

FRILLED LIZARD

Renowned for the spectacular frill that encircles its neck, the frilled lizard is a large, powerful dragon. The frill is normally folded neatly over its neck and shoulders, but when the dragon is alarmed it erects the frill, supporting it with a U-shaped combination of bone and cartilage in its throat. Juveniles have poorly developed frills, but in large males the frill may reach the size of a dinner plate.

Adults are generally brown with a pattern of dark irregular lines and blotches. The lower half of the frill is often strikingly coloured with red, orange, yellow or white. Juveniles are protected by a camouflage pattern of mottled grey and black.

Frilled lizards are very vigilant and have excellent eyesight. They are quick to see an observer and quietly sidle to the opposite side of a tree trunk. Male frilled lizards, which grow larger than the females, sometimes reach a total length of a metre, about two-thirds of which is tail.

Although they are tree-dwellers frilled lizards often descend to the ground to search for insects, other invertebrates and, occasionally, small vertebrates. They often move about on two legs, especially if they are surprised on the ground, when they usually race on their hind legs to the nearest tree; sometimes, however, they stand their ground and,

■ CHAMELEON DRAGON
When confronted, this dragon turns side-on and lowers its dewlap – a loose fold of skin under its throat – to create the illusion of a larger head.

with gaping mouth and erect frill, jump at their potential predator.

Common in the monsoonal woodlands of northern Australia and southern New Guinea, frilled lizards range as far south as south-eastern Queensland, although they are not common in the southerly part of their distribution. They are most

active during the wet season, when they spend less time in the tree tops and more on the ground. During this season, pregnant females excavate a burrow 15–20 cm deep in a sunny patch of soft soil and deposit 4–23 eggs. The eggs take about ten weeks to incubate.
Scientific name: *Chlamydosaurus kingii*

CHAMELEON DRAGON

The chameleon dragon is flattened from side to side, with a high ridge down the spine and a small eye aperture surrounded by granular scales. It is reddish brown to putty coloured and patterned with dark mottling or lines radiating from the eyes. Its tail is broadly banded and stops abruptly, without a fine point. Its body is 12 cm long and it is about 36 cm in total length.

This retiring, slow-moving lizard inhabits tropical woodlands in the north-west, from the Kimberley region of Western Australia to far north-western Queensland. It lives mainly in trees but is rarely seen in them, as it slides from view when approached. The female is occasionally encountered between June and September, during the dry season, when she descends to the ground looking for a place to bury her eggs. Females lay clutches of two to nine eggs, which they deposit in shallow burrows.
Scientific name: *Chelosania brunnea*

DISTRIBUTION

▫ JACKY LIZARD
■ GRAVEL DRAGON

▫ FRILLED LIZARD

▫ CHAMELEON DRAGON

■ FRILLED LIZARD
Although the frilled lizard lifts its spectacular frill (left) to intimidate predators, recent research has shown that the frill is also used during the breeding season when territorial mature males put on a display to warn off other males. The frill lies in folds to the shoulders when the lizard is at rest (above).

CTENOPHORUS DRAGONS ■

Dragons in this large genus – pronounced 'tenoforus' – are well adapted to arid conditions. Most are small, with tapering tails at least twice as long as their body. The males of most species have black markings on the throat and belly, which they use to threaten other males and to identify themselves to females. Hawks are one of their main predators, so camouflage from above is important and their backs usually match the ground colours.

These lizards, like many others, signal each other with head bobs, raising the front of their body, jerking their head up and down and flashing their underside.

Because the environments they inhabit vary, different ctenophorus dragons have different characteristics. Some are burrowers, some live in rock crevices and others are fast runners on the ground.

The burrowers are stout, with blunt snouts and short limbs. On their lower eyelid is a series of cone-shaped scales that help to keep sand and dust out of their eyes. They use their burrows as retreats from predators, for hibernation, and to conserve

■ CTENOPHORUS DRAGON
The spectacularly coloured red-barred dragon, *Ctenophorus vadnappa*, has a blue throat and red bands across its sides. When defending their territory, males raise a crest on their back, lower their throat skin and perform vigorous press-ups.

water – there is more moisture below ground than above. Burrows also provide shelter from the heat of the day; this is especially important for the Lake Eyre dragon (*C. maculosus*), which lives on the salt flats of dry lake beds where the surface temperature often rises well above 50°C. This dragon burrows beneath the salt crust to the cooler sand below.

Another burrower, the central netted dragon (*C. nuchalis*), has a light brown body (12 cm long) with a darker pattern. It is widespread across arid Australia and is adapted for exploiting disturbed habitats. In the female's first year she may produce several clutches of eggs. This ability to quickly produce young allows the species to spread into new habitats. These dragons move along dirt roads in the outback, burrowing into dirt thrown up by machinery. In much of central Australia they can be seen guarding their burrows along the roadside.

Extreme desert heat, followed by sudden thunderstorms, causes rocks to crack and peel, creating crevices where a group of flattened lizards retreat. The most flattened of this group is the ornate dragon (*C. ornatus*) from Western Australia, which is about 8 cm long in body, with black and white or pale yellow markings and a banded tail. Several other species live in boulder cracks in the Flinders Ranges and the Eyre Peninsula of South Australia. The red-barred dragon (*C. vadnappa*) occurs in the northern part of the Flinders Ranges.

Most dragons are capable of bursts of speed but the ground-dwelling crested dragon (*C. cristatus*) has endurance as well. The dragon performs long sprints through scattered trees and undergrowth, making it

■ WHITE-LIPPED DRAGON
The long-snouted white-lipped dragon spends much of its life in the trees along watercourses, feeding on insects.

almost impossible for a larger predator to keep pace, or even a bird of prey. The crested dragon lives in the mallee deserts of South Australia and eastern Western Australia and grows up to 10 cm in body length. It has a strongly banded tail and a scaly crest extending back from its neck. Large males are splashed with orange and black and have a distinctive black stripe down the throat. Both sexes stand with front legs extended and head held high, presumably searching for food.

The closely related ringtailed dragon (*C. caudicinctus*) lives in rocky areas of northern inland Australia. This species uses its speed to run to shelter among rocks.

Some smaller ctenophorus dragons (with a body length of about 5 cm), which are confined to spinifex grass in sandy deserts, also rely on speed to escape. The mallee dragon (*C. fordi*), one of Australia's best studied lizards, belongs to this group.
Scientific name: *Ctenophorus* spp.

WHITE-LIPPED DRAGONS ■

These are medium-sized, slender lizards with bodies up to 12 cm long and elongated limbs and tails. For most of the year they are patterned in shades of grey, but in spring the males darken and develop a large crest on the back of the neck and middle of the trunk. Their most striking feature at this time is a thick white stripe that runs from the snout to the back of the head and acts as a territorial signal to other males. In inland Australia both Gilbert's white-lipped dragon (*Lophognathus gilberti*) and the long-snouted white-lipped dragon (*L. longirostris*) occur along tree-lined watercourses that run dry most of the time. Males are easy to find in spring but are difficult to observe during other seasons. Females are rarely seen at any time. Scientific name: *Lophognathus* spp. or *Amphibolurus* spp.

TWO-LINED DRAGONS ■

All members of this genus are slender and have long, thin tails. The northern two-lined dragon (*Diporiphora bilineata*) inhabits the sand dunes, woodlands and forests of northern Australia. Since it feeds mostly on small insects, including grasshoppers, it is probably an asset to farmers. It usually hunts on the ground but sometimes perches in shrubs or low trees, where it is often found sleeping. Active during the day, it is particularly vulnerable to predators such as hawks. If confronted, the dragon's only defence is to open its mouth wide and hiss. Its total length is 17–30 cm, two-thirds of which is tail. It is grey to reddish brown, with a distinct narrow white or yellow line running down either side of its body. During the breeding season males develop bright colours – brick red heads, yellow stripes and black patches on the throat, neck and armpits.

The superb two-lined dragon (*D. superba*) was discovered by

■ TWO-LINED DRAGON
The slender shape and vibrant lime green colour of *Diporiphora superba* camouflage it as a wattle twig.

scientists in 1974. Little is known about this species except that it lives in wattle trees in the Kimberley region of north-western Australia. Its body is 8–9.5 cm long and its tail, which is thin and tapers to a pale tip, is about four times the length of its body.

The canegrass two-lined dragon (*D. winneckei*) is grey or brown with two stripes running along its body. It has a total length of up to 24 cm,

over two-thirds of which is tail. This fast-moving little dragon is active in the heat of the day. It basks in the sun in beach spinifex, canegrass or hummock grasses before setting out to hunt for arthropods on the scorching sands of inland or coastal dunes. To prevent overheating, it stands on its heels with its toes and body raised from the hot ground and lifts each leg in turn. It also climbs into shrubs to escape the ground heat. Scientific name: *Diporiphora* spp.

EASTERN WATER DRAGON ■

Water dragons are perhaps the most primitive of the Australian dragons. Water dragon fossils over 20 million years old, found at Riversleigh in north-western Queensland, scarcely differ from the skeletons of modern water dragons.

They are large dragons, the male's body length reaching up to 30 cm with a tail at least twice as long. They are usually steel grey with a black stripe passing through the eye. Males in most of eastern Australia develop a red belly in the spring, while in Gippsland they develop a blue-green belly. They eat invertebrates as well as vertebrates small enough to swallow. Unlike most other dragons, water dragons move around to find food. Larger individuals also eat berries and flowers, and some scavenge at picnic spots. Scientific name: *Physignathus lesueurii*

DISTRIBUTION

■ CTENOPHORUS DRAGONS

■ WHITE-LIPPED DRAGONS

■ TWO-LINED DRAGONS

■ EASTERN WATER DRAGON

■ EASTERN WATER DRAGON
Walking by clear water, you may see a water dragon clinging to the rocks on the bottom of the creek, or hear a loud splash as it dives into the water from an overhanging tree limb.

■ RAINFOREST DRAGON
When it is disturbed, the male Boyd's forest dragon opens its mouth and extends its large yellow throat pouch in a display of aggression.

RAINFOREST DRAGONS ■

Australia has only two rainforest dragons – the southern forest dragon (*Hypsilurus spinipes*) and Boyd's forest dragon (*H. boydii*). These two dragons are relatively large and slow-moving and they rely on camouflage and complete stillness to avoid predators.

Southern forest dragons sometimes raise their crests threateningly, especially when defending their territories, while Boyd's forest dragons show their colourful yellow throat pouches.

The two species differ not only in distribution but also in diet. Whereas southern forest dragons feed mostly on insects, Boyd's dragons eat rainforest fruit and invertebrates such as snails and slugs.

Both species of rainforest dragon are brown to grey, or sometimes the colour of green lichens, and have chunky, angular heads with spiny crests. Boyd's forest dragon also has large spines on its throat and is bigger than the southern forest dragon with a body length of about 15 cm compared with 11 cm for the southern forest dragon. Both have tails twice as long as their bodies.

Female rainforest dragons lay their eggs in shallow burrows in the forest floor, where sunlight falls and incubates them. These dragons often perch on tree trunks or lie on the forest floor basking in shafts of sunlight that pierce the canopy after rain. They are rarely seen by humans, and little is known about their habits.
Scientific name: *Hypsilurus* spp.

HEATH DRAGONS AND EARLESS DRAGONS

Heath dragons occur in the heathlands of southern Australia, including Tasmania, while earless dragons are widespread in central Australia. Both species are small, with a body length of about 5 cm and tails only a little longer. Active by day, they are ground-hugging species that rely heavily on camouflage for their survival. Their coloration is a subtle patterning of browns and greys that is designed to blend in well with their various habitats.

Species that live on the fringes of the east and west coasts have ears, but inland species do not. Scientists speculate that the reason for their earless state is that predators recognise eye and ear shapes as potential food and that earless dragons living in open landscape, with little chance to camouflage themselves, avoid being recognised as prey by dispensing with ear shapes. They can still hear – although probably not as acutely as other dragons – through contact between the inner ear and the bones of the skull.

In the presence of potential predators, earless dragons press their whole body against the ground. In this position they may be able to sense the movements of a predator. Remaining so close to the ground also eliminates shadows, which is another way of avoiding detection. If they are seen, earless dragons are capable of moving fast, at least for a short distance, and scuttle swiftly under cover.

The western heath dragon (*Tympanocryptis adelaidensis*) lives in coastal heaths near Perth, while the mountain dragon (*T. diemensis*) lives in the heathlands and dry eucalypt forests of south-eastern Australia. Despite the bold marking of some individuals of these two species, they almost disappear in leaf litter because their triangular patterning

---

SAVING OUR WILDLIFE

The lined earless dragon, *Tympanocryptis pinguicolla*, is found only in a few hectares near Canberra. In winter this species shelters in spider burrows, and in warmer weather it lives and hunts in tussock grasses. The introduction of livestock to native grasslands has led to the extinction of this lizard in most of its former range. Sheep trample spider burrows and eat tussock grasses, while farmers plant grasses that are unsuitable for the lizard. Since their plight was brought to the attention of politicians, a few of these lizards have been rescued from extinction by the erection of a fence in natural grassland near Canberra airport.

looks like irregularly shaped leaves. The blotch-tailed earless dragon (*T. cephalus*) is almost patternless and has scattered, roundish scales that blend with the gravelly soils where it usually lives.

All species lie in wait for small insects – especially ants, which form a large proportion of their diet.
Scientific name: *Tympanocryptis* spp.

THORNY DEVIL

This unmistakable lizard has a striking pattern of red, brown, yellow and white, and is covered in large, robust spikes. There is a small spiky lump on the back of its neck that looks a little like a head. Confronted by a predator, the thorny devil lowers its head, presenting this lump for attack rather than its head.

Head, body, limbs and tail are all short. Its body length may exceed 10 cm, and its tail is shorter than its body. The colours and uneven shape of the body provide the dragon with good camouflage in the sandy country where it lives.

Perhaps the thorny devil's most famous characteristic is its unusual way of drinking. The tiny channels between the devil's scales operate like capillaries to carry water up, against gravity, towards the corner of the lizard's mouth, where it can be drunk. These dragons live in the arid spinifex grasslands of Australia's central and western deserts, and this adaptation allows them to drink from damp sand as well as picking up dew from plants in the early morning.

The thorny devil feeds almost exclusively on ants. Positioning itself beside an ant trail, it flicks

thousands of ants into its mouth with its tongue at a single sitting. Most Australian dragons have front canine teeth for holding prey, but the thorny devil has lost these, probably because it catches prey with its tongue alone.
Scientific name: *Moloch horridus*

BEARDED DRAGONS

These dragons defend themselves by opening their mouths and pushing their throat skin forward to make a 'beard'. The lining of the mouth is usually yellow, which creates a startling effect. However, if a predator remains undaunted by this display, there are strong spikes along the side of the dragon's body that make touching these animals distinctly uncomfortable.

Bearded dragons are active by day, mostly on the ground in open habitats from dry eucalypt forests to deserts. They eat mainly insects but also feed on some plant material, especially yellow flowers. They are sometimes known as jew lizards or carnies, and in southern Australia

they are usually referred to as frillies. They have a triangular head and are greyish or brownish. Young bearded dragons are boldly patterned in shades of grey that become less distinct as they grow. The larger bearded dragons have almost no patterning as adults.

Until recently, bearded dragons from different areas were thought to be variations of a single widespread species, but several species are now recognised. The western bearded dragon (*Pogona minor*) occurs over much of the area of Australia west of an imaginary north–south line through Adelaide. Like most bearded dragons, this species grows to a body length of 14 cm, but its tail is unusually long for this group – almost twice the length of its body.

In the eastern half of the continent there are two giant species of bearded dragon, both growing to 25 cm in body length and 55 cm in total length. The eastern bearded dragon (*P. barbata*) occurs along the length of the Great Dividing Range but is replaced in more arid areas by the inland bearded dragon (*P. vitticeps*). *Vitticeps* means 'wide-head', and this is the most obvious characteristic of both these species.

Along their lower eyelids all bearded dragons have 'eyelashes' very like those found in the burrowing species of *Ctenophorus* (page 320), where they give protection to the eyes. While bearded dragons have been recorded as digging burrows for hibernation, burrowing is not a daily way of life for these lizards. Their eyelashes are probably a legacy from an ancestor common to both them and the burrowing ctenophorus dragons.
Scientific name: *Pogona* spp.

■ BEARDED DRAGON
Similar to the eastern bearded dragon, the Nullarbor dragon, *Pogona nullarbor*, is found on the Nullarbor Plain in South and Western Australia.

■ THORNY DEVIL
Active during the day, the thorny devil moves around in open areas, where its camouflage and armoury of spikes are essential defences.

DISTRIBUTION

■ RAINFOREST DRAGONS

■ HEATH DRAGONS AND EARLESS DRAGONS

■ THORNY DEVIL

■ BEARDED DRAGONS

GOANNAS

A TOUGH BABY
This lace monitor's egg was opened to reveal the baby goanna inside. Happily, the hatchling survived the experience.

■ **OCELLATED RIDGE-TAILED GOANNA**
The ground-dwelling goanna *Varanus acanthurus* lives among spinifex grasslands and rocky outcrops, picking up the scent of prey with its long forked tongue.

Of all the lizards, only the goanna has a deeply forked tongue, like that of a snake, which slots into the floor of the goanna's mouth. Goannas also resemble snakes in having a highly developed Jacobson's organ (see page 341) in the roof of their mouth. These two features help goannas to detect prey, and perhaps to find mates. Goannas have a long, slender neck, a flattened head, and tough, loose-fitting skin. Their tail is strong and muscular, but – unlike the tail of most other lizards – it cannot drop off or regrow. Their powerful legs bear five toes, each with a strong, sharp claw. Like all lizards, male goannas have two penises, either of which may be used when mating.

Goannas are known in other countries as monitor lizards. The word 'goanna' is an Australian corruption of 'iguana', which is the name of an unrelated group of reptiles from the Americas. There are about 35 species in the goanna family, all from a single genus (*Varanus*), and they are found throughout Africa, southern Asia and Australia. At least 25 species live in Australia.

Most of these lizards are ground-dwellers, though some live in trees, and a few are semi-aquatic. They occupy a wide range of habitats, with some being specific about where they live. The pygmy mulga monitor (*V. gilleni*), for example, is found across much of arid Australia but lives mainly under the bark of mulga and desert oak trees, and the mangrove monitor (*V. indicus*) lives its whole life in the mangroves and adjacent closed forests that line much of the northern Australian coast.

Living and breeding

Goannas are active during the day and, like all lizards, they bask to absorb energy from the sun. They avoid extreme heat or cold by sheltering in tree hollows and burrows. In the tropics they are active throughout the year, and even in colder climates they do not hibernate in winter but remain fairly active by basking wherever there is sunshine.

We know surprisingly little about goannas, especially the smaller ones, but their behaviour appears to vary among species. The courtship and mating ritual of Rosenberg's goanna, for example, is a languorous and tender affair, whereas that of the lace monitor is more aggressive and short-lived. The sand goanna, the lace monitor and Mertens' water goanna intimidate their rivals by raising themselves on two legs and inflating their throat pouch.

All goannas lay eggs, often in tree hollows, depressions in the ground or termite mounds. Some have communal nest sites.

If alarmed, some large goannas dash up the nearest tree. According to folklore, these goannas sometimes make a mistake and run up the leg of a human or a horse. Smaller species usually beat a hasty retreat.

Cold-blooded predators

Goannas are carnivores, and are among Australia's top predators. They eat almost anything they can catch – from insects to fishes to possums – and raid the nests of reptiles and birds for eggs, or scratch about in the ground for beetles and other arthropods. They are also scavengers, keeping the bush clean by eating dead animals.

They track food by sight, which is often keen, and also by sensing prey with their tongue. Some give chase to their prey and are surprisingly fast. The sand goanna, for example, is nicknamed the racehorse goanna for its ability to run at great speed.

BIPEDAL STANCE
Goannas sometimes rear up on their hind legs and totter along on two feet.

Other species, such as the lace monitor, climb trees to get into nesting hollows and steal birds' eggs.

Because they do not have to keep their body temperature constant (unlike mammals and birds), goannas need to eat only about five times their weight in a year. By comparison, every year the eastern quoll eats 65 times its weight and the little penguin consumes 115 times its weight; clearly there is a survival advantage for goannas and other reptiles in being cold-blooded (ectothermic).

Goannas gulp their food, often whole, aided by their large, sharp teeth and specialised throat muscles. Like most lizards, they can move their upper jaw independently of the base of their skull, and this allows them to move prey into and within their mouth. They can close their jaws rapidly to capture fast-moving prey. The throat and jaws of larger species are adapted to feeding on large prey, which they dismember by gripping it with their front feet and wrenching it apart with a jerking movement of their head. Smaller species live mainly on insects, but also eat other lizards and their eggs.
Family: Varanidae

OCELLATED RIDGE-TAILED GOANNA

This beautiful goanna is most easily recognised by its spiny tail banded with yellow rings. It is generally brown with creamy yellow spots on its body and stripes on its head, and a cream-coloured underside. It grows to a total of about 70 cm long. It occurs across the northern arid, semi-arid and tropical parts of Australia, mostly inhabiting rock outcrops and ranges. Although quite common, it is rarely seen because it is quick to seek shelter under rocks or in crevices, hollow logs or even termite mounds.

The ridge-tailed goanna breeds in early spring, and incubation of the eggs takes three or four months. The young reach sexual maturity at about one or two years of age. This goanna probably eats small prey such as insects, spiders and some lizards. In its turn it is preyed upon by larger predators, particularly black-breasted buzzards, dingoes and humans. In the Tanami Desert in central Australia, ten ridge-tailed goanna carcasses were found underneath a single buzzard nest.
Scientific name: Varanus acanthurus

ROSENBERG'S GOANNA

Growing to a total length of about a metre and weighing up to 2 kg, this species was first thought to be a smaller, black form of the sand goanna (page 326).

The courtship behaviour of Rosenberg's goanna is uncharacteristically tender. The male digs a burrow beside the female and they remain together for several days. During copulation, the male nuzzles and licks the female. If another male approaches, he is chased away.

These goannas inhabit the coastal heaths, moist woodlands and eucalypt forests of the south coast of Australia, from Adelaide to Perth; they also occur in patches throughout Victoria and New South Wales. They feed on insects, birds, lizards, frogs, mammals and carrion.

On Kangaroo Island these goannas remain active throughout the year, foraging for longer periods during summer. They sometimes shelter in shallow burrows that they have dug themselves, but they also use rabbit burrows. These protect them not only from the weather but from their killers – humans, vehicles and wedge-tailed eagles. Females lay their eggs in termite mounds.
Scientific name: Varanus rosenbergi

PYGMY GOANNAS

At 20 cm long, the short-tailed pygmy goanna (*Varanus brevicauda*) is the smallest of the goannas. It is a ground-dweller that lives throughout the arid parts of central and western Australia.

Although it is not a common species, the pygmy goanna is widespread in sandy spinifex country. Its burrows have been found under spinifex clumps, and it feeds on the invertebrates that live there. It is reddish brown, with small dark spots on its back and tail. Its snout, legs, toes and tail are relatively short.

Scientists know little about its breeding habits in the wild; in captivity, eggs incubated at a constant temperature hatched after 77 days.

The rusty desert goanna (*V. eremius*), also referred to as the pygmy goanna, has a similar distribution to the short-tailed pygmy goanna but is about twice its size and is found in a greater variety of habitats.
Scientific name: Varanus spp.

BLACK-PALMED ROCK GOANNA

Often, all that is visible of a black-palmed rock goanna is the whitish end of its long, slender tail as it disappears inside a rock crevice. These reclusive lizards live in the rocky outcrops of tropical Northern Territory, north-west Queensland and Western Australia, where they find shelter in caves and crevices and under boulders.

This goanna grows to a total length of about a metre, over half of which is tail. Its head and back are covered in a dark brown and fawn netlike pattern and its darker legs are spotted with fawn.

The black-palmed rock goanna has shiny black, rounded scales on the soles of its feet, from which it gets its common name. This agile animal forages, mostly for insects, during the day and sometimes at dusk or just before dawn.
Scientific name: Varanus glebopalma

ROSENBERG'S GOANNA
The coastal heaths, woodlands and eucalypt forests of southern Australia are home to Rosenberg's goanna.

BLACK-PALMED ROCK GOANNA
The shy black-palmed rock goanna, seen here in its rocky habitat, has a long, dark brown tail with a pale tapered end.

DISTRIBUTION

■ OCELLATED RIDGE-TAILED GOANNA

■ ROSENBERG'S GOANNA

■ PYGMY GOANNAS

■ BLACK-PALMED ROCK GOANNA

DISTRIBUTION

■ MERTENS' WATER
GOANNA

■ SAND GOANNA

■ SPOTTED GOANNA

■ PERENTIE
■ LACE MONITOR

■ BLACK-TAILED
GOANNA

■ SAND GOANNA
In hot weather, when
its body temperature
rises to 38°C, the sand
goanna, *Varanus gouldii*,
opens its mouth and
flutters its throat pouch
to increase evaporation
from its mouth and to
cool its brain.

MERTENS' WATER GOANNA ■

This tropical species, found from
the Kimberley Range in Western
Australia to western Cape York, is
named after the German herpetolo-
gist Robert Mertens, who carried
out much of the early research into
Australian goannas.

Mertens' water goanna is amphibious, always foraging and feeding in
and around water, on the banks of
billabongs and along streams.

Like the black-palmed rock goanna
(page 325), Mertens' water goanna
grows to a length of about a metre,
but it is more heavily built, with a
larger body and a shorter tail. It is
dark olive brown with tiny creamy
yellow spots and a cream-coloured
underside. It forages under water,
remaining for several minutes at a
time, and its nostrils are set particularly high on its head so that it can
breathe while only just breaking the
surface. It obtains much of its food –
such as crustaceans, fishes and frogs
– from the water, but it also eats
insects and some lizards, birds,
mammals and carrion.
Scientific name: *Varanus mertensi*

SAND GOANNA ■

Sand goannas are the most common
and widely distributed of the Australian goannas. They are found
throughout Australia except in the
temperate south-eastern corner, in
Tasmania and in the wet southern
forests of Western Australia. They
inhabit sand plains and dunes but
are also found in dry forests.

■ MERTENS' WATER GOANNA
Basking on a log overhanging the
water, Mertens' water goanna drops
noisily into the water when disturbed.

Sand goannas are extremely variable
in colour, ranging from light yellow
to black with light and dark flecks
and spots. Their undersides and tail
tips are usually yellow or cream
coloured. Some adults grow to a
total length of 1.6 metres, but sizes
vary between populations.

These goannas eat substantial
amounts of invertebrates, some reptile eggs, lizards, birds and rabbits.
Although they are ground-dwellers,
they can climb trees and will escape
into them if frightened. They shelter

in borrowed burrows, rabbit warrens and hollow logs, or even among
dense litter. Sand goannas also dig
their own sloping burrows up to
40 cm below ground. Some burrows
have an ancillary vertical shaft,
which provides a handy exit if a
predator enters the main hole.

The patterns of activity of sand
goannas vary according to climatic
conditions. In the tropics they are
active throughout the year, while in
the deserts they retreat to their burrows in extreme heat or cold. Like
the lace monitor (opposite page), the
female sand monitor may incubate
her eggs in termite mounds.

Sand goannas are also called
racehorse goannas because of their
speed. They are vulnerable to predators such as birds of prey, dingoes,
snakes and larger goannas, and are
also a favoured Aboriginal food.
Scientific name: *Varanus gouldii*

SPOTTED GOANNA

The spotted goanna is very similar
to the sand goanna (this page);
indeed, it was not described as a
separate species until 1980. The most
obvious differences are the spotted
goanna's rows of large dark spots
alternating with rows of small pale
ones on its back, and the dark spots
that cover the rest of its body.

This large goanna grows to a total
length of 1.4 metres. It is common in
tropical regions across the north of
Australia, and is also found in the
arid central west of Western
Australia. Little is known of its biology, but there is some evidence that
it buries its eggs deep in the soil,
choosing sites along creek lines, and
that these are communal nest sites.
Scientific name: *Varanus panoptes*

LACE MONITOR ■

The lace monitor lives throughout eastern Australia. It is a very large goanna, reaching a total weight of 14 kg and a total length of 1.5–2 metres. It has a very long tail and is usually dark blue to black with scattered cream or yellow spots and blotches. These markings are especially striking just after the goanna has shed its skin.

An inhabitant of woodlands and forests, the lace monitor often scavenges around picnic and camping grounds, even entering houses built in bushland. It eats a wide variety of food, including mammals, lizards, insects and eggs. The lace monitor is surprisingly agile on trees and is a major predator of nestling birds – hence its alternative common name, the tree goanna.

The lace monitor's most common form of shelter is a tree hollow, but it also uses hollow logs and burrows. If alarmed it is likely to scurry up the nearest tree, where it spirals up the trunk with its enormously powerful claws, attempting to remain hidden from its tormentor.

Lace monitors are most active during spring and early summer, when mating occurs. They reach sexual maturity when they are four or five years old, and most females breed every year, laying their eggs in termite mounds (see box, 'Termite mound incubators').

Goannas are usually solitary, but during the breeding season lace monitors often congregate in small groups. In autumn and winter they retreat to shelter for several months, emerging on sunny days to bask.

Scientific name: *Varanus varius*

PERENTIE

This magnificent lizard stands on its hind legs and tail to survey the surrounding bush. It can grow up to 2.5 metres long, making it the second largest lizard in the world – the largest of all lizards is the Komodo dragon (*Varanus komodoensis*), which is found only on Komodo, Rinca and Flores islands in Indonesia.

Perenties have a dark brown or black skin that is strikingly marked with yellowish spots. They occur within a broad band of Australia's deserts, but they are not commonly seen. They live mainly in and around rocky outcrops and ridges, sheltering under the rocks in large burrows they have dug themselves, or in ones they have commandeered, and travelling into nearby sandy country and claypans to forage. One perentie has been observed

submerging itself in a salt lake and remaining there for some time.

Like all large goannas, perenties feed on a range of prey, including insects, birds, other reptiles, and mammals. They are active foragers and use a 'sit and wait' strategy to catch larger prey such as rabbits.

Scientific name: *Varanus giganteus*

BLACK-TAILED GOANNA

A widespread and common species, the black-tailed goanna is found all over Australia except in the temperate eastern and southern parts. It is a tree-dweller and shelters in tree hollows. It is also found in rocky hills and outcrops, where crevices provide shelter, and is sometimes seen clinging to steep rock surfaces.

The black-tailed goanna reaches about 80 cm long. Adults are grey to dark brown or black. Some are an almost solid colour, while the body of others may be marked with numerous small, cream-coloured rings. Juveniles are more strongly marked than adults, and those in the north are paler than the southern populations. They produce large clutches of eggs, but do not lay them until the embryo is well developed. These goannas feed on insects and lizards, as well as the eggs of birds, turtles and lizards.

The Latin species name of the black-tailed goanna is *tristis*, meaning sad or gloomy; it refers to the earliest found specimens from the Swan River in Western Australia, which were entirely black.

Scientific name: *Varanus tristis*

■ LACE MONITORS
Locked in combat, these male lace monitors are engaged in the ritual battle for a mate. This aggressive behaviour often escalates into a full-scale wrestling match.

TERMITE MOUND INCUBATORS

Lace monitors mate during November and December. Four to six weeks later, the female digs through the walls of a termite mound and lays about eight eggs in a chamber. When the termites repair the hole they enclose the eggs, providing a safe nest site. The large eggs develop slowly over the winter. Between October and November, the female returns and releases the hatchlings. They may not leave the mound immediately, but when they do they move away quickly, keeping to cover. It is a mystery how the lizards remember in which termite mound they have laid their eggs, but it may be because they have a very detailed knowledge of their territory.

It is possible that Rosenberg's goanna and the sand goanna use a similar strategy for incubating their eggs.

DISTRIBUTION

RAINBOW SKINKS

RAINFOREST
COOL-SKINK

BARTLE FRERE
COOL-SKINK

SNAKE-EYED SKINKS

SKINKS

There are about 26 families of lizards in the world, and of these the skinks are the most diverse, with 1200 species worldwide. In Australia there are 390 skink species. These species are often quite diverse in appearance and habits.

Skinks have tough, unwrinkled skin covered by overlapping, fish-like scales. In most skinks these scales are shiny or iridescent, but some skinks have ridged or grooved scales and a few have very rough, even spiny, scalation. In most species, their head, short neck and long body are so smoothly joined that there is no noticeable distinction between the parts. While most skinks have scaly, movable eyelids, a significant number have a transparent disc in the lower lid, through which they can see even when their lids are closed. Most skinks produce leathery eggs, but others bear live young.

Many skinks are quite small, reaching no more than 8–10 cm in total length, but the largest grow to about 75 cm and weigh up to a kilogram. Skinks are generally ground-dwellers, although some species in this diverse family are specialised climbers, living on trees or rock outcrops.

Most skinks hunt by day, feeding on invertebrates, although many of

RAINBOW SKINK
This adult male rainbow skink, *Carlia longipes*, shows the full reddish brown breeding flush on its body.

the larger skinks also eat small vertebrates and often include vegetation in their diet. Most skinks prefer high body temperatures, which they maintain by alternately basking and seeking shelter. Many species, however, are burrowers or litter and soil 'swimmers', and these do not bask, as they prefer lower body temperatures. Burrowers characteristically have elongated, snake-like bodies, and legs greatly reduced in size. A few skinks are limbless.
Family: Scincidae

RAINBOW SKINKS

These lively, sun-loving lizards bask and forage among leaf litter for small insects. For reasons unclear to scientists, they wave their tails sinuously as they move – possibly tail waving, along with the bright colours of the males, is a social signal for signalling mates, status or personal space. These skinks are quick to flee or dive under leaves to escape predators, such as kookaburras, which are possibly attracted by the skinks' conspicuous behaviour.

Australia is home to 22 species of rainbow skinks, all of which have four toes on the forelimbs and five toes on the hind limbs. They all have a movable lower eyelid enclosing a window-like transparent area, and most have rows of ridges called keels running down their backs. Rainbow skinks are common in northern Australia, and their stronghold is the tropical woodlands and rock outcrops of north-eastern Queensland.

All species lay two soft-shelled eggs, sometimes deposited communally under logs, rocks or dense leaf litter.

The desert rainbow skink (*Carlia triacantha*) is the only species to penetrate the deserts of central and western Australia. It attains a total length of 15 cm and prefers rocky areas, where it hides under spinifex and leaf litter. The adult male of this species has a brilliant coppery green head and neck and a bright orange flush on its sides.

Different species of sexually mature male rainbow skinks are generally identifiable by their beautiful colours, which are brightest during the breeding season. The females and the young, however, are quite difficult to tell apart.

The male lined rainbow skink (*C. jarnoldae*) is among the most splendid. On its brown back are up to seven black stripes; its upper flanks are black with vivid blue spots, its lower flanks are bright orange, and its lips and throat are pale green. The female is greyish brown with a simple white stripe along its sides. The lined rainbow skink is quite small, growing to a total of only 12 cm long. It lives on stony soils in the tropical woodlands of north-eastern Queensland.

Rock outcrops around Coen on Cape York Peninsula are home to the Coen rainbow skink (*C. coensis*). Males and females are black with silver markings, a wide wavy stripe from neck to hips and two rows of large spots along the outer back and sides. With a total length of 18 cm, it is one of the largest of the rainbow skinks. It lives on boulders situated along thickly vegetated creeks; head held high and tail lashing, it perches to survey its surroundings and catch passing insects.

RED-THROATED SUITORS

Most skink species do not show distinct marked colour differences between the males and the females, but there are a few species that do. Among the most vivid of these are the rainbow skinks, the breeding colours of which vary from species to species. Other species whose males are clearly recognisable during the breeding season are the red-throated skinks – of which *Bassiana* (sometimes *Acritoscincus*; pictured below) is one – from the temperate regions of Australia. These males develop bright red patches on their throat and chin that signal their approach before they are close enough for a female to recognise them by scent.

The closed-litter rainbow skink (*C. longipes*) is a large, robust inhabitant of woodlands and monsoon forests on Cape York Peninsula and the north-eastern Northern Territory. Growing up to 18 cm in total length, males are plain brown with grey necks and bright orange sides, while females have a flecked dark and pale back and dark flanks marked by a pale line and a few pale spots.

The black-throated rainbow skink (*C. rostralis*) lives in open forests and woodlands at the base of Cape York Peninsula. It is of similar size and appearance to the closed-litter skink, except that the males have black throats and both sexes have a pale line down the outer back.

The red-throated rainbow skink (*C. rubrigularis*), with a total length of 12 cm, is a rainforest inhabitant of the wet tropics of north-eastern Queensland. It is often seen near Cairns basking in sunlight. Both sexes display a red throat. As well as insects, it eats small skinks, including the young of its own kind.
Scientific name: *Carlia* spp.

RAINFOREST COOL-SKINK

Commonly found among leaf litter in the upland rainforests and temperate beech forests of far northern New South Wales and southern Queensland, this skink is coppery brown with dark and pale flecks on the back, a fine pale line along the outer back and dark brown to grey sides. Its belly is yellow and its tail has a distinctive red flush.

The rainforest cool-skink grows to a total of 14 cm long. It is a shy lizard, and if approached is quick to hide under logs and dense leaves. It feeds on a wide variety of small insects and other ground-dwelling invertebrates. In summer it lays between three and six eggs beneath rotting logs and debris.
Scientific name: *Cautula zia*

BARTLE FRERE COOL-SKINK

On Mount Bartle Frère, which is Queensland's tallest mountain, 1400–1600 metres above sea level, lives the Bartle Frère cool-skink. This attractive 20 cm-long lizard has a coppery brown back with black and cream flecks and black sides marked with a broken white stripe. It forages for small insects and spiders on exposed boulder faces and shelters in narrow rock crevices.

In common with many rock-living skinks, the Bartle Frère cool-skink has evolved a flat head and body

and long, slender limbs to ensure a secure grip on bare rock.

Due to its lofty, isolated habitat, not much is known about the Bartle Frère cool-skink, although one female has been recorded as having a clutch of four eggs. Its entire range is contained in national parkland and the World Heritage-listed Wet Tropics, so its future is fairly secure.
Scientific name: *Bartleia jigurru*

SNAKE-EYED SKINKS

Members of this genus of skinks have the common name 'snake-eyed' because their transparent lower eyelid is fused to the upper eyelid, forming a fixed protective lens similar to that found in snakes.

There are seven species of the genus in Australia, and most are remarkably similar in appearance and habits. These small, agile, smooth-scaled sun-lovers are either tree-dwellers or live among rocks. Growing to less than 13 cm in total length, they are mostly grey or black

and are usually patterned with a pair of pale dorsal stripes.

Most snake-eyed species are abundant, and it is not unusual to see the common species on buildings and other man-made structures. They are active hunters, preying on virtually any insect or other invertebrate small enough to be eaten. They are egg-layers, the usual clutch being two eggs.

The species *Cryptoblepharus carnabyi*, *C. plagiocephalus* and *C. virgatus* are common tree-dwellers with widespread distributions. The rock-dwelling, reddish form *C. megastictus* lives in the rocky ranges of far northern Australia while the large, dark coloured rock-dweller *C. fuhni* has been found only in the Melville Range on Cape York Peninsula in Queensland. Another dark rock-dweller is *C. litoralis*, which lives on rocky beaches and headlands in northern Queensland and the Northern Territory.
Scientific name: *Cryptoblepharus* spp.

■ SNAKE-EYED SKINK
The beautiful blue-tailed skink, *Cryptoblepharus egeriae*, is a tree- and rock-dweller, occurring only on Christmas Island in the Indian Ocean. It is most common in human settlements and in forests, where it loves to bask in the sunlight that pierces the canopy.

■ RAINFOREST COOL-SKINK
Bushwalkers along the border of New South Wales and Queensland may encounter this small skink basking in sunlight among leaves.

DISTRIBUTION

☐ EGERNIAS

■ WHIPTAIL-SKINKS

■ WHIPTAIL-SKINK
The shrub whiptail-skink *Emoia longicauda*, which lives on tree trunks, branches and foliage in rainforests and vine thickets, has specialised scales under its toes to help it to climb.

EGERNIAS ■

Egernias are stout, medium-sized to large skinks found over most of Australia. There are 30 species in this genus, and all but one of these (*Egernia frerei*) are native to Australia. Large species are either herbivorous or omnivorous, while smaller species tend to be insectivorous. Egernias give birth to live young in spring or summer. The litter size is usually fewer than six.

Four egernia species, commonly known as spiny-tailed egernias, have short tails and sharp spines on their body scales, which they use to anchor themselves in rock and tree crevices. They live in small colonies that are probably family groups. Individuals in the same colony defecate in one site so that their droppings (scats) mark inhabited rock outcrops. They eat leaves, flowers and berries, generally feeding in the day, although some feed at night.

The most common egernia near human habitation is Cunningham's skink (*E. cunninghami*), which lives in south-eastern Australia among outcrops of rock. It grows to a body length of up to 21 cm and has a tail about twice as long. The smaller gidgee skink (*E. stokesii*) has a short, flat tail that is only about a third of its body length. It lives in the arid interior of southern Australia in rock crevices and the branches of gidgee trees. In the east of its range it is dark brown, but in the west it is more variably coloured.

Another group of egernias are the crevice egernias. They have flattened heads and bodies that allow them to live in narrower cracks than the spiny-tailed skinks. With body lengths of 10–12 cm, they are also smaller and have a longer tail – as long or longer than their body. Their scales do not have sharp spines and can be either smooth or rough, and their belly is reddish to yellowish. Within this group are the tree skink (*E. striolata*) of eastern Australia; the goldfields crevice skink (*E. formosa*) of inland Western Australia; and the south-western crevice skink (*E. napoleonis*) of south-western Australia. All mostly eat insects.

The rock and desert egernias usually burrow in the soil beneath rocks, but in the sandy deserts some species dig extensive burrows under spinifex tussocks. Most of these smooth-scaled burrowers have a body length of up to 11 cm and a tail longer than the body. They include White's skink (*E. whitii*) of south-eastern Australia, the desert skink (*E. inornata*) and the nocturnal desert skink (*E. striata*) of inland Australia. The latter species has cat-like eyes with elliptical pupils.

Several egernias do not fit into any of these groups. The mourning skink (*E. luctuosa*), which lives in the swamps of south-western Australia, is one of these. Others include the largest egernias, such as the land mullet (*E. major*) of the wet forests of eastern Australia, with a maximum body length of 31 cm and a longer tail, and King's skink (*E. kingii*) of south-western Australia, with a body length of up to 25 cm and a tail one and half times its body length.
Scientific name: *Egernia* spp.

■ EGERNIA
Australia's largest skink, the land mullet *Egernia major*, inhabits rainforests and nearby wet gum forests.

WHIPTAIL-SKINKS ■

Whiptail-skinks are slender, with pointed snouts, long toes and thin, tapering tails. All are fast, agile climbers. They are widespread from southern Japan to the Pacific islands, but only two – the littoral whiptail-skink (*Emoia atrocostata*) and the shrub whiptail-skink (*E. longicauda*) live on mainland Australia. Both are confined to Cape York and the islands of Torres Strait. Their ancestors probably reached Australia across ancient land bridges between Australia and New Guinea, or rafted across on floating debris.

The littoral whiptail is grey with dark and pale flecks across its back and a broad black zigzag stripe on its sides. It has a body length of 10 cm and reaches a total of 26 cm long. It lives among intertidal rocks and mangroves and forages for insects and crustaceans along the shore, dodging waves and returning when they subside. It lays clutches of two eggs in rotting mangroves or debris above the high-tide mark.

The shrub whiptail-skink is brown above and yellowish green below. Its body measures 9 cm long and its tail is 15 cm long.

A third species, the Christmas Island whiptail-skink (*E. nativitatus*), inhabits Australia's island territory in the Indian Ocean. It is brown with dark and pale scales. Its body is 7 cm long and its total length is 22 centimetres. It lives in rainforests, often foraging in sunny clearings.
Scientific name: *Emoia* spp.

In cold blood

We often refer to reptiles as 'cold-blooded', and it is true that they function best at a body temperature slightly lower than that of mammals and birds.

But cold-blooded is not an entirely accurate expression. In fact, in common with most other animals except mammals and birds, the body temperature of reptiles is regulated by the environment outside their bodies, rather than by their internal metabolic processes. Scientists call this characteristic ectothermy, from the Greek *ektos*, 'outside', and *therme*, 'heat'. Mammals and birds, by contrast, are described as warm-blooded, or endothermic (*endon* is Greek for 'inside'), which means that they maintain a constant body temperature by generating heat from within their bodies as they metabolise food into energy and into materials for the growth and maintenance of body tissues.

While mammals and birds must eat regularly to fuel the metabolic process, reptiles can survive long periods of inactivity without eating. In fact, reptiles require only around 10 per cent of the food that mammals and birds need. A slow metabolism is also an efficient way of conserving water, so that reptiles are able to live in very arid areas where food is scarce.

Warming up and cooling off

Reptiles control their body temperatures very precisely during the daytime by basking in the sun to warm up and sheltering in the shade or positioning

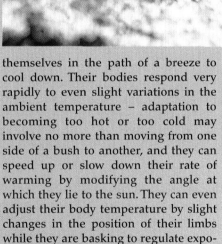

Crocodiles regulate their body temperature by filling their lower jaw with water and gaping to cool themselves by evaporation.

themselves in the path of a breeze to cool down. Their bodies respond very rapidly to even slight variations in the ambient temperature – adaptation to becoming too hot or too cold may involve no more than moving from one side of a bush to another, and they can speed up or slow down their rate of warming by modifying the angle at which they lie to the sun. They can even adjust their body temperature by slight changes in the position of their limbs while they are basking to regulate exposure to air flow and sunlight.

Some lizard species are able to make their skin darker so that they can absorb more heat when they need it and lighter when they need to cool down. The speed with which a reptile's body takes up heat is also affected by blood flow; in order to absorb as much heat as possible, the surface blood vessels dilate while the animal is basking and constrict when it is trying to conserve heat.

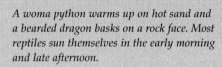

A woma python warms up on hot sand and a bearded dragon basks on a rock face. Most reptiles sun themselves in the early morning and late afternoon.

The need for warmth

Reptiles can tolerate much wider body temperature ranges than birds and mammals; a drop in body temperature that would kill a human merely renders a reptile temporarily inactive.

On the other hand, although reptiles can control their body temperatures to a considerable extent, ectothermy does limit the time during which they can remain active, so during the night or in winter months, when external temperatures drop, reptiles slow down; their movements become lethargic, their heart and breathing rates slow down, and they may enter a state of dormancy.

Ectothermy therefore has its disadvantages for reptiles, since they cannot grow or produce young when they are sluggish or dormant, and they are also vulnerable to predators at such times. The need for a comparatively high ambient temperature in order to survive, grow and reproduce means that most reptile species must live in warm conditions.

CTENOTUS ■

A characteristic feature of the genus *Ctenotus* (pronounced te-NO-tus) is the pointed or rounded scales along the front edge of the ear openings in most species. Known also as striped skinks, these ground-dwellers form the largest genus of skinks in Australia. Scientists have only recently named some of the 90 species.

Many ctenotus species are very similar in appearance and are difficult to tell apart. Most have pale and dark stripes on their back and sides, and some also have pale spots. Their bellies are usually pearly white, although some are yellowish or pinkish. Their tail is slender and often much longer than their body. Some of the small sand-dwelling species, such as the blue-tailed ctenotus (*Ctenotus calurus*) and the buff-tailed ctenotus (*C. colletti*) from the north-western desert area, have narrow, blade-like scales under their toes to help them grip the loose sand when running.

Probably the most unusual of these skinks is the leopard ctenotus (*C. pantherinus*), which is brown and covered with small white spots. This species, found over much of arid Australia, runs with a stiff action, carrying its body off the ground.

All of the ctenotus species that scientists have so far studied lay eggs, usually between one and five in a clutch, and generally in spring or early summer. They feed largely on insects and spiders, although a few eat some plant material as well.

Although they live over almost the whole of mainland Australia, except in the highest parts of the Australian Alps and the rainforests of the east coast, most ctenotus species live in the desert regions – especially in spinifex deserts, where up to seven species can exist in one area. Where several species coexist, there are frequently differences between them – in size, diet, time of activity (daily and seasonal) and exact habitat – differences that have probably evolved as a way of avoiding competition for food, mates and shelter.

In the mallee and spinifex sand plains of southern Australia the southern mallee ctenotus (*C. atlas*) grows to a total length of 21 cm and has a strongly striped pattern. It forages around the base of the same spinifex tussocks as the barred wedge-snout, or Schomburgk's ctenotus (*C. schomburgkii*). This much smaller species, which has a total length of up to 15 cm, has a pattern of coloured stripes and large blotches. Scientists speculate that the difference in size of these two species probably avoids competition for food, as they take different sized

prey. Further to the north, in the same kind of sand plain habitat, lives the fourteen-lined ctenotus (*C. quattuordecimlineatus*) – a similar lizard to the southern mallee ctenotus. The orange-tailed or Lea's ctenotus (*C. leae*) occupies spinifex sand dunes in southern Australia.

In north-western spinifex deserts lives a very large species, the grand ctenotus (*C. grandis*), which grows to a total of up to 35 cm long. It has a more spotted pattern on its sides than most other species.
Scientific name: *Ctenotus* spp.

PRICKLY FOREST SKINK ■

The prickly forest skink has a body 8.5 cm long and a tail a little longer. Its has well developed limbs, each bearing five toes. Its eyes are black.

This skink is restricted to the rainforests of north Queensland, including the Atherton Tableland, where it lives in rotting logs on the forest floor and in holes at the base of the buttress roots of rainforest trees.

Inside its damp log home the prickly forest skink remains moist, and its skin is usually shiny with moisture when it first emerges from its shelter but, when it is handled, its skin dries and becomes a dull brown. A drop of water placed on the dry skin immediately spreads out over the surface, helping to keep the lizard moist.

During daylight hours the prickly forest skink remains in its hole, with just its head sticking out. It emerges at night to forage for insects. The females, which are more commonly found than males, bear up to five live young during the tropical wet season. The young take several years to reach maturity, and live for about ten years.
Scientific name: *Gnypetoscincus queenslandiae*

■ PRICKLY FOREST SKINK
The small body scales of the prickly forest skink do not overlap. Each one has a high, backward-facing keel that gives the skink its prickly appearance.

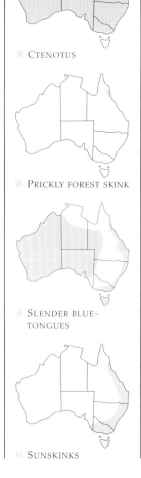

SLENDER BLUE-TONGUES

The slender blue-tongue skinks are closely related to the blue-tongued skinks (*Tiliqua* spp., page 339), but they are smaller and more slender. There are only nine species, all of which are restricted to Australia. Except for the pink-tongued skink (*Cyclodomorphus gerrardii*), all adults in this group have blue tongues.

The pink-tongued skink lives in the rainforests of eastern Australia and is a less slender species than other blue-tongues, with longer legs and toes and a narrow neck. It has a pattern of dark and light grey to pinkish bands across its body and reaches a body length of 25 cm, with a tail as long again. It has peg-like teeth, and also a single large, flattened tooth in each jaw, which it uses to crush the shells of the snails on which it feeds. The pink-tongued skink is active mostly at night – especially on hot nights after rain – and can climb bushes and trees in search of food. These skinks mate in spring and produce large litters of up to 53 live young in early summer.

The gill-necked skink (*C. branchialis*) is a small, pinkish brown lizard with a body length of up to 9 cm and a tail about two-thirds as long. Its common name refers to the three black 'gill' markings on the side of its neck. Until recently the gill-necked skink was thought to occur over much of the dry interior of Australia, from the west coast through to western New South Wales and Queensland. However, recent studies have shown that several different species were included under the one name. The true gill-necked skink is restricted to the Geraldton area of Western Australia, where it is now very rare.

The giant slender blue tongue (*C. maximus*), with a body length of up to 23 cm and a tail as long again, is similar in body shape to the gill-necked skink. It is found only in the northern Kimberley region of Western Australia, where it shelters in deep leaf litter and dense vegetation around large rock outcrops.
Scientific name: *Cyclodomorphus* spp.

SUNSKINKS

All five sunskink species occur in eastern Australia. They are small lizards that can live in a wide range of habitats, provided there is enough moisture. They all lay clutches of between two and six eggs, and several species nest communally.

The dark-flecked garden sunskink (*Lampropholis delicata*) is widespread from north-eastern Queensland right through to South Australia, including Tasmania. It grows to a total length of 10 cm and is found in wet and dry eucalypt forest, woodland and heathland. It is also a very common inhabitant of suburban gardens. It forages in leaf litter and other ground debris for arthropods. This skink has been accidentally introduced from Australia into Hawaii and New Zealand, and is now established in those regions.

The pale-flecked garden sunskink (*L. guichenoti*) is about the same size and is often found in the same areas. This skink lives under leaf litter and rock piles in dry eucalypt forest, woodland, heathland and tussock grassland, and is often found in suburban gardens in eastern Australia. It feeds on small insects and other invertebrates. It is intriguing to see a number of these sunskinks entangling themselves into a ball, each individual firmly gripping the next and reluctant to let go, but the reason for this activity is not known.

A very rare skink is the montane sunskink (*L. caligula*) which is found at high altitude around Barrington Tops and adjacent parts of the Great Dividing Range in New South Wales. It inhabits tufts of the snow grasses that grow in upland woodlands, usually in the vicinity of swamps or watercourses. This little lizard, which reaches a total length of 10 cm, favours places where there is plenty of leaf litter.

Another unusual member of this group is the saxicoline sunskink (*L. mirabilis*), which is found on Magnetic Island and neighbouring areas of the Queensland coast. It lives on granite rock outcrops and has long legs, strong claws and a flattened body – all adaptations to its rock-dwelling lifestyle. The largest of the sunskinks, it reaches a total length of 13.5 cm long.
Scientific name: *Lampropholis* spp.

■ SUNSKINK
The garden sunskink, *Lampropholis guichenoti*, shown here with a clutch of eggs, is one of the sunskink species that nest communally.

■ SLENDER BLUE-TONGUE
The pink-tongued skink, *Cyclodomorphus gerrardii*, is born with a blue tongue, like its relatives, but when it is mature its tongue turns pink.

MULCH SKINKS AND BAR-LIPPED SKINKS ■

Many of the species in this genus lack common names. All are small to moderate-sized skinks with smooth glossy scales and relatively short limbs with five toes on each. Most have a pattern of black and white spots on the sides of their body and on their tail, which differs from the pattern on their back. Their body length varies from 5 cm to 9 cm, measured from snout to vent (anus).

Fourteen of the 17 species of this genus occur in Australia, and the others in the Lesser Sunda Islands of New Guinea. Most are found in northern Australia, but one, *Glaphyromorphus gracilipes*, is restricted to the moist forests and woodlands of extreme south-western Australia.

Some species, such as *G. mjobergi* from the rainforests of the Atherton Tableland, are very slender, with tails up to twice their body length. Members of this group, known as mulch skinks, live in leaf mulch and under logs in shady areas of moist forests and woodlands – although *G. cracens*, also from the Atherton Tableland, is found in drier woods.

Species in the group known as bar-lipped skinks have a more stocky body and a short fat tail, usually about the same length as their body or a little longer. They are more active on the surface of leaf litter at the edges of sunny patches. This group includes the dark-tailed skink (*G. nigricaudis*) of eastern Cape York and eastern Arnhem Land woodlands – also found in southern New Guinea – and the brown-sided bar-lipped skink (*G. brongersmai*), found in forests along rivers and streams in the extreme north Kimberley region of Western Australia.

Most are egg-layers, usually producing between one and five eggs during the tropical wet season, but *G. gracilipes* and one population of the dark-tailed skink in southern Cape York are unusual in giving birth to live young.

Scientific name: *Glaphyromorphus* spp.

WATER SKINKS AND FOREST SKINKS ■

These skinks usually live near water or in humid environments. They are medium to large lizards with well-developed limbs. Their colouring is shades of yellow and black and they are often banded or spotted. Adults grow to between 15 cm and 28 cm long. They eat mostly insects and

■ FOREST SKINK
Usually, all that is visible of the wary yellow-blotched forest lizard, *Eulamprus tigrinus*, is its head protruding from a sheltered spot.

some plants, and all bear live young. Skinks from this genus can be divided into two distinct groups – the forest skinks and the water skinks.

The most restricted of the forest skinks is the orange-speckled forest skink (*Eulamprus luteilateralis*), which lives only in the Eungella National Park in central eastern Queensland. Growing to about 20 cm long, it is a rich brown with dark flecks on the back and orange sides with white spots. Active during the day and evening, it inhabits rainforest or closed woodland and shelters in litter or logs. It produces between three and five live young.

The yellow-blotched forest skink (*E. tigrinus*) is found only in northeastern Queensland and is often seen around the Cairns region. Mid-brown with darker flecks and yellow blotches, it reaches a similar size to the orange-speckled forest skink. It inhabits rainforest and wet forest, hiding in hollows, under the bark of trees or among rocks. It is an occasional tree-dweller and is active during the day and evening.

The bar-sided forest skink (*E. tenuis*) occurs from Cape York Peninsula to southern New South Wales, where it prefers moist areas of woodlands and wet forests. Reaching a total length of 18 cm, it has a greyish brown back and black sides with lighter bars. The most arboreal of the forest skinks, it usually forages early in the day or evening, feeding on arthropods and berries. It stays close to the shelter of rock crevices or tree hollows, and quickly vanishes if disturbed. Sometimes it occurs in suburban areas, where it makes use of brick or stone walls. It produces two to six young.

Water skinks are found near waterways, swamps or seepages, as their

■ BAR-LIPPED SKINK
Glaphyromorphus nigricaudis, the dark-tailed skink, does not always have a tail tipped with black – its colouring varies according to its habitat, and the pale colour of this example fits the coastal territory near Cairns, where it was photographed.

common name suggests. Bolder and more sun-loving than forest skinks, they can frequently be observed basking in full sunlight.

The most commonly encountered member of the group is the strongly built eastern water skink (*E. quoyii*). Usually seen around waterways, it runs for cover when disturbed, only to reappear minutes later to see if the coast is clear. It readily takes to water and can stay under for some time. Coppery to greyish brown, sometimes with a green tinge, it has a yellowish stripe on either side of its spine and grows to a total of 28 cm long. It feeds on insects, tadpoles and crustaceans and has been known to eat native berries. The female bears from two to nine live young in December or January.

The cool temperate water skink (*E. tympanum*) occurs in higher altitudes and more southerly locations than the eastern water skink, which it resembles – except that it has a darker back with black marks and is smaller, reaching a total of only 22 cm long. It lives in moist meadows, woodlands and tussock grasslands and near watercourses, and shelters in burrows beneath logs and rocks, which it also uses as basking sites. Within its habitat, this lizard can occur in large numbers. Like the eastern water skink, it feeds on invertebrates. Two to six young are born in January.

The Blue Mountains swamp skink (*E. leuraensis*) is restricted to a few areas in the Blue Mountains and the Newnes Plateau, west of Sydney. It lives in moist meadows and swamps in lower areas and shelters in dense grass tussocks and in burrows. Reaching a total length of 18 cm, these skinks are dark brown to black with four thin golden stripes along their back, and a black and gold or turquoise mottling on their sides. The Blue Mountains swamp skink is more wary than other water skinks, and if alarmed quickly disappears into thick grass. Very little is known about this lizard, which was not described until 1984.

Australia has two separate populations of alpine meadow skink (*E. kosciuskoi*): the one in the Snowy Mountains has a distinctive dark stripe down the back; the other, which has no stripe or only a faint one, lives on the New England plateau. Found in high-altitude tussock grassland, heathland and woodlands, it shelters under timber and rocks, in some areas utilising burrows. In the Snowy Mountains the southern population shelters

under snow for the coldest winter months. This species reaches a total length of 19 cm and gives birth to two to five young in January.
Scientific name: *Eulamprus* spp.

SAND-SWIMMERS ▧
Although the two skinks in this genus are commonly known as sand-swimmers, they do not merit this name as much as the truly sand-swimming skinks of the genus *Lerista* (this page). While they do wriggle into sand to hide, both species hunt on the surface and occur in areas without loose sand.

Both the narrow-banded sand-swimmer (*Eremiascincus fasciolatus*) and the more robust broad-banded sand-swimmer (*E. richardsonii*) are strictly nocturnal, prowling at night in search of insects and smaller lizards. Although common throughout arid Australia, they are more sensitive to heat stress and dehydration than most other desert lizards.

The habitats of these two species vary considerably across Australia. Generally, the narrow-banded species is more closely tied to sand dunes and looser soils, while the broad-banded species lives in heavier soils, and even on stony plains.

Both species undergo distinctive colour changes as they grow. As hatchlings they are bright yellow above with bands of contrasting intense purple, although banding is usually confined to the tail in the narrow-banded species. At night this colour and patterning gives the young skinks the appearance of large centipedes; this disguise may give the skinks protection, as centipedes are ferocious combatants. By the time the young have doubled their size, the contrasting colours are subdued. Their backs become fawn to sandy coloured and the bands

become grey-brown to tan, with the exact colour and patterning varying to enhance camouflage. On the white sand dunes around the Lake Eyre basin, where narrow-banded sand-swimmers are unbanded and almost white in colour, they are sometimes known as ghost skinks.
Scientific name: *Eremiascincus* spp.

SANDSWIMMING SKINKS ▧
Sandswimming skinks are common in semi-arid and arid regions of Australia. Most are burrowers that live in leaf litter or sand, under stones, logs or grass tussocks.

They are small, slender and smooth-scaled with varying degrees of limb and digit reduction. The primitive south-western plain slider (*Lerista microtis*) has well-developed limbs with five toes on each limb; the lesser robust fine-lined slider (*L. karlschmidti*) has no forelimbs and a single toe on each hind limb; and the limbless fine-lined slider (*L. ameles*) has no limbs at all. Due to their underground lifestyle they do not

▧ SAND-SWIMMER
The broad-banded sand-swimmer, *Eremiascincus richardsonii*, often occurs in areas without loose sand, hiding instead in burrows or leaf litter.

▧ SANDSWIMMING SKINK
The keeled slider, *Lerista planiventralis*, is active in the open during the day – an exception among sandswimming skinks. It tends to move around just under the surface, with occasional forays above ground.

HARD-NOSED LERISTAS

Lizards and snakes periodically shed their outer layer of skin, which is replaced from beneath. In most cases the reptile's skin comes off its body all in a piece, and areas inhabited by reptiles are often littered with shed skins.

Sandswimming skinks (*Lerista* spp.) also moult in this way, but in between times they shed their nose scales. Pushing through leaves and sand wears their nose down faster than other body parts, and to compensate for this they continually replace their nose scales. The photograph below shows *L. macropithops* about to shed its nose scales.

need good hearing, and all leristas have tiny ear-openings. Their lower eyelids have a transparent lens that allows them to see even when the lid is closed – an obvious advantage for skinks that burrow through leaf litter and sand. In many, such as the north-eastern orange-tailed slider (*L. orientalis*), the eyelid permanently covers the eye.

Sandswimming skinks are very active under cover during the day, but generally wait until nightfall before foraging in the open. Anyone walking in sandy areas may see the characteristic wavy tracks left by sliders moving beneath the surface.

All sandswimming skinks feed on soft-bodied insects, and are in turn eaten by spiders, scorpions, centipedes, birds, small mammals and burrowing snakes. Most lay eggs, but a few bear live young. There are more than 80 known species in this Australian genus.

The north-western sandslider (*L. bipes*) bears no trace of forelimbs, and its hind limbs have only two toes. It reaches a total of 13 cm long. It is pale yellow to reddish brown with two parallel rows of brown dots along the centre of its back and tail. It has a white belly and a broad, dark brown stripe along the upper part of each side. It has an endearing habit of poking just its head out of the sand to look around.

The north-western sandslider occurs from the arid region of Western Australia, east throughout the north-western corner of South Australia and the southern half of Northern Territory to the extreme west of Queensland. Inhabiting sparsely to densely vegetated coastal dunes, sand plains and sand ridges, it forages just beneath the surface on warm nights. It feeds on a variety of soft-bodied insects that either live in or fall onto the sand. It lays two eggs in a clutch, probably in spring.

Another species, the south-eastern slider (*L. bougainvillii*), is a primitive slider with five fingers and toes on each limb. It is greyish brown with two or four narrow, broken stripes along its back. It has a broad black stripe along the upper part of each side, which becomes indistinct on the tail. Its belly is white, and in many the tail is yellow or orange.

It reaches a total of 14 cm long. This skink occurs from central eastern New South Wales to the Eyre Peninsula, South Australia, and to north-eastern Tasmania, including the islands of Bass Strait. It lives beneath surface debris on heaths, woodlands and granite outcrops. On the mainland it produces one to four eggs in summer. In Tasmania and the islands of Bass Strait it gives birth to two to four live young in late summer or early autumn.

The rapid housing development on Australia's western coast between Perth and Mandurah may affect the long-term survival of the Perth lined lerista (*L. lineata*), which lives in the southern suburbs of Perth, ranging south as far as Mandurah, and is also found on Garden Island and Rottnest Island.

The Perth lined lerista is a pale silvery to brownish grey, with two parallel black stripes along the centre of its back and tail and a broad black stripe along each side, and its white belly is dotted or flushed with grey. It grows to a total of 11 cm long. Inhabiting coastal heathlands, shrublands and banksia woodlands, it feeds on small invertebrates as well as their eggs and larvae. It lays two or three eggs in mid-summer.
Scientific name: *Lerista* spp.

LITTER SKINKS ■

These tiny, sun-loving skinks inhabit leaf litter in the dry forests of north-eastern Australia. They have a body length of about 3.5 cm and they reach 9 cm in total length. Mature males develop a red flush on the hips, the tail and sometimes the

■ LITTER SKINK
This slender, short-limbed skink is a beautiful shiny russet brown colour. It has four toes on its forelimbs and five on its hind limbs.

LITTER SKINKS

DWARF SKINKS

NANGUR SPINY SKINK

throat. The lower eyelid, with its transparent window, is movable on all species except *Lygisaurus foliorum*. This skink, which is often found in leaf litter at the base of trees, has a fused eyelid. All litter skinks feed on small invertebrates and most of them – perhaps all – lay two eggs.

The sleek Chillagoe litter skink (*L. rococo*) from Chillagoe in north Queensland is a uniform copper colour with long limbs and toes. The largest of the litter skinks, it grows to a total of 10 cm long. Unusually among skinks, this species favours open rock faces. This skink is sometimes included in the genus *Carlia*, along with the sun skinks.
Scientific name: *Lygisaurus* spp.

BOWRING'S SKINK

This small, shiny, ground-dwelling lizard has short legs that it uses only when it is moving slowly. When it is alarmed and needs to move fast, it tucks its legs in beside its body and burrows rapidly, with snake-like movements, into soil or leaf litter. It grows to a total of 10 cm long.

Found naturally throughout much of South-East Asia, it was apparently introduced onto Christmas Island in imported soil or agricultural produce some time between World War II and 1978.

On Christmas Island it has been found only in disturbed areas, and not in the primary rainforest that still covers much of the island.
Scientific name: *Lygosoma bowringi*

DWARF SKINKS

Dwarf skinks are the smallest reptiles in Australia. The largest, the common dwarf skink (*Menetia greyii*) grows to a total length of no more than 9 cm – although it is sexually mature at about 7 cm, when it weighs about half a gram. Other species, such as the top-end dwarf

■ BOWRING'S SKINK
This small skink is characterised by a bronze back, a black stripe running from each eye to the base of its tail, and orange flanks speckled with brown.

skink (*M. alanae*) and the dwarf litter skink (*M. timlowi*) reach their maximum size at a tiny 7 cm long.

The common dwarf skink may well be the most widely occurring Australian lizard, being found almost everywhere except the cool, humid south-east and Tasmania.

This little skink seems equally at home in the stony deserts of central Australia and the gardens of Perth and Adelaide. Throughout its range it varies only slightly in colour and pattern, being greyer and with fewer contrasting stripes in coastal areas and more metallic in desert areas. Males of at least some dwarf skinks develop bright breeding colours: for example, the entire underside of the common dwarf skink becomes a bright lemon yellow, and sometimes the throat turns a vivid orange.

Dwarf skinks have an uneven toe count, with four toes on their front feet and five on their hind feet. They all have the fixed, snake-like

transparent eyelid that is common in small skinks that live in arid or semi-arid climates.
Scientific name: *Menetia* spp.

NANGUR SPINY SKINK

Remarkably, this distinctive animal remained unknown to scientists until 1992. The nangur spiny skink has prominent raised ridges on its scales, particularly on its tail base, which make it look rather like a miniature crocodile. In colour it is a fairly drab yellowish brown with darker narrow bands, and it has large, liquid black eyes. It reaches a total of 17 cm long.

The nangur spiny skink excavates its burrow among roots and tree buttresses in heavy volcanic soils. Being extremely shy, it seldom ventures far from home; it prefers to sit at its burrow entrance, with only its head or forebody exposed, ready to ambush passing insects. None has been seen to stray more than two body-lengths from the safety of its burrow – which probably explains how this skink remained undetected for so long.

Scientists do not know how many young nangur spiny skinks are born, but one baby is known to have lived in its mother's burrow for at least seven months. On several occasions baby nangur spiny skinks have been observed emerging from burrows riding piggyback on their mother, but this is probably not a case of parental care, which is virtually unheard-of in lizards.

The nangur spiny skink is rare and endangered. It is known from only about ten occupied burrows along the banks of a small seasonal creek in a vine thicket near Murgon, a mere three hours' drive north-west of Brisbane. Since its discovery, efforts have been made to protect this vital habitat.
Scientific name: *Nangura spinosa*

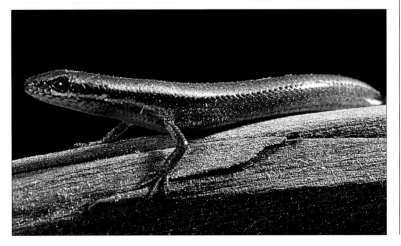

■ DWARF SKINK
The greyish brown dwarf skink *Menetia greyii* has a dark, almost black, stripe running along its flank, from nostril to tail. Found in a variety of habitats, this skink is active during the day.

DISTRIBUTION

■ YELLOW-BELLIED
THREE-TOED SKINK

■ HIGHLAND FOREST
SKINK

■ SHADESKINKS

■ BLUE-TONGUED
SKINKS

YELLOW-BELLIED THREE-TOED SKINK ■

Often the first indication of this lizard is a brown and orange tail disappearing into the loose soil when it is disturbed under rocks or surface debris. Slim, very glossy brown, and usually with a bright yellow or orange underside, this lizard can reach a total of 20 cm in length. Its limbs are very short, each with three very small toes.

The method of reproduction in this species is unusual. The female retains up to seven developing young inside her body until they are almost fully formed, and then lays transparent to opaque eggs just before the young are ready to hatch.

The yellow-bellied three-toed skink lives along the eastern side of New South Wales and in south-eastern Queensland, in a number of habitats ranging from wet forests to suburban gardens. It prefers moist, shaded areas and soil containing a lot of organic matter. It rarely comes to the surface, remaining most of the time in leaf litter, where it forages for the insects, worms and other invertebrates that also live there.
Scientific name: *Saiphos equalis*

OCEANIC SKINK

This rare skink has been recorded only on the oceanic island groups of Norfolk and Lord Howe. It became extinct on the main island of Norfolk, probably after early Polynesian visitors introduced the Pacific rat (*Rattus exulans*).

On Lord Howe Island its numbers declined dramatically after the accidental introduction of the black rat (*R. rattus*) following a shipwreck nearly 90 years ago. However, it persists in small colonies among outcrops of coral rock, and is still common on smaller offshore islands.

Growing to about 13 cm in total length, oceanic skinks are ground-dwellers that live among rocks, rock crevices and other ground debris – especially in areas just above the high-water mark. They feed on a variety of small insects, spiders and crustaceans, and are mostly active during the summer months, when they emerge from cover on warm nights, often moving into the intertidal zone at low tide to feed on small sand fleas and their relatives. They usually spend the colder winter months deep within crevices or in tunnels in the soil beneath large boulders.

The colour and patterning of the oceanic skink are recognisably different on the two island groups, but common identifying features are the pale golden-brown back (with or without dark flecks and spots) and the dark band along the upper flanks. On both islands the tails are sometimes bright rusty red.

Females lay up to three or four eggs in a clutch during the summer, often in communal nest sites. It is not known whether they lay more than one clutch in a season.
Scientific name: *Oligosoma lichenigera*

■ YELLOW-BELLIED HATCHLINGS
The eggs of the yellow-bellied three-toed skink, *Saiphos equalis*, are laid when the young inside are almost fully developed. They hatch within seven days. Shown above are three newborn young, one just emerging from the egg.

HIGHLAND FOREST SKINK ■

The highland forest skink is a small species with a body less than 5 cm long and a tail that is about the same length. It is golden brown to reddish brown, with a slender body, a finely pointed snout and bulging eyes.

This skink is the sole Australian member of a genus that is otherwise found only in New Caledonia. It is restricted to the extreme south-east of the Australian mainland, where several isolated populations occur in highland areas, usually in wet forests. There it finds shelter in moist leaf litter and under logs in very shaded positions.

The highland forest skink is sensitive to heat and rapidly dehydrates and dies in warm, dry conditions. It mates in spring and summer, and the females lay up to nine small eggs in moist soil. The hatchlings emerge about a month later.
Scientific name: *Nannoscincus maccoyi*

SHADESKINKS ■

Shadeskinks are small, slender lizards with long tails. They are reddish to mid-brown, usually with dark and pale flecks on the underside. They all have a pale spot immediately behind the hind limb, and most have a reddish orange tinge to the tail. All shadeskinks are active during the day, feeding on small insects and spiders.

■ HIGHLAND FOREST SKINK
This litter-dwelling species inhabits wet forests throughout its range and is often found on fallen timber, where it can be seen to good effect.

There are five shadeskink species, and all live along the east coast of Australia. The russet-brown weasel shadeskink (*Saproscincus mustelinus*) occurs along the coast and ranges of New South Wales and eastern and southern Victoria, where it frequents moist and humid localities with dense ground cover. It often lives in suburban gardens, but is usually only seen in the late afternoon or on overcast days. The weasel shadeskink grows to a total length of about 14 cm, of which 65 per cent is tail. It is distinguished by a pale mark behind its eyes.

The orange-tailed shadeskink (*S. challengeri*) occurs in the south-east of Queensland and northern New South Wales, where it inhabits rainforest or closed moist forest. It is usually seen, often in large numbers, at the edges of the forest or where shafts of sunlight reach the ground, foraging among leaf litter and fallen timber. It grows to a length of about 15 cm, of which just over half is tail.

The northernmost species of this group is the pale-lipped shadeskink (*S. basiliscus*), which occurs in two distinct populations in northern and central Queensland. It lives in rainforest and forages on the forest floor among ground debris. This skink grows to a length of about 13 cm, of which about 8 cm is tail.

All shadeskinks are egg-layers, and clutches range from two to nine eggs. Some species lay their eggs in communal nesting sites.
Scientific name: *Saproscincus* spp.

BLUE-TONGUED SKINKS
Among the most familiar Australian lizards are the blue-tongued skinks – at least one species makes its home in the gardens and parks of every capital city, as well as in most other parts of the country.

Blue-tongued skinks are among the world's largest skinks, and have relatively long bodies and short tails and limbs. Unusually among skinks, their third and fourth toes are of equal length.

Blue-tongues eat both plant and animal material and give birth to litters of live young in summer.

Although blue-tongues will bite if handled, they are not venomous, and the bites rarely break the skin.

There are six blue-tongued skink species, five of which live in Australia and one in New Guinea and eastern Indonesia. The common blue-tongue (*Tiliqua scincoides*) was one of the first Australian lizards to receive a scientific name. It is one of the world's two largest skinks, reaching a body length of up to 37 cm with a tail that is about two-thirds to three-quarters as long again. Its body is light grey to yellow or orange and its tail is strongly banded with dark grey or brown. There are two subspecies – the northern blue-tongue (*T. scincoides intermedia*) of northern Western Australia, the Northern Territory and north-western Queensland, and the eastern blue-tongue (*T. scincoides scincoides*) of eastern and south-eastern mainland Australia, from Cape York to Victoria and eastern South Australia. Common blue-tongues give birth to litters of up to 18 young.

The Adelaide pigmy blue-tongue (*T. adelaidensis*) is the smallest species, with a body length of less than 10 cm and a tail about two-thirds as long. Its body is greenish brown with irregular dark marbling. Unlike other blue-tongued skinks, it has a pink tongue. This species was first named in 1863, from two examples collected just north of Adelaide.

BLUE-TONGUED SKINK
When defending itself, the common blue-tongued skink thrusts out its blue tongue and hisses. Shown here is the subspecies *Tiliqua scincoides scincoides*, the eastern blue-tongue.

SHADESKINK
True to its common name, this shade-skink lives in shady moist areas, such as rainforest, avoiding direct sunlight except for very brief periods.

DISTRIBUTION

■ SHINGLEBACK

Although several more were collected in the next 35 years in the same area, and another pair in the mid-1940s and again in 1959, the species was not seen again until late 1992, when one was found inside a dead brown snake near Burra, north of Adelaide. Since then, scientists have found several colonies of Adelaide pigmy blue-tongues near Burra, where they live in spider burrows in native grasslands growing on hard soils. Females give birth to litters of up to four young.

The second smallest blue-tongue is the centralian blue-tongue (*T. multifasciata*), which reaches a body length of up to 29 cm and has a tail about half as long again. Its bluish grey to yellow body is transversely marked with narrow orange bands, and there is a dark streak behind its eyes. It is mostly found in the spinifex deserts of northern central Australia. In cooler weather this lizard is often seen during the day on desert roads, and in hot weather it is seen in the evenings. It gives birth to litters of up to 12 young.

SURVIVAL BY ADAPTATION

Skinks are the most diverse reptiles in Australia. While all other Australian lizards lay eggs, many skinks are live-bearers – the embryos develop inside the mother's body until they are born as fully-formed, self-supporting young. This allows skinks to live in very cold climates where egg-laying lizards could not persist because their eggs could not properly develop. By basking in sunny, sheltered spots during the day female livebearing skinks can keep themselves and their embryos warm. Their usually dark bodies improve heat absorption, as does flattening their bodies to increase their surface area when basking. Two skink groups – the tussock skinks (*Pseudemoia* spp.) and the snow skinks (*Niveoscincus* spp.) – are cold-climate specialists, living at high altitudes and in southern areas. The species pictured is *N. greeni*.

In hot climates, heat avoidance and moisture loss are the main problems for skinks. In some areas, prolonged exposure to desert heat would quickly kill these lizards, so many are active only at night, or in the early morning or late afternoon. In the hot middle of the day they shelter in deep burrows, or in areas shaded by overhanging vegetation. Eggs have little trouble developing in hot climates, and so egg-laying skinks tend to predominate in such areas.

The blotched or southern blue-tongue (*T. nigrolutea*) occurs in Tasmania, the lowlands of southern Victoria and adjacent South Australia, and in the highlands of the Great Dividing Range in northern Victoria and southern New South Wales. It grows to a body length of 37 cm with a tail about half to two-thirds as long again, although those from northern highland populations tend to be larger than those from southern populations. This skink's body is dark brown to black with paler blotches of orange, pink or light grey-green. It gives birth to up to ten young.

The western blue-tongued skink (*T. occipitalis*) lives in the mallee and heath country of dry parts of southern Australia, from the west coast to central New South Wales. It grows to a maximum body length of 32 cm, with a tail about half as long. Its body and tail have broad dark brown bands on a pale brown or cream background, and there is a dark streak behind the eye. The western blue-tongue gives birth to up to seven young.
Scientific name: *Tiliqua* spp.

SHINGLEBACK ■
The shingleback is a very large skink, common in the dry parts of southern Australia. It has several common names: in Western Australia it is sometimes called the bobtail or bob-tailed goanna; in South Australia the sleepy lizard, reflecting its lethargic nature; and in eastern Australia the stump-tailed lizard or boggi, or the pine cone lizard, in reference to its huge scales.

It is very closely related to the blue-tongues, and many biologists place it with them in the genus *Tiliqua*. Like the blue-tongued

■ SHINGLEBACK
A large, thick body and tail scales and a short, blunt tail distinguish the shingleback from the blue-tongues, which it resembles in many other ways.

skinks, the shingleback has a dark blue, almost purple, tongue, which it puts out in an attempt to create a fierce appearance and deter predators. It has short legs with the third and fourth toes of equal length, and is very variable in colour, from all-black to light blue-green with pale bands on the body and tail. Some banded examples have an orange head. The shingleback reaches a body length of up to 34 centimetres.

The shingleback lives anywhere within its range that is not densely forested or moist. Its habitats include mallee, heath and grassland (including cultivated grass), saltbush, spinifex and scrub lands. Shinglebacks are mostly herbivorous, favouring moist plant material such as flowers, berries and succulent leaves. However, they eat almost anything that is edible – and even some things that are not!

These large skinks breed in spring, when males follow females for several weeks, and the same breeding pairs form year after year. One to four young, but more usually two, are born in late summer or early autumn. They are very large at birth.

Shinglebacks live for a long time, with wild females taking four to five years to reach maturity. Captive animals have lived for at least 15 years, and there are unconfirmed reports of greater ages. Biologists estimate that in the wild these animals must live for more than 20 years if the population is to remain stable. Since they are common, they may live longer.
Scientific name: *Trachydosaurus rugosus*

SNAKES

Most of the world's most venomous snakes are found in Australia. Of the country's 172 species, 115 are venomous. Although snakes belong to the same order – Squamata – as the lizards, they differ from them in several ways. The most obvious differences are the snake's legless, elongated body and modified backbone. This great elongation has required a rearrangement of the internal organs. Most snakes have only one functional lung, and paired organs such as the kidneys are placed one in front of the other rather than side by side.

In comparison with most lizards, a snake's tail – measured from vent (anus) to tail tip – is short in proportion to its body. In many snake species the females are larger than the males.

venom gland

venom duct
fang
backward-slanting teeth

Jacobson's organ analyses sensory input from flicking tongue

groove
outlet

back fang

forked tongue

The movable eyelids of lizards are replaced in snakes by a fixed, transparent scale. Scientists still do not know how well developed the eyesight of snakes is. Snakes also lack the external ear openings of most lizards; for 'hearing' they seem to rely mostly on low-frequency vibrations rather than higher frequency airborne sounds.

All snakes possess a deeply forked tongue, which, among the lizards, is seen only in the goanna. The tongue plays no part in striking prey but flicks regularly in and out of the snake's mouth to 'taste' or 'smell' the air or ground. These sensations are then analysed by the Jacobson's organ, well-developed in goannas and snakes, which is in the roof of the mouth. Snakes can follow scent trails left by prey, or by members of their own species, and this may be one of the main ways in which they find food and mating partners.

Snake lifestyles

Snakes live on the ground, in trees, in the sea or in other watery places, and most can swim. They shelter under rocks or logs, inside rotting logs or in underground holes. If food or shelter is limited snakes congregate in areas, but such behaviour is unusual in Australian snakes except when flooding forces individuals together onto high ground.

Lifestyles also differ from species to species. Some are nocturnal, others are active by day. In cold places, snakes usually breed in early summer, but in the tropics some breed only during the wet season, some in the dry and others year round. Some snakes lay eggs, while others bear live young. Eggs are mostly laid in holes in the ground or under rocks

or logs, but some pythons make a sort of nest in leaf litter. Only the pythons, however, play a part in actually incubating the eggs. The mother stays with her eggs to protect them from predators.

Quite a mouthful

All snakes are carnivorous. While most predators eat animals much smaller than they are, snakes can swallow prey larger than themselves and two or three times their own diameter. The scrub python, for example, can swallow a wild pig.

To subdue large animals, some snakes immobilise or kill their prey with venom, while others squeeze their prey to death. Many others just seize their prey and swallow it live. Whipsnakes chase down their prey, while others – such as pythons – are ambushers, and death adders lure their prey by wriggling their tail to

imitate a lizard. Many nocturnal snakes take their victims while they are asleep. All snakes have sharp, backward-slanting teeth that prevent their prey from escaping once part of it is in the snake's mouth. Small snakes can last several weeks without feeding, and big pythons can survive for at least a year on a single, large meal.

Snakes have to swallow their prey whole because their teeth cannot tear. The two halves of the lower jaw are connected by tendons rather than fused together, allowing the jaws to stretch hugely. A snake's head, with its many slender bones connected by mobile joints, can expand while food is moving through, and its stomach can also expand considerably.

A SNAKE'S FANGS
In venomous snakes, muscles deliver poison from glands at the back of the mouth into the fangs, which are hollow teeth at the back or front of the snake's mouth. A bite from front fangs is much more effective in venom delivery than one from back fangs. Illustrated above is the front-fanged eastern tiger snake (top) and the back-fanged bockadam (bottom).

A STRETCH OF THE JAW
Snakes can grip with their teeth but cannot tear, so they have to swallow their catch in one gulp. This diamond python illustrates the way in which a snake's jaw stretches in order to engulf its prey.

DISTRIBUTION

■ BLIND OR WORM SNAKES

BLIND OR WORM SNAKES

These shiny, worm-like snakes have a blunt head and a short tail ending in an unusual, small conical spine. Their eyes are reduced to dark spots which are light sensitive. This allows them to distinguish between light and dark, but they probably have no other visual sense. Blind snakes are quite harmless, but when alarmed, they often give off a pungent smell. They consume ant and termite pupae, larvae and eggs. Although active during the day, they are usually hidden beneath ground debris and rocks or in termite and ant nests. Sometimes at night, after rain, they are seen on the surface.

There are about 42 species of blind snakes in Australia, and 38 of these live there exclusively. They sometimes gather under rocks or inside rotting logs in writhing knots of up to nine individuals. All blind snakes are presumed to be egg-layers.

Probably the most commonly seen blind snake in eastern Australia is

the blackish blind snake (*Ramphotyphlops nigrescens*).The small-headed blind snake (*R. affinis*), on the other hand, although widely distributed across Australia, is seldom seen. The fattest blind snake is the robust blind snake (*R. ligatus*), which grows up to 50 cm long; the 30 cm-long brown-snouted blind snake (*R. weidii*) is probably the slenderest. The interior blind snake (*R. endoterus*), which is found in the arid centre of Australia, grows to 35 cm long.

The small flowerpot blind snake (*R. braminus*) was introduced into Australia accidentally from South-East Asia. It grows to about 17 cm long and occurs in suburban Darwin and Katherine, where it is found sheltering in flowerpots or under compost and other debris. All flowerpot blind snakes are females that reproduce without mating.
Family: Typhlopidae

SMELLY BUT HARMLESS
Blind snakes can give off a strong odour when threatened. This is the blackish blind snake, *Ramphotyphlops nigrescens*, found in eastern Australia.

PYTHONS

DISTRIBUTION

■ CHILDREN'S PYTHON

■ BLACK-HEADED PYTHON AND WOMA

■ GREEN TREE PYTHON

Most of the world's pythons are found in Australia, and the group probably evolved here. The largest Australia python is the scrub python (*Morelia amethistina*), which grows to over 7 metres in length, and the smallest is the pygmy python (*Antaresia perthensis*), which is less than 70 cm long. Since pythons are relatively large, and large snakes take longer to warm up than small ones, it is perhaps not surprising that they live only in the hotter parts of Australia, mostly in the deserts and the tropics.

Australian pythons are quite slow-moving and most live on the ground – not unexpected in a continent that is dominated by desert rather than forest. A few, such as the green tree python (*Morelia viridis*), do live in trees, and many of the tree-dwellers have tails that can wrap around branches to give them grip.

All pythons lay eggs and – unusually for snakes – the female remains with her eggs to protect and warm them until they hatch. The number and size of eggs produced depends on the size of the female snake. The smaller species, such as the pygmy python, lay only two or three eggs, while the large scrub pythons may lay more than twenty. Female pythons exhaust most of their

reserves of energy in producing and then incubating their eggs, so it may take them two or three years to build up sufficient physical condition to reproduce again. During the breeding season the males of some python species wrestle over females.

Most pythons are ambushers. They overpower their prey by squeezing it until it stops breathing. Although several different kinds of snake – including many venomous species – use constriction to kill their prey before eating it, the pythons are the most powerful and effective constrictors. As soon as it has bitten its prey, the python throws loops of its body around its hapless victim; although the pressure of these coils is not great enough to break bones, it stops the prey from breathing, and may also prevent blood from reaching vital organs.

The smaller pythons prey on frogs, lizards and other snakes, while large species take mostly birds and mammals – up to the size of wallabies. In their turn, pythons are preyed on by birds of prey, jabirus, foxes and dogs.
Family: Pythonidae

■ CHILDREN'S PYTHON
This python is not so named because it eats children. It was called after a British scientist, John George Children.

CHILDREN'S PYTHONS ■
The common name of this genus does not mean that these snakes eat children, nor that their small size makes them ideal children's pets. In fact, they were named after the British zoologist, John George Children, in 1842.

Widely distributed across the northern half of Australia, all four members of this genus are relatively small. None of them grows to more than 2 metres long, and the pygmy python (*Antaresia perthensis*), also known as the ant-hill or dwarf

python – is the smallest python in the world. A desert species from Western Australia, it grows to a total of less than 70 cm long. It is brick-red or terracotta in colour, with a pure white area around the lower jaw. It is found in rocky country covered by spinifex grasses, and often takes up residence in large termite mounds, where it feeds on lizards and small mammals.

Children's python (*A. childreni*) is somewhat larger than the pygmy python, and occurs across much of northern Australia. The drab brown coloration of the adults provides good camouflage against the dark soils of the monsoonal tropics. The hatchlings are more sharply patterned, with dark blotches against the brown, but these colours fade as the snake grows older. Its diet also changes as it grows from a hatchling 27 cm long to its maximum size of about a metre. The juveniles eat frogs and lizards, while the adults feed mostly on mammals. In some rocky areas, Children's pythons linger near the entrances of bat caves to ambush bats as they fly past.

The other two species belonging to this genus are the spotted python (*A. maculosa*) and the large blotched python (*A. stimpsoni*).

The spotted python is brown with chocolate markings which, unlike those of Children's python, do not fade when the snake reaches adulthood. It is the largest species in the genus, growing to well over a metre in length. Spotted pythons are found along the Queensland coast, but do not penetrate west of the ranges.

The large blotched python is found in dry central areas across much of Australia. It has blotchy brown-on-brown markings.
Scientific name: *Antaresia* spp.

BLACK-HEADED PYTHON AND WOMA

Perhaps the closest living relatives of the earliest pythons are the two *Aspidites* species. Both species are exclusively ground-dwellers, and they spend much of their time in burrows underground. Long and slender, with relatively small heads, they resemble members of some other snake groups, such as the colubrids and elapids, rather than pythons.

Some claim that the black-headed python (*A. melanocephalus*) is one of the most beautiful snakes in the world. It has a light and dark brown banded body, a cream to yellow belly with brown blotches, and a glossy, jet black head and neck. It looks as if it has dipped its head in tar, which probably accounts for one of its common names, tarpot.

Found across the northern third of Australia, from the arid deserts through to the monsoonal tropics, the black-headed python is most common in savanna woodlands. Measuring up to 3 metres long and weighing 16 kg, it is a large, powerful snake that lives almost entirely on other snakes and lizards. Unlike all the other large python species, the black-headed python very rarely preys on mammals or birds.

The woma (*A. ramsayi*), also known as the sand python or Ramsay's python, is found throughout the arid regions of central Australia. At 2 metres long, it is smaller than the black-headed python, and its head is not glossy black, but it is similar in colouring and patterning. The woma cruises at night through the red sandy plains and spinifex clumps searching for lizards and mammals. Sometimes it agitates the tip of its tail to lure small animals close enough for a strike. Aboriginal people consider womas good food, and track them to their burrows.
Scientific names: *Aspidites* spp.

GREEN TREE PYTHON

These slender snakes with large, triangular heads are found only in pockets of rainforest in the eastern region of Cape York and in islands to the north. They are the most exclusively tree-dwelling of all the pythons, spending their whole life in the forest canopy.

Growing to over 2 metres long, these pythons conceal themselves tightly coiled among the thick forest canopy, waiting for unwary reptiles and mammals. The hatchlings, which are around 30 cm long, are either bright yellow or brick red; they turn green over a period of only a few weeks while they are still young.

Male green tree pythons fight lustily during the mating season, and individuals in captivity have been known to kill each other.
Scientific name: *Morelia viridis*

■ GREEN TREE PYTHON
With its brilliant lime green colouring, sometimes flecked with white, the green tree python is perfectly camouflaged in the lush canopy of its habitat in the rainforests of north Queensland.

■ WOMA
The woma, or sand python, is found on the sandy plains of central Australia. It feeds at night, taking shelter during the day in animal burrows or vegetation.

DISTRIBUTION

■ WATER PYTHON

■ OLIVE PYTHON

■ SCRUB PYTHON
■ ROUGH-SCALED PYTHON
■ OENPELLI PYTHON

■ CARPET PYTHON
■ CENTRALIAN PYTHON

■ SCRUB PYTHON
The scrub or amethystine python is one of the longest snakes in the world, growing to at least 7 metres long. It easily swallows prey considerably larger than itself, such as wild pigs and tree kangaroos.

WHITE-LIPPED PYTHON

The glossy scales of this python look dark brown until they are lit up by direct sunlight, when they sparkle in rainbow hues, with a strong irides-cent sheen. The head of this snake is darker than its body, except for the white lips and chin. It is a medium-sized python, growing to about 3 metres long.

This northern species, which is found mostly in New Guinea and surrounding islands, also occurs in a few islands in the Torres Strait. It probably feeds mostly on mammals, but, as with most tropical snakes, little is known of its biology. Recent studies suggest that this species may in fact be two separate species.
Scientific name: *Leiopython albertisii*

WATER PYTHON ■

This medium-sized python occurs mostly around bodies of water in the tropical north of Australia and in New Guinea. Water pythons can sometimes be found in very large numbers around the edges of bill-abongs and other waterways where the rats that form the major part of their diet are likely to live.

■ WATER PYTHON
Usually found alongside streams and lagoons, water pythons take to the water when disturbed. They feed largely on native rats, and stop reproducing when few rats are available.

The water python reaches a length of 3 metres and has a bright yellow belly and a dark brown back. Studies undertaken near Darwin have shown that water pythons feed for the most part on native dusky rats, and that the snakes migrate long distances every year in order to follow seasonal shifts in the distribu-tion of these rats.

When monsoonal rains fill the flood plains, the pythons may travel more than 10 kilometres to reach the higher ground where the rats have been forced to concentrate by the ris-ing floodwaters. In years when the monsoonal rains are less intense, the flood plain dries out quickly and the rats therefore stop breeding early in the dry season. During subsequent wet seasons, when rats are difficult to find, the pythons lose condition and stop reproducing.
Scientific name: *Liasis fuscus*

OLIVE PYTHON

Although this species looks like a water python at first glance, and is often found in the same general area, a closer examination reveals many differences. The olive python is generally lighter in colour and has a larger head, and its underside is white rather than yellow.
Olive pythons also inhabit drier country than water pythons and are often found among rocky outcrops in savanna woodlands. They grow much larger than water pythons, in some cases reaching well over 40 kg in weight and 5 metres in length. They are not the longest Australian snake – scrub pythons grow longer – but they are the heaviest.

The large size of the olive python enables it to feed on quite large mammals, including wallabies. There are reports of home owners in the Darwin area finding olive pythons in pursuit of their dogs, cats or chickens, but there are no records of olive pythons – or any Australian pythons – ever eating humans. Such stories belong strictly in the realms of fiction.
Scientific name: *Liasis olivaceus*

SCRUB PYTHON ■

Also known as the amethystine python, this giant snake is restricted to the forested areas of Cape York Peninsula and the islands to the north, including New Guinea. In the winter, scrub pythons may gather in open valleys to bask and mate.

This is the longest Australian species of snake, and one of the longest snakes in the world. Reports of specimens over 8 metres long are probably exaggerations, but there are many reliable records of scrub pythons 7 metres long, and they

While females of several types of snake stay with their eggs to protect them from predators, female pythons not only protect their eggs but keep them warm, so that they develop quickly and are not exposed to harmfully low temperatures. Like all reptiles, pythons are cold-blooded (ectothermic), but they have very muscular bodies, and the female is able to twitch her muscles at regular intervals to generate heat – exactly as shivering humans do when they are cold. By this means, the female python can remain 'warm-blooded' throughout the incubation period. But when the eggs finally hatch, she takes no further interest in her offspring.

have been known to take animals as large as tree kangaroos.

The scrub python is a relatively slender, rich golden or olive brown snake with dark bars and blotches along its body. The juveniles are quite often found in trees as well as on the ground, while the adults are thought to be more terrestrial.
Scientific name: *Morelia amethistina*

ROUGH-SCALED PYTHON

The rough-scaled python is known only from a small number of specimens that have been collected in the remote Kimberley region of Western Australia. Growing to at least 2 metres long, it is a heavy-bodied snake, blotched in brown and cream. Its body scales are keeled (ridged), giving it a rough texture.

This species of python appears to be restricted to small patches of thick monsoonal forest, but it may be more abundant than has been so far supposed. It probably spends most of its time in the trees.
Scientific name: *Morelia carinata*

OENPELLI PYTHON ■

Despite growing to a length of at least 4.5 metres, possibly more, this is the most slender python in the

world. Also known as the Oenpelli rock python, it lives in the sandstone escarpment country of western Arnhem Land. Its drab brown daytime colour changes to an elegant silvery grey at night.

Oenpelli pythons are believed to feed for the most part on birds and mammals. Local people talk of seeing these giant snakes draped motionless in the branches of fruiting trees, apparently lying in wait for birds attracted to the fruit.
Scientific name: *Morelia oenpelliensis*

CARPET PYTHON ■

The carpet python, better known in New South Wales as the diamond python, is familiar to quite a number of Australians. Growing to more than 2 metres long, it is found over much of the continent.

Its colours vary considerably across its extensive geographic range, with the typical form being a blotched brown in colour. The bright yellow and black spotted form is encountered only in south-eastern New South Wales. This python's social system also varies from area

to area. In some populations males fight vigorously during the mating season, but in other places they tolerate each other without aggression.

This python has adapted very well to human civilisation, and remains common in the outlying suburbs of Sydney and Brisbane. Traditionally, farmers have encouraged it as a natural means of controlling rodents in barns and grain storage areas.
Scientific name: *Morelia spilota*

CENTRALIAN PYTHON

This arid-zone species is sometimes known as the desert carpet python or Bredl's python, and is a close relative of the carpet python (this page). Red to yellow in colour and growing to about 2.5 metres in length, these pythons are mostly found in rocky outcrops and in trees beside usually dry watercourses. They are mainly nocturnal, especially when the weather is hot, and feed chiefly on mammals and lizards.

The centralian python has never been studied in any detail, and is awaiting further investigation.
Scientific name: *Morelia bredli*

■ CARPET PYTHON
The carpet python is commonly known in New South Wales as the diamond python. It is found from coastal forests in the east and north-east of Australia to arid inland areas.

■ OENPELLI PYTHON
The Oenpelli python is found in tropical woodlands among the sandstone gorges of western Arnhem Land. Oenpelli is the name of a settlement in the region.

DISTRIBUTION

ARAFURA FILE SNAKE

ARAFURA FILE SNAKES

The rivers, creeks and billabongs of tropical Australia and New Guinea are home to an entirely aquatic, non-venomous snake. The most distinctive feature of the Arafura file snake (*Acrochordus arafurae*), one shared with its smaller Australian relative *A. granulatus*, is its loose-fitting skin,

A FISH-EATING SNAKE
This water-dweller lives exclusively on fishes. It moves swiftly in its aquatic environment but is helpless on land.

which seems far too large. This skin is covered with small spiny scales, and its rough texture is responsible for the common names of file snake and elephant's trunk snake.

File snakes are probably only distantly related to other types of snake, and are unusual in a number of ways. For example, the females are considerably larger and much more heavy-bodied than the males. The average female has a length of about 1.55 metres and weighs 1.5 kg, while the male averages 1.22 metres in length and only 700 g in weight. In addition, their metabolic rate is somewhat lower than that of many other snakes, which enables it to survive dry seasons, when food is sometimes in short supply.

Both sexes feed entirely on fishes, but females consume mostly large, deep-water varieties while males take smaller, shallow-water species. File snakes hunt for their prey after

dark, and the snake's rough, loose skin enables it to constrict the fish in the same way as pythons do.

The file snake's biology is greatly affected by the seasonal climate of the monsoonal tropics. During the dry season, when the billabongs are small and isolated from each other, file snakes mate, but rarely feed. When wet-season flooding joins up the billabongs, the file snakes move out into the large areas of shallow water and feed more frequently. Females give birth to live young at the end of the wet season, with most females probably reproducing only once every few years.

File snakes are a popular food for Aboriginal people in some parts of tropical Australia. The snakes are caught by feeling around under logs and floating grass-mats. Despite this harvesting, and despite predation by other species such as crocodiles, sea eagles and jabirus, Arafura file snakes can be found in high densities in large, downstream, murky, crocodile-infested billabongs where fishes are plentiful.
Family: Acrochordidae

COLUBRIDS

The Colubridae, numbering nearly 2000 species in a dozen or so sub-families, are the largest and most successful family of serpents in the world. In Australia, however, this family is represented by only a handful of species in two subfamilies, Colubrinae and Homalopsinae. A third subfamily, Lycodontinae, occurs on Christmas Island since the accidental introduction of an Asian wolf snake (*Lycodon capucinus*).

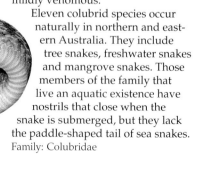

BROWN TREE SNAKE
This slim snake forages at night; during the day it hides in rock crevices and tree hollows.

Colubrids vary a great deal in body shape, behaviour and size. Species range from 20 cm to 4 metres in length. Some are egg-layers, while others bear live young. Many of them resemble the highly venomous elapids in appearance, although very few of the world's colubrids are deadly to humans. The exception to this rule is the African boomslang (*Dispholidus typus*) – a dangerous snake that has caused numerous deaths. Unlike elapids, whose fangs are at the front of their mouth, most colubrids are either solid-toothed, and so completely non-venomous, or back-fanged, making them only mildly venomous.

Eleven colubrid species occur naturally in northern and eastern Australia. They include tree snakes, freshwater snakes and mangrove snakes. Those members of the family that live an aquatic existence have nostrils that close when the snake is submerged, but they lack the paddle-shaped tail of sea snakes.
Family: Colubridae

BROWN TREE SNAKE ■
Many a pet canary has been the downfall of a brown tree snake. The slender snake slips easily between the bars of a bird cage, but difficulties arise when it is trying to leave. The bird owner may wake to find the canary missing and the snake coiled up in its place – the suspicious-looking lump in the snake's body has made it too large to pass back through the bars.

The brown tree snake is slender and flattened sideways, and has a broad head and large eyes with elliptical pupils like a cat's. Its body is pale brown to reddish brown with darker transverse blotches that may form narrow bands, and its belly is salmon pink to pale red. It grows to a length of 1.6 metres.

The brown tree snake occurs from the Kimberley across to Cape York Peninsula, south to Sydney and inland to the Great Dividing Range. It lives in sparsely to densely timbered areas, particularly near rocky outcrops. It feeds on frogs, lizards, mammals, birds and birds' eggs.

The brown tree snake is a venomous back-fanged snake, but it is not regarded as dangerous to humans. When disturbed it pulls back its head, folds its neck into an S-shape and strikes repeatedly.

Large numbers gather in caves and in the roofs of old buildings. They have turned up in places like New Zealand and Perth, accidentally transported in fruit packing cases.

During early summer in the south and in the spring in the north, the brown tree snake deposits 4–12 eggs in crevices or hollow logs, or beneath litter. The newly hatched young are 25–30 cm long.
Scientific name: *Boiga irregularis*

BOCKADAM

This stout-bodied water snake has a broad, distinct head, small, upward-bulging eyes with round pupils, and nostrils on top of its snout. It grows to 60 cm long and has keeled (ridged) scales. Its upper body is grey to brown marked with irregular blackish transverse bars, and its belly is white, yellow or pink with dark transverse bars. A dark streak on each side passes through its eyes onto its neck.

The bockadam is found coastally from northern Western Australia to Cape York Peninsula. Inhabiting flooded mangroves and mud flats, it feeds during the night on crabs and fishes. It rarely leaves its watery habitat: when disturbed on the surface it dives close to the bottom and swims away. It is back-fanged and mildly venomous, but harmless to humans. During summer it produces 8–26 live young in water.
Scientific name: *Cerberus rynchops*

COMMON TREE SNAKE

The body colouring of a common tree snake is quite varied – it can be greyish black, olive brown, bright green, blue or golden. Its lips and lower forebody are white or lemon yellow, while its belly is a similar colour to the back. It is a slender, long-tailed snake with smooth scales, large eyes and round pupils. It attains a length of 1.7 metres. Being solid-toothed, it is not venomous. When threatened it inflates its body, displaying the bluish skin between the scales.

Occurring along the coast and adjacent areas from the Kimberley to Queensland and as far south as

southern New South Wales, it is found in woodlands and thickets, especially near water, and hunts during the day for frogs, lizards and birds. It is equally at home on the ground or climbing through trees. At night it sleeps in tree hollows and rock crevices. The common tree snake deposits 5–12 eggs beneath bark, in hollow logs or under leaf litter during early summer in the south and in spring in the north.
Scientific name: *Dendrelaphis punctulata*

MACLEAY'S WATER SNAKE

The young of this snake are born in the water. During the summer the female gives birth to a litter of up to 15 young. The babies immediately cluster together to give themselves some protection from predators.

Macleay's water snake grows to a length of 80 cm. It is stout-bodied and has smooth scales and small eyes. Its upper body is greyish brown to dark brown and its sides are paler. Its lower sides and belly are cream to yellow, often mottled on the underside of the neck with black, and it has a narrow black stripe along the underside of the tail. Queensland individuals often also have a sparse mottling of black over their back and sides. It is back-fanged and mildly venomous, but harmless to humans.

This snake occurs in the northernmost parts of Queensland and the Northern Territory. Inhabiting freshwater swamps, billabongs and rivers, it hunts both by day and by night. It anchors itself by using its tail to grasp something, such as a submerged branch, and then grabs passing fishes, frogs and tadpoles.
Scientific name: *Enhydris polylepis*

MACLEAY'S WATER SNAKE
This snake of northern Australia is found in creeks and areas of water that are left behind at the end of the wet season. It bears live young in the water.

DISTRIBUTION

BROWN TREE SNAKE

BOCKADAM

COMMON TREE SNAKE

MACLEAY'S WATER SNAKE

COMMON TREE SNAKE
When threatened, this nonvenomous snake puffs itself up and flattens its neck and body so as to display the light blue skin between its scales.

DISTRIBUTION

■ WHITE-BELLIED
MANGROVE SNAKE

■ SLATY-GREY SNAKE

■ KEELBACK

■ RICHARDSON'S
MANGROVE SNAKE

WHITE-BELLIED MANGROVE SNAKE

As its common name suggests, the lower sides and belly of this snake are either white, cream or yellow. Its body may be white, grey, brown, red or black, with or without pale or dark blotches. This stout-bodied water snake grows to about 80 cm, has smooth scales and a blunt head.

The white-bellied mangrove snake is found in mangroves and mud flats along the coast from the Pilbara region in Western Australian to the Northern Territory. It forages at night, making its way over the mud during low tide by throwing loops of its body forward, anchoring them in the mud, and then dragging the rest of its body along. This action tends to move the snake sideways across the mud rather than straight ahead. It eats crabs, which it holds against the ground with its coils, removing and eating each of the legs before swallowing the body.

In 1995, during rough seas caused by cyclone Bobby, thousands of these snakes were seen entwined along the top of a wire fence near Karratha in Western Australia. By the following day, when the storm had subsided, they had left.

This snake is back-fanged and mildly venomous but harmless to humans. It gives birth to as many as 13 live young on the mudflats and in the water at the end of summer.
Scientific name: *Fordonia leucobalia*

SLATY-GREY SNAKE

The slaty-grey snake lives in damp areas near billabongs, rivers, swamps and water tanks in the northern parts of Queensland and the Northern Territory. Although usually found on the ground, it is

a good swimmer and climber. It is a moderately large, muscular snake with smooth, iridescent scales. Growing to a length of 1.3 metres, it is a uniform dark grey, dark brown or black on the top and has a pale yellow belly, lips and lower neck. On the underside, especially towards the tail along the outer edges, it is flecked with black.

It hunts for frogs at night, and also sometimes eats lizards and mammals. It is solid-toothed and harmless, but will bite when handled. This snake lays up to 12 eggs beneath rotting vegetation during summer.
Scientific name: *Stegonotus cucullatus*

KEELBACK ■

Sometimes known as the freshwater snake, the keelback is about a metre long with keeled (ridged) scales. It has large eyes with round pupils. Its body is yellow brown to dark brown with numerous black flecks or blotches, sometimes in irregular cross-bands. Its belly is pale yellow, olive, brown or pink. Like a lizard's tail, the tail of a keelback will break off if grasped by a predator.

■ KEELBACK
This foraging keelback's shed skin can be seen just behind the snake, lying across a partially submerged log.

The keelback occurs in coastal areas and adjacent parts from the Kimberley in Western Australia to northern New South Wales. It is found in damp areas near billabongs, rivers and swamps, where it hunts both by day and night, feeding on lizards and frogs. It even eats the young of the poisonous cane toad, with no adverse effects, and is also known to eat the squashed bodies of frogs from roads.

The keelback is solid-toothed and harmless. In spring and summer it deposits 5–15 eggs beneath rocks, logs and under rotting leaf litter.
Scientific name: *Tropidonophis mairii*

RICHARDSON'S MANGROVE SNAKE ■

This is a small snake – up to 50 cm long – with weakly keeled scales. Its body is grey to pale brown, with large darker blotches often forming irregular cross-bands. Its head is usually darker than its body and is unmarked except for a darker streak sometimes present along each side and passing through its eyes. Its belly is cream, grey or brown.

Richardson's mangrove snake occurs coastally from the Kimberley of Western Australia to the Northern Territory. It occupies mangrove swamps and mud flats, sheltering in crab holes and among roots. From its hiding place it ambushes and constricts fishes. This snake is back-fanged and mildly venomous, but harmless to humans. It is rare, and little else is known about it.
Scientific name: *Myron richardsonii*

■ RICHARDSON'S MANGROVE SNAKE
This small colubrid is found along the northern coast of Australia, generally among the mangroves and mud flats.

ELAPIDS

More than half the land snakes in Australia – about 85 species – are elapids. Worldwide, only about 10 per cent – no more than about 300 species – belong to this family.

All elapids are venomous, injecting venom into their prey through a pair of hollow teeth (fangs) at the front of their upper jaw. Because their fangs are at the front of their mouth rather than the back, they can defend themselves from larger animals by injecting venom into them. Many elapids are therefore dangerous to humans.

In Africa and Asia the elapid family includes cobras, kraits and mambas, and in South and North America it includes the coral snakes. In Australia and New Guinea these front-fanged land snakes are more closely related to sea snakes and sea kraits than to the elapids elsewhere in the world. Scientists therefore think that the elapid family probably evolved in Asia, with the Australian group being descended from a single species that came from Asia.

Elapids vary in size from 20 cm in some species to up to 4 metres in large taipans. Elapids eat mainly lizards, but some eat frogs or mammals, and some take a range of prey, including fishes and insects. About half the Australian elapids lay eggs and the rest give birth to live young.

About a third of all elapid species are too small to bite humans, while the bite of most of those that can is no more dangerous than a bee sting. Up to 20 elapid species are thought to be deadly to humans, but as only three or four dangerous species are ever found in one locality, it is easy to identify and then avoid them.
Family: Elapidae

RAINFOREST CROWNED SNAKES

These snakes live in rainforest along the east coast of Australia, and are nocturnal. They shelter under rocks, logs or moist leaf litter, where they forage for frogs and blind snakes as well as lizards and their eggs. They are dark brown or black above, with pale lines along the sides, mottled markings on their face, and a yellow or white collar. Females are larger than males and lay 2–15 eggs – the size of the clutch increasing with the snake's size. These snakes usually strike with their mouth closed, so bites are rare, but they should be treated with caution.

The golden-crowned snake (*Cacophis squamulosus*) grows up to 80 cm long, has a yellow collar broken at the mid-line, yellowish eyes and a reddish underside with black markings. When threatened it raises the front of its body in an S-shape, flattening its head and tilting it down.

Other species have a similar display, without the S-shaped coil. The white-crowned snake (*C. harriettae*), which grows to 56 cm, has a broad whitish collar, brown eyes and a dark grey underside. The northern dwarf crowned snake (*C. churchilli*) is also dark grey underneath, but with a yellow or cream collar. It grows to about 45 cm and has white eyes.
Scientific name: *Cacophis* spp.

WHIPSNAKES ▨

Whipsnakes, with their long, slender bodies, are among the fastest snakes in Australia. Occurring throughout the continent except in the far south, they prefer high temperatures and dry, open conditions. They have

large eyes, and nearly all have a dark line below each eye. Most also have other dark lines or spots on their head, or a dark collar. There are at least ten whipsnake species in Australia and New Guinea.

Generally active during the day, whipsnakes eat lizards and frogs. Detecting their prey either by scent or by sight, they then give chase. To see further, a whipsnake often holds its head above ground while cruising among grass and rocks, pausing to bob up and down to gauge distance. If it loses sight of its prey during a chase, it wiggles its tail, which usually scares the lizard into motion. To subdue larger prey, whipsnakes use constriction as well as venom.

Females, which lay 2–13 eggs under a rock or in soil cracks, do not grow as large as males. In tropical areas they breed at any time during the year, but in the south they breed only in summer and their communal nests may contain hundreds of eggs.

▨ WHIPSNAKE
The Percy Island whipsnake, *Demansia torquata*, is found on rocky hills in woodland or rainforest areas on the Queensland coast and islands.

DISTRIBUTION

▨ RAINFOREST CROWNED SNAKES

▨ WHIPSNAKES

DISTRIBUTION

■ RED-NAPED SNAKE
AND RELATIVES

■ BROAD-HEADED
SNAKES

■ BROWN SNAKES

The yellow-faced whipsnake (*Demansia psammophis*), which grows to just over a metre, is found over most of the continent. Both this snake and the smaller, northern olive whipsnake (*D. olivacea*) vary in colour from grey to a bright pattern of russet, olive green and yellow.

The grey whipsnake (*D. simplex*), of the north-west, is the smallest whipsnake, at a maximum of 53 cm long. The greater black whipsnake (*D. papuensis*) is the largest, reaching 1.8 metres. It is dark reddish brown to black, its head paler but without any markings. It can easily be mistaken for a young taipan, and has also been confused with the lesser black whipsnake (*D. vestigiata*).

Whipsnakes usually flee when disturbed, but if cornered or handled they may strike without any bluff or warning. Bites are painful but not considered dangerous, except for those of the two black whipsnakes.
Scientific name: *Demansia* spp.

RED-NAPED SNAKE
AND RELATIVES ■
These are all nocturnal snakes. They have small eyes, glossy scales and white bellies. Most species have a bar of contrasting colour across a black or dark brown head. They live in leaf litter, under rocks and logs, in soil cracks or in ant or termite nests. From these shelters, or from under litter, they ambush and kill lizards, using constriction as well as venom. The females, which lay one to ten eggs, are larger than the males.

The brown-headed snake (*Furina tristis*), which grows up to 95 cm long, is very dark brown except for

white edges on its body scales and a yellowish brown bar at the nape. Dunmall's snake (*F. dunmalli*) is a thick-bodied species growing to 70 cm and lacking a pale bar on the nape. It may be endangered by clearing of its brigalow habitat.

The 40 cm-long red-naped snake (*Furina diadema*) and the 70 cm-long orange-naped or moon snake (*F. ornata*) have dark edges on their body scales surrounding yellow and red pigments that form a net-like pattern. Black patches on their head and neck outline a bright yellow to red spot or bar. Yellow-naped snakes (*F. barnardi*) look like orange-naped snakes when young, but they darken with age. Adults, which reach 37–70 cm in length, are more like the brown-headed snake.

With the exception of the brown-headed snake, none of these species usually bites in self-defence.
Scientific name: *Furina* spp.

■ ORANGE-NAPED SNAKE
This snake has a yellow to reddish bar across its dark head. It feeds at night, ambushing lizards, which it then kills using constriction as well as venom.

BROAD-HEADED SNAKES ■
The common name for this group of three species of venomous snakes derives from their intriguing defensive strategy. If they are threatened, the snakes raise their head and the front part of their body from the ground in a stiff S-shape and flatten their head, giving the impression that they are larger than they really are. This display is not all bluff, as all three species will readily strike. No human deaths have been recorded, but a bite from a large specimen may cause quite severe symptoms.

These tree or rock-dwelling reptiles are restricted to coastal eastern Australia. Usually hunting lizards, frogs and small mammals by night, they can sometimes be found active – or merely sunbaking – on warm days. Usually, however, they spend the day resting in narrow crevices or tree hollows or behind large pieces of flaking bark on tree trunks.

Stephen's banded snake (*Hoplocephalus stephensii*) lives in moist forests, from the New South Wales central coast northward to southern Queensland. At about 1.2 metres long, this is the largest species in the group, and is distinctively marked with black and white bands along the body. These markings are particularly bright in newly born snakes, but they tend to fade with age.

Although it is the most widespread species, the pale-headed snake (*H. bitorquatus*), which attains a total length of up to a metre, is probably the least often encountered. Often living around large trees lining rivers and creeks, it inhabits wooded

■ BROAD-HEADED
SNAKE
A small, slim broad-headed snake species, *Hoplocephalus bungaroides* is found only in sandstone gorges in the Sydney area. It is an agile climber, capable of negotiating sheer rock faces using any small ridges and cracks to obtain a grip.

areas from Sydney to northern Queensland. It ranges further inland than its close relatives.

Like all broad-headed snakes, the pale-headed snake produces litters of live young. The normal litter size is about five or six, although as many as eleven have been recorded. As soon as they are born the juveniles slither away, avoiding the attention of hungry kookaburras, magpies and goannas, to find food and fend for themselves. Mostly dark grey in colour, this snake is distinguished by a light grey collar that is often surrounded by black spots.

The broad-headed snake (*H. bungaroides*) is a small, slender species, averaging around 60–70 cm long, with black and yellow markings. It is restricted to the Sydney region, where it lives among sandstone gorges and cliffs.

These reptiles are often found beneath loose slabs of sandstone warming their body with the heat of the sun that has been absorbed by the rock. Unfortunately, this species is on the decline, as these same rocks are highly prized by landscape gardeners who, in removing the rocks, also destroy an essential part of the species' habitat.

Scientific name: *Hoplocephalus* spp.

BROWN SNAKES ■

Although brown snakes have short fangs and small venom glands, their venom is extremely neurotoxic, and all species are potentially deadly. Even bites from the ringed brown snake (*Pseudonaja modesta*), the smallest of the brown snake species, can cause serious symptoms.

The largest brown snake is the eastern brown snake (*P. textilis*), and it is also the most aggressive. As well as being very large and not at all timid, it is common wherever mice – its favourite prey – abound, and it is not difficult to understand why this snake is considered the most dangerous of all Australian snakes. Before the discovery of an effective antivenom, about 40 per cent of bites from the eastern brown snake proved deadly.

Brown snakes vary greatly in colour – so much so that their common name is misleading. They may be pale yellowish grey, shades of russet or greenish brown, or even black – darker individuals usually being found in cooler or moister habitats. The underside of a brown snake is pale, with most of the belly scales bearing paired darker dots or blotches. The rostral scale (above the mouth at the front of the snout) is

Most Australian snakes mate in spring, and males are most active at this time as they search for females, often staying with them for days or weeks. It is common to find pairs together, and two or more males can be found with one female. In many species the males compete for the chance to mate by wrestling. Here, two male carpet pythons are wrestling in a creek.

large and thick, and helps to push earth particles aside as the brown snake burrows. These snakes are such competent burrowers that even large brown snakes can stay completely hidden while crossing lawns by bulldozing through the topsoil between grass roots. All species have dark markings on their head and nape when young, and most have a series of broad or narrow bands on their back, which usually fade with age. Brown snakes vary in size from 60 cm to 2.2 metres, with males being larger than females.

Brown snakes inhabit dry, open grassy areas of mainland Australia. They are usually active during the day but also on warm nights. They shelter under logs or slabs of rock, in deep soil cracks or in mammal burrows. They prey on lizards and frogs, and larger specimens also take mammals, smaller snakes – including their own species – and birds, all of which they constrict while the venom takes effect.

Mating occurs in spring, or early wet season, and males may compete in wrestling matches. Females lay 2–38 eggs in a clutch, and when food is abundant they may mate again and lay a second clutch in the summer.

There are at least seven brown snake species in Australia. The eastern or common brown snake (*P. textilis*), grows to 2.2 metres, while the western brown (*P. nuchalis*), the peninsula brown (*P. inframacula*), the dugite (*P. affinis*) and Ingram's brown (*P. ingrami*) reach lengths of 1.6–1.8 metres. The ringed (or five-ringed) brown (*P. modesta*) grows up to 60 cm and the speckled brown (*P. guttata*) to 130 cm; both mainly eat lizards, especially skinks.

Brown snakes are fast-moving and generally attempt to escape if they are disturbed, but some species are easily provoked. They have two kinds of threat display. The speckled brown and Ingram's brown flatten their neck and swing their head and forebody above the ground in a low arc. All the other species may begin with a similar display, but they then form a high double S, facing their attacker to display their speckled underside. This concertina action of the body allows the snake to make a long strike.

Scientific name: *Pseudonaja* spp.

■ BROWN SNAKE
Brown snakes are extremely venomous, and the eastern brown snake is considered the deadliest of all snakes in Australia because of its size, its aggressiveness, and its preference for cultivated areas where there are plenty of mice. This Queensland specimen is 1.8 metres long.

DISTRIBUTION

TAIPANS

BLACK SNAKES AND
MULGA SNAKES

BURROWING ELAPIDS

TAIPANS ▦

Australia's two taipan species are, among the venomous snakes, the largest and deadliest in the world, and have caused a number of human deaths. The combination of long fangs and the ability to produce large amounts of highly neurotoxic venom make them potentially even more dangerous than brown snakes, but since they are much less common and widespread, fewer people have been attacked.

Taipans usually bask and forage on the surface in the morning, but in cool weather they emerge only in the course of the afternoon. When it is hot they become nocturnal. Often stalking their prey in soil cracks or burrows, adults feed mainly on rats and mice, but they also consume small marsupials and birds. They are unique among Australian snakes in feeding exclusively on warm-blooded prey, even when young.

Breeding occurs from August to December and, as in other species where males are the larger sex, they may fight each other for access to females. From 7 to 17 eggs are laid at a time, and two clutches are laid in good years. Hatchlings are 40–50 cm

HOW DEADLY ARE AUSTRALIAN SNAKES?

The taipan (*Oxyuranus scutellatus*), pictured below – and snakes in general – have received much bad publicity, and many people fear them. Australia is home to more venomous snakes than any other country, but our species are not the world's deadliest. Many of them are fatal only to small creatures, and the annual number of deaths per million people is only 0.13 in Australia, compared with 10 deaths per million in South America, 13 in India and close to 50 in Sri Lanka.

Nor are snakes particularly aggressive. Indeed, 15 per cent of snakebite deaths in Australia have been caused by people trying to kill the snake instead of letting it slither away.

Snakes have learnt that where there are people there are mice, and most snakes tolerate the presence of humans to obtain this prized delicacy. If a snake should wander into your garden, the best strategy for both parties is to leave it alone. It is unlikely to bite unless you provoke it.

long at birth, and grow very rapidly on a diet of mice and rats.

The species *Oxyuranus scutellatus*, known simply as the taipan, sometimes reaches a length of 4 metres, making it Australia's longest venomous snake. It occurs in moist, open coastal plains ranging from the Kimberley in Western Australia to Fraser Island in Queensland and into northern New South Wales.

Sugarcane cultivation, land clearing, and rodent-rich rubbish dumps have favoured this species. The spread of cane toads has diminished the populations of all other large elapids in Queensland but has not affected the taipan, and numbers have increased in recent decades.

Like the brown snakes, the taipan is pale to dark yellowish or reddish brown above – sometimes nearly black – and paler below. Its head is also pale, and the scales on its neck are keeled. It shelters under logs, in long grass or vine thickets, in piles of leaf litter, or in animal burrows.

The taipan does not usually seize its prey after striking but quickly releases it, reducing the chance of being bitten by its prey, and also allowing it to kill several prey in quick succession. The taipan is likely to retreat when approached but, if provoked, holds its forebody in an open, slightly raised coil and strikes upward several times, often at the arms or upper body, embedding its fangs without closing its jaws.

The other taipan species, the inland taipan (*O. microlepidotus*) often stands its ground when approached, in an upright S-stance like that of some brown snakes.

Also known as the small-scaled or fierce snake, the inland taipan grows to a length of 2.5 metres and has smooth scales. Its head and neck are slightly darker than its body in

▦ TAIPAN

The inland taipan is also known as the fierce snake. It frequently stands its ground when approached, holding its body in an upright S threat display.

the summer but glossy black in winter. It is seldom seen, as it lives on the flood plains, gibber plains and dunes of the Channel Country (Cooper Creek and the Diamantina River, Lake Eyre Basin) of south-western Queensland, and in the north-east of South Australia. It is occasionally found in neighbouring drainage basins, but this is probably the result of widespread flooding in its normal distribution. It is thought to breed only when its principal prey, the long-haired rat, is abundant, which is usually only after several years of good rain.

The inland taipan holds onto its prey after biting, probably because its venom is so effective that bites from its catch are rare.
Scientific name: *Oxyuranus* spp.

BLACK SNAKES AND MULGA SNAKES ▦

The red-bellied black snake (*Pseudechis porphyriacus*) is one of the most familiar snakes in south-eastern Australia. It is glossy black on top and mainly bright red on its lower sides. Its underside is a duller red or pink, and the underside of its tail is black. This snake is active during the day, sheltering in hollow logs, thick vegetation and animal burrows, or under large rocks. It is usually seen on the edges of creeks, swamps and lagoons. It eats frogs, mice, lizards and smaller snakes, and sometimes hunts under water for eels and tadpoles. The males wrestle during the spring breeding season and grow much larger than the females, sometimes exceeding 2 metres.

The other members of this genus are similar in their habits, except that they mostly live in drier parts of the country and are active on warm nights as well as during the day. They have smaller eyes than the red-bellied black snake, and all have different colour patterns.

The mulga snake, or king brown snake (*P. australis*), is the largest of the genus, growing to nearly 3 metres long. It is found over most of the country in a wide range of habitats, and is either uniform reddish, greenish or grey brown, or has a dark or light spot on each body scale, forming a net-like pattern.

A similar but smaller species is the spotted mulga snake (*P. butleri*) from inland Western Australia, which grows to 1.6 metres long. Another species, *P. guttatus*, from woodland habitats in New South Wales and southern Queensland, grows to nearly 2 metres in length and has two colour forms – the blue-bellied black, which is black all over, and the spotted black, which is grey or brown with a darker head and scattered lighter and darker spots.

The most spectacularly coloured member of this group is Collett's snake (*P. colletti*), found on the black-soil plains of western Queensland. It grows up to 2.5 metres long and has irregular reddish bands and blotches on a brown to black body.

Snakes of this genus are generally shy, and if disturbed they usually try to escape. If cornered, they defend themselves by flattening their neck into a hood and swinging their head and neck in a wide arc close to the ground, meanwhile hissing loudly and making sweeping sideways strikes. Their venom is less neurotoxic than that of other large elapids, but their bite can be very painful; it can cause local tissue damage, and can even be fatal. The venom from a New Guinean black snake species, *P. papuanus*, is used to manufacture antivenom for all black snake bites.

Members of the *Pseudechis* genus lay 4–19 eggs; in most species these have the usual leathery shells and take several months to hatch. The red-bellies are the exception to this, with females retaining the eggs in their body until they are almost ready to hatch. The young are then laid in transparent egg membranes, from which they emerge either immediately or within a few days. This seems to be an adaptation for cool climates, as it allows the female to speed up incubation by basking.
Scientific name: *Pseudechis* spp.

BURROWING ELAPIDS

Burrowing snakes are difficult to observe in the wild; their behaviour is known only from capture records or observation in captivity.

Most shelter in sandy soil under leaf litter, or logs in open forest or woodland, but some dig into harder soil or under rocks. They eat lizards and their eggs. In spring males of most species can be found at night on the surface searching for mates. The females of all species are larger than the males, and lay one clutch of one to eight eggs in late summer.

Burrowing elapids are less than 45 cm long, with small eyes, glossy scales and a white belly. All have a pair of black patches on their head and nape, and most have a net-like red and yellow body pattern. They

BLACK SNAKE
One of the best known snakes in south-eastern Australia, the red-bellied black snake can sometimes be seen swimming across bays and estuaries.

have a relatively thick, muscular neck, a short tail and an enlarged scale on the tip of their snout.

Both *Neelaps* species have a narrow, cylindrical head and a rounded snout. They swim through sandy soil, and prey only on small sand-swimming lizards. The black-striped burrowing snake, *N. calonotus*, which grows to 28 cm, is endangered by habitat destruction in its restricted range around Perth. The stripe along its back is formed by the black edges on a single row of scales. The black-naped burrowing snake, *N. bimaculatus*, is longer and very slender.

The genus *Simoselaps* includes several groups with thicker bodies and flattened or conical heads. The most primitive is *S. warro*, found in eastern Queensland, but little is known about it. Most other members of this species have narrow or broad dark bands on their body and tail. The eastern shovel-snout, *S. australis*, which grows to about 37 cm, eats skinks and eggs, while the southern shovel-snout snake, *S. semifasciatus*, takes only eggs. They sniff out clutches of lizard eggs soon after they are laid, and then dig them up using their strong snout, and slit them open with blade-like teeth in the roof of their mouth.

Three burrowing elapids occur in central and Western Australia, collectively known as desert banded snakes: they are *S. bertholdi*, which grows to 33 cm; *S. littoralis*, growing to 39 cm; and *S. anomalus*, growing to 21 cm. They have short, powerful bodies encircled with solid black bands, and deep, wedge-shaped heads. Like the *Neelaps* species, they 'swim' through leaf-litter or sand.

They ambush prey at night or during the day, waiting with just the top of their head exposed to seize and then constrict passing lizards. They prey mainly on small skinks, but adults also take relatively large, strong-limbed lizards.
Scientific names: *Neelaps* and *Simoselaps* spp.

BURROWING ELAPID
The desert banded snake, *Simoselaps littoralis*, is found mainly in sandy shrubland and on coastal dunes. It burrows into the sand, leaving only the top of its head exposed, and preys on passing lizards.

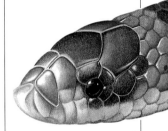

DIGGING AND DELVING
An enlarged scale on the tip of its snout, sometimes equipped with a shovel-shaped edge, enables the burrowing elapid to live mainly underground.

DISTRIBUTION

■ DEATH ADDERS

■ BARDICK
■ DE VIS' BANDED SNAKE AND ORNAMENTAL SNAKE

■ BANDY-BANDYS

■ COPPERHEADS

■ BARDICK
A native of mallee shrubland, the bardick is a primitive death adder. Its bite is not lethal, but can be serious.

DEATH ADDERS ■

Because of their long fangs, potent venom and unwillingness to move away when disturbed, death adders are very dangerous snakes. Before the use of antivenom, about 60 per cent of bites to humans were fatal. Their defence display involves flattening their body and hissing loudly before striking repeatedly. Generally, they move to escape danger only as a last resort, but there have been occasions when a person has walked close to a death adder, or even stepped on it, and the snake has stayed completely still – which accounts for their other common name, deaf adder.

Death adders look different from most other elapids. Their body is short and thick, their head broad and triangular, and they have small eyes with elliptical pupils. Body colours vary, but the tail, which is slender with the tip flattened from side to side, is yellow, white or black. Their narrow, irregular light and dark bands and their unusual body shape provide excellent camouflage.

Death adders spend most of the time partly hidden by leaf litter, sand or overhanging vegetation, moving around only in the late afternoon or at night. They are most often seen on hot nights in early summer, when the males are searching for females.

Death adders trick their prey by twitching or waving the tip of their tail just in front of their head. In the belief that the tail is an insect, frogs, lizards, birds or small mammals will investigate and are struck with terrifying speed. The snake's fangs sink deeply into the victim's flesh and inject it with a fast-acting neurotoxin, so that the snake does not have to move far to recover its meal.

The common death adder (*Acanthophis antarcticus*) is found in many habitats, including rainforest, coastal heath, sand dunes and arid grassland. Its body may be red, grey, brown or olive green, ranging from pale shades to nearly black. Its head and neck scales are smoother than those of other species. Females grow larger than males, averaging about 50 cm in length, but they can grow to just over a metre. These adders breed only every two or three years, giving birth to up to 20 live young.

The three other Australian adder species are generally less than 75 cm long, less thickset, and have strongly ridged scales on their head and neck. The desert death adder (*A. pyrrhus*) is bright reddish, matching the colour of most of its arid-zone habitat, which includes shrubland, sandy deserts and rocky hills. The northern death adder (*A. praelongus*) is brown, grey or dull reddish, and usually has prominent horn-like scales over its eyes. This species is found in rocky or woodland habitats.
Scientific name: *Acanthophis* spp.

■ DEATH ADDER
The desert death adder is found in arid regions in all mainland Australian states except Victoria.

BARDICK ■

The bardick is found in mallee shrubland in southern Australia. It grows to a length of 60 cm and, like the adders, has a relatively broad head and thick body. It is uniformly reddish, grey or olive brown, with scattered dark and light markings on its head.

As well as foraging actively by night, the bardick also ambushes prey while sheltering under logs or grass tussocks. It feeds on lizards and frogs, and sometimes birds, mammals and insects.

When disturbed, it can be quite aggressive. Bites can be treated with death adder antivenom.
Scientific name: *Echiopsis curta*

DE VIS' BANDED SNAKE AND ORNAMENTAL SNAKE

The two species of *Denisonia* are relatively thick-bodied and broad-headed. They shelter under logs or in soil cracks and hunt frogs at night. They also eat soft-skinned geckos, but they avoid the pricklier ones.

De Vis' banded snake (*D. devisii*) attains a length of 52 cm and is yellowish brown, olive or reddish brown with broad darker brown bands on its back. It lives west of the Great Dividing Range, on the flood plains and western slopes of New South Wales and Queensland. The ornamental snake (*D. maculata*), 46 cm long, looks similar, except that it lacks the dark bands. It occurs east of the Great Dividing Range in the Fitzroy River drainage basin, including in brigalow woodland.

Females of both species are slightly larger than males, and give birth to 3–11 relatively large young.
Scientific name: *Denisonia* spp.

BANDY-BANDYS

Bandy-bandys have distinct black and white bands encircling their body. The more widespread of the five species is the bandy-bandy *Vermicella annulata*, which is found in the east. It has broad black and white bands around its body and, at about 80 cm, is the longer species. The northern bandy-bandy (*V. multifasciata*), found in the north-west, has narrow, pale grey bands and grows to about 54 cm long. In both species the females are much larger than the males.

These snakes occur in a wide range of habitats over most of Australia except the south-west, but they are not often seen because they live mostly underground. They travel on the surface only when they are forced out by heavy rain, or on summer nights when they are looking for mates or new shelter sites.

Bandy-bandys have the narrow head, little beady eyes and short, blunt tail that are typical of burrowing snakes, but their slender, cylindrical body and rounded snout are not adapted to tunnelling in hard soil. Bandy-bandys can make their way through soft earth, but they probably live mainly in pre-existing tunnels, where they feed on blind snakes, which in turn feed on ants.

Female bandy-bandys breed only every few years, laying 2–13 eggs. The hatchlings are relatively large at a length of about 18 cm, and reach maturity at 30–40 cm long.

Scientific name: *Vermicella* spp.

COPPERHEADS

Copperheads live in the cooler parts of south-eastern Australia, including the highlands of New South Wales and the lowlands and ranges of Victoria, Tasmania, and South Australia, where they usually live among grass tussocks that grow close to streams or swamps.

Copperheads are capable of being active at far lower temperatures and higher altitudes than most other Australian snakes. They use rocks, logs or mammal burrows for shelter, and often a number of them take shelter together to make the most of a food glut.

They are moderately thick-bodied snakes with a head barely wider than their neck, which is marked by a dark collar. The front half of their body is reddish brown with a narrow, dark line along the middle of the back, and sometimes other lines or blotches on either side. The underside of the neck and lower sides are light grey to yellowish white, which

accounts for their other common name – yellow-bellied black snakes. The back and underside of the rear part of the body and tail are dark.

The pygmy copperhead (*Austrelaps labialis*) of the Mount Lofty Ranges and Kangaroo Island in South Australia, which rarely reaches more than 85 cm long, and the highlands copperhead (*A. ramsayi*) both have coppery heads and cream and dark brown bars on their upper lips. This feature distinguishes them from the lowlands copperhead (*A. superbus*), whose head is more uniformly dark. The highlands copperhead grows to about 1.2 metres, while the lowlands species can reach a length of as much as 1.7 metres on some of the Bass Strait islands.

Copperheads are active during the day, but they also forage on warm nights. They eat mainly small skinks and frogs, sometimes small snakes (including the young of their own species), and occasionally insects or small mammals. Unlike most snakes of their size, their diet hardly differs between juveniles and adults.

These snakes bear live young, and most females breed only every two years. The clutch may contain from 3 to 32 young, depending on the size of the mother, but all the hatchlings are about 15 cm long.

Although copperheads are dangerous and abundant, few people come in contact with them, as they usually retreat when disturbed. If a copperhead is cornered when it is too cold to move quickly, it flattens its neck into a hood and swings its head and neck in a wide arc close to the ground while hissing loudly and making sweeping sideways strikes.

Scientific name: *Austrelaps* spp.

COPPERHEAD

Living in cooler parts of south-eastern Australia, most copperhead species are able to be active at lower temperatures than other Australian snakes. This alert specimen is the lowlands copperhead, *Austrelaps superbus*.

BANDY-BANDY

The distinctive black and white bands around its body make a bandy-bandy easy to identify.

BEWARE THE TAIL THAT WAGS

Death adders are not the only snakes to use their tail to help them catch prey. Some elapids, such as whipsnakes and marsh snakes also use their tail – but not as a lure.

These snakes respond to nearby motion by raising their head and twitching or shaking their tail in the grass or leaves. This is often an alarm or territorial response to predators or another snake. But it has also been suggested that this motion and sound can disturb potential prey such as a lizard that, in attempting to escape the snake, breaks cover and is more easily captured. Illustrated here is a death adder about to strike a lizard that has been attracted to its twitching tail.

■ TIGER SNAKES

■ SOUTHEASTERN GRASS SNAKES

■ SOUTHWESTERN GRASS SNAKES
■ MARSH SNAKES

■ ROUGH-SCALED SNAKE

■ SMALL-EYED SNAKES

■ MARSH SNAKE
The black-bellied swamp snake is the most common marsh snake. It usually lives near water and shelters under rocks, sheets of bark and dense vegetation.

TIGER SNAKES ■

Tiger snakes are the largest and most dangerous live-bearing elapids. They have a fairly thick body and a short, broad head. Their body flattens when basking or during defensive displays.

These snakes live in cool, moist coastal heathlands, forests and alpine grasslands, usually among tussocky grass. They shelter in dense vegetation, under logs, or in burrows made by mammals or birds. They forage during the day and on warm nights. Sometimes they climb into trees to bask or to search of food.

Small tiger snakes eat frogs and lizards, while larger ones take small mammals, birds and small snakes. On some islands the adults feed largely on nestling sea birds. Males are a little larger than females and compete for mates in spring. The young are born in middle to late summer, varying in number from six to just over a hundred.

The eastern tiger snake (*Notechis scutatus scutatus*) is widespread on the south-eastern mainland. Usually light to dark brown with broad or narrow yellowish bands on its back, it is sometimes unbanded or mainly black. Tiger snakes living in cold areas are dark coloured, enabling them to warm up quickly in sunlight, while paler individuals predominate in the warmer parts of their range.

The western tiger snake (*N. scutatus occidentalis*) is found in the south of Western Australia. It is dark brown to black, with either narrow or faint bands or no bands at all. Other subspecies are found in South Australia and Tasmania.

Most tiger snakes grow to about 1.6 metres long, although bird-eaters

■ TIGER SNAKE
Large and dangerous, tiger snakes have been responsible for quite a number of human deaths. This is an eastern tiger snake, *Notechis scutatus scutatus*.

on Bass Strait islands can attain lengths of 2.4 metres and those living on islands where only lizards are available grow to less than a metre.

Tiger snakes usually try to escape when disturbed but, if cornered, they spread their hood and flatten their body in an open curve, hissing loudly, slightly raising the front of their body and swinging it from side to side with the head facing the threat. During forest clearance and inland settlement, many people were killed by tiger snakes, but they are now uncommon in many areas where they used to be abundant.
Scientific name: *Notechis* spp.

SOUTHEASTERN GRASS SNAKES

These are slender snakes with large eyes and a narrow head. They live in coastal and alpine regions in southern Australia, where they shelter under rocks, logs or vegetation. Feeding

mainly on skinks, they are active during the day and on warm nights.

Their undersides are whitish, lemon yellow, orange or pink, or a mottled combination of these colours. Males and females are about the same length. Females on the mainland breed nearly every year, bearing two to ten live young. Pregnant females gather in colonies, several basking together on a log.

The white-lipped snake (*Drysdalia coronoides*) grows to 50 cm and is grey, olive green or reddish in colour. Tasmanian individuals tend to be thicker-bodied and dark green, and breed only every two or three years.

The two species of yellow-crowned snakes are reddish or greenish grey overall, with a dark head patch and yellow collar. *D. mastersi* grows to 33 cm long and has a black-edged white lip stripe. This stripe is absent in the 46 cm-long *D. rhodogaster*.
Scientific name: *Drysdalia* spp.

SOUTHWESTERN GRASS SNAKES

The short-nosed snake (*Elapognathus minor*) is 50 cm long, and the crowned snake (*E. coronatus*) is 65 cm long. The crowned snake is grey, greenish or reddish brown above, with a dark collar and a pale-edged dark line though the eyes and across the snout tip. The short-nosed snake is dark grey with black and yellow markings on the neck. It has larger eyes than the crowned snake and no teeth on its upper jaw apart from its fangs. Both have pale yellow to bright orange undersides.

Both species live in heath or woodland in the cool, moist southern part of Western Australia. Active during the day, they feed on skinks and frogs. The smaller species gives birth to 8–12 young and the crowned snake has about 3–9 offspring.
Scientific name: *Elapognathus* spp.

MARSH SNAKES ■

The black-bellied swamp snake (*Hemiaspis signata*) is generally found close to water and is active by day and on warm nights, feeding on lizards, tadpoles, frogs and other snakes. It grows to 80 cm long and is olive green above, or sometimes brownish or black, with a glossy black underside and two dark-edged yellowish stripes on each side of its face. Males are slightly larger than females, and 3–16 young are born in late summer.

This normally docile snake flattens its body and neck in defence. Its bite is painful but not dangerous.
Scientific name: *Hemiaspis* spp.

ROUGH-SCALED SNAKE ■

This snake is similar in appearance to a tiger snake, but its head and body are narrower and it has strong keels (ridges) on its body scales. It is light to dark green or coppery brown above with narrow darker cross-bands, and grows to 1.2 metres in length. Males and females are about the same size.

The rough-scaled snake is a forest-dweller and, like its relatives the tiger snakes and broad-headed snakes, can climb trees. It is active from dusk to dawn, often emerging during rain. It both searches for prey and ambushes it, feeding mainly on frogs and small mammals, and sometimes birds and lizards. Females bear 5–18 live young in summer but do not breed every year. The young are keen climbers from birth, when they are about 20 cm long. They eat frogs until they are large enough to catch mice.

If disturbed, rough-scaled snakes attempt to escape, but they can be irritable and may raise their neck in an S-shape and point their head at the offender, hissing loudly with their mouth partly open. They make quick, accurate strikes, and may bite several times if unable to escape. Like that of the tiger snake, their venom can kill humans.

Scientific name: *Tropidechis carinatus*

SMALL-EYED SNAKES ■

These snakes, mostly less than 60 cm long, have relatively small but prominent or beady eyes and glossy scales. The top of their head is normally blackish and most have dark edges on the body scales, forming a stripe down the back in some species. The rest of the upper surface may range from bright pink to dark brown or black, but is usually reddish. Their belly is generally white.

Most are strictly nocturnal, sheltering by day under rocks, logs or grass hummocks, or in soil cracks or animal burrows. They usually catch their prey by searching shelter sites at night, when most lizards and other small snakes are asleep, but they also ambush prey. Some species also eat frogs, small mammals or the young of their own kind.

Males grow larger than females and will fight for females. They mate in spring, and it is common to find a male and a female together under a rock or log. Up to eight live young are born in late summer.

When disturbed, these snakes flatten their body into stiff, open coils, hiss loudly and make violent, thrashing motions and sideways strikes – though some species are more docile. Large specimens can

inflict a painful bite, and at least two species, the eastern small-eyed snake (*Cryptophis nigrescens*) and the curl snake (*Suta suta*), are dangerous.

The eight or so species of the genus *Parasuta*, known as hooded or black-headed snakes, are brown or reddish above with a black head patch. They inhabit mallee, woodlands and dry forests, and most occur in South Australia, with some species extending to Western Australia, Victoria and inland New South Wales.

The square-nosed snake (*Rhinoplocephalus bicolor*) has a dark stripe on its back and enlarged scales on its snout for burrowing. It lives in coastal woodland in the south of Western Australia, sheltering in the lower chambers of abandoned stick-ant nests. It ambushes lizards on the surface, near the entrance tunnel.

The eastern small-eyed snake (*Cryptophis nigrescens*) is black above with a white, yellow or pinkish red underside. Reaching a length of 95 cm, this snake prefers moist forest habitats. The northern small-eyed snake (*C. pallidiceps*) and the Carpentaria snake (*C. boschmai*), which are mostly brown above with orange or yellow sides, often shelter in deep cracks in the earth.

Suta species, which inhabit dry inland areas, have a dark line through their eyes and around the tip of their snout. The curl snake (*S. suta*), a relatively thick-bodied species growing to 85 cm, is usually pale to rich brown above, though sometimes reddish or greenish. It is usually found on flood plains. Rosen's banded snake (*S. fasciata*) and the little spotted snake (*S. punctata*) are smaller and more slender. Usually bright reddish with darker markings, they can range from pale yellow to dark reddish brown.

Scientific name: *Cryptophis*, *Suta*, *Parasuta* and *Rhinoplocephalus* spp.

■ ROUGH-SCALED SNAKE
This snake has strongly keeled (ridged) body scales, which give it a rough texture. It lives in wet forest and sometimes climbs trees.

■ SMALL-EYED SNAKE
The monk snake, a small-eyed snake, is more colourful than other members of the genus *Parasuta*. It is orange or pink above and has very little dark pigmentation, except for its hood.

DISTRIBUTION

HORNED SEA SNAKE

REEF SHALLOWS SEA
SNAKE

SEA SNAKES AND SEA KRAITS

Sea snakes and sea kraits evolved from land snakes possibly no more than 20 million years ago. Although scientists are not clear about their exact evolutionary relationships, there is little doubt that their nearest living relatives are the venomous elapid land snakes of the Australian region; in fact, these two groups are sometimes included with the elapids as a single family.

The most important difference between sea snakes and sea kraits is that only sea snakes give birth to live young in the sea. Because of this adaptation, sea snakes do not need to come onto land – indeed most cannot do so. Sea kraits, on the other hand, regularly come ashore in order to rest and digest their food and to lay their eggs on land.

The two groups also differ in their belly scales. The sea kraits spend a considerable amount of time on land, so they have retained the broad belly scales that help land snakes to maintain a grip on land surfaces. Most sea snakes, since they have no need for land adaptations, have belly scales that are scarcely larger than the rest of their body scales, and they are more stream-lined and eel-like than the sea kraits.

However, the two groups have in common various other adaptations to life at sea. Both have nostrils with fleshy valves that close off their respiratory passages and prevent water from entering their lungs when they are diving, as well as extended lungs to retain more oxygen. They are able to stay under water for long periods – typically half an hour or so, but some can stay down for two hours or more. They also have special glands under their tongue that serve to concentrate and excrete the extra salt in their bodies from the sea, and distinctive paddle-shaped tails.

Although several species that feed on fish eggs have virtually lost their teeth and venom glands, most sea snakes and sea kraits are extremely venomous, since they need quick-acting venom to immobilise their prey in the open sea. The venom apparatus of both groups is similar to that of Australia's venomous land snakes: hypodermic fangs at the front of the upper jaw, connected on each side by a duct to a large venom gland under the skin of the cheek.

Sea kraits range from India to the islands and reefs of the western Pacific Ocean, while sea snakes –

with one exception – range from the Persian Gulf to the western Pacific. The exception is the yellow-bellied sea snake (page 360), which extends from the east coast of Africa to the tropical west coast of the Americas. Ashmore Reef, on Australia's north-west shelf, has one of the world's most diverse sea snake faunas. Sea snakes and occasionally sea kraits are caught, sometimes in large numbers, in fish and prawn trawls in tropical waters. There are no marine snakes in the Atlantic Ocean.
Families: Hydrophiidae (sea snakes), Laticaudidae (sea kraits)

HORNED SEA SNAKE

This sea snake occurs from eastern Indonesia throughout Australia's tropical seas to New Caledonia. Growing to just over a metre in total length, it is usually pale brown with a series of blackish bands or saddles along the back alternating with another series on the belly. Its scales are very rough – even spiny in older individuals – but it is this snake's head that becomes most distinctive with age. Keels, or ridges, start to grow on the scales over and around the eyes, and these become more and more spiny as the snake grows, so that the head of the adult is spiky and fearsome in appearance.

Horned sea snakes live in both clear reef and muddy coastal waters. Little is known about their habits.
Scientific name: *Acalyptophis peronii*

LEAF-SCALED SEA SNAKE

This species of sea snake occurs only in waters among the complex of reefs, such as the Hibernia Reef and the Ashmore Reef, on Australia's

REEF SHALLOWS SEA SNAKE
Like others of its genus, but unlike most sea snakes, this sea snake has broad belly scales that may enable it to move over coral, boulders and sand.

north-west shelf, which is situated between the Kimberley coast and the island of Timor.

The leaf-scaled sea snake averages only about 60 cm in total length. It lives mostly in the shallow waters of the coral reef flats, where it feeds on a wide variety of small fishes that live in crevices. It gets its name from the long, overlapping, leaf-shaped scales on its body. It is usually dark brown to black with obscure darker and paler cross-bands along its body and tail. Its head is rather small and sharp-snouted.
Scientific name: *Aipysurus foliosquama*

REEF SHALLOWS SEA SNAKE

Ranging widely from the waters of Irian Jaya and Australia's north-west shelf, through Australia's tropical waters as far east as New Caledonia, this snake is usually associated with coral reefs. It is of moderate size, growing to about a metre long. Usually it is dark purplish brown – often with creamy edges to its scales, a creamy belly and a series of darker cross-bands – but uniformly brown individuals are also not unusual.

Although this snake is a common species, little is known about its habits. Like other members of its genus, it has much broader belly scales than most other sea snakes, suggesting that it can use these scales to move slowly over surfaces.
Scientific name: *Aipysurus duboisii*

TAILS LIKE PADDLES
Rather than having tails with a tapered end, like those of land snakes, sea snakes and sea kraits have flattened oar-shaped tails. This adaptation helps them make their way more effectively through the water.

GOLDEN SEA SNAKE

Growing to nearly 2 metres long, this snake, also known as the olive sea snake, is the largest member of its genus. It is abundant in Australia's tropical waters and ranges from southern New Guinea and Western Australia to New Caledonia.

This snake has the alarming habit of approaching divers and even coiling itself around them. Some divers say that it is naturally aggressive, but generally it is just curious. In pushing the snake away, however, a diver certainly risks being bitten.

The golden sea snake is found around coral reefs, in muddy coastal and estuarine waters, and in the Gulf of Carpentaria and the Arafura Sea, where it feeds on a variety of fishes. It varies in colour, but is typically an almost uniform olive grey or olive brown, sometimes with obscure darker cross-bands.
Scientific name: *Aipysurus laevis*

STOKES' SEA SNAKE

This large, bulky sea snake attains a length of 1–2 metres, and a very large girth of up to 10–15 cm in diameter. It ranges from the waters of Indo-Malaysia to Australia's east coast, and feeds on a variety of fishes. It is commonly seen at sea, and it dives if

disturbed. Large fangs and large venom glands in a massive head make it extremely dangerous.

It is usually grey above with a whitish belly. Younger specimens may be strongly banded with black, but older ones tend to have only a vestige of banding. Females produce five to ten large young in a litter.
Scientific name: *Astrotia stokesii*

SPECTACLED SEA SNAKE

The pale spot in front of each eye is responsible for this snake's common name. Confined to the waters of Australia and southern New Guinea, it is a slender snake and grows to 1.5 metres in length. It has a small black head and nape. Its body is grey-brown, with a series of about 50 black cross-bands or saddles, and there is a distinctive narrow black line along the middle of its belly.

Although it is widespread, little is known about this species. It seems likely that it feeds on burrowing and crevice-living eels, but it certainly eats free-swimming fishes as well.
Scientific name: *Distiera kingii*

TURTLE-HEADED SEA SNAKE

As a result of living entirely on fish eggs, this species has virtually lost its teeth and venom glands, neither of which are needed for such a diet.

Averaging about 60 cm in length, it ranges from the Timor Sea to New Caledonia and Fiji. It is abundant throughout Australia's northern seas. It is common on coral reefs and in the shallow waters of the Gulf of Carpentaria, the Arafura Sea and the north-west shelf.

It varies in colour and pattern, ranging from dark brown or black through various degrees of obscure banding to brilliant bands of black

and white. Males typically have a large spine on the scale at the tip of the upper snout, which may be used in courting or mating behaviour.
Scientific name: *Emydocephalus annulatus*

NORTH-WESTERN MANGROVE SEA SNAKE

This small sea snake occurs only along the coast of north-western Australia. It usually lives in mangroves, where it shelters among roots at high tide. At low tide it moves across the mud flats feeding on mudskippers and other small fishes in tidal pools. Being only about 60 cm long, it is not thought to be dangerous to humans.

Unlike most other sea snakes, this species has relatively large belly scales, which it seems to use to help it to move across the tidal flats. It is greyish, with about 30–40 dark grey or black blotches, or sometimes bands, along its back and tail.
Scientific name: *Ephalophis greyi*

BEAKED SEA SNAKE

This snake rarely visits Australian waters, but when it does, it is often in quite large numbers. It occurs from the Persian Gulf through the tropical waters of India, South-East Asia, Indonesia, Australia and New Guinea. Often caught in fishing nets, it is aggressive and highly venomous. It often swims into river mouths; it even swims long distances into the freshwater reaches of larger rivers.

The beaked sea snake averages about a metre in length and is slender, rough-scaled, and usually pale grey above and whitish below. It has projecting jaws with an overhanging snout and small beady black eyes that tend to look upwards.
Scientific name: *Enhydrina schistosa*

■ GOLDEN SEA SNAKE
These snakes sometimes swim right up to a diver and entwine themselves around the diver's body, but they seem to be more curious than aggressive.

■ STOKES' SEA SNAKE
Potentially one of the most dangerous sea snakes in the world, this bulky creature is usually seen out at sea, floating on the surface.

DISTRIBUTION

GOLDEN SEA SNAKE

■ STOKES' SEA SNAKE

SPECTACLED SEA SNAKE

TURTLE-HEADED SEA SNAKE

■ NORTH-WESTERN MANGROVE SEA SNAKE
■ BEAKED SEA SNAKE

DISTRIBUTION

BLACK-RINGED
MANGROVE SEA SNAKE

ELEGANT SEA SNAKE

ORNATE SEA SNAKE

YELLOW-BELLIED OR
PELAGIC SEA SNAKE

**BLACK-RINGED
MANGROVE SEA SNAKE**
A denizen of Australia's
northern coastal waters,
this species likes the mud
flats around mangroves.

BLACK-RINGED MANGROVE SEA SNAKE

This is another small snake that
spends most of it time among mangrove forests, moving about the
mud flats at low tide to feed. As
with many other sea snakes, little
is known about its life and habits.

It is found around the coast of
northern Australia, from about
Dampier to Torres Strait, and along
the southern coast of New Guinea.
It is conspicuously marked with
about 40 bluish-black cross-bands
alternating with narrower bands
of white or cream. Growing to only
about 50 cm in total length, it is not
thought to be a danger to humans.
Scientific name: *Hydrelaps darwiniensis*

COGGER'S SEA SNAKE

Cogger's sea snake is one of a group
of sea snakes that have tiny heads,
narrow necks, and a very slender
front half of the body with a considerably larger and deeper rear half.
This unusual shape has evolved to
enable these snakes to feed on the
slender eels that live in narrow burrows on the sea bottom. The snake
enters an eel's burrow, seals off the
entrance with its narrow body, and
then bites and immobilises the eel
before swallowing it.

This snake lives in seagrass beds,
on coral reefs and on the large sandy
flats of large reef lagoons, as well as
in the deeper water between reefs. It
ranges from Australia's north-west
shelf to the coral reefs of the western
Pacific and east to the Fijian islands.

The young have black heads and
their bodies are banded black and
pale yellow. As they grow, their
head becomes olive-grey and the
bands on their olive-grey body
become less marked. Growing to
just over a metre in total length,
these snakes are believed to dive
and feed at considerable depths –

sea snake belly
scales are usually
small and narrow

paddle tail

valves in nostrils shut
when sea snake dives

YELLOW-BELLIED SEA SNAKE
This snake is carried by currents and
winds across the open ocean. It is often
found in slicks of seaweed and other
debris that form where currents meet.

perhaps as much as 65 metres – and
can stay under water for long periods. The venom of this sea snake is
one of the most potent known, but
its tiny head and its small fangs and
venom glands mean that it is an
unlikely threat to humans.
Scientific name: *Hydrophis coggeri*

ELEGANT SEA SNAKE

One of the most common sea snakes
in tropical and temperate Australian
waters, this snake ranges from the
North West Shelf and the coast of
Western Australia to the Great
Barrier Reef. It is found on coral
reefs in both shallow coastal and
shelf waters, and often wanders
south during summer to the coast
of New South Wales and the south-
western part of Western Australia.

It grows to nearly 2 metres in total
length, and its body is fairly slender
at the front but becomes bulkier and
deeper towards the rear. It is usually
fawn or brown above and whitish
below, and has a series of darker
cross-bands or saddles along its
length. Dark spots along its flanks
alternate with the saddles; as in
many other sea snake species,
these saddles start as highly contrasting cross-bands in the young,
but become less marked with age.
Female elegant sea snakes produce
about 20 young in a litter.

This species is often taken in prawn
trawls. Its venom is very toxic.
Scientific name: *Hydrophis elegans*

ORNATE SEA SNAKE

Ranging from the Persian Gulf to the
east coast of Australia, this species
grows to about a metre in total
length. It is found in clear coral reef
waters, but it is most abundant in

murkier, inshore waters and in the
shallow, silty waters of the Gulf of
Carpentaria and the Arafura Sea.
Little is known of its habits except
that it feeds on a fairly wide range of
fishes. Except for its paddle-like tail,
it is shaped much like a land snake.

This snake gets its common name
from the series of large, dark spots
with pale centres running along
its flanks. These spots are usually
conspicuous in the young, but
they become indistinct or absent altogether in large adults. The remaining colour pattern is usually whitish
on the lower half of the body and
grey on the upper half, with a series
of incomplete dark bars or saddles
along the middle of the back.

The venom of the ornate sea snake
is extremely toxic, and has been responsible for a number of fatalities
in Asian fishing communities.
Scientific name: *Hydrophis ornatus*

YELLOW-BELLIED OR PELAGIC SEA SNAKE

Like other snakes, the yellow-bellied
sea snake (also known as the pelagic
sea snake) periodically sheds its
skin. Most land and sea snakes
achieve this by rubbing their bodies
against rough surfaces to dislodge
the skin, but pelagic species, which
live on the surface of the open
ocean, do not have this option.
Instead, yellow-bellied sea snakes
shed their skins by tying their bodies in knots. As they squirm out of
the knots the rough skin on one part
of the body rubs against that of
another part, gradually enabling
the snake to free the entire skin.

The yellow-bellied sea snake is
the most wide-ranging of all the
sea snakes, extending from the east
coast of Africa through the Indian
and Pacific Oceans to the tropical
east coast of the Americas. It floats

on the surface of the ocean, feeding on small surface-swimming fishes.

Being pelagic, it is carried by the winds and currents across the deeper expanses of the ocean, and is encountered in mid-ocean as often as it is in coastal waters. It is often found among the slicks of seaweed that are brought together where ocean currents converge. These slicks also attract many of the fishes on which the snake feeds.

Yellow-bellied sea snakes typically have a black back that contrasts sharply at mid-flank with their yellow or pale brown lower half. Their paddle tail is usually banded or spotted with the same two contrasting colours. In the Indian and western Pacific Oceans, yellow-bellied sea snakes grow to more than a metre, but they are considerably smaller in the eastern Pacific Ocean, suggesting that there is little intermixing of the two populations.

The venom of this species is very potent. Although yellow-bellied sea snakes rarely bite if encountered by swimmers and divers, they are often washed ashore exhausted or injured after storms at sea, and they are likely to bite at such times, despite being almost helpless on land.
Scientific name: *Pelamis platurus*

SPINE-BELLIED SEA SNAKE
This is a large, bulky sea snake that grows to about a metre in total length. It ranges from South-East Asia to Australia and occurs in large numbers in northern Australia, where it is often caught in prawn trawls. It is pale fawn or brown above – usually with obscure, broad cross-bands – and whitish on the lower flanks and belly. It has rough scales that can become very spiny, especially on the belly of adult males.

The spine-bellied sea snake is usually found in shallow coastal and shelf waters, and also frequently swims into the estuaries of larger rivers. It is common, but little is known about its habits and life cycle. Its venom is very potent and can be fatal to humans.
Scientific name: *Lapemis curtus*

NORTHERN MANGROVE SNAKE
Like the north-western mangrove snake, this is a small species; it grows to only about 50 cm long. It is an inhabitant of coastal mangrove flats, where it shelters among the mangrove roots during the day and makes its way over the exposed mud flats to feed, mostly at night. It is bluish to olive-grey above with a

series of about 40–50 irregular blackish cross-bands. Its belly scales are quite wide, and it probably uses them, as land snakes do, to help it to move across the mud flats.

This snake is found along the tropical coast of northern Australia and the southern coast of New Guinea, including islands in the Arafura Sea. It is believed to feed on small fishes.

Nothing is known about its venom, but its small size makes it an unlikely threat to humans.
Scientific name: *Parahydrophis mertoni*

SEA KRAITS ▦
Altogether there are six species of sea kraits, but only two – the white-lipped sea krait (*Laticauda colubrina*) and the black-lipped sea krait (*L. laticaudata*) – are found in Australian waters. Even these two species appear only occasionally, and do not seem to either live permanently or breed in this area, although they are abundant in nearby countries such as Papua New Guinea, the Solomon Islands, Vanuatu and New Caledonia.

Except for their paddle-shaped tails, sea kraits, look much like land snakes – indeed, they spend much of their lives on land, where they digest their food and where the

females lay their eggs in deep crevices well above the high-tide mark – usually in a clutch of between five and twenty.

While sea kraits are active at any time of day, they tend to leave land to feed in the sea just after dusk and return just before daylight. Both the white-lipped and the black-lipped sea kraits eat little but eels. They rarely venture far inland, tending to shelter within a hundred metres or so of the high-tide mark. Many individuals – occasionally as many as a hundred or more – may coil together in the same shelter.

The background colour of the white-lipped sea krait is usually greyish or metallic blue, and that of the black-lipped sea krait is a brilliant blue. Both species have numerous black cross-bands along their body. Their common names derive from the colour of their upper lip. Males average about 80 cm long, but females can reach 1.5 metres or more.

Sea kraits have extremely toxic venom, which they produce in large quantities, so a bite is potentially very dangerous. Fortunately they are very docile and rarely bite, even if roughly handled or injured.
Scientific name: *Laticauda* spp.

DISTRIBUTION

▦ SPINE-BELLIED SEA SNAKE

▦ NORTHERN MANGROVE SNAKE

▦ SEA KRAITS

▦ SEA KRAIT
The white-lipped sea krait is an occasional visitor to Australian waters. Sea kraits spend much of their time on land, within a hundred metres or so of the high-tide mark, in grass or under debris or boulders.

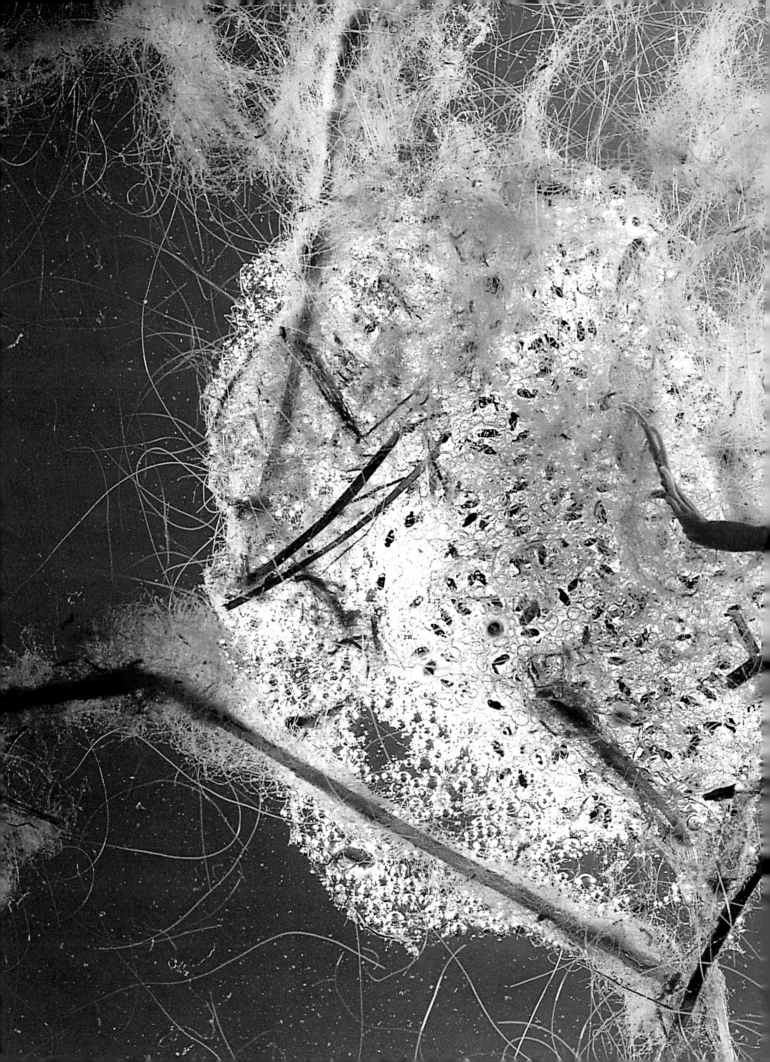

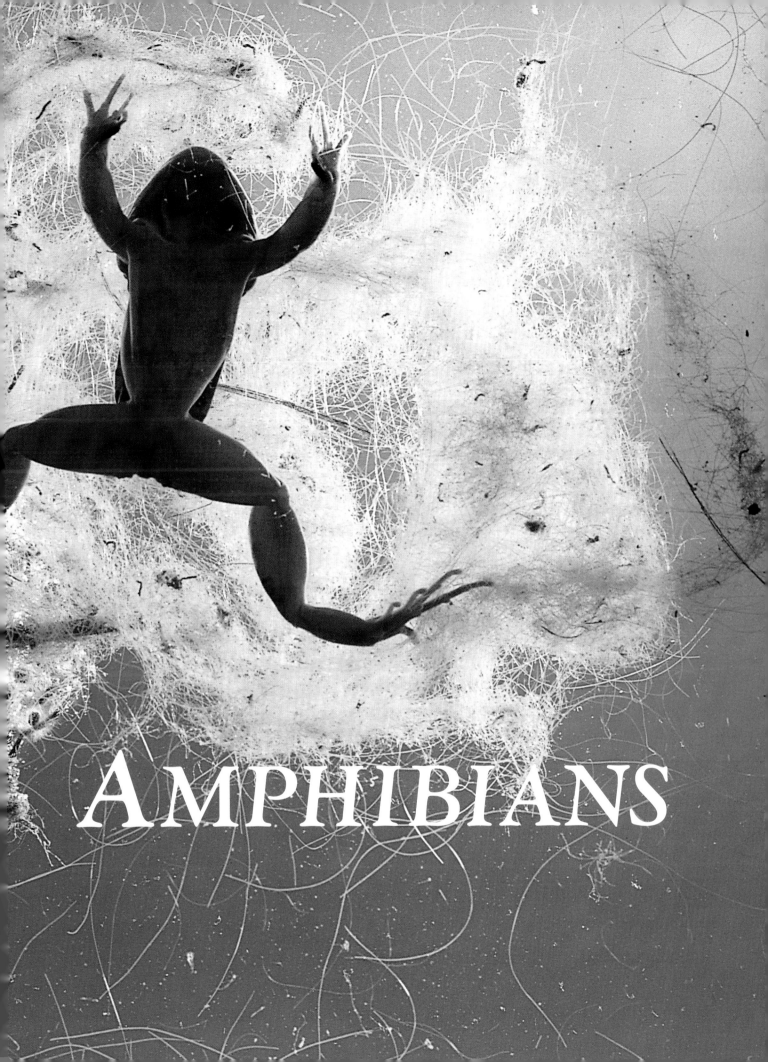

AMPHIBIANS

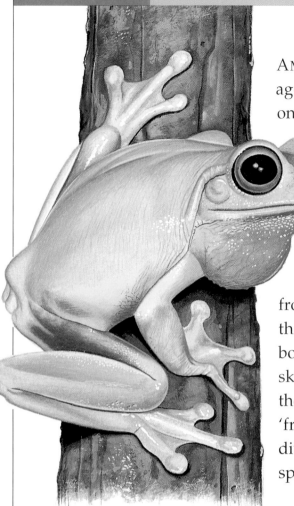

AMPHIBIANS FIRST APPEARED ABOUT 370 million years ago, and were the first vertebrates to live, at least partly, on land. There are three main surviving groups – newts and salamanders, caecilians, and frogs and toads – but frogs are the only amphibians that occur naturally in Australia, which has more than 210 of the world's 4000 known frog species. They are found from the mountains to the interior, but most inhabit warm, moist environments.

In Europe, there are structural differences between frogs and toads: frogs have a chest wall that is united in the middle by bone, whereas toads have two overlapping, boomerang-shaped cartilages. European frogs have smooth skins and European toads have rough, warty skins, and so the two forms are clearly differentiated. But all Australian 'frogs' have a toad-like chest, and in this country the division of species is merely historical – many Australian species were named by European naturalists.

FROG FEATURES
Frogs have large, high-set eyes with true eyelids and a third eyelid to keep the cornea clean and moist. They do not have a distinct neck, so they cannot move their head sideways. Most species have inflatable vocal sacs that act as resonating chambers, amplifying sound up to a hundred times. Their fingers and toes are rounded, or flattened and end in discs. In climbing species, these discs are expanded to provide a greater surface area, and there is usually extensive webbing between the fingers and toes.

Most adult frogs capture their small invertebrate prey by flicking out their long, muscular tongue. Frogs are ectotherms, drawing their body heat from the environment rather than generating it by metabolic processes that rely on a constant food supply, so they do not need to eat frequently.

In most frog species, males are smaller than females. The limbs are usually developed for leaping and swimming, although some frogs can burrow, run, scuttle, waddle or climb.

Sight is important to frogs for capturing fast-moving prey and avoiding predators, and they use colour vision to recognise mates. Most frogs are nocturnal and have well-developed night vision, though a few Australian species are active during the day. Frogs have highly developed vocal communication, but are especially attuned to the sounds produced by other frogs, usually of the same species. Many have distinctive calls that are useful in identification.

Miracle skin
Frogs do not drink; instead, they absorb water through their skin. The skin is also important in respiration, absorbing oxygen and releasing carbon dioxide across its surface, and in regulating the body's salt content.

A frog's skin is studded with glands. Some secrete mucus to keep the skin moist and cool; some produce fats that waterproof the skin; and some contain substances that may blend to form toxic compounds that deter predators.

Most frogs can change colour slightly over a period of days, or even hours, by means of chromatophores – pigment cells in their skin. This allows them to take on the colour of their surroundings in order to avoid predators,

GREAT AND SMALL
The green tree frog dwarfs the dainty green tree frog, though the two species are members of the same genus, *Litoria*.

or to impress a potential mate. Some frogs are brightly coloured to alarm predators or to give warning that they are toxic.

If captured, some frog species feign death in the hope that the captor will release its hold, providing a last opportunity for escape.

When frogs go a-wooing

Typically, males and females meet beside fresh water in an embrace known as amplexus, and the males release sperm at the same time as the females deposit eggs. The eggs are small, with yolks and gelatinous outer capsules; they have no protective membrane or shell, and may dry out in hostile conditions.

Many females release their eggs into a frothy mass that floats on the water. They create this raft for their living cargo by gently trapping bubbles at the water's surface with specially developed paddles on the inner fingers and throwing the bubbles of air backwards, where they become trapped in the mucus surrounding the eggs emerging from their bodies. Buoyed by the bubbles, the fertilised eggs are abandoned to float and develop. Scientists have found that these sticky rafts of mucus supply rich oxygen to the developing embryos. The rafts may also offer some protection against fungal infection and hungry predators.

A free-swimming tadpole, with external gills and a tail but no limbs or mouth, emerges from the egg and attaches itself to a surface by means of an adhesive organ. At first it lives off its yolk supply, but after a mouth and internal gills form, it scrapes food particles from rocks or plants or traps them in mucus secreted by its gills. Those that survive undergo a dramatic metamorphosis – limbs, lungs and other adult features develop, and finally the tail is fully absorbed. Tadpoles are at the mercy of many predators, and most frogs lay large numbers of eggs – thousands in some species – to increase the species' chances of survival.

Some Australian frogs vary this basic pattern. Desert-dwelling frogs breed whenever there is enough rain, but may have to wait years. When the rains do come, the desert resounds with frogs calling and mating. The tadpoles must grow into fully formed adults in the short time before the water seeps away and evaporates.

Southern frogs show an evolutionary trend towards egg-laying and tadpole development away from water. Laying eggs on land affords some protection from aquatic predators, but there is always a risk that the eggs will dry out.

The corroboree frog lays its eggs in jelly-like capsules on land. The tadpoles develop inside the egg jelly until the nest sites are flooded and the tadpoles are washed into streams. Species of *Heleioporus* also lay their eggs on land in a dry burrow. Once again, the developing tadpoles must wait for floodwaters to flush them from their underground nursery chambers.

Some tadpoles never swim in water, but develop entirely within the egg capsule. The eggs are laid in small clutches and are typically large and yolky, since the tadpoles rely on the yolk for all their nutrients until metamorphosis: the sphagnum frog may lay no more than 30 eggs, and the moss froglet only ten.

gelatinous eggs

developing tadpoles

free-swimming tadpoles

tadpoles with limbs developing

adult frog

A FROG'S LIFE
In a typical life cycle, fertilised eggs hatch into tadpoles, which grow legs and lose their tails before metamorphosing into adult frogs. Most frogs must lay their eggs in or near water, but some Australian frogs have adapted to this continent's arid conditions and are able to lay their eggs on dry land.

Parental care

It is a rare phenomenon for frogs to care for their young, but there are notable exceptions. After the tadpoles of the marsupial or pouched frog hatch from eggs laid under leaf litter, the adult males position themselves so that the tadpoles can squirm into pouches near their hind limbs. The males then carry the developing tadpoles wriggling around in their little 'hip pockets' until metamorphosis is complete.

The gastric brooding frog demonstrates the most extraordinary of all parenting behaviour: the female frog swallows her fertilised eggs and the tadpoles develop in her stomach and emerge from her mouth as tiny adults able to care for themselves. Sadly, gastric brooding frogs have not been observed in the wild since 1981, and the species may now be extinct.

DISTRIBUTION

- SANDHILL FROG
- TUSKED FROG

- KARRI FROG
- MOSS FROGLET
- MARSUPIAL FROG

SANDHILL FROG
To escape the heat, the Western Australian sandhill frog plunges its head into soft sand or shell grit and digs with its hands until it slowly sinks from sight.

SOUTHERN FROGS

The southern frogs are so named because of their ancestral links. Many millions of years ago, South America, Antarctica and Australia formed part of the southern supercontinent known as Gondwana. Australia's southern frogs evolved from this time and are close relatives of other frogs found today in other parts of the southern hemisphere, especially in South America. Indeed, the fossil record shows that the skeletons and muscles of these frogs are so similar to those of a South and Central American group, the Leptodactylidae, that many frog experts believe them to belong to one family.

There are about 115 species in around 20 genera of southern frogs, all of which live on the ground. Like the tree-dwelling frogs, or hylids, southern frogs are widespread throughout Australia, except in the driest deserts. Many southern frogs spawn in water, where the hatched tadpoles are fully aquatic before they metamorphose into terrestrial frogs, but one striking family feature is the trend towards increasing independence from free water for the developing larvae. Some *Geocrinia* and *Pseudophryne* species lay large eggs in damp litter around ponds, where the tadpoles develop to a late stage before hatching and completing their larval life in water. In other groups, such as *Arenophryne* and *Myobatrachus*, tadpoles complete

their development within the egg capsule with no need for free water.

Perhaps the most extraordinary southern frog life cycles are those that involve parental care of the young – marsupial frogs (page 367) and gastric brooding frogs (page 377) are examples.
Family: Myobatrachidae

SANDHILL FROG ■
Thousands of people visit Monkey Mia at Shark Bay to watch the dolphins, unaware that only a few kilometres away there is an even more extraordinary animal – the sandhill frog. Only 3 cm long and stippled light and dark brown, it lives only in the sand dunes along a narrow stretch of the coast of Western Australia. The sandhill frog is protected by legislation, but it is common over its range of several hundred kilometres and there are no known threats to its survival.

The sandhill frog has a number of strategies for coping with high temperatures during the day. At dawn it burrows headfirst into the sand to a depth of 30 centimetres or so. Here it finds pure, fresh water, and replenishes its moisture reserves by absorbing water through the skin. At night the sandhill frog emerges from the sand and waddles across the dry surface, leaving a telltale track as it pursues its main food source – ants.

■ TUSKED FROG
The male tusked frog is easily distinguished from the female by a pair of prominent bony 'tusks', which are probably used in territorial skirmishes.

All Australia's other burrowing frogs, except the turtle frog (page 374), dig holes with their back feet. Sandhill frogs dig with their hands.

Sandhill frogs have no fresh water in which to breed. Instead, they lay large eggs, each up to 5 mm in diameter, 80 cm deep in the moist sand layer. The tadpoles develop entirely within the transparent egg capsule, and the tiny frogs emerge from the capsules after about two months.
Scientific name: *Arenophryne rotunda*

TUSKED FROG ■
The ground-dwelling tusked frog has a drab, olive green to brown back with a rough, warty texture, but its underside has vivid white splashes on a black background and a bright red groin and thighs. The males (about 5 cm long) are larger than the females (about 4 cm long).

Tusked frogs have long, narrow fingers and toes. The male's head is wider than the body and he has a pair of large bony 'tusks' at the front of the mouth, which zoologists believe are used to defend territory. These projections can be long and quite sharp. If picked up by humans, the frogs do not attempt to bite. Males are aggressive, and fight over territories and females.

This is a secretive frog that breeds beside still water or gently flowing streams on the coastal plains and adjacent ranges from central eastern Queensland southward to southern New South Wales. The male selects a well-hidden site at water level, and then calls with a soft 'plop' or 'blik' sound. When the female arrives at the water's edge, he takes her in amplexus – the mating embrace. She then lays her eggs in a frothy, floating egg mass.
Scientific name: *Adelotus brevis*

KARRI FROG

The karri frog is about 2.5 cm long, with a black back and a smooth, bright, luminous pink to peach belly. The male's throat is black, but the female's throat is the same colour as her belly.

In spring and early summer, male karri frogs call with a continuous 'tick … tick … tick' sound from moist hollows under litter, moss or dense vegetation, deep in the karri forests of south-western Australia. It is impossible to mistake their calls, but finding adults or eggs is a different matter. The triangulation method of searching gives the best results (see 'In the spotlight', page 381).

Males commonly frequent creek lines, but never enter water, nor do their eggs or tadpoles. The eggs are laid, surrounded by jelly, in the small hollows from which the males call. These eggs have large yolks, and when the tadpoles hatch into the jelly this supply of nutrients feeds them until they are fully formed miniature frogs.

Karri frogs live only in karri forest, and their distribution is centred on the main forest belt from Manjimup to the Shannon River. *Geocrinia rosea* is closely related to *G. lutea*, *G. vitellina* and *G. alba*. All four species have similar breeding biology, and all are confined to the wettest parts of south-western Australia.

The orange-bellied *G. vitellina* and the white-bellied *G. alba* have very small ranges and are considered to be endangered species.

Scientific name: *Geocrinia rosea*

MOSS FROGLET

Somewhat similar in appearance to the common eastern froglet (page 369), moss froglets are small and brown, 2–3 cm long, and variably coloured and patterned. They live in remote south-western Tasmania, among dense undergrowth in heathland and rainforest. Their habitat is periodically enveloped in thick cloud, and during these misty intermissions the froglets crawl leisurely across the surface vegetation. At other times they shelter in concealed chambers built into moss, from which the males may advertise their position with a series of rapidly repeated 'toks' that sound like a bouncing ping-pong ball.

The moss nests also serve as nurseries for the eggs deposited during spring and summer. Clutches are small – around ten eggs only, each one rich in yolk. The entire life cycle takes place on land, with the tadpoles developing in gelatinous fluid

from the egg capsules. The yolk provides nutrients until the tadpoles metamorphose into tiny 6 mm-long froglets a year after the eggs are laid. The froglets' habitat may be under snow for several months in winter, but the insulating moss can maintain a temperature up to 10°C higher than that of the air.

Scientific name: *Crinia nimbus*

MARSUPIAL FROG

The marsupial frog, pouched frog or hip-pocket frog is restricted to the coastal ranges around the border of New South Wales and Queensland. It lives in Antarctic beech forest and rainforest in mountainous areas, spending most of its time in damp leaf litter and under rocks and logs.

This tiny frog grows to only about 2.5 cm long. It is grey to red-brown, with a pink spot on the base of each arm and variable darker markings, usually in the form of two V-shaped bars, on its back and sides. The male bears a pair of pouches, one on each hip, hence its common names.

Males call throughout the year in a series of repeated 'eh … eh …' sounds, the chorus peaking in October and November. Marsupial frogs do not need free water to breed. The female lays up to 16 large, toughly coated eggs under leaves on moist soil. The eggs are encased in fluid-filled capsules that stop the embryos from drying out.

The marsupial frog is one of the few frogs that care for their young. When the eggs are ready to hatch, the male lowers part of his body into the cluster of eggs. The egg capsules rupture and the male coats himself with the egg's clear fluid. The tiny tadpoles wriggle onto the moist skin and enter one of the two pouches, where they remain for 48–69 days, feeding on egg yolk. Meanwhile the male, encumbered by his offspring, snatches at prey, but is restricted in his hunting. Once the juvenile frogs are fully formed, at 4–5 mm long, they emerge from their pouch and must then fend for themselves.

Scientific name: *Assa darlingtoni*

■ MARSUPIAL FROG
Responsibility for raising the family falls to the male marsupial frog. After they hatch, the tiny tadpoles shelter in his two brood pouches, where they feed on egg yolk until they are tiny, fully formed frogs.

■ MOSS FROGLET
The well-concealed moss froglet lives only in the remote mountains and lowland forests of south-western Tasmania. These little frogs hide so effectively that they were not discovered until 1992.

367

■ WALLUM FROGLETS
In the breeding season, the loud chirping calls of male wallum froglets pinpoint their positions. Lovers of acid water, they are facing an ever-shrinking habitat.

DISTRIBUTION

■ WALLUM FROGLET
■ QUACKING FROG
■ CHIRPING FROGLET

■ STREAMBANK FROGLET
■ COMMON EASTERN FROGLET

WALLUM FROGLET ■

Behind the beautiful sandy beaches of southern Queensland and northern New South Wales lies the high dune country known as the wallum, which is vegetated with heaths and banksia. From Fraser Island south to Myall Lakes, the wallum is home to a unique group of frogs called acid frogs. The most common of these is the wallum froglet, which is also known as the tinkling froglet.

The wallum froglet is one of Australia's smaller frog species, growing to a mere 1.9 cm long. Its back is variably patterned in brown and black; underneath it is white with black and soft pastel pink and blue speckling. It has a distinctive bright white line of spots running down its throat.

When wallum froglets are calling in large numbers, they are easy to observe. Calling males can be seen with a torch at the base of herbs or under partly raised leaves. Their mating call sounds rather like a sparrow chirping, as does that of the chirping froglet (this page).

The wallum froglet breeds from October to April, and its favourite breeding sites are the lakes and swamps of the wallum country. The water in these lakes and swamps is tea-brown and acidic. The colour comes from decaying vegetation and the acidity from the organic acids that the rotting vegetation releases. Some swamps have waters with a pH of 4.5 – acid enough to eventually dissolve false teeth. The frogs lay small eggs in clumps, which they attach to submerged vegetation. The tadpoles are fat-bodied, short-tailed and low-finned.

The sandy wallum country is in great demand for tourist development, so the wallum froglet's range has contracted over the past 30 years. This froglet was once at home along the Gold Coast, but it can no longer be found there. More and more of these frogs are becoming restricted to government reserves.
Scientific name: *Crinia tinnula*

QUACKING FROG ■

In rainy winter weather in the jarrah forests of Western Australia, a sound like the cry of a duck can be heard – but it is more likely to be the call of the quacking frog. This is one of the most common frog species in south-western Australia, and it is found throughout forested areas on the Swan coastal plain and eastward across the southern coast as far as Cape Le Grand in Western Australia.

Quacking frogs are about 3.5 cm long. Their colouring is variable, but falls into the same three main patterns found in common eastern froglets (page 369). Females are white underneath. Males are more colourful – mottled grey and white, with a darker chin. They may also have bright red patches in the groin and across the underside of the body and legs.

When large groups of male quacking frogs begin to call, the chorus often starts with a single quack and then quickly builds up as more and more courting frogs join in. Because male quacking frogs respond so readily to each other, they also respond to crude imitations of their call; when a human 'quacks', the frogs will call right back. Males call throughout the winter from shallow water, 1–2 cm deep, from small depressions in moss, from hollows, or sometimes from around larger ponds. Fights often break out between males over calling sites.

Females deposit discrete clumps of eggs in very shallow water in mosses or hollows or among flooded grasses. The tadpoles are aquatic and develop rapidly, making the most of their limited water resource.
Scientific name: *Crinia georgiana*

CHIRPING FROGLET

Deserts look too dry and unpromising for little frogs to roam and feed. But at night, when the dew begins to fall, chirping froglets are on the move, foraging along the ground through the moistened brush. They hunt for small arthropods, with ants forming the largest part of their diet. During the day these froglets remain inactive, sheltering under leaves, logs, and other debris near water.

The chirping froglet, sometimes called the desert froglet, is small (1.8 cm long) and delicate, with a pointed snout. It is greenish brown above, and its underside is white with sparse flecks of pastel pink and blue and a peppering of brown. Sometimes it has a longitudinal line of paler white spots down its throat.

■ QUACKING FROG
The male quacking frog is distinguished by its duck-like call. The marbled patterning of its skin, so useful for camouflage, is sometimes relieved by splashes of bright red.

This little frog is best known in the dry country of western Queensland and the adjoining parts of New South Wales, South Australia and the Northern Territory.

The chirping froglet does not depend on rain to breed, but in a dry summer matings are fewer. Mating usually takes place along the permanent waterholes of drying rivers and creeks. When the rains come, the desert is suddenly alive with the chirping of these frogs; like the wallum froglet (previous page), they sound like chattering sparrows, but it is easy to distinguish which is calling because the ranges of the two species do not overlap. The males call from the base of vegetation or from under leaves on the ground.

Chirping froglets lay their small eggs in the water in clumps that they attach to submerged plants. The eggs hatch into globular tadpoles with short tails and low fins.
Scientific name: *Crinia deserticola*

STREAMBANK FROGLET

The streambank froglet is confined to South Australia. It is only about 2.5 cm long and has a brown, grey or blackish back that may be patterned or uniform, making this frog generally hard to spot. It lives in the creek beds of the Flinders Ranges and shelters by day beneath flat stones at the edges of the region's numerous shallow creeks, which are crisscrossed by roads and tracks. These creeks are subject to flash flooding, when huge quantities of water surge down the channels. The streambank froglet's eggs and tadpoles are adapted to cope with these major

changes in their normally placid environment. The eggs stick to the undersides of rocks to prevent them from being swept away, and the tadpoles are equipped with flattened mouthparts to enable them to hang onto submerged rocks or vegetation in the rushing currents.

Not many species of frogs are found in the Flinders Ranges, so most regular campers are familiar with the high-pitched clicking call of the streambank froglet. Happily, despite its restricted distribution, this frog seems to be present in large numbers and is not endangered.
Scientific name: *Crinia riparia*

COMMON EASTERN FROGLET ■

The small, ground-dwelling common eastern froglet is one of the most widespread species in eastern Australia. It occurs in almost every habitat – in coastal swamps, dry and wet forests, river flats, open and disturbed areas, and alpine grasslands.

The froglet's 'crick crick crick crick …' can be heard throughout the year, particularly after rain. The froglets call day and night from small ponds, swamps, dams, creeks, ditches and flooded depressions.

Common eastern froglets, which are also known as common froglets, grow to about 2.5 cm long; the females are characteristically slightly larger than the males. The patterning and colouring on the backs of these frogs can be very variable, even among individuals living in the same location. Three common patterns are recognised: a uniform brown to grey colouring on a

■ COMMON EASTERN FROGLET
Note the differences in the back patterns and colours of these common eastern froglets engaged in mating. There is much variation in the somewhat restrained appearance of this species, even when the froglets are sharing the same territory.

smooth back; a raised ridge forming a V-shape between the eyes, and more long, raised ridges down either side of the midline, which are banded in brown or black and earthy reds to sandy yellows, giving the creature a striped appearance; and a mottled reddish brown and grey colouring, textured with numerous bumps over the back.

The female common eastern froglet lays her small, darkly pigmented eggs in little clumps directly into water; the eggs then sink to the bottom. The tadpoles are aquatic and can be found at any time of year, even in winter. The adult frogs hide in moist, sheltered sites beneath logs and other debris near ponds, even in towns and cities.
Scientific name: *Crinia signifera*

FROGS AND THE FOOD WEB
Frogs play a vital role in the food web of ponds and streams – if frogs disappear from an area, the ecosystem can become unbalanced.

Typically, tadpoles eat algae and plant and animal detritus from pond bottoms; in turn they are eaten by fishes, tortoises and birds. Those that survive to become adult frogs live on insects and spiders, and some unfortunate ones are devoured by snakes.

GIANT BURROWING FROG ■

The giant burrowing frog, or eastern owl frog, first described by English naturalists in 1795, is not often seen today. It sometimes crosses warm roads at night during heavy rain. This species is the only one of the genus found in eastern Australia, and is very rare in the southern part of its range. Its main stronghold is the outskirts of the Sydney area, where it is threatened by urban development and polluted creeks.

The frog is about 9.5 cm long; the bumps on its slate grey, warty skin are sometimes dotted along the sides with white or yellow spots. Males have enlarged forearms and are thought to use the spines on their front feet in territorial combat.

Adult giant burrowing frogs travel widely in search of food, and often stray far from water. They eat spiders, centipedes and insects, some of which other frogs find noxious. They also prey on small crayfish.

These frogs have spade-like protuberances on their back feet and can dig powerfully, even into clay. At breeding time, the male excavates a deep burrow in a creek bank with a chamber at the bottom, and calls with a gentle, owl-like hoot. The female lays her eggs in a foamy nest in the burrow chamber. When the black tadpoles hatch, they are flushed by rain into creeks, where they grow as long as 8 cm before metamorphosis occurs.
Scientific name: *Heleioporus australiacus*

MOANING FROG ■

In autumn after the first rains, around mid-April through to early June, moaning frogs become the scourge of suburban Perth – their repetitive calls drive many people almost crazy. The males signal from well-concealed burrows and, unlike many other species, more or less synchronise their outbursts, so that the sound of amorous frogs runs in unison around the perimeter of a large swamp. In the early l950s moaning frogs and their relatives, *H. psammophilus* and *H. inornatus*, were identified as separate species from their distinctive calls.

Moaning frogs are about 6 cm long. The backs of both males and females are mottled light to dark grey, and in some animals there is a splash of yellow on the flank. They have distinctive calluses on the backs of their heels, which they use to dig steeply backwards into the soil. In early autumn, the creamy white eggs are visible through the females' belly skin. The eggs look like those of the western spotted frog, and develop in the same way (next entry).

Moaning frogs occur only in Western Australia, from Dongara through the south-west forest, and across the south coast to Cape Arid. Within their range, they live almost anywhere that floods in winter, and have been observed travelling as far as three kilometres from their breeding sites.
Scientific name: *Heleioporus eyrei*

WESTERN SPOTTED FROG

The western spotted frog is 8 cm long with enormous eyes. It has calluses on the backs of its heels, with which it burrows backwards into the soil. It has small white or cream spots on its dark back. Breeding males have one large and two smaller sharp black conical spines on their inner fingers.

Males call from the entrances of long burrows that twist and turn, sometimes up to a metre or more, into creek banks. Their loud whooping call travels long distances, particularly after the first winter rains.

Females deposit eggs at the end of the burrow in a foamy mass that looks like detergent suds but is sticky. The eggs develop slowly for several weeks until rising water levels flood the burrow. Eggs in moist burrows may hatch before the burrows flood. The eggs are white – not the characteristic black and white of frogs' eggs exposed to sunlight.

The western spotted frog's range extends from the wheat belt of Western Australia west into the jarrah forest. Although these frogs are frequently seen on summer nights and in autumn, it has been suggested that their range and abundance are being dramatically reduced by increasing salinity and vegetation clearance across the wheat belt.
Scientific name: *Heleioporus albopunctatus*

■ MOANING FROG
At the end of the summer, moaning frogs often end up in gardens, attracted by artificial watering systems.

■ GIANT BURROWING FROGS
Two giant burrowing frogs display the black conical spines on their front feet: the largest of these spines can puncture human skin. The warts on the frog's back, sides and chest may also bear tiny spines.

DISTRIBUTION

■ GIANT BURROWING FROG
■ MOANING FROG

■ WESTERN SPOTTED FROG

■ EASTERN BANJO FROG

■ BROWN FROG

■ EASTERN BANJO FROG
The calls of the eastern banjo frog ring musically through the forests and heathlands of south-eastern Australia.

EASTERN BANJO FROG ■

When the male eastern banjo frog calls to attract females, a single 'bonk' or 'plunk' almost always provokes a response from a second male. This 'bonk-bonk' sound has been likened to 'four-bob' – the call of not one frog but two – and has given the frog its second common name, the four-bob frog.

The four-bob frog grows to about 7 cm long and is usually dark brown. It is one of several species that have in common a stumpy body, short and muscular hind limbs, a golden glandular ridge at the angle of the jaws and a large, oval gland on the upper surface of the calf. This calf gland contains a toxin that has been found to repel rats, and may protect the frog against some of its enemies.

The eucalypt forests and heathlands of south-eastern Australia are home to this burrowing frog. Here it favours light soils, in which it burrows with a hard, spade-like structure on the sole of each foot. It digs down at dawn and emerges each dusk to feed.

This frog calls and mates in October. It lays its spawn clump, containing as many as a thousand eggs, in a foam nest in pond water, and the tadpoles develop slowly over the summer months as the temperature of the water rises. In February, when the pools begin to dry up, the tadpoles absorb their tails and leave the water to begin their life on land. In the colder parts of the continent, however, the tadpoles can take up to 15 months to develop into adult frogs.
Scientific name: *Limnodynastes dumerilii*

BROWN FROG ■

Adult brown frogs, which grow to a length of about 6.5 cm, have a moderately pointed snout, a flattened body, strong limbs, and long fingers and toes. They are found in a variety of still-water habitats, both natural and disturbed, including swamps, ponds, flooded grasslands and dams. In urban areas, brown frogs often make their homes in convenient garden ponds.

The brown frog's back is patterned in a series of light and dark brown longitudinal stripes and frequently has a cream-coloured midline. The skin is smooth and exudes a mucus that makes the animal quite slippery. The frog has muscular hind limbs and is a strong jumper.

Males call from sites discreetly hidden among vegetation at the edge of the water. The mating call is a single 'bock' sound, repeated every three or four seconds. A group of males calling around a pond sounds very much like a long table tennis rally.

The female deposits her eggs in a floating foamy nest, usually protected by vegetation, which she makes by using her hands to sweep bubbles of air beneath her body to join the mucus expelled with the eggs. This process is aided by a flap of skin on the second finger of each hand called a spatula. These flaps occur only on females.
Scientific name: *Limnodynastes peronii*

■ BROWN FROG
The robust ground-dwelling brown frog, also known as the brown-striped frog and the striped marsh frog, is common in eastern Australia. This juvenile still has the remnant of its tadpole tail.

■ ORNATE BURROWING FROG
During the breeding season the ornate burrowing frog calls to attract a mate. It stops calling if it is disturbed.

ORNATE BURROWING FROG ■

The ornate burrowing frog inhabits moist places on coasts and tablelands throughout north-eastern New South Wales, north and east Queensland, the northern half of the Northern Territory and north Western Australia. It is also adapted to some of the more arid regions of Australia.

The frog's body, about 4.5 cm long in both sexes, is stout, almost globose, and the head is broad with a short snout and large eyes. Its limbs are also short and stout. It lives in sandy soils, particularly on the flood plains of large rivers. It burrows with a shuffling movement of its hind limbs, and disappears gradually backwards in a circular motion into the soft ground.

The head and back of this frog are usually a yellowish brown, often splashed with small or large patches of darker brown, and dotted with many small, raised bumps. There is often a large, butterfly-shaped patch of yellow or cream on the top of the back. In some brightly marked individuals the small bumps are tipped with red or cream. In inland areas many specimens have a yellow or cream stripe down the middle of their backs.

Females lay their eggs in still, shallow water in a floating foam raft, which rapidly disintegrates as the embryos hatch out. The tadpole stage may be as short as two weeks: shallow ponds dry out quickly in the hot sun and, as for other species that use temporary pools, rapid embryonic development has distinct advantages for this frog.
Scientific name: *Limnodynastes ornatus*

SPOTTED GRASS FROG ■

Percussive noises like machine-gun fire resound from garden ponds when spotted grass frogs begin to call. This common species is familiar to many people living throughout south-eastern Australia.

The spotted grass frog ranges from 3 cm to 5 cm in length. Its coloration varies greatly with locality, and its spotted appearance usually helps it to blend well with grasses or other green, yellow or brown vegetation. At the extreme south of its range, the spotted grass frog bears narrow, bright red stripes down the middle of the back; these stripes are absent in other populations.

The spawn is typically a floating raft of eggs suspended from a mass of bubbles that resembles a blob of detergent. Normal raft production involves a synchronised pattern of arm movements in which the female traps bubbles at the surface and throws them backwards with her paddle-like hands. The bubbles bounce on her stomach, pass between her legs and become trapped in the jelly surrounding the eggs emerging from her body. In the south-east of South Australia, however, the females lay their eggs in a clump without bubbles – they flail their arms wildly, and this totally unsynchronised behaviour means that few bubbles engage with the egg mass.

The spotted grass frog is a successful colonist – there are even isolated populations at Kununurra in the extreme north of Western Australia and at nearby Newry Station in the Northern Territory. The Kununurra group may have been transported there as stowaways beneath transportable homes loaded from a paddock in an outer Adelaide suburb.
Scientific name: *Limnodynastes tasmaniensis*

FLETCHER'S FROG

Fletcher's frog inhabits the rainforests and wet eucalypt forests of north-eastern New South Wales and south-eastern Queensland, but not the relatively large rainforest area of north-eastern Queensland. However, fossil evidence indicates that members of this group were once more widespread in northern Australia. Fletcher's frog is the only member of its genus in Australia, but it has three close relatives in the rainforests of New Guinea.

Fletcher's frog is hard to see in forest leaf litter because its colouring and texture closely resemble decaying leaves. Its matt-textured back varies from reddish to dark brown, sometimes with irregular mottling, and its legs are faintly barred. Females are slightly larger than males, reaching about 5 cm, and both sexes have a flattened body shape that also aids in camouflage.

Fletcher's frogs breed in temporary pools, some as small as a teacup, that form after heavy rain: they commonly use water-filled hollows in tree roots. Males produce a soft 'g-a-r-r-up' call that is repeated at intervals of four to five seconds. When a female responds, the couple mate at the water's edge and eggs are laid into a foamy mass produced by the female, which then floats on the surface. The tadpoles develop rapidly once they hatch. This speedy growth is necessary because the small pools tend to dry out quickly and the tadpoles must metamorphose into tiny juvenile frogs, about 4 mm long, before this happens.
Scientific name: *Lechriodus fletcheri*

■ SPOTTED GRASS FROG
A male spotted grass frog clasps a female in his embrace. This frog is a prolific breeder – a captive female once laid 25 clutches of eggs in a year.

■ GREAT BARRED FROG
The great barred frog is large, with a solid, strikingly marked body and long, muscular hind limbs.

GREAT BARRED FROG ■
The ground-dwelling great barred frog lives in the moist forests of the coastal plains from north-eastern Victoria to south-eastern Queensland. It has a broad head and wide mouth. Its back varies from light brown to bronze or tan, and is mottled in darker hues of brown and tan. Its legs and arms are the same colour with darker crossbars – the feature that gives this frog its common name. Females are about 8 cm long and are slightly larger than the males. The great barred frog is well camouflaged and shelters by day beneath decaying leaf litter, often burrowing into loose soil.

Males call in the warmer months – a loud 'wark … wark … wark' followed by a short, guttural 'ruckle ruckle'. It is thought that the first part of the call attracts the female and the second part deters other males from entering the territory.

Eggs are deposited in a rather unusual way. As the couple float together on the water, a small number of eggs are laid and fertilised. The female holds the eggs on the expanded webbing of her foot and, with a rapid swish, flicks them on to the overhanging bank, to which the sticky, jelly-coated eggs adhere. The couple repeat this process many times until between 1000 and 2000 eggs have been deposited beyond the reach of aquatic predators. After a period of embryonic growth, the tadpoles hatch out and drop into the water below – where many of them subsequently perish.
Scientific name: *Mixophyes fasciolatus*

NICHOLLS' TOADLET ■
In the south-western corner of Western Australia, Nicholls' toadlet is abundant and widespread. It occurs in all sorts of vegetation types and is not dependent on watery habitats. Its call, a short 'cree-eek', can be heard from late spring through summer to early autumn, especially after rain or on damp nights.

The toadlet grows up to 2.5 cm long. Its back is dark brown, almost black, and it has small orange or yellow spots on the chest under the arms. The rest of the underside has light blue to white spots or mottling, like the soil fungi under logs or leaf litter where this frog is often found.

There is a mystery about the Nicholls' toadlet: it can breed almost anywhere, but there is little information about where and when it lays its eggs. Only two sightings of eggs have been reported, both in ants' nests. Most males call from dense vegetation along creek lines and from beneath burnt logs or piles of logging debris. The females lay only a very few large eggs, which are heavy with yolk. The nutrients in these yolks are enough to sustain the tadpoles until they become fully formed miniature frogs. In this they resemble karri frogs (page 367), but, unlike the eggs of the karri frog, Nicholls' toadlet egg capsules remain intact until the tiny frog is ready to emerge and crawl away.
Scientific name: *Metacrinia nichollsi*

WOODWORKER FROG
Throughout most of the Kimberley in the rugged north-west of Western Australia and in the rocky outcrops of Arnhem Land in the Northern Territory, a single, remarkable sound may issue from a sheltered position beneath a large flat rock or a crevice in the ground. This sound, like a piece of timber being struck, is the male woodworker frog's mating call.

Woodworker frogs are commonly found on the floors of caves, where they seem to pass the dry season. The species is characterised by its very large external ear, or tympanum. The frogs range in length from 4 cm to 6 cm, and have a dull purple back with darker markings and a pinkish underside.

The female lays about 350 black eggs in a foamy nest in shallow water, hidden from the light. The tadpoles are dark brown or black and have large, sucker-like mouths on the undersurface of their heads enabling them to stick to rocky surfaces during heavy rainstorms, when they are in danger of being washed away. The tadpoles reach a length of up to 5.5 cm and complete their development in slightly less than nine weeks.
Scientific name: *Limnodynastes lignarius*

DISTRIBUTION

□ ORNATE BURROWING FROG

□ SPOTTED GRASS FROG

□ FLETCHER'S FROG

■ GREAT BARRED FROG
■ NICHOLLS' TOADLET
■ WOODWORKER FROG

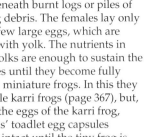

■ NICHOLLS' TOADLET
The fingernail-sized Nicholls' toadlet crawls rather than walks – that is, when it moves at all, for this toadlet often plays dead, lying on its back with its legs in the air, not moving a muscle.

TERMITES FOR TEA

In the deserts, heavy rains are indispensable to both termites and burrowing frogs. Drenching rains are a cue for the release of the winged stage of the termite's life cycle. A good downpour also wakes up dormant burrowing frogs. The adult frogs emerge from their burrows deep below the surface of the ground to feast on the swarms of termites. Some desert frogs eat several hundred termites in a single meal. The rich protein and fat of the plentiful insects is converted into fat reserves inside the frogs. These reserves sustain the frogs while they remain underground until the next deluge awakens them from their torpor.

GOLDFIELDS BULLFROG

After heavy summer rain in inland desert areas of Western Australia, the goldfields frog appears in large numbers, as if by magic. It is gone again almost as quickly.

The goldfields bullfrog is found from the southern end of Exmouth Gulf, along the coast southward to Carnarvon and Mullewa, and inland to just north of Wiluna and Kalgoorlie. It is a burrowing frog, 6 cm long, with large eyes, relatively short arms and legs, and a globular body. Its back is blotched yellow and chocolate brown. It is the easiest member of the *Neobatrachus* species to recognise, because of its distinctive markings – a Y-shaped yellow line radiating from the sides of its head along both sides and a yellow stripe down its backbone.

The goldfields bullfrog can live underground for several years. It forms a waterproof cocoon around its body by repeatedly renewing its skin but leaving the old layers in place, like so many pieces of tissue paper. These loose wrappings prevent its body from drying out. The frog also goes into a state of torpor, during which its heartbeat and breathing slow down so much that it barely uses any of its reserves of fat. The only water then accessible to the animal is stored in its bladder.

Unlike mammals, frogs can reabsorb water from their bladders, and in the goldfields bullfrog more than half its body weight may consist of water in the bladder.

Possibly alerted by changes in barometric pressure, or by moisture seeping into their chambers, these frogs never fail to respond to the onset of a desert storm. Rain galvanises them into action, and they scramble to the surface to take advantage of the brief wet conditions. As the desert comes to life (see box, 'Termites for Tea'), goldfields bullfrogs lose no time in building up their strength by eating voraciously. They then mate and produce a new generation before the landscape and the creatures in it once again become parched. The frogs gorge themselves on insects, and the melodious call of the males – a slightly drawn-out, ringing 'bonk' – fills the desert air. They lay their eggs in ephemeral ponds, and the aquatic tadpoles develop speedily before their watery habitat dries out.
Scientific name: *Neobatrachus wilsmorei*

TURTLE FROG ■

The turtle frog looks like no other frog in the world. It has a narrow, short head, short muscular legs, and a chest and body like those of a sumo wrestler. Adults are up to 6 cm long. Their skin, which is slightly bumpy, is pinkish grey above with flecks of yellow on the legs. This creature looks more like a baby turtle that has lost its shell than a frog, so its common name is extremely apt.

Often thought to be rare, the turtle frog is in fact very abundant in certain parts of Western Australia, but is seldom seen because of its strange burrowing and breeding habits. It is a sand-dweller and uses its front legs to burrow deep underground, where it spends most of its time.

Turtle frogs feed on termites and are widespread in the wheat belt and along the coast of south-western Australia. They call on just one or two wet nights of the year in early November when, in and around Perth, it is not unusual to hear huge numbers of males making their simple 'gwarp'-like sound.

Courtship among turtle frogs is a long-term affair. Pairs of frogs team up in early November and spend the whole summer underground, but the female does not produce eggs until the autumn. The eggs are large – up to 7 mm across – and are laid in moist soil to a depth of 1.2 metres.

These remarkable Australian frogs have adapted to the lack of water in their habitat by producing a tadpole that never needs to swim or chase food. It develops buried in the soil, feeding upon its own yolk-rich egg, until, when autumn rains fall, it comes to the surface and emerges as an adult frog.
Scientific name: *Myobatrachus gouldii*

■ TURTLE FROG
Myobatrachus gouldii digs head first, shovelling away sand with its front legs. Close examination reveals that its inner fingers are shaped like miniature triangular trowels.

HASWELL'S FROG

Haswell's frog is a rare species that is restricted to coastal areas from just north of Sydney in New South Wales southward to eastern Victoria. It lives in wet and dry eucalypt forests and among vegetation along the edges of creeks, ponds, dams, ditches and swamps, usually within coastal heathland, and has been found hiding in rushes and reeds or beneath stones in rocky creek beds.

Haswell's frog, about 3.5 cm long, has a smooth, light grey to brown back, flecked with darker marks. A black band runs from its nostrils down the sides of its body, and a pale, thin stripe may run down its back. Its most obvious distinguishing features are the bright orange to red patches in its armpits and groin and on the back of its thighs.

Scientists' knowledge of the life history and biology of Haswell's frog is scanty – in fact, virtually nothing is known about the eggs and tadpoles of this species. Males repeat a short 'wronk' sound from about August to March, usually from concealed vegetation in the water, or while under cover of litter and vegetation on the bank.

Scientific name: *Paracrinia haswelli*

CRUCIFIX TOAD

The very distinctive crucifix toad, sometimes called the holy cross toad, is shaped rather like a slightly squashed golf ball. It has an almost spherical body, short limbs, a short snout and a small mouth, and is able to inflate its body with air when disturbed. It lives west of the Great Dividing Range in New South Wales and southern Queensland.

A sphere is the most efficient shape for storing water and minimising the surface area for evaporation. When it is hot and dry, the crucifix toad remains deeply buried, emerging after heavy rains to breed and feed. Its adaptations for storing water and burrowing prevent it from being a strong jumper; rather it moves in a series of small hops.

Despite its bulky appearance and apparent inability to move fast, this frog catches insects by such rapid flicks of the tongue that the action

■ HASWELL'S FROG
Haswell's frog seems to occur in only a few patches of its known range, but within these patches it is thought to be fairly common.

is invisible. It does not need a wide mouth to ingest its diet of ants and termites. It usually squats on a termite trail and snaps up individual termites as they march along.

Both sexes of the crucifix toad grow to about 5 cm long. Biologists assume that the bright colours act as a warning against predators. When the frog is disturbed, glands in the skin secrete a thick, yellow, glue-like substance, which is thought to be poisonous and used as a natural defence against predators.

Scientific name: *Notaden bennettii*

GOLDFIELDS BULLFROG

TURTLE FROG

HASWELL'S FROG

CRUCIFIX TOAD

■ CRUCIFIX TOAD
The yellow back of the crucifix toad, or holy cross toad, is strikingly marked by a cross-shaped pattern of red and black round bumps – hence the toad's common names.

DISTRIBUTION

■ SPHAGNUM FROG

■ BAW BAW FROG
■ RED-CROWNED
TOADLET

■ WESTERN TOADLET
■ CORROBOREE FROG

■ SPHAGNUM FROG
Seldom seen above
ground, sphagnum
frogs are associated
with seepages and
water-filled spaces.

SPHAGNUM FROG ■

Not common, and restricted in distribution, the sphagnum frog lives in New South Wales in the high wet forests of the Great Dividing Range and the coastal slopes between Gibraltar Range National Park to the north and Werrikimbe National Park to the south. The sphagnum frog was discovered in 1952 at Point Lookout, 60 kilometres east of Armidale in New South Wales. It is a smallish, chunky creature that closely matches and blends in with the fallen leaves of the forest floor.

Females are about 3.5 cm long; males are somewhat smaller. The frogs' colouring is variable, but females are typically reddish brown and males are greenish grey. Each has fine black spotting or splashes. There are black stripes on the sides of the head, along the flanks and across the lower back in an inverted 'V' formation. A short black stripe runs across the thigh.

Between November and December breeding males call from water-filled burrows, which they excavate in moss or mud. Here mating takes place and the female lays 30–90 large, creamy white eggs as a foamy mass. The duration of development from fertilised eggs to new froglets in the wild is not yet accurately established, but it is believed to be about four months.

Most frog species lay numerous small, darkly pigmented eggs, and these develop into tadpoles that must feed to gain the energy for development once they have exhausted the small reserves of egg yolk. In the case of the sphagnum frog, the large egg contains enough yolk to fuel development of the tadpole until it reaches the feeding froglet stage of its life cycle.
Scientific name: Philoria sphagnicolus

■ RED-CROWNED TOADLET
Despite its name, this frog's handsome crown is not always red. It has a red stripe along the end of its backbone and bright white arm and leg bands.

BAW BAW FROG

Like many species of Australian frogs found at higher altitudes, the Baw Baw frog seems to have suffered dramatic population declines in recent years – but nobody knows why. This frog is found only in Victoria, and even there it is confined to alpine and subalpine areas of the Mount Baw Baw Plateau.

With an adult body length of 4 cm in males and about 5 cm in females, Baw Baw frogs are generally dark brown. They have pronounced glandular development on the shoulders, and often a cream to yellow mark on the head, which sometimes extends down the back.

These frogs are secretive and hard to find. In fact, like so many other species of Australian frogs, scientists know very little about their biology outside the breeding season. Males call in late spring and early summer from concealed positions under logs, rocks or dense vegetation, or from burrows formed within sphagnum moss. The call has been described as a short, regularly repeated 'clunk'.

Females lay around 100 large, creamy coloured eggs in foamy egg masses. The developing tadpoles hatch into free-swimming forms, but they do not feed; instead, they live off their yolk reserves until they are ready to metamorphose into small froglets. All *Philoria* species have similar life histories.
Scientific name: Philoria frosti

RED-CROWNED TOADLET ■

The red-crowned toadlet is a small, brightly coloured frog, about 3 cm long, that can be found only in the sandstone areas around Sydney in New South Wales. It lives in colonies along very small drainage lines below cliffs from which water flows into the larger creeks below.

This frog has a very dark brown or grey upper surface, and distinctive red and white markings. It is called a toadlet because it has short limbs and, although it is quite able to hop, walking is its more usual method of moving about.

Males call throughout the year to attract females. The females lay their eggs under leaf litter or rocks and the tadpoles develop within the egg capsule until the back legs start to appear. At this stage, development is arrested until heavy rain generates a flow of water through the nest. The tadpoles then break out of the capsule and are swept into small puddles, where they eventually metamorphose into frogs.

Unfortunately, the distribution of the red-crowned toadlet coincides with the metropolitan region of Sydney, and the areas in which it is found are being destroyed or degraded as houses are built for the growing city population.

This species lives just below the ridges, which are prime housing areas commanding magnificent views. Protection measures will have to be adopted if red-crowned toadlets are to continue to live side by side with humans and close to the suburbs of Sydney.
Scientific name: Pseudophryne australis

WESTERN TOADLET ■

Male western toadlets call from shallow burrows beneath logs, in the banks of claypans or under grass, where the eggs are deposited after summer and autumn rains. They start with a short 'crick' and then utter a much longer 'cree-ee-eek'.

The western toadlet is 3 cm long, with a dark brown to almost black back dotted with fine black bumps. It has smooth black and white skin on its underside and orange marks on its upper arms, its head and the very back tip of its body. These marks give it its other common name, the orange-crowned toadlet.

Western toadlets are found in Western Australia in granite desert outcrops and the central wheat belt, east into the goldfields, and north to Leonora, Mount Magnet and the southern end of Shark Bay. They have also been observed in north-west South Australia.

In the central wheat belt this species appears to have hybridised with another *Pseudophryne* species, Gunther's toadlet. The two distinct species have mated and produced frogs with an intermediate appearance. A magnifying glass is necessary to tell these two toadlets apart. Gunther's toadlet has only one inner toe joint – not two, like the western toadlet and most other frogs.
Scientific name: *Pseudophryne occidentalis*

CORROBOREE FROG ■

The adult corroboree frog is about 2.5 cm long. Its common name comes from its striking bright yellow and black stripes, like Aboriginal body decoration for corroborees.

This species occupies the wettest and coldest part of the continent in

■ WESTERN TOADLET
A western toadlet spreads protective arms over its clutch of eggs. The eggs will hatch when the rains come.

areas covered by deep snow for several months of the year. It lives above an altitude of about 1000 metres in the Snowy Mountains in the southern Alps of New South Wales, sheltering and feeding in dense understoreys of heath on the slopes of snow-gum woodlands. In summer the males move down to gather at pools in sphagnum bogs and seepages.

Corroboree frogs lay their eggs in depressions in thick moss at the edges of shallow pools. The males form these cavities and protect them by uttering warning territorial calls. They then summon females to the water's edge, and fertilised eggs are deposited in the depressions, well concealed from roaming predators.

The tadpoles hatch within two or three weeks but remain in the jelly-like mass to prevent them from drying out. Here they develop to an advanced stage, feeding on their abundant yolk over many months, and leaving the capsules only when the burrows are flooded by rain or snow melt. The tadpoles then swim to nearby water to complete their growth as free-swimmers. In December or January, almost a year after the eggs were laid, the young, fully formed frogs emerge from the pools and move up into the heath.
Scientific name: *Pseudophryne corroboree*

GASTRIC BROODING FROG ■

The female gastric brooding frog swallows her fertilised eggs, and a chemical in the surrounding jelly deactivates the glands that produce the digestive juices. The stomach becomes as thin as plastic film and the eggs hatch into tadpoles that

live on egg yolk. The mother does not feed during this time and, as the tadpoles grow her stomach enlarges into the space previously occupied by the lungs, so that she breathes through her skin. After about six weeks, the tadpoles turn into small frogs and the mother gives birth to them one by one through her mouth.

The frog is dull brown or slate coloured with a pale yellow underside, and has a very slimy skin. This species is one of the very few truly aquatic frogs; like fishes, it has a series of 'distant touch' receptors on its sides to monitor the movements of possible enemies in the water.

Scientists fear that *Rheobatrachus silus*, first identified in south-eastern Queensland, has vanished for ever. *R. vitellinus*, was discovered in Queensland at Eungella National Park near Mackay in 1984, but it too has since disappeared.
Scientific name: *Rheobatrachus silus*

■ CORROBOREE FROG
This spectacular and rare species is found only high in the cold, wet mountain country of south-east Australia.

■ GASTRIC BROODING FROG
A fully formed baby gastric brooding frog emerges from its mother's mouth after its six-week incubation inside her body. This amazing little frog was last seen in the wild in 1981 and may now be extinct.

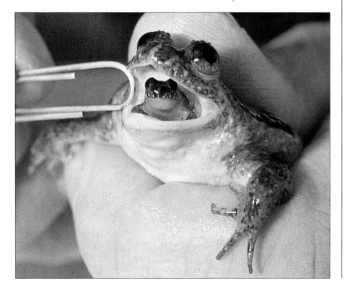

DISTRIBUTION

■ NORTHERN
TINKER FROG

■ SOUTHERN DAYFROG

■ UPEROLEIAN
TOADLETS

■ NORTHERN
TINKER FROG
This frog's range has
contracted to a few iso-
lated mountain tops
near Cooktown, and
even there populations
are critically low.

NORTHERN TINKER FROG ■

Previously widespread in mountain
country between Cooktown and
Cardwell in northern Queensland,
the northern tinker frog is now one
of Australia's most endangered frog
species and is quite possibly extinct.

This small, sharp-snouted frog is
olive brown on top with a thin,
light-coloured ridge along the edge
of the body and a broad black stripe
beneath. There are darker brown
bars across the legs, and frequently
one or more V- or W-shaped markings on the back and a white spot at
the base of each arm. The belly is
greyish white with darker flecks.
Females grow up to 3 cm long.

Northern tinker frogs live along
crystal-clear streams in cool upland
rainforest, and are active during the
day. At night, when other frogs call
for mates and search for food, northern tinker frogs find safe places to
sleep. Some climb onto fern fronds
lining stream banks, where they
perch precariously above the flowing water, apparently oblivious to
other frog species calling loudly
all around them.

At first light, males call vigorously
to attract mates or defend territory
with a soft chirping call or a loud,
musical 'tink tink tink', like a spoon
tapping a glass. They warn off rival
suitors by rising on their front legs,
and pointing their snouts skywards,
exposing their white throats in
conspicuous threat displays. If this
does not deter the intruder, a fight
may ensue to determine which male
wins the female or piece of territory.
Scientific name: *Taudactylus acutirostris*

SOUTHERN DAYFROG

The southern dayfrog has not been
seen since 1979, and it may now be
extinct. This frog was not discovered
until the early 1960s, but during that
short time it was commonly seen in

■ UPEROLEIAN TOADLET
Legs outstretched, the uperoleian
dusky toadlet shows off the patches of
orange and bright yellow on its groin
and thighs and behind its knees.

daylight hours basking on wet
rocks beside the mountain rainforest
streams of the D'Aguilar, Blackall
and Conondale areas of south-east
Queensland. Its other common
names are the Mount Glorious
torrent frog, the southern torrent
frog, and the diurnal frog.

In late afternoon dayfrogs leave
the rocks to forage on the ground
and beside creeks for insects and
other arthropods. At night they
shelter amongst leaf litter, under
rocks, and in dead rolled-up palm
fronds. When disturbed, they dive
into rock pools or plunge fearlessly
into fast-flowing torrents.

These charming frogs are only
about 3 cm long, and brown on top
with darker chevrons on the back
and legs. Their underside is cream
to custard yellow with some grey
markings. Unlike most frogs, the
southern dayfrog has no vocal sacs.

Eggs are laid between October and
May in gelatinous clumps under
rocks in streams. The tadpoles are
dark brown and fat-bodied, with
large lips forming umbrella-shaped
suckers for adhering to rocks and
logs in fast-flowing water.
Scientific name: *Taudactylus diurnus*

UPEROLEIAN TOADLETS ■

Members of this group are rarely
seen, but they make distinctive,
easily identified advertisement calls.
About half are 'clickers', uttering
single explosive clicks; the rest have

a longer call and are 'squelchers'.
Uperoleians are inconspicuous,
and are seldom more than 3 cm
long. For years zoologists thought
that there were just three species
in Australia, but in 1981 the number
recorded increased to 16, and 24 are
now recognised. The number of
species and their distribution has
made uperoleians difficult to study;
In fact, the tadpoles of only four
species are known.

Almost all uperoleians are confined to northern and eastern Australia; there are none in the south-
west of Western Australia and only
one in South Australia. The marbled
toadlet (*Uperoleia marmorata*) has not
been seen since George Grey collected it near the Prince Regent River
in Western Australia in 1841. The
oriental toadlet (*U. orientalis*) has
been sighted only once since
William Stalker first found it
in the Northern Territory in 1905.

Uperoleian frogs are short-legged
and dull to slate grey; some have
small carmine or orange patches in
the groin and on the thighs. The skin
of the back is warty or has large,
smooth bulges containing special
skin glands that exude chemical
compounds. Just what purpose
these chemicals serve for the
toadlets is unknown. In some
species they contain antibiotics that
may enable the frogs to counteract
infections in their environment.

About 40 years ago, a unique
chemical was found in uperoleians
and named uperolein. It was considered as a possible drug for people
with high blood pressure, but the
research program was abandoned.
Scientific name: *Uperoleia* spp.

TREE FROGS AND THEIR RELATIVES

Tree frogs is the common name for hylids, and many species of tree frogs do live in trees in wet forests. These frogs have large round suction pads on their fingers and toes, which help them to climb efficiently. A tree frog can scale the smooth vertical surface of a window with ease.

Australia's tree frogs are defined mostly by uniformity of skeletal and muscular structure. Three groups are recognised in Australia – *Cyclorana*, *Litoria* and *Nyctimystes*. Surprisingly, however, many hylids are ground-dwellers, and some even live in the arid interior of Australia. The genus *Cyclorana* are burrowers – the pads on their fingers and toes are very reduced, but they have hardened structures on their feet that they use as shovels for digging.

Like the southern frogs, Australian hylids are members of a widespread and ancient family, but – unlike southern frogs – tree frogs are found all over the world. They probably evolved, diversified and spread out from the great southern continent of Gondwana. Today, the greatest variety of hylids is found in South America and Australasia, both of which were once part of Gondwana.

The larval development of the tree frogs generally follows the typical pattern: eggs are laid in water, and then aquatic tadpoles develop. For species in arid environments, however, larval development must be rapid so that the tadpoles can achieve metamorphosis before pools dry up. In wetter climates, tadpoles may take six months or more to metamorphose.

In wet places frogs play a role in keeping down the number of flying insects. Tree frogs eat large quantities of mosquitoes, moths, cockroaches and flies. Frogs in these environments usually have large mouths because they often pursue flying prey, leaping into the air from leaves and twigs to catch a meal.
Family: Hylidae

ROUND FROG

Sometimes called the giant frog, this is the largest ground-dwelling frog in Australia. It is sandy to dull brown or occasionally bright green, usually with a paler stripe down the middle of the back. Viewed from the front, it has a dark stripe running from the tip of the snout through the eye to the shoulder, giving it a rather ferocious look. This impression is

■ ROUND FROG
When the heavy rains of the wet season arrive, the round frog is one of the first of the northern tree frog species to breed, laying up to 7000 eggs.

not false – the round frog is cannibalistic and capable of eating any other frog that can pass between its jaws. A 10 cm female in a vivarium at the University of Adelaide swallowed her 7 cm mate whole.

The tadpoles are pale cream or gold and live in water coloured cream because the underlying soil is clay. They develop into small frogs in fewer than 30 days, and then sit at the edge of the ponds feeding on the smaller frog species as they emerge from the water.

The round frog basks in the sun at the edge of shallow, temporary pools in the northern half of western Australia and the Northern Territory as far south as Barrow Creek. Considerable research has been devoted to finding out how these

frogs minimise water loss. It would be fascinating also to find out how they can sunbake for so long without blistering.
Scientific name: *Cyclorana australis*

SHORT-FOOTED FROG ■

Short-footed frogs are up to 4.5 cm long and burrow deep underground. After heavy summer rains, they emerge in their thousands to converge on temporary water bodies and indulge in a frenzy of mating. The mating call is an extremely loud and long moaning sound that can be heard for several hundred metres.

The female lays a long string of eggs and the tadpoles grow rapidly. Development from egg to frog takes as little as three weeks, but still many millions of tadpoles die, unable to develop fast enough to escape being marooned in evaporated pools.

After the rains cease, the frogs dig into the soil again, burrowing backwards with small 'shovels' on the backs of their feet. Once underground, the frogs produce a thin but water-resistant cocoon from dead cells shed from their own skin, which covers the entire body except for the nostrils. This cocoon reduces water loss so that the frog can breathe quietly under the dry soil for at least a year without replenishing its water supply. When the frog emerges from its cocoon after the next rains, its first act is to eat its wrapping. In environments as harsh as these, no food goes to waste.
Scientific name: *Cyclorana brevipes*

DISTRIBUTION

■ ROUND FROG

■ SHORT-FOOTED FROG

■ SHORT-FOOTED FROG
This species is stout, with dark brown marbling and a silvery stripe down its backbone. It is common in arid and semi-arid regions of eastern Queensland, but is rarely seen, spending most of its life buried deep in the soil.

SURVIVING IN THE
AUSTRALIAN DESERT
Some 27 species of
desert frogs live in the
arid zones of Australia.
They have adapted to
harsh droughts and
unreliable rainfall by
devising ingenious ways
of surviving until the
rains come.

WATER-HOLDING FROG

There are three distinct populations of water-holding frogs in Australia, one in the arid portion of the south-west of Western Australia, a second in the south-east of the continent, and a third on blacksoil plains in the Northern Territory.

This large (up to 6 cm long), bulky and usually greyish frog has uncharacteristically small eyes in a flat head. It attracted the attention of early explorers when they found that Aboriginal people used the frogs as a source of water. The fluid in the bladder is almost pure water, and can be squeezed out – but the unfortunate victims may not survive this treatment.

The water-holding frog is renowned for its capacity to live underground for years during periods of drought. It reduces water loss by shedding its skin several times to form a cocoon like a transparent plastic bag around its body and limbs, and lives in a state of torpor entombed in a cavity in the clay soil. Only summer cyclones bring sufficient flooding rain to soak the soil and so release the frog.

As soon as the frogs emerge from the softened soil, the males congregate in the water of claypans and strike up a deafening chorus to attract the females. During mating the eggs are deposited in water, and the newly hatched tadpoles feed on particles of organic debris on the pond floor. They are about 2.5 cm long when the tail is absorbed into the body – very large for baby frogs. They then join the adults in a feeding frenzy, gobbling up termites and

ants to build up fat reserves for when the waters disappear and they must burrow down for their long sleep until the next summer rains.

Despite its adaptation to extremely dry conditions, the water-holding frog is adept at life in water and can actually feed under water, grabbing food with its hands and stuffing it into its mouth. The tongue, so important to land-dwelling frogs for capturing food, is greatly reduced.
Scientific name: *Cyclorana platycephala*

■ SLENDER TREE FROG
A slender tree frog has limited powers of camouflage, but here it changes the colour of its back from brown to green to blend into its environment.

SLENDER TREE FROG ■

The slender tree frog is one of only three species of tree frog in south-western Australia. It has a distinct eardrum (the tympanum) behind the eye and large suction pads on the toes to help it to climb. Females grow up to 6 cm long; males are considerably smaller. In many permanent swamps, where it is one of the most abundant frogs, large choruses of males make their short 'gr-ra-arp' call throughout the winter and into the spring.

The slender tree frog is quite distinctive and cannot be confused with any other frog species in south-western Australia. The backs of its thighs are dark brown to almost black, with bright orange to red spots. Remarkably, it can change the colour of its back from brown to bright green to match its surroundings, but its legs never change colour. The function of such gaudy coloration is not known for certain: it may be a device to frighten predators when the frog jumps away, since these frogs often rest on reeds or vegetation during the day and are clearly visible to snakes, birds or other frogs that might eat them.

Unlike many frogs from south-western Australia, this one has a conventional breeding cycle. Males call from reeds and rushes, and females lay brown eggs in a jelly mass attached to vegetation just below the surface of the water. Tadpoles are striking, with long, streamlined tails, gold and dark green or black stripes, and silvery cream to white underbellies.
Scientific name: *Litoria adelaidensis*

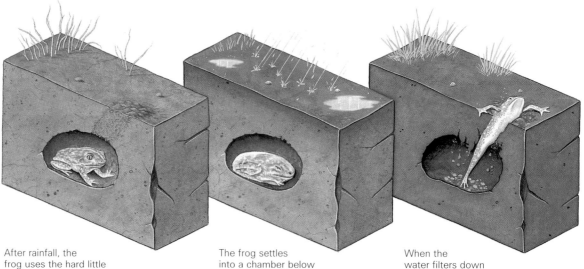

After rainfall, the frog uses the hard little 'spades' on its back feet to delve into the still-wet soil and make a burrow where it can cushion itself against drought.

The frog settles into a chamber below the surface, wrapped in a watertight cocoon formed by its shed skin, until the rains come again.

When the water filters down into the underground chamber, the frog eats its cocoon and digs back up to the surface to breed.

ROCKET FROG

The rocket frog is a swift, strong jumper, with a streamlined body and long, muscular legs. It is usually found in areas surrounding flooded grasslands, coastal swamps, streams and ponds from central New South Wales to the Kimberley in Western Australia. In these relatively open habitats, strong jumping is useful for escaping from predators. When disturbed, these frogs move rapidly with jumps of up to four metres.

Longitudinal rows of raised ridges along the back, usually dark black interspersed with smooth cream to brown stripes, accentuate the frog's streamlined body shape. The face has a black mask above a white lip, and there is a cream spot at the front of the eye. Females grow up to 5 cm long – slightly larger than males.

Males call from groundlevel, usually within a metre of water. After heavy summer rains they often form a large chorus. Their call can be likened to a series of raucous 'yap yap yap yap' sounds. Females lay their eggs in water, where they float on the surface in a film of jelly.
Scientific name: *Litoria nasuta*

GREEN AND GOLDEN BELL FROG ■

The green and golden bell frog's back is green with lines and splashes

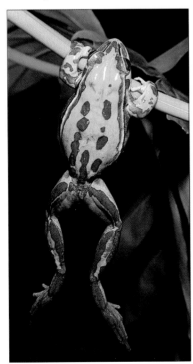

■ GREEN AND GOLDEN BELL FROG
This pretty tree frog is, at 8.5 cm long, among Australia's biggest. It still survives in New Zealand, New Caledonia and Vanuatu where it was introduced.

of gold or bronze, and it has groin patches of brilliant turquoise. It is also known as the golden bell frog, the grass frog and the green and golden swamp frog

Although the bell frog is still common in north-east Victoria, its numbers have dwindled drastically in eastern New South Wales over the past 30 years. It has disappeared from the highlands and is regarded as locally extinct in other areas. In New South Wales, the bell frog once lived mostly on rushes and herbs along streams, swamps, lagoons and billabongs. Since its decline, it has moved into disturbed areas such as dumps, drains and quarries.

There is growing evidence that introduced fish species, such as mosquito fishes, carp and goldfish, have caused this shift of habitat, since they consume spawn and tadpoles and eat frogs into local extinction. Only in disturbed areas that are as yet free from such enemies can the green and golden bell frog breed successfully.

Males call while floating in water in drawn-out groans ending with grunts. During mating the female lays about 4000 eggs, wrapping the spawn around vegetation. This floats at first but sinks after a time. The tadpoles are very large, and have high fins. They are heavily pigmented above and the overall effect is yellow to golden.
Scientific name: *Litoria aurea*

DAHL'S AQUATIC FROG ■

Huge numbers of Dahl's aquatic frogs live on the flood plains of the Northern Territory. By day they float in the water or bask in the sun on lily pads. They are green to dull purple with an emerald stripe down the middle of their back.

Around the beginning of December, at the start of the wet season, Dahl's aquatic frog lays more than a thousand eggs in large floating clumps.

Being abundant and fairly large – up to 7.5 cm long – Dahl's aquatic frog makes a good meal for many creatures: Mertens' water goanna (*Varanus mertensi*) and file snakes (*Acrochordus* spp.) are keen predators. The frog's sleek form equips it to escape from its enemies, and it is able to exude copious amounts of mucus, making it extremely slippery and hard to grasp. This mucus has an acrid smell, and is so toxic that it can kill other frogs.
Scientific name: *Litoria dahlii*

■ DAHL'S AQUATIC FROG
Flattened and slimy, Dahl's aquatic frog is an extremely common species throughout the Top End of Australia.

IN THE SPOTLIGHT

Frog specialists have devised an ingenious way of locating individual frogs. This night-time activity is called 'triangulation': three people with a strong torch each and good gumboots form a triangle roughly around the supposed location of the frog, each trying to work out the direction of the call. When all are satisfied that they have identified the direction, they switch on their torches. The point where the torch beams intersect usually pinpoints the position of the calling frog.

■ GREEN TREE FROG
The green tree frog is a fearless and skilful acrobat and moves about with graceful ease.

■ MAGNIFICENT
TREE FROG
As yet, no one has heard this frog's breeding chorus. There is also still much to discover about its egg-laying habits.

NORTHERN DWARF TREE FROG ■

This tiny, slender green frog is widely distributed across northern Australia and swampy regions of southern New Guinea. In Australia northern dwarf tree frogs prefer swampy areas in open woodland, but they are quite at home in suburban gardens where, during summer, males frequently start calling when lawn sprinklers are switched on.

Northern dwarf tree frogs gather in their thousands among tall reeds and grasses, hopping about in their search for food. The females are up to 3 cm long. At night the male frogs sit high in the reeds and call for mates with a bleating sound that is remarkably loud for their size. The noise attracts predators, and calling males frequently fall prey to nocturnal snakes cruising around the swamps in search of food.

These frogs are unusual among Australian tree frogs in that they perch on leaves for long periods in the blazing summer sun. Most frogs would dry out and die within hours under these conditions, because water evaporates rapidly through frog skin. Northern dwarf tree frogs, however, have developed behaviour to diminish water loss – they tuck their limbs in close to their bodies, thus reducing the area of skin that is exposed to sun and wind. It is likely that they also have a special water-resistant skin layer.

Scientific name: *Litoria bicolor*

TASMANIAN TREE FROG

Undoubtedly, the most distinctive of Tasmania's 11 species of frogs, the Tasmanian tree frog was first described in 1942 by Eric Scott from four specimens collected in north-western Tasmania by Myrtle

■ NORTHERN DWARF TREE FROG
A northern dwarf tree frog perches on a leaf, showing the characteristic cream stripe running along its lip to the edge of its mouth and the pale yellow inner side of its thigh.

Burrows. Scott reported an 'elegant' frog up to 7 cm in length, strikingly patterned in a marbled brown overlaid with patches of vibrant green.

The Tasmanian tree frog is now known to be widespread but rarely abundant in the wet western half of the island. It occupies habitats ranging from rainforest and eucalypt forest to sedgeland and alpine heath.

The males call in a distinctive, goose-like 'quank … quank' when they are trying to attract females to a breeding pond, but emit a low growling call when engaging in territorial encounters. Male frogs are visible when calling at night, either floating spreadeagled in the open water among emergent vegetation, or sitting elevated on reeds. The frogs are adept climbers and have been seen perched in eucalypt trees 15 metres above the ground.

The frog appears to breed whenever conditions are suitable in spring, summer or autumn in large permanent ponds, often in peaty, acidic soils, where they attach their egg masses to vegetation below the surface. The tadpoles hatch when they are 9 mm long and feed and grow to 6 cm before becoming frogs. Some tadpole populations suspend development – but not growth – through the winter until spring. This enables them to metamorphose in warmer temperatures when food is abundant, and thus improves their chances of survival.

Scientific name: *Litoria burrowsae*

MAGNIFICENT TREE FROG ■

The vast skin gland, shaped like a loose beret or cushion, that covers most of its head sets the magnificent tree frog apart from all other frog species. At 12 cm, this frog is one of the largest and heaviest in Australia, and one of the most handsome. With its superb green body spotted with beautiful pale cream to yellow, it deserves its Latin name, *splendida*.

First discovered in 1975 in a public toilet at Lake Argyle in the far northwest of Western Australia, this species is now known to range across the inland areas of the Kimberley, just reaching into the Northern Territory at Keep River National Park on the Victoria Highway. Some of the specimens collected at Lake Argyle are possibly still alive. They were adults when they were picked up, so they have lived until at least 25 years of age.

The natural habitat of the magnificent tree frog appears to be between rocks or in caves, but it is rarely seen and is probably not abundant anywhere. So far no one has ever been around at the right time and place to hear a breeding chorus. Females in captivity carry their mates on their backs, deposit a few hundred eggs in water, and then walk around the perimeter of their enclosure before returning to the water to lay more. This suggests that in the wild the female may deposit eggs in several pools rather than in just one in order to diminish the risk that, if a pool dries up, all the tadpoles will die before they complete their development. Nobody is sure that this is what happens in the wild – but if it does, this method of egg-laying is unique among Australian frogs.

Scientific name: *Litoria splendida*

SPOTTED-THIGHED FROG ■

Female spotted-thighed frogs reach a length of up to 8 cm; males are slightly smaller. The upper body is olive brown with numerous bright green spots on the back, the head and the upper sides of the thighs.

The species occurs in south-eastern Western Australia, from east of Albany to Cape Arid, and usually lives in permanent water, even well into the arid zone – for example, at waterholes around the granite outcrops south of Balladonia.

Males call in spring and early summer and sound like a motorbike warming up and driving off with a run of gear changes. This distinctive calling pattern is common to several related *Litoria* species found in both eastern Australia (*L. raniformis*, *L. aurea* and *L. castanea*) and western Australia (*L. moorei*). They begin with roughly synchronised long, slow moans and then all switch to a series of grunts – the 'gear change'.

Spotted-thighed frogs reproduce by conventional egg development in permanent water sources such as rock holes, seeps and farm dams. The large, aquatic tadpoles may reach a length of 8 cm before undergoing metamorphosis.

Spotted-thighed frogs and motorbike frogs, or bellfrogs (*L. moorei*), will mate with each other where their ranges overlap. This produces frogs with a variety of intermediate groin patterns.

Scientific name: *Litoria cyclorhynchus*

RED-EYED GREEN TREE FROG

The red-eyed green tree frog is one of the most common Australian frogs, widespread in the wet forests of the east coast from Gosford in New South Wales to southern Queensland. It is also called the red-eyed tree frog and the north coast green tree frog. Like most Australian frogs, it is nocturnal and can best be observed with a torch or spotlight.

It has an immaculate light green back with a metallic tint and a velvet sheen, and a yellow belly. The irises of its large, protruding eyes are bright orange to red. Behind its thigh is a streak of dark purple.

The body of the red-eyed green tree frog is relatively long – 6.5 cm – and flat, and its limbs are also long, with toes bearing large, rounded suction pads that help the frog to climb even the smoothest tree trunks. Apart from descending to the ground to breed in pools, this tree frog spends its entire life in

■ SPOTTED-THIGHED FROG
This spotted-thighed frog displays the typical tree frog features of a distinct eardrum and discs on the toes.

foliage, often high in the canopy of rainforest and wet eucalypt forest. At night it emerges to eat flying insects, such as moths and flies, which it collects by flicking out a large sticky tongue, and it actively jumps in pursuit of prey.

Breeding usually occurs in temporary pools that appear after heavy rain. Males form choruses around these sites in spring and summer. Their call consists of a series of strident, slow 'waa-aa waa-aa waa-aa' sounds, followed by a soft trill. This chorus can be almost deafening at close range. Because the tadpoles occupy ephemeral pools, they must develop fast and metamorphose into adults within a few weeks.

Scientific name: *Litoria chloris*

GREEN TREE FROG ■

The green tree frog, or White's tree frog, was probably discovered by the botanist and explorer Joseph Banks. When it was described in 1790 it became the first frog species to be reported from Australia. This was an appropriate honour, since this species is amongst the most abundant, best known and most widespread of all Australian frogs. It inhabits much of the northern half of the continent.

Its species name, *caerulea*, suggests that the creature is cerulean blue. It acquired this misnomer in England, where the first specimen was sent for examination. The months spent preserved in alcohol during the voyage turned the green frog blue.

These frogs are pale green above and cream or white beneath, and grow to about 10 cm long. They are unique in the way they respond to modifications in their environment. The species has fully exploited human constructions; they live in letter boxes, toilet cisterns, shoes, vases – anywhere, in fact, that provides a temporary refuge where the frogs can hide themselves away during the daytime.

The green tree frog feeds readily on a variety of food, ranging from insects to mice, and has been known to live for as long as 23 years in captivity. It deposits its eggs on surface rafts at the onset of summer rains. For breeding to take place in controlled conditions, the frogs seem to need more space than a standard aquarium provides. Some breeders raise the moisture level by spraying a fine mist when the frogs are mating to ensure that they lay and fertilise their eggs.

Scientific name: *Litoria caerulea*

DISTRIBUTION

■ NORTHERN DWARF TREE FROG

■ TASMANIAN TREE FROG
■ MAGNIFICENT TREE FROG

■ SPOTTED-THIGHED FROG
■ RED-EYED GREEN TREE FROG

■ GREEN TREE FROG

■ GREEN TREE FROG
The colour of the green tree frog sometimes verges on an exquisite greenish blue. It can also be white or pink with black spots.

383

■ WHITE-LIPPED
TREE FROG
Australia's largest frog
can change colour to
dark green or brown.

DISTRIBUTION

■ WHITE-LIPPED
TREE FROG

■ GREEN-EYED
TREE FROG

■ PERON'S TREE FROG

■ TORRENT FROG

WHITE-LIPPED TREE FROG ■

The white-lipped tree frog, which
is sometimes called the giant tree
frog, is Australia's largest frog: the
females can reach 13.5 cm long.
Indeed it is one of the biggest tree
frogs in the world. It is common
throughout mainland New Guinea
and the nearby South Pacific islands,
but in Australia it is restricted to
an area north of Townsville in
Queensland, around the coastal
edge of Cape York Peninsula.

These frogs are normally bright
green, but they can change colour
depending on the temperature and
the surface where they are sitting.
They can always be recognised by
their size and by the distinctive
white stripe around their lower lip.

In Australia the white-lipped tree
frog lives in a variety of habitats
ranging from rainforest to seasonally
arid monsoon woodland, and over
much of its range comes into close
contact with humans.

Large numbers congregate in
shower blocks and toilet cisterns,
taking advantage of the permanent
water supply laid on by their human
hosts, and are also attracted by the
insects that flock to the lights around
human dwellings. Others often find
refuge in banana plantations, and
are frequently transported to New
South Wales, Victoria and South
Australia in shipments of bananas.
Unfortunately, most of these travellers die because the species is truly
tropical and cannot survive the cold
southern Australian winter.

After summer storms males gather
around swamps and ponds and call
to attract females, often from perches high in the surrounding trees. The
mating call sounds like a dog barking rapidly twice, and a large chorus
is quite deafening.

Scientific name: *Litoria infrafrenata*

GREEN-EYED TREE FROG ■

The attractive green-eyed tree frog
is found in the rainforests of northern Queensland between Townsville
and Cape York Peninsula, as well
as throughout New Guinea. It is a
mottled rich brown colour, with
varying degrees of green on the
back and a green tinge on the top of
the eye, from which it gets its common name. Females are up to 8.5 cm
long and males 4.5–5 cm long.

A series of flaps or serrations along
the outer surface of each arm and
leg break up the frog's outline, helping it to blend with rainforest leaves
and thus confuse potential predators
looking for a frog-shaped meal.

In the daytime, these tree frogs
normally seek refuge high in the
rainforest canopy, where they rest
among thick clumps of foliage. They
are most commonly seen at night,
when they climb down, sometimes
head first. Males perch on streamside vegetation to call for mates.

After heavy rain, when humidity is
high, these frogs may become active
during the day, basking on rocks in
the sun. During this time the territorial males are combative, stretching
out their hind limbs and vibrating
them rapidly at each other and then
leaping on top of one another to

■ GREEN-EYED TREE FROG
In the breeding season the green-eyed
tree frog utters a soft, ticking call that is
scarcely audible above running water.

initiate wrestling bouts on branches overhanging the stream.
Scientific name: *Litoria genimaculata*

PERON'S TREE FROG ▨

The unusual call of Peron's tree frog is its most distinctive feature. The call is long and drawn out, increasing in loudness as it progresses, and has been variously described as 'a long rattle', 'a loud chuckling trill', 'the sound of a pneumatic drill' and 'a maniacal cackle'.

Peron's tree frog is widespread in many natural and settled areas, such as wet and dry forests, woodlands, pastures and the outskirts of urban developments. It occurs through south-east Queensland and all of New South Wales to the Murray River Valley in Victoria. Breeding occurs in swamps, ponds, dams, rivers and flooded regions.

Females, up to 6.5 cm long, are slightly larger than males. Their flattened heads and bodies help them to conceal themselves in narrow crevices in trees and fallen timber. The round suction pads on their fingers and toes help them to clamber about and grip.

Peron's tree frog is able to change colour rapidly. By day, when the frog is inactive, it is grey with little patterning. At night, however, it changes to a reddish brown with irregular darker brown mottling. Superimposed on this general brown colour are small patches of emerald green, which give the frog its other common name, the emerald green tree frog; there is also a strongly contrasting pattern of black and

■ PERON'S TREE FROG
Males and females of this species, renowned as agile climbers, live separate lives, often a long way from water. They come together to breed in low areas flooded by summer rains.

yellow markings at the backs of the thighs, under the arms and in the groins. These vivid patches are believed to deter potential predators as bright colours usually indicate that an animal is distasteful.
Scientific name: *Litoria peronii*

TORRENT FROG

Adult torrent frogs, also known as waterfall frogs, perch on rocks near or directly behind waterfalls and are active both day and night. The species lives along the rocky streams of Queensland's world heritage rainforests, which stretch between Townsville and Cooktown and include the Daintree.

This mottled olive green and dark brown frog grows to about 6.5 cm long. Like the northern tinker frog (page 378), males of this species put on complex visual displays to communicate with other males, and possibly also to attract females. Unlike the northern tinker frog, which exposes its chin as a threat display, the torrent frog uses its arms and legs to warn off other males. When approached, a resident male faces the intruder, calls vigorously, and waves its limbs in wide circular motions. This display normally scares rival suitors, and is used at night as well as during the day. Males of this species have no

balloon-like sac below the throat, so their mating call is rather quiet. Breeding takes place in fast-flowing streams. In the breeding season the male develops large black spines on the thumbs and chest. These provide an excellent grip as he presses against the female during mating, and prevent him from being swept off her back by the current. The eggs are glued under rocks in a gelatinous mass, and the tadpoles are also well adapted to flowing water – they have large, sucker-like mouths with which they can grip the rocks to prevent themselves from being washed away by the current.
Scientific name: *Litoria nannotis*

■ BLEATING TREE FROG
To produce its bleating call, this frog forces air from its lungs through its vocal chords into its vocal sac. This becomes a large, bubble-like resonating chamber.

ROCKY RIVER FROG ■

There are two similar, closely related species of rocky river frog. Common along flowing streams, creeks and rivers, in both open and heavily forested areas in coastal and adjacent ranges from central Victoria to far north Queensland, on warm spring and summer evenings males call for females from the sandy banks near pools or from exposed stones within the water. They have no vocal sacs and make a soft 'chuckle chuckle chuckle' sound barely audible above the sound of the water.

A black stripe delineates the sides of the head, starting at the snout, passing through the eyes and over the external ears before widening to terminate near the junction of the arms. A number of irregularly shaped black spots decorate the sides of the body. The rears of the thighs and groins are black and peppered with white or cream spots. Females grow up to 7 cm long and males reach about 5 cm long. The frog's streamlined body shape and long legs equip it to jump strongly.

Rocky river frogs lay their eggs in the quiet reaches of streams – during mating the pair lie underwater on the bottom. Eggs clump together and usually stick to rocks or pebbles. Outside the breeding season, these frogs roam widely at night, foraging among forest leaf litter.
Scientific name: *Litoria lesueuri* and *L. wilcoxi*

NAKED TREE FROG

The naked tree frog is one of the most widespread species in Australia. During

summer it is often found pressed against the outside of a window. In this position the working of the frog's internal organs are visible through the glass of the window and the creature's translucent body, which is about 3.5 cm long.

Naked tree frogs vary from flesh-coloured to brown but always seem suffused with pink, with a darker stripe along the side. Other common names are the desert tree frog, the purple tree frog, the red tree frog and the red-purple tree frog.

Naked tree frogs live in rocky ranges, woodlands, open forests and farmland, and along the permanent watercourses of arid Australia. They forage for insects and other arthropods, mostly at ground level, but are also quite adept climbers. The species benefits from water tanks and farm dams. In homesteads it likes to sit inside toilets, often in the company of green tree frogs.

The naked tree frog's mating call is a high-pitched trill, in chorus almost as high-pitched and deafening as that of the bleating tree frog (next entry). Suitors position themselves on the ground close to still or slow-moving water. The females lay their eggs in a thin film as a loose collection on the water's surface. Tadpoles are uniformly brown in colour.

Naked tree frogs prefer to live near semi-permanent waterholes. They have developed cunning behaviour to conserve moisture and keep warm and fed. They cram together in narrow rock crevices, in damp soil under rocks, or in tree hollows, regularly rotating their position within the group. In this way the frogs take turns at being on the outside of the cluster to feed and in the middle to remain moist and warm.
Scientific name: *Litoria rubella*

■ ROCKY RIVER FROG
When mating, the much smaller male rocky river frog male turns a yellowish bronze colour, but at other times the males have bronze-brown backs like those of the female.

BLEATING TREE FROG ■

The bleating tree frog, sometimes called Keferstein's tree frog, is distinguished by its extremely high-pitched call, which sounds rather like the song of a cicada. When many males call together, the synchronised chorus has a pulsing effect that can be painful to the ear.

This long, rather flattened frog grows to about 4.5 cm; females are slightly larger than males. It has a rounded snout and limbs of moderate length with rounded suction pads on the fingers and toes. Its back is a light grey to brown with a darker longitudinal patch running down the centre. The irises of its eyes are a rich wine red.

These frogs live in the coastal plains and ranges of south-east Queensland and eastern New South Wales, mostly in moist forests but sometimes in open areas. They breed in spring and summer, usually only after heavy rainfall. Large numbers of males call together from ground cover around temporary pools. Females deposit their eggs in small clumps attached to the vegetation. A population may complete its entire annual breeding within a few weeks.

Adults are hard to find at other times. They hide beneath bark or in the cracks and hollows of trees, their flat shape enabling them to slip into narrow spaces. Thus, if observers do not see these frogs during the breeding season, they may mistakenly think the species is uncommon.
Scientific name: *Litoria dentata*

LACE-EYED TREE FROG

The stream-dwelling lace-eyed tree frog is found only in the tropical rainforests of northern Queensland between Townsville and Cooktown. It shares its habitat with a number of other tree frogs, but its closest relatives are not Australian – they live along streams in the mountains of New Guinea.

The lace-eyed tree frog is an attractive frog that often bears pale, lichen-like markings on its back to enhance camouflage in its lush rainforest habitat. It has large, conspicuous eyes and a distinctive network of thick gold lines on the lower eyelid, a feature shared by no other species of Australian frog. Males reach a length of up to 3.5 cm and females grow up to 5 cm long.

Like the torrent frog (*L. nannotis*, page 385), this species breeds in swiftly flowing mountain streams. It lacks a balloon-like vocal sac for producing a loud call. The males perch next to small cascades and call to the females gently with single, soft, squeaking notes. The mating pair climb into the stream and lodge their gelatinous clump of large, yolk-filled eggs under a rock to prevent them from being washed away.

Because the developing embryos have a large amount of yolk in their guts, they are bright yellow until after they have hatched. The tadpoles stay under the rocks until their sucker-like mouths are big enough for them to move into the water current and graze on algae-covered rocks without being swept away.
Scientific name: *Nyctimystes dayi*

ROCKHOLE FROG

The rockhole frog lives in the escarpment country of Arnhem Land in the Northern Territory. Despite the intense heat of its habitat, the rockhole frog is active by day and often basks on hot rocks at the edges of pools. Just how it can survive on surfaces that are hotter than 50°C is a complete mystery.

This brown and yellow mottled frog is 2–2.5 cm long. It is not particularly striking in appearance, but its movement is spectacular. When disturbed, it takes a powerful leap across the surface of the water and continues at speed in a series of bounces until it reaches the far side of the pool, where it hops out and away. It manages this by kicking rapidly each time it hits the water, travelling at such speed that it does not sink. This ability to skim across the surface of the water is based on the same principle as that demonstrated when smooth, flat stones are skimmed across water so that they bounce several times before they eventually slow down and sink.

Rockhole frogs often gather in vast numbers; it is not unusual to see as many as a hundred gathered in a shallow rock pool with a surface area of only five square metres. Together, these water bouncers are a phenomenal sight – the water surface seems alive with splashes, as though heavy raindrops are falling.

At the beginning of the wet season, when shallow depressions in the rocks fill with water, the frogs lay up to 115 eggs in these pools. The tadpoles take around 30 days to complete their development and metamorphose into small frogs.
Scientific name: *Litoria meiriana*

VERREAUX'S TREE FROG

In all but densely forested areas, Verreaux's tree frog is common around dams, slow-flowing streams and swamps. It is found throughout the Great Dividing Range and the coastal plains from south-eastern Queensland to near Ballarat in western Victoria. The whirring chirps of calling males are a familiar sound throughout winter and spring and serve to attract females that are ready to mate and lay their eggs.

Small clumps of eggs adhere to vegetation under the water and, depending on water temperature, tadpoles usually compete their larval development in two to three months. The adult Verreaux's tree frog is no more than 4 cm long.

Two subspecies of Verreaux's tree frog are recognised: a widespread lowland form, and a distinctive high-altitude form found in most alpine and subalpine areas of south-eastern Australia from the Bogong high plains to the Kosciuszko region, and including isolated populations on Lake Mountain and the Baw Baw Plateau in Victoria. Both subspecies are attractive frogs. The flanks of the pale to dark brown lowland form have striking black splashes on a yellow background. These markings are visible only when it jumps. The high-altitude frogs are usually bright green but can sometimes be brown, with two or more distinctive dark stripes.

Verreaux's tree frog was once confused with the common brown tree frog of eastern Australia, *L. ewingii*. It was only the differences in call in places where the two species occurred together that identified them as different. Interestingly, where these two species live apart their calls are remarkably similar but where their distributions overlap their calls are unmistakably species-specific, so that the females can distinguish males of their own species.
Scientific name: *Litoria verreauxii*

■ LACE-EYED
TREE FROG
The unique feature of this frog – an interlacing pattern of veins on the lower eyelid – is clearly visible here.

■ VERREAUX'S
TREE FROG
The colouring of this species is highly variable. It is one of the few frog species to call throughout the winter.

DISTRIBUTION

■ COPHIXALUS SPP.

■ AUSTROCHAPERINA SPP.

■ COPHIXALUS
SAXATILIS
The rock frog is
found only on the
Black Trevethan Range,
south of Cooktown
in Queensland.

MICROHYLIDS

Microhylids are small, secretive, nocturnal frogs with a limited distribution in Australia. The largest Australian species is only 4.6 cm long and the smallest, at about 1.5 cm long, is scarcely larger than a human thumbnail.

There are many microhylids in North and South America, Africa, Madagascar, Asia and New Guinea. Australian microhylids are members of the subfamily Genyophryninae. They arrived here from New Guinea, where the subfamily is numerous and highly evolved.

Australian microhylids spend much of their time on the ground, although several climb into bushes or even trees. None of them has the webbed toes that make water frogs good swimmers, since they never go to water, even to breed. However, although they can live away from ponds or streams, they still need moist conditions during the breeding season, when they hide their eggs in damp places, such as under stones or rotting logs. Females lay

10–20 relatively large eggs, instead of the hundreds to thousands laid by frog species whose tadpoles grow up in water.

One frog, usually the male, stays with the eggs until they hatch into tiny frogs. Each egg yolk contains enough food for the embryo to grow into a small adult without any external nourishment. The feeding habits of microhylids have not been studied, but it seems certain that, like other frogs, they eat small invertebrates – insects, spiders and worms.

Rainforest dwellers
One microhylid genus is *Cophixalus*. Typically, these frogs spend the day hiding on the rainforest floor. They emerge on wet nights, the males climbing into bushes or low trees to call. Most species have enlarged discs on the tips of their fingers and toes for climbing.

The ornate frog (*C. ornatus*), about 2 cm long, is the species most likely to be heard by someone venturing into the rainforest on a wet night. It is found throughout most of the tropical rainforest of Queensland and is common. It calls in a fairly loud but short beep from leaves, twigs or tree trunks one to two metres above the forest floor.

Other *Cophixalus* species make clicking or buzzing calls from leaf litter or low shrubbery. The soft nocturnal buzz of the tiny buzzing frog, *C. bombiens*, is easily mistaken for the sound of an insect.

The rock frog, *C. saxatilis*, lives only at the edge of rainforest about 20 kilometres south of Cooktown on the Black Trevethan Range in Queensland. In daytime the loud

clicking calls of these frogs echo in the warm, moist cavities between the black granite boulders; at night the frogs are active in the open.

Members of another microhylid genus, *Austrochaperina*, are typically found in leaf litter on the forest floor or under rocks or logs. The Northern Territory frog (*A. adelphe*) and the slender frog (*A. gracilipes*), of Cape York Peninsula and southern New Guinea, are much more widely distributed than other Australian microhylids and live where there is no rain for much of the year. They are 'sibling species' – meaning that they are so similar that they can be told apart only by slight differences in colour and in the calls of the males. At times large numbers congregate in a moist spot during the dry season.

Three *Austrochaperina* species live in the tropical rainforests of north-eastern Queensland. The rain frog (*A. pluvialis*) is about 2.5 cm long, with a silvery stripe along each side of its nose and red in its eyes. In the summer rainy season, males call at night from beneath fallen leaves or other ground shelter in a series of short, high-pitched, whistle-like notes. All Australian frogs of this genus call with a similar series of high-pitched peeps or whistles, differing mainly in the rapidity with which they repeat the notes. The other two rainforest *Austrochaperina* species, the robust frog (*A. robusta*) and Fry's frog (*A. fryi*) are also 'sibling species'. They are most easily distinguished from each other by their call patterns: the robust frog calls in couplets, whereas Fry's frog calls in a series of even whistles.
Family: Microhylidae

DISTRIBUTION

■ AUSTRALIAN BULLFROG

RANIDS

AUSTRALIAN BULLFROG
The Australian bullfrog, or wood frog, was discovered on Cape York Peninsula, but it is also common in New Guinea, so the common name 'Australian bullfrog' is misleading. In Australia it lives in swamps and creeks in rainforests and open forests in northern Queensland between the tip of Cape York Peninsula and Townsville. It is the only Australian representative of the family Ranidae, which is common throughout the world.

The Australian bullfrog is large (about 8 cm long) and agile, with long, muscular legs, a narrow snout and fully webbed feet. Its back is brown and a fold of skin runs from each eye along the side of its body.

In daytime, Australian bullfrogs frequently bask in the sun at the edge of swamps. This raises their body temperature, and allows them to digest their food more rapidly and grow faster, but it also exposes them to predators, particularly large birds. Australian bullfrogs are

extremely wary. They have large ears and at the slightest threat leap into the water, emerging to bask again only when danger has passed.

This frog is unique among Australian frogs in having not one but two distinct balloon-like vocal sacs, with which it produces a loud and unusual mating call that sounds like a duck quacking. At night males call from the edge of swamps or from floating vegetation in the water.
Family: Ranidae
Scientific name: *Rana daemeli*

BUFONIDS

CANE TOAD ■

The cane toad was introduced into Queensland from Hawaii in 1935 to help get rid of the cane beetle, a pest of sugar cane crops. The toad failed to control the beetle and has since become a major pest itself.

Cane toads live in almost all habitats, including wet forests, open grasslands, sand dunes and even suburban gardens.

Cane toads are native to South and Central America. In Australia their present distribution stretches from the Northern Territory and far north Queensland to northern New South Wales, and they are extending their range further south and west at a rate of 27 kilometres every year.

The rate at which cane toads multiply, combined with a lack of natural predators resistant to their venom, has led to massive population explosions of cane toads. Kookaburras, owls and water rats are known to consume some parts of the toad's body such as the tongue, stomach and intestines. So, perhaps, do tawny frogmouths though, as yet, this has not been conclusively proven. Crocodiles have been observed washing the toads by shaking them very vigorously in water for several minutes before eating them.

Compared with most of Australia's frogs, cane toads are very large, reaching about 15 cm in length. Their skin is warty and is coloured grey to reddish brown. They have a pair of large, bulbous glands on the back of their heads and shoulders. These glands and the cane toad's flesh are poisonous to most native wildlife, and this deters many animals, including dogs, from eating them. Tadpoles and mature adults are especially poisonous.

Cane toads eat insects, as well as lizards and mice, which they swallow whole. They have also been known to eat dog food and corn cobs. They appear to use their power of smell to find food.

The males call from the water's edge during summer rains from September to March; the call sounds rather like a high-pitched telephone dialling tone. In the breeding season females produce 10 000 to 25 000 eggs, which they lay in strings and attach to vegetation and rocks in the water. Fertilised eggs later hatch into shiny, black tadpoles.

Scientific name: *Bufo marinus*

MEDICINAL FROGS

Medical science is investigating the potential benefits of substances secreted by the granular glands of frog skin. For example, a substance called caerulein from the skin of northern Australia's green tree frog (*Litoria caerulea*, page 383) has been found to restore gut movements after major abdominal surgery. *L. splendida*, the Australian magnificent tree frog (page 382) is just one of many frog species worldwide that are known to produce secretions with antibacterial, antifungal and antiviral properties.

Chemicals secreted by the glands on the shoulders of cane toads are being extracted, dried and exported to China for use in traditional medicine as diuretics, heart stimulants and tonics.

DISTRIBUTION

■ CANE TOAD

■ CANE TOAD
Australia's notorious cane toad is ample evidence of an attempt at biological control that went wrong. Introduced as a natural predator of the cane beetle, this species now preys on native wildlife, including hapless frogs.

FISHES

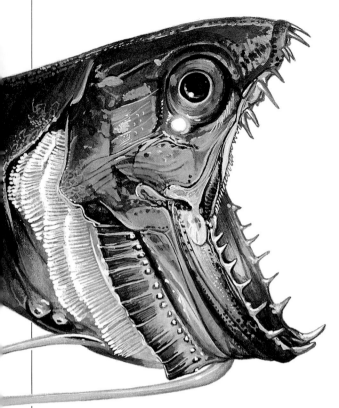

OVER 500 MILLION YEARS AGO, the oceans around the southern supercontinent of Gondwana were the setting for a new act in the drama of evolution. The fishes – the first creatures with a backbone – had joined the prolific but boneless sea life of the period.

Scientists call the earliest fishes agnathans, which means 'jawless'. Many had a bony head shield and body armour made up of minute scales or bony plates, and these fishes are called ostracoderms, meaning 'bony-skinned'. So well developed was their armour that they have left an excellent fossil record. During the age of fishes, 420–390 million years ago, the ostracoderms were numerous, but today they are extinct. By 360 million years ago, the three main groups of fishes known today had evolved.

DENIZENS OF THE DEEP Strange fishes lurk in the deep seas – possibly early-evolving species that were kept out of the upper waters by faster, more highly evolved species. In order to identify species, attract mates and lure prey, many emit light (bioluminescence) – like this star-eater, which has a spotlight below its eye, light-emitting organs on its sides and a luminous whisker (barbel).

The three groups are the jawless fishes (the hagfishes and the lampreys), the cartilaginous fishes (the sharks) and the bony fishes (the lungfishes, lobe-finned fishes and ray-finned fishes). All but the lobe-finned fishes are found in Australian waters, which are home to 3500 of the world's 23 000 fish species.

Australian fishes come in all sizes, colours and shapes, and have adapted to habitats from the ocean depths to the shallow tropical waters of the Great Barrier Reef and the temporary pools of the arid interior. Australia has some of the finest fossil deposits of early fishes in the world, including a collection of extinct bony-skinned fishes called Gogo fish, after the Gogo geological formation in north-west Western Australia's Kimberley region.

A typical fish of today – a bony creature with a streamlined body, a pointed head, jaws and paired fins – springs from a long evolutionary process. It was preceded by many strange and even bizarre forms, but throughout their evolution all fishes have shared certain characteristics: they all have gills, fins and a backbone.

Surviving change

When fishes first evolved, their only problem was survival of the fittest. The slow process of evolution developed highly sophisticated swimmers, hunters, grazers, reproducers and survivors for every aquatic environment.

When our own species emerged half a million years ago, humans were just another predator on fishes but, over the past 5000 years, fishes, like all other wild animals, have had to face a new kind of threat. Not only has predation increased to an enormous extent, but humans have also changed whole environments and destroyed ecosystems in the space of fewer than 20 generations of some fishes. The development of agriculture and the spread of industrialisation in the late twentieth century has had an enormous impact on the distribution, abundance, and ultimately the survival, of many fish species throughout the world.

Jaws

Fishes make up by far the majority of vertebrates on Earth today, and their survival stems from the advantage that they gained from the evolution of jaws about 400 million years ago.

Fossil records suggest that jaws may have evolved as an extension of the armour that the early jawless fishes carried on their head. Once the bones about the eyes developed, evolution continued the work, eventually making paired jaws that opened and closed. These jaws may have developed to surround existing teeth, with other teeth evolving to complement them, or they may have evolved from the first pair of gill arches – bony structures behind and below the eyes, bearing the gills through which the fish takes in oxygen.

Jaws were a formidable weapon for fishes in the battle for survival. Jawed fishes could eat other fishes, graze on large marine algae, and crush molluscs, crustaceans and marine worms in their mouths. Complex food webs began to develop, in which herbivorous fishes grazed on algae, carnivorous fishes preyed on herbivorous fishes, and large carnivorous predators devoured smaller ones.

Reproductive strategies

All fishes reproduce sexually – that is, they require sperm from a male and an egg from a female to produce offspring – but they achieve fertilisation in many different ways. Usually, a female fish lays eggs and a male (or males) squirts sperm (called milch) into the surrounding water to fertilise them. Many fishes lay hundreds of thousands of tiny, free-floating eggs that drift with the wind and surface currents; others lay a few large eggs in a burrow or nest and guard them until they hatch.

Fish spawning times are controlled by water temperatures, tides, currents and the phases of the moon, all of which affect the survival of both eggs and larvae. Some fish eggs drift to the bottom, some float near the surface, and others stick in clusters to rocks, logs or plants.

A small number of fishes are monogamous, with one male fertilising one female's eggs. More often, however, males fertilise eggs from a number of females. An unusual feature of many Australian fishes is that they change sex as they grow older, some from male to female, others from female to male.

Breathing under water

All living creatures need oxygen to survive. Land animals use their lungs to take oxygen from the air and their blood carries it around their body, but fishes must get their oxygen from the water around

them. To do this they have gills, which are remarkably efficient at extracting oxygen from water. But there is far less oxygen in water than in air, so a huge quantity of water must pass through the gills for the fish to get the oxygen it needs.

Some fast-swimming fishes that live in the open ocean, such as tunas, mackerels and certain sharks, must keep moving to ensure that enough water flows over their gills, but most fishes can rest sometimes, pumping water over their gills by flapping their gill covers and swallowing.

Living in salt water

A process called osmosis evens out the concentrations of salt in solutions by drawing water from places where there is less salt to places where there is more. Some marine fishes, such as hagfishes, deal with this by keeping their blood about as salty as the surrounding sea water, while sharks retain salty waste in their bodies as urea. But most marine and freshwater fishes must continually adjust the water and salt levels in their body to maintain a balance with the surrounding water, or they would become dehydrated or suffer from loss of salt. This process is called osmoregulation.

The blood of marine fishes is less salty than the sea water around them, so osmosis forces fresh water out of the fish's body into the sea. To prevent dehydration, marine fishes ingest sea water and produce very little urine. Excess minerals, such as calcium and sulphates, are excreted with other body wastes and other salts, such as sodium, potassium and urea, are discarded through the gills.

Freshwater fishes, on the other hand, have blood that is saltier than the surrounding water, so osmosis forces large quantities of water into the fish's body through its gills, mouth membranes and

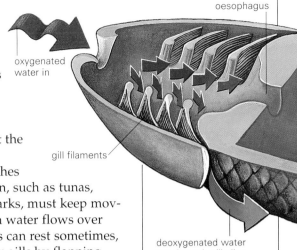

oesophagus

oxygenated water in

gill filaments

deoxygenated water out through gill slits

FRILLY GILLS
The gills are fine, frilly filaments with which a fish breathes. As the fish swims, water flows into its mouth and over its gills. Each tiny filament has a network of minute blood vessels that take up oxygen directly from water. As the used water is pushed out through the gill slits, more water flows in from the front. The delicate gills are protected by a flap behind the fish's eyes called the operculum.

ON THE ROCKS
Jumping blennies live in rock pools and shallow reefs around the south-western coast. They sometimes leap right out of the water onto the rocks.

intestine. To get rid of the excess water, freshwater fishes produce a lot of very weak urine. But this urine also eliminates salts, which the fishes need, since the water where they live and the foods they eat contain very little salt. To compensate for this, freshwater fishes absorb salt from water as it passes over their gills.

Staying submerged

Fishes have evolved various ways of remaining at the right depth in the water, neither sinking nor rising, or moving between shallow water and deep water.

Cartilaginous fishes, such as sharks, have a big, oily liver that provides some buoyancy, but most of them must also swim continually, which requires large, wing-like pectoral fins and uses a great deal of energy.

Bony fishes have a gas-filled swim bladder in the middle of their stomach cavity, just under the spine, to keep them weightless so they can stay at the right depth. A little gas in this bladder keeps the fish afloat in shallow water, but in deeper water increasing pressure compresses the bladder and more gas is needed in the swim bladder to keep the fish afloat. This phenomenon is called neutral buoyancy. In most fishes, gas is taken into the swim bladder by pumping it in from the blood with a gas gland, and is released from the swim bladder into the bloodstream through a network of blood vessels. Gas cannot be diffused into and out of the swim bladder rapidly, so most fishes must move slowly up and down in the water.

Most bottom-dwelling fishes do not have swim bladders, since they need to live and hunt on the ocean floor; buoyancy is not required for such a lifestyle.

lateral line

swim bladder

GOING SWIMMINGLY
In some fishes the sensory lateral lines are clearly visible. The swim bladder that the fish uses to control buoyancy is just below its spine.

Hearing without ears

Fishes do not have external ears, but they are able to 'hear' by sensing vibrations travelling through the water by means of their lateral lines – organs running the length of their body – and their ear bones (otoliths).

The lateral lines, which run along both sides of a fish's body and branch out to its snout and lower jaw, are made up of tiny, sensitive cells (neuromasts) filled with a soft, jelly-like substance that responds to changes in pressure. As the fish swims, it generates a bow wave that bounces off nearby objects, both stationary and moving. The neuromasts register the changes in water pressure and notify the fish's brain. Schools of fishes can move as one by sensing the changes in water pressure through their lateral lines. Because sound waves in water cause changes in pressure, fishes can also 'hear' low-frequency noises through their lateral lines.

Fishes can also sense where they are in the water through their otoliths, two small bones that sit inside a fish's head in liquid-filled cavities. As the fish swims, the otoliths move around, touching the surrounding nerves, which relay messages to the brain, so the fish can judge which way it has turned.

A management challenge

With European settlement, change in our aquatic environments began to take place at an unprecedented rate. The spread and growth of the urban population around the coastline has put huge pressure on inshore and continental-shelf fish stocks. Unfortunately, the impact of human activities in Australia falls mainly on the very places that fishes need the most – their breeding and nursery grounds. Mangroves, estuaries, inshore reef areas and river systems are all key areas for the survival of many fish species. Another threat comes from modern fishing technologies such as echo sounders, satellite navigation systems, portable freezers and access to remote locations.

Much remains to be discovered about Australia's fishes, particularly regarding how fish populations respond to the pressure of environmental change and exploitation. Fisheries management and conservation agencies must strike a balance between the short-term benefits of exploitation and the long-term benefits of conservation. It will be a challenge for all Australians in the next decade to contain the exploitation of fish at a sustainable level and protect the habitats that fishes depend upon from further degradation.

LAMPREYS AND HAGFISHES

The lampreys and the distantly related and more primitive hagfishes belong to the superclass Agnatha – sole survivors of the jawless fishes, which represent an early stage in the evolution of vertebrate animals. Unlike the bony-skinned ostracoderms, a group of jawless fishes now extinct, lampreys and hagfishes do not have an external skeleton. Both are eel-shaped, but neither is closely related to eels, which are jawed fishes. They usually occur in temperate waters.

LAMPREYS

Only three of the 40 or so known lamprey species occur in Australian waters – the pouched lamprey (*Geotria australis*), the short-headed lamprey (*Mordacia mordax*) and the nonparasitic lamprey (*M. praecox*).

In Australia, pouched lampreys in the freshwater stage mainly inhabit rivers in south-western Australia, South Australia, western Victoria and Tasmania. Adults probably spend two years at sea, growing from about 9 cm and 0.9 grams to about 65 cm and 250 grams. Then, they stop eating and re-enter rivers.

Accumulated fat helps them to survive for the next 15–16 months as they migrate upstream to spawn and then die. During this migration, the males develop a huge, jowl-like sac below the head and just behind the suctorial disc. The function of this bizarre structure, found neither in northern hemisphere lampreys nor in the two other Australian lamprey species, is not known.

The short-headed lamprey spends its juvenile and spawning phases in the rivers and streams of southern New South Wales, eastern Victoria and Tasmania. Its spawning run is believed to last for about a year.

The nonparasitic lamprey, known only from the Moruya and Tuross Rivers in southern New South Wales, may have evolved from the short-headed lamprey through the elimination of the marine parasitic phase in the adult stage of the life cycle. This species lives permanently in fresh water, and becomes fully mature at about ten months. The nonparasitic lamprey does not feed during its metamorphosis from larva to adult, but it develops teeth, eyes and a suctorial disc, so that it looks like a small version of the full-grown short-headed lamprey. It reaches only about 13 cm in length and 2 grams in weight, whereas the short-headed lamprey grows to about 35 cm and 40 grams.

Lamprey larvae are worm-like, toothless and blind. They live in burrows in soft river mud and sand, feeding on small algae and detritus. All three Australian species remain in the larval stage for at least three years, growing to 7.5–15 cm long.

Young adult pouched and short-headed lampreys have eyes, two fins along the back and a large suctorial disc at the front. On reaching adulthood, they swim downstream to the sea. Parasitic feeders use their sharp teeth, situated on a tongue-like piston in the middle of the disc, to cut or rasp tissue from their host.
Order: Petromyzontiformes

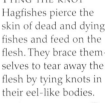
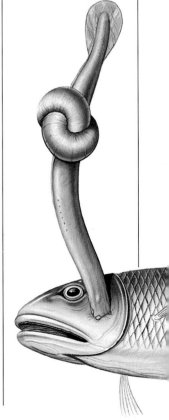

HAGFISHES

A hagfish captured by a predator simply ties itself into a knot then gradually moves the knot along its body and uses it to push its captor away. Hagfishes can do this because they have a flexible rod called a notochord, rather than a backbone made up of vertebrae. The sliding process is facilitated by mucus – hagfishes produce so much slime that they use the knotting technique to brush off excess mucus.

Hagfishes also use this knotting technique to provide leverage for tearing flesh from their prey. Hagfishes scavenge on dead and dying fishes and invertebrates on the sea floor. They have a tongue-like piston, which bears two long cutting plates that are used to cut and tear flesh from their prey. Often they penetrate the body of their prey and eat it from the inside out.

Hagfishes live only in the sea, burrowing into soft sediments and leaving only their snout protruding to enable them to breathe and sense the presence of prey.

Of the 50 or so hagfish species known worldwide, only two have been located in Australian waters – *Eptatretus cirrhatus* and *E. longipinnis* – and virtually nothing is known about their biology. *E. cirrhatus*, which grows to over 60 cm long, has been trawled from depths of between 300 metres and 700 metres in the Pacific Ocean off the coast of New South Wales, but one of only two *E. longipinnis* specimens so far caught, measuring 42 cm in length, came from a depth of only 40 metres in the Indian Ocean off the coast of South Australia.

Young hagfishes establish themselves in burrows shortly after they hatch from eggs as miniature adults.
Order: Myxiniformes

CARTILAGINOUS FISHES

The skeletons of sharks, rays and chimaeras (class Chondrichthyes) are made of cartilage rather than bone. It is now believed that the first sharks may have had a bony skeleton that was modified into cartilage – perhaps because it is lighter and more flexible, allowing the development of larger, faster fishes.

Of about 300 species of cartilaginous fishes known in Australian waters, more than half are unique to this continent. Around 170 shark species have been identified here, ranging from aggressive predators like the great white shark to the world's largest fish, the gentle whale shark. Australia also has over 120 ray species and at least 13 chimaera species.

MERMAID'S PURSE
Inside a dogfish's egg case, the tiny embryo clings to the food-rich yolk. These eggcases are often washed ashore, and their structure shows how they got their popular name.

THE LATERAL LINE
Like all fishes, sharks have a sensory lateral line that responds to both vibrations and pressure changes, and is used to detect prey at middle range.

SHARKS

Sharks have fairly large brains and sophisticated sensory systems. They can smell fish oil and blood at concentrations as low as one part per million. In addition to the sensitive lateral line, electro-receptors around the snout detect weak, close-range electrical fields around the muscles of prey – even in fishes buried in sand. Sight, taste and touch are also acute, and are used at short range.

Sharks seldom rest, because they do not have a swim bladder to pump gases in and out of the blood-stream and hold them at the right depth in the water. Their large, oily liver helps them to stay afloat, but they must keep swimming to maintain their position in the water. They cruise at about 5 kilometres an hour, but can achieve short bursts of up to 30 kilometres an hour.

Some sharks live mainly on squids, others on crustaceans, others on small fishes, large fishes, or even other sharks. Being large predators, their only threat is from other sharks – and humans. Sharks keep the population size of their prey in check, and also help to maintain genetically strong fish populations by picking off weak and sick fishes.

Design perfection
Sharks, among the earliest jawed fishes, emerged around 400 million years ago. By about 130 million years ago, modern shark design was firmly established. It has changed very little, although many species have evolved and become extinct.

A shark's impressive rows of teeth are not attached to the jawbone; instead, several rows grow in a membranous tooth bed and new teeth move to the front as older ones are lost or broken. Sharks grow slowly; some species live for over

50 years. They range from less than 20 cm to 18 metres long. Shark skin is covered with scales called dermal denticles, which are like miniature flat teeth in structure.

Cartilaginous sex
Some aspects of shark biology are quite complex. Sharks fertilise their young internally. Males have a pair of sexual organs called claspers, used to deliver sperm into the female's sexual opening. About 70 per cent of sharks and rays bear live young; the rest lay eggs protected by thorny cases.

The period from fertilisation to birth is usually nine to ten months, and two to 40 young are born. At birth the babies, called pups, are between 20 cm and 1.4 metres long. Females often breed every two years, but sometimes less frequently.
Subclass: Elasmobranchii

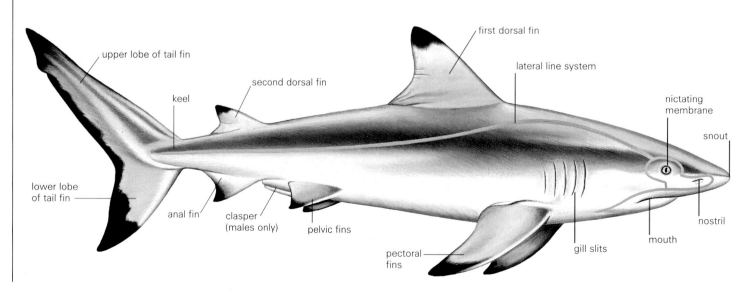

upper lobe of tail fin

keel

second dorsal fin

first dorsal fin

lateral line system

nictating membrane

snout

lower lobe of tail fin

anal fin

clasper (males only)

pelvic fins

pectoral fins

gill slits

mouth

nostril

BLINDSHARKS

Blindsharks have a slender, rounded body, a small mouth located slightly behind the tip of the snout and ahead of the eyes, two dorsal fins without spines, an anal fin and a lobe and groove around the outer edges of the nostrils. Adults can be up to 1.2 metres in length, but most species reach about 70 cm long.

Blindsharks are so named because they close their eyes when caught by rock anglers. They live only in the eastern waters of Australia from Cape York in northern Queensland to Jervis Bay in southern New South Wales, and are thought to feed primarily on small fishes and shellfish. Litters of seven or eight live young are born in the spring.
Family: Brachaeluridae

LONGTAIL CARPET SHARKS

Longtail carpet sharks have the same build, size and physical characteristics as blindsharks (above). They are found in coral reefs in tropical waters around Australia's northern coast.

The juveniles of one species, *Chiloscyllium punctatum*, are strikingly patterned with dark, wavy bands that change to a drab, uniform grey as the fish matures. *C. punctatum* grows to just over a metre long.
Family: Hemiscylliidae

MEGAMOUTH SHARK

Megamouths were discovered in 1976 when one became entangled in the anchors of a research vessel in deep water near Hawaii. Since then, specimens have been recorded from Japan, The Philippines, Indonesia, South America, Africa, the USA and Australia. The Australian specimen

■ COLLARED CATSHARK
Most collared catsharks have a well-defined 'dog collar', like this striking *Parascyllium variolatum* specimen.

was washed ashore in 1988 at Mandurah, just south of Perth.

Megachasma pelagios is the sole member of this family. Its huge mouth contains large jaws with about a hundred rows of teeth in each jaw. Every row contains three or four tiny teeth, designed for eating small prey. Megamouths feed on plankton, krill and sea jellies and grow to just over 5 metres long.
Family: Megachasmidae

TAWNY SHARK

The tawny shark (*Nebrius ferrugineus*) is the only member of this family. Adults grow as long as 3.2 metres, but have small mouths and are harmless to humans.

Tawny sharks are common and widely distributed throughout the Indo-Pacific on continental shelves and atolls. In Australia they are most abundant in tropical waters.

The tawny shark hunts at night. Although found from the intertidal zone to a depth of about 70 metres, it seeks out sheltered crevices and caves on reefs to rest. It feeds on a variety of small reef animals, including corals, crabs, octopuses, sea urchins and fishes, sucking whole prey into its mouth cavity, which acts as a powerful pump.
Family: Ginglymostomatidae

COLLARED CATSHARKS ■

The collared catsharks resemble the blindsharks and the longtail carpet sharks (this page). Temperate Australian waters are home to the collared catshark genus *Parascyllium*.

Their slender, flexible body, less than a metre long, enables these sharks to slip into very small crevices and holes in search of the small fishes and crustaceans that are their prey.
Family: Parascylliidae

HORN SHARKS ■

Three members of this primitive group of sharks are found on Australia's continental shelf, all marked with dark bands or stripes. The very rare zebra horn shark (*Heterodontus zebra*) lives in deep, tropical waters; the crested shark (*H. galeatus*), of temperate waters, is also hardly ever seen.

Horn sharks – known as bullhead sharks outside Australia – have hard ridges above the eyes. Unlike other sharks, they have both an anal fin and strong, horny spines in front of each dorsal fin. Adults can reach a length of 1.6 metres, but are mature at 60–95 cm long.

One species, the Port Jackson shark (*H. portusjacksoni*), sleeps all day in caves and under ledges. At night, it feeds on sea urchins, crabs, lobsters, abalones and periwinkles, crushing their spines and shells with its flattened back teeth.

In winter, females lay a few large, spiral-flanged egg cases, which they drill into the sand and mud using their mouth. After about five months the young, about 23 cm long, emerge from the eggs and immediately begin to fend for themselves.
Family: Heterodontidae

■ HORN SHARK
The Port Jackson shark is a common horn shark species in coastal waters off southern Australia. It swims sluggishly or crawls over the ocean floor, using its greatly enlarged, flap-like pectoral fins to propel itself slowly along.

■ WHALE SHARK
The whale shark is easily identified by its size, its broad, flat head and its enormous mouth, which is situated close to the tip of its snout. It is also distinctively marked in a checkerboard pattern.

FRILLED SHARK

The frilled shark *Chlamydoselachus anguineus*, lone member of its family, is one of the oldest living shark species. It has been recorded from isolated locations in temperate and tropical oceans throughout the world, where it lives near the bottom at depths of 120–1280 metres. It is quite commonly caught off the coast of Japan, and has been caught off Tasmania and New South Wales.

The frilled shark is dark brown, grows to about 2 metres long, and gives birth to 8–15 live young. Six long, frill-like gill slits, the first encircling the throat, give it its name. With its serpentine body, single low dorsal fin, reptilian head and fang-like teeth near the tip of its snout, the frilled shark looks more like a snake than a shark. Its sinuous body enables it to hunt in caves and crevices, and its jaws gape wide to take in relatively large prey. Little is known about its life cycle.
Family: Chlamydoselachidae

WHALE SHARK ■

Sole species in this family, the adult whale shark (*Rhincodon typus*), the world's largest fish, grows to at least 12 metres long. This huge shark is harmless to humans. It has minute teeth and eats plankton and small fishes, drawing food from the water through its gills, which have internal mesh-like screens for filtering out tiny creatures. Whale sharks swim with their huge mouth open to force

water through the gill filters. They also feed by hanging vertically in the water, opening their mouths to allow water and food to pour in.

Whale sharks are seen worldwide in tropical and subtropical oceans. Generally loners, they gather in groups of up to a hundred to feed. In Australia they inhabit oceanic and inshore tropical northern waters, but may venture as far south as New South Wales and, very occasionally, to the fringes of the Great Australian Bight as the water warms up.

Between March and May, whale sharks congregate off Ningaloo Reef in northern Western Australia. Scientists believe that they are drawn to the area by the spawning of corals after the March and April full moons. The coral spawn attracts masses of plankton and krill, which in turn attract huge schools of small fishes – a shark feast.

Little is known about reproduction in whale sharks, but the young, about 50 cm long at birth, are thought to be born alive.
Family: Rhincodontidae

WOBBEGONGS ■

Wobbegongs have a flattened, mottled body, beard-like skin flaps (which probably act as sensors for detecting prey) and formidable fang-like teeth at the front of the jaws. Adults are 60 cm to 3 metres long.

Most wobbegongs occur in Australian waters, and many are unique to Australia. They live near reefs and mainly rest during daylight. At night, they hunt live fishes and invertebrates. The spotted wobbegong (*Orectolobus maculatus*) and the banded wobbegong (*O. ornatus*) can be aggressive feeders.

Wobbegongs give birth to large litters of 20 or more that swim from the female after developing in eggs held in the uterus.
Family: Orectolobidae

HOUND SHARKS AND WEASEL SHARKS

These two shark families are long and slender like the catsharks (see page 403) but more plainly coloured. They resemble their larger relatives, the whaler sharks (opposite page).

Hound sharks are found throughout Australian waters, but weasel sharks occur only in warm waters. Some species have shortened mouths and small teeth, which may help them when they are suction-feeding on soft, slippery prey, such as squids and octopuses. Others have larger mouths and stronger teeth that are better adapted to feeding on fishes.
Families: Triakidae (hound sharks), Hemigaleidae (weasel sharks)

■ WOBBEGONG
Waiting on the sea floor to ambush its prey, the banded wobbegong *Orectolobus ornatus* is well camouflaged.

WHALER SHARKS

Also known as requiem sharks, in Australia these fishes are dubbed whalers because they feed on the carcasses of harpooned whales.

The 30 whaler species found in Australian seas prefer the surface coastal waters of the tropics, but during the summer some move southward, particularly down the east coast. A few whalers cruise in the middle of the oceans, and two inhabit fresh water: the bull shark (*Carcharhinus leucas*) and the rare speartooth shark (*Glyphis glyphis*).

Whalers have the classic shark appearance – a streamlined body, a mouth on the underside of the head, five gill slits, two dorsal fins (the second often much smaller than the first) and a tail with the upper lobe longer than the lower.

Some whalers can be dangerous to humans, but most prefer to eat small fishes and squids. All produce live young, and have litters varying from two to over a hundred pups, depending on the species.

Reef-dwelling whaler sharks found in Australian waters include the grey reef shark, *Carcharhinus amblyrhynchos*; the black-tip shark, *C. melanopterus*; the silver-tip shark, *C. albimarginatus*; and the white-tip reef shark, *Triaenodon obesus* (not to be confused with the oceanic white-tip shark, *Carcharhinus longimanus*).

Reef sharks generally occupy small territories in different parts of the reef. The grey reef shark, patrolling the outer edges of the reef where it drops away to deeper waters and deeper lagoon channels, puts on territorial threat displays. If a rival comes too close, a display of arched body and lowered pectoral fins may be followed by attack or flight. Grey reef sharks are very aggressive and have been known to drive off tiger sharks large enough to kill and swallow them whole. Black-tips occupy lagoons and reef flats, often swimming in water so shallow that their backs are exposed. Silver-tips are found mainly on the seaward side of reefs. White-tips rest during the day and hunt in the same area at night.

Three of the four sharks potentially most dangerous to humans are whalers – the tiger shark (*Galeocerdo cuvier*), the bull shark (*Carcharhinus leucas*) and the oceanic white-tip shark (*Carcharhinus longimanus*).

Named for the stripes of juveniles, the tiger shark, the largest of the whaler sharks, sometimes grows to about 6 metres long. As adults, tiger sharks lose their stripes and tend to be grey. They inhabit all the world's

tropical oceans. In Australia they swim as far south as southern New South Wales and Perth in warmer months. Found mainly in coastal waters, they are more active at night, swimming close to shore after marine and sometimes terrestrial prey. Their size, indiscriminate diet and prevalence in inshore waters make them dangerous to humans.

The bull shark penetrates further into fresh water than other sharks – in South America's Amazon River system it has been found nearly 4000 kilometres from the sea – but it can also tolerate water much saltier than normal sea water. Bull sharks, which grow up to 4.2 metres long, are found in river and lake systems in northern Australia, extending as far south as the Swan River in Western Australia and Sydney in New South Wales. This aggressive shark has powerful jaws, and its extraordinarily varied diet includes mammals, birds, turtles, sharks, rays and carrion, so it can be dangerous to humans.

A shark of the open waters, the oceanic white-tip rarely appears

close to land. Although it does not seem to be very active, it has been found with fast-swimming prey in its stomach. One theory suggests that its mottled white dorsal fin looks like a school of small fishes, and that this lures fast prey, such as tuna, into attacking range.

Only two whaler species have been seen as far south as Tasmanian waters – the blue shark, *Prionace glauca*, and the bronze whaler, *Carcharhinus brachyurus*. The blue shark has long pectoral fins and a cobalt blue upper body with silvery blue sides. Blue sharks make transoceanic migrations of as much as 7000 kilometres, riding the ocean currents. The females often bear love bite scars inflicted by males during mating, and hence have developed thicker skins than the males. Tuna fishermen catch blue sharks in huge numbers, usually taking the fins for the oriental sharkfin soup market and dumping the carcasses.
Family: Carcharhinidae

■ WHALER SHARK
Reef whaler sharks in a feeding frenzy present a terrifying sight. At times like this, these carnivorous eating machines are fully focused on getting a meal, and will attack any living creature near them, even sometimes setting on one another.

FINDING FOOD
Around its snout the blue shark has a scattering of sensitive receptor pores that detect the electrical field of prey.

PERPETUAL MOTION

Many sharks lead extremely active lives, so they need an efficient supply of oxygen to their muscles and organs. Sharks extract oxygen from the water by taking it in through their mouth, allowing it to flow over their gills and then expelling it through their gill slits.

Sluggish, bottom-living species such as catsharks and wobbegongs use special muscles to pump water over their gills, even while at rest. But fast, highly active species such as mackerel sharks use their forward motion to force water through their gills – a process known as ram-jet ventilation. These sharks must keep swimming in order to breathe. Between these extremes are species such as the grey nurse shark, which pumps water over its gills at rest but switches to ram-jet ventilation when swimming to save energy.

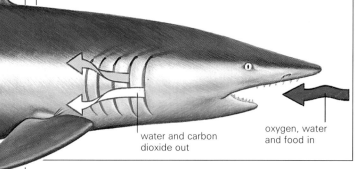

water and carbon dioxide out

oxygen, water and food in

GREY NURSE SHARKS ■
Grey nurse sharks are relatively stout-bodied, with conical snouts, long, slender, pointed teeth, small eyes, two large dorsal fins and a tail with the upper lobe longer than the lower one. The family contains two genera and four species, two of which occur in Australia.

The grey nurse shark *Carcharias taurus* inhabits tropical and warm temperate oceans throughout the world (with the exception of the eastern Pacific), and is found in waters around all Australian states except Tasmania. It lives near the sea bottom in shallow waters ranging to depths of about 200 metres.

■ GREY NURSE SHARK
The film *Jaws* gave all sharks a bad reputation, and grey nurse sharks were aggressively hunted in the mistaken belief that they were dangerous. As a result, their numbers were so drastically reduced that in 1985 they became the first sharks to be protected.

This shark has a bronze upper body, and is paler below with brownish spots towards the rear, especially in juveniles. Despite its fearsome long, pointed teeth and great size – up to to 3.2 metres – this shark is harmless unless provoked. Although protected since 1985, it remains endangered because accidental capture by anglers and entrapment in nets set to protect swimmers are causing continued population decline.

During the day, grey nurses of different ages and sizes gather in groups, but at night they probably feed alone, mainly on fishes. Grey nurses swallow air at the surface and hold it in their stomachs to give themselves just enough buoyancy to hang almost motionless above the sea bottom, thus staying in the same place, near their chosen feeding site, without using energy unnecessarily.

Like many shark species, the grey nurse shark gives birth to live young but produces only two very large offspring, about a metre long. The young are cannibalistic inside the uterus, which in sharks is actually two uteri. Over several months, females produce millions of tiny eggs, packaged in capsules. Inside each uterus, a strong embryonic shark feeds initially on its own egg yolk, but once it develops teeth (which happens when it is around 10 cm long), it gobbles up the other eggs in its capsule. It then breaks the capsule and hunts down and eats its siblings, so that only one baby shark in each uterus survives. This ensures that only healthy, well-developed young that are capable of looking after themselves at birth are born.

The sand tiger shark (*Odontaspis ferox*) looks very like the grey nurse shark, but inhabits deeper waters.

It is known only from a few locations in the Mediterranean, Pacific, Indian and Atlantic Oceans, including around the coasts of New Zealand, New South Wales and north-western Australia. It lives on the sea bottom in waters 150–420 metres deep.
Family: Odontaspididae

THRESHER SHARKS
All three species of the world's thresher sharks are found in Australia. They inhabit tropical and temperate seas, preferring to live near the surface in both coastal and oceanic waters.

The thresher shark's enormous tail, about as long as the rest of its body, makes this shark quite unmistakable. The tip is strengthened by enlarged vertebrae, making it very solid, and the shark wields it like a baseball bat to stun its fishy prey. Threshers often attack schools of small fishes, stunning several of them before turning round and eating them.

Like the mackerel sharks (page 402), threshers can keep their body temperature higher than that of the surrounding sea water. This allows their muscles to work very efficiently. These fast-swimming, powerful sharks are even capable of jumping clear of the water.

The most commonly encountered thresher shark in Australia is the whiptail shark or thintail thresher (*Alopias vulpinus*). This shark occurs around the southern half of the continent from Brisbane to central Western Australia. It is blue-grey above with a metallic lustre, and white underneath. Like mackerel shark embryos, thresher shark embryos feed on unfertilised eggs produced by the mother. Thresher sharks bear two to four pups in each litter, each measuring 115–150 cm at birth. Mature sharks grow to a maximum length of about 5.5 metres.

The other two thresher species, the pelagic thresher (*A. pelagicus*) and the bigeye thresher (*A. superciliosus*) are restricted to somewhat warmer waters than the whiptail shark. In Australia, both species have been recorded on the North-West Shelf in Western Australia, and the bigeye has been observed on Middleton Reef in Queensland and also off the coasts of New South Wales and South Australia. True to its name, the bigeye has enormous eyes that extend right up to the top of its head. This seems to be an adaptation to its habitat, as it can be found at depths of up to 500 metres.
Family: Alopiidae

ZEBRA SHARK

This shark (*Stegastoma fasciatum*) is the only member of its family. It grows to over 3 metres long and is common on continental shelves and atolls. It abounds in Australian tropical waters, but is sometimes caught in temperate waters in summer.

Zebra sharks are distinctive in colour and shape, with a very long tail and hard ridges along their back. Little is known of their reproductive behaviour, except that they attach their large egg cases to the ocean floor with bunches of hairy fibres. They rest on the sea bottom during the day and grub lazily around reefs at night in search of sea snails, small fishes, bivalves and crustaceans.
Family: Stegostomatidae

CROCODILE SHARK

The rare crocodile shark (*Pseudo-carcharias kamoharai*) grows to only 1.1 metre long, and inhabits the world's deep offshore waters. In Australia it has been found off Queensland's coast.

Its distinctive features include large eyes, long gill openings, long, sharp teeth (hence its name) and small keels on the base of its tail fin. This slender shark is dark brown on top, and becomes whitish below. It probably eats small fishes, squids and crustaceans.
Family: Pseudocarchariidae

GOBLIN SHARK

The goblin shark (*Mitsukurina owstoni*), the only member of this family, is found throughout the world but has been seen in only four locations in Australian waters: off South Australia, off Sydney and the southern coast of New South Wales, and off Tasmania. It inhabits waters 100–1000 metres deep.

A bizarre-looking creature, it has a long, blade-like snout, and its awl-like teeth often protrude from its

mouth. It probably feeds on smaller sharks and fishes, and is unlikely to be harmful to humans. It is grey to reddish brown, and grows to a length of at least 3.8 metres.
Family: Mitsukurinidae

BASKING SHARK

The single species in this family, *Cetorhinus maximus*, is a harmless, filter-feeding shark growing up to 10 metres long. Basking sharks are the second largest living fishes; only the whale shark (page 398) is bigger.

Basking sharks are found in the world's temperate coastal waters, often close to shore. In Australia they are quite rare, but have been seen around the southern part of the continent from Sydney to Perth. They have a stout body, a conical

ZEBRA SHARK
Juvenile zebra sharks are attractively patterned with dark and light vertical bands, but the adults are yellowish with dark spots, rather like a leopard.

snout, two dorsal fins, with the first much bigger than the second, and a tail fin with equal-sized lobes. Pale underneath and brownish grey above, they can be clearly identified by their minute teeth and by the long gill slits almost encircling their head. Juveniles have a much more elongated and cylindrical snout.

Despite their size, basking sharks feed on tiny plankton. In spring and autumn, when plankton is abundant, basking sharks congregate to feed together. But plankton levels decline in temperate winters, and then these sharks may shed their gill filters and hibernate on the sea bottom at the edge of the continental shelf, or they may live on energy stored in their enormous livers. But this is speculative – so far, scientists have had little success in tracking the movements of basking sharks.

Nor is much known about their reproductive behaviour. The ovaries of adult females may contain up to six million small eggs, and possibly the embryos feed on unfertilised eggs inside the mother. Since young basking sharks less than 2 metres long are rarely seen, newborns may be big – perhaps 1.5–2 metres long.
Family: Cetorhinidae

BASKING SHARK
Basking sharks cruise below the surface at a gentle 4 kilometres an hour, mouths gaping and gills flared. About 2000 tonnes of water an hour pour through their gills, and the shark filters out the plankton on which it feeds.

MACKEREL SHARKS

Five species of mackerel sharks are known throughout the world: the great white shark, two mako shark species and two porbeagles. All inhabit Australian waters except for one porbeagle species, *Lamna ditropis*, which is unique to the North Pacific. Most mackerel sharks live mainly in temperate oceans, but some are found in the tropics and a few in subpolar regions.

Mackerel sharks have bodies adapted for fast swimming. Most fishes have their maximum diameter about halfway along their bodies, but these sharks have the greatest width just before their mid-point. Their trim outline, tapering at the back, forms the perfect hydrodynamic shape. They are quite stout and have a tail fin with equal-sized lobes, which provides the greatest thrust with the least drag. Large gills extract the maximum amount of oxygen from the water, and abundant red muscles permit continuous cruising. Mackerel sharks keep their body temperature higher than that of the surrounding sea water, so that their muscles work very efficiently.

Unborn embryos feed on the unfertilised eggs that the female produces inside her body for much of her pregnancy. Litters range from 2 to 16, depending on the species.

Great whites (*Carcharodon carcharias*), sometimes called white pointers, are found mainly in temperate oceans; they seldom appear in the tropics. Little is known about their movements or reproductive behaviour; only a few pregnant females have been observed. They produce up to ten pups weighing up to 30 kg and measuring 1.2–1.4 metres long at birth. The young appear to grow at a rate of about 30 cm per year, so a great white 4 metres long would be around ten years old. Males reach sexual maturity at about 3.5 metres, while females are mature at about 4 metres and grow to about 6 metres long – slightly larger than the males. Great whites are a bronze-grey above and pale on the underside.

Young great whites feed mainly on fishes, but when they are about 3 metres long, these huge, powerful predators add marine mammals such as seals and dolphins to their diet. They are cautious with large seals, attacking them and then retreating until the seal dies.

The fastest shark in the sea, the shortfin mako (*Isurus oxyrinchus*) can jump spectacularly clear of the water, especially when hooked on a line. Its large body (up to 4 metres), beautiful cobalt blue above and white below, makes it an impressive sight. Living in the surface layers of all tropical and temperate oceans, shortfin makos are most common in oceanic waters beyond the continental shelf. They frequent Australian waters, except for a few parts of the Northern Territory, feeding mainly on surface-living fishes and squids. Large shortfin makos may take fast, powerful prey, such as the broadbill swordfish. The longfin mako (*Isurus paucus*), mostly restricted to tropical waters, has much longer pectoral fins than the shortfin mako.

One porbeagle species, *Lamna nasus*, is found in Australian waters. It inhabits many temperate waters, including those around the southern coast of Australia from about Sydney to Perth, and is most abundant in the Tasman Sea. Porbeagles have been caught in subantarctic waters with bottom temperatures of around 2°C. Of all the mackerel sharks, they have the most efficient system for raising their body temperature several degrees above that of the surrounding water.

Porbeagles feed mainly on fishes and squids. They grow to about 3 metres long, and usually give birth to two pups, which are about 60 cm long at birth.
Family: Lamnidae

SIX-GILL SHARKS AND SEVEN-GILL SHARKS

Like the frilled shark, six-gill sharks have a single dorsal fin and six pairs of gill slits; their body is typically shark-like and their mouth is on the underside of their head. Two species live in Australian waters: the bluntnose six-gill (*Hexanchus griseus*) and the bigeye six-gill (*H. nakamurai*).

Seven-gill sharks look like six-gills, with a single dorsal fin and seven pairs of gill slits. The sharpnose seven-gill (*Heptranchias perlo*) and the broadnose seven-gill (*Notorynchus cepedianus*) live in Australian waters.

Six-gill and seven-gill sharks inhabit the world's temperate and tropical oceans, where they usually live near the bottom in deep water, although broadnose seven-gills occupy fairly shallow bays and estuaries. These sharks, 1.4–4.8 metres long, prey on marine mammals and other sharks and rays. They give birth to up to a hundred live young.
Family: Hexanchidae

■ MACKEREL SHARK
In Australia the great white shark is seen mainly in waters off the southern mainland coastline, from south Queensland to the North-West Cape in Western Australia.

HAMMERHEAD SHARKS

These sharks are easily identified by their extraordinary hammer-shaped head. This remarkable head acts rather like the wings of an aeroplane, providing lift additional to that of the pectoral fins at the front of the shark and enabling the shark to rapidly change direction and so catch fast prey, such as squids.

Growing to a length of 1–6 metres, depending on species, hammerhead sharks are brown-grey to bronze-grey above and white below.

Hammerheads live in tropical and warm temperate seas. Three species have been observed around the northern Australian coast: the winghead (*Eusphyra blochii*), which has a head around half the length of its body; the great hammerhead (*Sphyrna mokarran*), which eats bottom-dwelling fishes, including sharks and rays, and is the only one of the hammerhead family likely to be dangerous to humans; and the scalloped hammerhead (*S. leweni*), which travels to a latitude of about 34 degrees south (the latitude of Sydney) in the warmer months. A fourth species, the smooth hammerhead (*S. zygaena*) frequents the southern coast of Australia, and seems to be absent from the tropics.

Hammerheads live mainly in coastal waters, occupying the region from the surf line to a depth of about 275 metres. Most species have relatively small mouths and teeth – ideal for consuming their diet of small fishes, and in some cases small cephalopods and crustaceans.
Family: Sphyrnidae

DOGFISHES

The dogfish family includes both the smallest of sharks, the smalleye pygmy shark (*Squaliolus aliae*), mature at about 15 cm, and one of the largest fishes, the sleeper shark (*Somniosus pacificus*), which grows to

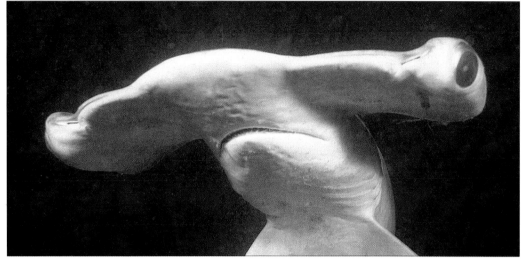

well over 4 metres. Most species, however, mature when they are between 50 cm and a metre long.

Dogsharks lack an anal fin and have two dorsal fins, both preceded by spines. Generally black or grey, some species have pale spots. Most dogfishes bear live young.

More than 40 species of dogfishes are known in Australian waters, and they occupy a broad range of habitats, from the brackish reaches of estuaries to the open ocean, where they may live near the surface or down more than 6000 metres at the bottom of the abyss. They are found all around the Australian coast.

Dogfishes eat a variety of prey, including fishes, other sharks and marine mammals. Some, such as the cookie-cutter shark (*Isistius brasiliensis*), which dwells in the open ocean, attack fishes much larger than themselves, as well as dolphins and whales. The cookie-cutter, which is less than 50 cm long, uses its large sucking lips and needle-like upper teeth to attach itself to its prey and then, rotating its body quickly, removes a circular plug of flesh from its victim with its enlarged, razor-

sharp lower teeth. Larger dogfishes, including the sleeper shark, have also been known to feed in this way. Sleeper sharks feed on large prey, including marine mammals, but there are no accounts of it attacking humans. However, dogfishes will bite the hand of a careless angler. The strong, sharp fin spines of spurdogs (*Squalus* spp.) can also give a painful wound.

In Australian waters dogfishes are caught for their oil, called squalene. Inuits catch these sharks for oil, and use their skin for boots and their lower jaw teeth as knives for trimming hair. The flesh is toxic when fresh, but there are traditional methods of drying it to make it edible.
Family: Squalidae

CATSHARKS

These slender, elongated sharks are widely distributed in Australia – they are found all around our coast – and they are large, with adults reaching lengths of 2.3 metres. They dwell on the sea floor, from near the coast down the continental slope to depths exceeding 1000 metres.

The draughtboard shark (*Cephaloscyllium laticeps*) intimidates its enemies by swallowing water or air to expand its stomach when it is disturbed. Young draughtboard sharks may take almost a year to hatch from egg cases attached to the sea bottom. Other catsharks bear live young from eggs that are held in the mother's body. Catsharks feed on small bony fishes, small sharks, and sometimes small crustaceans.
Family: Scyliorhinidae

■ **CATSHARK**
Gulf catsharks of inshore regions are mostly blue, brown and orange with spots and bands, though deep-water species are usually drab in colour.

■ **HAMMERHEAD SHARK**
The hammer on the shark's head may provide a directional sense of smell, improved electro-reception (which allows sharks to pick up nerve impulses from prey), and binocular vision. These sharks have been seen using the hammer rather like a metal detector to seek prey buried in the sand.

This shark's common name presumably comes from its 'wings' – the expanded and flattened pectoral fins that make the shark look like a ray. Unlike those of rays, however, the angel shark's pectoral fins are not joined to the head.

ALL IN THE TAIL
Rays (top) and skates (bottom) can be easily distinguished from one another by their tail characteristics.

PRICKLY DOGFISHES

Also known as rough sharks, these bizarre-looking creatures have very tall, sail-like dorsal fins, extremely rough skin and well-defined ridges along the belly. The liver, which can constitute up to a quarter of the fish's body weight, is thought to assist in buoyancy control, enabling the fish to hover above the bottom so that it can remain in its feeding ground without using up energy. It probably feeds on bottom-dwelling invertebrates and small fishes.

The single Australian species, *Oxynotus bruniensis*, lives on the continental slope of southern Australian and New Zealand waters in depths of up to 650 metres.
Family: Oxynotidae

ANGEL SHARKS ■

These fishes have ecclesiastical common names – angel shark, monkfish, archbishop and sand devil.

The four Australian species are unique to Australian waters; two are recent discoveries that do not yet have scientific names. Each species has a limited range, but together they occur from Cairns in Queensland around the southern coast to Broome in Western Australia, from close to shore to depths of 400 metres. The largest Australian species (*Squatina australis*) is more than 1.5 metres long.

Angel sharks propel themselves along with side-to-side motions of the tail and undulating movements of the pectoral fins. Camouflaged in sand or mud, they launch lightning attacks on passing prey. They feed aggressively, grasping virtually anything within reach of their strong, extendable jaws. Their sharp teeth can inflict painful cuts, but they rarely bother humans. Commercial fishers are most at risk: angel sharks can still bite savagely 40 minutes after being taken from the water.
Family: Squatinidae

BRAMBLE SHARKS

Within this family, only two species, both of the genus *Echinorhinus*, occur worldwide, and both appear to be

rare in Australian waters. Their skin is covered in large, thorny scales, like prickles. Unlike their relatives the dogfishes, bramble sharks lack spines before each dorsal fin. They are very large – up to 4 metres long – but quite harmless to humans.

Bramble sharks are thought to be suction feeders, sucking water and prey – fishes and invertebrates from the sea bottom – into their mouth. The females hold their eggs inside their body, and bear two to 20 live young.
Family: Echinorhinidae

SAWSHARKS

The snouts of sawsharks have been modified into long, flattened, saw-like blades, armed on each side with long, bony, needle-sharp teeth. They have whisker-like sensory structures called barbels on the undersurface of their snout for detecting prey, and gills on the side of their head.

In Australia sawsharks mainly occupy deep water in cooler habitats on the continental shelves and the upper slopes. They use their long, sharp saws to stir up the sea bottom in search of food or to stun small fishes and crustaceans. In some ways, sawsharks are rather like sawfishes (opposite page), but the two groups are not closely related.
Family: Pristiophoridae

RAYS AND SKATES

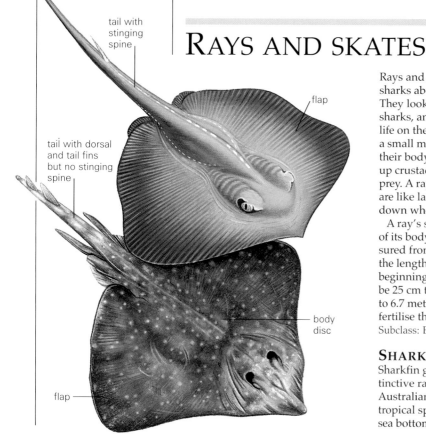

tail with stinging spine

tail with dorsal and tail fins but no stinging spine

flap

body disc

flap

Rays and skates evolved from sharks about 200 million years ago. They look rather like flattened sharks, and most are adapted for life on the ocean floor. They have a small mouth on the underside of their body that sucks in and chews up crustaceans, shellfish and other prey. A ray's pectoral fins, or 'flaps', are like large wings that flap up and down when the creature swims.

A ray's size is described in terms of its body disc – the width is measured from one flap to the other, and the length from the snout to the beginning of the tail. The disc may be 25 cm to 8.8 metres long and up to 6.7 metres wide. Like sharks, rays fertilise their young internally.
Subclass: Elasmobranchii

SHARKFIN GUITARFISHES

Sharkfin guitarfishes are large, distinctive rays. Widely distributed in Australian waters, with most being tropical species, they dwell on the sea bottom, feeding on small fishes

and crustaceans. They can reach lengths of 80 cm to 3 metres and have a well developed oval or shovel-shaped disc, two dorsal fins, a tail fin, and a long and relatively robust tail but no stinging spine.

One member of the family, the shark ray (*Rhina ancylostoma*), has the tail and dorsal fins of a shark, but also some characteristics of rays: a rounded head with the mouth on the underside, and large, pointed pectoral fins. Its back is sculpted in hard ridges formed by clumps of large, horny thorns to protect it against predators.

The white-spotted guitarfish (*Rhynchobatis djiddensis*) is a related species. A powerful ray capable of great acceleration, it is occasionally seen in tropical seas. This creature is characterised by its curiosity; it will approach a diver and use the tips of its pectoral fins to prop itself up on the sea bottom to get a better look, but it is not dangerous to humans.
Family: Rhynchobatidae

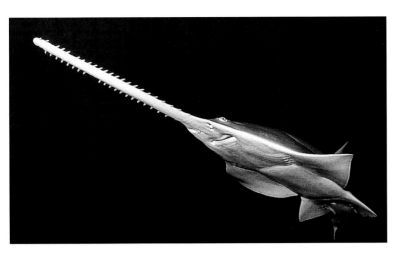

BUTTERFLY RAYS

Their body shape makes members of this family ideally suited to life on the sea floor. Their disc is very broad and flattened, recalling the shape of a stealth bomber, and this configuration probably enables the ray to drift down undetected onto its prey of very small fishes and small crustaceans. Butterfly rays live offshore on the continental shelf, and so are rarely seen.
Family: Gymnuridae

SIX-GILL STINGRAYS

These rare, floppy-bodied fishes live on the sea bottom where the water is a kilometre or more deep. Unlike most sharks and rays, they have six pairs of gill slits, rather than the usual five. Uniformly greyish pink, they have heart-shaped bodies and measure up to a metre across.

Their can move their long, mobile snout with the flexibility of a finger, and they use the tip, which bears organs sensitive to vibration and taste, to probe for prey hidden under the sea floor.
Family: Hexatrygonidae

SKATES

The skates are the most diverse, widely distributed and possibly least known of all the ray families. Most live in cool waters on the sea floor, ranging from the shallows to the dark abyssal depths. Each group has a preferred depth range, usually narrow; for example, *Raja* skates live only near the coast of southern Australia, while related species occur at specific depths on the continental slope in the tropical north.

One *Raja* species, the maugean skate, is found only in two large estuaries of south-western Tasmania – Port Davy and Macquarie Harbour. Its closest relatives live off the coasts of New Zealand and South America, suggesting that its ancestors may

■ SAWFISH
Sawfishes use their 'saws' to stir up sediments on the sea and river floors in search of food and to stun their prey.

have been in the region more than sixty million years ago, when Australia was part of the supercontinent of Gondwana.

Some Australian skates reach lengths of 1.7 metres, but most are smaller than this – less than a metre long. They use their snout to grub about in sea-floor sediments to find fishes, crustaceans, soft-shelled molluscs and worms.

Adult males, like the males of other cartilaginous fishes, copulate by inserting one of their two unusually large claspers into the female. They hold the female in position using sharp thorns embedded in the upper surface of their pectoral fins. In most species these thorns can be

erected or retracted into grooves in the skin. The females lay one to four horny egg cases in the sea bottom.
Family: Rajidae

SAWFISHES ■

Sawfishes are rays rather than sharks; unlike sawsharks (opposite page), which are true sharks, sawfishes have no sensory organs (barbels) on their snout, and their gills are on the underside of their head. Again, while sawsharks live in deep waters, Australian sawfishes occupy rivers, estuaries or inshore waters in the tropical north. At more than 7 metres long they are much larger than sawsharks, but, like sawsharks, they are bottom-dwellers.

Sawfish populations have declined all over the world in recent years. The freshwater sawfish (*Pristis microdon*), which is Australia's largest freshwater fish, used to be moderately common in northern rivers, but it is now considered to be a threatened species.
Family: Pristidae

SHOVELNOSE RAYS ■

Shovelnose rays, which are very closely related to sharkfin guitarfishes (opposite page), are common in Australian waters.

Temperate fiddler rays (*Trygonnorhina* spp.), found only in Australian waters, have a scroll-like pattern resembling the sound holes of a violin on their back. They are active scavengers and are often drawn to lobster pots in search of food.
Family: Rhinobatidae

■ SHOVELNOSE RAY
Shovelnose rays eat small fishes and invertebrates from the sand and mud; some move to the shallows on the incoming tide to feed. Their shovel-shaped head is well adapted to digging into the soft sediments on the sea floor.

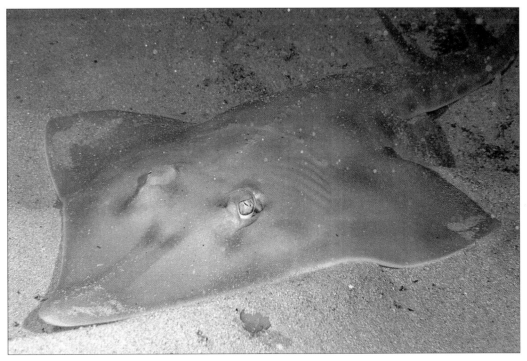

■ STINGAREE
Stingarees, disc-shaped like stingrays, favour sand and reef habitats around the coast of eastern Australia. They are frequently encountered upstream from the mouths of estuaries, but are also seen offshore.

STINGAREES ■

Stingarees are probably more abundant and diverse in Australian waters than in any other part of the world. Stingarees are very like stingrays but are generally smaller and have a shorter tail with a small, leaf-like fin at its end. The tail is slender and about the same length as the body, and usually bears one or more serrated stinging spines, which can inflict a painful wound.
Family: Urolophidae

STINGRAYS ■

More than 20 stingray species inhabit Australian waters. When fully grown, they range between 20 cm and 2.1 metres in width and reach up to 4.5 metres in length.

All stingrays have very large, flattened bodies, with the head and trunk joined to form a large disc. The disc shape varies, but its outer flaps are rounded, rather than pointed like those of the related eagle and cownose rays. Some stingrays have striking patterns on the disc, such as irregular splashes, bluish spots, wiggly lines or circles. The thin tail of most species has a stinging spine used for defence. Most bear live young and feed on small fishes and invertebrates that dwell on or in the sediments. Stingrays eject swallowed sand or grit through holes (spiracles) behind their eyes.

These rays occur from upstream in rivers to the surface layers of the open ocean. Most species stay inshore in tropical waters, but the smooth stingray (*Dasyatis brevicaudata*), possibly the world's largest species at 2.1 metres wide and 4.5 metres long, inhabits Australia's southern coast. Females weighing more than 300 kg bask off surf beaches during the summer. Large rays provoked by divers often raise their tail over their body and direct their long, sharp, stinging spine towards their tormentor – but they sting only if forced to.

Many species swim alone, but some, such as the pink whipray (*Himantura fai*), sometimes gather in schools of up to 50 individuals that are observed regularly in the Great Barrier Reef from offshore islands. Young pink whiprays ride the backs of adults of other species, apparently enjoying the company. The unpatterned pink upper surface and the extremely long, whip-like tail are distinctive of this species.
Family: Dasyatididae

EAGLE RAYS AND COWNOSE RAYS

These rays sometimes gather in schools. As thousands of cownose rays swim just below surface level beating their 'wings', the pointed tips of their powerful pectoral fins often break the surface, sometimes resulting in shark warnings on beaches. At times, these rays leap spectacularly clear of the water.

┌─ A STING IN THE TAIL ─┐

Many species of ray have a bony spine on the tail, covered by a sheath of skin. The spine has serrated edges and tapers to a sharp point. Venom is produced in glands near its base. When the spine punctures a victim, the sheath ruptures and releases the venom.

Large stingrays (*Dasyatis* spp.) have spines that may be more than 30 cm long and can cause serious injury and even death. Stingarees are most likely to inflict injury, particularly when they are accidentally touched. The highly flexible tail of some species can deliver multiple thrusts in any direction.

These fishes are medium to large, diamond-shaped and heavy-bodied. The white-spotted eagle ray, *Aetobatus narinari*, is reportedly more than 3 metres wide. The snout of eagle rays is rounded; in cownose rays it is indented. Both eagle rays and cownose rays use the stinging spines on their whip-like tail for defence, but they rarely injure humans.

Most of Australia's five species of eagle rays are decorated with spots, bands or stripes, in white, cream, bluish green or dark brown, on sandy brown or olive green to dark

■ STINGRAY
Most stingrays live on soft sea floors, but this dramatically patterned tropical ray, the blue-spotted fantail (*Taeniura lymma*), rests under ledges and on coral formations. Other rays, such as the mangrove whipray (*Himantura granulata*), hug the tops of small coral outcrops.

brown bodies. Every part of the coastline has at least one species occupying the zone between close inshore and depths of 200 metres. The most common is the southern eagle ray (*Myliobatis australis*), which is often seen off beaches and on sandflats in southern Australia.

Only two cownose rays have been recorded in Australian waters: the Australian cownose ray (*Rhinoptera neglecta*) and the Javanese cownose ray (*R. javanica*). Both are dark greyish brown and have no markings.

Large depressions in intertidal areas may mark the feeding sites of these rays: they burrow in sea-floor sediments with their pectoral fins to find prey, particularly crabs and shellfish, which they crush with their plate-like teeth.

For both eagle and cownose rays, fertilisation is internal. Cownose rays produce litters of just one. Eagle rays normally bear litters of one to four live young, but litters of up to 12 have been reported.

The white-spotted eagle ray reaches sexual maturity after four to six years, and has a gestation period of 12 months. Its young are about 26 cm wide and 50 cm long when they are born.
Families: Myliobatididae (eagle rays), Rhinopteridae (cownose rays)

ELECTRIC RAYS

Dwelling at the bottom of the world's oceans, electric rays often burrow in the sand and grub for shellfish or molluscs, but they may also stun large fishes that come into contact with them while they are swimming or buried in sand. They do this by delivering an electric shock from a unique kidney-shaped organ on each side of their flattened body disc. These organs are usually visible through the ray's skin; each is made up of many hundreds of vertically arranged thin plates, each richly supplied with nerves.

Electric rays have disc-shaped bodies and two dorsal fins. Their tail is usually shorter than their body. Unlike the stingrays, they do not have spines on their tail.
Order: Torpediniformes

NUMBFISHES
The largest of the numbfishes in Australian waters reaches a length of 45 cm, but most of them, all belonging to the genus *Narcine*, are smaller. All five species live in the

soft sediments of the continental shelf, where they search for worms, prawns and shellfish. Inhabitants of shallower waters are spotted or banded with dark brown or pinkish yellow; deep-water dwellers are light brown above and white below.

N. westraliensis is commonly trawled in Shark Bay in Western Australia; another species, as yet unnamed, is found in the Gulf of Carpentaria; and the Tasmanian numbfish (*N. tasmaniensis*) is taken in shallow waters around Tasmania and at depths of 640 metres off the coast of northern New South Wales. The other two species, which are also not yet named, are known from north-western and north-eastern Australian waters respectively.

These relatively small fishes can deliver electric shocks that surprise anyone taking them from nets, but the shocks are rarely powerful enough to discourage handling; they usually cause no more than a tingling in the fingers and arms.
Family: Narcinidae

COFFIN RAY
The sole member of the coffin ray family, *Hypnos monopterygium*, is known only from Australia. It is reddish brown and about the size of a large dinner plate. It inhabits ocean waters around the southern coast to depths of 220 metres, from southern Queensland to Broome in Western Australia.

It has lost the function of its tail and dorsal fins and is a poor swimmer, so it buries itself in the sand and relies on its remarkable electrical powers to stun passing crabs, prawns and small fishes. In a single attack it can deliver a battery of up to 50 shocks. These quickly diminish in strength, but the coffin ray can stun quite large prey: some fishes

swallowed by coffin rays are so large that it is a wonder the coffin ray's small mouth can engulf them.
Family: Hypnidae

TORPEDO RAYS ■
Found along the sea bottom of deep offshore waters of the continental slope, torpedo rays are widespread, but they are rarely encountered, except by trawlers. Being relatively large – up to 60 cm long – they sometimes envelop their prey of lobsters and fishes in the flaps of their disc as they deliver a powerful electric shock. Anglers have been thrown to the ground by the charge from these rays.
Family: Torpedinidae

■ TORPEDO RAY
Like all electric rays, torpedo rays are sluggish movers, despite their common name. Other rays use the wing-like flaps of their body disc for propulsion, but electric rays drive themselves along with their tail and tail fin.

THE SHOCK OF HIS LIFE

In 1958 a Western Australian lobster fisher trapped a saucer-shaped ray, brown above and white below, with a very small tail, no tail spine, and two dorsal fins close together at the rear. When he pulled it cautiously from the pot, the ray flexed its body and the fisherman was knocked backwards by a severe electric shock. Not realising that the ray had generated the shock, he checked his boat for a short circuit. Then he tried to remove the fish from the pot with a gaff – but as he impaled it, he received another powerful shock. Only then did he realise where the electrical impulse was coming from. Later, he learned that the creature was a coffin ray, rarely found in lobster pots but well known to prawn trawlers.

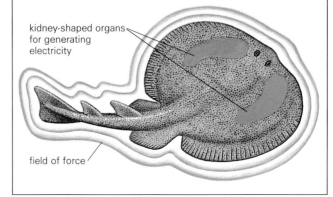

kidney-shaped organs for generating electricity

field of force

DEVIL RAYS ■

Propelled by their wing-like body disc, devil rays swim gracefully through the surface waters of tropical and subtropical oceans. They usually travel alone but sometimes form groups of up to fifty. Unlike most rays, devil rays drop to the ocean floor only occasionally to have their parasites removed by cleaner wrasse (see page 467).

Devil rays are among the largest of all fishes: the manta ray (*Manta birostris*) reportedly grows up to 9 metres wide. Others of the family are smaller: the pygmy devil ray (*Mobul eregoodootenkee*), for example, grows to about a metre wide.

There are probably four devil ray species in Australia's northern waters, ranging from Geraldton in Western Australia around to Sydney. Their upper surface is grey to black, and the lower surface is white. Some species have a spine on the tail, but they are generally harmless to human swimmers.

Devil rays feed with mouth agape to strain out crustaceans and small fishes from the water. They direct their prey towards their mouth with a pair of huge, fleshy, horn-like lobes that protrude from their head.

Devil rays can leap right out of the water, sometimes even somersaulting two or three times before splashing back into the sea. One

■ MANTA RAY
At 9 metres wide and weighing in at a massive 1360 kg, the manta ray is the giant of the devil ray family.

female was seen ejecting its young as it leapt into the air. Most devil rays bear one or two young per litter.
Order: Myliobatiformes;
Family: Mobulidae

CHIMAERAS

Chimaeras, also known as ghost sharks, probably evolved about 400 million years ago from an ancient shark group. These primitive creatures look quite unlike any other fishes. Although they belong to the class of cartilaginous fishes, they are not cartilaginous – but neither can they be classified as bony fishes.

The group contains the elephant fishes or plownose chimaeras, of the family Callorhinchidae; the shortnose chimaeras, also known as ghost sharks or ratfishes, of the family Chimaeridae; and the spookfishes or

SILVER GHOST
Propelling itself through the water with its greatly enlarged pectoral fins, this baby elephant fish is a fine illustration of the ghostly quality that has earned chimaeras such common names as ghost sharks and spookfishes.

longnose chimaeras, of the family Rhinochimaeridae. Chimaeras are most closely related to sharks, but have only one gill opening on each side of the head instead of five or six. Their skin has no scales or denticles, and their jaw is not hinged like a shark's – rather, the upper jaw is fused to the skull. In front of the first dorsal fin, all species have a prominent spine that can deliver venom.

Adult chimaeras may grow to 2 metres long, but generally they range between 60 cm and 1 metre. They feed mainly on bottom-dwelling invertebrates, and their teeth are either plate-like for grinding up shellfish, or in the form of a beak-like structure for slicing through soft-bodied invertebrates such as squids and octopuses.

They detect food using a well-developed system of sensory pores on their highly specialised snout. In the elephant fishes, the snout forms a bizarre, plough-shaped structure. Shortnose chimaeras have a bluntly rounded snout, but the snout of spookfishes, or longnose chimaeras, is extended into a long, flabby 'nose' called a proboscis. How these structures function is not completely understood, but the more highly

modified snouts are probably used to detect prey in sediment.

Chimaeras have among the most complex external reproductive structures of all vertebrates. Like sharks and rays, they fertilise their young internally, but males have strange recessed claspers on their head and before their pelvic fin, as well as pelvic claspers like those of cartilaginous fishes.

It is possible that the claspers on the head function as stimulators during sexual activity; alternatively, it has been suggested, they may be vestiges of defensive spines that have lost their function over time.

At least 13 chimaera species live in Australian waters. Most local species occur in deep water, where some have been caught at depths of 1500 metres near the sea bottom.

Possibly the best known chimaera species, the elephant fish (*Callorhynchus milii*), appears in large sheltered bays in southern Australia in late spring and summer during the breeding season, and then disperses into deeper waters. The young develop inside elongated rubbery egg cases that are tadpole-shaped with side flanges.
Subclass: Holocephali

BONY FISHES

A skeleton of bone rather than cartilage characterises members of this group (class Osteichthyes). Other features include teeth fused to the jawbones, segmented fin rays, and gills to extract oxygen from the water. They usually have a double nostril on each side of the snout and a swim bladder. Fertilisation is generally external. Bony fishes are found in every watery environment, from deep ocean trenches to mountain streams. They range from gobies 2 cm long to gropers weighing more than 400 kg, and they come in an amazing variety of shapes, from the worm-like eels to the picture-book seahorses.

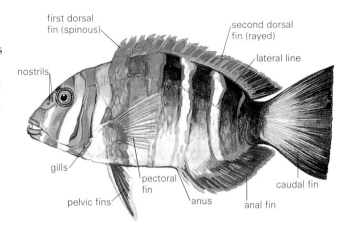

first dorsal fin (spinous)
second dorsal fin (rayed)
lateral line
nostrils
gills
pectoral fin
pelvic fins
anus
anal fin
caudal fin

Bony fishes evolved from jawless fishes about 400 million years ago. Their skeleton, with many vertebrae, makes them extremely flexible. Bones give muscles solid support and enable the tail to move efficiently, resulting in a fast-moving animal able to hunt prey, escape predators and survive severe injury. Some of the best known members of the class are salmon, trout, herrings, sardines, billfishes, snappers and tunas.

There are three subclasses of bony fishes: lungfishes (Dipneusti); lobe-finned fishes (Crossopterygii); and ray-finned fishes (Actinopterygii).

Ninety-six per cent of all known fishes are ray-finned fishes. Therefore, with the exception of the Australian lungfish, all the fishes discussed here are members of this subclass.

A TYPICAL BONY FISH
The harlequin tuskfish, *Choerodon fasciatus*, with its bony skeleton and covering of scales, is characteristic of most fishes of this huge class.

AUSTRALIAN LUNGFISH

Lungfishes were common throughout the ancient supercontinent of Gondwana, but today only six species are extant: four from Africa, one from South America and one from Australia.

The Australian lungfish (*Neoceratodus forsteri*) is also known as the Queensland lungfish. Seven species with an almost identical appearance were scattered throughout Australia during the Cretaceous period, about 100 million years ago.

Lungfishes are remarkable because they are able to breathe air as well as extract oxygen from the water. They breathe air through an opening from the gut into one or two pouches. These are supplied with a network of blood vessels to form a primitive lung (or lungs) that functions in much the same way as the lungs of land-dwelling vertebrates.

The African and South American species of lungfish are eel-shaped, with thread-like pectoral and pelvic fins, relatively small scales and a long, tapering tail. They grow to between 40 cm and 2 metres long. The Australian lungfish has a stouter body, smaller paddle-like pectoral and pelvic fins, large scales, and a broad tail that tapers to a point. It can reach 1.8 metres in length and 40 kg in weight.

The Australian lungfish has only one lung, whereas other species have two. The South American species breathes only through its lungs, but African species use both their gills and lungs when in water. The Australian lungfish normally relies on its gills for extracting oxygen from the water, but in an emergency, such as during vigorous activity or in stagnant ponds where oxygen is limited, it uses its lung as well as its gills. Young Australian lungfishes are also able to breathe through their skin. Some African lungfishes can survive drought by burrowing in mud.

The natural distribution of the Australian lungfish is restricted to the Mary and Burnett river systems in south-eastern Queensland, but it has also been introduced to the nearby Brisbane, Fitzroy and neighbouring river systems. Adults favour deep waterholes, but smaller lungfishes are frequently seen in the shallows. Sluggish during daylight hours, the lungfish becomes active at night, when it feeds on tadpoles, frogs, fishes, prawns, snails and aquatic plants. Large adults have few predators, but the young are taken by larger fishes and ducks.

Spawning occurs during spring, before the summer rainy season. Each female deposits up to 100 eggs among weeds, frequently at night, which are simultaneously fertilised by the male. The eggs, which are about 3 mm in diameter, hatch after one to two months, and the young begin feeding after about 50 days, when their yolk sac is depleted. These fishes may live at least 50 years.
Subclass: Dipneusti;
Family: Ceratodontidae

A LIVING FOSSIL
The Australian lungfish is now the country's only lungfish species, but millions of years ago there were seven similar species in Australia.

BONY TONGUES

PROMINENT WHISKERS
The gulf saratoga, also known as the gulf barramundi, is equipped with sensory spines, called barbels, near the tip of its lower jaw.

Fossilised members of this family dating back to 40 million years ago have been found in Australia. The seven living representatives are found mainly in the southern hemisphere – in Australia, New Guinea, South-East Asia, Africa and South America – suggesting that their ancestors inhabited the supercontinent of Gondwana.

The two Australian species of bony tongue are popularly known as the saratoga (*Scleropages leichhardti*) and the gulf saratoga or gulf barramundi (*S. jardinii*). Unlike most Australian freshwater fishes, which developed from marine ancestors, these fishes appear to have evolved entirely in fresh water.

Saratogas are tropical fishes that live in the still waters of ponds and billabongs in the north of Australia. They have thick, bony scales, a pair of whiskers (called barbels) on the lower jaw, a large, near-vertical

mouth, a single dorsal fin, and one anal fin that is positioned well back towards the tail. They can grow to a length of up to 90 cm and feed on insects, fishes, crustaceans and other marine invertebrates.

Saratogas are sometimes seen near the water's edge among dense weed growth and lily pads. They usually spawn just before the wet season. As soon as the 130 or so eggs are fertilised, the female gathers them up in her mouth and holds them there for one to two weeks, until they hatch. During this time she is therefore unable to feed.

Once the babies have hatched, the mother releases them into the water but they remain close to her mouth, for protection, for about a month. Young saratogas begin feeding well before they have absorbed their yolk, and they reach a length of about 10 cm after three months.
Family: Osteoglossidae

GIANT HERRINGS AND TARPONS

■ **TARPON**
This fish is known for making spectacular leaps out of the water. It swims rapidly up to and through the surface of the water and then hurls its body into the air.

Like their cousins the bonefishes, giant herrings and tarpons comprise a primitive group of bony fishes, dating back about 135 million years. Although they are not true herrings, several families in this group are commonly referred to as such because they look like herrings.

Along with eels and spiny eels, these fishes have thin-headed larvae known as leptocephali. The larvae, which are transparent and leaf-like, drift on ocean currents. As they mature, the larvae sink downward

to the sea bed, shrink, firm up, and take on the colouring and body form of the juvenile or adult fish.
Order: Elopiformes

GIANT HERRINGS
Also known as bananafishes, ladyfishes, ten-pounders and Torres Strait herrings, giant herrings are cylindrical silvery fishes. They have a metallic blue-green sheen on their back, a blunt snout and fatty eyelids. They grow to 1.2 metres in length. The two giant herring species found

in Australia live mainly in open tropical and subtropical coastal waters, although they occasionally venture into brackish and fresh water.

The most common of the two species, *Elops hawaiiensis*, occurs from Coffin Bay in South Australia, where it is rare, around the western and northern coasts to Port Hacking in New South Wales. *E. australis* is somewhat smaller, and is found mainly in tropical waters.
Family: Elopidae

TARPONS ■
The tarpon (*Megalops cyprinoides*), sometimes called the ox-eye herring, resembles a giant herring, except that the last ray of its dorsal fin is thick and elongated. This probably acts as a rudder and provides propulsion as the fish leaps from the water.

The tarpon ranges from Port Hedland in Western Australia north and east to southern New South Wales. In the coastal waters that they mainly inhabit, these fishes can grow to a length of 1.5 metres and a weight of 18 kg, but in creeks and estuaries they may be less than 50 cm long. It is said that the tarpon can breathe surface air when the oxygen content of the water is low.
Family: Megalopidae

BONEFISHES

Of the five or so bonefish species that occur in warm waters all over the world, Australia's tropical and subtropical inshore marine waters harbour at least one species of the genus *Albula*, possibly two.

Also known as ladyfishes, these silvery fishes are slim and extremely bony, with a snout longer than the lower jaw and fatty eyelids. They eat crustaceans, shellfish and worms, which they dig from the sandy sea bottom by squirting it with a jet of water from their mouth.

In Australia these fishes weigh about 7 kg and grow to about a metre in length. They are often found in schools over sandflats, from Coral Bay in central Western Australia northward and eastward round to Port Hacking in central New South Wales.
Order: Albuliformes; Family: Albulidae

SLENDER AND BONY
Schools of silvery bonefishes can often be observed over sandflats, their tails breaking the water surface as they feed.

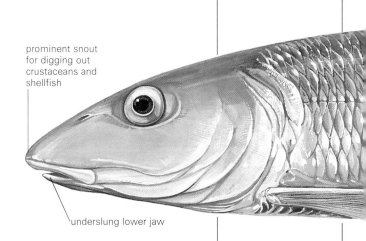

prominent snout for digging out crustaceans and shellfish

underslung lower jaw

EELS

Australia has about 140 eel species in its streams, lakes and seas. Most of them favour the warmer waters from north-western Western Australia to Queensland.

Although sometimes regarded as primitive fishes, eels are a most successful group, displaying a great diversity of form and way of life. Their long, snake-like bodies enable them to insinuate themselves into crevices, bury themselves tail-first in soft bottom sediments or hide among boulders or in the banks of streams. They swim with sinuous undulations and all but a few have long dorsal and anal fins continuous with the tail fin, giving them an extra propulsive surface. Most eels lack scales, or have tiny, scarcely visible ones embedded in the skin. The smooth surface of their body and their slimy skin help them in their snake-like burrowing habits.

Some eels are unpatterned, but others are spotted, mottled or barred in various colours. When mature, they may be only a few centimetres in length or as long as 2–3 metres. They live in a wide range of aquatic habitats. Most live solitary lives, but a few species live in colonies of many individuals.

All eels are carnivores. Some have large mouths and sharp teeth for feeding on a variety of active prey, such as other fishes and crustaceans, while others have small mouths and feed on plankton.
Order: Anguilliformes

LIFE CYCLE OF AN EEL
In the course of its life, an eel takes on a variety of forms, from larva, to glass eel, to elver, to adult.

AN EEL AND ITS VALET
This fimbriated moray eel, a species found on the Great Barrier Reef, is having its parasites removed by a cleaner shrimp. Eels live in both freshwater and marine environments, from inland lakes and streams to estuaries and deep ocean waters.

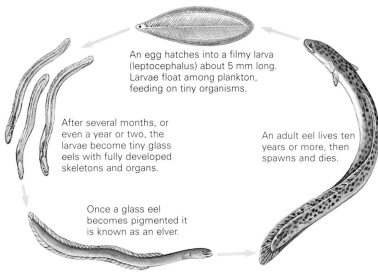

An egg hatches into a filmy larva (leptocephalus) about 5 mm long. Larvae float among plankton, feeding on tiny organisms.

After several months, or even a year or two, the larvae become tiny glass eels with fully developed skeletons and organs.

Once a glass eel becomes pigmented it is known as an elver.

An adult eel lives ten years or more, then spawns and dies.

FRESHWATER EELS

Members of this family spend most of their lives in fresh water, migrating to the ocean when they reach sexual maturity. The four freshwater eel species found in Australia all have muscular bodies (up to 2 metres long in one species), thick lips, tiny teeth crowded in bands on the jaws and roof of the mouth, and tiny embedded scales. Their bodies are slimy, which helps them to slither over wet grass to feed on earthworms, and to reach the sea at the start of their breeding migration.

The four species are distinguished mainly by their body colour and the length of their dorsal fin. This fin begins roughly above the front of the anal fin in shortfins and much closer to the head in longfins. The number of vertebrae also differs among the four species.

All species are predators and feed mainly at night, when they can be seen by torchlight foraging in lakes and waterways. Small eels eat insect larvae and molluscs, which they locate mainly with their well-developed sense of smell. Large ones eat fishes, and even ducklings.

The shortfin eel (*Anguilla australis*) inhabits coastal streams and lakes from southern Queensland to South Australia, including Tasmania. It is found mostly in the south-east of the mainland. It also occurs in New Zealand, New Caledonia and Fiji. The body is olive green above and lighter or silvery below.

Female shortfins grow to 1 metre long and males to about 50 cm long. The shortfin's dorsal and anal fins begin about opposite each other.

The Pacific shortfin eel (*A. obscura*) and the Indian shortfin eel (*A. bicolor*) are similar in appearance to the shortfin eel. The Pacific shortfin lives in fresh water on the north-eastern Queensland coastal strip and in Papua New Guinea eastward to the central Pacific. The Indian shortfin lives in fresh water on the north-western coast and widely throughout Indonesia and the Indian Ocean.

The longfin eel (*A. reinhardtii*) inhabits freshwater coastal streams and lakes from Queensland to Tasmania; it is also found on Lord Howe Island and in New Caledonia. Adult longfins have an olive green

THE LONG SWIM TO THE SPAWNING GROUNDS Mature freshwater eels migrate long distances from their freshwater habitats in Australia and New Zealand to the open sea and to their breeding grounds in the South Pacific Ocean.

FRESHWATER EEL
An inhabitant of freshwater coastal streams in eastern Australia, the longfin eel spawns in the open ocean.

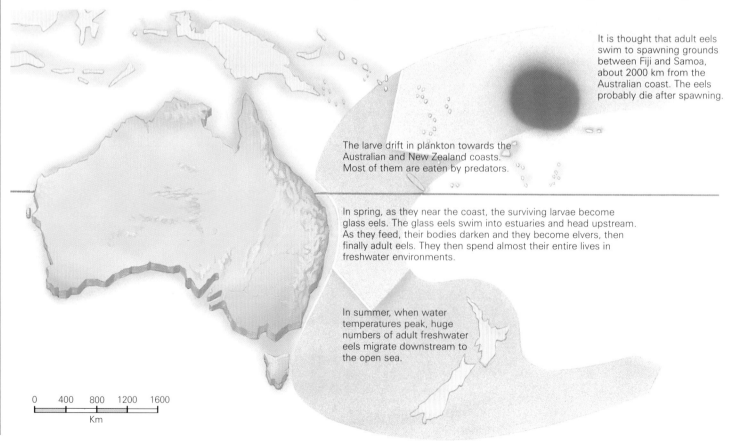

It is thought that adult eels swim to spawning grounds between Fiji and Samoa, about 2000 km from the Australian coast. The eels probably die after spawning.

The larve drift in plankton towards the Australian and New Zealand coasts. Most of them are eaten by predators.

In spring, as they near the coast, the surviving larvae become glass eels. The glass eels swim into estuaries and head upstream. As they feed, their bodies darken and they become elvers, then finally adult eels. They then spend almost their entire lives in freshwater environments.

In summer, when water temperatures peak, huge numbers of adult freshwater eels migrate downstream to the open sea.

| 0 | 400 | 800 | 1200 | 1600 |
Km

spotted or marbled body, 2 metres long in females and about 1 metre long in males. The dorsal fin begins well in front of the anal fin and this, together with the difference in body colour, distinguishes the longfin eel from the shortfin eel.

Huge numbers of freshwater eels swim downstream to the ocean in summer to spawn. It is thought that they swim to ancestral spawning grounds, where they mate.

Years ago, European freshwater eels were found to spawn in the Sargasso Sea, thousands of kilometres from their freshwater homes, but it was not until 1995 that the spawning grounds of Australia's shortfin eel were discovered, when a Japanese research vessel collected about 150 of their larvae near Fiji. Now we know that all Australian freshwater eels spawn somewhere between Fiji and Samoa – about 2000 km from the Australian coast.

The larvae drift on currents towards the Australian coast. Most are eaten by predators, but in spring the survivors turn into glass eels as they near the coast and then enter river estuaries. As they feed, their bodies darken and grow and they move upriver to find a stream or lake in which to spend at least ten years as adults. As they near sexual maturity, they make the summer migration to the sea and back to their birthplace to spawn and die.

Scientists do not know how the adult eels find their way back to the spawning grounds, but it may be that eels (and other fishes) can sense differences in Earth's magnetic field at different points on the globe, and thus determine where they are. Alternatively, they may follow ocean salinity or temperature patterns.
Family: Anguillidae

SNAKE EELS AND WORM EELS

Buried in the sea floor, with only their head or snout projecting above the surface, snake and worm eels lie in wait for passing fishes or crustaceans. They lunge with lightning speed, grasp their prey and sink back into the sand to devour it. To stop sand particles entering the mouth, many of these eels have a fringe of tiny tentacles on their lips.

Instead of a tail fin, most of these creatures have a hard, pointed tail tip that is ideal for burrowing tail-first into the sand around coral reefs or on the continental shelf.

Most of the 35 Australian species in this group live in the warmer waters around northern Australia.

The giant snake eel (*Ophisurus serpens*), known from New South Wales around the southern coast to Albany in Western Australia, has a muscular body like a broom handle and grows to a length of 2.5 metres. Its long, slender snout and jaws bear a few prominent, needle-like teeth.

The long-finned worm eel (*Muraenichthys breviceps*), known from Victoria along the south coast to south-west Western Australia, has a greenish brown body above and grows to about 60 cm long. It is more worm-like than the giant snake eel, and its snout is blunter. These eels are sometimes swallowed whole by larger fishes and can penetrate their stomachs, becoming mummified in their body cavities.
Family: Ophichthidae

MORAY EELS

Morays are marine eels that live mainly in crevices on coral reefs. They may reach lengths of 3 metres, but most are only about a metre long. They may be plain, speckled, spotted, mottled, or marked by bands or bars of contrasting colour, but each species is distinctive. All lack pectoral fins but have folds of skin on the throat, rounded snouts, hole-like gill openings, and fleshy dorsal and anal fins.

Aggressive hunters, active at night, morays lunge from their hiding places to seize passing fishes, crustaceans or shellfish. Most have sharp teeth, but the shellfish-eaters have blunt, rounded teeth. Even a small moray can inflict a deep wound if an unwary diver pushes a hand into its home crevice. About 50 species are known in Australian waters, but only four are common or distinctive.

Green morays (*Gymnothorax prasinus*) are common within their range from southern Queensland to south-western Western Australia. They are mainly found in near-shore reefs. They have a bright green body, often with a yellowish head, or even a completely yellow body. Their teeth are large and sharp, and the front ones below the tip of the snout can be pushed down so that the mouth can close completely.

The mosaic moray (*Enchelycore ramosa*) lives among the crevices of coastal rocky outcrops and islands off New South Wales. It reaches lengths of up to 1.5 metres and has a pale yellow body overlaid by a network of dark, sprawling lines, which are more obvious in juveniles. It has a long snout with very sharp teeth, which are so large that its mouth cannot completely close.

Broad black and yellow vertical stripes identify the zebra moray (*Gymnomuraena zebra*), which is sometimes seen by reef divers off the north-western coast of Western Australia. Its heavy body grows to 1.5 metres long, and it has a blunt snout and blunt, molar-like teeth.

The slender ribbon moray (*Rhinomuraena quaesita*), up to 90 cm long, is sometimes seen on the Great Barrier Reef. Juveniles are black, but adult males are fluorescent blue and adult females bright yellow. Ribbon morays burrow tail-first into rubble and sand, with their head projecting to reveal long, tube-like nostrils and jaw tentacles extending upwards.
Family: Muraenidae

■ MORAY EELS
The adult male ribbon moray (above) is a fluorescent blue and the female is bright yellow. The green moray (left) is another brightly coloured member of the Muraenidae family.

CONGER EELS ■

Congers are marine eels, living mainly on sandy or muddy sea floors from inshore out to the continental slope, although garden eels are found only on or near coral reefs.

Garden eels are slender-bodied and most are distinctively coloured. Unlike most other eels, they have forward-facing eyes and short snouts, and they feed on tiny planktonic animals. Of the 35 species worldwide, the only one known from Australian waters is Hass's garden eel (*Heteroconger hassi*). It lives on the Great Barrier Reef and is widespread in the Indo-Pacific. It is very slender, and its speckled body has three prominent black patches – on its head, on the side of its body and around its anus. Garden eels live in colonies, partially burying themselves, tail-first, in tubes that they excavate in the sandy sea bottom.

About 18 conger eel species are found in Australian waters. They are rather drab grey, brown or olive green, and variously silver on their head and below. They generally look like freshwater eels, except that they have no scales and their dorsal fin begins more or less above the pectoral fin. Adults may grow as heavy as 20 kg and as large as 2 metres long. Some have quite large mouths, but they generally have tiny teeth arranged in bands on the jaws.

Some congers bury themselves tail-first in the sandy bottom, but most forage actively on the sea floor. Many tend to be active at night, when they feed on crustaceans and small fishes. Little is known of other aspects of their behaviour.

The southern conger eel (*Conger verreauxi*) is found in estuaries and well offshore around Victorian and Tasmanian reefs. The adults are very heavy-bodied, with thick lips, small eyes and triangular teeth set close together. Their body is typically dark grey to bluish black above and lighter below, with the dorsal fin beginning just above the pectoral fins. Large southern congers are known to hide in the same rocky crevice, where they can be observed time and again.

The smaller and more slender eastern conger (*C. wilsoni*), with a dorsal fin beginning further back, has a much wider distribution, ranging from southern Queensland southward and westward to Western Australia. The tropical conger (*C. cinereus*), notable for the dark markings below its eye and on its pectoral fins, is more typical of reef areas from north-western Western Australia to Queensland.

Among the less commonly seen conger eels is the silvery ladder conger, *Scalanago lateralis*, which has a distinctive, ladder-like pattern of sensory pores along its sides. These help it to sense its surroundings in the silty inshore waters of the New South Wales coast, where it lives.

Off the coast of the Northern Territory coast lives the luminous conger eel, *Lumiconger arafura*, with its protruding teeth and snout and a light-emitting organ in its stomach that shows through its body wall.
Family: Congridae

GULPERS

In addition to true eels, Australian waters are home to a variety of eel-like fishes, some of which are very strange indeed.

The bobtail snipe eel (*Cyema atrum*) has long, very thin, diverging jaws, covered with tiny, file-like teeth with which it snares small crustaceans. It has a distinctive blunt tail and grows to 15 cm long. It lives in the midwater of the deep sea around Australia.

The swallower eel (*Saccopharynx schmidti*), which grows to 1.8 metres long, and the deepsea gulper (*Eurypharynx pelecanoides*), which grows to 75 cm, also live in the deep ocean midwater. Among the most bizarre of eel-like fishes, they have tiny eyes, jet black, slender bodies, and huge, cavernous mouths.
Order: Saccopharyngiformes

GULPING EQUIPMENT
The deepsea swallower, *Saccopharynx lavenbergi*, with its enormous hinged jaw, is related to the swallower eel that is found in Australian waters.

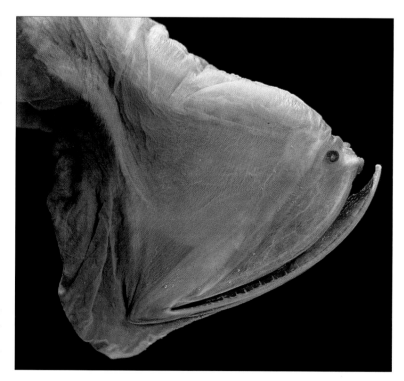

BAITFISHES

Most baitfishes, such as pilchards and anchovies, are small, slim marine species that live in large groups, called shoals or schools, near the surface of open seas or in inshore waters.

Baitfishes have large, round silvery scales that are easily shed, a small mouth with small, weak teeth, a single short-based dorsal fin and fins lacking spines. Most have filamentous gill rakers – bony projections on the gill arches – that are often used to strain plankton from the water. As well as feeding on plankton, these fishes also eat tiny invertebrates and algae.

Baitfishes frequently follow their prey in vertical migrations to and from the surface. Shoals of herrings and sardines, for example, rise to the surface to feed each evening and at dawn. Shoals also form when oceanic upwellings of cold water create blooms of plankton on the surface.

The habit of shoaling provides individual fishes with some protection from predators. Although the shoal may suffer heavy losses (see box, 'Feeding frenzy'), enough fishes always survive to form a breeding nucleus for the future.

Baitfishes provide roughly half the world's fish harvest. Apart from their use to humans as food and bait, these fishes are eaten by large fishes, birds and aquatic mammals.
Order: Clupeiformes

HERRINGS, SARDINES AND PILCHARDS ■

Herrings, sardines and pilchards are found throughout the world's tropical to temperate zones in both marine and fresh waters. About 30 species in the large Clupeidae family live in Australian waters, eight being found nowhere else. Most are tropical and marine, but six species live in temperate waters and about five live in fresh water.

Herrings, sardines and pilchards live in open water, but bony bream (freshwater herrings) live both near the bottom and in open water. Most sardines, pilchards and herrings are marine. They shoal in coastal waters and juveniles enter estuaries. Many species migrate seasonally along the coast. Freshwater baitfishes can tolerate wide ranges of water salinity, temperature and clarity. Baitfishes spawn by scattering large numbers of eggs (up to 200 000 in larger species) in the water.

The length of these fishes' life cycle depends on the stability of their food supply. When food is plentiful, populations multiply quickly. Baitfishes that feed on plankton blooms grow fast and may live for only 18 months to two years, timing their spawning to take advantage of the blooms. Those living in more stable environments, such as lakes, can live for up to six years and grow larger. Fisheries based on baitfishes can usually make large harvests without unduly harming the resource.

Also known as bloater, mulie and blue bait, the pilchard (*Sardinops neopilchardus*) is widespread in southern coastal waters from central Queensland to Shark Bay in Western Australia, and in the northern and eastern coastal waters of Tasmania. Adults school in coastal waters and juveniles enter estuaries. Pilchards grow to 21 cm long and can live for six years. They are mature at one to three years, and large females spawn about 45 000 eggs each season.

The sandy sprat (*Hyperlophus vittatus*), also called whitebait, glassy, or white pilchard, schools in bays and estuaries from southern Queensland south to Bass Strait and around to the Murchison River in Western Australia. These fishes reach 15 cm in length and live about two years.

The bony bream (*Nematalosa erebi*), a freshwater herring, is found only in Australia, where it is widespread in the warm waters of all mainland states. It reaches a length of 48 cm and has a prominent, blunt snout and an elongated, thickened last ray in its dorsal fin. Bony bream feed on plankton when young, switching to algae and aquatic plants as they age. They live for about ten years.

Perth herrings (*Nematalosa vlaminghi*) are found only in the southern part of Western Australia. Although they are found in inshore marine waters, they live mainly in fresh water, moving upriver to spawn. They grow to about 40 cm in length and live for about eight years.
Family: Clupeidae

ANCHOVIES

Huge quantities of these small fishes are caught every year and used commercially. The family contains about 160 species worldwide.

The 15 cm-long Australian anchovy (*Engraulis australis*) lives in shallow seas off the southern coast, where it gathers in huge schools.
Family: Engraulidae

■ HERRING
The freshwater herring, or Nepean herring, is a schooling fish found in waterways along the south-east coast, mainly to the north of Sydney.

FEEDING FRENZY

In June 1993, observers noticed hundreds of sharks milling restlessly around the fringes of an enormous inky blob in the ocean that followed the shoreline contour of a bay at Cape Cuvier in Western Australia. The amorphous dark shape was later found to be a massive conglomeration of small, silvery anchovies.

The frenzied, hungry sharks were plunging headlong into the anchovies. Hundreds of trevallies, tunas, and other pelagic fishes also became part of the action. Finally, a number of gigantic Bryde's whales arrived to join the feast.

Schools of baitfishes are seen regularly along Western Australia's remote central coast during spells of winter calm. The Cape Cuvier incident was unique, however, because of the size of the school and the fact that it remained there for much longer than usual – nearly three weeks.

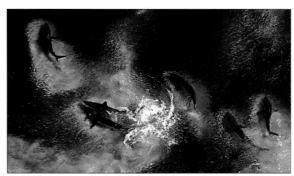

MILKFISHES

Milkfishes are toothless, and with their long, silvery bodies they look a little like herrings. Only two families are found in Australian waters.
Order: Gonorynchiformes

MILKFISH ■
Easily recognisable because of its elongated, silvery body, single dorsal fin without spines and strongly forked tail, the milkfish (*Chanos chanos*) is the sole species in this family. Other features include a milky white belly, which gives this fish its common name, a small, toothless mouth and a sheath of semitransparent fatty tissue that covers the eyes. Adults may grow to 1.8 metres in length and more than 20 kg in weight.

The milkfish occurs throughout the tropical Indo-Pacific, from the shores of East Africa to Australia and the Melanesian islands. In Indonesia and the Philippines, baby milkfish are netted in huge quantities and introduced into lagoons, ponds and rice paddies. In these environments they grow to a considerable size, but they seldom breed there.

In Australia, schools of milkfish are sometimes observed feeding in mangrove-lined bays and estuaries,

■ MILKFISH
The milkfish is so named because of its milky white belly. It lives in the open sea and in brackish water.

and occasionally on coral reefs, with their tails protruding from the water. They mainly consume dead organic matter and microscopic organisms that they find in the mud.
Family: Chanidae

BEAKED SALMONS
Beaked salmons, sometimes known as sand fishes or sand eels, are slender, cigar-shaped inhabitants of southern coastal waters. They are closely related to carps and catfishes and have nothing to do with northern hemisphere salmons, which are raised on southern Australian fish farms, nor with Australian salmons, which are well known to anglers.

Previously thought to constitute a single species widespread in cooler waters of the Indian and Pacific Oceans, the family is now considered to contain about seven species with more restricted distributions. One, *Gonorynchus greyi*, which occurs from southern Queensland to Shark Bay in Western Australia, is known only in Australian waters.

This fish is easily recognised by its long, tubular body, the placement of its dorsal, anal and pelvic fins close to the tail, and its tiny scales, which give the body surface the appearance of sharkskin. Attaining about 50 cm in length, beaked salmons are most frequently encountered as small individuals in shallow, sandy areas within and outside bays, although larger adults are trawled to depths of about 160 metres.

Beaked salmons are sometimes seen ingesting sand while searching for food. The single, hair-like barbel (whisker) beneath the snout that extends in front of the mouth helps them to locate the invertebrates on which they feed. When disturbed, beaked salmons dart into the sandy bottom and may be mistaken for eels if only their snout is protruding.
Family: Gonorynchidae

■ CARP
The European carp, *Cyprinus carpio*, an introduced species, infests waterways throughout south-eastern Australia, competing with native species for food.

CARPS

Of more than 1450 carp species worldwide, at least five have been introduced into Australian rivers and lakes. The European carp, or common carp (*Cyprinus carpio*), is native to Asia, but is now probably the most widely distributed freshwater fish in the world; there are introduced populations on every continent except Antarctica.

Other carps in Australian waters include the goldfish (*Carassius auratus*), the tench (*Tinca tinca*), the roach (*Rutilus rutilus*) and the rosy barb (*Puntius conchonius*).

The European carp and the goldfish are found in waterways from central Queensland to southern Western Australia; the tench occurs in Tasmania and throughout the Murray–Darling river system; the roach seems to be limited to southern Victoria; and the rosy barb, an Indian native that was imported as an aquarium fish, is now common in several streams in the Brisbane area.

Carps favour slow-flowing rivers and lakes and can survive extremes of temperature, low concentrations of oxygen and high salinity. They feed mainly on aquatic plants and insects, and on bottom sediments, which they suck and strain, sometimes increasing the turbidity of water in confined areas.

The European carp may live for more than 20 years and reach about 85 cm in length and 20 kg in weight. It has been declared a noxious fish in many states because of fears about its impact on the environment. In order to keep populations down, a commercial fishery has been opened and there is a ban on the release of these fishes by anglers.

Carp catches have been declining in recent years, and juvenile carp are known to be a source of food for native predators, including Murray cod, golden perch, water rats, and birds such as pelicans.
Order: Cypriniformes; Family: Cyprinidae

CATFISHES

Long barbels like cats' whiskers around their mouths give these scaleless, bottom-dwelling fishes their common name. The sensitive barbels help the fishes to detect motion in the water and locate prey.

Over 2000 catfish species have been identified, mostly in America. Only two families occur in Australia.
Order: Siluriformes

FORK-TAILED CATFISHES ■

Fork-tailed catfishes are also known as salmon catfishes, crucifix catfishes or cobblers. They have three pairs of fleshy barbels around their mouth, a strong, serrated spine at the front of their dorsal and each pectoral fin, an adipose (fatty) fin on their back, and usually a deeply forked tail. Their spines can inflict considerable pain, though their sting is much less painful than that from the spines of an eel-tailed catfish (next entry).

Australia's 15 fork-tailed catfish species live in tropical and subtropical marine, estuarine or fresh waters. A few live only in fresh water and a few never leave the sea, but most can live in both environments.

A species often takes on the colour of its habitat – deep blue in coastal waters and pale fawn or orange far inland. Australian species range in maximum length from about 30 cm to nearly 2 metres. Their diet can be exceedingly broad or highly selective, some species eating only fishes or molluscs or sea urchins.

Fork-tailed catfishes demonstrate remarkable reproductive behaviour. The female spawns 25–150 large, heavily yolked eggs, which she extrudes in two clumps resembling bunches of grapes. The male then scoops up the egg clumps in his mouth, and for four to six weeks he incubates them there, periodically churning the eggs around to help free the hatching larvae. He finally releases the young catfishes when they are 2–6 cm long.

Fork-tailed catfishes generate noises using their tough-walled swim bladder, and probably their ear bones (otoliths), to help them find one another in the often murky water in which they live.
Family: Ariidae

EEL-TAILED CATFISHES ■

About 20 eel-tailed catfish species inhabit the tropical and temperate waters of Australia. More than half of these live in fresh water, and 11 species occur only in Australian waters. These fishes, with maximum lengths of 15 cm to 1.4 metres, have four pairs of barbels (whiskers), a slimy skin and an elongated body.

Freshwater species inhabit still or running water and eat algae and bottom-living invertebrate, such as worms, crustaceans and aquatic insects. Marine species live in turbid inshore and estuarine waters and include fishes in their diet.

The most widely known freshwater species is the tandan (*Tandanus tandanus*), which can reach 90 cm and 6.5 kg and inhabits the coastal rivers of central eastern Australia and the Murray–Darling river system. Other freshwater species live in the Kimberley drainage systems of Western Australia, the Lake Eyre drainage system of central Australia, and coastal river systems of Western Australia, the Northern Territory and Queensland.

The best known marine or estuarine species are the cobbler or estuary catfish (*Cnidoglanis macrocephalus*), of southern Australia, and the striped catfish (*Plotosus lineatus*) of tropical Australia. Juvenile striped catfishes swim in closely packed groups that take on various shapes, such as balls or tree branches, apparently to camouflage themselves from predators.

Eel-tailed catfishes have poison glands at the base of their serrated dorsal fin spine and pectoral fin spines. The venom secreted when the spine punctures skin is extremely painful and can make an adult human very ill for several days.

These catfishes lay thousands of eggs in a shallow-water gravel nest up to 2 metres wide. Spawned eggs sink and lodge among the stones. One of the parents remains at the nest for the two to seven days it takes for the larvae to hatch.
Family: Plotosidae

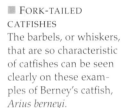

■ FORK-TAILED CATFISHES
The barbels, or whiskers, that are so characteristic of catfishes can be seen clearly on these examples of Berney's catfish, *Arius berneyi*.

■ EEL-TAILED CATFISHES
The striped catfish is an eel-tailed catfish found in tropical Australia. Fishes of this family have spines that secrete venom when they puncture skin, causing great pain.

SALMON-LIKE AND TROUT-LIKE FISHES

These fishes live mostly in fresh water, and many have soft, fine scales on their streamlined bodies. The group includes species that have been introduced to Australian waters, such as salmons and trouts, plus many native fish species such as galaxiid minnows.

Often patterned with spots, some of these fishes have powerful jaws for crushing their prey. Some species migrate from the sea into fresh water to spawn; others migrate from fresh to salt water and can adapt to life in a marine environment.
Order: Salmoniformes

■ SMELT AND GRAYLING
The Australian grayling (above) and the Australian smelt (right) live in freshwater habitats.

SLICKHEADS
Poor swimmers with soft bodies and weak bones, slickheads live close to the sea floor, where they feed off the bottom on animal plankton and small fishes. They may reach over 50 cm in length. Many slickhead species are known from Australian waters in depths to 1500 metres.
Family: Alepocephalidae

SALAMANDERFISH ■
The salamanderfish (*Lepidogalaxias salamandroides*), the sole member of its family, is found only in rivers and temporary pools between Albany and Augusta in south-western Western Australia.

The region's rivers often flow only after winter rains. At other times they are a series of pools, many of which dry out. The salamanderfish, which grows 4–6 cm long, is a fine

example of adaptation to such a harsh environment. It spawns in late winter, when the rivers are full. The young grow rapidly and, as the pools shrink, build burrows in the mud, linked to the surface by a tube. They lie dormant throughout the summer, becoming active when water returns with the first rains of autumn.
Family: Lepidogalaxiidae

SMELTS AND GRAYLING ■
Small schooling fish, smelts inhabit freshwater streams, swamps, and brackish estuaries. They are usually found in still or slow-flowing waters.

The Australian smelt (*Retropinna semoni*) is found from the Fitzroy River system in south Queensland, throughout south-eastern Australia,

to eastern South Australia, while its cousin, the Tasmanian smelt (*R. tasmanica*), inhabits Tasmania's coastal streams. Smelts feed on zooplankton, aquatic insects, crustaceans and algae. They are mature at about one year old, when they are 5–7 cm long. It is believed that they migrate upstream to spawn.

The Australian grayling (*Prototroctes maraena*) is one of only two species in the subfamily Prototroctidae, and the second is thought to be extinct.

Graylings live in the cool creeks and rivers of south-eastern Australia, where they favour gravel bottoms between pools and rapids. Their range extends from the Grose River near Sydney to eastern South Australia, King Island in Bass Strait and Tasmania, but they are most common in Victoria's Gippsland.

Graylings are usually about 14–23 cm long but they can reach 33 cm in length, and live for six years. They eat small crustaceans, insects and their larvae, and algae.

These fishes often form large schools before spawning. The female lays 25 000–68 000 eggs, which drift down to the river bed. Two to three weeks later the larvae hatch and are swept downstream to an estuary or the sea. In flood or drought years many die. The survivors return upstream about six months later to complete their life cycle.
Family: Retropinnidae

■ SALAMANDERFISH
This salamanderfish is emerging from its burrow. Salamanderfish resume their aquatic existence after rain has fallen and the previously dry creek beds have refilled with water.

GALAXIID MINNOWS

All 40 species in this family are confined to the southern hemisphere, and over half of them are unique to Australian waters. Ten species are found in Tasmania alone.

Galaxiid minnows are small, scaleless freshwater fishes that live in a range of environments across the southern half of Australia, from Tasmania's cold lakes and streams to the warm, often saline coastal streams of southern Western Australia. Some species are widespread, but many are unique to a single river system. They feed on aquatic insects, small crustaceans, and algae or plant debris and generally grow 4–8 cm long.

Some species, such as the spotted minnow (*Galaxias maculatus*) migrate from fresh to salt water to spawn. The short-fin or climbing galaxias (*G. brevipinnis*), found in fast-flowing streams in areas such as the Blue Mountains in New South Wales and the Tasmanian Highlands, uses its pectoral and pelvic fins to climb rocks and waterfalls, moving far inland to spawn in remote streams and lakes.

The Tasmanian whitebait (*Lovettia sealii*), another galaxiid, is transparent and has a distinctive silver lateral band. This 5–8 cm-long fish inhabits the estuaries and shallow coastal seas of Tasmania. Adults migrate upstream in large schools to spawn in fresh water. The eggs stick to submerged stones, logs or plants, and, after hatching, the larvae are washed down to the sea. The adults die soon after spawning.
Family: Galaxiidae

SALMONS AND TROUTS

All members of this family have similar features. Their streamlined bodies, powerful jaws, spotted silvery sides and dark olive to brown backs are the signs of successful, well-camouflaged predators.

Salmons are the largest of the family: some species reach 1.5 metres long and 40 kg in weight, although individuals larger than 60 cm and 4 kg are rare in Australia. Trouts generally weigh 1–3 kg, but they can live for over ten years and grow to 1 metre long and over 15 kg in weight.

Salmons and trouts were brought to Australia from Europe in the nineteenth century, partly to improve recreational fishing in local streams and rivers, which contained few species of interest to anglers, and partly because Australia was seen as a Noah's ark where European species under threat from the expansion of agriculture and industrialisation could be saved from extinction.

Five species of this family now live in Australia, and many lakes and rivers are stocked for sport fishing with young, known as fry, reared in government-run hatcheries. The first imports were the European Atlantic salmon (*Salmo salar*) and the brown trout (*S. trutta*). Later came the North American chinook or Pacific salmon (*Onchorynchus tshawytscha*), the rainbow trout (*O. mykiss*) and the brook trout (*Salvelinus fontinalis*).

Salmons and trouts are cool-water fishes. In their native habitats, both Atlantic and chinook salmon spend most of their lives at sea, returning to fresh water to spawn. Trouts, on the other hand, generally spend their lives in fresh water. However, both brown trout and rainbow trout can tolerate high salinity and may establish adult populations that are permanently adapted to sea water. They then become known as sea trouts and steelheads, respectively.

At spawning time, the female trout, like the salmon, migrates into shallow streams and uses her tail to dig a depression, known as a redd, in the gravel for the eggs. She then engages in a courtship vibration with the male, resulting in the release of sperm and eggs into the redd.

In cool regions, particularly in Tasmania, Victoria and New South Wales, trouts established wild breeding populations many years ago. Salmons, in contrast, survived in southern fresh water, but after leaving the rivers in their traditional migration to Arctic feeding grounds they never returned. Atlantic and chinook salmons are now stocked in a limited number of enclosed waters in south-eastern Australian for sport fishing, and are farmed in Tasmania.

Trouts and salmons feed on many small fishes, insects and insect larvae, and crustaceans. Trouts eat galaxiid minnows and compete with native fishes, such as graylings. In many waters galaxiids and trouts seem to coexist, but in others a decline in native fish numbers has been linked to the presence of trouts, as well as to changes in the environment.
Family: Salmonidae

■ GALAXIID MINNOWS
The colouring of the mud minnow is variable, blending in with the colour of the water in which the fish lives.

■ SALMONS
The chinook or Pacific salmon is a native of North America. In south-eastern mainland Australia, Atlantic salmon are stocked for anglers in some areas of enclosed water, and in Tasmania they are farmed in sea cages.

LIZARDFISHES

■ FLAGFIN
The flagfin that is known as the sergeant baker lives in coastal waters around the southern half of Australia.

The long bodies of these fishes are patterned like those of lizards, and the pointed head and large eyes are also lizard-like. Only two lizardfish families live in Australian waters.
Order: Aulopiformes

FLAGFINS ■

The large, pennant-like dorsal fin of these fishes accounts for their common name. Of the three species found in Australia, the best known is the sergeant baker, *Aulopus purpurissatus*, which is widespread in coastal waters around the southern half of the continent. Although often seen on near-shore reefs, it also occurs around rocky offshore areas to depths of nearly 250 metres.

Attractively mottled in pink, red and blue and growing to a length of 68 cm or more, the sergeant baker has sizeable anal and pelvic fins, which, like its enlarged dorsal fin, are supported entirely by soft rays. Males are easily recognised by their extended second and third dorsal fin rays. The small, rayless, fleshy, fin on the back, immediately in front of the tail, is a primitive feature that is found in few other shallow-water Australian fishes. Sergeant bakers remain motionless on algae-covered reefs awaiting the arrival of the crabs, shrimps and small fishes upon which they feed.

The more tropical flagfin *Aulopus curtirostris* is found off eastern Australia from central Queensland to central New South Wales; a third species, which is known to occur away from the coast on sandy or muddy bottoms in north-western Australian waters, is yet to be given a name. Both these species are relatively small, and are seldom seen other than by commercial fishers.
Family: Aulopodidae

LIZARDFISHES ■

Common in warm continental-shelf waters off Australia, lizardfishes resemble lizards, with their tooth-lined jaws and pointed head. They may reach lengths of 60 cm, and one species lives in waters more than 1000 metres deep. The related Bombay ducks, of the Harpadontidae family, get their name from a dried lizardfish species sold in Bombay.
Family: Synodontidae

■ LIZARDFISH
The lizardfish, *Saurida nebulosae,* has the distinctive reptilian appearance of the order Aulopiformes.

LANTERNFISHES

Lanternfishes form one of the most widespread and abundant fish families in the world. So far 225 species have been recognised, but there are undoubtedly more. About 40 species inhabit Australian waters alone.

Coloured black and silver, lanternfishes reach 4–15 cm in length and are covered with luminous tissue and light-producing organs called photophores, the patterning of which is unique to each species. The photophores are thought to be important in species recognition for shoaling and in avoiding predators. Lanternfishes are a major part of the diet of many fishes and marine mammals, particularly whales.

Normally lanternfishes are thinly distributed, but they are sometimes found in huge numbers and harvested for fish meal. Although species have been reported from depths below 2000 metres, a few live in the surface 10 metres. At night most adults move from their daytime depths of 450–900 metres into the upper 200 metres in order to feed on crustaceous plankton. Some also feed on fish and algae.

Lanternfish species that inhabit temperate regions spawn in spring, but tropical species may spawn all year round. Some of the smaller species reach sexual maturity at six months and live for no more than a year, but lanternfishes generally live for three to five years.
Order: Myctophiformes;
Family: Myctophidae

■ LANTERNFISH
These fishes are characterised by species-specific patterns of light-producing organs on their bodies. These photophores are thought to provide camouflage and identification for shoaling. This is a brooch lanternfish, *Benthosema fibulatum.*

The twilight zone

Many fish families live in the ocean depths and have evolved an extraordinary array of adaptations to cope with life in the darkness, where food is scarce.

A surprising assortment of marine creatures live in the midwaters of the open oceans of Australia, 500–1000 metres below the surface. Food supplies are low at these depths, which are far from the site of production at or near the surface. These fishes encounter nourishment infrequently, so they must grasp every opportunity for a meal. Fishes that live here are generally shorter than about 30 cm, but are highly adapted to catching prey and swallowing very large meals – sometimes almost as big as themselves.

Hunting by stealth

Many of the deep-ocean fishes are wily hunters. Black dragonfishes have a scaleless form that is designed for cruising and pouncing, not for chasing; scaleless dragonfishes lure prey into striking distance with their luminous mouths and chin whiskers; and anglerfishes use lures on 'fishing rods' developed from fin rays on top of their heads.

Deep-sea fishes often catch and hold their prey with specialised teeth. The hinged, needle-like teeth of the scaly dragonfish lie flat as the fish's prey slides into its mouth, but then pull erect to prevent the prey from escaping. The bristlemouths have multiple rows of teeth, whereas the teeth of sabretooth fishes are long and blade-like.

The swallowing of large prey requires a big mouth, a flexible skeleton so that prey can pass down the throat, and a muscular stomach capable of great expansion. These are features of the loosejaws, whose gape is maximised by a very long jaw and a floorless mouth.

In the clear midwaters, offshore, the sunlight is just detectable. In this gloom, and in the darkness beyond, fishes generate light to communicate, to find or attract prey, and to camouflage themselves. To do this they use light-producing bacteria in specialised organs called photophores, which are visible on the fish's body in many forms – rows of dots in the lighthousefishes or larger oval marks in the hatchetfishes.

Deadly hide and seek

Many predators lurk below their prey, looking upward for silhouettes, so prey species hide by illuminating their lower surface to match the light filtering from

The fangs of the viperfish are so large that they slide into special channels on the outside of its head.

above. But many predatory fishes have light-emitting organs on their cheeks that they can switch on to spotlight their prey. These predators use wavelengths of light that their prey are unable to see.

Some deep-sea species, such as scaly dragonfishes, also have a light-emitting organ on a fleshy stalk on their chin. This lure attracts prey, or can signal to other members of the same species.

With its hinged mouth, the remarkable eel-like deep-sea gulper can engulf prey that is almost its equal in size.

A living 'fishing rod' projects from the head of the deep-sea anglerfish, topped by a lure containing bacteria that glow in the dark. The fish remains still until its prey is within reach, then grabs its victim with its cavernous mouth.

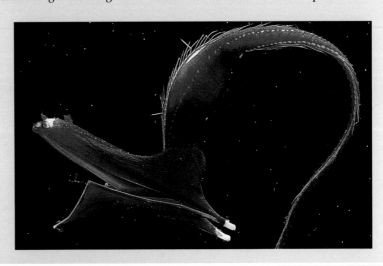

■ WHIPTAIL AND PREY
The toothed whiptail, *Lepidorhynchus denticulatus*, is one of the many whiptail species that live in the depths of the ocean close to the sea floor. Whiptails communicate with each other by luminous organs on their body; in this species these organs are seen as a series of lateral silver and black lines.

DEEP-SEA CODS AND HAKES

These fishes are marine creatures, and mostly feed on other fishes and crustaceans. Their bodies are usually silver-bronze, with small scales and fins containing soft rays. They are often striped from gills to tail. In the northern hemisphere these fishes are important to commercial fisheries.
Order: Gadiformes

CODS

Cods are mainly northern hemisphere fishes and, of the 55 species, only one is known from Australian waters: the New Zealand rock ling (*Gaidropsarus novaezelandiae*). Most cods have three separate dorsal fins, two anal fins and a separate tail fin, but body shape is variable. Lengths vary from 15 cm to 2 metres.
Family: Gadidae

PELAGIC CODS

Long black tapering fishes, pelagic cods reach only about 15 cm in length. The two known species are widely distributed in both tropical and temperate oceans, and occur around Australia. Pelagic cods live in the open ocean at depths below 200 metres, but they are rather rare and little is known about them. They have a distinctive blunt head, covered with parallel fleshy ridges.
Family: Melanonidae

WHIPTAILS ■

Long, tapering fishes, whiptails, also called rattails or grenadiers, range from 12 cm to 1.5 metres long. They occur in all the world's oceans except the high Arctic, mostly at depths of 100–2000 metres, though they have been found deeper than 6000 metres. Around 300 species are known, and more are being discovered in deep-sea trawler catches.

In Australia, whiptails outnumber the species of all other deep-sea fish families. Most live on or close to the deep-sea floor, but a few species live in open water.

In the darkness of the deep oceans, whiptails communicate using light and sound. Light-emitting organs on their belly or around their vent are uniquely shaped in each species so that they can recognise other fishes as friends or foes. Male whiptails can make sounds by drumming on their swim bladder with special muscles – behaviour that probably has more to do with locating a mate than with avoiding predators.
Family: Macrouridae

MORID CODS ■

Sometimes known as beardies, morid cods have a rounded, tapering body and a distinct tail fin. They range in length from a few centimetres to at least 1.4 metres. Mostly deep-sea species, they occur in all oceans, and about 30 of the 70 known morid cod species are found in Australian waters. Shallow-water species are commonly caught by anglers in estuaries and bays.

A number of morid cod species house light-producing bacteria in special organs on their belly and around their anus. These patterns of light may assist in species recognition during spawning.
Family: Moridae

HAKES

The largest of these long, slender fishes reaches about 1.5 metres in length and 15 kg in weight. Found in temperate latitudes in depths to about 1000 metres, most hakes live near the sea floor, making extensive migrations at night up into the water column to feed. These voracious predators have streamlined bodies, large jaws at the front of the head and well-developed teeth.

Around south-eastern Australia, the blue grenadier, *Macruronus novaezelandiae*, feeds near the surface at night on lanternfishes. The long upward swim is worthwhile because lanternfishes, which also feed near the surface at night, are easy prey. After feeding, the blue grenadiers spend the day on the sea floor.
Family: Merlucciidae

UNICORN CODS

Known as unicorn cods, or codlets, these slender fishes reach about 12 cm long. Six of the 12 known species are found in Australian waters, living between the surface and depths of 200 metres in the open water of tropical and sub-tropical seas. Some unicorn cod species are found near the shore, while others inhabit the open ocean.

Unicorn cods are so named because of the distinctive single strong ray of the first dorsal fin on top of their head. They are also distinguished by long pelvic fins that extend well back along their body from below their head.
Family: Bregmacerotidae

■ MORID COD
The bearded rock cod is found around reefs and rocky areas, where it feeds on small fishes, crabs and shellfish.

EEL CODS

Grey-brown to reddish, often with an iridescent sheen, eel cods are small, elongated fishes that grow to about 40 cm in length.

All four known eel cod species are native to the cold waters of the Antarctic or subantarctic over the continental shelf and slope, down to about 1600 metres deep. Eel cods live near the sea bottom and feed entirely on animal plankton.

These fishes have a laterally flattened body, a small head, continuous dorsal, tail and anal fins, and long scales that do not overlap.
Family: Muraenolepididae

CUSK EELS

Cusk eels are not true eels, but they are similar in appearance. They have long, slim bodies that taper off gradually at the end. Rather than having the triangular shape that is normally associated with a fish's fins, their fins run along most of the length of the body, above and below.
Order: Ophidiiformes

PEARLFISHES

Adult pearlfishes have the extraordinary habit of living inside the body cavities of other animals. While some species just shelter in sea squirts, sea stars or clams and emerge to feed, those living in sea cucumbers may also eat the internal organs of their hosts.

Pearlfishes reach about 50 cm in length. Their slender, scaleless bodies are well adapted to slipping easily into their animal homes. Thirteen of the 30 known species are found around Australia.
Family: Carapidae

LIVE-BEARING CODS

As their name suggests, these fishes bear live young. Males are equipped with a copulatory organ to transfer sperm into the female.

Live-bearing cods are distributed worldwide and occur in coastal waters and in the deep sea. The largest species reach only 20 cm in length. At least 20 of the 86 known species occur around Australia.
Family: Bythitidae

LINGS

Elongated fishes, lings range in length from a few centimetres to around 2 metres. At least 26 of the 165 known species are found in Australian waters. Most live close to the sea floor on the continental shelf and slope, but several species occur down to 6000 metres. The deepest-living fish ever recorded was a ling – an *Abyssobrotula galatheae* specimen found at a depth of 8370 metres.
Family: Ophidiidae

BLINDFISHES

Living at depths of 700–6000 metres, blindfishes have several characteristics that are associated with life in the deep ocean, including tiny eyes and transparent, gelatinous skin.

All of the 20 known species of blindfish, two of which are found in Australian waters, bear live young. Most blindfishes grow to only about 10 cm in length.
Family: Aphyonidae

LIVE-BEARING COD
This live-bearing cod was photographed in the coastal waters of south-eastern Australia.

FROGFISHES

Of about 70 species worldwide, only nine frogfish species occur in Australian waters. Also known internationally as toadfishes, these creatures are characterised by a broad, flattened head with fleshy flaps and whisker-like barbels around the mouth and a rather long, cylindrical body. Their frog-like appearance is enhanced by large, forward-facing eyes, a down-turned mouth and smooth, slimy skin.

Australian frogfishes have three to four short, sharp spines on the gill cover, and another three in their small spiny dorsal fin. None of these spines is venomous, but they can still produce a painful wound. Some species from Central and South America do have venomous spines.

Frogfishes are drably patterned in greens, browns and greys that blend perfectly with their surroundings as they sit motionless on the sea floor, waiting for octopuses, crabs, prawns and shellfish to pass by. These they usually swallow whole.

The best known Australian frogfish species are the banded frogfish (*Halophryne diemensis*) found in northern Australia; the eastern frogfish (*Batrachomoeus dubius*) from southern Queensland and New

South Wales; and the pink-headed frogfish (*B. rubricephalus*), which is native to south-western Australia.

The young hatch out in a nest, which may be a rocky cave, an empty shell, or even a discarded jar. The female departs after laying the eggs, and the male cares for the young until they can fend for themselves. Frogfishes produce relatively few eggs, so this parental care is important for the survival of the species.
Order: Batrachoidiformes;
Family: Batrachoididae

FISHES LIKE FROGS
The banded frogfish, *Halophryne diemensis*, from northern Australia has the typically frog-like appearance of this family. Frogfishes can grunt loudly when they are disturbed, and they bite if handled.

ANGLERFISHES

Anglerfishes are sluggish creatures, mostly less than 60 cm long, with a variety of body forms and life strategies. Some live hidden beneath the sediments or lie motionless on the sea bottom, disguised by their chameleon-like skin tones. Others inhabit the deep midwater of the open ocean, the tiny males living as parasites on their female hosts.

They are named anglerfishes because many species have a rod-like projection on the head, at the tip of which there is often a small lure that they wiggle to attract prey.
Order: Lophiiformes

GOOSEFISHES, COFFINFISHES AND BATFISHES ■

Goosefishes, coffinfishes and bat-fishes are deep-water relatives of anglerfishes. Of the 16 or so species in Australian waters, almost all live in the tropics on the bottom of the continental slope at depths of 200–1200 metres. Most species are less than 20 cm long, but a few reach lengths of 60 centimetres.

Goosefishes are the largest members of the group, their flattened bodies making them well adapted to life on the bottom. They were named goosefishes because of a shallow-water Atlantic species that is said to have caught and eaten whole diving birds as the birds foraged near the bottom. Goosefishes are voracious feeders, with a huge mouth armed with multiple rows of long, needle-

like teeth. They are certainly capable of eating fishes as big as themselves, using their lure to attract prey.

Coffinfishes have a small fishing apparatus recessed into the snout. Their rough, flabby skin is pinkish, often with bright yellow spots. As with other members of these families, little is known of their biology.

Batfishes are typically less than 10 cm long, with a triangular or disc-shaped body covered with small, warty scales or sharp spines. Like their relatives, they are awkward swimmers, and they prefer to walk over the bottom using their pectoral and pelvic fins.
Families: Lophiidae (goosefishes), Chaunacidae (coffinfishes), Ogocephalidae (batfishes)

ANGLERFISHES ■

Most temperate-zone Australian anglerfishes are found only around Australia, but tropical members of the family tend to be distributed more widely. They are often brilliantly coloured, primarily in red, yellow, black and white, and are capable of rapid changes in tone.

Anglerfish reproductive biology is highly evolved. Females of some species produce large numbers of small eggs that are trapped in a raft of mucus, which then drifts near the surface, helping with dispersal. Others produce a small number of large eggs that require parental care. Some parents carry the fertilised eggs attached to their sides or dangling from their dorsal fins. Others conceal the eggs in a 'pocket' formed by the pectoral and tail fins.
Family: Antennariidae

HANDFISHES ■

Handfishes are one of the few marine families confined to Australian waters, most species occurring only off Tasmania and Victoria. Some have extremely narrow ranges. The spotted handfish (*Brachionichthys hirsutus*), for example, is confined to the Derwent Estuary and nearby bays in south-eastern Tasmania. Once common, this species now seems to be facing extinction. Predation of eggs by the introduced Pacific sea star (*Asterius amurensis*) is thought to be the most likely cause.

Handfishes prefer to walk slowly over the bottom rather than swim, though they can gallop when necessary, using their 'hands' and pelvic fins together. Handfishes are normally inactive and seem to live for extended periods in one area. This makes them vulnerable to collecting for aquariums, and some species are now considered endangered.

Handfishes lay their very large eggs in clusters in flask-like structures that are connected by fine threads to form a nest. The nest is then attached to some object on the sea bottom. The eggs are protected, probably by the female, until they hatch. To avoid fouling the nest, adult handfishes package faecal material into small capsules joined together by strands. These are then presumably washed away from the brood site, preventing a build-up of potentially harmful bacteria.

Nothing is known about the larvae or habitat of young handfishes.
Family: Brachionichthyidae

DEEP-SEA ANGLERFISHES

Living at depths of 300–2000 metres, many of these anglerfishes are not well known. About 20 families live in Australian waters, including the seadevils, devil-anglers, prickly anglerfishes, smooth anglerfishes and slender anglerfishes.

Most anglerfishes grow no longer than 15 cm, but some, such as the northern seadevil (*Ceratias holboelli*) reach 90 cm or more. They are generally brown to black.

Their name comes from a rod-like structure projecting from their forehead, with a fringed or bulbous tip. Some tips contain bacteria that glow in the dark. Anglers remain still and dangle their lure to entice their prey, such as other fishes, squids or crustaceans. Once in range, the victim is snatched into the angler's enormous mouth, where its large, backward-pointing teeth prevent escape.

The most bizarre feature of anglerfishes is the mode of reproduction of some families. In the seadevil family, for example, the male must parasitise the female in order to reproduce. The female releases a pheromone to attract the male, and the male attaches himself to the female's body with specialised hooks on his snout and chin. In some species, the body tissues and blood supplies of the two merge. Some females have been found with more than one male attached.

It is only quite recently that deep-water submersibles have made it possible for scientists to study anglerfishes in their natural environment.
Families: Ceratiidae (sea devils), Melanocetidae (devil anglers), Himantolophidae (prickly anglerfishes), Oneirodidae (smooth anglerfishes), Gigantactinidae (slender anglerfishes)

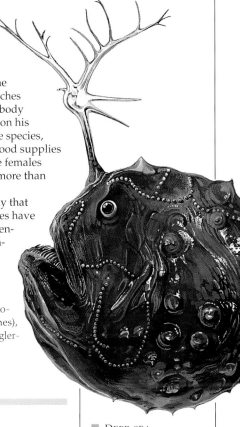

■ DEEP-SEA ANGLERFISH
Life in the ocean depths, where food is scarce, has led to a striking adaptation in deep-sea anglerfishes, such as this prickly anglerfish. They have rod-like structures projecting from their forehead which act as a lure to catch prey.

CLINGFISHES

Small and shy, most clingfish species hide under ledges, in crevices and in seagrass beds. Their name comes from their pelvic fin, which is modified into a suction disc that allows the fish to adhere to almost any surface. The members of one subfamily of clingfishes, the Alabetinae, have lost this sucker and, being more elongated than most clingfishes, are called shore-eels (genus *Alabes*).

Thirty-three clingfish species, from a world total of over 120, live in Australian seas. The seven shore-eel species are found only in Australia.

Clingfishes come in various shapes, from the tadpole-like members of the genus *Aspasmogaster* to the slender rat clingfish, which does not yet have a scientific name. Some clingfishes have short, triangular snouts, while others have spade-like ones. The shape of the long-snouted urchin clingfish (*Diademichthys lineatus*) varies according to the fish's sex; the female has a narrow, elongated snout, whereas the male's is much broader. Some species have a relatively large spine on each side of the head, but many species lack spines.

Shore-eels reach a maximum of 12 cm in length. Australia's largest clingfish – the western clingfish, *Alabes occidentalis* – grows to 11 cm long, and the smallest species is the rat clingfish, at only 2 cm long.

CLINGING CLEANERS
Cleaner clingfishes feed on the skin parasites on other sea creatures. This western cleaner clingfish is resting on the intake siphon of a sea squirt.

Clingfishes tend to be coloured in order to blend with their surroundings: those living among weeds and in seagrass beds are mostly green, while reef-dwellers are more diverse in colour. The Tasmanian clingfish (*A. tasmaniensis*), for example, is banded in colours ranging from orange, red and green to yellow, pink and blue.

Most clingfishes inhabit shallow coastal waters, living in a variety of habitats – under rocks, among coral or sea urchin spines, and on weeds. Some prefer areas of heavy wave action, where they put their suction disc to good use, while others like sheltered bays. Some even ride on the backs of other fish species.

Shore-eels are found among rock-pool weeds and in seagrass beds. Two species – the dwarf shore-eel (*A. hoesei*) and the pygmy shore-eel (*A. parvulus*) – are almost transparent, their internal organs clearly visible through the sides of their body.

Clingfishes lay quite large eggs, which they usually guard until the young hatch. The two cleaner clingfish species – the western cleaner clingfish, *Cochleoceps bicolor* (found from western Victoria to Western Australia) and the eastern cleaner clingfish, *C. orientalis* (native to the coasts of New South Wales and eastern Victoria) – lay their eggs on sea squirts, sponges or kelp fronds, and one parent remains with the eggs to prevent predators from eating them.

The sticky eggs of the spiny clingfish (*Posidonichthys hutchinsi*) are laid on a piece of seagrass. Here they are fertilised by the male, who guards them until the young hatch.
Order: Gobiesociformes;
Family: Gobiesocidae

HARDYHEADS AND RAINBOWFISHES

Elongated, generally small schooling fishes, hardyheads and rainbowfishes are usually silvery in colour or have a silvery stripe down the sides of their body. They have two separate dorsal fins and rounded scales.
Order: Atheriniformes

HARDYHEADS

Australian hardyheads (also known as silversides, minnows and whitebait) rarely exceed 10 cm in length. They are torpedo-shaped, and have two dorsal fins and mouthparts that they can thrust forward. Their colour varies from yellow to green to grey, with a silvery or black stripe on their sides. Marine species often have iridescent scales, and some have a habit of jumping out of the water at night, creating luminous trails.

Superficially, hardyheads resemble mullets. They occur in both temperate and tropical shallow waters and, of the 200 or so species worldwide, about 35 live in Australian waters. Hardyheads also occur in estuarine and freshwater environments.

Many marine species form schools and are food for larger fishes and birds. Hardyheads themselves have a varied diet: some eat insects; some eat small fishes and invertebrates; others seem to eat vegetation as well.

Hardyheads scatter their eggs on the sea bottom or attach them to plants. One exception is an overseas species, the Californian grunion (*Leuresthes tenuis*): it deposits its eggs on the beach to hatch.
Family: Atherinidae

■ BLUE EYE
The Pacific blue eye, *Pseudomugil signifer,* lives in streams and swamps within 30 km of the sea and among coastal mangroves along the east coast of Australia.

FLOWERS OF THE WAVE

Of the seven species known worldwide, only one – *Iso rhothophilus* – is recorded in Australia, but the group is widely distributed throughout the Indian and Pacific Oceans. The fish's

body is as thin as a leaf, and the front part has no scales. Flowers of the wave are less than 7 cm long and have a keeled belly. Their body is translucent, but their sides have a silvery sheen that may form a stripe.

Surprisingly, these fragile fishes usually live in strong surf, close to rocky shores. Flowers of the wave often school in large numbers.
Family: Notocheiridae

RAINBOWFISHES ■

Rainbowfishes, or sunfishes, are freshwater fishes found throughout tropical Australia and ranging south into the Murray–Darling river system. They are abundant in New Guinea and northern Australia, forming a major part of the fish community in rivers, drainage ditches, billabongs, lakes, ponds, and even puddles in stream beds. Many species are restricted to a single lake or river system.

Fifty-four rainbowfish species are recorded, 13 of which are found in Australian habitats. Of these, the Australian rainbowfish (*Melanotaenia splendida*) is the most widely distributed, ranging from Western Australia to eastern Queensland.

Rainbows are minnow-like fishes, usually less than 10 cm long. Their common name is based on their bright colours – shades of red, blue, green and yellow. They often gather

■ RAINBOWFISHES
The chequered rainbowfish, a subspecies of the Australian rainbowfish, is found in Northern Territory rivers.

in shallow, sunlit waters, where they eat a variety of small insects that fall onto the surface.

Rainbows breed year round, with spawning often triggered by the onset of monsoonal rains. Mates swim side by side among aquatic weed or submerged roots, and eggs are shed and fertilised with an intense vibrating action. The tiny eggs stick to plants with thread-like filaments. There is no parental care, but floodwaters provide extensive shallow habitat, helping the young to escape predators. Growth is rapid, and most species are mature before they are a year old. Rainbows live for about five years.
Family: Melanotaeniidae

BLUE EYES ■

Delicate, often semitransparent freshwater fishes, blue eyes are rarely more than 4 cm long when mature. Most of the 17 species occur in New Guinea, but six are found primarily in eastern and northern Australia.

Blue eyes are found in the same freshwater and brackish habitats as rainbowfishes, but most species do not penetrate as far inland.
Family: Pseudomugilidae

GARS

These slim, silvery blue fishes share a distinguishing beak. Some have a protruding lower jaw that resembles a needle; others have long upper and lower jaws lined with teeth.
Order: Beloniformes

SAURIES

The 45 cm-long southern hemisphere king gar (*Scomberesox saurus*) is the only member of this family so far recorded from Australia.

Members of the offshore ocean fish community in subtropical and temperate seas, sauries, or king gars, often live far from shore, feeding on plankton. Schools sometimes leap from the water in unison when fleeing from predators such as tunas.

Sauries look like longtoms (this page), but have short jaws and five to seven separate finlets behind both the main dorsal and anal fins.
Family: Scomberesocidae

GARFISHES

There are 18 species of garfish, or halfbeak, in Australia: worldwide there are around 80 species. Most live in coastal seas, but there are also several estuarine and freshwater species. They are slender, silvery fishes with a short upper jaw and an unusually long lower jaw.

Garfishes frequently swim in schools close to the surface. The ribbon halfbeak (*Euleptorhamphus viridis*), one of the largest members of the family, grows to about 40 cm long. It can leap from the water and glide for considerable distances, using its enlarged pectoral fins in the same way as flyingfishes do. Most other garfishes can jump when alarmed or pursued by predators, but they do not actually glide.

Although garfishes are basically marine, freshwater forms have evolved in Australasia, including members of the genera *Arrhamphus* and *Zenarchopterus*. These freshwater species patrol the edges of streams, feeding chiefly on insects that fall on the surface. In Australia these fishes usually live within a few kilometres of the sea, but in New Guinea they penetrate well inland: the river garfish (*Zenarchopterus novaeguineae*), for example, has been seen nearly 1000 km upstream in the Fly River.
Family: Hemiramphidae

FLYINGFISHES

Known for being able to glide great distances above the waves, flyingfishes occur in all temperate and tropical open seas, living near the surface. The family contains about 60 species, ranging from 10 cm to 30 cm in length. Flyingfishes have a colouring known as counter-shading: bluish on the back and silver to white below, they are camouflaged from birds above and fish predators below.

Spawning females lay thousands of tiny eggs among floating seaweed.
Family: Exocoetidae

LONGTOMS

The elongated shape of these fishes has given rise to the common name longtom; their other name, needlefish, refers to the sharp, slender teeth that cover their jaws. Most species are silvery with a counter-shading colour scheme similar to that of flyingfishes.

Longtoms are voracious predators of small fishes, favouring herrings and anchovies. Some larger species, such as the 150 cm-long crocodile longtom (*Tylosurus crocodilus*), of northern Australia, can be a threat

CAN FLYINGFISHES REALLY FLY?

Photographic studies have shown that flying fishes are not true fliers. Rather than flapping their wing-like pectoral fins, they hold these fins quite rigid – the resulting gliding action is similar to that of the flying lizards of South-East Asia. To really fly, they would need to be able to flap their fins sufficiently for their body to be supported in the air. Only one fish can do this: the freshwater hatchetfish of South America.

Flyingfishes swim rapidly at an upward angle and propel themselves rapidly from the surface. If the initial burst of speed is insufficient, they uses their tail like an outboard motor, vibrating it as rapidly as 50 beats per second, until they are airborne. Their average gliding speed is 56 km per hour, and flights as long as 15 seconds have been observed. Their flight allows them to elude predators such as tunas.

to humans. It bursts from the water with great force, sometimes impaling people paddling in the shallows.

This family, which contains about 30 species, is distributed in all tropical and temperate seas. Some species inhabit brackish estuaries, and a few, such as the 60 cm-long freshwater longtom (*Strongylura krefftii*) of northern Australia and southern New Guinea, are found only in inland waters.
Family: Belonidae

■ LONGTOM *Strongylura krefftii*, which reaches a length of 60 cm, is one of the few longtoms, or needlefishes, found in fresh water. It lives in the inland waters of northern Australia and southern New Guinea.

RIBBONFISH
After metamorphosis, this scalloped ribbonfish larva will have the red fins and silvery body that are characteristic of ribbonfishes.

PINEAPPLE FISH
The Japanese pineapple fish is known in Australian waters only from a few specimens. They have light-emitting organs on their jaw.

Opahs

Marine fishes with flattened, often brightly coloured bodies, opahs are found worldwide. Some look like flounders, and others resemble eels. They have protruding mouths, and though many are toothless they are very effective predators.
Order: Lampridiformes

Moonfishes

Moonfishes, or opahs, are open-ocean fishes. There are two species, both found in Australian waters, but they are rarely seen by anyone except operators of deepwater commercial trawlers.

The southern moonfish (*Lampris immaculatus*) and the spotted moonfish (*L. guttatus*) can exceed 110 cm in length and 100 kg in weight. Both have a compressed oval body with sickle-shaped pectoral fins and forward lobes on the dorsal and anal fins, and a crescent-shaped tail to give great speed. The southern moonfish is more slender than the spotted moonfish and lacks the silvery spots.
Family: Lamprididae

Veilfins

Veilfins have deep, laterally flattened bodies and are open-ocean dwellers. They occur at depths of less than 200 metres in northern Australia and along the continental rims of the tropical Indian and Western Pacific Oceans. *Velifer hypselopterus* has large, sail-like dorsal and anal fins and a compressed

striped body, whereas in *V. multiradiatus* only the front of the dorsal fin is especially high.

Both species have unique attachments and modifications that allow their mouth to protrude as a feeding tube. This probably helps them catch fast-moving prey or suck up shrimps.
Family: Veliferidae

Oarfishes

Scarce, strikingly coloured and frequently large, the ocean-dwelling oarfishes are responsible in part for 'sea serpent' sightings. One species, *Regalecus glesne*, is the longest bony fish in the world. It has a large head and eyes and a slender silvery white body with a red dorsal fin along its entire length. Adults are reported to reach about 11 metres, but the largest found in Australian waters have been no more than 6 metres long.
Family: Regalecidae

Ribbonfishes

Like the oarfish, the ribbonfish (*Trachipterus jacksoniensis*) is brightly coloured and large, but it is shorter and deeper-bodied. Ribbonfishes have telescopic mouths that form a tube when extended. When the gill cover is opened, small fishes and invertebrates are sucked inside.

Ribbonfish species are reasonably common in the open ocean off southern Australia. They vary greatly in shape with size and age.
Family: Trachipteridae

Crestfishes

Members of this family are not well known, and only a few specimens have been collected from Australian waters. Like oarfishes and ribbonfishes, they are large (up to 8 metres long). Their forehead protrudes, and their dorsal fin starts further forward – above or before the snout tip – than in related groups. They also have ink sacs, which probably release ink when the fish is trying to avoid a predator.
Family: Lophotidae

Hairyfish and ribbonbearers

Both the hairyfish (*Mirapinna esau*), with its wing-like pectoral fins, and the elongated, smooth-sided ribbonbearers (*Eutaeniophorus* and *Parataeniophorus* spp.), which are named for the banner-like central extension of their tails, have small, trapdoor mouths that are ideal for snapping up free-swimming invertebrates. These fishes grow to between 4 cm and 5 cm in length.
Family: Mirapinnidae

Jellynose fishes

Along the sea bottom in deep waters swim the elongated, flabby-bodied jellynose fishes, with their underslung jaws and jelly-filled flexible snouts. These fishes grow to 2 metres long and extract their invertebrate food from the sea bottom.
Family: Ateleopodidae

Squirrelfishes

Deep-bodied marine creatures, squirrelfishes are large-eyed and have spiny fins. Some live in shallow waters, but most prefer the deep sea. They are usually reddish in colour.
Order: Beryciformes

Pineapple fishes

The small pineapple fish family includes only three species, two of which are found in Australian waters. One, the Japanese pineapple fish (*Monocentris japonicus*), is extremely rare. The other, *Cleidopus gloriamaris*, occurs only in Australian waters and consists of two subtropical populations, one on the east coast and one on the west.

Pineapple fishes, also known as pinecone fishes and knight fishes,

have a body resembling the skin of a pineapple, being yellow and covered with plate-like scales. A feature of these fishes is the presence of light-emitting organs on the sides of the lower jaw. This light is produced by bacteria.

During the day, pineapple fishes hide in caves or in the shade of overhanging rocks near the sand, but at night they move out over the open sea bottom to feed on shrimps and other crustaceans, which they locate with their own spotlights.

Common in the waters off New South Wales and southern Western Australia, the pineapple fish *Cleidopus gloriamaris* grows to about 20 cm long. It is nocturnal but not particularly secretive, so it is often

seen by divers. During the day pineapple fishes shelter in caves and beneath ledges in rocky reefs, often forming small groups. At night they hunt individually over the sandy bottom, frequently venturing a long way from their daytime shelter but usually returning home by daybreak. They live in relatively shallow waters and sometimes enter estuaries, but they have also been trawled from deep water.
Family: Monocentrididae

ROUGHIES ▨

This is not the largest family in this group, but no other family has members with such a variety of lifestyles. Six genera and more than a dozen species inhabit Australian waters.

At first glance roughies, also known as sawbellies or slimeheads, have few distinguishing features, although a prominent bony head is apparent, and some have enlarged, pointed scales along the belly, giving their underside a serrated appearance.

Detailed studies have revealed a variety of depth preferences and ways of life among roughies. The common roughy, *Trachichthys australis*, is a small southern Australian species that lives beneath shallow rocky reef ledges during the day, emerging at night to feed.

The recently discovered golden roughy (*Aulotrachichthys pulsator*) acquired the label 'pulsator' from its ability to emit rapid pulses of

▨ ROUGHY
When disturbed, the common roughy often releases a noxious substance that is capable of killing other fishes.

clicking sounds when kept in an aquarium – an ability apparently restricted to males. Unlike other members of its genus, which seem to be confined to quite deep waters, the golden roughy is known only from rocky reefs at depths of about 25 metres off South Australia. This species, and the eight or more others in the genus, have strips of luminescent tissue along the lower edge of the sides, at the base of the pectoral fins and on the underside of the head.

The orange roughy (*Hoplostethus atlanticus*), widely distributed in temperate waters throughout the world, is found in Australia's southernmost regions at depths of 700–1400 metres. It may live to a great age (about 175 years), but reaches only 56 cm in length and 5 kg in weight, possibly because it has a low metabolic rate due to the great depths at which it lives and the low temperatures.
Family: Trachichthyidae

FLASHLIGHT FISHES ▨

The outer edge of the northern Barrier Reef and adjacent seas of New Guinea, Indonesia and the Philippines are the domain of the flashlight fishes. The most distinctive feature of these 10 cm-long creatures is a large light-emitting organ under the eye, which contains luminous bacteria and produces an incredibly bright light. By day these fishes live deep within the reef, emerging at night to feed on plankton. They are most active on dark nights, when large numbers light up their surroundings.

During their nightly forays the lights are intermittently flashed on and off. Presumably this helps the fish maintain contact with members of their species. It may also help to entice larval fishes and crustaceans.

The family contains seven species, most inhabiting the tropical Indian and Pacific oceans. Two species are common in Australasia: the great flashlight fish (*Anomalops katoptron*) and the small flashlight fish (*Photoblepharon palpebratus*). They are distinguished from each other by the number of dorsal fins, the great flashlight fish having two and the small flashlight fish one.
Family: Anomalopidae

▨ FLASHLIGHT FISH
The small flashlight fish, *Photoblepharon palpebratus*, is active on the darkest nights. Legions of these creatures literally light up reef shallows when they are feeding.

BLACK FANGTOOTH AND SPINYFINS

Perch-like in body form, the black fangtooth (*Anoplogaster cornuta*) has needle-like fangs, suggesting a diet of larger fishes, squids and prawns. A deep-sea fish, it is found world-wide and grows to 15 cm in length.

Spinyfins, or black dories, also live in the open ocean. These quite flattened fishes have a large mouth but tiny teeth that are suited to eating smaller crustaceans. Two species are found in Australian waters – the black spiny fin, *Diretmoides parini*, which grows to 32 cm long, and the little dory, *Diretmus argenteus*, which grows to only 13 cm long.

Families: Anoplogasteridae (black fangtooth), Diretmidae (spinyfin)

REDFISHES ■

Members of this small family of predominantly red or orange fishes have large eyes and a preference for deep water. Most species school, feeding on animal plankton at depths of 150–700 metres. Just a few enter shallow waters as adults.

The two genera and nine species of redfishes dwell in temperate waters throughout the world. Both genera have representatives in Australian waters, and seven species occur in the cool southern waters.

Redfishes are superficially similar to bream or snapper – indeed, one species is commonly known as red snapper – but the high number of pelvic-fin rays, and other features, such as the internal bone structure of the head, suggest that they are more primitive.

Only two redfish species are known, taken by trawls in depths of 300–700 metres: the imperador

■ SQUIRRELFISH
Squirrelfishes are reef dwellers that are active at night. They make clicking sounds that are thought to be for communication between school members.

(*Beryx decadactylus*), which is the largest member of the family, reaching a length of 52 cm, and the alfonsino (*B. splendens*). Best known are the four nannygai species, which generally form sizeable schools. Small juveniles sometimes enter shallow estuaries with rocky reefs.

The bight nannygai (*Centroberyx gerrardi*), also known as red snapper, shelters in caves and on ledges during the day, then moves out at night to hunt various invertebrates. Its bright colour makes it stand out from its normally dull surroundings, and the white margin on its fins distinguishes it from similar species. It grows to a maximum of 46 cm long. It is commonly encountered by divers on rocky reefs at depths of 10–300 metres in South Australia and southern Western Australia. A few specimens are known from Port Philip Bay in Victoria, but the species is rare in this area.

The most common species in the family, the nannygai (*C. affinis*), grows to about 40 cm long and is caught by both commercial trawlers

and anglers. It is also often seen by divers around moderately deep reefs of the southern New South Wales coast, from where it ranges to western Bass Strait off Victoria and Tasmania. Reports of this species from South Australia and Western Australia are based on the similar looking and also common yellow-eye nannygai (*C. australis*). This species, sometimes referred to as yellow-eye red snapper, grows to a maximum of 51 cm long. It is usually taken by hand-line or bottom-trawled at depths of 80–300 metres.

The swallowtail (*C. lineatus*), a slender species with a distinctively long forked tail fin and a maximum length of 43 cm, is found from the southern coast of New South Wales to southern Western Australia, but it is not often seen in the eastern part of its range. Small groups of swallowtail have been seen off Bermagui in southern New South Wales, in depths of about 25 metres, and some specimens have been trawled in Bass Strait.

In South Australia, where swallowtails are common, they form large schools on shallow offshore reefs, and in southern Western Australia they are frequently seen inshore as well, even under jetties.
Family: Berycidae

■ REDFISHES
The most common redfish species is the nannygai (*Centroberyx affinis*). It usually occurs in large schools, as shown here.

SQUIRRELFISHES ■

Although squirrelfishes are abundant on coral reefs, they are rarely seen. During the day they remain hidden deep in caves and crevices, appearing in the open shortly after sunset to join the nocturnal hunt (see box, 'The night patrol'). Many invertebrates, particularly crustaceans and echinoderms, try to avoid fish predators by feeding at night, but squirrelfishes feed mainly on crustaceans and have adapted their feeding times to take advantage of their prey's behaviour.

Squirrelfishes are easily recognised by their red colour, coarse scales and large eyes, which resemble those of a squirrel. The family contains two genera. The true squirrelfishes of the genus *Sargocentron* have a long, sharp, backward-projecting spine on the lower edge of the cheek, a feature lacking in the genus *Myripristis*, commonly known as soldierfishes. Both genera produce clearly audible clicking sounds. These are believed to be used for communication between members of the school.

Most species are less than 30 cm long when fully grown, but the sabre squirrelfish (*Sargocentron* *spiniferum*) reaches 45 cm in length. The family occurs in all warm seas where coral reefs exist. About 70 species are known, 32 of which occur in northern Australian seas.
Family: Holocentridae

RIDGEHEADS

A family of rather small deep-sea fishes (maximum size 16 cm), ridgeheads, also known as bigscale fishes or crustheads, are found at depths of 500–4000 metres. They are not known to migrate into shallower water, although they do sometimes swim from the depths to the surface.

Of the 45 known ridgehead species, just six are known from Australian waters. They are generally black or brown and covered with large, smooth scales. They have a large ridged head, a large blunt mouth with small teeth, and one dorsal fin.

Some species of ridgehead are restricted in distribution, but as a group they are found throughout the world, other than in the Arctic and Antarctic regions. Ridgeheads feed on plankton and are preyed on by larger fishes. They are thought to be long-lived.
Family: Melamphaidae

WHALEFISHES

Food is not easy to come by in the midwaters of the deep ocean, and finding a mate can be an adventure. But in these seldom-visited regions, bizarre is often beautiful.

It is not clear whether members of the Centomimidae, Rondeletiidae and Barbourisiidae families emulate their mammal namesakes by cruising the depths with their enormous mouths agape in order to sieve small items of food from the water, or whether their expandable stomachs have developed so as to accommodate their occasional – but indispensable – large prey.
Order: Cetomimiformes

FLABBY WHALEFISHES

At depths of more than 1000 metres in the open ocean, the flabby whalefishes dominate. Shaped like whales, they have reduced eyes that merely sense light, no pelvic fins, and supersensitive cavernous lateral lines that provide virtually their only means of detecting whether there are other creatures in the vicinity. The tiny 5 cm-long males are dwarfed by their female partners, which may grow to eight times the male's size. It may be that the female needs a large body to produce the mass of eggs for their single mating in this food-poor environment.
Family: Cetomimidae

REDMOUTH AND VELVET WHALEFISHES ■

Redmouth whalefishes are found in shallower waters than flabby whalefishes, and they have well-developed, though small, eyes and functional pelvic fins. The similar velvet whalefish, or red whalefish (*Barbourisia rufa*), sole member of its family, differs most noticeably from the redmouth in having spiny skin.
Families: Rondeletiidae (redmouth whalefishes), Barbourisiidae (velvet whalefish)

■ VELVET WHALEFISH
The velvet whalefish, *Barbourisia rufa*, is bright red and has a spiny skin. It is a deep-sea species that has been found in all major oceans.

DORIES

Most dories have a round or oval body that is flattened sideways, and a mouth that they can thrust forward. They are rough to touch because they have small spines on the head or fin bases, or sharp projections on their scales, or both. Dories are 10–65 cm in length, and are widely distributed in temperate and tropical oceans. Nearly 30 species in six families occupy Australian waters.

Members of four of these families live in tropical waters to 900 metres, so they are rarely seen. Most are small, such as the two Australian members of the Macrurocyttidae family, which grow to only 10 cm long. The largest of the four families is Grammicolepididae, the scaly dories, or tinselfishes – so named because of their vertically elongated scales – which grow to 33 cm long. The orange, pink or red boarfishes (family Caproidae) live in midwater as juveniles and on the sea bottom as adults. *Parazen pazificus*, the single member of the family Parazenidae, shares the colouring of the boarfishes.

Members of the remaining two families, Zeidae and Oreosomatidae, are fished commercially in Australia, mostly in the south-east.
Order: Zeiformes

DORIES ■

Popular as food throughout most of their worldwide range, dories occur from inshore to depths of over 700 metres. They approach small fishes, squids or crustaceans slowly and, when in range, shoot out their tubular mouth to engulf their prey.

Nine dory species are found in Australian waters. The king or look-down dory (*Cyttus traversi*) reaches 65 cm in length and 6 kg in weight, but the rare *Cyttomimus affinis*, of northern Australian waters, grows to only about 10 cm long.

The john dory (*Zeus faber*) is green to olive grey, with a dark blotch, circled in yellow, on each side. It may weigh more than 8 kg and grow to 60 cm long. The mirror dory (*Zenopsis nebulosus*), which is similar in size, is silvery with black spots on each side and has spiny plates, called bucklers, around the edge of its body.
Family: Zeidae

OREOS

Oreos, or warty dories, live in the deep waters (400–1400 metres) of most temperate oceans. There are six species in Australian waters, off the southern two-thirds of the continent.

Oreos probably live for more than 100 years, making them among the longest living fishes in the world. They range in length from 22 cm to 68 cm; the largest species, the smooth oreo (*Pseudocyttus maculatus*), reaches up to 6.5 kg in weight.

Most species are brown or black. Juveniles are often paler with dark bluish spots, and most have a large abdomen with one or two rows of cones or warts. Adults feed mostly on molluscs, shrimps and fishes.
Family: Oreosomatidae

SEAMOTHS

When these little flattened fishes spread their large pectoral fins they somewhat resemble a moth. They are also known as dragonfishes.

Most of their body is encased in bony plates and the snout is elongated. The small mouth beneath thrusts forward to suck up minute animal life from the sandy sea bottom.

All three Australian seamoth species live in shallow coastal waters, mainly on the sandy sea floor near the edges of reefs or seagrass beds. They are coloured to blend in with the sand, in which they often bury themselves, leaving just their eyes exposed. They rarely swim, but rather glide, pushing themselves along with their pelvic and pectoral fins.

Males display to females with their ornamental pectoral fins. To spawn,

UNIQUE TO AUSTRALIA
The sculptured seamoth is common along the southern coast of Australia but is found nowhere else in the world.

the pair rise slowly above the sea floor, releasing their eggs and sperm simultaneously into the current.

The sculptured seamoth (*Pegasus lancifer*), 12–14 cm long, is native to the south coast of Australia. Dozens congregate in sheltered bays and sandy coves in late winter or spring, forming pairs to breed. Males are distinguished by a small olive-green spot on each pectoral fin.

The similar-sized slender seamoth (*P. volitans)* and the dragonfish (*Eurypegasus draconis*), which is smaller at 8 cm long, are widespread in Australia's tropical waters.
Order: Gasterosteiformes;
Family: Pegasidae

TRUMPETFISHES, PIPEFISHES AND SEAHORSES

Members of this well-known group of fishes are both fascinating and beautiful. Even for fishes they have unusual shapes, resembling horses and dragons. They usually live in shallow marine waters.
Order: Syngnathiformes

TRUMPETFISHES

These fishes are easily recognised by their long, slender body and tubular snout with the mouth at the very tip. Trumpetfishes are highly variable in colour, usually matching their surroundings. Sometimes the entire fish is bright yellow. Inhabitants of both coastal waters and outer reefs, they are solitaries that prey on other fishes, often approaching them by staying close to large, nonpredatory species.

In Australian waters, the family is represented by the Pacific trumpetfish (*Aulostomus chinensis*), which grows to 50 cm long. It is common in tropical waters, but stray specimens are found down the eastern coast to southern New South Wales.
Family: Aulostomidae

FLUTEMOUTHS

Flutemouths are similar to trumpetfishes but are more slender and have long rays projecting from the centre of their tail fin. In juveniles these rays are connected to each other by a large membrane. Flutemouths feed on small fishes, which they suck up with their long tubular snouts.

Two Australian species are widespread in the tropical Indo-Pacific. Both inhabit depths to 200 metres and reach a length of 2 metres. Although tropical, the rough flutemouth (*Fistularia petimba*) ranges into temperate zones, including Australia's southern coast, while the smooth flutemouth (*F. commersonii*) ranges no further south than about Montague Island off Narooma on the New South Wales coast.
Family: Fistulariidae

BELLOWFISHES AND SHRIMPFISHES

Also known as snipefishes, bellowfishes grow to about 28 cm long and have a greatly compressed body and a tube-like snout with a toothless mouth at its tip. They live near the sea bottom and usually swim in large schools. About six species are found in Australian waters. Best

known is the common snipefish (*Macroramphosus scolopax*), which occurs in the southern half of Australian waters, from depths of 60–500 metres. Another widespread temperate species is the banded bellowfish (*Centriscops humerosus*), which is found at 35–1000 metres. Juveniles are silvery until they are almost adult, when they become banded silver and black. For a long time they were thought to be a separate species.

Shrimpfishes are mainly silvery in colour, but often with a dark band running along the body from the snout to the tail. Adults average about 15 cm in length.

The best known Australian species is the coral shrimpfish (*Aeoliscus strigatus*), which swims in large schools on coral reefs. Equally common, but not as well known, is the rigid shrimpfish (*Centriscus scutatus*), which lives in more coastal, and sometimes silty, waters. It differs from the coral shrimpfish in having an inflexible dorsal spine.
Family: Centriscidae

GHOST PIPEFISHES

Members of this small tropical family closely resemble the related pipefishes (page 434). At present about five species are known.

Ghost pipefishes have a pipefish-like head and a body encased in bony armour, but, unlike pipefishes, they have well-developed fins – two dorsal, one anal, and large tail and pelvic fins. They also differ from

pipefishes in their breeding behaviour, as the female, not the male, incubates the eggs. She keeps the brood in a pouch that she forms by hooking her pelvic fins onto tiny spines on her body.

The most common species is the ornate ghost pipefish (*Solenostomus paradoxus*). Its colouring is usually white, yellow, red and black, or transparent in parts. It often hovers near rocks, corals or feather stars – backgrounds against which it is well camouflaged. The 10 cm-long robust ghost pipefish (*S. cyanopterus*) is more leaf-like and is green or brownish in colour. Most ghost pipefishes pair as adults, and occasionally they are found in small groups.
Family: Solenostomidae

TRUMPETFISH
Widespread in tropical waters, the Pacific trumpetfish ambushes its prey. It rests motionless in the water behind coral or the body of a larger fish until an unsuspecting smaller one swims close by. It then darts forward and grabs its meal.

SHRIMPFISHES
Shrimpfishes are also known as razorfishes because of their very compressed, thin bodies. They normally swim in a vertical posture, with their head down.

Living legends

Seahorses, seadragons and pipefishes are among the most exotic of marine creatures, looking more like characters from a fairytale than fishes.

The large family of seahorses, sea-dragons and pipefishes has some 220 species worldwide, about half of which are found in Australian waters. Common features of these creatures are a body armoured with bony plates (instead of scales), a tubed snout with a small mouth at the tip, and no teeth or pelvic fins. Seahorses, and some pipefishes, have a muscular tail that they use to hold onto fixed objects or floating weeds while feeding and sleeping.

Australian seahorse species may be anything from 2.5 cm to 35 cm long. Most live in weed or seagrass habitats, but a few dwell in deep water, where they cling to sponges or soft corals.

Right, the leafy seadragon (Phycodurus eques) *cunningly imitates drifting seaweed to disguise itself as it floats among weeds close to the sea floor.*

Some tropical species are very striking, but most are superbly camouflaged, enabling them to elude predators and get close to their prey – mainly small crustaceans, which they suck in with their long snout and swallow whole.

Elegance and breeding

Seahorses swim slowly and elegantly, holding their bodies upright and driving them through the water by rapidly beating their large dorsal and pectoral fins, with a motion rather like that of a helicopter. They use their dorsal fins for forward and backward movement and their pectoral fins for turning. The arch of the neck and poise of the head bear a resemblance to those of a horse, giving them their common name. Their belly often has a distended appearance.

Seahorses usually occur in pairs, and several pairs may form a small group. When they are not breeding, males may live separately from females, but they come together in October in southern waters.

White's seahorse (Hippocampus whitei) *is drab coloured when living among seagrasses but often matches its bright surroundings when on sponges or near kelp.*

The weedy seadragon (Phyllopteryx taeniolatus) *grows up to 45 cm long. This male is carrying eggs under the skin of his tail.*

The breeding season lasts for most of the summer, with activity peaking each month near the full moon. Three or four days before mating, the male seahorse grows a pouch on his underbelly. While they are courting, the male and female coil around each other and the female squirts thousand of eggs into the male's pouch. These are fertilised by the male, who carries them around for about 25 days, feeding them with a fluid secreted from the lining of the pouch.

When the baby seahorses are ejected from their father's pouch they make their way to the surface, where they attach themselves to floating weeds and begin feeding on zooplankton. Brood sizes depend on the size of the species: small species bear about 50 young, larger species about five hundred.

Seadragons and pipefishes

Seadragons are magnificent creatures that are unique to southern Australian waters. They have a seahorse-like head and an armoured body with long spines on which elaborate lobes of skin grow, so that the animals resemble seaweed. They breed annually in early summer and usually produce one brood per season. The 250 or so eggs are carried by the male while they develop, embedded in the skin under his tail.

Pipefishes look rather like seahorses, but they swim horizontally instead of vertically and their bodies are straight rather than curled. Slender, stick-like and armoured, they are more flexible than seahorses and vary considerably in size and way of life. Some are tiny, worm-like and secretive; others are large and lie openly on the sea bottom. Many free-swimming pipefishes hide in caves and beneath ledges when they are not feeding, and some masters of disguise entwine themselves in weeds.

SWAMP EELS

Although swamp eels are not true eels, they do greatly resemble them. Worm-like, they have a strong, muscular body and poor fin development: the dorsal and anal fins form low ridges around the tail, and they lack pectoral fins. Worldwide, the family is represented by about eight species, found mainly in the tropical regions of Australia, Asia, Africa, and Central and South America. Swamp eels live mainly in fresh or brackish water.

The three Australian species – the swamp eel (*Ophisternon gutturale*), the blind cave eel (*O. candidum*) and the belut (*Monopterus albus*) – are seldom seen, as they live in ditches, dark cracks and crevices, or concealed under bottom sediment.

The most unusual member of the trio is the blind cave eel from Western Australia. It lives in darkness in the crevices that riddle the coastal plain near Exmouth. It grows to a length of 40 cm, is about the same diameter as a pencil and has no eyes. It probably feeds on tiny crustaceans and possibly another blind fish (a gudgeon) that shares its underground habitat.
Order: Synbranchiformes;
Family: Synbranchidae

AMPHIBIOUS FISHES
Swamp eels are remarkable because they can remain active out of water for several months at a time. The specimen shown here is *Ophisternon gutturale*, which grows to about 60 cm long. It is found around the lagoons on the Gulf of Carpentaria.

SCORPIONFISHES, STONEFISHES AND FLATHEADS

Of various shapes, these fishes defend themselves by pumping venom out of their spines into unwary intruders. Their beautiful mottled coloration acts as perfect camouflage against the seabed.
Order: Scorpaeniformes

SCORPIONFISHES ▪

The scorpionfish's common name comes from the venomous spines on its dorsal and anal fins, which can inflict a dangerous – sometimes fatal – sting (see box, 'Scorpions of the sea', page 436).

These fishes range from 2.5 cm to 50 cm in length, and there are about 80 species in Australian waters. Certain scorpionfishes, such as the firefishes, have flamboyant long rays projecting from their fins and brilliantly striped bodies that may serve to warn potential predators of the fish's toxicity.

Scorpionfishes, a group that includes the deadly stonefishes, are dangerous to humans. These fishes are often quite difficult to see and seldom move when approached. Some stonefishes bury themselves in the sea bottom, with only the top of the head and the venomous spines along the back exposed. In Hervey Bay, in Queensland, divers have reported the sandy bottom near a particular reef as being covered with partly buried stonefishes.

Most scorpionfishes are found in tropical waters, although many also occur in Australia's southern waters.

Except for one freshwater species, the bullrout (*Notesthes robusta*), all Australian scorpionfishes inhabit marine or estuarine waters. Most are bottom-dwellers, living hidden in reef crevices, but some, such as the firefishes, swim in open water.

Scorpionfishes generally ambush their prey. They remain hidden and motionless, waiting for fishes or crabs to pass, and then they seize their prey and swallow it. Stonefishes are particularly adept at this because they are so effectively camouflaged.

There are four stonefish species in Australian seas: the estuarine stonefish (*Synanceia horrida*), one of the most feared animals in the sea; the reef stonefish (*S. verrucosa*); the monkeyfish (*Erosa erosa*); and the Dampier stonefish (*Dampierosa daruma*). All inhabit tropical waters, but some have been found as far south as Lancelin in Western Australia and Ballina in New South Wales.

The spectacular red firefish (*Pterois volitans*) is also extremely dangerous. Also known as the lionfish and the butterfly cod, it grows to 38 cm long. It can move each spine of its dorsal fin independently of the others, and has been known to jab the hands of divers reaching towards it.
Family: Scorpaenidae

▪ SCORPIONFISH
To frighten predators, the red firefish swims slowly through the water with the long, decorative rays of its large pectoral fins spread out like butterfly wings. When resting on the bottom, it folds these cumbersome fins alongside its body.

435

■ VELVETFISH
As their name suggests, velvetfishes have velvety skin. This is the moss-back velvetfish, which is found along the Queensland coast and as far south as Sydney.

VELVETFISHES ■

Few velvetfish species are well known because they are small and secretive and extremely well camouflaged. The 20 cm-long southern Australian velvetfish (*Aploactisoma milesii*), however, is a species that is commonly encountered by divers in southern New South Wales and Victoria. Its range extends from Sydney Harbour to Western

---

SCORPIONS OF THE SEA

The venomous spine of a scorpionfish is needle-sharp, with several grooves running lengthwise along its surface. In most species the venom glands are in these grooves, but in the stonefishes the bulbous glands lie mostly outside the grooves.

Spine and glands are covered with skin, which slides back when the spine pierces the victim. The glands then rupture, releasing their contents: generally, the deeper the penetration, the more toxin enters the victim's body. The contents of the venom glands of the stonefish, however, are expelled at the spine tip, so little penetration is needed for a full release of toxins. Stonefish venom is at least ten times stronger than that of other scorpionfishes and has caused many deaths, but an antivenom is available and most victims in Australia recover.

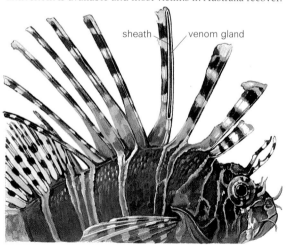

sheath   venom gland

Australia, including Tasmania, and it is found on shallow rocky reefs, where it hides under rocks or partly buries itself in sand.

Also common, but not often noticed, is the threefin velvetfish, *Neoaploactis tridorsalis*, which is often mistaken for the juvenile of another species, as it reaches only about 45 mm in length. Threefin velvetfishes are widespread in Australia's southern waters from One Tree Island in Queensland to Shark Bay in Western Australia, but only a few specimens have been reported. This species inhabits reefs and is usually found when rocks are turned over in shallow water.

The tropical mossback velvetfish (*Paraploactis trachyderma*) is one of the largest velvetfish species, growing to about 30 cm long. Off the coast of Queensland the adults are often trawled with prawns, on which they probably feed; juveniles are found as far south as Sydney. Family: Aploactinidae

PROWFISHES ■

This is a small family of temperate-zone Australian fishes. They can be recognised by their enormous dorsal fin, which begins at the front of the head, runs the entire length of the back, and sometimes joins the tail fin.

Prowfishes have no pelvic fins and use the large pectoral fins low on their body to perch on the sea floor among reefs. They are well camouflaged and often sit next to sponges, matching their colours perfectly. They feed mainly on crustaceans, especially shrimps, which they catch by motionless ambush. When its prey walks in front of its mouth, the prowfish snaps up its victim.

If they are disturbed, these slow-moving fishes just rotate themselves gently, as if nudged by the current. If they need to make a quick escape, they expel a jet of water from a small gill opening below the base of their dorsal fin. This, combined with a thrust by their pectoral fins against the sea floor, provides the momentum they need to get away.

Prowfishes reach a maximum of about 25 cm long. They have no scales; instead, they are covered with tough skin. Plants and animals, such as algae, tubeworms, sea mats and other invertebrates, take advantage of the prowfish's sedentary lifestyle to set up residence on its skin. To prevent this growth from becoming uncomfortable, prowfishes regularly shed their outer layer of skin in almost one piece, rather in the way that snakes do.

There are three genera of prowfishes, each with a single species.

The rare and secretive whiskered prowfish (*Neopataecus waterhousii*) occurs mainly on the south-western coast of Western Australia, but has also been reported from Victoria.

The warty prowfish (*Aetapcus maculatus*) is most commonly observed in southern waters, and is found from shallow, protected reefs to deep-water sponge beds. It varies from drab brown to yellow and orange, and sometimes has dark spots. Small juveniles are usually paler, white or yellow, with dusky pectoral fins and smooth skin. The warty prowfish can be found in Bass Strait and west as far as Shark Bay in Western Australia.

In New South Wales, divers sometimes see the red Indianfish, *Pataecus fronto*. It can be easily recognised by the tall dorsal fin above the head

■ PROWFISH
The red Indianfish is one of three prowfish species found in Australian waters. Its huge dorsal fin makes this prowfish easy to recognise.

and usually lives deep in sponge habitat, where it is often taken in fish traps. This fish occurs in the southern half of Australia's oceans, from southern Queensland to a similar latitude on the west coast, but is apparently absent around southern Victoria and Tasmania.
Family: Pataecidae

CORAL VELVETFISHES

This is a small, tropical, Indo-Pacific family with two species that live in Australian waters: the spotted coral velvetfish (*Caracanthus maculatus*), which is grey with tiny red spots, and the pygmy coral velvetfish (*C. unipinnus*), which is grey-brown.

These small fishes, which grow to only about 50 mm long, live wedged in branched corals. Although they are widespread in tropical waters, velvetfishes are rarely seen. They are frequently mistaken for gobies.
Family: Caracanthidae

RED VELVETFISHES

A single species, *Gnathanacanthus goetzeei*, belonging to the family Gnathanacanthidae is found only in southern Australian waters. It grows to a length of about 30 cm and, although closely related to prowfishes (page 436), is readily distinguishable from them by its large pelvic fins and deeply notched dorsal fin. Like scorpionfishes (see page 435), to which it is also related, *G. goetzeei* is reported to have venomous spines in its dorsal fin.

Adult red velvetfishes vary in colour from brown to red, usually according to the depth of water they inhabit; specimens trawled from deep water are bright red. Small juveniles are semitransparent and are ornamented with red blotches over their body and fins.

Red velvetfishes live hidden in kelp reefs, where they feed almost entirely on shrimps. They are generally seen only at night, when they are out hunting.
Family: Gnathanacanthidae

GURNARDS ■

In certain parts of the world gurnards are known as sea robins because of the chirping noises they make when they are removed from the water. They are easily recognised by their prominent, often beautifully marked pectoral fins, the lower few rays of which are not connected by membranes. Their prominent bony head often has forward-pointing spines at the tip of the snout. In some groups, backward-pointing spines probably deter predators.

Most members of the family are quite small, ranging from just over 10 cm to about 30 cm long.

Gurnards are extremely important in the food web, bridging the broad gap between small, soft-sediment invertebrates and large predatory marine creatures. Well adapted to life on the ocean floor, gurnards perch or amble about on the free rays of their pectoral fins. They thrust these rays, which are studded with taste buds, into soft sediments in order to detect food. Deep-water armoured gurnards also have taste buds on their elongated, often many-branched bristles (barbels), which are occasionally almost half their body length.

Over 30 gurnard species live in Australian waters, at depths from a few metres to more than 600 metres.

The bodies of the deep-dwelling subfamily Peristediinae are completely encased in bony plates; members of the more broadly distributed unarmoured subfamily Triglinae have sides covered with small to tiny scales.

The snout spines of some of the armoured gurnards, such as the crocodilefish (*Satyrichthys lingi*) of southern Australian waters, are enlarged and spatula-like, and may be used as spades for digging up food detected by the animal's intricate barbels. Still more modified are the distinctly fluted lobes around the rather flattened, circular head of the gargoyle gurnard (*Gargariscus* sp.), which occurs at great depths along the northern coast of Western Australia. The purpose of these structures is not known.

■ RED VELVETFISH
The red velvetfish, *Gnathanacanthus goetzeei*, is found only in southern Australian waters. It is said to have venom glands on the spines in its dorsal fin.

■ GURNARD
The 20 or so Australian species in the genus *Lepidotrigla* can be told apart by the colours and patterns on the upper surface of their pectoral fins. This is the colourful butterfly gurnard, *Lepidotrigla vanessa*.

WINGED FISHES

Several fish families have enlarged, webbed pectoral fins resembling birds' wings. These fins are cumbersome and do not help the fishes to swim – so what is their purpose? Flyingfishes use their wings to glide above the waves and elude enemies. But other winged fishes cannot propel themselves out of the water, so they must use this adaptation differently.

Some scorpionfishes use their wings to capture small crustaceans and fishes. As the fish swoops on its victim on the sea bottom, it extends its pectoral fins and thrusts them forward, forming a net that cuts off the prey's escape routes.

The fan-like pectoral fins of flying gurnards are spectacularly patterned with multicoloured spots and false eyes. When threatened, these fishes display their wings to frighten the potential predator, causing it to flee or back off. The wings are also probably used for display in courtship rituals.

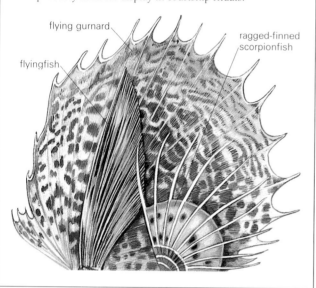

flying gurnard

flyingfish

ragged-finned scorpionfish

There are at least 20 *Lepidotrigla* species in Australian waters, many of which are found nowhere else in the world. These mostly pink and white fishes look alike, but individual species can be identified by the colours and patterns on the upper surface of the pectoral fins. These range from drab browns, mustard yellows and oranges to brilliant turquoises and jet black.

Markings may be fin-edgings, subtle splashes, or even spots that look like eyes. Fin coloration may help to deter predators, but it is probably chiefly used in behavioural displays, particularly at breeding times, and possibly to establish territories. The pectoral fins of these fishes have little, if any, use for swimming.

Most *Lepidotrigla* species are found only along short sections of the Australian coastline, but examples of two species – the minor gurnard (*L. modesta*) and the spiny gurnard (*L. papilio*) – have been found right around the southern coast.

The latchet (*Pterygotrigla polyommata*) and the red gurnard (*Cheilodonichthys kumu*) are both southern Australian species. They are uncharacteristically large for gurnards, growing to 60 cm long. The latchet, which has a prominent pair of slender, forward-pointing spines at the tip of its snout and backward-pointing shoulder spines, is found only in Australian waters.

By contrast, the red gurnard is the most widely distributed of Australian gurnards, and is also found along the coasts of South Africa, Japan and New Zealand.

The cold-water painted latchet (*P. andertoni*) and the tropical half-spotted gurnard (*P. hemisticta*) are among the few representatives of this family with bodies patterned with distinctive dark spots.
Family: Triglidae

FLYING GURNARDS

The bizarre-looking flying gurnards make their way methodically over the sea bottom by moving their pelvic fins alternately – just as if they were walking! They have a box-shaped head and are protected by a stout bony armour and a lengthy spine that projects backwards from the cheek. Their most conspicuous feature is a pair of enormous fan-like pectoral fins that resemble wings (see box, 'Winged fishes').

The family Dactylopteridae is represented by four species, all but one of which are basically tropical: the exception, the 38 cm-long oriental sea robin (*Dactyloptena orientalis*) ranges down to southern New South Wales. The oriental sea robin is quite often seen in very shallow water, but flying gurnards more commonly range over the continental shelf to a depth of 250 metres.
Family: Dactylopteridae

■ FLYING GURNARD
The dramatic, wing-like pectoral fins of the oriental sea robin are typical of flying gurnards.

■ FLATHEAD
Flathead species change colour to match their environment, but they can be identified by the unique colouring of their tail fin. This is the sand flathead, *Platycephalus bassensis*, which is found mainly in Victorian and Tasmanian waters.

FLATHEADS ■

These fishes spend much of their time motionless on the sandy or silty bottom or buried just below the surface. Flattened in both head and body, many are able to adjust their patterning to match their environment, so that flatheads living over sandy bottoms are usually a pale colour with darker bands, whereas those living in weedy areas may be almost black with a scattering of white spots and pale splashes.

This characteristic would make it difficult to identify flatheads, but for the fact that many have one feature that is unique to each species – the coloration of the caudal or tail fin. Some have dark stripes running along the fin, while others have dark spots and blotches. The bar-tailed flathead (*Platycephalus endrachtensis*), for example, has a bright yellow dash near the top of its caudal fin, while the southern blue-spotted flathead (*P. speculator*) has a row of rounded black splashes down the rear margin of its caudal fin.

Flatheads are found worldwide, and at least 44 species occur in Australian waters. They are as much at home in tropical as in temperate waters. Many flathead species inhabit shallow coastal regions, and even swim into estuaries, but most prefer the deeper offshore areas. Some species live among rocky and coral reefs, but they are generally found on soft sandy bottoms.

Most flatheads grow to around 60 cm long, but the dusky flathead (*P. fuscus*) can reach a length of 1.5 metres. Its legendary size has resulted in some anglers mistaking a very large specimen for a shovel-nose shark. The dusky flathead favours sandy areas near coastal and estuarine reefs. It is found along the east coast of Australia from central Queensland to eastern Victoria.

The most spectacular member of the family is probably the tassel-snouted flathead (*Thysanophrys cirronasus*). This fish grows to 38 cm long, and the splashes and bands on its head and body can range from purple, red or orange to brown. It is found in or near rocky reefs, which suggests that it uses its bright markings to conceal itself among the colourful life on the reef. This species inhabits the southern half of the Australian coast.

Most flathead species have prominent spines on the sides of the head; these are not toxic, but they can inflict a painful jab. The dorsal spines on the back behind the head are sharp and slightly venomous; anglers who injure their hands removing a flathead from a hook may suffer considerable swelling.
Family: Platycephalidae

GHOST FLATHEADS

Sometimes known as spiny flatheads, ghost flatheads are found off the coast of Australia in waters up to 1500 metres deep. They have an extremely flattened head and grow to about 50 cm in length.

Superficially, ghost flatheads look very like true flatheads, but the characteristic flattened appearance of the two families is believed to have evolved independently.

One of the most noticeable differences between the two is that ghost flatheads have no scales on their bodies, whereas true flatheads are scaly all over. Ghost flatheads also have three or four finger-like rays detached from the lower edge of the pectoral fin – a characteristic that true flatheads lack.

Not very much is known about ghost flatheads; specimens are rather difficult to observe, since they are generally taken only by trawlers operating in deep waters.
Family: Hoplichthyidae

SCULPINS AND BLOBFISHES

Sculpins and blobfishes, which are sometimes known as fatheads, are not well represented in Australian waters, where there are only six or so species. All local species occur on the continental slope at depths of 600–1400 metres, and they are most abundant in temperate regions. The adults of some species reach about 40 cm in length.

These fishes are typically drab grey in colour and look rather like puffer-fishes (page 488), although some species are spotted. Superficially, all sculpin and blobfish species look alike, which makes them difficult to identify. The smell given off by sculpins and blobfishes after they have been caught suggests that their flesh may be toxic.

More than 200 sculpin species are found in the northern hemisphere, in both fresh- and sea-water habitats, but only two species occur around Australia, and they are from a single genus, *Antipodocottus*. These very poorly known species are less than 10 cm long when adult.

The common blobfish (*Psychrolutes marcidus*) is appropriately named – the skin is loose and flabby, and the abdomen flops around like a jelly when the fish is held out of water. Only the tail and head have a distinct shape, and even then the head is so fat and puffed up that the eyes often seem to be partly obscured by flesh. After death, the flesh around the head collapses to reveal a rough, bony skull. The fish's belly is very elastic, and can expand to several times its normal size in order to accommodate large prey.

Little is known of blobfish biology, and some of the Australian species are probably new to science.
Families: Cottidae (sculpins), Psychrolutidae (blobfishes)

PERCH-LIKE FISHES

This large and varied order contains more species than any other group of vertebrates. The perch-like fishes share a few broad similarities: one or two dorsal fins; pelvic fins close to the head, usually bearing a spine and five rays; and rounded scales covering the body.

Families in the order include fishes in a great variety of shapes, sizes and colours. Most live in inshore marine waters, but habitats range from shallow waters to the deep seas.
Order: Perciformes

■ GLASS PERCHLET
The backbone of a glass perchlet, such as this *Ambassia agrammus*, is clearly visible through its transparent flesh.

BARRAMUNDI AND SNOOKS ■

The barramundi (*Lates calcarifer*) inhabits estuaries and freshwater rivers in northern Australia and Papua New Guinea, and northward and westward to southern China and the Persian Gulf. Seven similar species belonging to the same genus live mainly in African fresh waters.

Snooks (*Centropomus* spp.), found in marine and estuarine habitats in the tropical Americas, look very much like barramundi, but have a sharper snout and a forked tail.

The sand bass (*Psammoperca waigiensis*) somewhat resembles the barramundi. It frequents weedy parts of coral reefs in northern Australia and neighbouring oceans.

Spawning usually takes place in brackish estuaries or off river mouths at the beginning of the winter rainy season. A second wave of spawning may occur after the onset of rains, when young adults living in fresh water move downstream into the

estuaries. Spawning coincides with either the new or the full moon, as the tide begins to move in.

Each female lays several million eggs, which are swept into mangrove swamps and estuaries. The eggs hatch within about 24 hours, and the young develop in the estuaries or, as the wet season develops, swim into nearby swamps and flood plains. In larger river systems, the young barramundi eventually move well upstream until they reach the first impassable barrier, such as a waterfall or dam.

Young barramundi may live in fresh water for several years until they become sexually mature, when they migrate back to the coast in order to spawn. Juveniles feed on a

wide variety of aquatic insects, small crustaceans and fishes; adults prefer mainly prawns and fishes.

Barramundi grow rapidly, reaching about 20 cm long in ten months and about 50 cm by the end of their third year, at which time they are sexually mature. For the next two years they fertilise eggs, and then, at about six years old, they become female. Most barramundi more than 1.2 metres long are female: mature specimens may be 1.8 metres long and more than 50 kg in weight.

The barramundi is a prized game fish and is renowned for its eating qualities, so barramundi fishing is strictly controlled, but it is also important to protect the coastal wetlands that are havens for the young.
Family: Centropomidae

GLASS PERCHLETS ■

Glass perchlets are usually characterised by translucent muscle tissue, through which their vertebral column and swim bladder are visible. A microscopic view shows that the margins of their eyes and cheeks are generally armed with tiny spines. The largest members of the family reach about 25 cm long, but most are much smaller; the Australian pennyfish (*Denarusia bandata*) reaches only 2.5 cm in length.

Glass perchlets live in the coastal seas and fresh or brackish waters of India, East Africa, South-East Asia, the Melanesian Archipelago and Australia. About half the estimated 40 members of this family live in fresh water, including six Australian species. Little is known about their lives, but most seem to be nocturnal, spending the day in stationary groups. Their diet consists mainly of small crustaceans and insects.
Family: Chandidae

■ BARRAMUNDI
The barramundi (*Lates calcarifer*) used to be called the giant perch, but the name barramundi – an Aboriginal word meaning 'bearing large scales' – is now used throughout Australia.

AUSTRALIAN PERCHES

Despite this family's common name, only 15 of the 22 known species live in Australian fresh waters. The remainder are from South America. In the northern hemisphere, these fishes are often called bass.

The Murray cod (*Maccullochella peeli*) is the largest Australian perch, growing to 1.8 metres long and weighing as much as 114 kg. It is distributed widely in the Murray–Darling river system, and has been introduced into lakes and dams in Victoria and New South Wales. It is often found under submerged tree stumps and rocks in turbid, slow-flowing streams.

Spawning occurs in spring, the female depositing up to 40 000 eggs, usually inside a hollow log or on a rock. These are simultaneously fertilised by the male and hatch after one to two weeks. Newly hatched larvae are 6–9 mm long and have a large yolk sac. They begin to resemble juveniles after about a month. At first they feed on plankton, then they eat fishes, crustaceans and bivalves.

The Murray cod is probably the longest-living Australian freshwater fish; some specimens live as long as 30 years, and a few individuals may live twice this long.

Other Australian perch species that inhabit various parts of eastern Australia are the trout cod (*Maccullochella macquariensis*) and the eastern cod (*M. ikei*), which are now both endangered; the golden perch (*Macquaria ambigua*); the Macquarie perch (*M. australasica*); the estuary perch (*M. colonorum*); and the Australian bass (*M. novemaculeata*). Family: Percichthyidae

FRESHWATER BLACKFISHES

Freshwater blackfishes are found only in the cool streams of south-eastern Australia and Tasmania. The two species are elongated black to dark grey fishes with forked pelvic fins dangling beneath the throat.

The river blackfish (*Gadopsis marmoratus*) is found from the Murray–Darling river system in southern Queensland to Victoria, northern Tasmania and South Australia. The two-spined blackfish (*G. bispinosus*) is confined to some streams on the slopes of the Great Dividing Range in central Victoria. Both species feed mainly at night on crustaceans, insects and small fishes. They may reach 60 cm in length and 5.5 kg in weight, but are usually less than 30 cm long and 500 grams in weight. Females lay 20–500 eggs, which stick

together on the undersides of logs and rocks or the insides of hollow logs. One parent – possibly the male – guards the eggs until they hatch about 16 days later. The larvae take about five weeks to become free-swimming; during this time they are vulnerable to predators such as dragonfly nymphs and crayfish.

Blackfishes are no longer as widespread or abundant as they were 50 years ago. Environmental change, river-clearing and dam-building are thought to be contributing to the reduction in numbers. In 1971 they were listed as a threatened species, but recent studies suggest that they are still common in many areas. Family: Percichthyidae

PYGMY PERCHES

This Australian group of freshwater fishes has six species. They occur in the streams and lakes of coastal southern Queensland and all the southern states, including the larger Bass Strait islands. They are closely related to the freshwater Australian perches (this page).

They are often as little as 3–4 cm in length, and even the largest species reaches no more than 10 cm long. They resemble goldfishes, with small mouths and large body scales.

Males become gaudily coloured when spawning, and in some species the fins turn red or their belly turns orange. They feed on insects and other invertebrates. Most pygmy perch species prefer to live in gently flowing streams with plant growth along the banks.

Balston's perchlet (*Nannatherina balstoni*) is found around Albany in south-west Western Australia. All other pygmy perches belong to the genus *Nannoperca*, of which the most common species is the southern pygmy perch (*N. australis*), known from the Murray and Murrumbidgee river systems, from Flinders and King islands, and from Tasmanian

■ AUSTRALIAN PERCH
Golden perch travel hundreds of kilometres upstream to spawn, their migration apparently triggered by a rise in the water level. This seems to be nature's way of ensuring that eggs are distributed downstream without being washed out to sea.

■ FRESHWATER BLACKFISH
The river blackfish, also known as the marble cod or slimy, is found in cool, slow-flowing streams with abundant overhead cover, and in lakes and dams.

■ ROCK COD
A deep body marked with spots and a large mouth characterise members of the rock cod family. This coral cod (*Cephalopholis miniatus*) is having parasites removed from its mouth by a cleaner shrimp.

rivers that flow into Bass Strait. It is common in streams near Melbourne.

The Ewen pygmy perch (*N. variegata*) is restricted to Ewens Ponds in South Australia and some tributaries of the Glenelg River in western Victoria. A species also restricted in range is the Oxleyan pygmy perch (*N. oxleyana*) from south-eastern Queensland and northern New South Wales. This fish is now rare because stream channelling and forest clearing have destroyed a great many of its habitats.

The Yarra pygmy perch (*N. obscura*) from southern Victoria and eastern South Australia and the Westralian pygmy perch (*N. vittata*) from the south-west of Western Australia are quite common, living in most coastal streams and lakes within their respective ranges.
Family: Nannopercidae

ROCK CODS ■

Rock cods, or gropers, form one of the largest families of marine fishes, with an estimated worldwide total of nearly 400 species. Most of them live primarily in the tropics, and the rest inhabit cooler temperate seas. Many are oval in shape and stout-bodied, but members of this family are extremely diverse in form and habits. They range in size from the colossal Queensland groper (*Epinephelus lanceolatus*), which grows to a length of 2.7 metres and a weight of more than 400 kg, to small basslets that are fully grown at no more than 3–4 cm long.

It is difficult to tell members of this family apart on the basis of a single physical trait. In general, rock cods have a deep, small-scaled body that is often spotted, and a large mouth with three spines on the gill cover. Some species have more than one row of teeth in each jaw and tiny spines on the edges of their cheeks.

Most rock cod species have subtle colour patterns, often in shades of brown or green overlaid with spots, stripes and bars, or with a dappled or marbled effect, but fairy basslets (*Pseudanthias* spp.) are a notable exception. These small inhabitants of Indo-Pacific coral reefs are among the world's most exquisitely coloured fishes, in striking shades of red, purple, pink and yellow.

This large family of fishes can be conveniently split into a number of groups. The most abundant are the true gropers and the fairy basslets. Members of these groups are found around coral and rock reefs. In these habitats, most species occur at depths of 1–40 metres, but some are found at 100–200 metres, and others live as deep as 500 metres. A third group, the soapfishes, are small, inhabitants of caves and ledges.

Most true gropers are more than 20 cm long and lead solitary lives. True gropers and soapfishes mostly frequent hard rocky or coral sea floors, although juveniles sometimes lurk in the cover of seagrass beds, and the adults of a few species prefer sand or mud bottoms. In contrast, fairy basslets are 3–15 cm long, and swim in large schools well above the bottom.

With the exception of fairy basslets, which feed for the most part on current-borne animal plankton, all members of this family are ambush predators, constituting one of the major predatory groups of coral reef communities. These fishes capture prey by hiding until an unwary victim passes and then rushing forward at tremendous speed to grab their target with a quick snap of the jaws.

Many of the larger groper species feed on relatively large fishes. Smaller gropers feed on a variety of crustaceans, particularly crabs and prawns, as well as smaller fishes. The large head and mouth of most species of groper enable them to engulf their prey in a large volume of water in less than a second. They seize the victim with their numerous inward-slanting teeth and thus prevent its escape.

Some gropers follow moray eels and other large foraging fishes in order to pounce on the small fishes and crustaceans that the eels accidentally frighten from their hiding places in their search for food.

Small gropers and fairy basslets are the prey of a large number of larger fishes, such as snappers and other gropers. However, the soapfishes, as their common name suggests, have evolved an ingenious mechanism to discourage their enemies – most predators instantly

■ ROCK COD
The potato cod, or potato groper (*Epinephelus tukula*), is among the largest of the reef fishes. This specimen is considerably bigger than its accompanying white-tip reef sharks.

NEW DISCOVERIES

Australia's tally of more than 3000 fish species is still growing; few other places in the world approach this number. New species are discovered by scuba-diving scientists, mainly on northern coral reefs, and by experimental vessels, and there have been a number of freshwater finds. Some are species previously unknown in Australian seas, but the most exciting are species that have never been collected anywhere else.

New discoveries are often small fishes that spend most of their time hiding in cracks and crevices. A surprising recent discovery was the red-finned blue eye, *Scaturiginichthys vermeilipinnis*, shown below, which was found in 1990 living in spring-fed puddles in a paddock in central Queensland.

release them after tasting the bitter, toxic mucus that covers their bodies.

Many gropers are sequential hermaphrodites – that is, their growth triggers sex changes (see box, 'Gender benders', p. 470). Specimens under a certain size are female, but once they reach that size they change into males. Fairy basslets have a harem-like social structure, with the largest, most socially dominant fish being a male. If this fish is killed by a predator or removed for experimental purposes, the most dominant female becomes a male. According to research, carried out mainly in the Caribbean, most gropers gather to spawn from early spring to early summer, but there is considerable variation according to locality.

Large gropers may live for 30 years or more, and it is believed that mature Queensland gropers may live for well over 50 years. These large, fleshy fishes are highly coveted for food. They have few enemies other than humans.
Family: Serranidae

DOTTYBACKS AND EEL BLENNIES ■

These fishes mainly inhabit the coral reefs of northern Australia and the Indo-Pacific. Some of the most brilliantly coloured of all fishes belong

to this family. They are shy species, and seldom stray far from cover.

Most resemble miniature gropers and rarely exceed 10 cm in length, but eel blennies have an eel-like body and may grow to 45 cm long.
Family: Pseudochromidae

LONGFINS ■

Longfins are a relatively small Indo-Pacific family that consists mostly of tropical fishes. All seven longfin genera are represented in Australian waters by 17 of the 25 known species, including a number that live in temperate waters.

Further taxonomic studies could result in several groups of longfins being placed in subfamilies. The largest such group comprises longfins (*Plesiops* spp.), blue devils (*Paraplesiops* spp.) and comets (*Calloplesiops* spp.). Longfin species generally live secretively in reefs – either alone, in pairs, or in small, loose groups – feeding on invertebrates that dwell on the sea bottom. These fishes deposit their eggs in crevices, and then either the male or both parents undertake guard duty to deter predators.

The eastern blue devil (*Paraplesiops bleekeri*) is a reef fish that grows to a maximum of 40 cm long. This species typically lives beneath rocky ledges, where the adults erect their fins in order to display their broadly banded black and white bodies and yellow and turquoise markings. The eastern blue devil is sometimes found in rocky estuaries but prefers clear water around reefs. Its range extends from southern Queensland to Montague Island off the southern New South Wales coast.

The southern blue devil (*P. meleagris*) is found around the southern coast. It lacks the yellow colouring and banded pattern of the eastern blue devil, but is a brilliant turquoise with subtle markings.

The comet (*Calloplesiops altivelis*) is black with small white spots all over

its body and fins. Its common name comes from its long, trailing dorsal, tail and anal fins, which reach a length of about 16 cm, making the fish look considerably larger than it really is. This tropical species shelters at the back of ledges and caves in coastal to inner reef habitats.

Hulafishes (*Trachinops* spp.) are small, long and slender. Found in temperate Australian waters, they feed on plankton, and usually form schools near rocky reefs. Hulafishes live in current-prone areas where fresh supplies of plankton are regularly available. They deposit their eggs in narrow crevices, and the male protects them by wrapping his body around the egg cluster.

The eastern hulafish (*Trachinops taeniatus*) grows to 10–15 cm in length. It features longitudinal yellow and red splashes and stripes on a black background, and it has a white belly. This species is common in the waters of New South Wales, usually forming large schools on coastal reefs.

The most distinctive group of longfins are the scissortails (*Assessor* spp.). Males brood their young in their mouth – a highly specialised behaviour that suggests that they may belong in a separate family.

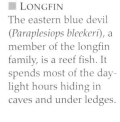

■ LONGFIN
The eastern blue devil (*Paraplesiops bleekeri*), a member of the longfin family, is a reef fish. It spends most of the daylight hours hiding in caves and under ledges.

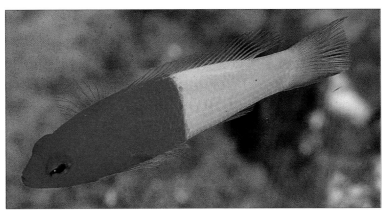

■ DOTTYBACK
Dottybacks are retiring but vividly coloured inhabitants of coral reefs. This little fish is the royal or bicolour dottyback, *Pseudochromis paccagnellae*.

The yellow scissortail (*Assessor flavissimus*) is brilliant yellow and grows to 6 cm in length. It has a large, scissor-like tail. Living around tropical reefs in northern Queensland and in the waters of Papua New Guinea, yellow scissortails swim in small schools along the gutters of inner reefs and upside down near the ceilings of caves.

The blue scissortail (*A. macneilli*) is dark blue and ranges to the southern edge of the Great Barrier Reef.
Family: Plesiopidae

■ PEARL PERCH
The West Australian jewfish, the largest of the pearl perches, lives in the southern waters of Western Australia.

PEARL PERCHES ■

The pearl perch, *Glaucosoma scapulare*, from eastern Australian waters is closely related to two species from western waters: the deepsea jewfish, *G. buergeri*, and the West Australian jewfish, *G. hebraicum*. (Confusingly, 'jewfish', sometimes spelt 'dhufish', is also the common name of the family Sciaenidae; see page 456.)

This group of fishes have robust, rather deep bodies and look very like some members of the rock cod family (page 442). Generally a silvery grey, they sometimes have a more dusky coloration. They frequently have a dark, curved band passing through the eye and across the cheek, but this is often faint in adults. The pearl perch has a

prominent, silvery black blotch behind the head which the other two species lack, while a black coloration on the inside of its mouth distinguishes the deepsea jewfish from the other two species.

The largest of the three is the West Australian jewfish, which lives in the southern waters of Western Australia and grows to about 1.2 metres in length. The deepsea jewfish of northern Western Australia and the pearl perch are usually less than half this size.

These large-mouthed species feed on smaller fishes, octopuses and prawns. While it prefers deeper off-shore reefs, the West Australian jewfish migrates seasonally to nearshore reefs, and divers frequently see individuals in caves and under ledges at depths of 10–30 metres. Similarly, the pearl perch, which is more of a schooling fish, sometimes moves into shallow areas during the day, returning to deeper waters at night. The deepsea jewfish remains constantly at depths of 50–200 metres.
Family: Glaucosomatidae

GRUNTERS ■

Grunters are oval, somewhat stout fishes that live in marine, brackish and fresh waters. They are called grunters because they use their swim bladders to produce peculiar grunting sounds. There are about 45 species in the family; except for a dozen primarily marine species living in shallow coastal waters in tropical areas, all are confined to the freshwater environments of northern Australia and nearby New Guinea. These freshwater species no doubt evolved from marine ancestors, and a fossil that was found in Queensland indicates the family has been present in Australia for at least 30 million years.

Colours vary from overall silver to drab shades of black and brown, although some species are marked with distinctive spots, bars or stripes. The dorsal fin is usually notched and the front portion incorporates strong spines. Grunters are generally 12–45 cm long. The silvery white crescent perch (*Terapon jarbua*), with its bold brown to blackish horizontal stripes, grows to a maximum of 30 cm long and inhabits estuaries, river mouths and the lower reaches of streams. The inland habitats of

most other Australian species range from lakes and quiet, lowland creeks to swift-flowing mountain streams. Most stream-dwelling species prefer deep rocky pools, often below rapids or waterfalls.

The larger species – for example the 45 cm-long sooty grunter, *Hephaestus fuliginosus* – are generally carnivorous, feeding on aquatic insects and their larvae, crustaceans, molluscs, fishes and frogs. Some species also eat algae and the floating seeds, leaves, fruits and flowers of terrestrial plants.

Grunters lay their eggs on gravel bottoms, where the eggs sink into the crevices out of the reach of predators. The young hatch after three to four days. Baby grunters are attractive, but older juveniles and adults have aggressive natures and voracious appetites.
Family: Terapontidae

BANJOFISHES

This small Indo-Pacific family, which consists of only a few species, lives mainly in northern Australian coastal waters. Banjofishes live in the turbid waters above sandy sediments, and so are rarely seen. One species, the banjofish *Banjos banjos*, occurs from the Abrolhos Islands, Western Australia, northwards. It grows to about 30 cm in length.
Family: Banjosidae

FLAGTAILS

Flagtails are active fishes that swim just above the bottom. They are laterally compressed, reaching about 20 cm in length. They are strong swimmers and this, together with their stream-lined shape, enables them to live in turbulent waters that are subject to waves and strong currents. Flagtails are generally silver, and separate species look very similar except for their tails, which are distinctively marked with dark margins, blotches or stripes.

Flagtails feed on crabs, prawns and small fishes. Freshwater species, such as the jungle perch (*Kuhlia rupestris*), which inhabits fast-flowing rainforest streams, also eat insects and their aquatic larvae. Marine species, such as the fiveband flagtail (*K. mugil*), form large aggregations in the wave zone or in tidal pools along rocky shores. The fiveband flagtail, which is marked by blackish bands on its tail, inhabits coastal shallows and rock pools on the eastern coast of Australia from Cape York in Queensland south to Seal Rocks in New South Wales.
Family: Kuhliidae

■ GRUNTER
The coal grunter, *Hephaestus carbo*, is found in streams in the Northern Territory.

REDFIN PERCH ■

The redfin perch (*Perca fluviatilis*) is the only member of the northern hemisphere freshwater perch family in Australia. It was introduced in Tasmania in 1862 for angling, but a release in Victoria in 1868 is thought to be the source of populations now living in dams, lakes and rivers from the Murray–Darling river system to western Victoria, and in south-west Western Australia.

Redfins commonly grow to 0.5–2 kg, but may reach 60 cm in length and 10 kg in weight. They prefer cool, still or slow-flowing waters with plenty of aquatic plants, and feed on crustaceans, worms, insect larvae and small fishes.

Mature at between one and three years old, these fishes are prolific breeders, spawning at night in late winter and spring and laying over 100 000 eggs in a gelatinous mass up to 3 metres long. The juveniles grow rapidly, and may reach 11 cm by the end of their first year.

Redfin perch compete with native fish species and trout, particularly in dams, and have been blamed for the decline of trout populations.
Family: Percidae

BIGEYES ■

This small tropical family comprises about 17 species, at least eight of which occur in Australian waters. As their name suggests, bigeyes have very large eyes. Most species grow to about 35 cm long. They are mainly nocturnal, but divers often notice them in caves or along ledges during the day. Occasionally they form schools and hover above reefs. At night bigeyes move to open water where they feed on animal plankton, shrimps, young squids and larval fishes. Despite their large mouths, they prefer to filter small prey from the water through their gill rakers, which act like fine-toothed combs.

The crescent-tail bigeye (*Priacanthus hamrur*) is widespread and common throughout the tropical Indo-Pacific, and is the most observed big-eye species in Australian waters. It lives in the sheltered parts of reefs, and is easily distinguished from similar species by its distinctive crescent-shaped tail. The similar glasseye (*P. blochii*) is also common, but it lives in coastal areas and is often found in turbulent waters.

The blotched bigeye (*Heteropri-acanthus cruentatus*) is widespread and known from all tropical seas. At night it enters shallow depths and floats, almost motionless, above reefs looking for prey. It is deeper-bodied than other bigeye species and has a distinctive blotched pattern on its body.

The spotted bigeye (*Priacanthus macracanthus*) somewhat resembles the blotched bigeye, but is more slender and has distinctive spots on its dorsal and anal fins. It also grows

■ REDFIN PERCH
Native to Europe, this fish was introduced into Australia in the nineteenth century. In enclosed waters redfins often overpopulate, so that the young become stunted through lack of food.

larger, reaching 46 cm in length. The adults usually live in deep water and are rarely seen.
Family: Priacanthidae

NURSERYFISHES
Pearly white to bronze brown, these fragile-looking fishes inhabit the coastal marine and brackish waters of northern Australia and Papua New Guinea. Nurseryfishes are usually about 30–40 cm in length, but they can grow to 60 cm long. They have a deep, humped body, a large mouth and a forked tail fin, and males have a hook on the nape, in front of the dorsal fin. This hook is the clue to their name: the male carries bunches of eggs twisted around it until they hatch. Egg-carrying males have been found in nearly fresh water in the Northern Territory and in freshwater billabongs of rivers flowing into the Gulf of Carpentaria.

Little is known about the lifecycle of these fishes – they are difficult to observe in the wild, since they live in the turbid coastal rivers of northern Australia where saltwater crocodiles are common. They eat mainly small fishes and prawns.

Several aquariums are trying to breed nurseryfishes to find out more about their behaviour – for example, how the egg bunches become twisted around the male's hook.
Family: Kurtidae

■ BIGEYE
The blotched bigeye, *Heteropriacanthus cruentatus*, lives in all tropical seas. During the day it is usually found deep in caves, but at night it moves to open water to feed. The large eyes of the members of this family give them enhanced vision for their nocturnal activities.

CARDINALFISHES ■

Cardinalfishes are dominant members of the coral reef fish community, but most species are inconspicuous due to their nocturnal habits and small size – they are usually less than 10 cm long. Only scuba divers who visit reef areas after dark are in a position to fully appreciate their abundance and diversity.

Typically, these fishes have relatively large eyes, two separate dorsal fins (the first with six to eight spines), two anal spines, and a moderately large mouth. Their common name is derived from the red coloration of so many species, but these fishes also come in shades of black, brown, yellow and white. In addition, some cardinalfish species are translucent, so that their backbone and internal organs are visible.

The family occurs worldwide in tropical and temperate seas, but about two-thirds of the estimated 250 species inhabit shallow coral reefs and surrounding habitats in the Indian and western Pacific oceans. Nearly a hundred species have been recorded from Australian seas, which boast the world's largest total. Seven species of *Glossamia* –

■ CARDINALFISH
The reef habitat of this tiny transparent cardinalfish (*Apogon* sp.) is clearly visible through the fish's muscular tissue.

commonly known as 'mouth almighty' because of their huge mouth – are found in fresh water, sometimes several hundred kilometres from the sea, and all of them are restricted to northern Australia and southern New Guinea.

Cardinalfishes are found in many different types of habitat, but each species occupies a relatively narrow ecological zone. For example, some live in mangrove areas, others prefer sandy lagoons, and many inhabit the caves and crevices of outer reef slopes. At dusk they emerge from these retreats to feed. Their diet is variable but most consume animal plankton, such as copepods, and small bottom-dwelling invertebrates, such as crabs and prawns.

About a dozen species of cardinalfishes from the tropical Indo-Pacific live in association with poisonous long-spined sea urchins. During the day the fishes swim close to their urchin hosts, retreating deep into the spines when danger threatens. Another variation on this theme is seen in members of the genus *Siphamia*, which sometimes live among the spines of the crown-of-thorns sea star.

Cardinalfishes brood their eggs in their mouth, although some do this only when the eggs are in danger, and they lavish an unusual degree of parental care upon their young. While courting, prospective mates engage in chasing bouts, interrupted by periods of hovering, during which they rapidly flick their dorsal and pelvic fins back and forth. After the female has released the eggs and the male has fertilised them, the male sucks the egg cluster into his mouth in order to incubate them. (see box, 'Protective papas').

Once hatched, the larvae of most cardinalfishes swim around in the open water and are carried by ocean currents until eventually they settle on new reefs, sometimes tens or even hundreds of kilometres away from their hatching ground.

Recent scientific investigations reveal that the male Banggai cardinalfish (*Pterapogon kauderni*) from Indonesia retains the larvae in his mouth until they are large enough to venture out without the risk of being eaten by predators. The young then settle in among the spines of nearby poisonous sea urchins. Because these fishes are well protected in their youth, the Banggai cardinalfish lays only about 15–20 eggs at a time.

The cardinalfish's practice of protecting the young by holding them in the mouth is unique among marine fishes, although it is common among cichlids (page 461) and a few other freshwater fishes.
Family: Apogonidae

■ CARDINALFISHES
Cardinalfishes, such as these ring-tailed cardinalfishes (*Apogon aureus*), are mainly found around coral reefs.

PROTECTIVE PAPAS

A number of fish families care for their young, including catfishes, pipefishes, sea horses and cardinalfishes.

Parental care in fishes bestows considerable evolutionary advantage. The females of most fish species produce vast numbers of eggs to ensure that at least some survive the vagaries of the environment and predators. In contrast, fishes that use parental care produce fewer but larger eggs, because their guardianship of the eggs ensures high survival rates.

During spawning the female cardinalfish releases a mass of several hundred eggs. After fertilisation, the male sucks up the eggs and incubates them in his mouth. Males that are brooding eggs can be identified by their swollen throat, and the eggs are visible when the mouth is partly open, as can be seen in this photograph of a ring-tailed cardinalfish (*Apogon aureus*). During the incubation period of several days, the brooding male forgoes food.

LONG-FINNED PIKE ▦

The long-finned pike, *Dinolestes lewini*, is the sole representative of its family. Although considered a close relative of the cardinalfishes, the long-finned pike is not nocturnal, nor does it live, as cardinalfishes do, on small pelagic or planktonic prey. Instead, it has a javelin-shaped body and impressive sabre-like teeth that make it a successful predator of schooling fishes and shrimps.

Long-finned pike are restricted to the southern Australian waters where they developed their body form, perhaps in response to the absence of competition from local barracuda representatives. They are often found in enormous schools over reefs close to the coast and inside bays. They grow to about 90 cm long.
Family: Dinolestidae

WHITINGS ▦

Whitings are slender fishes with pointed snouts. In countries throughout the Indian and Western Pacific oceans they are commonly referred to as sandborers because they burrow quickly into the sand when there is the slightest threat. The family is represented in Australian waters by 12 of the 31 species currently recognised.

Schools of whiting favour sand bars or gutters in shallow waters, and open bays with sandy or silty bottoms. They do not live on coral or rocky reefs, although they will inhabit sandy coral lagoons. They dig in the soft sea floor for small crustaceans, beach hoppers and juvenile crabs. On more silty ground, their diet consists mainly of marine worms.

The large spotted whiting, or King George whiting (*Sillaginodes punctata*), which reaches 72 cm in length and almost 5 kg in weight, and the trumpeter whiting (*Sillago maculata*) frequent the seagrass beds of temperate shores. Other species, such as the poddy whiting (*S. bassensis*) and the sand whiting (*S. ciliata*), inhabit the surf zone. The rough-scaled whiting or yellow-finned whiting (*S. analis*) and the yellowfin whiting or western sand whiting (*S. schomburgkii*) live in estuaries and occasionally enter fresh water for brief periods. Most whitings live in shallow coastal waters, but the adult trumpeter whiting and the mud whiting (*S. lutea*) feed on the silty or muddy bottoms of more open water and are commonly found at depths of about 180 metres.

Nearly all whitings have highly sophisticated sensory equipment that they use to locate prey buried in sand and to 'hear' any disturbance in their vicinity. Scientists think that subtle vibrations emitted by buried organisms are picked up by the thin membrane of a closed tube that extends from the swim bladder to the rear end of the fish just before the anus, and that these vibrations are then conveyed to the whiting's swim bladder, which may consist of several elaborate echo chambers. These amplify sound and send it on to auditory capsules on each side of the fish's bony skull.

The King George whiting has no such tube and swim bladder, since this species is exceptional and feeds on small fishes and crustaceans in the open sea, not in sand.

Whitings usually trail the small, slender, soft first ray of their pelvic fins over the sea bottom to maintain contact with the sand. In the club-foot whiting (*S. chondropus*), this first ray has become thickened to form a sled-like runner that remains in firm contact with the bottom.
Family: Sillaginidae

TILEFISHES

Tilefishes live on the soft sea bottom in coastal waters throughout the tropical and subtropical regions of the world's oceans. Their elongated bodies and correspondingly elongated dorsal and anal fins are suited to sheltering in burrows or hovering above them in search of food.

The black-striped blue blanquillo, *Malacanthus latovittatus*, reaches 40 cm in length. It generally inhabits quite shallow waters, often burrowing among rubble at the base of coral reef slopes and feeding on plankton. Larger tilefishes, which are placed by some zoologists in a separate family, have a deeper and more flattened body. The six tilefish species known from Australian waters are all found at depths of 100–300 metres.
Family: Malacanthidae

FALSE TREVALLY

The false trevally, or milk trevally (*Lactarius lactarius*), is the sole representative of its family. It is a pelagic, inshore inhabitant of the tropical Indian and western Pacific oceans, where it is both common and commercially important, though less so in Australian waters. It resembles true trevallies (page 449), but it is distinguished from them by the deep base of its tail, by its mostly straight lateral line, and by anal fin spines that are attached to the rest of the fin by a membrane.
Family: Lactariidae

▦ LONG-FINNED PIKE
This fish resembles a barracuda with a long-based anal fin. Although they evolved from different ancestors, these two species have developed similar specialised characteristics to suit their similar lifestyles.

▦ WHITING
Whitings have a pouting mouth that is perfectly designed for grubbing up crabs, shellfish, crustaceans and worms from the soft sea floor. This is a sand whiting (*Sillago ciliata*), a species found in the surf zone.

TAILOR ■

Pomatomus saltatrix, a species known in Australia as tailor, is found around the world in coastal waters in cool tropical and warm temperate latitudes. This streamlined, powerful fish has a low first dorsal fin supported by spines that can be lowered into a groove on its back, and a longer-based second dorsal fin of similar size and shape to the anal fin beneath. A bluish cast across the back, which helps to conceal this surface-dwelling fish from sea birds, gives the species its American common name, bluefish.

Its Australian name comes from its shear-like jaws, which have opposing serrated edges formed from close-set, triangular teeth. The tailor uses these to slice neat plugs of flesh from its prey or to chop up smaller fishes. There are stories of tailors tearing into dense schools of small fishes and then regurgitating what they have eaten when their stomachs can hold no more, but such events probably take place only when food is extremely plentiful.

Individual specimens are most often encountered along surf lines and off rocky points, pursuing schools of pilchards or grey mullet. They are usually 30–60 cm long, but they can reach a maximum of 1.2 metres in length and 14 kg in weight. At this formidable size these fishes can be hazardous to bathers, especially in areas of reduced visibility, where pale human skin might be

mistaken for a frightened mullet in the froth of waves. Attacks on swimmers have been reported in surf off Miami Beach in Florida.

In eastern Australia, the presence of large concentrations of tailor larvae in the coastal waters of southern Queensland during the spring months indicates that spawning takes place in areas such as Fraser Island, where the species congregates. Its pelagic eggs and larvae are then carried down the coast by the southern-moving Eastern Australian Current. Larval settlement occurs in estuaries as far south as southern New South Wales, where the voracious young fishes devour crustaceans, squids and other fishes. Juveniles grow rapidly and mature at about two years when they are around 30 cm long. In late winter and early spring, Australian tailors migrate northward with their prey.

■ TAILOR
In Australia, *Pomatomus saltatrix* is known as tailor because it has jaws that scissor smaller fishes to pieces.

Despite the species' extensive and greatly disrupted distribution, it is believed to be the sole representative of its family. Nevertheless, recent research shows that isolated populations, such as those on Australia's eastern and western coasts, have recognisable differences.

Commercial and recreational fishing must be managed to protect these populations from overfishing.
Family: Pomatomidae

COBIAS ■

This family contains only one species, the migratory *Rachycentron canadum*, which inhabits all tropical seas except the central and eastern Pacific Ocean.

Also known as the black kingfish and the crab-eater, the cobia is a large pelagic fish, reaching at least 2 metres in length and almost 70 kg in weight. It has brown and silver longitudinal stripes that are visible when it leaps from the water. The cobia is very similar in appearance to remoras, to which it is related, but instead of a sucking disc it has a row of short dorsal fin spines from its nape to the base of its soft dorsal fin.

In Australia, the cobia is found from about Shark Bay in Western Australia around the northern coast to at least as far as Jervis Bay on the southern coast of New South Wales. Juveniles occur singly on coastal reefs, but large adults usually swim in small groups, sometimes in coastal waters as shallow as 2–3 metres. Cobias mainly eat crustaceans, but also consume other invertebrates and fishes.

These fishes spawn in the summer, the large females producing millions of eggs. Females grow faster than males and reach a larger size.
Family: Rachycentridae

■ COBIA
This large fish is found around coastal reefs, where it sometimes leaps from the water. Adults tend to swim in groups of three to six.

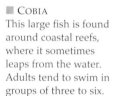

REMORAS ◼

These fishes have streamlined, elongated bodies with flattened heads, protruding lower jaws and low dorsal and anal fins. Like cobias, they have brown and white longitudinal stripes. Worldwide there are eight species, and all but one have been recorded from Australian seas.

Remoras are also called diskfish, sucker fish and lousefish. They live in the tropical and temperate waters of the open ocean, usually attached by large oval sucking discs on the tops of their heads to sharks, rays, billfishes, other large fishes, sea turtles, porpoises, dolphins and whales.

This unique feature is a modified first dorsal fin consisting of a series of transverse movable plates, called laminae, and a fleshy margin. The remora swims alongside a fish, puts its disc against the fish's body and creates a partial vacuum by operating the laminae like the slats of a Venetian blind. This provides enough suction for the remora to adhere to its host. To detach itself, the remora simply works the laminae in reverse.

As larvae, remoras are planktonic and grow into free-swimming juveniles; they do not become 'passengers' until they are 4–8 cm long. Some remoras are host-specific, attaching themselves to certain animals rather than to others. They may change hosts as they grow, larger remoras choosing larger hosts.

Free-swimming remoras feed on plankton, tiny crustaceans and small fishes, but once they have attached themselves to a host, they live on the host's skin parasites and food remnants. Remoras do not have a swim bladder, and, because moving through the water requires so little effort for them, they have fewer red blood cells than most fishes.

At a metre long, the slender suckerfish, *Echeneis naucrates*, is the largest remora in Australian waters. It has worldwide tropical and subtropical distribution; in Australia it ranges from Busselton in southern Western Australia to Port Hacking in central New South Wales. The lousefish (*Phtheirichthys lineatus*) inhabits coastal waters from the Great Barrier Reef to Sydney. The whalesucker (*Remora australis*) is a temperate species that is found in the waters off South Australia and south-west Western Australia. As its common name suggests, its favoured hosts are whales and porpoises, but one specimen found at Port Adelaide was attached to a ship that had arrived from overseas.
Family: Echeneididae

JACKS AND TREVALLIES ◼

Jacks and trevallies are generically known as carangids. This marine group has a worldwide distribution in tropical to temperate waters. Of around 140 species, 63 have been recorded from Australia.

Adults are pelagic and tend to have the silvery coloration that has evolved widely in fishes with this lifestyle. They often occur in large schools and are fast swimmers with streamlined, laterally compressed bodies. They have a slender tail base and their tail fin is strongly forked.

Their maximum adult size varies widely. One of the smallest species in Australian waters is the southern mackerel scad, *Decapterus muroadsi*, which lives down the eastern coast as far as southern New South Wales. It grows to 20 cm long. At the other end of the spectrum are the giant trevally, *Caranx ignobilis*, which can reach 1.7 metres in length and 62 kg in weight, and the amberjack, *Seriola dumerili*, which can reach 2 metres in length and 80 kg in weight.

Carangids are carnivorous, smaller species feeding on animal plankton and larger species preying on other fishes, molluscs and crustaceans. The pilot fish, *Naucrates ductor*, which grows to about 70 cm long and is found in coastal waters around Australia, lives on scraps of prey caught by larger predators. Pilot fishes often swim alongside sharks, whales, turtles and even ships, waiting to scavenge a meal.

Carangids release their spawn into the water, producing huge numbers of tiny, buoyant, planktonic eggs from which pelagic larvae develop. Floating on ocean currents, larvae and juveniles can be transported over great distances. This accounts for the wide distributions of many species. The larvae and juveniles of some species are commonly swept up into estuaries and can survive in brackish or even fresh water.

Adults typically range over wide areas, and many species migrate great distances each year, returning seasonally to particular locations.

Carangids are renowned both as game fishes and for food. However, *Caranx* species have been linked to poisoning (see box, 'Ciguatera poisoning', p. 450), and yellowtail kingfish (*Seriola lalandi*) from the southern coast of Queensland can be infested with a parasite.
Family: Carangidae

DOLPHINFISHES

The family contains two species: the dolphinfish (*Coryphaena hippurus*) and the pompano dolphinfish (*C. equiselis*). They are similar in

◼ TREVALLIES
Trevallies are powerful swimmers and tend to occur in large schools. Shown here is a school of big-eye trevally, *Caranx sexfasciatus*.

◼ REMORA
This slender suckerfish (left) has attached itself to a Queensland groper. Remoras have a modified first dorsal fin (above), with which they adhere to a host. They feed on the host's skin parasites and leftover food scraps.

CIGUATERA POISONING

Ciguatera is a form of fish poisoning. Fortunately, its incidence in Australia is relatively low, with only 920 cases recorded in Queensland between 1965 and 1992.

People who eat fishes containing this toxin may experience various symptoms. If the fish is only slightly toxic, the victim feels weak and may suffer diarrhoea. More severe poisonings may cause tingling sensations in the palms or soles. Nausea, joint pain, severe itching, extreme weakness, and confusion of the sensations of hot and cold are also common. In extreme cases, there is paralysis, coma, and respiratory or heart failure.

The agent that causes this toxin is a tiny protozoan that lives on seaweed, algae and dead coral. The toxin accumulates in the food web and large predatory fishes may be very toxic.

Because of ciguatera, it is illegal to sell the following snappers in Australia: chinaman fish (*Symphorus nematophorus*), paddletail (*Lutjanus gibbus*) and red bass (*L. bohar*).

paddletail

chinaman fish

red bass

shape, but pompano dolphinfishes are much smaller than dolphinfishes – maximum length 50 cm, compared with 2 metres – and have fewer scales along the lateral line.

Dolphinfishes have an elongated body tapering towards a deeply forked tail and a long dorsal fin extending backwards from the head. They have a green-blue back grading into a golden belly, an electric blue dorsal fin, and yellow to orange lower fins. They live near the surface of tropical and subtropical oceans, larger species sometimes entering inshore waters and passing along Australia's southern coast.

They often school in small groups close to drifting objects, such as offshore yachts. Their diet consists mainly of pelagic fishes, such as flyingfishes and garfishes, and they can track flyingfishes and catch them as they re-enter the sea.
Family: Coryphaenidae

■ STRIPED PONYFISH
The striped ponyfish *Leiognathus fasciatus* has a downward pointing mouth, feeding on bristleworms, small fish and small crustaceans. It occurs in Australia in tropical coastal waters.

PONYFISHES

Ponyfishes inhabit the tropical and subtropical waters of the Indo-Pacific and the western Pacific from East Africa to Tahiti. They generally live in coastal marine waters, but some species enter estuaries where the water is brackish, and they may also move into rivers for short periods. In Australian waters they occur between Shark Bay in Western Australia around the northern coast to as far south as Sydney at depths of 10–170 metres. Ponyfishes are also known as slipmouths, slimies, dollarfish and silverbellies.

Of a total of around 25 ponyfish species throughout the world, about 17 are found in Australian waters. They are small, laterally compressed fishes that grow to no more than 20 cm long. Their bodies are silvery and slimy, and are covered in small scales. There are bony ridges on the top of their head and their fin spines are weak. Many species live for no more than about a year.

Ponyfishes can extend their mouth either forward, down or up, depending on the species' food preferences. They produce bioluminescence in their throats, which is projected through their belly. This 'living light' is strong enough to read by at close quarters. Ponyfishes can vary the amount of light they emit in order to confuse predators and, since the light-producing organ in males is considerably larger than in females, it is presumably used as a sexual attractant as well.
Family: Leiognathidae

MOONFISHES ■

Mene maculata, the single member of this family, is found in Australian tropical and subtropical waters. Growing to 30 cm long, it is a silvery fish with brown spots on its back. It

has a small mouth and an oval body, and the first ray of its pelvic fin is very long. Scientists know little about the moonfish's life history.
Family: Menidae

■ EASTERN AUSTRALIAN SALMON
This Australian salmon, *Arripus trutta*, can grow up to 89 cm long. They can swim in reef water that is barely deep enough to cover their body.

POMFRETS ■

Pomfrets are among the most abundant and widespread large pelagic fishes. Adults vary in length from less than 10 cm long to more than a metre; most species are mature at a length of 30–70 cm and a weight of less than 10 kg, but they may reach as much as 45 kg in weight.

Members of this family change dramatically in body form and fin shape as they grow, resulting in juveniles being taken for separate species from fully grown specimens.

Pomfrets are pelagic in all oceans but seldom venture inshore. They prefer to live near the surface, where

they are the dominant mid-level predators of this zone, eating small crustaceans, squids, and small fishes such as lanternfishes. They are, in turn, prey for billfishes and tunas.
Family: Bramidae

AUSTRALIAN SALMONS

This family of fishes is found only in Australia and New Zealand. Australian salmons are not true salmons or herrings; they were so named by early English explorers because their shape is similar to that of European salmons and herrings. They feed on both plankton and small pelagic fishes.

The eastern Australian salmon (*Arripis trutta*) and the western Australian salmon (*A. truttaceus*) have sleek, torpedo-shaped bodies with large, powerful, forked tail fins. The eastern species has been recorded at 89 cm long and the western species at 96 cm long. They are both silvery grey in colour – though they may vary from greyish green to steely blue – and their bodies are often spotted yellow or brown.

Australian salmons spawn at sea, taking advantage of currents to spread their eggs and young far and wide. Before spawning, adults migrate upcurrent to ensure that the flow will return some of the juveniles to the adults' normal haunts.

The spawning runs of the eastern Australian salmon take place in summer to coincide with the south-flowing East Australian Current. Salmon come from eastern Victoria and Tasmania, moving north to about Sydney. After spawning, the schools break up and the fishes return to more southerly waters.

The western Australian salmon migrates westward and northward in autumn to just north of Perth. Some schools start their journey from as far east as Tasmania, moving around the south-western corner of the continent and then north. After spawning they head back south.

During their spawning runs Australian salmons swim swiftly in tightly knit schools, occasionally resting near prominent headlands. They are nervous, and schools are easily scattered by disturbances.

For many years *Arripis trutta* and *A. truttaceus* were thought to be the only two species of Australian salmon, but in 1993 a species was described from Norfolk Island, Lord Howe Island and New Zealand, and was named the northern salmon (*A. xylabion*).

The fourth member of the family is the tommy rough. This species of fish (*Arripis georgianus*) is a smaller relative of Australian salmons, growing to about 40 cm long. It is found along the southern Australian coastline and is abundant in South Australia and Western Australia. It is similar in colour to the salmons, but its forked tail fin has two prominent black tips.
Family: Arripidae

BONNETMOUTHS ■

Bonnetmouths, or rovers, were once thought to be a diverse group of cylindrical, plankton-feeding fishes with widely opening mouths, but recent studies have shown that many of these fishes are specialised offshoots of the snappers, sweetlips and sea breams (families Lutjanidae, Haemulidae and Sparidae). In fact some scientists apply the common name bonnetmouth only to a specialised line of sweetlips (page 453).

What sets members of the family Emmelichthyidae apart from the members of the other three families is their expanded maxilla – the bone at the rear of their upper jaw. In the bonnetmouths this bone is covered with scales and does not slide beneath the bone forming the rim below and in front of the eye.

At present, at least two of the ten species placed in the family Emmelichthyidae are found in Australian waters. Both occur in open waters off southern coasts at depths of 30–500 metres.

The redbait, *Emmelichthys nitidus*, is recognisable by its slender body and the gap between the spiny and soft portions of its dorsal fin; in the more deeply-bodied rubyfish, *Plagiogeneion macrolepis*, the dorsal fin is continuous, despite its deep notch.

Both species grow to little more than 30 cm long. They are an important source of food for predatory fishes and sea birds.
Family: Emmelichthyidae

SNAPPERS ■

About a hundred members of the family Lutjanidae are distributed throughout tropical seas, but most inhabit the Indo-Pacific region. Australian waters harbour about 45 species, among the best known being the saddle-tail snapper (*Lutjanus malabaricus*), the red snapper (*L. erythropterus*), the red emperor (*L. sebae*) and the mangrove jack (*L. argentimaculatus*). These species are common in northern waters.

The members of this family are sometimes called sea perches to avoid confusion with another species also known as snapper (*Chrysophrys aurata*, page 454). This species, a popular eating fish across southern Australia, is not a true snapper but a sea bream.

Many snapper species have a characteristic shovel-headed appearance and sharp canine teeth. Snappers are one of the main groups of predatory

■ BONNETMOUTH
Bonnetmouths can be identified by their expanded maxilla – the bone forming the rear portion of the upper jaw. The species illustrated here is a rubyfish, *Plagiogeneion macrolepis*.

■ SNAPPERS
The hussar (*Lutjanus amabilis*) is one of the smaller snappers. It is found on reefs along the Queensland coast.

fishes on coral reefs and in deeper areas of the continental shelf. They feed mainly at night on a variety of prey; other fishes dominate the diet of most species, but they also feed on crabs, shrimps, molluscs, octopuses, squids and animal plankton.

Snorkellers on the Great Barrier Reef are able to see quite a variety of snappers. Large numbers of blackspot sea perch (*Lutjanus fulviflamma*) frequently congregate under jetties or around boat moorings. Other species include the colourful paddletail (*L. gibbus*) and red bass (*L. bohar*); the latter may grow to 75 cm long. Both species are frequently caught by anglers, but are not recommended for eating as they are frequently implicated in cases of fish poisoning (see box, 'Ciguatera poisoning', page 450).

The saddle-tail and the red snapper are common on the continental shelf at a depth of about 100 metres, and are important species targeted by commercial trawlers off the northern coast of Western Australia. Scientific studies have revealed that in the 1960s and early 1970s these species made up 20–30 per cent of all fishes on the North-West Shelf, but that this declined to less than 10 per cent after the area was intensively fished by Taiwanese trawlers.

The red emperor grows to more than a metre in length. It is pink or white, with three bold, dark bands running obliquely across its head and body. Young red emperors are sometimes found taking shelter among the spines of poisonous sea urchins, but they quickly outgrow their spiny host and become free-

■ SILVER BIDDY
The lowfin silver biddy (*Parequula melbournensis*) travels in large schools along the coasts of Victoria, South Australia and Western Australia. It is seen in shallow water in the summer but spends the winter in deep water.

swimmers. The distinctive body markings gradually fade as the fish matures, and sometimes disappear altogether in extremely large adults. The red emperor is a delicious eating fish and is popular with anglers on the Great Barrier Reef.
Family: Lutjanidae

FUSILIERS ■

Fusiliers are sleek, predominantly blue fishes that are related to snappers (page 451). They grow to about 30 cm in length and congregate in large, conspicuous schools high above the sea floor. This behaviour is a ploy to confuse predators, and also helps them to take maximum advantage of planktonic food.

Fusiliers are most common on outer reef slopes and passes, where the ocean currents are strong.

The family contains 20 Indo-Pacific species, including ten Australian representatives. The best place to see a good variety of fusiliers is on the outer edge of the Great Barrier Reef. These fishes sometimes swarm in a swirling mass, temporarily obscuring a diver from view.
Family: Caesionidae

TRIPLETAIL

The tripletail family consists of a single species, *Lobotes surinamensis*, which occurs in all tropical seas. It is characterised by large, rounded lobes on the back of the dorsal and anal fins, which are about equal in size to the rounded caudal fin.

Juvenile tripletails bear a close resemblance to floating leaves, and they use this disguise to confuse predators such as large fishes and sea birds. The young often float among sargassum seaweed and other debris, sometimes far from land, a mode of dispersal that no doubt accounts for the species' worldwide distribution.

Adults are commonly found around areas of mangroves, where they consume prawns, crabs and fishes. Full-sized tripletails are 100 cm or more long and can reach as much as 20 kg in weight.
Family: Lobotidae

SILVER BIDDIES ■

These are silvery fishes that occur mainly in the tropics, although a few are found in temperate and subtropical waters. They reach a maximum of about 25 cm long. They forage over sand or silty bottoms, feeding on marine worms, crustaceans and other small invertebrates.

Approximately 40 species are known worldwide, and about 12 of them occur around Australia. Most are marine or estuarine, but juvenile

THE LONG …
AND THE SHORT
Members of the snapper family vary enormously in size, from the the red emperor, at over a metre long when it is fully grown, to the four-lined snapper, which is less than 4 cm long.

■ FUSILIERS
Safety in numbers is the operative principle for schooling fishes. These are yellow-backed fusiliers, *Caesio xanthonota*.

silver biddies may swim into the lower reaches of rivers. In South Australia silver biddies are known as roaches, and in other places they are called silver bellies.

Reefs in tropical regions tend to be associated with the glamour of brilliantly coloured fishes and delicate coral seascapes, but there are other aspects of a reef community that are just as interesting and colourful. Reef habitats often contain scattered pockets of rubble and sand, or are surrounded by vast areas of sand. These submerged deserts may seem to harbour very few forms of life, but in fact they support an extensive variety of invertebrates and fishes.

Tasty worms, shellfish, crabs and prawns live in the sand and are keenly sought by an assortment of predatory fishes that have evolved extraordinary feeding methods. Silver biddies quickly thrust their telescopic mouth into the sand, suck in a mouthful of bottom sediment, sift out the food particles and expel the remaining sand and debris through their gill openings.
Family: Gerreidae

SWEETLIPS

Sweetlips are also sometimes known as rubberlips or grunts. They inhabit the Mediterranean Sea and the Atlantic and eastern Pacific oceans, but the family is most diverse in the Indian and western Pacific oceans.

These fishes have large, rubbery lips and six pores on the chin – the openings to their sensory canal system. Species range in length from 30 cm to about a metre.

The best known sweetlips genera, *Plectorhinchus* and *Diagramma*, dwell on subtropical and tropical reefs, sheltering in gutters and beneath rocky overhangs during the day and feeding on bottom-dwelling invertebrates after dark. Sweetlips suck their prey, such as worms and molluscs, from the sandy bottom with their loose, fleshy lips.

Most sweetlips species are ornately patterned. Those that frequent the clearer waters of coral reefs are more brightly coloured. Their markings can change dramatically as they grow, and so can their habitat and behaviour as adults venture from shelter and form schools, making species identification difficult.

The juvenile harlequin sweetlip (*Plectorhinchus chaetodonoides*) and the magpie sweetlip (*P. picus*) are attractively marked with large, pale areas on a dark brown or black background. The dark areas break up to form round spots on a pale background when the juveniles cease to move like undulating flatworms and begin to form loose schools that swim more directly.

Similarly, the juvenile brown sweetlip (*P. gibbosus*) has a brown body and a transparent or pink tail. It swims upright until threatened, and then flutters down to the bottom of the estuary mouth where it lives, and drifts, resembling dead leaves, with the tide. The adults are completely brown. They swim like other fishes, and frequent rocky and coral reefs inside bays, coming into estuaries only occasionally.

The yellow-spotted or gold-spotted sweetlip (*P. flavomaculatus*), another

inshore species, is known at the juvenile stage as netted sweetlip or morwong, although it is not related to true morwongs (page 465). It is found near coral and rocky reefs in temperate and subtropical waters around Australia. Juveniles are greyish green with yellow longitudinal stripes across the head and the front of the body. These stripes gradually split up into dense masses of golden spots all over the fish's body.

Javelinfishes (*Pomadasys* spp.) look like sweetlips but they have large scales and lack the rubbery lips. They have a central pit in the middle of their chin that contains two pores, one on each side. Javelinfishes have a long, strong second anal spine attached to their anal fin and long, sharp spines attached to their dorsal fin. These fishes are also known as grunters, from the grating sounds they make with their teeth at night when they are feeding. These noises are clearly audible through the hull of a small boat at anchor.

Adult javelinfishes are found in coastal bays and estuaries rather than around reefs. Although they often have spots or broken vertical bars across their body, they are not as brightly coloured as many species of sweetlip. Their diet consists mainly of small crustaceans, such as prawns, and small fishes.
Family: Haemulidae

■ HARLEQUIN SWEETLIPS
These harlequin sweetlips are queuing up at a cleaning station – a place on the reef where cleaner wrasse are found. The wrasse feed on parasites living on larger fishes, at the same time providing an extensive grooming service that sometimes includes entering the mouth and gills of their clients.

■ LINED SWEETLIP
The lined sweetlip, *Plectorhinchus gaterinoides*, clearly illustrates why these fishes are also known as rubberlips. Sweetlips suck their prey from the sandy sea bottom.

SEA BREAMS ■

This family of medium-sized fishes comprises an estimated 50 species worldwide. Most are found in South African waters but the family is well represented in Australia, with about one-third of all species.

Most sea bream species found in Australia live in tropical waters, but a few live in temperate waters and a few in southern waters. Those living in cooler waters grow much larger than their warm-water relatives. Major species in this family are the pink snapper (*Chrysophrys aurata*), the bream (*Acanthopagrus* spp.) and the tarwhine (*Rhabdosargus sarba*).

Sea breams are mostly silver. They sometimes have indistinct banding or blue spotting, but this is seen mainly in juveniles or at night. Some deep-water individuals may be pink to red. Their fins are prominent and feature strong spines, and they have conical teeth, usually with several large canines at the front.

Snappers change shape and colour as they mature. Breams and tarwhine are generally similar in appearance throughout their growth, except for proportional changes – especially in the eyes, which are large in juveniles and small in adults.

Most sea breams occur in coastal habitats, usually in bays and estuaries, and they often congregate near river mouths. Some of the larger

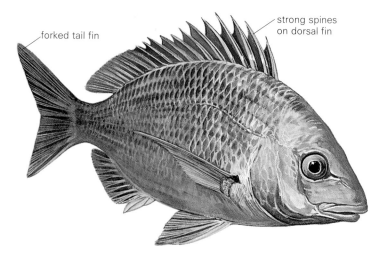

forked tail fin

strong spines on dorsal fin

■ SEA BREAM
The adult pink snapper, is not a true snapper but a sea bream. It is easily recognised by the hump above its head, which increases in size with age. Pink snappers with large humps are often called old man snapper, although both sexes develop these humps.

species enter shallow ocean waters, but usually only at night. While the juveniles of some species enter fresh water, few adults do. Sea breams eat a variety of small bottom-dwelling animals, and the larger species also feed on fishes. These fishes may occur singly or in small groups, and sometimes form large schools when migrating. They usually travel over sand and rubble bottoms near reefs. Their migratory and feeding habits alter with growth and the time of year, and vary between species.

There is often confusion about bream species because the same common name is sometimes applied to several species and because one species often has several local names. Members of several fish families are called snapper or bream, but scientists regard the Lutjanidae family (page 451) as the true snappers.

The pink snapper (*Chrysophrys aurata*) is common in the southern states, ranging north to subtropical waters, and there are separate eastern and western populations. It has a prominent hump above its head and can weigh 20 kg or more and grow to at least 1.3 metres long.

Pink snappers occur on sandy and rubble bottoms near rocky reefs or among low reefs dispersed over sand areas. They school seasonally and enter bays or estuaries to spawn. The larvae settle in the deepest parts of estuaries, where they feed on small bottom-dwelling animals.

As they grow they go through several changes, and the stages have different names – for example, small juveniles are called cockneys on the east coast. They grow to about 10 cm long and look rather like breams or tarwhine, but their blue spotting easily distinguishes them. Larger juveniles usually move out of estuaries and bays into deeper waters offshore. They are called red bream –

A TYPICAL BREAM
The silver bream, or yellow-finned bream, is typical of the Sparidae family. It has a deep, compressed body covered with moderately large scales.

though they are not red. Juveniles weighing up to about 1.5 kg still have blue spots, and are known as squires. Adults are silvery grey, sometimes pinkish, and in deep water are reddish pink or brown.

Another species, the long-spined snapper (*Argyrops spinifer*), is more tropical and mainly known from off the coast of north-western Australia.

The yellow-finned or silver bream (*Acanthopagrus australis*) is quite common on the east coast from central Queensland to eastern Victoria. It is usually silvery with yellow on its lower fins, but in turbid waters it may be dusky grey or brown. This species is replaced on the south coast by the similar southern bream (*A. butcheri*). Lacking yellow on the fins, the southern bream is often dark and is sometimes called black bream. Also known as black bream is the tropical pikey bream (*A. berda*), which can be almost black.

All breams are coastal, often preferring brackish waters, and some enter fresh water as adults. They usually move into the sea during floods, forming schools off nearby headlands. Juveniles eat bottom-dwelling invertebrates when in estuaries, and when in fresh water include insects in their diet. Adults take shrimps, molluscs and worms. Most bream species grow to about 60 cm in length and 4 kg in weight.

Only one tarwhine species, *Rhabdosargus sarba*, has been found in Australian waters, around the northern coast from Albany in Western Australia to southern New South Wales. It occurs mostly on coastal reefs and enters lagoons and

estuaries. Tarwhine are related to breams and similar in appearance, but unlike breams they have a rounded head profile and, usually, yellow lines on their sides. Their lower fins and tail are usually pale to bright yellow, especially in large adults. They reach a maximum of 45 cm in length and 1.4 kg in weight. They usually swim in small groups, often among schooling bream.
Family: Sparidae

EMPERORS ■

Emperors are small to moderately large deep-bodied fishes, variable in colour but often silvery with red, blue or dusky markings. Larger species grow to about a metre long and 5 kg, but red-throat emperors (*Lethrinus miniatus*) weighing up to about 9 kg have been caught.

The most abundant emperor species belong to the genus *Lethrinus*. About 17 of these occur in Australia in tropical and subtropical waters as far south as Houtman's Abrolhos on the west coast and Sydney on the east coast. Emperors inhabit waters of the continental shelf, including coral reefs and lagoons. Large numbers commonly occur on sand or rubble bottoms and on sea beds dominated by sponges, corals and sea fans. Most species inhabit waters 5–30 metres deep, but some, such as the red-spot emperor (*L. lentjan*), occur as deep as 90 metres.

The majority are bottom-feeding carnivores and have large, strong jaws with stout teeth. They feed mainly on crabs, gastropods, sea urchins, fishes and other bottom-dwelling animals. Most species, such as red-throat emperors, which rest on reef areas during the day and forage over adjacent sand bottoms at night, are nocturnal but some are daytime feeders. Emperors can be solitary or schooling fishes. They are not known to be territorial; tagging studies in Western Australia have shown that individuals may travel up to 100 kilometres.

Some species, such as the red-throat emperor, the red-spot emperor and the blue-spotted emperor (*L. choerorhynchus*), are known to function first as females and later become males. In northern waters emperors are known to spawn all year round, while in more southern waters spawning is restricted to the warmer months. Spawning is thought to occur at night, and is preceded by the formation of large spawning gatherings near the surface or at the bottom of reef slopes. Spawning activity reaches a peak

around the new moon. The eggs are less than a millimetre in diameter, and are carried by ocean currents.

Little is known of the early life history of emperors, although juveniles (2–3 cm long) are known to occur in shallow seagrass beds and mangrove areas and on rocky reefs, moving into deeper waters as they grow. Emperors are relatively long-lived, and it is estimated that some species may survive for up to 25 years.
Family: Lethrinidae

THREADFIN BREAMS ■

Common in tropical and subtropical Australian waters, these Indo-Pacific fishes are sometimes called butterfly breams. The family has 13 threadfin bream species (*Nemipterus* spp.), six whiptail bream species (*Pentapodus* spp.) and 12 coral bream species (*Scolopsis* spp., *Parascolopsis* spp. and *Scaevius milii*).

Threadfins and whiptails have elongated dorsal and caudal fin rays, and coral breams are usually

brightly coloured. Most members of the family are up to 30 cm long. They inhabit coral or rocky reefs or nearby sand or mud bottoms, generally to depths of about 30 metres, although a few species occur at 400 metres.

All threadfin breams are carnivorous and most are daytime feeders, preying mainly on other small fishes, crustaceans and worms.

Some coral bream and whiptail bream species have both male and female sex organs. They function first as females and later become males. Spawning behaviour is little researched, but threadfin breams are known to produce minute eggs that drift on ocean currents.

Juvenile coral breams often differ in colour from the adults. In order to protect themselves, juveniles of the brindled monocle bream (*Scolopsis bilineatus*) and the pearly coral bream (*S. margaritifer*) mimic the colouring of noxious blennies.
Family: Nemipteridae

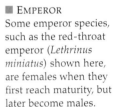

■ EMPEROR
Some emperor species, such as the red-throat emperor (*Lethrinus miniatus*) shown here, are females when they first reach maturity, but later become males.

■ THREADFIN BREAM
These are western butterfish (*Pentapodus vitta*), which are found around reefs in Western Australian waters. They belong to the group of threadfins known as whiptail breams.

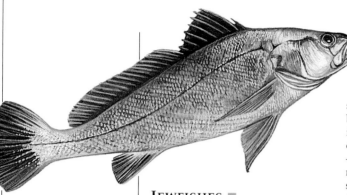

■ JEWFISH
The mulloway is the only jewfish found in cooler waters, occurring around the southern coast.

JEWFISHES ■

With about 270 species worldwide, jewfishes make up one of the largest families of perch-like fishes. They share the name jewfish with several species from the Glaucosomatidae family (Pearl perches, page 444).

Some of Australia's 19 jewfishes are found only here. Most live in tropical and subtropical waters; the mulloway (*Argyrosomus hololepidotus*) is the only one that inhabits cooler waters. It occurs around the southern coast from Bundaberg in Queensland to the North-West Cape in Western Australia.

Jewfishes normally inhabit coastal waters and estuaries. They are abundant at the mouths of large rivers. While they are chiefly marine, there are some species that live in fresh and brackish water. They live in a wide range of habitats, from the sea bottom to near-surface waters. Depending on species, jewfishes feed on a variety of prey, from bottom-dwelling invertebrates to free-swimming fishes.

Jewfishes are normally silvery in colour with iridescent green backs and upper sides. Some species have dusky spots, while others have orange or yellow fins. Different species appear to have the same body form, but there are subtle differences that allow them to occupy different positions in the ecosystem – the position of the mouth, the number of pores on their chin and snout, the tail shape, the amount of thickening of the pectoral fin rays, the tooth form and dental arrangement, and the possession (or not) of a chin barbel.

Most northern Australian jewfishes do not grow very large. The two better known tropical species are the orange croaker (*Atrobucca brevis*) and the spotted croaker (*Protonibea diacanthus*). However, some riverine forms grow larger, and the teraglin (*Atractoscion aequidens*), from the central eastern coast of Australia, can reach about a metre long and more than 10 kg in weight.

Jewfish are also known as croakers or drums because they can produce sound using their swim bladder and the muscles associated with it – a noise they often make when they are taken from the water. They probably make these noises to find each other in the murky waters where they live, and also to maintain cohesion of feeding or spawning schools.

The cooler water species, the mulloway, may grow to more than 2 metres long; the largest specimen recorded in Australia weighed 43 kg. In summer, spawning mulloways shoal in the surf zone and the young then move into estuaries, where they remain until they become young adults. Adult mulloways migrate several hundred kilometres along the coasts.

Young mulloways feed on planktonic crustaceans, while adults prey on fishes and squids in shallow coastal waters. Their spawning habits have not been widely studied, but it is known that a female mulloway weighing 10 kg can produce more than a million tiny eggs.
Family: Sciaenidae

GOATFISHES ■

Goatfishes have two separate dorsal fins and a pair of barbels on their chin. Their elongated bodies are covered in large scales and their tails are deeply forked. Colours vary according to species and, even though their colour may change between day and night, it is often the only way of distinguishing between closely related species. Most *Parupeneus* species feature a distinctive spot or band.

Most goatfishes form small schools in sheltered bays or protected parts of reefs. Some species enter shallow waters to feed and are common in bays and harbours with sand and rubble bottoms. They probe the bottom with their barbels in search of invertebrates to eat. About half of the world's 35 goatfish species live in Australian waters.

The southern goatfish (*Upeneichthys vlamingii*) is reddish brown, sometimes with blue lines or spots. It is the only goatfish found along the southern coast of mainland Australia and off Tasmania, where it occurs in large numbers near reefs. The blue-lined goatfish (*U. lineatus*), which occurs along the east coast, is similar in appearance but has a slightly blunter snout. Both species reach a maximum of 35 cm in length.

The black-spot goatfish (*Parupeneus signatus*) reaches a maximum of 50 cm long and is easily recognised by the black spot close to its tail. It is widespread in subtropical and tropical coastal waters from the south-west coast around the northern and eastern coasts to southern New South Wales.

The yellow-saddle goatfish (*P. cyclostomus*) has a yellow saddle just in front of its tail. The rest of the fish can be grey, pink or greeny grey. Juveniles – and sometimes adults – are entirely yellow. They grow to 40 cm and are widespread in tropical waters on the east coast as far south as northern New South Wales.

The banded goatfish (*P. multifasciatus*) is a widespread tropical species with a short black stripe behind its

■ GOATFISH
Goatfishes have two conspicuous dorsal fins and a pair of strong barbels, rather like a billygoat's beard, on their chin. This is the black-spot goatfish, *Parupeneus signatus*.

eyes and several broad black or brown bands set against a pale background at the tail end. This species reaches a maximum of 25 cm long. The similar round-spot goatfish (*P. pleurostigma*) does not have a stripe behind its eyes, and instead of banding it has a large, round black spot located at the centre of its side.

The dash-and-dot goatfish (*P. barberinus*) grows to 40 cm long and has a long black stripe running from its snout, through its eyes, almost to the black spot on the base of its tail fin. It is often bright yellow above the black stripe. Two similar species are the long-barbel goatfish (*P. macronema*), which has a very thick black stripe, and the yellow-spot goatfish (*P. indicus*), in which the black stripe is usually restricted to the head area and there is a bright yellow blotch on the centre of the side of the body.

The yellow-stripe goatfish (*Mulloidichthys vanicolensis*) is a slender species that is often seen in great numbers hovering in sheltered reef areas. It is greenish grey, dark above and silvery along the belly, with yellow fins. This species is often confused with the square-spot goatfish (*M. flavolineatus*) because the square-spot sometimes bears a similar yellow stripe. However, the square-spot can be identified by the elongated black spot in the centre of its side. Both species are widespread in tropical waters and rarely exceed 30 cm in length.

The bar-tail goatfish (*Upeneus tragula*) belongs to a tropical genus that includes many small, little-known species that school in large numbers. Several members of this genus appear to be undescribed, including one that is common in Sydney waters. Adult bar-tails can be distinguished from similar species by the yellow spotting on their first dorsal fin. They grow to 30 cm long and occupy various habitats from estuaries to outer reefs, where they feed among sand and rubble.
Family: Mullidae

BULLSEYES ◾

Bullseyes (known as sweepers outside Australia) have deep, compressed bodies tapering to a narrow tail-fin base, and large eyes. Their dorsal fin is tall and relatively short-based, in contrast to the long-based anal fin that originates below the end of the dorsal fin. The distinct lateral line continues right along the tail. They are small fishes, the largest reaching 12 cm long. Most species are drably coloured, although some species have distinctive markings, such as black fin tips or margins.

During the day most species hide in caves or in reef shadows, often in schools. At night they hunt the small shrimps and larval crustaceans that swim among the plankton.

Around the southern half of the Australian coast, including the coast of Tasmania, the common bullseye (*Pempheris multiradiata*) is plentiful. It occurs in a variety of habitats from shallow estuaries to deep offshore reefs. Juveniles are a little paler than adults and have yellow pelvic fins. Adults are drab brown to grey. The small-scale bullseye (*P. compressa*) is common in New South Wales, and the rough bullseye (*P. klunzingeri*) occurs in south-western waters.

Parapriacanthus species gather in large schools, the slender bullseye (*P. elongatus*) in temperate zones and the yellow sweeper (*P. ransonnetti*) in tropical zones.
Family: Pempherididae

ARCHERFISHES ◾

Archerfishes are distributed in fresh and brackish waters from India to Australia and the Melanesian Archipelago. Four of the six species – all in the genus *Toxotes* – are common in northern Australian waters.

Archerfishes bring down their insect prey with a jet of water. When the fish clamps its gill covers shut, water shoots from its mouth.

These fishes have pointed snouts and laterally compressed bodies. The seven-spot archerfish (*Toxotes chatareus*) lives in rivers and creeks in northern Australia. It is silvery white with seven black spots or bars on its back. It grows to about 25 cm long and usually schools.
Family: Toxotidae

◾ BULLSEYES
The yellow sweeper, *Parapriacanthus ransonnetti*, is a small tropical bullseye species that forms extensive schools.

◾ ARCHERFISH
When an archerfish sights food, usually an insect, it rises to the surface and shoots a jet of water from its mouth. The victim is usually knocked off its perch and devoured as soon as it hits the water. The fish's aim is accurate to a distance of 2–3 metres – an amazing feat, since when taking aim the fish must compensate for the refraction of light through water.

THE BEST OF BOTH WORLDS

Several fish species that normally live in estuaries enter rivers and creeks from time to time. There are several advantages in so doing. First, in fresh water there are fewer large predators; second, there are fewer fishes in general, so competition for food is less; and third, it is easier to find food in clear fresh water than it is in the silty waters of river mouths.

Some species, such as the silver batfish, remain near the mouths of streams, where they are exposed to either fresh or salt water, or a mixture of both. On the other hand, young barramundi, which begin life in brackish estuaries, make extensive migrations into fresh water. The young barramundi shown here is devouring a freshwater species – a rainbowfish.

DRUMMERS ■

Drummers inhabit shallow marine seas throughout tropical and temperate latitudes. Australia has 14 drummer species – half the worldwide total, and more than anywhere else in the world. Drummers, also known as sea chubs, are compressed oval fishes with small heads and mouths. They range in length from 16 cm to 85 cm, according to species. The family contains several major groups that were once considered separate families, but because of strong anatomical similarities scientists now list them as one family.

Drummers (subfamily Kyphosinae) are most common on tropical coral reefs, but a few, such as the buffalo bream (*Kyphosus cornelii*) and the silver drummer (*K. sydneyanus*),

■ DRUMMERS
The eastern rock blackfish (*Girella elevata*) is a nibbler and belongs to the drummer family. It is found along the southern coast of Australia. These two individuals are resting in the shelter of a cave.

are mainly found in cooler temperate seas. They are generally silvery grey and swarm over the reef's surface in schools, grazing on seaweed.

Nibblers (subfamily Girellinae) are similar to drummers in their habits and overall appearance, but Australian species tend to be darker than drummers or, in the case of the zebrafish (*Girella zebra*), marked with vertical dark bars. The luderick (*G. tricuspidata*), the eastern rock blackfish (*G. elevata*) and the western rock blackfish (*G. tephraeops*) are well known across the southern coast of Australia. They congregate to form dense pre-spawning shoals next to jetties and rocky outcrops. According to Polynesian anglers, the flesh of some species may have a mildly hallucinogenic effect.

Sweeps (subfamily Scorpidinae) are variously distributed around the Pacific Rim, but only the *Scorpis* genus, with four species, occurs in Australian waters. Sweeps are sometimes known as footballers because their bold patterns of highly contrasting bars, bands and stripes resemble those seen on football shirts. They are deep-bodied and compressed, and have tightly packed small scales. Their tails are large, but the other fins are small. In some juveniles the soft parts of the dorsal and anal fins are elevated into a point, giving the fish a diamond-shaped profile.

Sweeps are mainly midwater feeders, usually swimming in schools and feeding on floating algae or animal plankton. They prefer turbulent waters around rocky headlands, though juveniles are often found under jetties in bays.

The sea sweep (*S. aequipinnis*) is silvery grey with a broad, dark grey saddle over the middle of its back. It occurs commonly in southern Australia, from southern New South Wales to Shark Bay in Western Australia, and around Tasmania.

The silver sweep (*S. lineolata*) ranges north as far as southern Queensland and south to north-eastern Tasmania, and into Port Philip Bay in Victoria, where it is found in small numbers. It is common in New South Wales, where it occurs in huge schools on offshore reefs.

The banded sweep (*S. georgiana*) from Western Australian is less inclined to school than other sweeps, and is often found singly along rocky ledges or in caves in shallow water. This species has taller dorsal and anal fin tips than other sweeps, and is marked with distinctive dark bands over its body and tail.

■ BATFISH
This round batfish (*Platax orbicularis*) illustrates the enormously tall fins of this group of fishes, which make their bodies look larger than they really are.

The two genera and five species of stripeys and mados form a small subtropical group (subfamily Microcanthinae) that is best represented in Australian and New Zealand waters. The stripey (*Microcanthus strigatus*) has three subtropical populations, one on Australia's west coast, one on the east coast, and one in Japan.

On Australia's east coast, the Australian mado (*Atypichthys strigatus*) is often abundant, while on the south coast two other species are common: the footballer sweep (*Neatypus obliquus*), which bears a diagonally banded pattern, and the moonlighter (*Tilodon sexfasciatus*), which resembles the tropical butterflyfishes (opposite page). Most mados and stripeys reach a maximum length of 18–25 cm, although the moonlighter grows to 40 cm long.
Family: Kyphosidae

BATFISHES ■

Batfishes belong to a small global group of about ten species, half of which are called spadefishes. Only batfishes are commonly encountered in tropical Australian waters. The largest species reaches 60 cm long.

Batfishes are distinctively shaped, having extremely tall fins on their disc-shaped bodies. These fins provide good camouflage and make batfishes look considerably bigger than they are, thereby discouraging many predators. Batfishes feed on algae and various invertebrates. Nothing is known about their reproductive behaviour.

The tall-fin batfish (*Platax teira*) is one of the most common and widespread species. Juveniles swim under loose, floating weeds, often drifting considerable distances and becoming quite large before they settle on the sea bottom. Adults inhabit outer reef lagoons or shipwrecks.

The round batfish (*P. orbicularis*), whose juveniles look rather like leaves, prefers coastal reefs. Another common species, the shaded batfish (*P. pinnatus*), forms schools, and the small black juveniles, outlined in bright orange, look like bad-tasting flatworms, which provides them with a certain amount of protection from would-be predators.
Family: Ephippidae

SILVER BATFISHES

The 25 cm-long silver batfish (*Monodactylus argenteus*), sometimes known as the moonie, occurs in coastal areas of northern Australia and adjoining South-East Asia. Its silvery, diamond-shaped body is strongly compressed and it has triangular dorsal and anal fins. Silver batfishes school around wharves and jetties and sometimes make their way upstream into fresh water (see box, 'The best of both worlds').

Also belonging to this family are two species of fishes from the genus *Schuettea*. Commonly known as pomfrets, although they are not members of the family Bramidae (page 450), these species are found in the shallow seas of southern Australia. They are similar in appearance to the silver batfish, but their body is more oval in shape.
Family: Monodactylidae

SCATS

Tropical and widespread, the small scat family consists of two genera and about four species; one species from each genus occurs in Australian waters.

Scats mainly live in brackish coastal waters and can nearly always be found in freshwater runoffs from river mouths. Juveniles often move into pure fresh water. They grow to about 35 cm long and have spiny fins that can inflict painful wounds and are thought to be venomous. The spotted scat (*Scatophagus argus*) and the striped scat (*S. tetracanthus*) are scavengers that are able to tolerate fluctuations of temperature and salinity.
Family: Scatophagidae

BUTTERFLYFISHES

Gracefully shaped and striking in their colour patterns, butterflyfishes are probably the best known of all coral reef fishes. They are small to medium-sized (normally 13–30 cm long) with laterally compressed bodies, and in several species the dorsal fin ribbons out in long, fine threads. They have a single dorsal fin with six to 16 stout spines; this fin becomes erect when the fish is alarmed – an effective deterrent against predators. Dominant colours include orange, black and white. They are generally found in tropical seas, although a few occur in temperate waters. Most inhabit reefs less than 20 metres deep, although a few range down to 50 metres or more.

The family has about 120 species, and Australia has one of the richest butterflyfish faunas in the world

with about 50 species, many of which live on the Great Barrier Reef. Butterflyfishes occur in groups, in pairs or alone, depending on the species. Mated pairs are common, and these bonds may last a lifetime. Most are confined to an isolated patch of reef or to a relatively small section of a more extensive reef, but within their home area they travel widely in search of food.

Although few members of this family are territorial, one exception is the chevroned butterflyfish (*Chaetodon trifascialis*). It lives among formations of plate coral, which serve as its food supply. It zealously defends its territory against other fishes, whether of the same species or other coral-feeding butterflyfishes; however, if confronted by a large predator, such as a groper or snapper, it shelters among the coral.

Fighting is rare among most other butterflyfishes, although minor squabbling sometimes occurs at dusk in defence of night-time resting places. At sunset, feeding ceases abruptly and butterflyfishes retreat into crevices or coral heads, where they sleep throughout the night.

Butterflyfishes feed on a wide variety of small invertebrates. *Chelmon* and *Forcipiger* species have an elongated snout adapted for reaching crustaceans in narrow crevices. The chevroned butterflyfish feeds only on coral polyps. Another group, which includes the pyramid butterflyfish (*Hemitaurichthys polylepis*) and the schooling bannerfish (*Heniochus diphreutes*), swim high above the sea floor and consume animal plankton.
Family: Chaetodontidae

■ SCAT
Scats are widespread in tropical waters. They are generally found in brackish water at the mouths of rivers. Shown here is the spotted scat, *Scatophagus argus*.

■ BUTTERFLYFISH
The long-nosed butterflyfish (*Forcipiger flavissimus*) has an elongated snout that enables it to pluck crustaceans and marine worms from reef fissures.

ANGELFISHES ■

The brilliantly coloured angelfishes are found mainly on coral reefs. Many species – especially those belonging to the genera *Holacanthus* and *Pomacanthus* – undergo dramatic colour pattern changes between the juvenile form and that of the adult). Angelfishes are easily distinguished from their close relatives the butterflyfishes (page 459) by the enlarged, backward-projecting spine on their cheeks.

The smaller species of angelfish tend to be shaped rather like an egg and laterally compressed, while the larger species are frequently extremely deep-bodied and have graceful fins. Some angelfishes are a single colour; others have dazzling patterns of bars, stripes, bands or lines. A variety of shades of yellow and blue are particularly well represented on these fishes, but red, black and white are also seen.

The angelfish family occurs throughout the world and contains about 85 species. The majority are found in the Indian and the western and central Pacific oceans. About 30 species are known from Australian seas. Angelfish species found in Australian waters range in length from 7 cm for the white-tail pygmy

■ OLD WIVES
Because of their black and white stripes, old wives are sometimes called zebrafishes. This school of old wives is gathered under a wharf.

angelfish (*Centropyge flavicauda*) to about 50 cm for the six-banded angelfish (*Pomacanthus sexstriatus*).

Angelfishes spend the daylight hours near the sea bottom searching for food. Certain species feed almost entirely on algae and detritus; others, such as the large *Pomacanthus* angels, prefer sponges as their staple diet, which they supplement with a variety of small bottom-living invertebrates. *Genicanthus* angels forage on animal plankton high above the bottom on outer reef slopes, where the ocean currents are strong. Most angelfishes rely on boulders, caves or crevices in the coral for places to shelter. They are typically territorial, especially towards individuals of their own species.

Spawning occurs at dusk and usually involves a single pair, although a male may sometimes mate successively with several different females. Males establish their territory by driving away other male competitors. They then swim up from the bottom and await the arrival of one or more females. When a prospective mate approaches, the male puts on a courtship display that may include erecting his fins, swimming rapidly back and forth and quivering his body. Eventually the male and the female spiral slowly towards the surface. At the apex of the ascent they suddenly shed eggs and sperm and then swim back to the bottom. The eggs, which are less than 1 mm in diameter, hatch 15–20 hours later.
Family: Pomacanthidae

OLD WIFE ■

Although it looks very much like a cold-water angelfish, the black and white vertically striped old wife (*Enoplosus armatus*) is not related to

■ ANGELFISH
Just above its tail the yellow masked angelfish, *Euxiphipops xanthometapon*, has a false eye spot, which may serve to confuse potential predators.

the angelfishes and butterflyfishes that are found on tropical coral reefs. Unlike these warm-water families, the family Enoplosidae has a single representative and a distribution that is totally confined to the relatively shallow, inshore waters of the southern half of Australia.

Growing to a length of about 25 cm, old wives are common inhabitants of algae-covered rocky reefs and regions of seagrass, where they can often be seen swimming in pairs, gracefully weaving their way in and out of the underwater vegetation in search of the marine worms, small shrimps and other invertebrates on which they prey. Sometimes these fishes are solitary, but at other times they can be seen in large schools, perhaps sheltering under a jetty or a rock ledge.

Their high, spinous first dorsal fin, which is totally separated from an even higher soft second dorsal fin, sets the old wife apart from the tropical reef-dwellers. The needle-like spines are certainly a deterrent in themselves, but they can also deposit a painful venom in the flesh of a novice predator or an unsuspecting handler.

The old wife has received its common name not from this formidable array of 'knitting needles' on its body but because when it is removed from the water it produces grinding noises that some people think sound like the mumblings of an elderly person.
Family: Enoplosidae

BOARFISHES

Although boarfishes occasionally venture into the shallows, they prefer reef areas in deep water, and so little is known about their behaviour. They are identified by the strong spines on their dorsal fin, the armour-like bony plates of their head and their elongated snout.

There are 14 boarfish species found worldwide, eight of which occur in Australian waters. Quite common along the deeper reefs of Australia's southern coastline, the long-snouted boarfish (*Pentaceropsis recurvirostris*) is the best known of these. It has oblique black bars on its body and a long snout that it uses to probe the sandy bottom and rocky crevices for prey. It grows to 50 cm long.

The largest species is the giant boarfish (*Paristiopterus labiosus*), which may grow to over 90 cm long. While it normally inhabits deep offshore waters, it has also been found in such shallow areas as Port Phillip Bay in Victoria and Jervis Bay on the southern coast of New South Wales. The front dorsal spines of the juvenile are very long, but they become progressively shorter as the fish ages. Giant boarfishes have various colour patterns, including silver with oblique brownish bands and reddish brown with bright yellow spots; these spots have given it one of its common names, the yellow-spotted boarfish. It is found around the temperate coastline of Australia from northern New South Wales to southern Western Australia.

Similar in appearance to the giant boarfish is the brown-spotted boarfish (*P. gallipavo*) of South Australia and Western Australia. It can be distinguished from the giant boarfish by its elongated dorsal spines and the many small brown spots that cover its body – though these spots

are sometimes restricted to the brown bands of the body. This species grows to 74 cm long.
Family: Pentacerotidae

KNIFEJAW

The knifejaw, *Oplegnathus woodwardi*, is the sole Australian representative of this cool-water marine family. Apart from its boldly banded pattern of black on white, its deep body is not distinctive. Only when its mouth is opened, revealing fused teeth that form a beak-like edge to the jaws, is the knifefish unmistakable. Its jaws are constructed like those of parrotfishes (page 469) and toadfishes (page 488), though it is not related to these groups. Small but efficient, these jaws can break the hard shells of the invertebrates on which the knifejaw feeds.

Knifejaws have a rather long dorsal fin with a relatively even height, a slightly forked tail and a low, rounded anal fin. They grow to nearly 50 cm long.

Only juveniles are normally seen in shallow coastal waters, but adults occur at depths of up to 400 metres around the southern half of the continent, and are particularly common in the Great Australian Bight.
Family: Oplegnathidae

CICHLIDS

This large family of over 900 species inhabits the fresh waters of Africa and South and Central America. These fishes are so diverse that it is impossible to describe a typical species. Some species grow to nearly a metre long and greatly resemble marine snappers and emperors, but others are small and delicate.

Five cichlid species have been introduced into Australian fresh waters, but the Mozambique cichlid (*Sarotherodon mossambica*) is the only

one that is widespread here. Three other species – clearly released by aquarists – occur in ponds that are heated by discharge from a power station near Morwell in Victoria. The fifth species appeared briefly in a pond in a Perth suburb but is now thought to have been eradicated.

The Mozambique cichlid, which is mainly a plant-eater, is now a pest in some rivers of eastern Queensland, including those around Brisbane and Townsville. It has also been recorded in the Gascoyne River in Western Australia. Schools stir up the bottom when feeding, and nesting males build volcano-shaped nests that can occupy the entire bottom habitat, crowding out native fishes. Females are greyish yellow with black blotches on their sides, while males are black with white on the lower part of their head and a red fin margin. This coloration is intensified during the breeding season. Mozambique cichlids are mouth-breeders, the female taking the eggs into her mouth as soon as they are laid and fertilised. The young remain in her mouth until they are about 1 cm long.
Family: Cichlidae

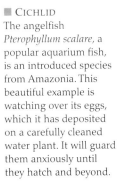

■ CICHLID
The angelfish *Pterophyllum scalare*, a popular aquarium fish, is an introduced species from Amazonia. This beautiful example is watching over its eggs, which it has deposited on a carefully cleaned water plant. It will guard them anxiously until they hatch and beyond.

■ BOARFISH
The long-snouted boarfish (*Pentaceropsis recurvirostris*) of Australia's southern coastline is easily recognised by the oblique black bars on its body and its long, tubular snout.

■ DAMSELFISHES
Anemonefishes, which are a form of damselfish, exhibit a strict pecking order that is related to size. They form groups of about five, in which the dominant member is always a mature female. The rest of the group are males at various stages of maturity. If the female dies, the next largest individual becomes a female within a few days. The anemonefishes shown here are from the species *Amphiprion chrysopterus*.

DAMSELFISHES ■

Damselfishes are one of the most conspicuous members of the coral reef fish community; during the day they literally swarm over the reef. Damsels are found worldwide in tropical and temperate seas. Over three-quarters of the 330 species are found in the tropical Indian and Pacific oceans. The tropical waters of Australia and nearby Indonesia have the largest number of damselfish species in the world, with well over a hundred species each.

Most species are territorial, notably those that feed on algae. They guard their 'gardens' jealously, particularly when the intruder is another damselfish. *Stegastes* species will even attack skin divers. Fortunately for the divers, these fishes grow to only 10 cm long, and the smallest species are 4–5 cm long when fully mature.

Feeding habits are diverse. As well as the algal feeders, there are many species that feed on animal plankton and small, bottom-dwelling invertebrates. Others prefer a combination of algae and invertebrates.

Egg-shaped and compressed from side to side, damselfishes range from drab hues of black, brown and grey to bright shades of orange, yellow, red and blue. The juveniles of many species have a bright yellow body with a neon blue stripe (or several stripes) running back from their head along the upper part of their back. This conspicuous livery fades with growth, often to a nondescript pattern bearing little resemblance to the original colours. The colour pattern for a single species may also vary, although to a lesser degree, according to locality, and – more rarely – in response to environment.

Just before spawning, the male damselfish attracts females to its nest site on the sea bottom by performing an up-and-down swimming motion, as though riding a roller coaster. This behaviour, which normally attracts several females, is called 'signal jumping'. Spawning often occurs in the morning and may last for more than two hours. Depending on the species, each female lays from 50 to 1000 or more eggs. The incubation period ranges from two to seven days, during which time the male takes the principal role in guarding the eggs.

Among the most colourful of all damselfishes are the anemonefishes, which have a symbiotic relationship with sea anemones (see box, 'Happily ever after'). Ten anemonefish species occur on Australian coral reefs. They are 8–16 cm long and their basic colour scheme is a solid background of orange, black or brown with up to three white crossbars, although two species have a narrow, pale stripe instead of the bars. The most popular species among scuba divers and photographers are the clown anemonefish (*Amphiprion percula*) and the false clown anemonefish (*A. ocellaris*). They are bright orange with three bold white bars edged with black. The clown is found on the Great Barrier Reef and the false clown in north-western Australia.

Like many fishes, anemonefishes undergo sex reversal (see box, 'Gender benders', page 470). They have both male and female sex organs, but when they are small adults only the male organs function. When the fish is larger, the male organs degenerate and the gonads turn into ovaries.

These fishes are often found in groups of five or more, with a mature female always dominating.
Family: Pomacentridae

HAPPILY EVER AFTER

For most fishes, swimming too close to a sea anemone means death. The anemone fires tiny poison darts to paralyse the victim and then eats it. However, anemonefishes are covered in a slime containing chemicals that prevents the anemone's tentacles from firing.

Anemonefishes can therefore live among sea anemone tentacles – a mutually beneficial arrangement. The anemone repels the fishes' enemies, and the anemonefishes attack anemone-eating creatures such as butterflyfishes.

Tropical treasures

Australia's Great Barrier Reef is famous worldwide, and its fishes are renowned for their vivid colours and patterns – but no one is sure why these fishes are so distinctively marked.

Many fishes, such as angelfishes and damselfishes, are brightly coloured as juveniles. In damselfishes, these colours often fade with growth and the adults are relatively drab. One theory about their striking colouring as juveniles is that the patterns are a form of camouflage, breaking up the outline of the fish so that it merges with the high-contrast environment of the reef. Once the fish has grown out of the vulnerable juvenile stage, it no longer needs to rely on camouflage to escape its enemies.

Giving predators the slip
Another possibility is that the dazzling patterns confuse potential predators, directing attention away from the most vulnerable part of the fish – its head. This may be why there is an ocellus – a false eye – on the rear part of the bodies of some juveniles. If a predator attacks the wrong end of its prey, there is a better chance of escape; and even if the attacker does inflict some damage, the wound will probably not be fatal.

Bright colours could also be a warning to stay clear; for example, it may be that the dazzling hues of the anemonefish warn its predators that they risk being stung by the fish's host, the sea anemone. Likewise, the colours of butterflyfishes may advertise the danger of impalement on their sharp dorsal spines.

Staying in touch
Reef fishes may use their colours to maintain contact with members of their own species, which is crucial for finding mates. If a reef is inhabited by 20 types of butterflyfishes, all of a similar shape, it is easier to pick out fellow individuals if each species bears a distinctive pattern. In some coral reef fishes the colouring of females is quite different from that of males of the same species. This may also be useful for mate spotting.

The vivid coloration of the adult emperor angelfish, shown here, differs greatly from the white on dark blue patterning of juveniles.

Staking a claim
For territorial species, colours may be a way of claiming a section of the reef and deterring intruders of the same species. Such discouragement eliminates competition for food supplies, nesting sites and living space, but the sitting tenant usually has to enforce such claims with some form of aggressive behaviour.

A pink anemonefish peeps from among the fronds of its anemone home.

As well as being brightly coloured, which may deter predators, boxfishes secrete a toxin that makes them taste unpleasant.

Jewel-like fairy basslets weave their way among whip coral. These are males; the female is without the blotch on the dorsal fin and has a yellow back and tail.

HAWKFISHES

Hawkfishes can be identified by the small tufts of filaments on the tips of the dorsal fin spines. These fishes perch on the thickened rays of their pectoral fins, normally on the bottom, and survey their surroundings for food. Their excellent eyesight allows them to see small prey from a long distance. Hawkfishes are around 10 cm long, though a few species are slightly larger.

About 35 species are known from the Indo-Pacific, 12 of which live in Australian waters. Hawkfishes are brown to red, and each species has a distinctive banded patterning of grey to green spots and blotches. Most species are widespread in tropical regions, although the splendid hawkfish (*Cirrhitus splendens*) is restricted to Lord Howe Island and northern New South Wales.

One of the most widespread and common species is the blotched hawkfish (*Cirrhitichthys aprinus*), which ranges down the east coast to southern New South Wales. It occurs in coastal bays and harbours, usually sitting on sponges or pylons, and is often seen in Sydney Harbour.

The similar coral hawkfish (*C. falco*) prefers tropical reefs. The freckled hawkfish (*Paracirrhites forsteri*) and the ring-eyed hawkfish (*P. arcatus*) occur mainly on coral reefs. The long-nose hawkfish (*Oxycirrhites typus*) is usually found among fan corals or in black corals along steep reef walls. As its common name suggests, this fish has an exceptionally long snout.

The lyre-tail hawkfish (*Cyprinocirrhites polyactis*) is unusual for this family because it often swims high above the bottom to feed on animal plankton. It has a long, half-moon-shaped tail and looks more like a basslet (see Rock cods, page 442) than a normal hawkfish. It is common, but is seldom seen, as it usually lives in deep water in sponge habitats. It is widespread in tropical waters and is found as far south as Montague Island off southern New South Wales.
Family: Cirrhitidae

KELPFISHES AND SEA CARPS

Kelpfishes and sea carps spend much time sitting on the sea floor, usually in areas of weed and reef. When they push off the bottom, they swim in a rather ungainly fashion. Each family has three species in Australian seas.

These two families are related to morwongs (opposite page), but they have longer bodies and their lips are not as thick and blubbery. Kelpfishes have elongated rays in their pectoral fins, but sea carps do not. Kelpfishes are generally small, some growing to a length of 40 cm, whereas sea carps may grow to 65 cm long.

The eastern kelpfish (*Chironemus marmoratus*) is fairly common in southern New South Wales, often schooling with others of its species in coastal waters. It is also found in eastern Victoria and in Tasmania, where its range overlaps with that of the western kelpfish (*C. georgianus*), which is distributed across the southern coast to southern Western Australia. The western kelpfish, however, is rarely seen in the open. Both species are pale brown with darker blotches and a silver spot near the top of the gill opening. Both have pointed snouts and small tentacles at the top of each dorsal spine. On the western species the tentacles are in a tuft on the dorsal spine, while the eastern species has a single tentacle. Eastern kelpfishes reach a length of 40 cm, but western kelpfishes grow to only 21 cm long.

The silver spot (*Threpterius maculosus*) is like the eastern and western kelpfishes but has a shorter, blunter snout and a more hunch-backed appearance, and its silver spot is on the pointed flap of its gill cover. This species hides in weedy areas on rocky reefs. Its colour is variable, including reddish brown, green and dark brown, usually with darker blotches. It grows to 40 cm long.

The southern sea carp (*Aplodactylus arctidens*) is quite common on exposed coastal reefs of Victoria and Tasmania, ranging as far west as south-eastern South Australia. It feeds on seaweeds and is greenish in colour. A close relative, the western sea carp (*A. westralis*), occurs in western parts of South Australia and southern Western Australia. This fish's snout is blunter than that of the southern sea carp, and it is generally more brown in colour. Both species grow to about 60 cm long.

The rock cale (*Crinodus lophodon*), an inhabitant of exposed coastal reefs of New South Wales and far eastern Victoria, is related to sea carps. Like the sea carps, it has a blunt snout and small mouth. This species is grey to brown with pale spots, especially on the fins. The rock cale's hunch-backed appearance distinguishes it from the sea carps. It grows to 45 cm long.
Families: Chironemidae (kelpfishes), Aplodactylidae (sea carps)

SEA CARP

The rock cale gathers in schools on wave-swept reefs in New South Wales and eastern Victoria where it feeds on weeds. It is related to sea carps.

HAWKFISH

Hawkfishes have excellent eyesight and can spot small prey, such as shrimps and worms, from some distance away. Shown below is an inhabitant of coral reefs, the ring-eyed hawkfish, which is often found resting on branching coral heads.

MORWONGS ■

Thick, rubbery lips and elongated rays in the lower half of their pectoral fins make morwongs easy to recognise. Some species also have small 'horns' in front of their eyes.

Australia has 11 species from a worldwide total of about 21. They are mainly found in temperate waters, though several species live in subtropical areas. Although Queensland's sweetlips (page 453) are sometimes called morwong because of their rubbery lips, they are in fact from another family.

The early stage of a morwong's life is known as the 'paper stage', because of its very thin, deep-bodied, silvery form, which is only about 25 mm long. During the paper stage, these silvery youngsters drift in the ocean looking like bubbles floating near the surface. They seem to be quite vulnerable to predators, and have been found in the gut contents of various fishes and birds. Their shape and silvery colour may help individuals to avoid detection during this early part of life.

The most spectacular member of the family is the queen snapper (*Nemadactylus valenciennesi*), which ranges from Victoria to southern Western Australia. It has an iridescent blue body and many yellow lines around its eyes. Queen snapper eat cowries, which they ingest whole, so some anglers check the gut contents of their catch in the hope of finding a rare deep-water cowrie. Queen snapper grow to one metre long, and have been found in water as deep as 240 metres.

A common species in New South Wales is the red morwong (*Cheilodactylus fuscus*), which often forms large schools near offshore reefs. It grows to 65 cm long and feeds on shellfish, which it removes from the rocks with its strong, rubbery lips. Late in the afternoon red morwongs can be observed resting on the sea bottom, or even sleeping in crevices. This species is mainly reddish brown, the lower portion of its head and body being whitish.

The banded morwong (*C. spectabilis*) from Tasmania and Victoria and the red-lipped morwong (*C. rubrolabiatus*) from Western Australia look very similar. Both are pale brown with some reddish areas on the head and brown banding on the body, but only the red-lipped morwong is also spotted with dark brown. These morwongs prefer coastal reefs and are very common in their respective areas. They both grow to about 80 cm long.

The blue morwong (*Nemadactylus douglasii*) is trawled commercially in offshore waters of New South Wales to depths of about 100 metres but is also found on inshore reefs. It looks like the queen snapper but does not have yellow lines around its eyes. Another relative, the jackass fish (*N. macropterus*), is also trawled commercially, but from waters to around 400 metres deep. It is distinguished from the blue morwong by a dark grey to blackish band on its back behind its head. The jackass fish grows to a length of 70 cm and is found around the southern coastline of Australia and to New Zealand.

The largest of this family is the dusky morwong (*Dactylophora nigricans*), at 1.2 metres long. It is silvery grey to greenish grey, sometimes with a bronze tinge on its sides. It often rests on the bottom, especially in seagrass beds near reef areas.
Family: Cheilodactylidae

TRUMPETERS ■

Trumpeters are a small group of temperate-reef fishes with a pointed head and fleshy lips. Most are silvery with a brown upper surface. Adults reach a length of 1.2 metres.

Most species of trumpeter live alone or in small schools, but the real bastard trumpeter, *Mendosoma lineatum*, is occasionally found off southern Tasmania in enormous schools. In New Zealand this species is commonly known as the telescope fish because it is able to extend its jaws forward and downward to suck in plankton.

Other trumpeters spend much of their time cruising around near the bottom eating small crustaceans, sea urchins and molluscs. Like young morwongs, young trumpeters are known as paper fish because they are very thin and have a well defined keel-like belly.

The striped trumpeter (*Latris lineata*) is the largest member of the group, reaching more than 20 kg in weight. It is greenish in colour with black stripes. As adults, striped trumpeters occur on deeper offshore reefs of the continental shelf.
Family: Latrididae

■ TRUMPETER
The bastard trumpeter *Latridopsis forsteri* is the most widely distributed trumpeter species in Australia. It is found from the central coast of New South Wales southward and westward as far as South Australia.

■ MORWONGS
Morwongs are common inhabitants of Australia's southern seas. This pair of painted morwongs (*Cheilodactylus ephipplus*) were photographed at Lord Howe Island.

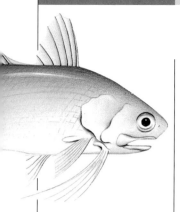

■ THREADFIN
The lower section of the pectoral fin on threadfin fishes consists of several thread-like filaments. These unattached rays vary in number from species to species, and the number of rays helps to identify species.

JAWFISHES ■

There are an estimated 70 species in this secretive, burrowing family – most of them not yet scientifically named. They have a number of common names: missing links, pugs, harlequins, grinners, smilers and monkeyfish – but are generally known as jawfishes.

These fishes construct burrows with stones that they carry around in their large, downward-curving mouths. Usually only their heads are visible as they stare out from large, dark eyes that are placed high and forward. The burrows double as brooding chambers.

Jawfishes come in many colours, but very bright ones are rare in Australian waters. They inhabit rubble zones near reefs where there are moderate currents, and feed on plankton as it drifts into range. Some species live in colonies, spacing their burrows evenly over a small area, and disputes over stolen building materials are not unusual.

Divers off New South Wales, at depths of about 20 metres, occasionally see smilers (*Opistognathus jacksoniensis*) up to 20 cm long. Their brown and white marbled skin camouflages them perfectly in their rocky reef home.

At 55 cm long, black jawfishes (*O. inornatus*), from northern Australia, are among the largest members of this family.
Family: Opistognathidae

BEARDED EEL BLENNIES

There are only a few species in this little-known family. The bearded eel blenny, *Notograptus guttatus*, occurs in northern Australia and New Guinea, and the Shark Bay eel blenny, *N. gregoryi*, is known only from Shark Bay in Western Australia. Eel blennies are coastal fishes, up to about 15 cm long, usually found in shallow silty habitats.
Family: Notographtidae

GREY MULLETS

Towards dusk on calm autumn days, greyish fishes with silver bellies may sometimes be seen jumping from the water in estuaries. These are grey mullet expressing *joie de vivre* as they gather in large schools before going to sea on their long spawning migration.

All the mullets are schooling fishes that are found all over the world, except in polar seas. Nineteen species occur around Australia, mostly along tropical coasts, although the biggest schools are found in cooler southern waters.

Mullet species range in length from 28 cm to 45 cm and look much alike, having elongated bodies that are rounded in cross-section behind the head and become laterally compressed towards the tail. They have two fins in the mid-line on the back, a single anal fin, and paired pelvic fins lying below the lateral pectoral fins just behind the head. Most have eyes on the side of the head, but in one tropical species the eyes are on top, providing aerial vision in the muddy waters of tropical rivers.

Mullets mostly eat microscopic algae and filamentous seaweeds, but some species include small animals, particularly copepods and worms, in their diet. Head down and tail up, they suck in food particles, often with sand and mud, by extruding their partly telescopic lips. On the edge of the lips are small teeth, connected to the jaw by fibrous strands, which act as sieves. A sorting apparatus in the gullet partly sorts the material and the fish coughs out the rejected mud or sand.

Australia's most common species, the sea mullet (*Mugil cephalus*), gathers in estuaries in great shoals in autumn. On a strong offshore breeze the shoal migrates out to sea and heads north. The eggs shed at sea then drift south on the prevailing currents, and the hatching fry enter the estuaries to gradually make their

■ JAWFISH
The jawfish (*Opistognathus* sp.) lurks in the burrow that it has built with stones carried in its large mouth.

way upstream, many even into fresh water. There they grow for three years before returning to the lower estuaries to take part in the spawning migration. Not all mullet species migrate up rivers, and some do not migrate at all, but all are nomadic.
Family: Mugilidae

THREADFINS ■

Despite their common name, these fishes do not belong to the same family as the threadfin breams (see page 455). In Australia, they are often called threadfin salmon. They are good to eat and are targeted by both anglers and commercial fishers.

Threadfins have several distinctive features, including a shark-like snout, a gelatinous membrane over their eyes, a silvery body, and pectoral fins that are divided into two parts: the upper part looks like a normal fin, but the lower section is separate and composed of several thread-like filaments. The number of filaments in this part is useful for identification purposes because many threadfin species look very alike except in this respect.

The family contains 33 species, of which eight occur in Australian waters. Most of the Australian species grow to 20–40 cm in length, but the giant threadfin, or Cooktown salmon (*Eleutheronema tetradactylum*), grows to 120 cm long.

Threadfins live mainly in tropical and subtropical seas, although they also frequent brackish estuaries and a few species travel up rivers. The best places to find them are tidal flats, river mouths and estuaries, where the water is usually turbid. Apparently, these fishes use their long, thread-like 'feelers' to probe the mud for food. Their prey includes small invertebrates – particularly crabs, prawns, worms and molluscs – that are found on soft bottoms.

Threadfins' relationship to other fish families continues to puzzle fish experts. It was once believed that they were close relatives of the mullets and barracudas, but the current opinion is that they are probably cousins of the jewfishes (page 456).
Family: Polynemidae

WRASSES ■

Many members of this family can be found sculling along between reef corals using their pectoral fins for locomotion, their tails dragging limply behind. Others spend their lives in quite different habitats – from inshore and estuarine areas, dense with seagrasses and algae, to smooth sandy regions. Some even make their home near rocky reefs more than 250 metres deep.

Among marine fish families, only the gobies comprise more species than the wrasses. Australian waters shelter nearly a third of the more than 600 species worldwide, mostly in the northern tropical regions.

During the day wrasses poke about in the sand in search of the invertebrates on which they feed, gulping occasional mouthfuls of sediment and spitting out the sand and shell fragments. At the lower back of their throat are fused bones (pharyngeal bones) paved with teeth; these make an efficient crushing plate for extracting the tender inner tissues of hard-shelled prey.

At nightfall wrasses bed down in one of a variety of ways. Many of the more slender species virtually dive into the sandy bottom – something they will also do in daylight if predators are in hot pursuit. Extreme among those that bury themselves are the highly compressed razorfishes, such as the pavo razorfish (*Xyrichtys pavo*), which has a forehead with a knife-like edge that allows it to penetrate the bottom at full speed when it is

being pursued. More robust members of the wrasse family tend to seek shelter more conventionally within nooks and crannies of reefs.

Some wrasse species have special feeding adaptations. The bird wrasse (*Gomphosus varius*) has slender jaws, for extracting food from tight places, and the slingjaw wrasse (*Epibulus insidiator*) can throw its mouth forward a great distance to snap up its prey. Adult tubelips have mouths adapted for feeding on coral polyps, although as juveniles they feed on parasites of other fishes (see box, 'You scratch my back', p. 468).

The body shape of wrasses varies between genera, being deep and perch-like in some and quite slender in others. A characteristic feature of

all wrasses, however, is their single long-based dorsal fin, rather uniform in height and supported by spines, which are often flexible, along the first half of its length. Wrasses also have strong jaws, usually bearing several pairs of prominent, curved canines at the front.

Most wrasse species grow no more than about 20–30 cm long, but the diminutive white-banded sharpnose wrasse (*Wetmorella albofasciata*) rarely reaches more than 5 cm, and the King Kong of the family, the humphead Maori wrasse (*Cheilinus undulatus*) has been known to grow to about 2.3 metres in length and 190 kg in weight. Large humpheads are virtually fearless, allowing divers to approach quite closely.

■ HUMPHEAD WRASSE
The largest wrasse is the humphead Maori wrasse, *Cheilinus undulatus*, which grows to over 2 metres long. These fishes live mainly around the deeper reefs along the Queensland coast north of Mackay.

■ WRASSE
The harlequin tuskfish, *Choerodon fasciatus*, is common all over the Great Barrier Reef. This wrasse is strongly territorial but will tolerate humans swimming nearby, so its striking colouring can be seen at close quarters.

YOU SCRATCH MY BACK

Like all animals, fishes are plagued by parasites; several members of the wrasse family help to rid their neighbours of this problem – and earn themselves an easy meal in the process. When they are juveniles, the yellowtail tubelips (*Diproctacanthus xanthurus*), the tubelip wrasse (*Labrichthys unilineatus*) and the southern tubelips (*Labropsis australis*) feed on the external parasites of their fish neighbours, while the cleaner wrasse (*Labroides dimidiatus*) undertakes this work as a lifelong task.

The juveniles all have distinct dark and pale longitudinal stripes, though the breadth and position of these changes according to species. The wrasses establish 'cleaner stations' at prominent spots on the reef, enabling their uncomfortable clients to find them easily. Here, two cleaner wrasses are tending a brown spotted groper, *Epinephelus coioides*.

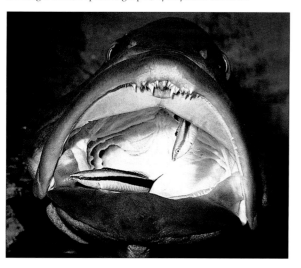

■ WEED WHITING
These cold-water fishes differ from almost all other perch-like fishes in having a spine in their pelvic fin.

Most wrasse genera are represented in Australia by a number of species, but few approach the richness of the genus *Halichoeres*, which has about 20 species living in Australian waters. Although they are somewhat on the small side, these fishes display the standard features of the slimmer type of wrasse. Probably the best known is the golden wrasse (*H. chrysus*), which is a brilliant yellow.

In contrast to the golden wrasse and its close relatives, the tuskfishes (*Choerodon* spp.) have extremely sturdy, rather deep bodies. More than half of the 16 species that are found in Australia are confined to Australian waters, where they appear to have originated.

A few members of this genus, such as the blue tuskfish (*C. cyanodus*), the blackspot tuskfish (*C. schoenleinii*) and the Venus tuskfish (*C. venustus*), grow to 65–90 cm in length and more than 15 kg in weight. These species are occasionally sold as bluebones because of the blue coloration of their teeth and skeleton.

The harlequin tuskfish (*C. fasciatus*) has a striking colour pattern of blue-edged orange bars on a stark white or white and black background.

The hogfishes (*Bodianus* spp.) are closely related to the tuskfishes, but they generally have a more pointed head. There are four hogfish species that are almost entirely confined to Australia's colder waters. They range in size from the deep-dwelling twospot hogfish (*B. bimaculatus*) and the Izu hogfish (*B. izuensis*) at about 10 cm long, to the goldspot hogfish (*B. perditio*) at 80 cm long. The blackspot pigfish (*B. unimaculatus*) is found in subtropical regions on the east coast. This is another of the larger wrasse species, reaching about 40 cm in length.

There are relatively few wrasse species in the colder waters of southern Australia. Among them are the western and eastern blue gropers (*Achoerodus gouldi* and *A. viridis*). These are closely related to the hogfishes, though they are somewhat larger, growing up to 1.7 metres long. These fishes share the common name groper with some members of the rock cod family (page 442).

Other species found in southern waters include the black-spotted wrasse (*Austrolabrus maculatus*), the southern Maori wrasse (*Ophthalmolepis lineolata*), the smaller pretty Polly (*Dotalabrus aurantiacus*), the little rainbow wrasse (*D. alleni*) and the snakeskin wrasse (*Eupetrichthys angustipes*). The bluethroat wrasse (*Notolabrus tetricus*) is common on near-shore reefs.

Family: Labridae

WEED WHITINGS ■

It is quite easy to tell the 11 species of this cold-water family apart, as they have a greater variety of body shapes than almost any other family – which is remarkable in view of the small number of species. Confined to southern Australian and New Zealand coastal waters, most weed whitings can be found in areas of seagrass or weed. Few grow more than 40 cm long.

These fishes are closely related to the generally more tropical wrasses (page 467) and parrotfishes (opposite page), with which some weed whitings have been confused in the past. Like parrotfishes, but in great contrast to wrasses, the jaw teeth of these southern dwellers are entirely fused into beak-like plates. Unlike both wrasses and parrotfishes – and virtually all the other perch-like groups to which they are related – weed whitings have a spine in their pelvic fin and only four soft rays, though there is one species that has no pelvic fin at all.

Perhaps most like the wrasses is the little rock whiting (*Neoodax balteatus*), common in the seagrass beds of bays and estuaries southward from about Sydney in the east and Perth in the west. Growing to about 16 cm long, this small, slender species could easily be mistaken for one of its close wrasse cousins, except for the arrangement of its teeth and its large number of dorsal fin spines. Little rock whiting are mainly tan-coloured and females have a dark, mid-lateral stripe.

Early scientists thought that the rainbow cale (*Odax acroptilus*) was a southern parrotfish because of its bright colours and rather deep body. However, these algal reef-dwelling fishes appear to feed on marine snails and similar invertebrates rather than munching on corals as the parrotfishes do. The closely

■ WEED WHITING
Seaweeds are the staple diet of the herring cale (*Odax cyanomelas*), a weed whiting that lives in the wave-tossed waters along the rocky coast of southern Australia.

related herring cale (*O. cyanomelas*), a much more slender fish with a crescent-shaped tail, is found in the waters along rocky coasts. It uses its powerful jaws to bite off pieces of leathery, broadleafed algae on which it feeds. Like their distant tropical relatives, male and female herring cale are very different in colouring, the males being blue to nearly black with iridescent blue lines on their tails, and the females brown with less distinctive blue markings.

Most various in shape are the six species of the genus *Siphonognathus*. These fishes range from the longray rock whiting (*S. radiatus*), which is a slightly more slender version of the little rock whiting, to the elongated tubemouth (*S. argyrophanes*), which is extremely stretched and looks more like a trumpetfish than a weed whiting. In the past this species was placed in a family of its own because of its lack of pelvic fins.
Family: Odacidae

PARROTFISHES

Parrotfishes are colourful, medium-sized fishes with strong teeth fused into plates that somewhat resemble a parrot's beak. This, and the bold coloration of the males, accounts for their very appropriate common name. There are about 80 species of this large tropical family worldwide, and 30 of these are found in Australian waters.

Parrotfishes occur in huge numbers on coral reefs. During the day they often form extensive schools to feed on reef-crests, scraping or biting off the algae that forms on rubble and corals and digesting everything – including portions of the limestone reefs. Their powerful teeth pulverise pieces of the reef and the fishes, and then discharge large quantities of white, powder-like sand, which often streaks the water along reef edges. At night they sleep in crevices or caves.

Males of each species are easily identified by their distinctive colouring. Females and juveniles, on the other hand, are often very similar in appearance across species, and are usually dull-coloured. Although a few juvenile parrotfishes have distinctive colours, many have similar brown longitudinal bands.

Parrotfishes frequently swim in schools consisting entirely of their own sex. Because of this, the only way to determine which fishes, at their various stages, belong to which species is to observe them during spawning – the time when males and females can be seen together.

Males spawn near the surface with a number of females, and eggs and sperm are released simultaneously.

The humphead parrotfish (*Bolbometopon muricatum*) is the largest of the parrotfishes, reaching a maximum length of 1.2 metres. Adults develop a hump on the head, which is largest in the leader of the group. Although drab in its colouring, which is dark brown to dark greenish grey, the humphead is very impressive when adult – especially if observed in a school, which looks rather like a herd of buffaloes. These fishes sleep in crevices in reefs, usually in the same place every night, often travelling considerable distances to feed and returning just before nightfall. The humphead parrotfish occurs from coastal to outer reef slopes in northern Australia and on the Great Barrier Reef.

The two-colour parrotfish (*Cetoscarus bicolor*) has three very distinct colour forms. Small juveniles are white with an orange band over the head. They are usually seen singly, swimming among large, branching corals. The female is grey with pale areas along the back and a pattern of small spots and lines along the lower sides. The male is bright green with small pink spots

■ PARROTFISH
This ember parrotfish (*Scarus rubroviolaceus*) is showing its powerful teeth. Parrotfishes use their teeth to crop algae from coral reefs, often also grinding up chunks of limestone.

and lines. Adults reach a maximum length of 80 cm and usually occur in small groups, each consisting of several females and one large male.

The adult long-nose parrotfish (*Hipposcarus longiceps*) has a longer snout than most other parrotfishes, and it is slightly pointed. Juveniles have a red or orange stripe that runs from the tip of the snout, over the

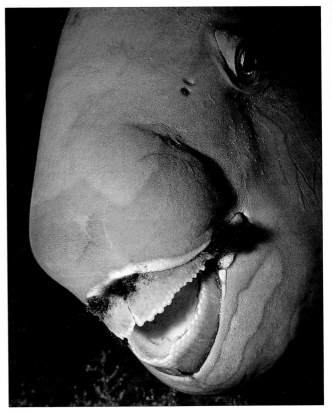

■ PARROTFISH
Parrotfishes, such as this steep-head parrotfish (*Scarus microrhinus*), secrete a covering of mucus each night, within which they sleep. This covering may offer some protection from predators that hunt by smell.

GENDER BENDERS

Scientists once thought that fishes changed sex, a process called hermaphroditism, only rarely during their lifetime. Nowadays we know that such changes are common in many fish groups, and are triggered by social interactions as well as factors related to size and age. Wrasses and parrotfishes are almost universally hermaphrodites.

As they grow, wrasses and parrotfishes often go through three colorations, as in the case of the minifin parrotfish, *Scarus altipinnis*, shown below. In the first phase (called the juvenile phase) they are sexually inactive; in the second phase (the initial phase) they are generally female; and in the third phase (the terminal phase) they are always male.

juvenile phase
minifin parrotfish

initial phase
minifin parrotfish

terminal phase
minifin parrotfish

lower part of the eye to the tail. Also known as the red-stripe parrotfish, the long-nose parrotfish reaches a maximum of 40 cm long. Adults school in lagoons near outer reefs, while juveniles live alone among the corals on coastal reef slopes.

The blue-barred parrotfish (*Scarus ghobban*) is a common and widespread species. Individuals reach a maximum of 75 cm long. They prefer coastal, often silty habitats, where they school both as juveniles and as adults. Although mostly tropical, blue-barred parrotfishes range into subtropical waters. Larvae float a long way in the currents and juveniles are found well beyond their tropical breeding range. In some summers larvae are plentiful as far south as Sydney Harbour, and individuals can reach at least half their maximum potential length before dying during the winter, when the water becomes too cold for them.

Forsten's parrotfish (*Scarus forsteni*), sometimes called whitespotted parrotfish because of the distinctive marking on the juveniles, has three easily identifiable forms. The juvenile is very dark with a small, distinct white spot on its sides. The female is dark to light brown with a green to blue metallic blotch, often outlined in gold, on the side. The male has thick blue-green banding on the head. This species reaches a maximum of 55 cm long.

The male king parrotfish (*S. flavipectoralis*) has yellow pectoral fins, and its head has a green horizontal stripe that passes over the lower part of its eyes. Females are rather plain, yellowish, and similar to

several other parrotfish species. This is a small species, reaching about 30 cm long. It prefers coastal and protected inner reefs, where females swim in small groups and males are usually solitary.

Schlegel's parrotfish (*S. frenatus*) grows to a maximum of 40 cm long. The male has large dark and pale areas and a bright yellow saddle-like marking in the middle of its back. The female has pale chevrons like those of the females of other parrotfish species, so identification is sometimes difficult. This species often mixes with other parrotfishes, forming large schools to feed. Such schools usually travel over extensive areas of reef, descending on patches of algae for quick feeding sessions.
Family: Scaridae

THORNFISHES ■

Also known as temperate icefishes, thornfishes belong to the dominant fish group of the Antarctic, the Antarctic cods. Australia's three thornfish species are confined to the southern part of the continent, where they have colonised fresh water as well as reefy marine habitats near the shore. The largest of these species grows to 36 cm long.

Thornfishes take their name from the largest and most widely distributed genus, *Bovichtus*, which has a greatly enlarged, sharp, thorn-like spine on the gill cover. They are among the most commonly encountered fishes in tidal pools, on pier pilings and under ledges near the tide mark. Their bright coloration and heavy ornamentation afford excellent camouflage. They eat small crustaceans that live within the diverse array of encrusting invertebrates, such as sponges and sea squirts, that dominate their habitat.

The congolli (*Pseudaphritis urvillii*) spends part of its life in rivers and streams but can tolerate a wide range of salinities and moves to estuaries to spawn. It feeds on a varied diet of worms, crustaceans and insect larvae. The congolli is also known as freshwater flathead because of its resemblance, when resting on the bottom, to the unrelated marine flatheads (page 439).

A marine relative of the congolli, the flathead congolli (*Halaphritis platycephala*) was discovered recently off Tasmania and Victoria. This small fish lives at the back of caves and under deep ledges in shallow water, revealing itself only after dark, when it swims about in search of food.
Family: Bovichtidae

■ THORNFISH
The congolli (*Pseudaphritis urvillii*) is a hardy thornfish species that is able to adjust to rapid changes in salinity. It lives mainly in estuaries in south-eastern Australia, but sometimes swims hundreds of kilometres inland.

Fishy facts

From space, Earth looks like an iridescent blue jewel, because no less than 70 per cent of the planet's surface is covered by water. This is why life was able to evolve on Earth – as far as we know, the only planet in the solar system where this has happened.

Fishes were the first vertebrates to evolve, and they are still among the most successful forms of life. They are perfectly adapted to life in water and are found in every aquatic habitat, from mountain streams to the deepest ocean trenches. Some are confined to fresh water, others to the sea, but many can withstand a broad range of saltiness in the water, and can live in estuaries or migrate between rivers and the sea.

Roughly 20 000 fish species have been identified, and and it seems likely that many more are yet to be discovered and named. Nearly half of the known species are found in fresh waters – an amazing proportion, given that fresh waters make up a tiny 0.01 per cent of our planet's water.

Australian oddities

Australia has about 3000 marine fish species, but because it is a dry island continent it has fewer freshwater fish species than any other continent (except

This blenny's large, dramatic eyes camouflage the fish against the colourful reef background.

Above, a fierce moray eel lurks in a crevice. Eels look primitive, but they have survived many years of evolution. Left, shoaling and sheltering in the tentacles of invertebrate marine life forms are species survival techniques for small fishes.

Antarctica, where there are many fossils of freshwater fishes but no living freshwater species). This is because Australia was isolated by oceans quite early in the geological upheaval that produced the present distribution of landmasses, and freshwater fishes cannot cross salt waters.

But Australia is home to some of the strangest of the freshwater fishes. The Australian lungfish, for example, is one of the few surviving fishes that can extract oxygen from air as well as water. This sounds like a huge step in the evolution of animals from an aquatic to a terrestrial existence, but fossil records show that lungfishes have lived here virtually unchanged for 100,000,000 years, and scientists believe that these fishes evolved air-breathing lungs quite independently of the development of air-breathing lungs in land-dwelling vertebrates. Blind gudgeons and blind cave eels are Australian freshwater fish species that have adapted to life in waters below the surface of Earth.

Antifreeze for fishes

Most fishes cannot raise their body temperature above that of the ambient water. Antarctic fishes have evolved ways of surviving at temperatures well below freezing point. Protein compounds – the biological equivalent of antifreeze – stop their blood from turning (literally) to ice. They also have low metabolic rates and are not very active, which conserves energy. Their skeletons are light, and stored fat deposits buoy them up so that they do not need to use precious energy to stay afloat.

ICEFISH
The blood of these unique fishes contains no haemoglobin at all. Unaffected by the very low temperatures of Antarctic waters, this thinner blood is able to circulate freely in the fish's body.

ANTARCTIC ROCK CODS

With about 50 species, this is the most abundant and diverse of the Antarctic cod families. The largest grow up to 2.2 metres long and are active midwater predators that feed on fishes and squids. Other species are modest-sized, bottom-living fishes that feed on a variety of small worms and crustaceans. The family also contains small species that look like pilchards and feed on small planktonic crustaceans.

Antarctic rock cods range from Antarctic coastal waters, where many species feed exclusively on krill, through subantarctic waters to Patagonia in the western hemisphere and New Zealand in the eastern hemisphere.
Family: Nototheniidae

ICEFISHES

Icefishes are unique among the vertebrates in lacking red blood cells and the red pigment, haemoglobin, which in other animals carries oxygen from the gills or lungs to the tissues. Most Antarctic cods have fewer red blood cells and a lower

concentration of haemoglobin than do other fishes, but icefishes lack haemoglobin altogether and have less than one hundredth of the red cells of most fishes. This reduces the viscosity of their blood, making it easier to pump around the body, which is an important consideration at low temperatures. It has been calculated that the lower red blood cell count in icefishes has about the same effect on blood viscosity as a 20°C rise in temperature.

Icefishes can exist perfectly well without functional red cells; the oxygen is carried from the gills and skin (these fishes lack scales) in the blood in simple solution. They have a relatively large volume of blood, which is pumped around the body quickly by a large, powerful heart. The low temperatures are an advantage in this process because more oxygen is dissolved in the sea water and in the blood plasma than in warmer conditions.

Individuals can grow up to about 50 cm long, and are more streamlined than the Antarctic rock cods. They have a large mouth and teeth, and many live in the midwater, feeding on krill and small fishes.
Family: Channichthyidae

SAND LANCES

The cigar-shaped sand lances are apparently closely related to the stargazers (next entry), though they are quite different in appearance. In Australia they live in rather shallow tropical waters. Often found in sand, sand lances use the soft bottom as a shelter from predators and as a place to sleep at night. During the day they hover above the sandy surface,

feeding on plankton that they collect by dropping their protruding lower jaw to form a funnel-like mouth. Though occurring in large numbers in some parts of their range, sand lances' speed, agility and ability to dive to the bottom to escape threats usually save them from capture.

A long, low dorsal fin, with the sensory lateral line positioned just below the base, embedded scales, a lengthwise skin-fold along the lower edge of each side, a forked tail and the absence of pelvic fins make these fishes easy to recognise.
Family: Ammodytidae

STARGAZERS AND SAND STARGAZERS

Remarkably similar in appearance, stargazers and sand stargazers both have bulldog-like faces with upward-looking eyes. Despite their similarities, it is thought that these two families developed from separate ancestors – a process known as convergent evolution – and that their almost identical lives have led to their similar body shapes.

They are ambushers that live buried in sandy bottoms, only their eyes protruding above the surface to watch for small fishes and shrimps. Both have protruding lower jaws and upward-turned mouths that position their gape at surface level so that they can act instantaneously when an unwary victim approaches. A fine, fleshy fringe along the edge of their lips forms a sieve that excludes sand particles when the fish draws water into its mouth for respiration while it is buried.

Stargazers inhabit the tropical and temperate marine waters of all major oceans, and can be found along the Australian coast from the shallow waters of estuaries to depths of almost 1000 metres. The species differ in their combination of features, which may include a separate spiny first dorsal fin, intricate sculpturing on their bone-encased head, and a pair of strange bony flaps on their chin. All have lateral (sensory) lines close to the base of their dorsal fin and a prominent protective spine, angled backwards, behind the upper end of each gill opening. Supplied with potent venom, these spines inject poison into aggressors. Human deaths from stargazer toxin have been suspected, though these are yet to be confirmed.

The smallest stargazers grow to at least 15 cm long. At the other end of the scale are species such as the coast-dwelling southern stargazer (*Kathetostoma laeve*) and the speckled

STARGAZER
Body buried in the sand, the western stargazer scans the water for prey with its upward-looking eyes. Its upturned mouth is perfectly suited to snatching and devouring unwary passers-by.

ALL THINGS COME TO THOSE WHO WAIT

Fishes that must wait for food to come to them stand a better chance of a meal if their prey can be enticed within reach. Stargazers have a slender, worm-like, fleshy lure that has developed from a strip of skin, called an oral valve, that borders the inner edge of their lower jaw. From its hiding place in the sandy sea floor the ambusher pokes this undulating morsel up into the water, inviting the unwary to investigate more closely.

The southern stargazer below shows the upward-turning mouth with its well positioned gape.

stargazer (*K. canaster*), of somewhat deeper waters, which can reach 75 cm long. But even they are dwarfed by their New Zealand cousin, the monkfish (*K. giganteum*), which grows to more than a metre.

Most very young stargazers live in surface waters until they are a few centimetres long, after which they settle down to a bottom-dwelling existence. The young of one species, the extremely deep-dwelling purple stargazer, *Pleuroscopus pseudodorsalis*, appear to live well away from the bottom until they reach nearly 30 cm long. When they reach this size, their compact, nearly cylindrical head and body become quite flattened and flabby, perhaps to equip them for life on a muddy bottom where they cannot easily dig in.

The small family of sand stargazers is confined to the cool waters of southern Australia and New Zealand, where individuals are most frequently found in very shallow waters along ocean beaches and in clean sandy estuaries. Also known as pygmy stargazers, these diminutive fishes reach little more than 10 cm in length. Like their stargazer cousins they have pelvic fins beneath their head, but unlike the close-set fins of their namesakes these fins are widely separated and well adapted for digging the fishes

into the sea floor. Other distinguishing features include a sensory line (the lateral line) running along the middle of each side; very long-based dorsal and anal fins; and the absence of head and fin spines.

All four Australian species have mottled cream and brown bodies that closely resemble the sandy bottom, making these fishes difficult to detect even when they emerge from the sand. One species, the robust pygmy stargazer (*Crapatalus munroi*), is apparently confined to Victorian and Tasmanian waters.
Families: Uranoscopidae (stargazers), Leptoscopidae (sand stargazers)

DUCKBILLS, SAND DIVERS AND SAND BURROWERS ■

Duckbills, sand divers and sand burrowers are seldom encountered because they are rare, well camouflaged or small, or because they dwell on the outer continental shelf and upper slope, out of sight of divers and anglers. Adults are typically less than 25 cm long and have an elongated body, tapering to the tail. They feed on small juvenile fishes and small invertebrates.

Members of the genus *Bembrops* look like flatheads (page 439). Their extremely flattened snout, with the lower jaw longer than the upper, resembles a duck's bill. Other duckbills resemble grubfishes (next entry), except that they have two well-defined dorsal fins instead of one. Large eyes on top of their head give good peripheral vision when the fish is buried beneath the sand. Each eye is capable of independent movement, so the fish can look in more than one direction at once.

More than a dozen duckbill species live in tropical Australian waters, but most are poorly known.

Sand divers are small, almost eel-like fishes that occur throughout the Indo-Pacific, though the Australian species are poorly known. Sand divers are striking, often colourful fishes, with tall dorsal and anal fins that are spectacular when raised. Most species remain buried in the sand, emerging only to feed.

With six species, Australia has almost half the world's sand burrowers. They are very small, rarely exceeding 8 cm long as adults, and extremely well camouflaged. Some have bodies that are almost transparent – so much so that their backbone is visible. The slender sand burrower (*Creedia haswelli*) lives on sand or gravel seabeds.
Families: Percophidae (duckbills), Trichonotidae (sand divers), Creediidae (sand burrowers)

GRUBFISHES ■

Of this moderately large family, with about 60 species throughout the world, only the genus *Parapercis*, with about 20 species, occurs in Australian waters. Many look alike, and some do not yet have scientific names. Most species are tropical, but two occur in shallow waters along Australia's southern coast. There are only slight differences between juveniles and adults, and between sexes. Grubfishes, which range from 12 cm to 22 cm long, feed on shrimps and other small invertebrates.

The spotted grubfish (*P. ramsayi*), a pale species with a series of dark blotches along its lower sides, occurs in sheltered bays of southern New

SIMILAR FAMILIES – DIFFERENT SHAPES Although their shapes are so different, sand divers (top) and sand burrowers (bottom), together with duckbills, belong to rather similar families of quite small bottom-dwelling fishes.

■ GRUBFISH Grubfishes, which are also known as weevers and sandperches, have an elongated body with a long-based dorsal fin over the back. Like most active daytime hunters that live on the bottom of the ocean, grubfishes have large eyes on top of their head.

■ THREEFIN
Most threefins live in shallow reef habitats, some in intertidal zones, generally occupying the walls or ceilings of caves and hiding under rocks. A few live on sponges in deep waters. Threefins usually have excellent camouflage and can change colour to suit their surroundings.

South Wales, South Australia and southern Western Australia. One common South Australian species is the wavy grubfish (*P. haackei*), which has a dark stripe, often wavy, from behind the eye to the tail.

Commonly observed tropical species are the sharp-nose grubfish (*P. cylindrica*), a pale grey species with thin dark banding over the top and a series of large black blotches along the lower half of its body, and the false-eye grubfish (*P. clathrata*), which has two eye-like spots on top of its head, not far behind the real ones. The widespread tropical pink-banded grubfish (*P. nebulosa*), which has brown and pink bands, is often seen in Sydney Harbour.
Family: Pinguipedidae

THREEFINS ■
More than 200 species of these tiny fishes are known, though many have not yet been given scientific names. About nine genera and an undetermined number of species inhabit Australian waters.

Tropical threefins are usually a few centimetres long, normally lack distinctive colouring and are difficult to identify. Sometimes males show bright coloration when displaying to females, and turn yellow, orange or red over the back. In more temperate waters, threefins grow larger and are easier to identify by their fin and head characteristics, and sometimes by their marking in various patterns of spots and bands.

■ COMMON THREEFIN
The widespread common threefin (*Norfolkia clarkei*) grows to about 8 cm long in the cooler waters around Tasmania. In the waters off central New South Wales it reaches about 5 cm long.

Also known as triplefins or threefin blennies, threefins are closely related to blennies (page 476) but, unlike blennies, they usually have scales on their bodies. Threefins are distinctive in having a dorsal fin in three sections, generally separated or joined only at the base. They are easily mistaken for gobies (page 478), which are also small but have only two dorsal-fin sections, and usually have pelvic fins joined into a cup-shaped disc.

Threefins occur in small, loose groups consisting mostly of females, while males often inhabit a territory that they defend against other males. Threefins feed on small invertebrates and sometimes on fishes just out of the larval stage.

The common threefin (*Norfolkia clarkei*) is a variable species and grows to different maximum sizes, apparently in relation to water temperature. It is longest in the coolest part of its range. Common threefins from cooler southern areas also have

more fin rays than those from warmer climates. The common threefin lives in most marine habitats, from shallow, silty environments to moderately deep offshore areas where sponges grow. In Tasmania it is known as Macleay's threefin. The very similar crested threefin (*N. cristata*) occurs along the south-west coast. It is best distinguished from the common threefin by its much higher first dorsal fin.

There are several more small species, most of which are very seldom noticed, in temperate as well as tropical waters. Some grow to a maximum of only 35 mm long.

The black-cheek threefin (*Enneapterygius rufopileus*) belongs to a tropical genus that comprises many small and similar species, most of which are inconspicuous. Only the male is brightly coloured, and then only when displaying to a female. Generally the species are difficult to identify unless the display colour of the male is known. This is usually a combination of a red or orange body, black fins and black dorsal fins, though sometimes the first fin is white. The female is usually a drab grey-brown with some white spotting, or sometimes with narrow dark bands on the body. Common along Sydney's rocky shores, usually in shallow protected reefs and rock pools, the black-cheek threefin is also known from Queensland and Lord Howe Island. Another common New South Wales species is the ring-scale threefin (*E. annulatus*), which prefers to live in estuaries. Both species grow to a maximum of about 45 mm long.

The jumping blenny (*Lepido-blennius marmoratus*) is 12 cm long and inhabits shallow inshore reefs and rock pools, often in turbulent zones, from the Bass Strait region

to the south-west coast of Western Australia. The jumping joey (*L. haplodactylus*), which occurs on the east coast from Byron Bay in New South Wales to Western Port in Victoria is very similar in size and appearance. It lives mainly in rock pools and on mud flats. When water levels drop because of wave action, the jumping blenny may be seen clinging to rocks out of the water. The two species may overlap in range in Victoria. Jumping joeys have smooth scales; jumping blennies' scales are rough.

The many-rayed threefin (*Forsterygion varium*) is common in Tasmania's Derwent Estuary. It ranges into brackish waters, and is found on rocky reefs and rubble bottoms. It and a closely related species also found only in Tasmania appear to have been introduced from New Zealand. The many-rayed threefin grows to about 15 cm long. The smaller bare-backed threefin (*Grahamia gymnotam*) grows up to 9.5 cm long and prefers clearer water. It inhabits rocky reefs and is often found on jetty pylons.
Family: Tripterygiidae

WEEDFISHES AND SNAKE BLENNIES ■

Most members of this large family of fishes live in the southern hemisphere, and more than 40 of the world's 100 species are found in Australian waters. In Australia many species are well known, although they have not yet been given scientific names. Snake blennies differ from weedfishes in being more elongated, having eel-like or snake-like bodies.

Secretive or well camouflaged, these fishes are rarely seen. Most species live in heavily vegetated reef and seagrass habitats, mainly in coastal regions in the southern half of the continent.

Weedfishes and snake blennies are usually small – about 10 cm long when fully grown – but a few species on the south coast reach 40 cm in length. They feed on small invertebrates and fishes living on or among weeds. Unusually for small fishes, they use internal fertilisation and give birth to live young.

The crested weedfish (*Cristiceps australis*) is a common south coast species. It is usually drab coloured when among weeds, but it may be brownish yellow when living in kelp. Above the head the dorsal fin is elevated as a separate section that is much higher than the rest. The almost identical golden weedfish (*C. aurantiacus*) lives among kelp

on the east coast. It is distinguished from the crested weedfish by the position of its dorsal fin, which begins further forward on its head, well in front of its eyes. Both these species grow to about 18 cm long.

Johnston's weedfish (*Heteroclinus johnstoni*) is the largest Australian weedfish, reaching 40 cm in length. It is best identified by the large, fleshy tentacles on its snout and above its eyes; these tentacles have a star-like lobe at their tips. Juveniles are strongly banded, and often the head is black with a white snout. Adults may have a series of eye-like spots along their back, one row in each dark band.

The common weedfish (*H. perspicillatus*) is one of the most common weedfish species, and is found under rocks or in seagrasses and often in habitats with little vegetation. The many similar species are all highly variable in colour – greywhite, pink, brown, green, yellow or red – and in pattern – spotted, blotched or banded. On Australia's southern coast the common weedfish can be identified by the eyesized dark spot on its head below its dorsal fin, but on the east coast Whitelegg's weedfish (*H. whiteleggi*) also has this spot. Both species grow to about 10 cm in length. Also similar is the banded weedfish (*H. fasciatus*) from the east coast, which grows to only 65 mm long.

The variable snake blenny (*Ophiclinus ningulus*) is one of the commonest snake blennies in

Victoria and Tasmania, although it is very secretive. It lives under rocks or debris on coarse sand or rubble. Its colouring is extremely variable, ranging from black with a white stripe over the snout to pale brown with light and dark mottled patterns. It reaches 10 cm in length. Also common in Victoria are the black-back snake blenny (*O. gracilis*) and the frosted snake blenny (*O. gabrieli*). Both live in seagrass areas, usually among decaying weeds accumulating against rocks. Frosted snake blennies can grow to 16 cm long.

The variegated snake blenny (*Ophiclinops varius*), which is one of the smallest snake blennies, reaches only about 5 cm in length. Its highly variable colouring always camouflages it well against the low reefs and seagrasses it typically inhabits. It is found in shallow protected bays along the entire south coast of the continent and the northern coast of Tasmania. Two other species of this genus have restricted distributions in South Australia and southern Western Australia, but they are poorly known from only a few specimens identified so far.

The sand crawler (*Sticharium dorsale*) lives in protected coastal bays along the edges of reefs or seagrass beds, spending nearly all its time under the sand with just its face exposed. Here it feeds on shrimps that swim just above the sand. Sand crawlers have specially modified pectoral and pelvic fins for dragging

■ WEEDFISH
Johnston's weedfish inhabits protected coastal bays around reefs, where it hides, and patrols seagrasses, in which it feeds. The adults of this species sometimes also live among sponges in deeper water.

■ TASMANIAN BLENNY
Parablennius tasmanianus,
a species from southern
waters, grows to a length
of about 13 cm and
blends easily with its
background. It feeds on
algae in rockpools and
tidal gutters, and also
lives in sheltered estuaries, where it is attracted
to jetty pylons.

long, is widespread in the Indo-
Pacific. The red-streaked blenny
(*Cirripectes stigmaticus*), which lives
on shallow reef flats with rich coral
growth, is one of the most common
blenny species. A shy creature, it
dives quickly into holes or under
corals if approached, and only the
large adults, with their bright red
markings, are usually seen. These
individuals, which grow to 10 cm
long, are more daring and often sit
openly on top of corals. They feed
on algae at coral bases.

The Tasmanian blenny (*Parablennius tasmanianus*) is a commonly
observed species in southern waters.
The only other blenny species there,
the oyster blenny (*Omobranchus
anolius*), is rare on the south coast
and lives intertidally among oyster
shells or clusters of tubeworms. The
Tasmanian blenny occurs in rock
pools and coastal bays, often around
jetty pylons. The very similar crested
blenny (*Parablennius intermedius*) is
common in the Sydney area and
ranges to tropical waters. All three
species, which feed on algae, reach
a maximum of 13 cm long.

The brown sabretooth blenny
(*Petroscirtes lupus*) is one of several
similar species in the tropical Indo-
Pacific. It is probably restricted to
eastern Australia and New
Caledonia, ranging well south of
Sydney. The short-headed sabretooth blenny (*P. breviceps*), with
several colour forms that mimic
harptail blennies, and the variable
sabretooth blenny (*P. variabilis*),
which inhabits seagrasses, both
occur in northern Australia. Males
of all three species use empty shells
or aluminium cans for nests, where
they guard the fertilised eggs. They
grow to 10–12 cm long.

themselves through the sand, leaving snake-like tracks behind them.
A second species, the dusky crawler
(*S. clarkae*) is more oceanic and is
usually found in the sandy bays of
islands. Both species grow to a maximum of 10 cm long.

The eel blenny (*Peronedys anguillaris*) is one of the most unusual and
also one of the rarest species in this
family. It has an eel-like body 13 cm
long and minute pectoral and pelvic
fins. Inhabiting the decaying seagrasses that lie below living seagrass
beds, it is known only from South
Australia, occurring in St Vincent
Gulf and around Kangaroo Island.
Because of habitat changes, the eel
blenny may now be restricted to
waters around Kangaroo Island.
Family: Clinidae

BLENNIES ■

Most of the well over 300 blenny
species are very small tropical fishes.
The family can be divided into two
groups: swimming species and bottom-dwelling species.

Swimming blennies usually have
bright colours and very elongated
bodies. They generally prefer deeper
water than bottom-dwellers, beyond
the intertidal zones, and swim just
above the sea bottom.

Species that rest on the bottom or
cling to the reef are usually thicker-
bodied and better camouflaged than

swimming species. Most live in very
shallow waters, many in the intertidal zone, where they feed on algae
that they scrape off rocks or rubble.
Some even cling to rocks out of the
water when wave action makes the
water level drop.

A few blennies mimic other fishes,
such as plankton-eaters or cleaner-
fishes, mainly to trick these larger
fishes into coming close enough for
the blenny to snatch a bite from
their fins or scales.

The pink-spotted blenny (*Exallias
brevis*) is a common tropical blenny
that usually lives secretively among
densely branched corals. It has distinctive coloration to suit its habitat:
juveniles have black spots and
adults become pink-spotted, particularly on the tail. The pink-spotted
blenny, which grows to 14 cm

■ SABRETOOTH BLENNY
The male short-headed sabretooth
blenny (*Petroscirtes breviceps*) guards its
eggs in hollow objects on the sea floor.

The tubeworm blenny (*Plagiotremus rhinorhynchos*) is a slender creature with blue, black and sometimes orange stripes along its body. It uses empty tubeworm casings for both shelter and nesting. The similar hit-and-run blenny (*P. tapeinosoma*) has white along the underside and a more blotchy body stripe. This fish, also known as the mimic blenny, often swims with other fishes. Although the mimicry is poor, it is sufficient for the fish to get close enough to its prey to bite off bits of skin or fin. Both these species occur commonly on tropical reefs, ranging into subtropical zones. They reach about 12 cm in length.

Harptail blennies (*Meiacanthus* spp.) are coastal fishes, usually swimming above rubble and sand along reef margins and feeding on small bottom-dwelling invertebrates. Most grow to about 12 cm long. Harptail blennies have a venomous bite and are distinctively coloured, often yellow with contrasting black lines. Some other blennies, and also some cardinalfishes (page 446), mimic the harptails in colour, shape and behaviour to protect themselves from predators.

The yellow-lined harptail blenny (*M. lineatus*), a common Queensland species, may extend into northern New South Wales. There are several similarly striped species, of which only the gold-stripe harptail blenny (*M. luteus*) occurs in the same area. Another common species, the eyelash harptail blenny (*M. atrodorsalis*), is yellow with a grey head and has a short black stripe behind the eye.

The eyelash harptail blenny is mimicked by the false harptail blenny (*Plagiotremus laudandus*), which swims with it in order to share its prey. Another blenny, the false cleanerfish (*Aspidontus*

■ MOYER'S DRAGONET
Moyer's dragonet is one of the many members of this family known to inhabit Australian waters. More than 30 species have already been recorded.

taeniatus), widespread and common, perfectly mimics the cleaner wrasse (page 467) in looks and behaviour. Fishes looking for cleaner wrasse to remove parasites are tricked into approaching the impostor, but instead of the expected cleaning service, they often lose a scale or a bit of fin. Only close examination of the mouth identifies the masquerader. Growing to a maximum length of 10 cm, false cleanerfish sometimes form small groups and, as well as feeding on larger fishes, occasionally eat algae scraped from the rocks.
Family: Blenniidae

DRAGONETS ■
Small bottom-dwelling marine fishes, the dragonets, or stinkfishes, are most diverse in tropical seas. More than 30 species occur in Australian waters; the five that inhabit southern Australian waters are found nowhere else in the world.

Adult dragonets grow to at least 35 cm long. Most species live on sand or muddy bottoms, but a few occur among seaweed or between rocks or corals. They are so well camouflaged that they are seen by only the most observant divers, or in catches taken by prawn fishermen. Most dragonets live in the shallow waters of the continental shelf, but some inhabit water up to 900 metres deep on the continental slope.

Dragonets have elongated bodies and enlarged fins. Small specimens may resemble gobies, but their large pelvic fins are situated forward of the pectorals and are not interconnected or transformed into a sucking

disc, as in gobies. They also have a slimy, scaleless body, a small pore-like gill opening and a triangular shaped head.

Most dragonets are extremely colourful. Males tend to be brighter than females and often have greatly enlarged dorsal fins. The first few spines of the first dorsal fin, in particular, are often very long and filamentous. These male structures are used as a flagging device to attract a mate of the same species during the period of courtship.

Their alternative common name, stinkfish, derives from the odour of the dragonet's flesh. The flesh of the largest temperate-water species, the common stinkfish (*Foetorepus calauropomus*), is very strong-smelling and bitter-tasting, and causes nausea when eaten.
Family: Callionymidae

SCHINDLER'S FISHES
It was not recognised until quite recently that these very small, slender fishes were related to gobies (page 478). Schindler's fishes live offshore in the open ocean or near coral reefs and look very much like larval bony fishes, even when adult.

Only two species have been discovered in the world, and very little is known about them. Both species are transparent and grow to about 22 mm in total length. They are among the lightest known vertebrates, with the adults reaching only about 8 mg in weight.
Family: Schindleriidae

■ DRAGONETS
This pair of common stinkfishes (*Foetorepus calauropomus*) clasp in a mating embrace as they drift through temperate waters. The bitter flesh of the common stinkfish repels other species.

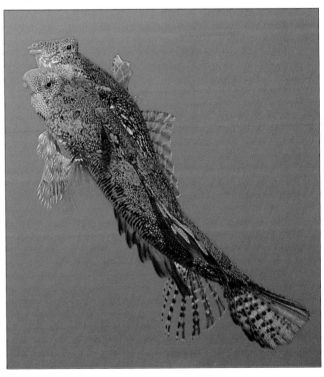

LIFE IN THE FAST CURRENT

Life is not easy in the intertidal zone. Fishes living there have to cope with swirling waves at some times, and at others with receding tides that can leave them isolated in pools or on mud flats. Generally they are small fishes (less than about 20 cm) with thin or flattened shapes for hiding in holes and crevices. Some have pelvic fins modified into suckers (clingfishes) or discs (gobies) to prevent them from being washed away by the continuous surge. A few, such as mudskippers (illustrated below) and rock-hopping blennies, have adapted to being exposed to the air at low tide, emerging from the water to graze the algal slime that covers the surface of mud and rocks.

Many intertidal fishes have pronounced homing abilities. Particularly striking are the pool-dwelling blennies, which leap into the air to view the surrounding terrain. They forage widely over the exposed reef flat at low tide, but always return to their home pools.

GUDGEONS AND GOBIES

Very similar in outward appearance, gudgeons and gobies occur around the Australian coast. Nearly all Australian gudgeons live in fresh or brackish water, only one species being found on coral reefs, but most Australian gobies are marine.

Rather stoutly built, gudgeons have two dorsal fins, and their paired pelvic fins are close together below their pectoral fins. Gudgeons usually have large mouths with fine, sharp teeth. They ambush their prey of small fishes, prawns, yabbies, insects and other aquatic animals.

■ GUDGEON
The carnivorous purple-spotted gudgeon, *Mogurnda mogurnda*, is most at home in slow-flowing water, where it seeks its prey of worms, tiny fishes, insect larvae and small crustaceans.

One of the cleverest ambushers is the crimson-tipped gudgeon (*Butis butis*), which mimics a dead stick or hides under a floating leaf in order to get close to its prey.

Gudgeons range from small – about the length of a human thumb – to nearly half a metre in length. The sleepy cod (*Oxyeleotris lineolata*), which reaches about 40 cm long, has brown and green markings arranged in subtle patterns like a Persian carpet. Some gudgeons, such as the purple-spotted gudgeon (*Mogurnda mogurnda*) and Cox's gudgeon (*Gobiomorphus coxii*), are good at leaping and climbing. Cox's gudgeon has even been seen climbing up dam walls when the adults are migrating upstream.

An enormously diverse group in tropical and subtropical seas, gobies are small fishes found in marine, brackish and fresh waters throughout the world, including Australia. If the goby-like fishes from the families Microdesmidae, Kraemeriidae, Xenisthmidae and Schindleriidae are included, gobies probably number almost 2000 species.

Gobies belonging to the subfamily Gobiinae look rather like gudgeons and can be confused with them. Many gobies in Australia are marine or estuarine dwellers, but a few live in fresh water. The goby's paired pelvic fins have joined to form a distinctive disc or cup, though some coral reef gobies have separate pelvic fins without a disc. Most gobies also have two dorsal fins. They live near the bottom, and many are protectively coloured to help them to blend in with the sand or rock on the sea floor and thereby avoid bottom-dwelling predatory fishes and wading birds such as reef herons.

Gobies come in all sizes, from the smallest known vertebrate – the centimetre-long coral reef goby

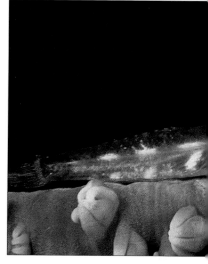

■ GOBIES
Many gobies have cup-like pelvic fins that help them to cling by suction to their home without being dislodged.

(*Trimmatom nanus*) – to giant freshwater gobies nearly half a metre long. A number of gobies have become specialists in particular ways of life. Some are plankton-pickers that hover in schools above the bottom, ready to grab tiny animals as they float past in the current. Others are sand-sifters that shovel up large mouthfuls of sand and strain it out of their gill openings before swallowing any very small creatures that have been trapped. Sea whip gobies (*Bryaninops yongei*), which grow to only 35 mm long, lay their eggs close to the tip of a sea whip so that, when the eggs hatch, the baby fishes will be swept away by the current to colonise a new group of sea whips.

One group of gobies has developed the ability to move over and in mud. These are the mudskippers (subfamily Oxudercinae), the best known of which leap and climb over mud and rocks in mangroves and other brackish habitats. Other mudskippers are probably better described as mud wallowers or mud burrowers, because they swim through the mud. Mudskippers have tiny eyes, so they depend on the sensory systems in their skin to find food or escape from danger.
Family: Gobiidae

SAND DARTS

Sand darts, or sand gobies, are goby-like fishes that are rarely seen because they burrow into fine coral or muddy sand in very shallow marine to brackish areas of tropical Indo-Pacific waters. They are slim, with very small, close-set eyes and

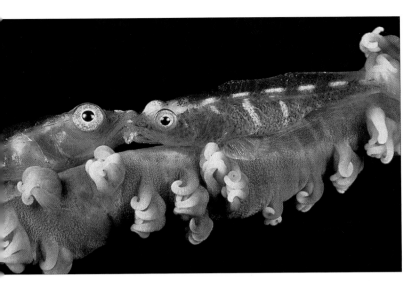

a pointed, protruding chin, which they use to force their way into the sand after tiny animals to eat.

Translucent, whitish or yellowish, sometimes with very light brown markings, sand darts occasionally grow to about 7 cm long, but they are usually smaller.
Family: Kraemeriidae

DART-GOBIES AND WORMFISHES ■

Some of the most beautiful of the goby-like fishes belong to this family. They are slender, elegant fishes, about 12 cm long, with long fins and large eyes, and are usually brightly coloured. They feed on plankton and small animals living in sand.

Dart gobies live around coral reefs in schools, pairs or small groups, and are rather shy and wary, diving into tiny refuge holes at the first sign of danger. The fire goby (*Nemateleotris magnifica*), which grows to about 7 cm long, has a long, banner-like first dorsal fin that it flicks gently, probably as a contact signal, though this explanation has not yet been confirmed by scientists.

■ DART GOBY
Dart gobies, such as the purple fire goby (*Nemateleotris decora*), pick plankton from the water as it drifts past.

Wormfishes are long and slender, with prominent rounded chins and very long fins. They are often blue, yellow and pink, and usually have a long dark stripe on their body. They hover over coral sand banks or seagrass beds around coral reefs.
Family: Microdesmidae

WRIGGLERS

Looking rather like thick matchsticks, wrigglers are about 3–5 cm long, with small eyes, low fins, a prominent bulbous chin and red to brown colouring, often with blackish spots and bands. They live in the tiny holes and crevices of Indo-Pacific coral reefs, such as the Great Barrier Reef, and are rarely seen.

Because of the inaccessibility of their habitat and the difficulty in observing them, very little is known about their life history.
Family: Xenisthmidae

RABBITFISHES ■

Primarily tropical fishes of the Indo-Pacific region, 16 rabbitfish species are known from Australian waters. Those of the subgenus *Lo*, with its distinctive protruding snout, are quite easy to distinguish from those of the subgenus *Siganus*.

Rabbitfishes range from about 20 cm to 35 cm in length. They have compressed oval bodies covered with tiny scales, and their fins have numerous venomous spines. Rabbitfishes have an unusually large number of spines in their anal fin and are unique in having a spine at each end of their pelvic fin, with three soft rays between them. They feed primarily on algae, but may also eat other plant matter – one has even been seen eating banana peel!

Several species of rabbitfishes live in seagrass beds, and are so abundant in certain regions that they

constitute an important food source for other fishes, despite their small size. Seagrass-dwelling species are drab coloured, usually a greenish grey, and each one has different spotted markings, in part or entirely covering its body and fins.

Coral reef species are much more brightly coloured, and some are a vivid yellow with blue or black markings. Most distinctive is the foxface (*Siganus vulpinus*), with its yellow body and black and white face. On coral reefs adults of most species move about in pairs swimming near the bottom, while the juveniles hide among corals.

The common species *S. nebulosus* is known by several common names – black trevally, black rabbitfishes or happy moments. It occurs in estuaries and coastal waters around the northern half of the continent. Another commonly seen species is the schooling rabbitfish (*S. argenteus*), so called because it forms large, dense schools. These bright blue fishes swim along reef slopes, grazing algae from the bottom.
Family: Siganidae

MOORISH IDOL

The sole member of its family, the Moorish idol (*Zanclus cornutus*) is deep-bodied with thick vertical black stripes on a yellow to white ground, and has a long, white, filamentous extension on its dorsal fin.

These striking fishes live on algae and plankton and reach a maximum of 22 cm long. They occur singly, in pairs or in groups, and occasionally in large schools. The species is broadly distributed in the tropical Indo-Pacific and ranges to southern New South Wales in the summer.
Family: Zanclidae

■ RABBITFISHES
Crowds of schooling rabbitfishes congregate to feed near reefs, nibbling algae from the ocean floor.

SURGEONFISHES AND UNICORNFISHES ■

Distributed throughout the world's tropical oceans, this family contains three groups: the surgeonfishes (subfamily Acanthurinae), which form the largest group; the unicornfishes (subfamily Nasinae), with 16 species; and the sawtails (subfamily Prionurinae), with just a few species. All three groups have representatives in Australian waters, and about 35 species are known from the northern half of the continent.

Surgeonfishes have a movable spine, venomous in some species, on their sides near the tail. The spines, often highlighted with bright blue, orange or yellow as a warning, are used for defence or fighting and can inflict painful wounds.

Unicornfishes have several fixed recurving spines that bend backwards, and sawtails have a series of bony plates with a short spine, both of which are used for defence.

These fishes are 25–50 cm long, with oval to oblong compressed bodies and tiny scales. Their mouth is small and their jaws have numerous tiny teeth adapted to various feeding methods, depending on genus. All species feed on algae, but some scrape it from flat surfaces, while others take a mixture of floating algae and plankton from the water. The plankton-eaters often form huge schools along reef walls, where currents are rich with food. Sometimes the bottom-dwelling grazers form large schools on reefs to overcome the defences of the very territorial damselfishes (page 462).

Many surgeonfishes have distinctive coloration and are therefore easy to identify, but juveniles are often different from adults. The young of the mimic surgeonfish (*Acanthurus pyroferus*) have rounded

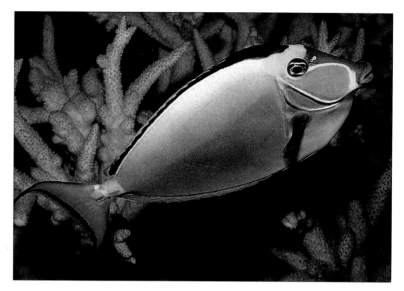

■ UNICORNFISHES
The spotted unicornfish, *Naso brevirostris* (right), bears the distinctive bony horn above its snout that gives most of these fishes their common name. The black-finned unicorn fish, *N. lituratus* (above), however, does not grow a horn. It is found around coral and rocky reefs in Australia's tropical waters and in the Indo-Pacific region.

■ SURGEONFISHES
Blue surgeonfishes occur commonly in loose schools in clear water over coral reefs, where they feed on animal plankton in open water. Usually a timid species, they quickly take refuge in narrow gaps in corals when they feel threatened. Small juveniles stay close to the corals, but adults may roam over large areas while grazing algae from the bottom of the ocean.

tails, unlike the typical half-moon shape, and adopt the coloration of local angelfishes of the genus *Centropyge*. Unicornfishes and sawtails are often dull grey. Species are identified by the shape and number or colour of the spines on the tail.

Convict surgeonfishes (*Acanthurus triostegus*) have black stripes on a pale greenish grey background. They grow to 26 cm long and are common in shallow coastal waters around Australia's north. Juveniles can be found as far south as Sydney during summer. Adults form schools, especially on reefs where there is some freshwater run-off from land, to feed on the usually prolific algal growth.

The lined surgeonfish (*A. lineatus*) is marked with orange and blue lines. It has a venomous spine on its tail and grows to 35 cm long. Adults school on shallow reef flats, usually in high-energy zones where waves roll over at high tides. They also live in narrow gutters or among large boulders. Juveniles hide among small boulders on shallow reefs, and can be found as far south as Sydney.

The immediately recognisable blue surgeonfish (*Paracanthurus hepatus*) is bright blue with black markings and a yellow and black tail. It grows to 30 cm long. These fishes gather in schools to feed around clear-water coral reefs.

The spotted unicornfish (*Naso brevirostris*) is among the most common and widespread unicornfishes in the tropical Indo-Pacific. Adults have a long, bony horn above their snout at eye level, projecting horizontally to well beyond their mouth. When spotted unicornfishes form schools to feed on surface matter, their horns are sometimes visible sticking out of the water. Juveniles feed on bottom-growing algae and are normally solitary. This species grows to 50 cm long, but some other horned species grow slightly longer.

Another easily identified common species is the blue-spine unicornfish (*N. unicornis*), which, as its name suggests, has blue spines on its tail.

The sawtail (*Prionurus microlepidotus*) is common around rocky headlands in northern New South Wales, where it feeds on loose algae or plankton in turbulent shallow waters. The juveniles inhabit algal reefs and often form small groups. The sawtail is found from central Queensland to southern New South Wales and Lord Howe Island.

The spotted sawtail (*P. maculatus*) has a similar range, but is readily distinguished from the sawtail by the yellow spotting all over its slightly deeper body. Both these species grow to a maximum of almost 50 cm long.
Family: Acanthuridae

Barracudas ■

Voracious predators of smaller fish species, barracudas occur throughout the world in tropical and warm temperate seas. Most inhabit shallow inshore waters, and a few species also live in estuaries. The family is relatively small, containing a single genus (*Sphyraena*) and about 20 species, six of which occur in Australian seas. All species are similar in appearance: the silver body is long and slender; there are two widely separated dorsal fins on the back; and the head is rather long and pointed, with large, powerful jaws equipped with an awesome array of long, sharp-edged teeth.

Its fierce appearance and large size (up to 1.8 metres) make the great barracuda (*S. barracuda*) the best known member of the family. It is a solitary hunter that patrols both coastal and offshore reefs and can strike with lightning speed. In the West Indies, where more than 30 attacks on humans have been recorded, these fishes are feared even more than sharks. However, most attacks have involved bathers in murky water or spearfishers who have provoked a barracuda; attacks are very rare in the clear waters of the Indian and Pacific oceans.

Most of the other species are considerably smaller and do not pose any sort of threat, although several, such as the 90 cm-long chevron barracuda (*S. qenie*), form impressive schools of several hundred fishes. The yellowtail barracuda (*S. flavicauda*) is one of the smaller species, growing to about 35 cm long.
Family: Sphyraenidae

Gemfishes

The gemfish, or escolar, family contains about 20 species worldwide, at least three of which are found in Australian waters. In America their long, slim, silvery grey body and protruding lower jaw with large teeth have given them the common name of snake mackerel.

The three Australian species are the gemfish (*Rexea solandri*), also known as the king barracouta or hake; the barracouta (*Thyrsites atun*); and the oilfish (*Ruvettus pretiosus*). These fishes inhabit the upper slope and deeper waters of the continental shelf from Brisbane right around the southern coast to the central west coast of Western Australia.

The gemfish usually occurs at depths of 100–700 metres, where it feeds on whiptails, deepwater cardinalfishes, royal red prawns and squids. It may grow to over a metre long and live for 16 years. In the autumn large schools of gemfish form off the north-eastern corner of Bass Strait and migrate to their only known spawning ground, off the coast of central and northern New South Wales, where the females lay 1–2 million eggs each. The eggs drift with the currents until they hatch. Migrating schools are heavily fished by commercial deepwater trawlers, but in recent years catches have declined significantly. Gemfish formed an important inshore fishery in southern Tasmania until the 1880s, but by 1900 the species had disappeared from inshore waters.

Barracouta are usually found in schools that migrate vertically between depths of 200 metres and the surface, where they feed at dawn and dusk on midwater shrimps and small surface-dwelling fishes, such as anchovies and pilchards. Juvenile barracouta use southern bays and estuaries as nursery areas. They may grow to about 1.4 metres long and live for more than ten years.

The oilfish is known to grow to at least 1.6 metres long. It inhabits deep waters over rocky reefs, and is occasionally caught by deepwater trawlers and commercial longline fishers off the south coast.
Family: Gempylidae

Hairtails

About 17 hairtail species are known throughout the world, and two of these – the largehead hairtail, or Australian hairtail (*Trichiurus lepturus*) and the southern frostfish (*Lepidopus caudatus*) – are found in Australian waters. Their long, flat, ribbon-like, bodies, silvery pointed heads and small tails explain why hairtails are also known as cutlassfishes outside Australia.

Schools of largehead hairtails are occasionally found in coastal bays and estuaries off both the east and west coasts of Australia; specimens over 2.3 metres long have been observed feeding on small fishes and juvenile hairtails.

The southern frostfish lives on the continental shelf at depths of 300–600 metres, where it spawns during the winter. Frostfishes are widely distributed, and are also found in the Mediterranean Sea, the north-west Atlantic, and the southern Indian and Pacific oceans.
Family: Trichiuridae

■ **Barracuda**
The great barracuda is a particularly active hunter at dawn and dusk. Light levels are low at these times, so the voracious barracuda is less likely to be seen by the small fishes on which it preys.

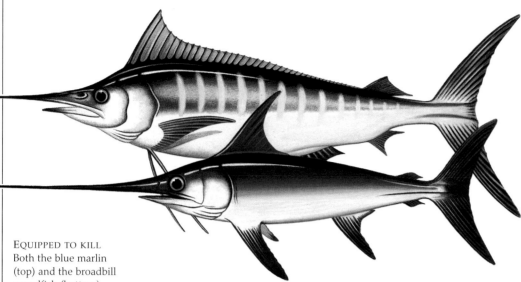

EQUIPPED TO KILL
Both the blue marlin (top) and the broadbill swordfish (bottom) use their spear-like upper jaws for stunning smaller fishes. Broadbill swordfish have been known to hole wooden boats, and even to pierce copper sheeting.

BILLFISHES AND MARLINS ▪

There are two families of billfishes: the Istiophoridae family comprises the marlins, the sailfishes and the spearfishes, while the Xiphiidae family contains only the broadbill swordfish. These distantly related families are linked because the members of both possess a long bill – a projection of the nasal bones. The marlin's bill is round and covered with fine teeth, whereas the broadbill swordfish has a smooth, flattened bill like a broadsword of old.

The Istiophoridae are all dark blue to black on the back and have white to silver bellies. When feeding, they seem to light up, their colour changing to phosphorescent blue, with purple stripes often appearing on their sides. These colour changes happen because dark pigmentation in the skin contracts to reveal highly reflective cells underneath. Broadbill swordfishes tend to be a dull grey or brown, but some have black to purple backs and pale bellies.

Billfishes hunt tunas and mackerels, and also squids. Extremely streamlined, they can swim at high speed, reaching as much as 80–100 kilometres an hour in short bursts.

The black marlin (*Makaira indica*) is one of the most awesome fishes in the sea, growing to at least 700 kg in weight and about 5 metres in length. This formidable predator is easily identified by its rigid pectoral fin. It also has a relatively low first dorsal fin, and its second dorsal fin is ahead of its second anal fin. Like other marlins, the black marlin

▪ BLUE MARLIN
Around Australia, the blue marlin occurs off the eastern coast from Cairns to Bermagui on the south coast of New South Wales, and off the western coast from Perth to Exmouth.

grows very rapidly. Pinhead-sized eggs are released in huge numbers in the Coral Sea each spring: one 500 kg female may produce 100–200 million eggs each season. Fertilised eggs take about two days to hatch into tiny larvae, about 2 mm long. After two years the juveniles weigh about 30 kg, and a 400 kg giant may be only ten years old. Black marlin are found along the east coast off north-east Queensland to as far as Mallacoota in Victoria, and down the west coast to the south-west tip of Western Australia.

The tropical blue marlin (*M. nigricans*) also grows to an enormous size – the largest specimen recorded so far weighed 819 kg. This species occurs in the Atlantic, Indian and Pacific oceans, and it spawns near Hawaii and Mauritius.

The striped marlin (*Tetrapturus audax*) occurs around Australia. It has prominent stripes and a characteristic very high first dorsal fin, measuring at least three-quarters the depth of its body; in smaller specimens the fin is equal to the body

depth. The striped marlin has the most slender bill of all the marlins and a long, acutely pointed lower jaw. Striped marlin are not as large as black or blue marlin; the largest on record, weighing 250 kg, was caught off New Zealand in 1994.

The sailfish (*Istiophorus platypterus*) is one of the most spectacular open-sea fishes. Its huge spotted dorsal fin is unmistakable, running the whole length of its body and at its highest point much deeper than the body. Early mariners thought that the fin was used like a sail – hence the common name sailfish – but this is not so. Hunting in groups, sailfishes round up schools of small fishes by leaping clear of the water and crashing down on their sides. They use their dorsal fins like capes to herd the small fishes into tight balls. Then, once by one, the sailfishes take turns to swim in for a meal.

Occupying tropical seas world-wide, sailfishes occur in all oceans, but they concentrate close to reefs and islands, often where baitfishes gather at the confluence of oceanic and nutrient-rich waters. Sailfishes weighing 100 kg have been caught, but Australian species average 30 kg off Queensland and 15–20 kg off Western Australia. Their back is dark blue to black and their sides and belly are a silvery white.

Sailors of earlier times feared the broadbill swordfish (*Xiphias gladius*), believing that it attacked and sank their ships by piercing the wooden hulls. It is now thought that the damage was caused accidentally when swordfishes chased small fishes sheltering under boats.

The broadbill swordfish occurs in all oceans and reaches over 500 kg in weight. It uses its flat, sword-like bill to stun or kill its prey by slashing

through schools of squids – its favourite food. Swordfishes have a remarkable brain-heating organ that is really a modified eye muscle; when they dive deeply to feed, their prey become cold and slow down but the swordfish remains alert, with a warm brain and efficiently functioning eyes.

Unlike marlins, which are oval in cross-section, the broadbill swordfish is round-bodied. Brown to black on the dorsal surface and cream on the belly, these fishes do not light up like marlins and sailfishes. During the day they remain in deep-water canyons, and at night they follow their prey of squids and deep-water fishes towards the surface. Broadbill swordfishes live in the temperate waters of the world's major oceans, and are also found in deep cold waters in tropical zones.

Families: Istiophoridae (marlins, sailfishes and spearfishes), Xiphiidae (broadbill swordfish)

TUNAS, BONITOS AND MACKERELS ■

Tunas can travel vast distances and can achieve bursts of speed up to 70 kilometres an hour. Between their tail and their second dorsal and anal fins they have rows of small finlets to reduce turbulence, and they can streamline themselves by folding their fins into slots in their body.

Tropical species such as skipjack and yellowfin tuna live in tropical and temperate latitudes in the three major oceans, while colder-water species such as bluefin and southern bluefin tuna live at higher latitudes. Most tuna species are marine, though some occasionally make their way into estuaries.

Members of this family produce extremely small eggs that float near the surface for several days before hatching into tiny larvae. A few species, such as the slimy mackerel (*Scomber australasicus*), feed by filtering plankton from the water, but all other members – tunas, bonitos, Spanish mackerels and little tunas – prey on fishes and squids.

The adult yellowfin tuna (*Thunnus albacares*) has greatly elongated second dorsal and anal fins. Yellowfin tuna occur throughout the world's oceans, including those off eastern and western Australia. Yellowfin grow very rapidly, reaching about 30 kg by the end of their second year of life. Nearly all those weighing more than 70 kg are males, since females are thought to expend their energy producing huge numbers of eggs – tens of millions over the two

or three months of summer. The largest yellowfin tuna recorded from Australian waters, weighing 124 kg, was landed off the south coast of New South Wales in 1994.

Yellowfin tuna like water warmer than 21°C, and so swim close to the surface, but the bigeye tuna (*T. obesus*) prefers cooler water and swims deeper. Albacore (*T. alalunga*) may be distinguished from yellowfin by their extremely long pectoral fins and the white margin on their tail.

The southern bluefin tuna (*T. maccoyii*) was once the most common tuna in Australian waters, but its numbers fell dramatically after heavy commercial fishing by Japan and Australia in the 1960s and 1970s. Strict controls have now reduced the total catches to a fraction of what they were. The southern bluefin prefers much cooler water than its tropical relative, the yellowfin. It occurs in a band between latitudes 30°S and 50°S throughout the Pacific and Indian oceans, where temperatures are 5–20°C. To spawn, adults enter much warmer waters off Timor and Bali, the only known spawning grounds of the species.

The Australian bonito (*Sarda australis*) is a small, tuna-like fish – up to a metre long – that prefers coastal habitats. Unlike other tunas, bonitos have prominent teeth and horizontal stripes covering their body. Watson's leaping bonito (*Cybiosarda elegans*) has a very high dorsal fin and dark spots on the upper body.

The dogtooth tuna (*Gymnosarda unicolor*) is a large coastal bonito. It can weigh up to 130 kg and is equipped, as its name suggests, with formidable teeth. Scuba divers are sometimes unnerved by its large shape, but it is a harmless species that feeds on fishes. Apart from its teeth, its main feature is a prominent

wavy lateral line. The dogtooth tuna lives near coral reef drop-offs – the vertical edges of coral reefs.

The skipjack tuna (*Katsuwonus pelamis*) is the most common of all tunas, occurring in huge numbers throughout the world's oceans. One of the so-called little tunas, it reaches a maximum of only 108 cm in length and 33 kg in weight; in Australian waters skipjacks can grow to about 80 cm long and 10 kg in weight.

World catches of skipjack tuna have topped a million tonnes in recent years, and many scientists believe that this is sustainable since the growth and reproductive rates of skipjack tuna are high. During the spring–summer spawning season, a female skipjack may produce tens of thousands of eggs every day. The other 'little tuna' occurring around Australia is the mackerel tuna (*Euthynnus affinis*).

Slender, elongated, fast-swimming fishes, mackerels use their razor-sharp teeth to slice through prey. Like other members of the family,

■ SOUTHERN BLUEFIN TUNA
These enormous fishes migrate over very long distances, sometimes from the southern coast of Australia to South Africa and back again. Large migratory tunas are sometimes known as fishes without a country.

■ MACKEREL
The narrow-barred Spanish mackerel (*Scomberomorus commerson*) lives in the waters of northern Queensland for most of the year, but visits northern New South Wales and central Western Australia in the summer.

they can reach 70 kilometres an hour in bursts of high-speed swimming at the height of the chase.

The narrow-barred Spanish mackerel, *Scomberomorus commerson*, is Australia's best known mackerel. It is commercially fished in northern Queensland. Four of the 18 mackerel species occur close to the coast of Australia; three are restricted to the northern half of the continent. Little is known about mackerel reproduction, but it is thought to be similar to that of other members of the family.

The related wahoo (*Acanthocybium solandri*) has a much longer snout than other mackerels and is reputed to be the fastest fish in the ocean, capable of speeds of more than 100 kilometres an hour. It is also the most widespread of all mackerel species, living throughout the world in the open ocean in tropical and subtropical regions.
Family: Scombridae

TREVALLAS, DRIFTFISHES, EYEBROW FISHES AND SQUARETAILS
These four families form part of a distinct group of marine fishes known collectively as stromateoids.

Australian species are typically oceanic, living in midwater or near the bottom on the continental slope or over deeper parts of the continental shelf. Some species have unique specialisations, but all have a distinctive fat-nosed and wide-eyed appearance. Most species are silvery,

NURSERY JELLY FOR ME Some young trevallas seek refuge among the tentacles of sea jellies, immune to their stinging tentacles. Not only are the fishes protected, but they also benefit from particles of food trapped in the jellies' tissues.

bronzeish or bluish, and many have blotches and spots, which are more pronounced in juveniles. Adults may grow to lengths of about 1.5 metres, but many species are mature at less than 30 cm long.

The trevallas are the best known of this group in Australia. The blue-eye or deepsea trevalla (*Hyperoglyphe antarctica*) is a large fish, reaching 50 kg in weight, that lives near the surface until it is about 50 cm long, when it descends to depths of 200–500 metres. This change is accompanied by changes in body form: the eyes increase in size and acuity to adjust to the lower light levels, the forehead becomes blunter, and the colouring becomes darker.

Like many of their relatives, trevallas are specialised feeders: adults feed mainly on hollow, sausage-like pelagic salps. Until recently, the habitat of very small juvenile blue-eye trevalla remained a mystery. Scientists searched for more than a decade until they discovered the first specimens in the winter of 1993 in the open ocean off eastern Tasmania under huge rafts of brown kelp. The young, which feed on copepods, resemble the adults in shape, but are a brownish colour that helps them to blend in with their habitat.

Warehous (*Seriolella* spp.), sometimes known as snotty trevallies, also belong to this group. They are taken in commercial quantities off southern Australia in the winter and

spring by trawlers. Large schools also occur inshore. Female warehous produce up to 1.6 million pelagic eggs, each about 1 mm in diameter. The young are pelagic too, and can live among the tentacles of the giant sea jelly, which are fatal to most fishes. In December these sea jellies occur in heavy concentrations along Australia's southern coast, and at times juvenile warehous are found with almost every sea jelly, their purplish bellies indicating that their host is a source of food as well as a protection from predators.

Driftfishes generally have very wide distributions in the open ocean, but most are rarely seen. The bluebottle fish (*Nomeus gronovii*) lives among the tentacles of the Portuguese man o' war. Like warehous with sea jellies, these fishes appear to feed on the man o' war's tentacles and to be immune to their venom. A covering of mucus over the fish's body may protect it from its host's battery of stinging cells.

Squaretails are unusual fishes, with their cigar-shaped body, rough, firm scales and large keel at their tail base. Their box-like upper jaw and knife-like lower jaw are ideal for slicing through the sea jellies and comb jellies that they feed on. Young squaretails can sometimes be found hiding inside salps.
Families: Centrolophidae (trevallas), Nomeidae (driftfishes), Ariommatidae (eyebrow fishes), Tetragonuridae (squaretails)

FLATFISHES

Most inconspicuous bottom-dwelling fishes have bodies that are flattened from top to bottom, but the flatfishes simply turn over on one side. So that they do not lose the benefit of the eye on the underside, this eye has, through the ages, migrated to join its partner on the upward-facing side of the head. And the basic design of a mouth opening on the right or left side is so successful that flatfishes are prominent bottom-dwellers in many of the world's oceans.

Flounders and other flatfishes hatch with an eye on each side of their head. While the fishes are still larvae, one eye begins to travel to the opposite side, either across the top of the head or through a notch or hole in its upper surface. When the eye reaches its destination, the free-swimming youngster is ready to take up a bottom-dwelling existence.

In all but one flatfish family, the adults' eyes consistently appear on the same side, be it the left or the right. The exception is the family Psettodidae, the primitive flounders, whose bodies have changed little from those of their early ancestors. Apart from a second eye that barely pokes over the top of the head and dramatically different colour patterns on the two sides – pale on the downward-facing side and much darker above – these fishes could be mistaken for more conventional, though rather deep-bodied, fishes.

Australian waters are home to a single member of this family, the Queensland halibut (*Psettodes erumei*), which is widely distributed in northern inshore areas. It is the largest Australian flatfish, reaching a length of 60 cm and a weight of 10 kg or more.

Two other families, the right-eye flounders and the left-eye flounders, have more than 80 members between them in Australian waters.

Both these families have estuarine, coastal and deep-living species variously distributed around the Australian coastline. Most prefer sandy regions where they can partially nestle into the bottom, their highly adaptable colouring changing to match the colours and textures of their immediate environment. Only their eyes protrude from the sand to survey their surroundings for potential prey or predators. Their mouth forms often indicate their food preferences: small mouths that mostly lack visible teeth indicate a diet of invertebrates, and larger gapes with prominent canines suggest a taste for larger prawns and fishes.
Order: Pleuronectiformes

EYES RIGHT! (OR LEFT) The eyes of newly hatched flatfish larvae are on either side of their head, but when the larvae are about 15 mm long, one eye begins to move up to join the other one on top.

RIGHT-EYE FLOUNDERS

The right-eye flounders, whose eyes are situated on the right side of the head in adults, form the bulk of the flatfish species. Among the right-eye flounders, the greenback flounder (*Rhombosolea tapirina*) is a fish of cool southern inshore waters. It is related to the Pacific halibut (*Hippoglossus stenolepis*) of Alaska but, at just 45 cm long, it falls far short of the 2.7 metre length and more than 475 kg weight attained by its much larger relative.
Family: Pleuronectidae

LEFT-EYE FLOUNDERS ▪

This family is best represented by the largetooth flounder (*Pseudo-rhombus arsius*), which grows to 40 cm long and is distributed around most of the continent. The slightly smaller smalltooth flounder (*P. jenynsii*), reaches about 35 cm long, and seems to be confined to waters off the southern half of Australia.
Family: Bothidae

SOLES AND
TONGUE SOLES ▪

Two flatfish groups that parallel the and right-eye and left-eye flounders in development are the soles and the tongue soles. In many ways, these fishes may seem to be inadequate versions of their counterparts, with their small eyes, hooked mouths that often open awkwardly, and, in some species, reduced or nonexistent pectoral fins. But the numbers of species in both groups indicate that they have adapted successfully to life in their sandy or muddy homes.

Most soles are found in relatively shallow, sandy coastal areas, some

▪ LEFT-EYE FLOUNDER
Like many species of flatfish, the left-eye flounder has a spotty appearance. This provides these fishes with camouflage on sandy seafloors, helping protect them from predators.

even invading brackish or freshwater streams. All have both eyes on the right side of the head as adults and, like the tongue soles, they can be distinguished from their flounder look-alikes by the uninterrupted scale-covered skin of their cheeks, which obscures the underlying cheekbone. It is the often sawtoothed hind edge of this bone in fishes that can be so hazardous to anglers unhooking their catch.

Perhaps the most remarkable of the soles are the *Pardachirus* species, including the peacock sole (*P. pavoninus*), which repels attackers by

releasing a foul-tasting, milky cloud of poison from skin pores along the bases of the dorsal and anal fins.

There are at least 40 sole species in Australian waters. The black sole (*Synaptura nigra*), which is distributed widely in inshore tropical waters, is broad and darkly hued, and has fins that are continuous around its tail. This species grows to about 35 cm long.

The small-headed sole (*Aesopia microcephala*), like several of its close relatives, develops its adult form while it is still unusually small. The adults are darkly banded, but the juveniles are vividly coloured and strikingly patterned – white with a bright blue and orange peripheral border – virtually identical to the noxious flatworms and sea slugs found in nearby areas, among which they camouflage themselves. To further the resemblance, small soles in this group move with an uncharacteristic, exaggerated undulation of their body and fins.

The tongue sole family – the left-eyed example of this pair of families – has only about 20 Australian representatives, many of which are found in slightly deeper offshore waters. Most Australian species have a greatly hooked mouth and a spade-like snout, as well as a characteristic slender, tongue-shaped body with joined fins and pointed tail. Like those of the soles, their rather feeble mouths are suited only for feeding on small invertebrates.

One of the larger species in this family, the lemon tongue sole (*Paraplagiusa unicolor*), is distributed in coastal waters off Queensland and New South Wales.
Families: Soleidae (soles), Cynoglossidae (tongue soles)

▪ SMALL-HEADED SOLE
The adult of this species (*Aesopia microcephala*) is more sombrely hued for bottom-dwelling camouflage than the juveniles, which mimic the colours of the poisonous flatworms and sea slugs near which they live.

PUFFERS, LEATHERJACKETS AND BOXFISHES

This group of mostly marine fishes have deep, rounded bodies. They are masters of self-defence, and each family has developed different ways of repelling would-be attackers. Some puff themselves up to double their size; some have sharp spikes covering their body; some make ferocious noises from their swim bladder; some have sharp teeth; and some have toxic flesh and internal organs that can kill.
Order: Tetradontiformes

DEEPWATER TRIPODFISHES

Also known as spikefishes, members of this family are found throughout the world in waters 40–1000 metres deep. At least eight of a total of 19 species have been found in Australia's northern waters. They are related to triggerfishes and leatherjackets (this page), but are easily distinguished from them by the two large, movable spines that project downward and outward from their undersides. When the spines are locked in the extended position, these fishes can sit on the sea floor, propping themselves up as if on a tripod, to lie in wait for small prey drifting in the weak currents close to the bottom.

Some tripodfish species, such as the trumpetsnout spikefish (*Macrorhamphosodes platycheilus*), have elongated snouts with mouths twisted to the right or left; others, such as the shortsnout spikefish (*Triacanthodes ethiops*), have much shorter snouts. Presumably those with long snouts use them to probe the ocean bottom in search of food.

Tripodfishes have been taken only by research trawlers operating in deep offshore waters. They grow to about 15 cm long.
Family: Triacanthodidae

TRIGGERFISHES AND LEATHERJACKETS ■

These two families are very similar in appearance. Both have a large dorsal spine at the back of the head, a small mouth with only a few teeth, small gill openings, and a rudimentary pelvic fin in the form of a bony spike or knob. The dorsal spine can lock in an upright position to make the fish more difficult for a predator to swallow, and in some species the bony pelvic knob can be locked in a downward position.

When both the dorsal spine and the pelvic knob are extended, a fish can easily wedge itself into a rocky or coral crevice, making it almost impossible to remove. These fishes also raise and lower their dorsal spines vigorously to demonstrate

■ LEATHERJACKET
With 60 species out of the world total of 90, Australia has the largest number of leatherjacket species. This horseshoe leatherjacket (*Meuschenia hippocrepis*) inhabits southern waters.

aggression to others of the species; these spines are sometimes serrated, but none is venomous.

Some of the larger triggerfishes and leatherjackets have strong, sharp teeth that can shear through human fingers and even steel fish-hooks. Some species feed by biting off pieces of hard coral, which significantly wears down their teeth, but most leatherjackets have small nibbling teeth for nipping pieces from seaweeds, sponges and worms.

Triggerfishes and leatherjackets can be distinguished from one another by the number of visible dorsal spines: triggerfishes have three, while leatherjackets have only one. Also, the body scales of triggerfishes are generally large and prominent, but those of leatherjackets are very small and difficult to detect.

Both families are found all over the world, occurring in both tropical and temperate waters, although triggerfishes prefer tropical areas near coral reefs.

Unlike many leatherjackets, which swim in pairs or in small schools, triggerfishes are generally solitary. With strong teeth well adapted for biting and crushing, triggerfishes feed on such prey as crabs, sea urchins and molluscs.

Three of the largest species, the yellow-margined triggerfish (*Pseudobalistes flavimarginatus*), the yellow-spotted triggerfish (*P. fuscus*) and the blue-finned triggerfish (*Balistoides viridescens*), scrape the sandy bottom out to make craters

■ TRIGGERFISH
The orange-lined triggerfish (*Balistapus undulatus*) is one of about 20 triggerfish species that occur in Australian waters around shallow coral reefs or at greater depths. Triggerfishes range from a minute 2 cm up to 75 cm long.

for nests, in which the female lays her eggs. They defend these nests vigorously; females will confront divers who come too close, and will even bite them.

The best known species in Australian waters are the starry triggerfish (*Abalistes stellatus*) and the white-banded triggerfish (*Rhinecanthus aculeatus*). The starry triggerfish is often caught in the nets of prawn trawlers, and the distinctive colour pattern of the white-banded triggerfish – brilliant blue lines across the head and alternating brown and white oblique stripes on the lower half of the body – always attracts the attention of divers.

Most leatherjackets are found in the continent's southern waters, but several also inhabit the tropical north. They range in size from the minute 25 mm-long diamond leatherjacket (*Rudarius excelsus*) to the large, long-tailed scrawled leatherjacket (*Aluterus scriptus*), which grows to almost a metre long.

Other species caught in southern Australian waters are the fan-bellied leatherjacket (*Monacanthus chinensis*), the Chinaman leatherjacket (*Nelusetta ayraudi*), the velvet leatherjacket (*Parika scaber*), the yellow-finned leatherjacket (*Meuschenia trachylepis*), the horseshoe leatherjacket (*M. hippocrepis*) and the six-spined leatherjacket (*M. freycineti*).

Perhaps the two most interesting species are the pygmy leatherjacket (*Brachaluteres jacksonianus*) and the bearded leatherjacket (*Anacanthus barbatus*). The pygmy leatherjacket, which grows to 9 cm long, is a poor swimmer and relatively easy to catch. To make it more difficult to swallow, this species has evolved an inflatable abdomen that can be expanded when danger threatens. Once swollen up, the pygmy leatherjacket becomes an unpalatable meal – it literally sticks in the throat of its predators.

The bearded leatherjacket, which grows up to 35 cm long, has an extremely elongated head and body, and looks more like a blade of seagrass than a fish. True to its common name, this species has a prominent beard-like whisker (barbel) on its lower jaw. This leatherjacket relies almost wholly on camouflage to avoid detection, so it has little use for its dorsal spine, which is consequently weak and not easily seen.

Most leatherjackets reproduce by laying thousands of small eggs, which, after fertilisation, are widely scattered by ocean currents. However, some small *Rudarius*

species produce only a small number of relatively large eggs. Possibly these species lay their eggs in nests and care for them, but as they are rarely seen by divers, little is known about their reproductive behaviour.
Families: Balistidae (triggerfishes), Monacanthidae (leatherjackets)

BOXFISHES AND COWFISHES ■

The rigid, box-like structure that provides a protective shell around their body gives boxfishes their name. This bony outer skeleton is formed by the fusion of body scales; openings allow the eyes, mouth, gills and fins to project. Some species have bony horns above or in front of their eyes, and are generally referred to as cowfishes. Poor swimmers, boxfishes are often washed up dead on beaches during storms.

In Australia there are two distinct groups of boxfishes, the tropical species and the temperate-zone species, which differ from each other in the positioning of the dorsal and anal fins. In tropical species the base of each fin is located entirely in a hole in the bony shell, whereas in the temperate species the bases are not surrounded, or are only partly surrounded, by the bony shell.

Boxfishes can secrete a toxic mucus called ostracitoxin through their skin, and this can contaminate their flesh. The strongest poison is produced by glands in the mouth that start to make toxin when the fish is under stress. In a small aquarium the toxic secretions of a boxfish can easily kill all the other inhabitants. The poison is apparently toxic to humans, so people should take care when handling these fishes.

Some boxfishes feed by blowing a jet of water through their mouth, aiming it at the sandy bottom. They then devour any small prey such as worms and small crustaceans that are flushed out by the water jet.

About 19 boxfish species, ten tropical and nine temperate, inhabit Australian seas. In all species the male looks different from the female.

■ SHAW'S COWFISH
Aracana aurita is a common boxfish species from southern Australia, where it inhabits shallow reef and weed areas. It is often seen by divers in protected bays along the coastline, but it is also taken by trawlers in deep offshore waters. The biggest Shaw's cowfishes are no more than 25 cm long.

■ LONG-HORNED COWFISH
When this boxfish species (*Lactoria cornuta*) is young, the horns above its eyes and near its tail are very long, but they gradually become smaller as the fish grows older. Care should be taken if handling one of these fishes.

■ TOADFISH
The saddled pufferfish (*Canthigaster valentini*) is a common but shy and retiring toadfish species that lives along the Great Barrier and other coral reefs. These fishes stake out small territories that are guarded by the females.

■ PORCUPINEFISH
Sensing a threat, this porcupinefish takes defensive action. To deter potential predators, it turns itself into a spiky sphere by filling its abdomen with water or air, causing its spines to become erect.

Usually the male is very brightly coloured, and has a more pronounced hump on either the head or the back than the plainer coloured female. The best known example is the yellow boxfish (*Ostracion cubicus*). Small juveniles of this species are like little yellow boxes covered with black spots, but as they grow larger the base colour becomes more brownish, and the spots grow more bluish to whitish and become enclosed in a black ring. This colour pattern is characteristic of the female; the male is purplish brown, with either no spotting or faint spotting, and with a bright yellow pattern on its cheeks and along the lower surface of its body.

The male ornate cowfish (*Aracana ornata*) is yellowy green, patterned with vivid blue lines and many small polygonal blue spots on the side of its body; the female is yellowish brown and marked with pale wiggly lines. The ornate cowfish grows to about 15 cm in length.

The spotted boxfish (*Ostracion meleagris*) lives in coral reefs and is probably the most common of all the species of tropical boxfish. Juveniles and females are dark brown to black with many small white spots; the male is bluish and has many bright yellow spots. Spotted boxfishes grow to a maximum of 20 cm long.

The long-horned cowfish (*Lactoria cornuta*), which grows to 50 cm long,

is often taken by prawn trawlers in tropical Australian waters. Although it has a toxic skin to protect it, the long-horned cowfish is sometimes eaten by large predators.
Family: Ostraciidae

TOADFISHES AND PORCUPINEFISHES ■
Toadfishes are also known as pufferfishes. The family contains about 140 species worldwide, more than 35 of which are found in Australian waters, from the tropics to the cool southern coast. Of the 15 species of their cousins, the porcupinefishes, about ten live in Australian waters.

A typical toadfish has a flattened body, a protruding, beak-shaped mouth and prominent eyes; porcupinefishes have similar features, but their body is more rounded. Markings and colours vary widely among species, but they both usually have a pale underbelly and spotted or patterned camouflage on top.

Both have small spines on their stomach, and sometimes on their sides and back, and when threatened they puff up their abdomen with water or air to erect these spines, which makes them look like a spiky ball. Out of water, the puffing-up process creates a croaking sound, giving them their common name of toadfish, or toado. In some parts of Australia toadfishes are also known as blowfishes or blowies.

Toadfishes are generally found in coastal waters and estuaries, often over weed or sand. Most species are 15–25 cm long, but some are much smaller or much larger. The tiny saddled pufferfish (*Canthigaster valentini*) – sometimes called Valentin's sharpnose pufferfish – from the Queensland and New South Wales coast grows to only 9 cm long; by contrast, the giant tropical silver toadfish – or northwest blowie – (*Lagocephalus scleratus*), can reach nearly a metre in length and over 6.5 kg in weight.

The three-barred porcupinefish (*Dicotylichthys punctulatus*) is common near coral or other reef areas in New South Wales, while other members of the family extend to deeper offshore waters.

Both these families have powerful jaws, with front teeth shaped a little like a parrot's beak, which they use to crush crabs and small shellfish or other particles scavenged from the sea floor. In larger specimens, such as the silver toadfish, this deadly set of teeth can easily shear through a wetsuit – and through the occupant's bones. They are fearless

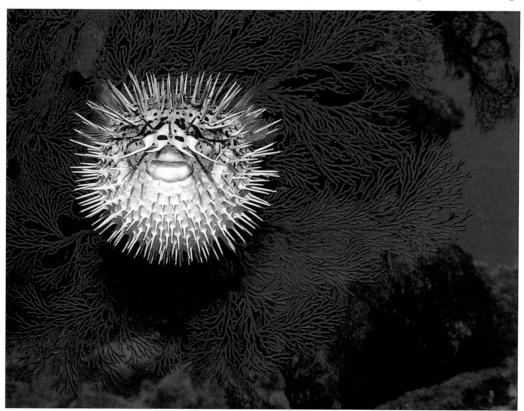

■ SUNFISHES
The adult giant sunfish (left) has a coarse, rough skin. The sunfish larva (above) is covered in bony tubercles.

predators, forming large schools that can be stimulated into a feeding frenzy by the presence of food or blood in the water. They frequently harass divers or swimmers, and sometimes bite them.

Cases of toadfish poisoning, and prohibitions on the consumption of these fishes, have been recorded for many centuries. Ancient Egyptian wall paintings depict poisonous pufferfishes, while Jewish dietary laws in the book of Leviticus in the Old Testament forbid the eating of fishes without scales, such as the smooth-skinned toadfish. An example from more recent history was the near-death of Captain Cook after tasting the flesh of a toadfish in New Caledonia on his second major voyage of exploration in 1773.
Families: Tetraodontidae (toadfishes), Diodontidae (porcupinefishes)

SUNFISHES ■

Sunfishes are distant ocean-going relatives of toadfishes and porcupinefishes (opposite page). They are called sunfishes because they have been frequently observed lying quietly on their sides as though basking in the sun, although it is possible that such specimens are sick or incapacitated in some way.

The cool southern waters between Victoria and southern Western Australia are home to three giant sunfish species: the short sunfish (*Mola ramsayi*), the oblong sunfish (*Ranzaenia laevis*) and the pointed-tailed sunfish (*Masturus lanceolatus*).

Sunfishes have an enormous oval body covered in extremely thick skin, with a beak-like mouth and large dorsal and pelvic fins placed well towards their tail. The colours and markings of the short sunfish vary from blue-grey with white blotches to brown, while the oblong sunfish has a distinctive pattern of grey and white stripes and blotches, usually on a grey background. The short sunfish and the pointed-tailed sunfish may reach a length of up to 3 metres, and their smaller relative, the oblong sunfish, grows to about 90 cm long. A notable feature of all species is their long dorsal and pelvic fins, which have sometimes been mistaken for the dorsal fins of large sharks. Very little is known about the reproductive behaviour of sunfishes, but a ripe female may produce 300 million tiny eggs.

Sunfishes rarely come close to shore, and are most likely to be seen when stranded. They spend most of their life in deep oceanic waters, drifting with the ocean currents and feeding near the surface on sea jellies, salps – a gelatinous form of zooplankton that may occur in dense swarms – and small fishes.

The world's largest sunfish so far recorded was caught on a ship's port propellor in 1908. The SS *Fiona* impaled it on a run between Newcastle and Sydney. So firmly embedded was the fish in the ship's propellor that the crew could do nothing at sea to free it. Running on the starboard engine only, the ship steamed slowly into Mosman Bay in Sydney Harbour. Here the body of the sunfish was extricated from the metal blades and winched on board. The fish measured 3 metres long by 4.25 metres between the upper and lower fins. It weighed 2.25 tonnes. A sunfish caught in New South Wales waters two years previously was at least a metre smaller from fin tip to fin tip.

The measurements of another large sunfish taken in Queensland were recorded in January 1929. This impressive specimen was dragged ashore on the beach at Mooloolabah. It was 2.7 metres long and 2.4 metres from dorsal fin tip to anal fin tip.
Family: Molidae

A DEADLY DISH

Toadfishes and porcupinefishes are highly toxic; their flesh and internal organs contain a powerful nerve poison known as tetrodotoxin, for which there is no known antidote. The highest concentration of poison occurs in the fish's liver and in the eggs.

Adults can deter predators by inflating themselves into a spiky ball, but larvae and juveniles have no such protection. The poison may well serve as a collective defence, giving predators a small dose each time they take a juvenile toadfish and thereby deterring them from consuming more.

In Japan toadfish flesh is highly valued and is prepared sashimi-style by trained and licensed fugu chefs. Part of the appeal reportedly lies in the mild euphoria and tingling sensations caused by low doses of the toxin. But people still die from lethal doses of the poison, and the aftereffects of even a nonfatal dish of fugu may include headaches, nausea, internal bleeding, skin rashes and paralysis.

INVERTEBRATES

THERE HAS BEEN LIFE ON EARTH for about four billion years. For the first three billion of these, it took the form of microscopic, single-celled organisms. Animals, as multi-cellular organisms, first appeared about 600 million years ago as a radiation of life forms. Animals are arbitrarily divided into two groups, the vertebrates and the invertebrates. The vertebrates – fishes, amphibians, reptiles, birds and mammals – have a backbone made up of vertebrae. All other animals are invertebrates, and their only common feature is that they do not have a vertebral column. More than 95 per cent of animals are invertebrates, but the diversity of invertebrate life remains one of the unexplored frontiers of biological science.

GREEDY ECHINODERM
The crown-of-thorns sea star feeds on living coral by settling on coral formations and thrusting out the stomach on the underside of its body to devour the coral polyps. Only the skeleton of its prey is left behind.

EVOLUTION IN ACTION
From the first true many-celled animals, such as sponges and sea jellies, invertebrate life evolved to produce the sea squirts (tunicates), which have a supporting structure along the back of their body that is the forerunner of the vertebrate backbone.

Many invertebrates are known to us by their exquisite shapes and colours and sometimes by the services they render us: corals beautify our tropical seas, sea shells adorn our beaches, and earthworms are a sure sign that the soil is healthy. The arthropods – a group that comprises three-quarters of all known animal species – are also familiar. This group includes the insects, crustaceans, centipedes, millipedes, scorpions and spiders.

But these familiar animals represent only the tip of the iceberg of invertebrate biodiversity. Many invertebrates are unfamiliar because of their microscopic size; for example, virtually every home harbours millions of invisible dust mites. Most invertebrates are concealed in the soil, in the canopies of rainforests, in the ooze of lakes, rivers and seas, as plankton floating on the ocean surface, or in the depths of the ocean. Only a fraction of these organisms are known to science at present, and we have, as yet, little knowledge of their life histories and functions in their ecosystems.

Zoologists classify animals into some 30 groups called phyla, and the members of a phylum share features that distinguish them from all other phyla. Many of the earlier animals were soft-bodied and did not easily fossilise, so the relationships among the phyla are still a riddle.

It is possible, however, to trace some of the fundamental steps through which animal life has evolved: the progression from single-celled organisms to animals with bodies composed of millions or billions of cells; the specialisation of cells to form tissues and organs; the development of body cavities to allow guts and hearts to expand and contract; the evolution of a segmented body with different segments dedicated to particular functions; and the development of protective and supporting skeletons.

Protozoans
Protozoans are single-celled organisms found wherever there is water – oceans, fresh water, damp soil, even within other organisms, where they live as parasites or as mutualists.

sponge
(poriferan)

sea jelly
(cnidarian)

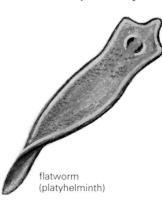

flatworm
(platyhelminth)

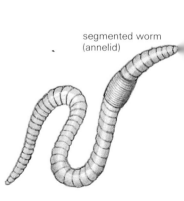

segmented worm
(annelid)

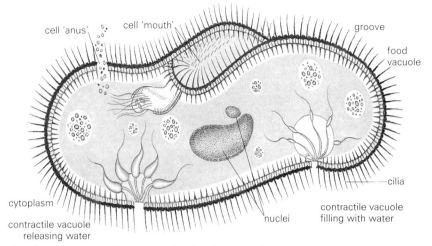

cell 'anus' cell 'mouth' groove

food vacuole

cilia

cytoplasm

contractile vacuole releasing water

nuclei

contractile vacuole filling with water

Sponges

Sponges are the simplest of all animals. They are communes of cells, rather than bodies in the usual sense. These cells are unusual in that they retain a capacity for changing into other cell types as required. The sponge body is supported by a leathery skeleton of protein fibres or by a filigree of inorganic spicules.

Cnidarians and comb jellies

The vase-shaped bodies of sea jellies, sea anemones and corals are made up of simple tissues. The mouth of the vase is the animal's mouth, fringed with stinging tentacles and opening into a gut cavity lined with a sheet of digestive cell tissue. The outer surface is a layer of skin cells that are capable of muscular contractions for movement, coordinated by a simple network of nerve cells. Between the two layers of cells is a supporting layer of non-living jelly, which is enormously expanded in the bodies of sea jellies. The bodies of the comb jellies are similarly constructed.

Worms

There are no fewer than 11 worm phyla, and worms were the pioneers of new evolutionary models. The bulk of a worm's body consists of masses of cells between the outer protective skin and the delicate inner digestive surface. Within this cell mass, true organs – specialised groups of cells – control the animal's movement, reproduction, excretion and coordination. This was the blueprint for the development of all subsequent life forms.

Flatworms have no cavities in this cell mass, so there is no space for a heart to beat, nor are the contractions of the gut independent of the movement of the whole animal.

The ribbon or bootlace worms are like flatworms in their basic organisation, but do have a circulatory system and a complete gut with a mouth at the front and an anus at the rear.

Several worm phyla have fluid-filled body cavities in which muscles work against the fluid pressure to change the body shape and bring about movement with minimal energy expenditure. These cavities also act as shock-absorbers to protect internal organs, and as circulatory systems to carry nutrients, gases and waste products around the body.

Earthworms, beachworms and leeches display a further evolutionary refinement: a body divided into segments, visible externally as a series of rings. Muscles act independently on the fluid in each segment, allowing great flexibility for swimming, crawling and burrowing.

Arthropods

The success of the segmented body plan is reflected in the arthropods – the insects, the centipedes and millipedes, the crustaceans and the spiders, scorpions, ticks and mites. These animals have an external armoured skeleton that must be shed periodically as they grow.

Originally, the arthropods had one pair of jointed limbs per segment. The diversity of form and function of these limbs shows how evolutionary forces can fashion complex forms from simple ancestral structures.

In the various groups of arthropods, the segments have fused in different combinations to make functional units. For example, the head of a common fly is six segments fused into one unit. The limbs belonging to these six segments have become sensory antennae and complex

NOT SO SIMPLE
While the body of a paramecium is single-celled, it is structurally quite complex, with two nuclei and the equivalents of a mouth and an anus. It moves through the fresh water where it lives by beating the tiny hairs (cilia) that cover the cell surface.

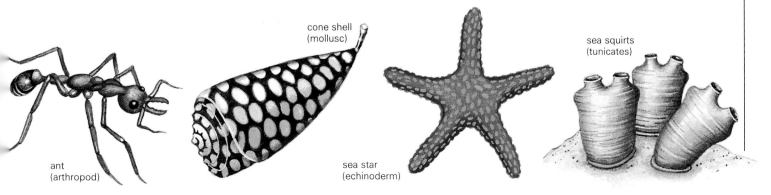

cone shell (mollusc)

sea squirts (tunicates)

ant (arthropod)

sea star (echinoderm)

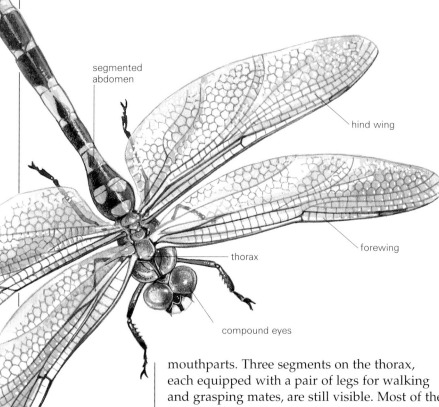

segmented abdomen

hind wing

thorax

forewing

compound eyes

mouthparts. Three segments on the thorax, each equipped with a pair of legs for walking and grasping mates, are still visible. Most of the abdominal segments now lack limbs, but the limbs on the hindmost segment have modified into the genitalia. Virtually every arthropod activity involves the use of specialised limbs, and insects have added to this versatility by developing wings – a feature that has greatly enhanced their evolutionary success.

Molluscs

The molluscs are not segmented, but are second only to the arthropods in numbers of species, and are perhaps even more varied in body forms and ways of life. Limpets, slugs, oysters, clams, and the squids and octopuses that rival vertebrates in their dexterity, speed and complex behaviour, are all within this phylum.

Most molluscs – though by no means all – have an external shell to protect the soft body, but some terrestrial and marine molluscs have entirely lost this structure, and others have internalised it to form a skeletal support. The cuttlefish 'bone' washed up on seashores is a familiar example of an internal shell.

Echinoderms

Like the molluscs, the sea stars and sea urchins do not have segmented bodies. They do not appear to be particularly active animals, but they have evolved ingenious ways of moving and handling their food. Their

bodies contain a system of water-filled canals that extend through their skin as tubular 'feet' called podia. These structures can be extended and contracted by fluid pressure. They are used by various groups of echinoderms to collect food, attach to the substrate or for locomotion.

Minor phyla

Some phyla that contain few species still deserve study because they are commonly encountered or they shed light on the course of evolution.

Some worm phyla have few members but are extremely common: the microscopic wheel animals (rotifers) are abundant in pond water, and some peanut worm and spoon worm species are widespread on rocky shores.

Other small phyla may represent the vestiges of ancient, once prolific groups. Fossil records are rich in lampshells and sea mats: paleontologists have described 30 000 lampshell species, compared with a mere 300 species alive today.

Some small phyla may suggest evolutionary relationships with major phyla: velvet worms and water bears display features that indicate they are ancestral to the arthropods, and acorn worms constitute a link between the echinoderms and the chordates – the phylum to which vertebrates, including humans, belong.

The web of life

Invertebrates fulfil almost every role in the cycle of life and death called the food web. On the water surface microscopic invertebrates feast on photosynthetic algae, and on land, the invertebrates graze and browse, suck sap and nectar, and burrow through the tissues of plants. These herbivores are preyed on in turn by their carnivorous relatives, which have developed an impressive array

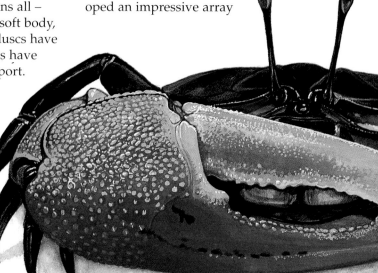

of tricks, traps, venoms and weapons to ensure the safety of their food supply.

Faeces and dead plants and animals are broken up by termites, earthworms, maggots and a myriad soil, mud and ocean-floor invertebrates, and fungi and bacteria process these materials to release nutrients for the plants.

In addition, every free-living plant and animal species is host to at least one invertebrate parasite species, and often many. Parasitism is, in fact, the dominant way of life in the animal world and plays an important part in keeping the numbers of animals and plants in check.

Life on Earth depends on the small invertebrates that form the bulk of the food web. If the invertebrate component were removed, or even reduced, the ecosystem would collapse.

With or without sex

There are two types of reproduction: sexual and nonsexual. Sexual reproduction is the union of two individuals and the exchanging of their genetic material to create a genetically different individual. Almost all animals reproduce sexually at some time to maintain genetic diversity within their group. But many invertebrates can also increase their numbers by nonsexual reproduction, where a single individual produces another identical individual – a clone.

Protozoans, for example, reproduce sexually when two parent cells unite to create an individual that is a genetic mixture of both. But protozoans can also simply divide a mature cell nonsexually to generate new individuals.

Nonsexual reproduction takes many forms. Sponges and some worms and echinoderms can grow new individuals from pieces broken off the adult body. Other invertebrates form buds that are released to create new individuals or remain attached to the parent to increase the size of the colony. Some female insects lay eggs that, without male intervention, hatch into daughters that are identical to their mothers. Flatworms, earthworms, leeches and terrestrial snails and slugs are

MARSH-DWELLER
The fiddler crab, a member of the huge arthropod group, burrows in tidal marshes, where it contributes to the food web by throwing up nutrients to the surface. The male has a greatly enlarged front claw, which he uses to attract females and drive away other males.

hermaphrodites – each individual has both testes and ovaries. Hermaphrodites usually reproduce sexually, though self-fertilisation does sometimes occur. Each individual receives sperm from a partner, to be stored until the eggs are released and fertilised.

Many marine invertebrates release their eggs and sperm directly into the water. This often synchronises with an environmental change – for example, a phase of the moon. The huge number of sex cells released ensures that enough male and female cells unite for fertilisation to occur and the species to survive. Each egg is tiny, and the larvae hatch in a form very different from the adults. The larvae make up much of the small aquatic life in the water that scientists call plankton. For immobile animals such as corals, this free-floating larval stage is essential in dispersing the species to new habitats.

Other animals have evolved different ways of depositing their sperm directly into the female to increase the chance of fertilisation. Males of some species have a penis for this purpose, but others have different methods: centipedes and scorpions deposit a package of sperm on the ground to be picked up by the female, and male spiders load their semen into syringe-like structures on their heads and inject the sperm into the female's genital opening. The developing eggs are then laid with a protective shell or the young are born live.

Parental care

Most invertebrates leave the fertilised eggs to develop on their own, but female centipedes guard their eggs and young ferociously, while the social insects – the bees, the ants and the wasps – have evolved sophisticated communities in which adults share the responsibility for looking after the next generation.

A TIMID MONSTER
Octopuses are molluscs, although they have no trace of a shell. They have provided the model for many a fearsome sea monster, but they are shy creatures, using their highly developed brains and eyes to hunt by stealth and cunning. Many can camouflage themselves by rapidly changing colour.

PROTOZOANS

Members of the phylum Protozoa are mainly single-celled; their scientific name means 'the first animals'. Some protozoans harness the sun's energy directly, like plants, but the majority eat food and can move, so most scientists regard them as animals. Many are microscopic, but some grow to about 1.25 cm, and fossils of extinct protozoans several centimetres long have been found.

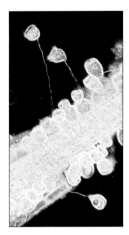

DRAWN INTO THE VORTEX
The cilia around the rim of the bell-shaped bodies of these *Vorticella* create a vortex, sweeping bacteria towards the centrally located 'mouth' of the cell. *Vorticella* attach to aquatic plants and animals by a stalk, which can be retracted like a spring when the organism is disturbed.

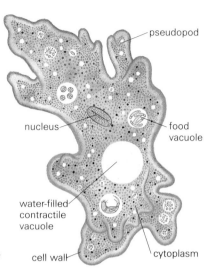

MULTIPURPOSE FEET
Amoebae use their pseudopods –'false feet'– not only to move but to engulf their prey in a bubble-like vacuole.

Protozoans form a vast assemblage of mainly single-celled organisms. As their name implies, they were once considered to be animals (as the phylum Protozoa) because the structure of their cells is similar to the individual cells that make up the bodies of true multicellular animals.

The other feature that protozoans share with animals is that they ingest and digest food as their source of materials to build their cells and provide energy. Indeed, the cells of protozoans carry out all life functions that are performed by the tissues and organs in animals. Their complex cell structure, together with recent genetic evidence, now indicates that protozoans actually form a large number of separate phyla of organisms that are so distinctly different to animals as to warrant a completely separate classification.

Protozoans are found all over the world where they can occur in vast numbers living in the oceans, fresh water, in the thin film of moisture surrounding plants and soil particles and within the bodies of animals. Most are microscopic but some can grow to about 2 cm or more and be seen with the naked eye. They feed in a variety of ways by enveloping their prey or directing it towards their body in currents created by the beating of tiny hair-like structures called cilia. Most protozoans reproduce nonsexually by splitting the cell into two identical cells.

However, many also reproduce sexually by dividing the cell to form the equivalent of sperm and eggs. These fuse in pairs to form a new individual that is genetically different to either parent cell. Some protozoans are supported by a variety of elaborate skeletons. On death, their skeletal remains can form a significant component of marine sediments.

The familiar protozoans
The best known protozoans are the amoebae, which live in the sea, fresh water or the film that surrounds plants and moist soil. In order to move, they extend projections from the body called pseudopodia. Foraminiferans have shells that enclose the cell and the pseudopodia, as a food entrapping net, extend through an opening in the shell. The foraminiferan, *Marginopora vertebralis*, is the largest protozoan with a disc-shaped body that can exceed 2 cm in diameter. They are very commonly found attached to the base of the macroalga *Halimeda* species on the Great Barrier Reef. *Paramecia* species are structurally more sophisticated than amoebae. They are very common in fresh water. Their cells have a constant shape, which resembles a slipper (see page 493). They rapidly propel themselves in a corkscrew fashion by beating thousands of hair-like cilia on the cell surface. Powerful cilia sweep particles of food into a groove leading to the 'mouth'. The bell-shaped cells of *Vorticella* species are also common in fresh water. The cell is attached to pondweeds by a stalk, which can contract like a spring when disturbed. The cilia beat to create a vortex, sweeping food particles to the centrally located 'mouth'.

Symbiotic protozoans
Many protozoans live inside the bodies of animals where they form relationships ranging from benign through beneficial to extremely harmful. Herbivorous animals often possess protozoans in their gut to aid the digestion of cellulose. Many termites have a special part of their gut where they cultivate a very large and spectacular protozoan – *Trichonympha* species – for this purpose. Many other protozoans are parasitic causing harm to their host, including the water-borne gut parasites *Giardia lamblia* and *Entamoeba histolytica*, and the blood parasite *Plasmodium* species causing malaria. Fortunately, neither the malaria parasite nor its vector, the anophaline mosquito, occurs in Australia.

SEDIMENTS OF SKELETONS
Foraminiferans are among the largest of all protozoan cells, reaching up to 3 centimetres in diameter. The cell is supported by an often highly sculpted external shell constructed of calcium carbonate. The accumulated skeletal remains of foraminiferans can form a significant component of marine sediments.

SPONGES

Sponges are among the most ancient of all animal life. The earliest species existed 600–700 million years ago, and their descendants can still be seen today. Worldwide, some 6000 sponge species have been recorded; there may be just as many in Australian seas, but all the sponges of Australia and the Indo-Pacific are still far from being discovered. Sponges belong to the phylum Porifera, meaning 'pore-bearing'.

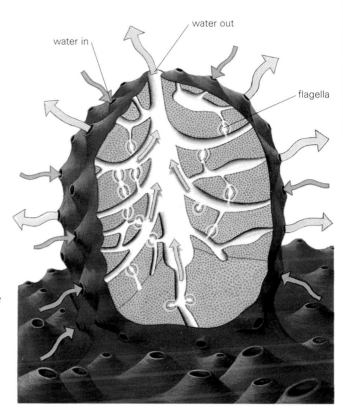

Before synthetics, natural sponges were popular bathroom equipment but the bath sponge is the skeleton of just one of the thousands of aquatic sponge species. Made of soft protein, the skeleton supports a labyrinth of canals and chambers – a framework that once housed tens of thousands of minute sponge cells. These cells act as individuals to form a colony. Each group of cells performs a different function in the sponge – for example, skeleton formation, feeding or reproduction.

In many sponges the soft skeleton is strengthened by small, sharp spikes called spicules, composed of either silica or calcium carbonate. However, the sponges that are used for commercial purposes have soft skeletons with no spicules.

Animal or plant?
Sponges have no mouth, tissues or organs that correspond to those of other animals, and they have long fascinated and puzzled naturalists. The Greek philosopher Aristotle, the first person to attempt classification of animals and plants, believed that they were an intermediate life form between plants and animals. It was not until 1825 that they were finally proved to be animals. By observing sponges through a microscope, the Scottish naturalist Robert Edmond Grant demonstrated beyond any doubt that they feed on particles of organic matter found in water.

Food filterers
To obtain enough nutrients from the sea, sponges have to filter bacteria and microscopic plants and animals from large volumes of water; many sponges filter their own volume of water every four to nine seconds.

Huge beds of sponges flourish in both tropical and temperate waters; most live in salt water, but a few have adapted to life in fresh water. Because they filter food, many sponges live where there is constant movement of nutrient-rich water –

for example, just below low tide levels on rocky shores. Those that cling to the shore usually resemble mats with a rough, smooth or slimy texture. Some species that live in deeper water form erect branching, vase or fan shapes.

Sponges vary greatly in both shape and size; even members of the same species may be as small as a human thumbnail or several metres wide. Some take a lifetime grip on rocks, while a few embed themselves in mud or sand; still others produce chemicals with which they bore into mollusc shells and corals in search of living space.

Many sponges that grow on coral reefs have evolved from spherical or tubular shapes into dish, cup or fan shapes or encrusting forms. These shapes efficiently trap the sunlight that is necessary for the animal to live and grow.

Shared resources
In waters around coral reefs, where the supply of nutrients is limited, sponge populations have formed a symbiotic relationship with algae. Algae in the water enter the sponge and become trapped in the sponge cells or in the fluid around the cells. Rather than eat the algae, the host sponge has developed a chemical mechanism to force the algae to leak energy-rich sugar compounds (valuable products of photosynthesis) directly into the sponge cells. The symbiosis works so well in some sponges that most of their nutrition is provided by the algae.

Perpetuating the species
Sponges are able to reproduce both sexually and nonsexually. In sexual reproduction, which ensures genetic diversity, one sponge releases both eggs and sperm into the water. Once fertilised, the eggs hatch to form minute, free-swimming larvae, which eventually settle on the sea bed and grow into new sponges. In nonsexual reproduction, where the

HOW SPONGES FEED
Sponges draw in water through tiny pores on their surface. Millions of hairlike flagella then drive the water and nutrients through canals. Particles of food are trapped, filtered and transported by special wandering cells.

genetic material of the new sponge is identical to that of the parent, the adult sponge produces buds that break off, settle on the sea bottom and grow into new sponges.

Sponges have remarkable powers of regeneration. Under the right conditions, the fragments of sponges that have been torn apart by storms will attach themselves to a solid object and grow. They have the capacity to do this because their structure is simple and they contain very few different types of cells.

Surviving drought
In Australia 25 species of freshwater sponges have been identified. The freshwater sponges have developed an ingenious reproductive technique to ensure their survival through even the most devastating droughts. When the rivers and creeks dry up, these sponges produce extremely hard, drought-resistant reproductive buds called gemmules, which remain in suspended animation until the drought breaks and the waters flow again. Only then do the buds come miraculously to life.

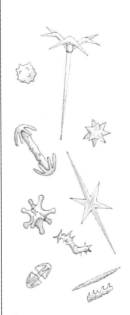

SPONGE SPICULES
The silica or calcium carbonate spicules that reinforce the soft skeletons of many sponges come in a wide variety of shapes, from simple needles to multipointed stars and spirals. The shape of the spicules and the way they are distributed in the body of the sponge are important for identification.

■ VASE SPONGE
Each 'finger' of the vase
sponge is a separate
individual, shaped like
a tall, slender vase. The
large openings that
expel water from the
sponge are viewed
here from above.

VASE SPONGES ■

Clusters of this creamy coloured
finger-like sponge are found on
temperate and tropical seashores
under boulders on rock platforms.
They also grow on coral reefs.
Individual vase sponges are usually
2–3 cm high and about 1 cm in diameter. Their spicules are made of
calcium carbonate.
Scientific name: Sycon spp.

GOLF BALL SPONGE

This small, bright orange, spherical
sponge is quite small, but it is easy
to spot. It usually grows in groups
on vertical rocky surfaces between
the tide levels. Found in temperate
waters, golf ball sponges are often
seen on rocks and in slightly deeper
water in south-eastern Australia.
Scientific name: Tethya popae

GOBLET SPONGE

This pale grey, goblet-shaped
sponge stands about 15 cm high.
Its beautifully sculpted skeleton,
which is soft and has no spicules, is
very distinctive. It lives in sheltered
areas of deep water, and sometimes
among corals on the outer reef flats.
   The goblet sponge has symbiotic
cyanobacteria living in its body.
These cyanobacteria use sunlight
to photosynthesise, producing
compounds that provide the host

goblet sponge with some of the
nutrients it requires.
*Scientific name: Carteriospongia
foliascens*

MAUVE SPONGES ■

This is one of a very diverse group
of sponges that are found throughout Australasian waters and are
common along the coastline of New
South Wales. The mauve sponge
lives between the tidal limits clinging to the sides of rock pools, tucked
into crevices and under large boulders. It appears to be one of the few
temperate-zone sponges that can
withstand full sunlight. It grows
upright and lobed where space
allows, or as a short, squat mat.
Scientific name: Haliclona spp.

BREADCRUMB SPONGE

This encrusting sponge, light creamy
yellow to green and brown and up
to about 2 cm thick, crumbles easily
if handled, hence its common name.
It occurs most frequently between
high and low tide levels, often covering quite large expanses of rocks
where there are shaded crevices or
overhanging ledges. It is also found
on wharf piles, in mussel beds and
on seaweeds. The breadcrumb
sponge is widespread in the
waters off temperate-zone coasts.
Scientific name: Halichondria panicea

BROWN REEF SPONGE

These brown, rough-textured reef
sponges form dome-shaped colonies
of various sizes on the dead coral
boulders of shallow reef flats, like
those surrounding Heron Island off
the coast of far north Queensland. In
the deeper water along reef slopes,
their shapes vary from dome-shaped
to upright and lobed.
Scientific name: Jaspis stellifera

■ MAUVE SPONGE
Some sponges are rather
drab in appearance, but
Haliclona species come
in attractive shades of
violet and mauve.

CNIDARIANS

The phylum Cnidaria contains many strange and beautiful animals, so different in shape, size and life history that it is difficult to believe they are all related. They vary from fern-like hydroids and flower-like sea anemones to corals and sea jellies. Although cnidarians are not highly evolved animals, their relatives may have been on Earth for as long as 650 million years. Most cnidarians are ocean-dwellers.

More than 10 000 species of cnidarians have been recorded worldwide, and new species are still being discovered in Australian waters. The phylum takes its name from the Greek word for a nettle, because all these creatures have a special armament for immobilising their prey: their tentacles contain cells called cnidocytes, each containing a coiled stinging thread and a supply of venom. On contact with prey, the stinging threads are released and the animal uses its tentacles to drag its stunned prey to its mouth.

There are two structural types of cnidarians: a stationary cylindrical polyp with a central mouth fringed by upward-reaching tentacles, and a free-swimming, umbrella-shaped medusa with a central mouth under its 'bell' and tentacles trailing from the edge. Some species go through both stages during their life cycle.

Like the sponges, most cnidarians are colonial animals, and usually the colony grows by budding new individuals that remain attached to the parent colony. But cnidarians are more advanced than sponges, since they have two layers of tissues with a gelatinous layer between and some basic organs.

There are four classes of cnidarians: hydrozoans, sea jellies, box jellies and anthozoans.

SEA MONSTERS
This huge example of a mosaic sea jelly, *Catostylus mosaicus* (page 502), almost dwarfs a diver. Sea jellies can be very tiny or very large; some are almost transparent, while others are opaque. Sometimes they swarm in vast numbers, either in open waters or in more sheltered bays and estuaries.

HYDROZOANS

Most hydrozoans are marine and colonial, and have both a polyp and, often, a medusa form. The group includes sea ferns (hydroids), hydrocorals and floating colonies.

Most hydroids form communities of thousands of polyps, often looking like fern fronds. They occur in large numbers on rocky reefs, in shallow temperate seas, and on coral reefs. Their larvae attach themselves to the undersides of boulders, the holdfasts of seaweeds, and sometimes the shells of small snails. They feed on plankton, and are preyed on by larger animals.

Hydrocorals differ from hydroids in that they have hard, limy skeletons in which the minute polyps are embedded.

Floating colonies look completely different from hydroids and hydrocorals. They have gas-filled floats from which numerous polyps and tentacles are suspended. At the mercy of winds and currents, they are tossed around on the surface of oceans and die if washed ashore.
Class: Hydrozoa

SISTERS UNDER THE SKIN
Although they do not resemble each other, the cnidarians' polyp form (top) and medusa form (bottom) are structurally similar.

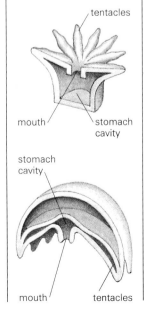

LIFE CYCLE OF A HYDROID
The hydroid's stems bear feeding polyps with tentacles for prey capture. Smaller, nonfeeding reproductive polyps bud tiny medusae, which may be male, female or bisexual. They produce eggs and sperm. Fertilised eggs develop into free-swimming larvae, which settle on the sea floor to form new polyps. The polyps immediately start budding.

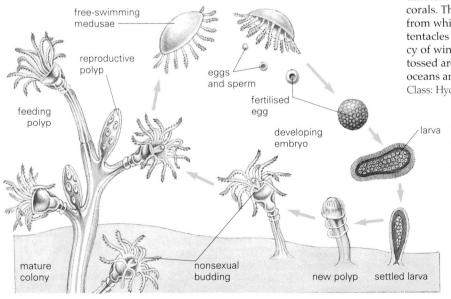

free-swimming medusae

reproductive polyp

eggs and sperm

fertilised egg

developing embryo

larva

feeding polyp

mature colony

nonsexual budding

new polyp   settled larva

HYDROIDS

HYDRAS
Hydras are found in freshwater lakes and streams all over the world, including Australia. Unlike most hydroids, hydras do not live as colonies but exist as individual polyps. They are difficult to see because they are so tiny and their bodies are transparent, but they gather in large numbers and are widespread. Hydras are extremely acrobatic; propelling themselves with their tentacles, they move about in the water from one object to another, preying on microscopic aquatic animals and even tiny fish.
Order: Hydroida
Scientific name: *Hydra* spp.

■ MAUVE HYDROCORAL
Most colonies of the mauve hydrocoral, *Distichophora violacea*, are quite small – around 3–5 cm – although some do grow larger. They are generally tucked away in protected cracks and crevices, but the larger ones grow in more open areas. They live at water depths of up to 30 metres. The skeletons of *Distichophora* species keep their strong colouring after the colony is dead.

HALOCORDYLE DISTICHA
Common around the temperate and subtropical coasts of South Australia, Victoria, New South Wales and Queensland, this hydroid is found in crevices and pools on rocky shores and on wharf piles in harbours. Its feathery colonies of brown stems often grow about 20 cm high and bear branches lined with tiny polyps.
Order: Hydroida

SOLANDERIA FUSCA
Widespread along the temperate coasts of Queensland, New South Wales, Victoria and South Australia, this hydroid is easily recognised by its flattened fan shape. Its many brown branches, which may reach 20 cm high, are covered with small white polyps with club-shaped tentacles. Small colonies may be found under boulders but larger, erect colonies are often seen by divers in caves and overhanging rocks on reef slopes in deeper water.
Order: Hydroida

FIRE WEED ■
As its name implies, a brush with this green, fern-like hydroid can be searingly painful. Attached to coral reefs in tropical waters around the northern coastline of Australia, it sometimes grows in colonies up to 30 cm high.
Order: Hydroida
Scientific name: *Aglaophenia cupressina*

STINGING SEA FERN
This species is found in Australia's tropical waters. It has long, brown, branched stems that reach lengths of up to 20 cm and are covered with white polyps. It occurs in deeper water than the fire weed and is finer and more feathery. It is usually found on the sides of reefs or in underwater caves.
Order: Hydroida
Scientific name: *Lytocarpia philippina*

HYDROCORALS

MAUVE HYDROCORAL ■
Along the tropical coast of Australia, colonies of mauve hydrocoral a few centimetres high are found under dead coral boulders on reefs, and larger examples grow in caves and under ledges down reef slopes. The sides of its flat, mauve, white-tipped branches are edged with pores from which its polyps emerge to feed.
Order: Hydroida
Scientific name: *Distichophora violacea*

LACE CORAL
A delicate, multibranched hydrocoral, usually pink, lace coral is found in sheltered back-reef areas and caverns throughout the Indo-Pacific region.
Order: Hydroida
Scientific name: *Stylaster elegans*

FIRE CORAL
Although this creature looks like a coral at first glance – it even lives among corals on tropical reefs – it is not a true coral but a hydrocoral. Vast pale yellow or white colonies shaped like dinner plates grow several centimetres high, forming limy skeletons covered with minute pores. Within these pores are several types of polyps that perform different functions, such as feeding and defence. Stings from the fire coral cause a painful burning sensation.
Order: Hydroida
Scientific name: *Millepora platyphylla*

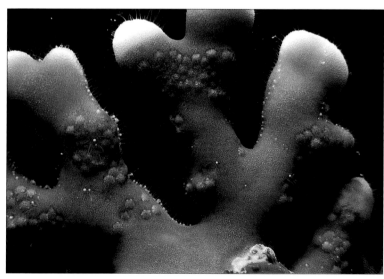

FLOATING COLONIES

PORTUGUESE MAN O' WAR ▪

The Portuguese man o' war, which is better known to most people in south-eastern Australia as the blue-bottle, is a notorious marine stinger. What is less widely recognised is that it is not a sea jelly but a floating colony of individual polyps called zooids. A blue gas bladder keeps the colony afloat, and beneath it hang three different types of zooids: some are used to catch prey, some to feed and others to reproduce. Usually each colony has a few very long (up to 30 metres) tentacles and a large number of smaller tentacles. These fishing tentacles are supplied with an enormous number of very potent stinging cells. When the fishing tentacles contact their prey, the stinging cells stun it and quickly contract the tentacle, bringing the food to the feeding zooids, which digest it.

Portuguese men o' war are carried on currents along the eastern and western coasts of Australia, and prevailing summer east winds blow them to shore in their hundreds. Even after stranding, the stinging tentacles remain potent for some time, but the float is harmless.
Order: Siphonophora
Scientific name: *Physalia physalis*

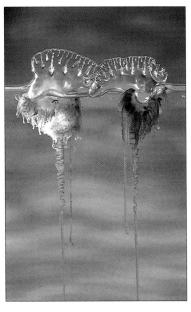

▪ PORTUGUESE MAN O' WAR
The float of *Physalia physalis* is set so that its direction of travel is 45 degrees to the wind, to the left for about half the swarm and to the right for the rest. So, while many Portuguese men o' war may be stranded inshore, just as many will be pushed out to sea.

BY-THE-WIND SAILOR

The by-the-wind sailor is found all over the world. Although it is often washed ashore with the Portuguese man o' war, the float of the by-the-wind sailor looks quite different; it is a flat, oval disc, 1–5 cm in diameter, kept afloat by hundreds of tiny gas-filled chambers. Sitting on top of the disc is a thin transparent 'sail' that enables the by-the-wind sailor to harness the wind to drive it across the sea. A large central mouth below the disc is surrounded by short zooids fringed with pointed tentacles that are harmless to humans but fatal to prey.

At least three other members of the floating community prey upon the by-the-wind sailor: the floating violet snail, *Janthina*, and two nudibranchs, *Glaucus* and *Fiona*, are each capable of denuding a whole flotilla. *Janthina* and *Glaucus* attack the underside, removing all the zooids, while *Fiona* eats all the surface tissues and leaves a bare float, on which it lays coils of tiny white egg ribbons.
Order: Chondrophora
Scientific name: *Velella velella*

PORPITA PORPITA

A surface drifter, this bright blue floating colonial animal has a round, flat disc up to 2 cm in diameter that is kept afloat by gas-filled chambers. Because its flat surface is not easily caught by the wind, *P. porpita* is rarely washed ashore.

This blue-green floating colony is best appreciated while it is still afloat, as its fragile tentacles are damaged when the animal is cast ashore. The tiny bunches of stinging cells along the tentacles are quite harmless to humans.
Order: Chondrophora

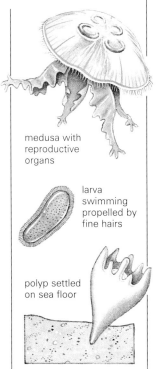

medusa with reproductive organs

larva swimming propelled by fine hairs

polyp settled on sea floor

cup-like disc leaving the polyp

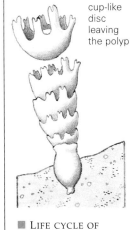

▪ LIFE CYCLE OF THE MOON JELLY
During the summer breeding season, the moon jelly's four pink, horseshoe-shaped reproductive organs appear in the centre of its bell. Here fertilised eggs develop into tiny larvae. When the larvae are large enough, they use fine hairs on their surface to propel themselves through the mouth of the medusa and into the sea. They then develop polyps with tentacles and find a place to settle. As the polyps develop, they grow cup-like discs that eventually bud off to form free-swimming, miniature medusae.

SEA JELLIES

Sea jellies are sometimes called jellyfishes – but they look nothing like fishes, so the more accurate name 'sea jellies' is being adopted. In summer, sea jellies are found, sometimes in their thousands, pulsating gently just below the surface of the sea.

Sea jellies range from a few centimetres to almost 2 metres across the surface of their 'bell' or 'umbrella'. Their bodies are transparent or translucent, and they may be pink, blue, mauve, yellow or brown. Many are decorated with spots or stripes of contrasting colours.

Seen at night from a small boat or the deck of a ship, many sea jellies are brilliantly luminescent. Luminescence in some animals is generated by a biochemical called luciferin that is produced in the animals' cells. Many sea-dwelling creatures are luminescent, but the reason why they have this property is still something of a mystery to scientists.
Class: Scyphozoa

MOON JELLY ▪

Sometimes known as the saucer jelly, this almost transparent sea jelly is perhaps the most common in the world. Found in rivers and estuaries along the entire Australian coast and in the open ocean, the moon jelly often assembles in vast shoals that extend for huge distances and may contain as many as 40 000 individual moon jellies per square kilometre.

The moon jelly's saucer-shaped bell is about the size of a small dinner plate and is fringed with short, fragile tentacles. Prey stunned by the tentacles are delivered to the central mouth by four mobile oral 'arms'.
Order: Semaeostomeae
Scientific name: *Aurelia aurita*

PURPLE STINGER

This pink-mauve sea jelly is an ocean dweller found occasionally in summer in the harbours and bays of eastern Australia, where it has been swept by the currents. It is often seen in the open sea during the summer. Hanging below its bell are four fragile, frilled 'arms', each filled with a labyrinth of canals with openings. These 'arms' are, in fact, secondary mouths, and through them the sea jelly obtains its food of minute planktonic animals. Just inside the bell's margin are eight trailing white tentacles. Both the surface of the bell (up to 14 cm in diameter) and the mouth-arms are covered with stinging cells. At night the purple stinger is brilliantly luminescent.
Order: Semaeostomeae
Scientific name: *Pelagia noctiluca*

■ MOSAIC SEA JELLY
A baby trevally darts into the umbrella of a sea jelly. Immune to the sea jelly's stinging tentacles, the tiny fish will live and travel in the umbrella until it is big enough to survive independently.

GIANT SEA JELLY

This magnificent sea jelly is sometimes called the lion's mane jelly because of its thick mane of long, stinging tentacles and the tawny colours of its scalloped bell, which may be up to a metre across. Its tentacles, 3–4 metres long and arranged in eight U-shaped clusters, hang just beneath the edge of the bell and can deliver a painful sting. Toward the centre of the bell are the thick, frilled mouth-arms from which the larvae develop. Although usually at home in the open ocean, young giant sea jellies, about a hand's width across, are sometimes seen in summer in estuaries and along surfing beaches.
Order: Semaeostomeae
Scientific name: *Cyanea capillata*

MOSAIC SEA JELLY ■

One of Australia's most common species, the mosaic sea jelly lives in rivers, estuaries and the open ocean. Fully grown specimens are at least the size of a large dinner plate, and can easily be seen in summer from the deck of a boat or from a low-flying aircraft. The jelly's thick, fringed bell has a coarse texture, and is marked with a blurred cross. Instead of tentacles it has eight thick 'arms', each filled with canals with openings, that hang beneath its bell. These 'arms' are secondary mouths through which the sea jelly feeds. Its colour varies according to where it is found: in the open ocean this sea jelly is usually a clear blue, but in estuaries it can be an opaque white – or even a yellowish brown, which is caused by algae sheltering within the sea jelly's tissues.
Order: Rhizostomeae
Scientific name: *Catostylus mosaicus*

SPOTTED SEA JELLY

This sea jelly is easily recognised by its spotted bell. It has creamy brown frilly mouth-arms, below which trail short white tentacles. In summer it assembles in large numbers in rivers, lakes and estuaries in temperate Australian waters, particularly in south-western Western Australia.
Order: Rhizostomeae
Scientific name: *Phyllorhiza punctata*

BOX JELLIES

The box jellies are sometimes called sea wasps. They are the most dangerous of all the cnidarians, and their stings have caused almost immediate death. Stinging tentacles trail from the flat, gelatinous lobes that hang from each corner of their box-shaped bells. Several species of box jellies, with stings that vary in potency, occur throughout the tropical waters of the Indo-Pacific.
Class: Cubozoa

JILGI

The jilgi, or four-tentacled box jelly, is found all around Australia's temperate shores from New South Wales along the southern coastline to Western Australia, but appears in bays and estuaries for only a short time in the summer. Its transparent bell is about 15 cm in diameter, with a single short mauve tentacle hanging from each corner.

The jilgi's tentacles can inflict a painful sting, but the creature moves so fast that swimmers are in little danger of being stung unless there are swarms of jilgi in the water.
Order: Cubomedusae
Scientific name: *Carybdea rastoni*

■ DEADLY BOX JELLY
All but invisible as it cruises in calm mangrove-flat shallows, *Chironex fleckeri* is one of the world's most dangerous marine stingers. Its tentacles, armed with stinging cells called cnidocytes, may trail as far as 3 metres behind the bell.

DEADLY BOX JELLY ■

The deadly box jelly is one of the most dangerous of all marine animals. Its sting has killed several people in the past, but no deaths have been recorded in recent years.

The jelly has a large bell – one specimen half a metre wide has been recorded – and up to 15 stinging tentacles extend from the four large lobes at each corner. It is so transparent in its young stages that it is almost impossible to see; larger forms become more translucent. It occurs only along Australia's tropical coasts in summer. Signs on the beaches in far north Queensland warn people not to swim during the summer months, when winds and currents bring the deadly box jelly close to the shore.

A lycra 'stinger' suit, or even pantyhose, seem to provide effective protection against stings. If someone is stung, drench the area with vinegar for 30 seconds and seek medical attention immediately. Never wash, scrape or pick off tentacles, and do not apply methylated spirits or other forms of alcohol to a *Chironex* sting. These actions may increase the intensity of the sting.
Order: Cubomedusae
Scientific name: *Chironex fleckeri*

ANTHOZOANS

Anthozoans include sea anemones and true corals, as well as soft corals, tube anemones, sea pens and sea whips. They are found from shallow intertidal waters to the depths of the ocean. Despite their variety of form and colour, they share the same structure: that of a polyp, a vase-shaped animal with a mouth fringed with stinging tentacles.
Class: Anthozoa

SEA ANEMONES

WARATAH ANEMONE ▩

Probably the best known Australian anemone, the waratah anemone is found in intertidal waters from the tropics to the southern coasts. It lives under stones, in rock pools and on vertical rock faces. It is common on the beach rock of coral cays.

At low tide, when completely exposed, it looks like a purple-red gelatinous blob; in deeper water its light red tentacles expand to feed. It is an aggressive carnivore, competing with its neighbours for food. Young anemones develop in brood pouches inside the adult, emerge through its mouth and settle nearby.

Fawn-coloured *Actinia australis*, a closely related species, clings to boulders on rock platforms and, if removed from a rock, quickly uses its tentacles to right itself.
Order: Actiniaria
Scientific name: *Actinia tenebrosa*

SPECKLED ANEMONE

Common along the coast from New South Wales to south-western Western Australia, the speckled anemone gathers in large numbers in shallow crevices on rock platforms. At low tide it camouflages itself cleverly with shell grit, sand or gravel, making it difficult to see. But when it is submerged at high tide the anemone 'blooms', its short, grey-white tentacles extending from a pale green, red-spotted column.
Order: Actiniaria
Scientific name: *Oulactis muscosa*

STINGING ANEMONE

The stinging anemone lives embedded in sand on coral cay beaches and on the fringing reefs of continental islands, such as the Whitsundays off the coast of far north Queensland. It can retract completely into the sand, but at low tide the anemone usually lies exposed, its mouth surrounded by grey-blue, multibranched tentacles armed with stinging cells. When covered by water at high tide, it resembles a miniature pine tree.
Order: Actiniaria
Scientific name: *Actinodendron plumosum*

GIANT REEF ANEMONE

Growing as much as 50 cm wide, this is one of the largest species of sea anemone found in Australia's tropical waters. The giant reef anemone favours the outer reef slopes. Its light brown column is fringed with beautiful short blue tentacles that provide a safe shelter for clown fishes (*Amphiprion* spp.).
Order: Actiniaria
Scientific name: *Stichodactyla gigantea*

▩ WARATAH ANEMONE
Actinia tenebrosa has tentacles of a vibrant, glowing red, lighter than its body. It is usually seen when it is completely retracted, so that it looks like a rather unexciting reddish-brown blob, but when the tentacles do emerge the anemone reveals its full beauty.

UNDERWATER GARDEN
Feather stars (page 599), which are related to sea stars, frolic in a garden of sea whips (page 506) on the sea floor of the Great Barrier Reef.

CONSERVING WATER
When they are left exposed by the retreating tide, anemones draw their mouth and tentacles into their body, thus minimising water loss. The depression in the domed top of the closed-up anemone is not its mouth but the retracted surface of its body.

Reef builders

Coral reefs are able to withstand the force of typhoons and cyclones, yet they are put together by tiny, fragile polyps that look like miniature sea anemones.

Polyps 'build' coral reefs by taking up dissolved calcium carbonate from sea water and laying it down as stony deposits around them. These deposits are often referred to as the coral's skeleton because they support the living polyps. Thousands of polyps may live in one colony and colonies may mass together to form an almost continuous cover over the sea floor.

Over time, the world's corals have formed massive reefs in warm tropical waters, usually no deeper than 60 metres. Australia has the most extensive of these – the 2300 kilometre Great Barrier Reef. Listed as a World Heritage Area, it is home to more than 350 coral species, many of which are also found on coral reefs off the coast of Western Australia.

Synchronised spawning spectacular

Corals reproduce in three ways. At any time of year, they may, by nonsexual budding, produce new polyps that remain attached to the parent coral, so that existing corals continue to grow upwards and outwards. To form new colonies, however, corals have two other strategies. The first is a simple approach: broken fragments of coral, carried by ocean currents, settle on a suitable

Staghorn corals are prolific on the Great Barrier Reef. This colony is in the process of spawning – releasing hundreds of bundles of egg and sperm into the Coral Sea.

reef and begin to grow. The second method – sexual reproduction – constitutes one of the great marvels of nature.

On the Great Barrier Reef the annual spawning occurs in the week following the full moon in late spring or early summer. At nightfall, millions of polyps

Fishes swim among the delicate tracery of sea fans – plant-like corals that grow in vivid colours.

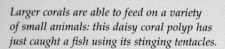

Larger corals are able to feed on a variety of small animals: this daisy coral polyp has just caught a fish using its stinging tentacles.

from dozens of different coral species spawn in the same few minutes – an unforgettable sight for those lucky enough to witness it. Most species are hermaphrodites and produce pinkish orange bundles of eggs and sperm about the size of poppy seeds, but some are single-sexed, producing either eggs or sperm. On reaching the surface, the bundles disintegrate and the sperm and eggs unite to form fertilised eggs. These become tiny larvae that are swept along by ocean currents until they lodge in a suitable place to grow. Huge amounts of eggs and sperm are devoured by other reef creatures, but they are produced in such abundance that dispersal of corals within the reef system is assured.

Symbiotic relationship

Compared with the plankton-rich waters of colder climates, the tropical seas are not plentiful feeding grounds for small carnivores like corals. For a long time people were puzzled by how these tiny polyps could flourish and form such mighty reefs. The mystery was solved when vast numbers of microscopic algae called zooanthellae were found living symbiotically within the tissues of the corals. Being plants, zooanthellae use sunlight to make their food in a process known as photosynthesis. Some of this food is absorbed by the coral. The algae also facilitate formation of the coral's skeleton by converting soluble calcium bicarbonate into insoluble calcium carbonate. Since the algae need sunlight to photosynthesise, the corals are found only in shallow water where sunlight can penetrate.

TRUE CORALS

STAGHORN CORALS

These are the best known and most familiar corals, found from low-tide level to the deep waters on the outer slopes of reefs. Seventy east-coast and 54 west-coast species have been described in Australia.

Colonies may be bushy, short, long or multibranched, or they may form flat encrustations or wide plates. Colonies form by budding and by the mass release of egg-and-sperm bundles in summer.

Staghorn corals range in height from a few centimetres to many metres. They can be fawn, purple, pale grey, mauve, green or blue.
Order: Scleractinia
Scientific name: *Acropora* spp.

HORSE'S TEETH CORAL

Viewed from the side, this coral looks like a horse's tooth. Its polyps are brown-green and about 2–3 cm wide. Short, stubby tentacles surround its central mouth. This species is widespread on Australia's eastern and western tropical coasts.
Order: Scleractinia
Scientific name: *Lobophyllia corymbosa*

NEEDLE CORAL

Perhaps the most fragile of all corals, this dainty species is found nestling in small colonies in the shelter of other corals on the outer reef flats. Larger, multibranched forms grow in reef lagoons. Its long, fine, tapering branches are sharp and its polyps minute. Colours vary from a creamy yellow to blue and pink.
Order: Scleractinia
Scientific name: *Seriatopora hystrix*

MUSHROOM CORALS

Mushroom corals are so named because they resemble overturned mushrooms with the stalks taken out. They are not colonies but very large individual polyps, leading a solitary life among other corals on the reef. In their early larval stages, however, they settle in groups, often on the dead skeleton of another mushroom coral, where they grow a short stem. There they remain until their sheer size and weight cause them to topple off and begin their existence as separate polyps.

The polyps of *Fungia fungites* are covered with short, pointed tentacles and can be seen only under water at night. In contrast, *Heliofungia actiniformis* has long, round, dark purple tentacles with light tips that are completely exposed during daylight hours.

Mushroom corals live throughout the Indo-Pacific and are common on both the eastern and western coastal reefs of Australia.
Order: Scleractinia

BRAIN CORAL

A massive, dome-shaped colony with convoluted walls, usually brown and grey and sometimes tinged with green, this coral, as its common name suggests, looks like the human brain. Deep inside the valleys between the walls are polyps that emerge only at night.

Some brain corals can be up to 2 metres wide and have patterns of maze-like intricacy. Most species live on upper reef slopes throughout the Indo-Pacific to the Great Barrier Reef and the Dampier Archipelago off the coast of Western Australia.
Order: Scleractinia
Scientific name: *Symphyllia recta*

MICRO-ATOLL CORAL

This coral forms massive, flat, dome-shaped colonies, 3–5 metres wide, usually fawn, blue, purple or green. When the centre of the colony dies from exposure and is worn away by wave action, the colony becomes ring-shaped – like a miniature atoll.

Micro-atoll corals are common on reef flats, in lagoons and on fringing reefs. They are found throughout the Great Barrier Reef and as far south as the Abrolhos Islands, off the coast of Western Australia.
Order: Scleractinia
Scientific name: *Porites lobata*

OTHER ANTHOZOANS

TUBE ANEMONES

Tube anemones do not attach themselves to solid objects, as true anemones do, but live in long, sand-encrusted tubes that project vertically from the sea floor in bays and estuaries and may be as much as a metre long. The tubes reach deep into the sediment, leaving only a fraction visible above the sea floor.

The beautiful burrowing anemone, with its outer ring of long, delicate tentacles and its inner ring of much shorter ones, lives beneath the low-tide mark and is a voracious predator of small fish and plankton.
Order: Ceriantharia
Scientific name: *Cerianthus* spp.

■ **TUBE ANEMONE**
Looking deceptively like a flower, its long, delicate tentacles trailing in the sea, the tube anemone waits for its prey.

■ **STAGHORN CORAL**
The staghorn coral grows faster and occupies more reef than any other coral. Corals with a definite staghorn form are very brittle and easily damaged, and are dangerous to walk on.

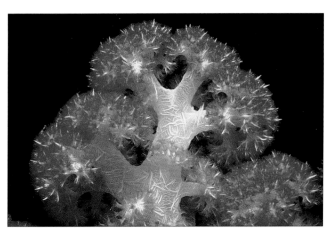

■ SOFT CORAL
With its feathery polyps extended, this soft coral maximises its chances of seizing planktonic food. The needle-like supporting spicules are visible in the transparent tissue.

■ SEA PEN
Sarcoptylum sp. shows the sea pen's quill-like plumes with their horny, flexible skeletons.

BLACK CORALS

Despite their common name, black corals are not true corals but they belong to the same group as the tube anemones (page 505). Usually confined to deep water among coral and temperate-zone reefs all over the world, black corals vary from dense, bushy growths to long, thin whips.

Black corals take their name from their black skeletons, which are much prized by jewellery makers. Unlike true coral skeletons, which fade when they die, the skeletons of black corals retain their colour. When they are alive, however, black corals do not look black but rather yellow, brown or orange because of their many colourful polyps.
Order: Antipatharia
Scientific name: *Antipathes* spp.

ORGAN-PIPE CORAL

Like black corals, the organ-pipe coral is not a true coral. Its skeleton is made up of parallel rows of small, limy tubes resembling organ pipes. Colonies several centimetres across live embedded among true corals on tropical reefs throughout the Indo-Pacific region. Fragments of their flame red skeletons are often swept up on the shores of sand cays.
Order: Stolonifera
Scientific name: *Tubipora musica*

SOFT CORALS ■

Unlike the true, or hard, corals, soft corals do not have a solid skeleton of calcium carbonate. Instead, minute needle-like spicules of calcium carbonate are scattered throughout their soft tissues to support the gelatinous colony.

Soft corals dominate parts of many reefs where true reef-building corals have been destroyed. Since they tend to grow much faster than the reef-builders, they can prevent true corals from regenerating.

Species vary enormously: some have flexible, snake-like branches; some have short, stubby, leathery lobes; others have little ridges across their surface. A few species occur in temperate and subtropical waters along the Australian coast, but most are found on tropical coral reefs.

Many soft corals have the power to alter their external appearance, often with dramatic effect. At low tide *Sarcophyton trocheliophorum*, which is found in the shallow intertidal waters of coral reefs, resembles a somewhat shapeless, flat mass of yellow or grey leathery tissue lying over dead coral. But as the tide rises, minute polyps emerge like flowers, transforming the colony into what looks like a miniature garden.
Order: Alcyonacea

SEA FANS AND SEA WHIPS

Sea fan colonies, which are sometimes known as gorgonians or horny corals, look very much like plants. They are found in both the tropical and cooler southern waters of Australia. Their numerous branches, which are often vivid yellow or orange and studded with tiny polyps, fan out from a stout main stem that is firmly attached to a hard surface – often coral.

The many brilliant, deep orange branches of the gorgonian sea fan (*Melithaea squamota*) grow up to 50 cm high on the vertical surfaces of coral or rock, and are dotted with white polyps. When the tentacles are extended for feeding, these polyps look like a dense white fuzz.

Sea whips form long, single stems up to a metre long, and live alone or in quite large clusters. Most embed themselves in sandy sea floors where there is a strong current. When they are among corals they usually occur in fairly shallow water, but in colder waters they live at greater depths.
Order: Gorgonacea

SEA PENS ■

Colonies of sea pens, about 30 cm to a metre high, grow vertically in soft silt or sand in the shallow waters of sheltered bays or in the ocean in warm temperate regions.

Cavernularia obesa has a short, blunt-ended stem about a third the length of the colony. The rest is covered with pores from which polyps emerge to feed. Found in both temperate and tropical Australian waters, *C. obesa* is particularly spectacular at night, for it glows with luminescence when touched.
Order: Pennatulacea

JEWEL ANEMONE

Densely packed colonies of jewel anemones cling to the sides of rocks just below low tide or in underwater caves in both tropical and temperate waters. Small clusters are also sometimes found under boulders on the outer edges of rock platforms. The jewel anemone's 2 cm-wide body is a brilliant orange, and the short, white-tipped, club-shaped tentacles are arranged in two rings around the mouth. This anemone resembles the true hard corals in structure, but has no calcium carbonate skeleton.
Order: Corallimorpharia
Scientific name: *Corynactis australis*

ZOANTHIDS

These colonial anemones do not produce a skeleton. The conspicuous disc-shaped polyps are embedded in a leathery mass of living tissue. It is this mass that attaches the anemones firmly to rock, or even to other animals, such as corals. Colonies may contain hundreds of individuals. They are usually found intertidally or in shallow water around Australia's tropical and temperate shores, but some live more than 30 metres deep in temperate waters.
Order: Zoanthidea

COMB JELLIES

Sometimes mistaken for sea jellies, comb jellies (phylum Ctenophora) are delicate marine animals whose translucency makes them inconspicuous in an environment without shelter. They form part of the large swarms of tiny animals, called the zooplankton, that drift on the surfaces of the world's oceans, coastal lakes, estuaries and shallow seas.

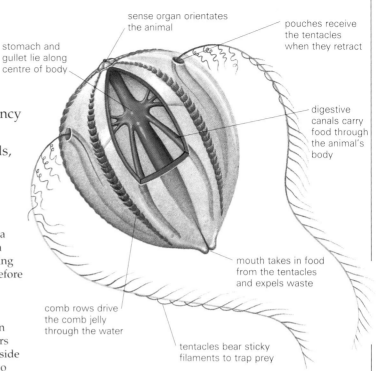

sense organ orientates the animal

stomach and gullet lie along centre of body

pouches receive the tentacles when they retract

digestive canals carry food through the animal's body

mouth takes in food from the tentacles and expels waste

comb rows drive the comb jelly through the water

tentacles bear sticky filaments to trap prey

The comb jelly's gelatinous body ranges in length from a few millimetres to over a metre, and comes in a variety of shapes. From top to bottom it bears eight bands made of tiny plates of fused hair-like cilia known as combs. These beat in unison to propel the comb jelly through the water. Internal canals fill with water to keep the animal's body in shape and support the combs.

Unlike sea jellies, comb jellies have no stinging tentacles, but some species have two thread-like tentacles, from which filaments with special 'lasso' cells flick out to catch prey and transfer it to the animal's mouth. Comb jellies are fierce predators, and they often devour small fishes, and even other comb jellies.

Each comb jelly has both male and female sex organs. The animals release eggs and sperm into the open sea, where the fertilised eggs develop into tiny comb jellies that look like their parents.

These animals are so fragile that it is extremely difficult to collect them alive without damaging them. With great care you can catch one in a small bucket and transfer it to a glass jar, and watch its fascinating gentle, pulsating movements before returning it to the sea.

COMB JELLY ▣
This comb jelly is often found in large numbers in harbour waters throughout the year. On either side of its mouth this species has two lobed flaps that help the combs to propel the animal through the water. Related species are at times very common over reef flats in the Great Barrier Reef.
Scientific name: *Bolinopsis chuni*

VENUS'S GIRDLE
Venus's girdle is exciting to watch as it propels its ribbon-like body, up to 1.5 metres long, with a gentle, sinuous movement. It is generally an oceanic species found in the Mediterranean Sea, the tropical Atlantic Ocean and the Indo-Pacific, but divers in Australian coastal waters sometimes see it.
Scientific name: *Cestrum veneris*

SEA GOOSEBERRY ▣
The sea gooseberry is one of the best known of the comb jellies. It is spherical in shape and about the size of a little fingernail. Its mouth is on its underside, and it has two fishing tentacles with specialised cells for catching prey. The tentacles retract into little pouches on either side of the animal.

Sea gooseberries occur in all the world's seas, and this Australian species can be seen in large swarms around all the coasts of Australia. Sometimes it is washed ashore and found in rock pools.
Scientific name: *Pleurobrachia pileus*

▣ SEA GOOSEBERRY
Roughly the same size and shape as a translucent gooseberry, the sea gooseberry has two thin, trailing tentacles fringed with filaments to trap its prey. The tentacles retract into pouches and pass the prey to the sea gooseberry's mouth.

▣ COMB JELLY
In sunlight the little combs of comb jellies flash with a brilliant iridescence; at night they emit a ghostly luminous glow.

WORMS

Although many worms become meals for early birds and other predators, and even for other worms, most species exist in great numbers. However, much is still unknown about these fascinating groups of invertebrates because their habitats are difficult to explore thoroughly. They live in soil, sea water, fresh water, and – in the case of the parasitic flukes and tapeworms – inside other animals.

Worms are so diverse that taxonomists have not attempted to group them into a single phylum; in fact there are no fewer than eleven separate phyla of worms, most of which are represented throughout the world.

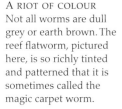

A RIOT OF COLOUR
Not all worms are dull grey or earth brown. The reef flatworm, pictured here, is so richly tinted and patterned that it is sometimes called the magic carpet worm.

Worms are often slimy, and most do not have obvious limbs for support and movement. They have a more-or-less distinct head end, where they take in nourishment, and this is sometimes crowned with sensory structures for detecting food.

Their elongated shape allows worms to squeeze into crevices to protect their soft, vulnerable bodies. Many parasitic worms fit neatly into the narrow internal cavities of their host, such as the gut.

Some worms move by the synchronised beating of tiny hair-like structures called cilia, which results in a smooth, gliding motion through water or over a surface. Others, particularly larger worms, use muscles to bend their bodies in sinuous swimming or crawling.

Worms also use their muscles to shorten or elongate their body, a movement that is particularly efficient when they are burrowing through mud, sand or soil.

Several groups of worms have fluid-filled body cavities. In these worms, the muscles work against the fluid pressure to rapidly change the shape of the body and bring about movement with as little expenditure of energy as possible.

The fluid-filled body cavities also act as shock-absorbers to protect the worm's delicate internal organs, and as circulatory systems to carry nutrients, gases and waste products around the animal's body.

FLATWORMS

Flatworms are the most primitive of worms. They do not have a fluid-filled body cavity or a circulatory system, and they absorb oxygen directly through their skin.

The mouth of the flatworm, which is surrounded by a muscular organ called the pharynx, leads into a gut with no opening corresponding to an anus at the rear end: these creatures regurgitate indigestible parts of their diet through their mouth. In larger forms, the gut may branch and extend to all parts of the body.

Most flatworm species have both male and female characteristics, contained in a complex hermaphroditic reproductive system that lies between the animal's thin skin and the digestive surface of the gut. However, flatworms do not self-fertilise; eggs are always fertilised with sperm from a different animal.

Some flatworms, such as the flukes and the tapeworms, are entirely parasitic. Free-living flatworms belong to the class Turbellaria – they have no common name.
Phylum: Platyhelminthes

organ (the pharynx) from their mouth to envelop their prey. Most turbellarians are 12 mm long or less, but some, such as polyclads and planarians, are more conspicuous. Many of this group can regenerate lost parts of their bodies.
Class: Turbellaria

POLYCLADS ■

Polyclads, 5 cm long or more, glide under stones in pools on Australia's rocky shores. Their name means 'many-branched' (from the ancient Greek), and refers to their branching gut, visible through their skin and radiating from a central mouth.

Some polyclads are almost transparent; others are white, pale pink, fawn or deep brown, though always pale on the underside.

The species *Callioplana marginata* is dark brown with conspicuous white to orange edges. On coral reefs, brightly patterned species of *Pseudoceros*, familiarly known as magic carpet worms, undulate gracefully as they swim. The wafer or oyster leech (*Stylochus* spp.), which is common on Australia's south-eastern coast, slips between the open shells of feeding oysters to consume their flesh.
Order: Polycladida

■ **POLYCLAD**
Pseudoceros bifurcus, a common reef species of marine flatworm, feeds under ledges on a variety of sea squirts.

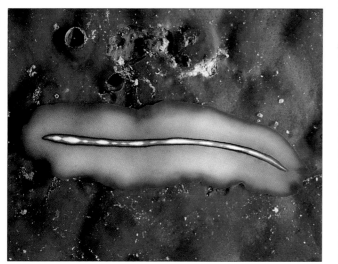

TURBELLARIANS

Turbellarians are primarily marine creatures, but they also inhabit fresh water or moist places on land. Most are bottom-dwellers, living in sediments, under stones, among aquatic vegetation, such as seaweed, or between the bodies of encrusting animals that cover underwater surfaces. They are carnivorous, wrapping themselves around other small invertebrates, dead or alive, entangling them in sticky mucus, and then shooting out a muscular

PLANARIANS

In oceans these worms are called triclads, but they more generally frequent fresh water and land, where they are known as planarians. Pond weed contains many inconspicuous dark grey to brown aquatic planarians, measuring about 1 cm long.

Land planarians are showier than their aquatic relatives – 10 cm or more long, they are often bright yellow, orange, green or deep blue, sometimes with contrasting stripes. They live in damp places, under stones, logs and leaf litter. They glide by beating cilia on their undersides, using muscle action for more vigorous movement. They secrete copious mucus that helps them to move and capture prey, and may repel or even be toxic to predators.

The shovel-headed garden worm (*Bipalium kewensi*), which can be identified by its light and darker brown stripes and its flattened, spade-like head, is common in suburban gardens. It is native to South-East Asia, but has now spread to many parts of the world.
Order: Tricladida

■ PLANARIAN
Recognised by its shovel-like head, *Bipalium kewensi* is so called because it was first identified when it turned up at Kew Gardens in London. In fact, the worm had travelled there in the soil surrounding plants from the warmer climate of South-East Asia.

TEMNOCEPHALIDS

Temnocephalids are only 1–12 mm long. They have stumpy bodies and numerous conspicuous tentacles around their mouth. They are commonly found attached to the surface of freshwater crayfish by suckers at the rear end of their body, so that people frequently confuse them with leeches. However, temnocephalids are not parasitic; they feed on small invertebrates, and possibly also on food scraps collected by their host.
Order: Temnocephalida

TAPEWORMS

In most cases tapeworms do not deserve their reputation for being repulsive parasites, as many are relatively harmless. They live attached to the intestines of vertebrates by a holdfast at the front, which is armed with suckers or hooks or both.

Individuals called proglottids bud from this region but remain attached to each other, forming a ribbon-like body that can reach several metres in length. Each proglottid contains a set of male and a set of female reproductive organs. Mating can occur between proglottids of a single worm or between proglottids of separate worms.

In a typical tapeworm life cycle, the eggs – often contained in the proglottids that break off from the hind end of the worm – are passed out in the vertebrate host's faeces and deposited in grass or water. They remain fertile for a long time, until they are ingested by their second host. They then hatch as minute larvae, burrow through the gut wall and lodge in the internal organs, where they develop into larvae. At this stage they are often called bladder worms.

When the second host is eaten, the bladder worms become active and attach themselves to the intestinal wall of the new host by their holdfasts. The life cycle continues as each holdfast buds to form a new worm.

Tapeworms and disease

Tapeworms have no gut – they do not feed on host tissue but absorb the host's digested food through their skin. Consequently, visible signs of tapeworm infestations are rare, unless the host has multiple infections or is malnourished.

Echinococcus granulosus, however, a tapeworm of dogs and other carnivores, is far from harmless. The adult is minute as tapeworms go, with only three proglottids, but the bladder worm stage, known as a hydatid cyst, can grow to the size of a golf ball in sheep and humans and disrupt the functions of vital organs. Health programs have publicised the danger of hydatid cysts, but they are still a problem in rural areas of Australia, where dogs may be fed raw sheep offal containing the cysts.

A tapeworm of dogs and cats, *Dipylidium caninum*, is passed on when the host animal ingests fleas containing the bladder worm larvae.
Class: Cestoda

FLUKES ■

Flukes are creamy brown and can grow to 7.5 cm long. They dwell inside vertebrates throughout Australia, lodging in the gut, the liver, the pancreas, the lungs, the bladder, the ureter, or even the blood. They feed on the tissues, fluids and intestinal debris of their host.

Flukes have a complex life cycle that depends on two or more hosts. The vertebrate host passes out fluke eggs in its faeces or urine, and the eggs hatch in water as microscopic larvae. These tiny, active creatures bore through the skin of marine or freshwater snails to invade the internal organs, where they multiply, feed and grow on soft snail tissue.

They emerge from the snails as cercariae, a strong-swimming stage in the life cycle. These cercariae re-enter their vertebrate hosts along with their food. Cercariae attach themselves to a plant if their host is a herbivore, or to an animal if their host is a carnivore. Blood flukes burrow directly through the skin to gain access to the bloodstream.

Australian fluke species

Relatively little is known about the indigenous flukes that infect our native fauna. The introduced sheep liver fluke (*Fasciola hepatica*) exists through its introduced host snail and some native snails that also act as hosts. This fluke has also been found in many species of native herbivorous marsupials. Another fluke, *Calicophoron calicophorum*, invades the stomachs of sheep and cattle.

Fortunately, Australia is free of human flukes. However, freshwater and estuarine snails host blood flukes that infest water birds; their cercariae can burrow into the skin of humans, causing allergic dermatitis.
Class: Trematoda

■ FLUKE
Unusually for flatworms, adult blood flukes have separate female and male individuals, seen entwined in this photograph. In Australia their main hosts are marine and freshwater birds.

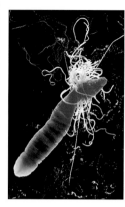

TENTACULAR DISPLAY
The marine ribbon worm
Gorgonorhynchus repens
is unmistakable with
its brilliant orange col-
oration and the writhing
tentacles of its proboscis.

RIBBON WORMS

About 1200 ribbon worm species have been described worldwide, but only 64 of these have been recorded from Australia. The long, flat form of these creatures is responsible for their two common names – ribbon worms and bootlace worms. They are also sometimes called proboscis worms because of the tentacle-like, elongated proboscis that emerges from a fluid-filled cavity, either through their mouth or through an opening immediately above it.

Like flatworms, ribbon worms, have no fluid-filled body cavity surrounding the gut. They resemble flatworms in appearance as well, but they have an anus and a much more muscular body, and are usually longer than flatworms, sometimes growing to several metres or more.

Most species are inconspicuously coloured, but ribbon worms may be bright yellow, orange, red or green, and are often longitudinally striped or horizontally banded.

Ribbon worms are carnivorous. They shoot out their proboscis with considerable force to ensnare small invertebrates, and then release

sticky toxins from the proboscis tip to immobilise their prey. In some species the proboscis is armed with a barb that penetrates the skin and injects toxins hypodermically.

Most ribbon worm species have separate sexes, but a few are hermaphrodites. Some marine species release their eggs and sperm directly into the sea, but in most marine and all freshwater and terrestrial species, the mating pair secretes a cocoon of mucus, into which they discharge their eggs and sperm.

Water-dwellers
The majority of ribbon worms are marine, living under boulders, in crevices, or buried in sand or mud. However, some species inhabit fresh water and damp places on land.

Marine ribbon worm species are found from the Great Barrier Reef down the coast of eastern Australia and south and west to the southern coast of Western Australia. Even for zoologists (except worm specialists) species identification is difficult. However, *Gorgonorhynchus repens* is a common, widely distributed and

distinctive marine species that occurs from the Great Barrier Reef to the coast of southern New South Wales. These bright orange worms, which are up to 10 cm long, have a unique proboscis that shoots out a mass of writhing tentacles.

Only three species of freshwater ribbon worms have been reported in Australia. They are generally smaller than their marine relatives – about 1 cm long – and yellow to bright red in colour. They are encountered only rarely, gliding over submerged vegetation in ponds and in the backwaters of creeks and rivers.

Land-dwellers
Four species of terrestrial ribbon worms have been described from the moist forests of eastern Australia. One species, *Argonemertes australiensis*, is widely distributed from southern Queensland to Tasmania. Looking like a small slug, it is up to 8 cm long. Its colour varies from cream to reddish brown, or it may have brown stripes or splashes on a lighter background.
Phylum: Nemertea

GREEN CARNIVORE
The long, pointed head
of the muscular green
ribbon worm snakes out
in search of its prey. This
specimen was found at
Heron Island on the
Great Barrier Reef.

THORNY-HEADED WORMS

All thorny-headed worms are parasitic, but they rarely invade human hosts. About 50 species have been identified in native Australian vertebrates, mostly from fishes.

They live in the intestines of their vertebrate hosts, attaching themselves to the lining of the gut by a proboscis armed with rows of backward-curving hooks. Like tapeworms, they absorb the host's digested food through their skin.

After mating, the fertilised eggs develop into larvae enclosed in thick capsules, which are passed out in the faeces of the host. The capsules are then ingested by insects or aquatic crustaceans, such as yabbies and ostracods, and the larvae then hatch and bore through the gut lining of this second host to lodge in the body cavity. Here they transform into another larval form and again become enclosed in a thick-walled capsule. When a vertebrate eats the second host, the second-stage larvae hatch and hook onto the intestinal wall, and the cycle continues.

Seldom seen

Because they are parasitic at all stages of their life cycle, thorny-headed worms are encountered only when the intestines of their hosts are examined. Compared with tapeworms and roundworms they are rare, so they are not considered to be of great economic significance to livestock industries.

One species, however, *Macroacanthorhynchus hyrudinaceus*, reaches a length of up to 80 cm and can infect pigs. *M. hyrudinaceus* is not common, but heavy infestations have been reported from the Darling Downs in Queensland, the south coast of New South Wales and Gippsland in Victoria. Pigs become infected by eating beetle species that contain the worm larvae.

Phylum: Acanthocephala

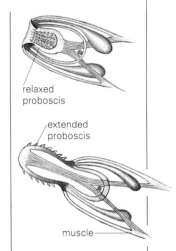

relaxed proboscis

extended proboscis

muscle

HOOKED ON THE HOST
This anatomical detail shows how the thorny-headed worm uses special muscles to thrust out its hooked proboscis and cling to its host.

ROUNDWORMS

Roundworms are among the most widespread of all groups of animals and thrive from polar to tropical regions. They live in oceans, from shallow soundings to great depths; on land, from the highest mountains to the driest deserts; and in fresh water, saline lakes and hot springs. Some are parasitic – the vast majority of plants and animals play host to at least one roundworm species.

About 12 000 species have been identified worldwide, but most are so tiny – 0.3 mm to 8.5 mm – that large numbers are still undetected. Research has concentrated on those that are parasitic on humans, domestic animals and crops.

Roundworms have a cylindrical body tapering to a point at each end, with a thick external covering, called a cuticle, that gives them shape. They move by contracting muscles that bend the body from side to side. Their shape and way of moving help them to penetrate sediments or soil, or to travel within confined spaces in the body of a host.

Roundworms reproduce sexually. The females release shelled eggs, and the eggs hatch into juvenile worms which grow into adults.

Contributors to the food web

Nonparasitic roundworms often collect in huge numbers in mud and sand in aquatic environments, or in soil on land. Here they engulf bacteria, microscopic creatures and algae, or hypodermically suck the juices from larger plants, fungi and animals. They are the largest group of animals that feed on bacteria and fungi, which makes them important members of the food web.

Human pinworm

Many children in the world's temperate regions are infected at some stage by the human pinworm, *Enterobius vermicularis*. The females, up to 8 mm long, emerge from the child's anus at night to lay their eggs on the surrounding skin. The child scratches to relieve the itch and the eggs lodge under the fingernails, on which they are then carried to the mouth to reinfect the child.

Pinworms are relatively harmless, and easily eradicated by medication.

Roundworms in pets

The most common roundworm in dogs is *Toxocara canis*, which can grow up to 18 cm long. Puppies can become infected by *T. canis* even before birth if the microscopic juvenile worms pass across the placenta from the bitch to the fetuses.

When the mature female roundworm releases her many eggs, they are passed out in their host's faeces. If the eggs are swallowed by dogs, they hatch out and the larvae wander through the dog's body, first to the liver, then to the lungs and then, in puppies, back to the intestines, where they weaken and even kill their host. In older dogs, most of the larvae reach the muscles and brain, where they lie dormant. In bitches they become active again in the last weeks of pregnancy and may cross the placenta to infect the puppies.

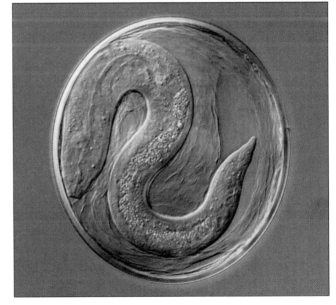

The common roundworm of cats, *Toxocara cati*, has a similar life cycle, except that it is not transferred to unborn kittens through the placenta.

Hand-washing after touching puppies and kittens is an essential precaution, especially for children.

Mosquitoes on mainland Australia transmit the dog heartworm (*Dirofilaria immitis*) after ingesting the larvae during a blood meal from a dog. The larvae grow inside the mosquito and enter a new host when the insect feeds on a second dog. The larvae make their way to the dog's heart, where they become adults and complete the life cycle, killing their host in the process.

Phylum: Nematoda

ROUNDWORM EGG
Over their four months of sexual maturity, female dog and cat roundworms release millions of eggs, which pass out in the faeces of the host animal and can remain infectious for many years.

ROTIFER ANATOMY
Rotifers are microscopic worms with complex body systems containing cells and organs. The fine, hair-like cilia on the rotifer's corona (crown) direct food to its mouth.

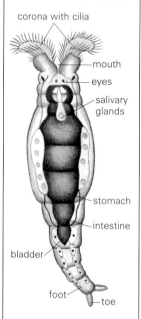

corona with cilia
— mouth
— eyes
— salivary glands
— stomach
— intestine
bladder —
foot — — toe

PSEUDO-PEANUTS
Even when the peanut worm elongates its body, its outer covering resembles a peanut shell in colour and texture.

HORSEHAIR WORMS

During warm weather horsehair worms suddenly appear in still water, and people often take them to museums for identification. They used to be seen in horse troughs, and this, with their elongated brown body, gave rise to the belief that they generated from horsehair – hence their common name.

Because they twist themselves into knots, they are also called Gordian worms, from the Greek myth of the Gordian knot. According to an oracle, whoever untangled the knot was destined to conquer Asia Minor. Alexander the Great achieved the feat by slashing through the knot.

'Spontaneous' generation
The life cycle of these worms explains their apparently spontaneous generation. Their thin body, up to a metre long, weaves itself into a tangled mass, especially in males, who mate by wrapping themselves around females. The males die, and the females lay gelatinous strings of eggs, which hatch as larvae that penetrate or are eaten by insects. Inside the host's body, they feed by absorbing fluids through their skin.

The adult worms emerge when the host animal is near water. They do not feed, but can live for several months until they find a mate.
Phylum: Nematomorpha

ROTIFERS

Rotifers are closely related to roundworms, thorny-headed worms and horsehair worms, but they differ in appearance and way of life.

All rotifers are microscopic, reaching no more than 1–2 mm in length. Most inhabit fresh water or inland saline lakes, but a few species are marine, and some occur in moist terrestrial situations, such as in the film of water surrounding the stems of mosses. Their abundance in freshwater ecosystems makes them an important link in the food web.

Although they are so small, the bodies of rotifers have hundreds of cells organised into tissues and complex internal organs. They are quite variable in form, but they usually have an elongated, cylindrical body divided into a short head region, a trunk, and a terminal foot.

The head bears a crown-like organ, the corona, which has hair-like cilia that beat in unison, creating a vortex in the water that drives microscopic particles of food to the animal's mouth. Rotifers are sometimes called wheel animals because these cilia look like a turning wheel.

In favourable conditions female rotifers produce eggs that do not need to be fertilised by males – a process called parthenogenesis.

Surviving hard times
In unfavourable conditions, such as the drying up or freezing over of a pond, rotifers reproduce sexually. Males appear and fertilise eggs, which then acquire a thick shell to protect them from dehydration or freezing. The eggs remain dormant and the wind disperses them; later, when good conditions return, they hatch as parthenogenetic females. This method of dispersing the eggs accounts for the wide distribution of many species of rotifers.

Moving around
Rotifers move with a leech-like, looping action over the surface of submerged plants, as well as swimming by beating their cilia. Some species, however, live permanently cemented to a solid object, sometimes in colonies that are attached by a single common foot.
Phylum: Rotifera

PEANUT WORMS

Peanut worms are so called because, when contracted, they look very much like peanuts with their shells on. They are marine animals that live in shallow water on the sea floor under boulders, in burrows in mud and sand, or in the crevices of encrusting animals, such as barnacles, that grow on the surfaces of rocks, wharf piles and seaweed.

Around 300 species have been described, of which about 50 are from Australia. *Phascolosoma noduliferum* is commonly found under boulders or in crevices on temperate southern shores from New South Wales to Western Australia.

Peanut worms release sperm and eggs into the sea, where fertilisation occurs to produce larvae like those of the bristleworms (pages 513–17).

After this planktonic stage, the larvae settle on the sea floor and change into juvenile peanut worms.

Peanut worm anatomy
The worm's body is enclosed in a tough, light brown skin held in shape by the pressure of the fluid in the body cavity. If the worm is left undisturbed, a narrower section of the body slowly emerges, as if someone were squeezing the hand of a rubber glove to extend a finger. The mouth at the tip of this 'finger' has a short fringe of tentacles that collect sediments, from which the worm extracts food scraps. The gut is a tube that coils tightly and threads back through the coil to open at the anus near the front of the body.
Phylum: Sipuncula

SPOON WORMS

The mobile proboscis extending from its front end is the most distinctive feature of the marine spoon worm. In members of the Echiuridae family this proboscis is spoon-shaped, but species of the Bonellidae family have a very long proboscis that is forked at the tip. The feeding animal thrusts out its proboscis, edges curled up to form a groove, to scoop food-rich sediments into its mouth. At the slightest disturbance, it rapidly retracts the proboscis.

The spoon worm has a sausage-shaped body, 1–10 cm long, that shows no sign of segmentation.

Most species of spoon worms burrow in sediments, but a few live in crevices in rocks or in coral rubble. Some are a dull grey; others are bright green, red, or even coal-black. Only about ten species have been found in Australia, and they are not commonly encountered.

Spoon worms have separate sexes; sperm from males and eggs from females are shed into the sea, where fertilised eggs develop into larvae.

After a short time the larvae of the echiurids settle on the sea floor, where they transform into juvenile spoon worms. The bonellids, however, have rather different sexual behaviour. In this family, some of the larvae settle on a mature female and migrate into her reproductive ducts. Here they become parasitic males, their bodies effectively reduced to a testis from which sperm fertilise the eggs as they pass out of the female's body. Bonellid larvae that settle elsewhere develop into females.

Phylum: Echiura

SPOON-FEEDING
The forked proboscis of a bonellid spoon worm scoops up a meal.

SEGMENTED WORMS

The segmented worms include bristleworms, earthworms and their aquatic relatives, and leeches. They range from microscopic to 3 metres long or more. Their elongated body is divided into segments, seen on the outside as a series of rings corresponding internally with partitions that divide the body into a series of fluid-tight compartments.

Each segment has its own set of muscles that contract independently of those in adjoining segments, but movement is coordinated by a brain linked to a double nerve cord on the underside of the body.

Synchronised muscular action on either side of the body produces undulations for crawling and swimming or contraction and elongation of the segments for burrowing. The gut has its own muscles for moving food from the mouth to the anus. Other organs, such as the reproductive and excretory systems, are often repeated in each segment.

Phylum: Annelida

BRISTLEWORMS ▪

Bristleworms are the most diverse of the segmented worms. They are predominantly marine, but they also occur in fresh water. Some are active swimmers but most are bottom-dwellers. They live under boulders or in crevices, or burrow through sand or mud on the ocean floor. Some species live permanently in tubes that they construct from a variety of materials.

Free-living bristleworms have a pair of paddle-like structures, called parapodia, on each segment. They move these forwards and backwards in phase with the wriggling of their body to increase their propulsive force. They also thrust out bundles of microscopic, needle-like bristles, called chaetae, from the parapodia while they make their backward propulsive stroke, in order to gain traction for movement over a surface. It is the large number of these chaetae that give bristleworms their scientific name – 'polychaeta' means 'bearing many bristles'. Burrowing and tube-living bristleworms tend to have small parapodia with chaetae embedded directly in the skin.

Some bristleworms reproduce by budding, but most have separate sexes and release their eggs and sperm into the sea. Here fertilisation occurs to produce microscopic larvae called trochophores, which look like little tops as they spin through the ocean before settling on the sea bottom to become juvenile worms.

Because of their diversity, bristleworms have been classified into about 80 families. Some are familiar enough to have common names but most have only a scientific name.

Class: Polychaeta

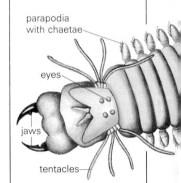

parapodia with chaetae
eyes
jaws
tentacles

PADDLING ALONG
Each segment of a bristleworm has a pair of paddle-like parapodia with tiny protruding bristles called chaetae.

FREE SPAWNING
Thousands of tiny bristleworm eggs spill out into the sea.

▪ BRISTLING ALONG
The large number of needle-like chetae covering the body of polychaetes gives them the common name of bristleworms. They may be used for traction.

■ FIREWORMS
Known throughout southern Australia for their painful sting, fireworms of the species *Eurythoe complanata* have fragile bristles that break off in the skin of their victims.

RAGWORMS

Ragworms are often used in textbooks to illustrate the main features of bristleworms. They have a distinct head end with sensory structures – eyes and tentacles. The mouth leads into a pharynx that has a pair of stout jaws and can turn itself inside out. All body segments are similar and possess a pair of well-developed paddles (parapodia).

Ragworms live on the open coast, among seaweed, under stones, and in crevices among the bodies of encrusting animals. *Australonereis ehlersi*, which grows to 10–15 cm, is found in estuaries from Queensland to Western Australia. The openings to its sandy tubes can be seen projecting above the mud flats.

A scavenger, it partially emerges from its burrows to feed on the carcasses of animals and plants. Its body is flimsy and easily broken, but it is popular with anglers as bait.
Family: Nereididae

■ EUNICID
Around the southern coast of Australia, the large segmented marine worm *Eunice aphroditois* lurks under boulders at low tide.

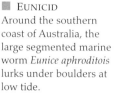

PHYLLODOCIDS

These slender worms are often found in crevices and under stones on rocky shores, and on mud flats in the estuaries of eastern Australia. Phyllodocids can be identified by a conspicuous, flattened, leaf-shaped lobe attached to the upper part of each paddle-like parapodium; in some species these lobes overlap to cover the surface of the body.

The gently undulating, emerald green bodies of *Phyllodoce novaehollandiae*, 4.5–7 cm long, emerge at low tide to feed on small invertebrates that frequent the mud flats.
Family: Phyllodocidae

SCALEWORMS

Some scaleworms are elongated, but many are short and oval with a more or less flattened body. The conspicuous hardened plates that often cover the upper part of their body give these worms their common name. The scales are attached to alternate pairs of paddle-like parapodia at the front of the body, becoming less regular towards the back.

Scaleworms are carnivorous and feed on a variety of small invertebrates that they find under boulders and in crevices.

In Australia, species of *Lepidonotus* are common. No more than 2–3 cm long, they have overlapping shiny brown scales adorned with distinctive white to cream patches.
Family: Polynoidae

SEA MICE

Sea mice get their common name from their short, fat, brown bodies and the thick mat of iridescent bristles (chaetae) that covers their upper surface like fur. They occur below the low tide level in shallow waters to depths of 60 metres.

Aphrodite australis, one of 12 species that occur in Australian waters, is 10 cm long and 5 cm wide. It is found from Sydney Harbour in New South Wales around the southern coast to Port Hedland in Western Australia. Sea mice are often washed up on beaches, collected in trawls, or hooked on baited lines by anglers.
Family: Aphroditidae

FIREWORMS ■

Fireworms have bundles of long, needle-sharp bristles, called chaetae. They erect these bristles to penetrate the flesh of predators – unwary humans are no exception – where they break off and cause irritation. Some species are thought to inject poison into the wound.

Eurythoe complanata, measuring 10–14 cm, is a very widespread fireworm species found under coral rubble in tropical regions and under boulders in rock pools between the tidal levels on temperate shores.

Chloeia flava, 7 cm long and 2–3 cm wide, is an active swimmer and is often caught in nets; it has to be carefully extricated from the catch.

One deep-sea fireworm, *Amphinome rostrata*, up to 25 cm long, lives on driftwood in warm seas and feeds on goose barnacles. It is sometimes washed up on beaches after storms.
Family: Amphinomidae

EUNICIDS ■

This family is closely related to the beachworms (below) and, like them, many eunicids reach a considerable size. One of the most conspicuous of the eunicids is the giant, dark purple, iridescent *Eunice aphroditois*, found at low tide under boulders on southern Australian shores. Its robust, muscular body can be as long as 2 metres.

The blood-worm (*Marphysa sanguinea*), so named because of its red gills, is about 25 cm long and is very common on mud flats.
Family: Eunicidae

BEACHWORMS ■

Monsters of the bristleworm world, beachworms grow to 3 metres or more. They scavenge on dead animals and seaweeds stranded when the tide recedes, tearing off pieces with their sharp jaws. They are equipped with chemical sensors that detect rotting carcasses from some distance. Their burrows, often in large numbers, undermine the sand of surf beaches from Queensland south and west to South Australia.

For a long time, biologists recognised only one beachworm species, the kingworm (*Australonuphis teres*). However, keen anglers distinguish several common beachworms by size, muscle tone, sliminess and coloration: they call the larger specimens kingworms, greenheads, bronzeheads or bullworms, the smaller versions stumpies (now identified as juvenile kingworms), high-tiders or standards, and the long, slender, slimy ones slimies, redheads, blueys or bungum worms.

Kingworms are found on beaches from Maroochydore in Queensland south to Lakes Entrance in Victoria.

Slimies are now classified separately as *A. parateres*. They are found in great numbers from half-tide to low-tide levels on sand flats or spits from Yeppoon in Queensland southward and westward to Adelaide.

A species often encountered in northern New South Wales is known as hairy Mary, wiry or whisker, and scientists have immortalised the first of these names by calling the worm *Hirsutonuphis mariahirsuta*.

Beachworms do not construct tubes; instead, they secrete large quantities of mucus to strengthen the walls of their burrows. It is assumed that, in their natural habitat, they live head up in vertical burrows, but move horizontally at a lower level as the sand shifts or in response to the presence of food, and then come up vertically again.
Family: Onuphidae

CIRRATULIDS

Cirratulids are usually found buried just beneath the sediments under boulders in rock pools or in crevices between boulders or encrusting animals. Their body is elongated and cylindrical, tapering at both ends.

Cirriformia filigera, 4 cm long, occurs in estuaries from Queensland south and west to Western Australia. It feeds by gathering organic debris from surfaces into grooves on the underside of tentacles that lead to the mouth. *C. filigera* has elongated, unbranched gills that occur in pairs down the length of its body. Both the feeding tentacles and the gills are bright red and form a writhing mass over the surface of the body.
Family: Cirratulidae

TEREBELLIDS

Terebellids spread a spaghetti-like mass of tentacles over the surface of sediments. These tentacles are attached to the head end of a delicate, elongated body, usually encased in a fragile tube of mucus encrusted with sand or mud. The terebellid's head bears a cluster of branched, bright red gills.

Terebellids are commonly found exposed at low tide under stones in rock pools, or between the bodies of encrusting animals. Their tentacles are like vacuum cleaners; they collect organic debris from surface sediments into grooves on their

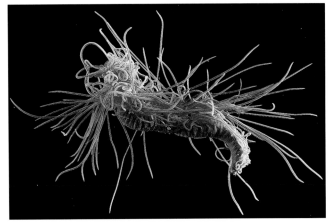

underside and direct it in a current of mucus to the animal's mouth.

The very conspicuous, metre-long, cream tentacles of a large species, *Reteterebella queenslandia*, are often seen spread out over the surface of coral rubble on a reef flat. When touched, the tentacles rapidly retract towards the worm, which is concealed under the coral boulders.
Family: Terebellidae

CHAETOPTERIDS

These rather fragile worms, up to 15 cm long, live permanently in the horny, leathery or parchment-like tubes of mucus that they secrete.

The pale yellow *Chaetopterus variopedatus* is a common chaetopterid species. Its U-shaped tube, and its inhabitant, extend into the mud for some distance, and the exposed part of the tube protrudes from the sandy mud in estuaries. Its body consists of three distinct regions. The front part contains the head and mouth, which secrete the tube that is its home. The middle part has a pair of large, horn-shaped paddles (parapodia) that secrete a bag-like net of mucus, and three more pairs of parapodia that form large, circular fans; these operate like pistons to drive water through the tube. Food particles in the water catch in the net of mucus, which is periodically rolled up and moved forward to the mouth. The rest of the worm consists of many identical segments.

C. variopedatus harbours pea crabs and scaleworms in its tube, and these feed on scraps of food brought in by the current.
Family: Chaetopteridae

GIANT BEACHWORM
Anglers prize the large, muscular body of the beachworm as the ideal bait – but grasping a beachworm behind the head and flicking its considerable length from its burrow can be a good deal more difficult than catching a fish!

■ CIRRATULID
Some species of cirratulids, inhabitants of rock pools and estuarine sand flats, have masses of thread-like feeding tentacles spreading out from their bodies.

■ CHAETOPTERID
The tube of the marine worm *Chaetopterus variopedatus* protrudes from the estuarine mud like a pale drinking straw.

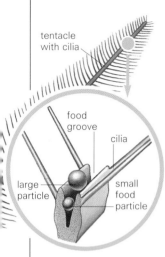

SIFTING FOOD
The feather-duster worm's hair-like cilia direct food particles along food grooves to its mouth. The grooves reject larger particles.

■ **FANWORM**
The spectacular fan-worm breathes and feeds through its light, feathery gills.

SABELLARIIDS

Sabellariids make tubes of sand grains that are so firmly cemented together and to the surface of rocks that they are very difficult to break open. The head of the worm bears a crown of large, erect, feathery bristles (chaetae) that fold down over the opening of the tube when the worm retracts. In the centre of the crown is a cluster of tentacles covered in minute hair-like cilia that drive a current of water between the tentacles. The cilia direct food particles to the animal's mouth and separate out small sand grains, which are used to build the tube.

The 2 cm-long tubes of the sabellariid *Idanthyrsus pennatus* form a surface covering that is quite common on boulders along the rocky shores of northern New South Wales; in the more southern parts of eastern Australia, single individuals cling to the undersides of boulders.
Family: Sabellariidae

FEATHER-DUSTER WORMS ■

Feather-duster worms, so named for the elaborate crown of feather-like structures extending from their tube opening, are among the most beautiful of all bristleworms – perhaps even of invertebrates in general. They live in tough, fibrous tubes, often reinforced with mud, sand, shells or other debris. Any slight

disturbance – even a faint passing shadow – causes the worm, complete with crown, to retract instantly into its tube. It slowly re-emerges once the danger has passed.

The crown consists of a pair of semicircular lobes bearing a number of erect filaments, each furnished with paired side branches. The whole structure forms a funnel leading to the central mouth at its base. As the beating cilia draw water through the crown, they sift particles of food and direct them down grooves on the filaments to the mouth. They also separate out small grains of sand and mud, to be used in the construction of the tube.

Sabellastarte indica is a common feather-duster worm that is found in rock pools from Queensland to Western Australia. Where individuals cluster together, their cream to light brown crowns, measuring 5 cm or more across, create an enchanting underwater flower garden.
Family: Sabellidae

FANWORMS ■

These worms are very similar to feather-duster worms – indeed, their common names are interchangeable. Fanworms, however, secrete calcium carbonate to makes their tubes, which are more substantial than those of feather-duster worms.

At low tide, the worms retract into their tubes and protect themselves from drying out by closing the tight-fitting trapdoors (opercula) of the tubes until they are covered again at high tide. When the opercula open, the tubes are concealed by the black fuzz of their feeding crowns.

■ FEATHER-DUSTER WORM
Unfurling a crown of tentacles from its tube, the feather-duster worm gathers food particles from the water. At the least disturbance, the crown retracts.

The tubes of fanworms may appear singly or, as in *Galeolaria caespitosa*, in a thick, encrusting mass that forms a vivid, white, limy band at mid-tide level along exposed rocky shores from southern Queensland southward and westward to South Australia, and more sparsely in Western Australia.

G. hystrix, a closely related species with a similar distribution, cements isolated light pink tubes to the undersides of rocks at low tide.

Galeolaria species, which are largely confined to open coasts, are replaced in estuaries by the thinner and more brittle tubes of *Hydroides elegans*, which form thick encrustations on wharf piles, marinas and the bottoms of boats.

On coral reefs, the crown of the beautiful Christmas tree worm, *Spirobranchus giganticus*, forms a conspicuous spiral of feathery arms resembling the branches of a miniature pine tree only a centimetre high; the resemblance gives the worm its common name. The branches come in a range of dramatic colours – from fawn, yellow, orange, red, purple and deep blue to black. The larvae of this worm settle on the surfaces of corals where a small area of polyps has been destroyed. Eventually the tube of *S. giganticus*, except for its opening, becomes enclosed in the regenerating coral.
Family: Serpulidae

SPIONIDS

Spionids abound in estuaries, where they live in burrows lined with secreted mucus. Masses of their fragile tubes are sometimes visible at low tide, when they are slightly higher than the surrounding sediments. Spionids have a single pair of tentacles with which they gather food particles from the surface sediments or the water above their tubes and direct them to their mouth.

The Victorian species *Polydora aciculata* excavates twisting galleries in abalone shells, and *P. websteri* is the infamous oyster borer; this species causes 'mud blisters' on oyster shells that weaken the shell and may kill the oyster. At low tide on coral reef flats many burrows of *Malacoceros indicus* are visible, surrounded by conspicuous, spaghetti-like strands of faeces (worm casts) consisting of undigested sediments.
Family: Spionidae

SPIRORBIDS

These white worms make their tubes from calcium carbonate, like their close relatives, the fanworms (page 516), but their tubes are tiny and coiled, unlike those of fanworms.

Spirorbids cover the surface of rocks, seaweeds, seagrasses or the bodies of other animals, such as mollusc shells, often in large numbers. *Janua* and *Pileolaria* species are common in warm Australian seas.

These tiny worms brood their young within their tubes – a reproductive strategy often adopted by small marine animals that cannot produce the numbers of eggs that are required for free spawning.
Family: Spirorbidae

EARTHWORMS AND THEIR RELATIVES ■

Charles Darwin (1809–1882), author of the theory of natural selection, noted how useful earthworms are in composting, and farmers and gardeners now realise that earthworms mean fertile soil. But few people know that many relatives of earthworms live in water – some in fresh water and some in the sea – where they fulfil the same functions in their aquatic environment.

Hard to tell apart

Earthworms and their relatives, collectively known as oligochaetes, are much more uniform than bristleworms, in both appearance and way of life. Most species can be distinguished from one another only by obscure aspects of their anatomy, particularly features of their complex reproductive systems. Despite their apparent uniformity, however, over 3000 species have been so far identified worldwide. These are divided into 25 families, of which four contain most of the terrestrial species called earthworms.

'Oligo' is an ancient Greek word meaning 'few', and oligochaetes, as their name implies, have fewer bristles (chaetae) than bristleworms. They do, however, have bundles of tiny, needle-like bristles embedded in their skin to provide traction for their smooth bodies as they burrow through sediments or soil. These

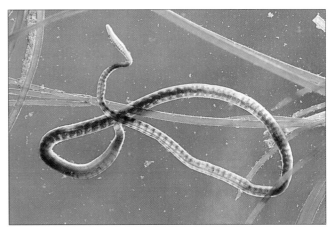

bristles are sparse, but if you run your fingers down an earthworm you will be able to feel them.

Unlike bristleworms, earthworms and their relatives do not have the crown-like structures for sensing the environment and directing food to the mouth, nor do they have paddle-like parapodia.

The reproductive process

Oligochaetes are hermaphrodites. Unlike bristleworms, which often carry reproductive organs in many of their body segments, oligochaetes have their testes and ovaries in their front segments only. The presence of a saddle-like structure called the clitellum about a third of the way down the body is a sign of sexual maturity; The glands it contains secrete the mucus that envelops the worms during mating.

When two worms get together, each releases sperm that are then stored in the sperm receptacles of the other. Some time later, the clitellum of each worm produces a sleeve of hardened mucus, out of which the worm wriggles backwards, first releasing eggs from its female genital opening and then sperm from the sperm receptacles. The sleeve containing the fertilised eggs drops from the head of the worm to form a sealed cocoon in which the eggs develop into juvenile worms.

Natural fertiliser

Earthworms benefit soil in many ways. They move through it by forcing their front end between earth particles, swallowing vast quantities of soil as they burrow. They make the burrows semi-permanent by reinforcing the side walls with sticky mucus – a process that opens up

■ AQUATIC WORM
Long, slender and agile, an aquatic relative of the familiar earthworm swims around above the sea floor.

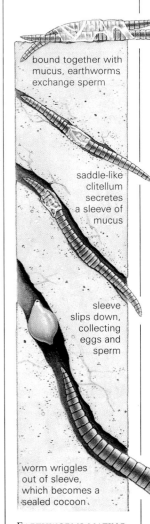

bound together with mucus, earthworms exchange sperm

saddle-like clitellum secretes a sleeve of mucus

sleeve slips down, collecting eggs and sperm

worm wriggles out of sleeve, which becomes a sealed cocoon.

EARTHWORMS MATING
The earthworm builds a sleeve of mucus to hold eggs and sperm. The sleeve later becomes a cocoon for the young.

■ FANWORM
Found on Australia's coral reefs, the colourful Christmas tree worm looks more like an exotic plant than a worm.

the soil to oxygen and water. Soils where earthworms live soak up water more efficiently than soils that lack these hard-working creatures. Plant roots penetrate spongy earth more easily than compacted earth.

Earthworms and their marine relatives also churn soil and sediments as they feed. Most species, including earthworms, are scavengers, eating dead organic matter in sediments and soil, which they swallow by turning their muscular pharynx inside out and then returning it, outside in, to their mouth.

They take dead vegetation down into the soil and deposit faecal matter at the surface in visible mounds called wormcasts, or vermicasts. Wormcasts themselves make a substantial contribution to the fertility of topsoil, since they contain beneficial bacteria from the worm's intestine that break down the soil even further, releasing minerals in a form that plants can use.

Imported versus native

Worm farms are now commercially viable, providing such species as reds (*Lumbricus rubellus*), tigers (*Eisenia fetida*) and blues (*Perionyx excavatus*) to regenerate gardens, pastures and agricultural land. Unfortunately, native species do not seem to do as well in cultivated land as introduced species do.

About 300 native earthworm species have been identified in Australia, but there are probably twice this number. They range from only a few millimetres in length to the giant Gippsland earthworm (*Megascolides australis*), one of the largest of all earthworms at over 2 metres when contracted. Nobody knows for sure whether the survival of this species, found only in the Korumburra region of Gippsland, is threatened, but the World Wildlife Fund has placed it on the vulnerable list.
Class: Oligochaeta

MEGAWORM
Some people claim to have seen specimens of the giant Gippsland earthworm 4 metres long, or even more.

LEECHES ■

Leeches in Australia have been sadly neglected by scientists, despite the abundance of terrestrial leech species in the moist forests of eastern Australia. Freshwater leeches are also common in still ponds, lakes, flowing creeks and rivers, and marine leeches are occasionally observed on freshly caught fish.

Bushwalker's bane

Leeches are slimy, and generally brown to black, with some land varieties sporting yellow to orange stripes. They are closely related to earthworms and their relatives and share many of their anatomical features, including a complex hermaphroditic reproductive system.

They have the unpleasant habit of sucking blood from vertebrates, including humans – much to the annoyance of bushwalkers. Even more repellent, they remain firmly attached to the skin while feeding and can be very difficult to remove.

Not all leeches are blood-suckers. The so-called jawless leeches are carnivorous, and feed by thrusting a proboscis like a hypodermic needle into the bodies of small invertebrates to suck out their entire body contents. Some of these pierce the bodies of larger prey, such as vertebrates, and suck out only blood. The jawed leeches have developed semi-circular cutting blades that slice a hole in the skin of their victim. They then suck the blood that oozes from the wound directly into the mouth.

To prevent their victims' blood from clotting, leeches inject an anticoagulant into the bite, along with a histamine that dilates the blood vessels and increases the blood flow to the area. This is why a leech bite

■ LEECH
All leeches possess suckers. They move with a distinctive looping action, attaching their front and back suckers alternately to the surface.

goes on bleeding for quite a long time after the leech has gorged itself and dropped off. Some scientists believe that leeches also produce an anaesthetic, so that the victim does not feel the bite and the leech can feast undisturbed.

Leeches can store large quantities of blood, enabling them to survive for months on a single blood meal. They have special bacteria that digest the blood slowly for them.

Leeches and medicine

In the past, doctors used leeches in the treatment (albeit ineffective) of ailments ranging from headache to syphilis. Today there is a more scientific resurgence in the use of leeches in microsurgery, where they can relieve congestion while veins heal.

Researchers are also exploring the potential of the pharmacologically active substances that leeches produce as part of their extraordinary feeding and digestive activities.
Class: Hirudinea

LEECH COCOON
Leeches breed in the same way as earthworms (see page 517). They produce a surprisingly beautiful cocoon.

VELVET WORMS

These elegant creatures are little known, but they have significance in evolutionary studies as some features indicate they are ancestral to the arthropods. Internally they are arthropod-like but their body is covered by a thin cuticle instead of a hard external skeleton. Also, they are categorised as 'living fossils' because fossils that look like present-day velvet worms have been discovered in sites dating back over 500 million years – a time when the major invertebrates were first appearing.

Today, velvet worms, ranging in size from one to several centimetres, are confined to the tropics and southern hemisphere landmasses. In Australia they live in damp coastal forests from north Queensland to Tasmania, in the Adelaide Hills in South Australia, and in the southwest corner of Western Australia. They are abundant in moist habitats, such as rotting logs, under stones, and within leaf litter and soil.

Multipurpose head

The velvet worm's head has a pair of mobile antennae, bright, beady eyes and a mouth with sharp, slashing jaws. It is carnivorous, and traps other small invertebrates by shooting sticky strands from turrets on each side of its head. It tears open the immobilised prey, injects it with saliva, and sucks the resultant mixture back into its mouth.

Some velvet worms mate with their heads. The males of many Australian species possess bizarre head configurations ranging from knobs to cavities, often adorned with tusks, hollow syringes or spikes. In some species a bundle of sperm has been observed enclosed within this structure. One species caught in the act of mating showed the head structure of the male turned inside out and wedged firmly against the rear genital opening of the female. Other species deposit sperm on the skin of the female, which makes its way into her body cavity to fertilise the eggs.

Some species of velvet worms in Australia and New Zealand lay shelled eggs that take 17 months to hatch. However, most give birth to live young, which look like miniature adults and are immediately capable of fending for themselves.

Common names

Velvet worms are so called for the velvety texture of their skin, which in many species resembles a Persian carpet richly patterned in deep blue, mauve, brown, orange, pale green and white. Their soft bodies are shaped by muscles acting against a fluid-filled body cavity.

The way they move on paired, unjointed legs gives them their other common name, peripatus – derived from the Greek for 'wandering'.
Phylum: Onychophora

WORMS WITH LEGS
The unusual velvet worm, or peripatus, resembles an arthropod as it moves along on its pairs of short legs, each with a flat sole and a terminal pair of claws.

WATER BEARS

The water bear's scientific name means 'slow-stepper', and its shape and slow, lumbering gait are reminiscent of a miniature bear. Water bears range in size from microscopic to just over 1 mm long. They have a globular body with four pairs of stumpy limbs ending in claws. The body has an outer covering, called a cuticle, which in some species is thick, sculptured and divided into plates. Needle-like stylets on its head allow the water bear to pierce the bodies of animals or plants and suck the juices into its mouth.

Water bears reproduce sexually, although males are usually rare and the parthenogenetic females of some species produce eggs that do not need to be fertilised by males. The eggs of terrestrial water bear species have thick shells that can withstand periods of desiccation.

Equipped for survival

Adult water bears, too, have the capacity to survive unfavourable conditions, such as freezing or dehydration, by contracting their body within its outer covering to become a resistant stage, called a tun.

Both the eggs and the tuns may blow about in the wind for great distances – sometimes even between continents – which accounts for the wide distribution of many species.

Water bears are found throughout Australia in virtually all habitats: in coastal and abyssal waters; in freshwater sediments; among aquatic plants; in the film of water that covers soils, terrestrial mosses and lichens; and even in the arid interior.

Arthropod cousins

Because these appealing animals are so small, zoologists have tended to neglect them, so there is still much to find out about them. Their relationship to other invertebrate groups is controversial, but many aspects of their anatomy suggest that they are closely related to arthropods.
Phylum: Tardigrada

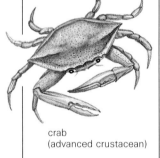

millipede

prawn
(primitive crustacean)

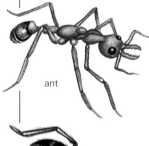

crab
(advanced crustacean)

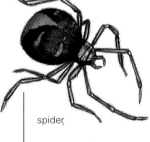

ant

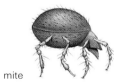

spider

mite

ARTHROPOD TYPES
The arthropods have diversified into shapes ranging from long and narrow to a more compact configuration with fewer legs. The arachnids, such as the spider and the mite, are the most versatile of this very large group.

ARTHROPODS

Arthropods (phylum Arthropoda) are, without a doubt, the most successful living creatures on Earth, not only in sheer numbers but in number of species. Three-quarters of the known living species of animals are the arthropods, and this group includes the insects, the crustaceans (lobsters, prawns, crabs), the horseshoe crabs and arachnids (scorpions, spiders, mites and ticks) and the myriapods (millipedes and centipedes). Throughout the world, at least a million species have been named and more are being discovered all the time.

Across these many forms are the shared features of jointed limbs, segmented bodies and an external skeleton called an exoskeleton.

Arthropods are found in most habitats – from the tropics to the poles, from ocean depths to alpine heights, and even living in or on other animals or plants.

The exoskeleton supports the soft body of the arthropod and protects it from predators. While the strong but lightweight carbohydrate, chitin, provides toughness to the exoskeleton, the leather-like protein sclerotin gives it rigidity. Flexibility is afforded by those parts lacking sclerotin. Although it is flexible around the joints to allow for movement, inside there is little room to grow. Several times during a lifetime, the arthropod must discard the outer layer of its exoskeleton (the inner layer is reabsorbed) and secrete a larger one, a process known as moulting.

While waiting for the new skeleton to harden, the arthropod is vulnerable to predators and disease and, on land, to dehydration. The difficulties associated with moulting may be the reason why few arthropods are larger than 60 cm (most, in fact, are much smaller), and why the largest arthropods are marine – it is easier to support a soft, skeletonless body in water than in air during moulting.

INSECTS

Insects live almost everywhere except in the open ocean – species have even been discovered in frozen Antarctica. There may be as many as 30 million insect species, with about 108 000 having been identified in Australia.

Flight, metamorphosis and their relationship with flowering plants are the main reasons for the success and diversity of insects. Because there are so many of them, they are vital in supporting many ecosystems. Some help to pollinate plants or provide food for other animals; others help to decompose dead animal and plant matter, or burrow into and aerate the soil.

The insect body
There are three regions – a head, containing the sensory and feeding appendages; the thorax, equipped with three pairs of legs (hence the Subphylum Hexapoda); and an abdomen with sensory (cerci) and reproductive appendages.

The circulatory system consists of a heart and blood vessels but at some stage the blood escapes from its confinement in vessels and directly bathes the body organs. So blood circulation is rather sluggish.

Insects breathe through openings (spiracles) leading into an extensive system of air-filled tubes (tracheae) that deliver oxygen directly to the body tissues. Insects that live in water either surface to breathe or have gills. Body functions are co-ordinated by a nervous system – a brain connected to a nerve cord that runs down the underside of the body. Insects also have a well-developed hormone system that controls major activities, such as moulting and metamorphosis.

Powered flight
Only some insects, birds and bats are capable of true powered flight, rather than just gliding. Wings are so important in insect biology that the scientific names of many insect orders contain the word 'ptera', meaning 'wings'. It is also significant that the largest and best known of the insect orders, such as beetles, butterflies and moths, flies, bugs and grasshoppers, are winged.

Wings allow insects to travel long distances, sometimes by gliding on the wind. They can seek out new food sources, escape from enemies, mix with different populations of their own species, find mates and disperse new generations. Wings may also be patterned to provide camouflage when an insect is at rest. In some cases, drab camouflaged wings cover flashes of bright colour that are revealed only when the wings are spread for flight. If the insect is fleeing danger, the flash of colour may startle its enemy and give it a chance to escape. Many insects combine the considerable advantages of flight with the extra innovation of metamorphosis.
Subphylum: Hexapoda; Class: Insecta

DRAGONFLY'S COMPOUND EYES
Made up of thousands of tiny lenses, the compound eyes of a dragonfly (above) detect the slightest movement. Insects' compound eyes resemble those of crustaceans, but it is thought that they developed independently.

LADYBIRD
The ladybird (below) is a small winged beetle. Like other winged insects, it is able to fly relatively long distances to search for food and mates, to pollinate flowering plants, and sometimes to escape from enemies.

SHAPE-SHIFTERS

Metamorphosis means 'change of form'. Some insects, such as silverfish, change little from the moment they hatch to when they become sexually mature adults. As they grow they moult, but their body shape remains the same.

Other insects, such as the true bugs, grow differently. When they hatch they look like small adults without wings. They are known as nymphs. Every time they moult their skeleton, the bud-like wings grow a little longer. On the last moult, the wings emerge fully formed. This kind of growth is called a gradual, or incomplete, metamorphosis.

A third mode of development is illustrated by butterflies. They hatch from the egg as caterpillars (larvae) and after several moults enter a stage called a pupa. Within the pupal case the larva is reorganised into a different body – that of the adult butterfly. This is complete metamorphosis. Many insect species undergo complete metamorphosis. It allows them to have a crawling larval stage to feed and grow, while the winged adult reproduces and disperses the species. Larvae and adults eat different foods and so do not compete.

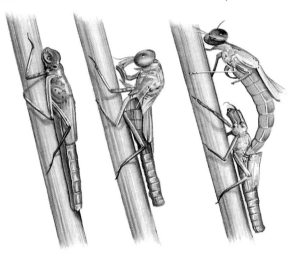

INCOMPLETE METAMORPHOSIS
When the nymphs of insects such as damselflies, dragonflies and mayflies are ready to change into adults, they crawl from the water on to a plant stem. The soft body of the adult gradually emerges from the nymphal skin.

COMPLETE METAMORPHOSIS
Butterflies change their bodies completely. The larva, called a caterpillar, hatches from the egg and, after shedding its skin several times, enters the pupal stage, or chrysalis. Transformed inside the pupa, it emerges as a butterfly.

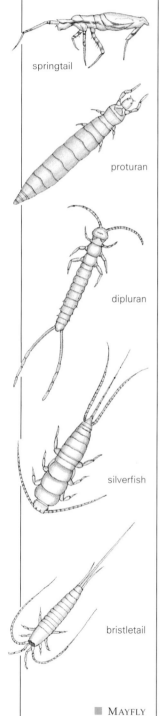

springtail

proturan

dipluran

silverfish

bristletail

INSECT ALLIES

Formerly believed to be a primitive type of insect, this small group of wingless hexapods differs anatomically from true insects. Their mouthparts do not protrude like those of insects but, like insects, they still have three pairs of legs. They do not undergo metamorphosis.
Class: Ellipura

SPRINGTAILS

Most springtails are less than 6 mm long. At the end of their abdomen, they have a fork-shaped organ called a furcula, which they use to propel themselves into the air. Although most of these small jumping insects live in moist soil and leaf litter or under bark, some species are found on the surface of fresh water and on seashores or reefs. Some springtails even live on snow and a few inhabit the nests of ants and termites. Springtails have been known to flock together in vast numbers, causing blockages in sewage pipes.

Most springtails feed on decaying matter, but some prefer lichens, fungi, algae and pollen. Their greatest enemies are spiders and beetles. The lucerne flea (*Sminthurus viridis*), which sometimes appears in millions, feeds on legume crops, causing considerable damage to them.
Order: Collembola

PROTURANS

Proturans were discovered only in 1907, and are structurally different from other insect allies. They are colourless, wingless creatures with no eyes, antennae or sensory tail appendages (cerci). All proturans are tiny – up to 2 mm long.

Proturans like humid conditions and are often found in deciduous woodlands in wetter parts of Australia. Using specially adapted mouthparts, they suck liquid from moist soil, leaf debris and decaying timber. Their forelegs, which are larger and longer than their other legs, serve as antennae. They are preyed upon by mites, tiny spiders, ground beetles and centipedes.
Order: Protura

DIPLURANS

Diplurans are wingless, elongated and blind with bead-like antennae and soft, cream-white bodies. Although most diplurans have bodies that are about 5 mm long, a few grow to as much as 5 cm in length.

Diplurans are widely distributed in Australia. Although many feed on decaying vegetable matter, some species are carnivorous. These diplurans burrow into soil, leaving their pincers exposed to seize prey, such as small insects and slaters.
Order: Diplura

BRISTLETAILS AND SILVERFISH

Creatures very similar to bristletails and silverfish are found in the earliest insect fossil records; possibly these are the ancestral types from which today's true insects evolved.

Bristletails are 3–15 mm long and found throughout Australia, including tropical rainforests, wet and dry eucalypt woodlands and coastal cliffs. They haunt moist dark places, such as leaf litter, where they feed on vegetable debris, algae and lichen.

Silverfish have tapering bodies about 8 mm long. A few species are familiar inhabitants of our homes, particularly in damp places. They come out at night to feed on wallpaper and bookbinding pastes, linen, starchy foods and the dead bodies of insects. Some species live in ant and termite nests.

Both groups have protruding chewing mouthparts typical of true insects. They are wingless and do not undergo metamorphosis. Their abdomen terminates in an elongate 'tail' flanked by two sensory appendages (cerci).
Order: Archaeognatha (bristletails)
Order: Thysanura (silverfish)

MAYFLIES ■

The nymphs of mayflies may take several years to develop, but the parents live for only a few days. During their fleeting life, adult mayflies do not feed – their sole purpose is to mate. At dusk they perform their lively mating dance above water. Females hover on the outskirts of the whirling mass of males, making sudden dashes into the swarm to be seized by the males. Mating pairs immediately leave the dance to alight on nearby leaves and branches. Later, the females dip the long egg ribbons that trail from their abdomen tips into running water. The eggs quickly sink and settle on submerged plant stems and stones.

Newly hatched nymphs have gills and well-developed mouthparts. They shelter from predators beneath stones and crevices in the banks or by burrowing into the mud. The nymphs are vegetarians, feeding on algae, plant tissue and decaying matter. When conditions are suitable, they crawl on to nearby rocks, plants or dead branches, shed their skin and emerge as winged insects – but not yet adults. Mayflies undergo incomplete metamorphosis (see page 521). When their wings are dry, they fly to a resting place, where they remain until their final moult into adults. Mayflies are the only insects that can fly before maturity.

Mayflies, 20–40 mm long, are usually found near lakes, streams and billabongs, although they do occasionally stray from water. During daylight, they rest on tree trunks and leaves, their forelegs extended in front and two pairs of transparent wings held erect above their body.
Order: Ephemeroptera

DRAGONFLIES ◾

Few insects can match the speed, manoeuvrability and endurance of dragonflies. They always take their prey on the wing, and the swooping style of bigger species has earned them the name 'mosquito-hawks'.

Dragonflies have excellent sight. Some of the larger species recognise members of the opposite sex from as far away as 40 metres as they dash in circular, territorial patterns up and down streams at speeds of up to 50 km per hour. When at rest, their two pairs of gauzy wings, of almost equal length, are spread horizontally, distinguishing the dragonfly from the damselfly (page 524).

Dragonflies are usually seen on warm, sunny days, often near water, where they feed on flying insects. They have bright, almost metallic bodies and huge complex eyes. Commonly seen dragonflies are the powder blue *Orthetrum caledonicum* and the bright red *Diplacodes bipunctata* and *D. haematodes*.

Miniature carnivores

Dragonflies are carnivorous at all stages of their life. As nymphs they have a unique folding lower jaw that shoots forward to seize their prey, such as water insects, tiny fishes and tadpoles. Their short, spiny legs form a basket for holding prey beneath the head.

Unlike the aquatic nymphs of mayflies, damselflies and stoneflies, those of the dragonfly have no tail, only pronounced sensory appendages (cerci). Dragonfly nymphs take in oxygen with water through special valves in their anus; the waste water is expelled through the same valve. The valve is useful when they need to propel themselves through the water, although nymphs also use their legs to swim. Fully grown nymphs leave the water just before dawn, to climb tree trunks or rocks, where they shed their skins.

Airborne breeding

During courtship, dragonfly pairs fly together, with the male in front, gripping the female on the top of her head with his specialised tail-claspers. To mate, the couple usually settle and the female loops her body forward and inserts her tail into the male's sperm pouch. The couple may continue to fly together until the female is ready to lay her eggs, the male supporting the female as she dips her tail into the water to deposit the strings of eggs.

GIANT DRAGONFLY

Fossil remains of dragonflies that flew about 300 million years ago show that they were once gigantic. The largest, *Maganeura monyi*, measured 70 cm across its wings. The largest living species in Australia is the tropical dragonfly (*Petalura ingentissima*), with a wingspan of 16 centimetres.

Maganeura monyi

Petalura ingentissima

Despite their remarkable flying ability, many dragonflies meet an ignoble end. It is not unusual to find them entangled in the webs of golden orb-weaving spiders, and often they are snatched on the wing by birds, such as bee-eaters, which swallow them whole.
Order: Odonata; Suborder: Anisoptera

◾ DRAGONFLY
In summer, dragonflies are often seen courting by ponds, lakes and rivers. During mating, which takes place in flight or on vegetation, the female (below) inserts her tail into the male's sperm pouch. Later she drops the eggs in or near the water.

■ DAMSELFLIES
Like dragonflies, damselflies perform a fleeting courtship in the air. After mating, which may be airborne or on nearby vegetation, the female damselfly drops her eggs singly into the water.

DAMSELFLIES ■

Nicknamed 'darning needles' because of their fine, straight, exceedingly long bodies, these delicate insects are smaller than dragonflies but larger than mayflies. Damselflies flutter rather than fly, and fold their membranous wings, which are of almost equal length, above their bodies when at rest.

Depending on the species, these creatures can be brilliant blue, green, red or gold. One of the most beautiful is the blue damselfly (*Diphlebia coerulescens*); other attractive and commonly seen damselflies include the brilliant electric blue males of *Ischnura heterosticta* and the vivid red males of *I. aurora*.

Damselflies share many characteristics with dragonflies, including their method of mating. The female damselfly, however, drops her eggs into water singly, rather than in a ribbon, as dragonflies and mayflies do. The nymphs are frail creatures that hide amongst aquatic plants and feed on water life such as mosquito larvae.

Damselfly nymphs, like mayfly nymphs, have three tails, but those of damselflies serve as gills. As well as being used for breathing, a damselfly's tail propels it through the water, swishing from side to side rather like a fish's tail. Like dragonfly and mayfly nymphs, damselflies crawl from the water just before dawn to shed their nymphal skin.

Damselflies are carnivorous at all stages of their life, most of which is spent near water, where many fall prey to birds and spiders. They are found all over Australia.
Order: Odonata; Suborder Zygoptera

STONEFLIES ■

Stoneflies are an ancient group, known to have been on Earth at least 270 million years ago. Although they have an aquatic nymph stage, stoneflies are actually more closely related to grasshoppers and crickets than they are to mayflies, dragonflies and damselflies. They have earned their name from their habitat. The nymphs live beneath stones in the clear, running water of creeks and streams, and on the wave-washed shores of freshwater lakes. They become less prolific as levels of pollution rise.

The aquatic nymphs live underwater for several months, breathing through their gills and eating plants and other small aquatic insects. They moult several times before crawling out of the water onto tree trunks or rocks to emerge as adults during late autumn to early spring.

Adult stoneflies seldom venture far from water. Measuring between 5 mm and 5 cm in body length, most species are drab-coloured, which provides good camouflage when they are resting on rocks or tree trunks. They have two pairs of gauzy wings, which they fold along their back. Their fan-shaped hindwings are broader than their forewings. Their fine antennae are many-jointed, and their abdomens end in a pair of long tails (cerci).

Adults live only a few days, during which time they do not eat but draw their energy from the fat reserves stored during their nymphal days. At dusk both males and females take to the air to take part in a courtship dance, which involves flying up and down a stretch of the water's surface.

Once the stoneflies find their partners, mating takes place on a tree trunk or rock. Females may produce more than 1000 eggs in a single laying. The eggs are either washed from the tip of the female's abdomen as she dips her tails into the running water, or dropped into the water from an overhanging branch. The outer coating of the eggs quickly swells and becomes sticky so that it adheres to rocks.

Stoneflies are most common in the cooler, high-altitude areas of Australia. Of the 2000 species described worldwide, 190 are known in Australia. The most frequently seen stonefly is *Stenoperla australis*. Members of the unusual genus *Eusthenopis*, found in Tasmania, are easily recognised by their short, rounded forewings and the bright red or purple underneath their hindwings. Despite their camouflage, many stoneflies are eaten by birds, freshwater fishes, dragonfly nymphs and water beetle larvae.
Order: Plecoptera

■ ADULT STONEFLY
With their wings folded flat against their backs, dull-coloured stoneflies are well camouflaged against tree bark, one of their favourite resting places.

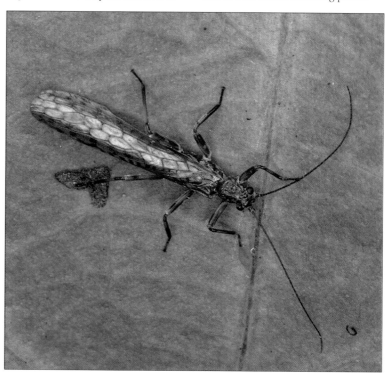

COCKROACHES

Cockroaches are believed to have been on Earth for 300 million years. They are extraordinary survivors, although it is not true – despite some people's belief – that they can withstand holocausts, fires and nuclear explosions. They are no more immune to radioactivity and heat than any other life form, but their fine antennae, their prominent tail appendages (cerci) and the specialised sensors on their legs make them acutely sensitive to air disturbances and light, so that they can react swiftly to danger. Their long, spiky legs help them to scuttle away quickly and their flattened bodies enable them to hide by crawling into the narrowest of cracks.

So sensitive are cockroaches that when these creatures have crawled into microwave ovens, they can position themselves out of the path of the deadly rays. Even with all their known light-receptors covered, and even when they are decapitated, cockroaches still respond to light – but scientists do not know exactly how they do this.

The body of a cockroach is well protected by a tough shield that covers its head and thoracic region and by leathery forewings that protect its large abdomen and enclose its delicate, membranous hindwings. All introduced cockroach species can fly, but a few Australian species have reduced wings or are entirely wingless. Some species are quite small (as little as 10 mm in length), while others can grow up to 7 cm long. Cockroaches have chewing mouthparts and stout, toothed jaws.

From egg to adult

A fertilised female cockroach usually produces 12–40 eggs, packed neatly into a single, well protected, tough, leathery egg capsule that protrudes from the end of her abdomen.

Depending on the species, she eventually drops the capsule or attaches it to a support in a warm, sheltered location. If a female is attacked, she will drop her capsule to ensure that the next generation survives. In some species, females can produce up to 50 egg capsules in their lifetime. Some species, such as the American cockroach (*Periplaneta americana*) are parthenogenetic and can reproduce without being fertilised. Unlike the introduced cockroaches, some native cockroach species give birth to live young.

When the nymphs are ready to hatch, the egg capsule splits along its ridge. The nymphs resemble their parents, and moult up to 12 times before completing growth. They become adult in anything from a few weeks to over 12 months – the smaller the species, the quicker it is to reach sexual maturity.

Pests and natives

The most commonly known cockroaches are the introduced pests that inhabit our homes and restaurants. These include the 35 mm American cockroach (*Periplaneta americana*), the 30 mm smoky brown cockroach (*P. fuliginosa*), the 15 mm brown banded cockroach (*Supella longipalpa*) and the 15 mm German cockroach (*Blattella germanica*). Another species, the 30 mm oriental cockroach (*Blatta orientalis*), is found in southern parts of Australia. The introduced species eat almost anything, often spoiling food with their excreta and an unpleasant odour that persists long after their departure. They also eat their own cast-off moults and their empty egg capsules, as well as their own deceased. Cockroaches have been known to carry salmonella onto food.

Of the 420 species known in Australia, 400 are native to the country. Native cockroaches are not pests but live in caves or under bark, stones and decaying logs. Most are active at night, but some species, such as those in the large *Polyzosteria* genus, rest on trees and rocks to

bask in the sunlight. The giant 6 cm native bush roach, *Polyzosteria mitchelli*, is commonly found in the heathlands of New South Wales. The pungent smell it produces to deter predators is unmistakable.

An unusual native species is the blind *Trogoloblattella nullarborensis*, which lives in the limestone caverns beneath the Nullarbor Plain.

The native flat cockroach (*Laxta granicollis*) is a flattened species that lives under bark. The females are entirely wingless, but winged males are sometimes seen during summer evenings around lights.

Cockroaches are an important part of the food web; they are eaten by many other arthropods, as well as by birds, reptiles, frogs, native marsupial mice and bandicoots. Their egg capsules, too, are often parasitised by little black wasps that live throughout Australia.

Order: Blattodea

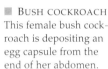

■ BUSH COCKROACH This female bush cockroach is depositing an egg capsule from the end of her abdomen.

■ STRIPED COCKROACH The *Polyzosteria mitchelli* cockroach shelters from the heat of the midday sun beneath some banksia flowers. This species has pale, diverging stripes on a green or brown body.

A TERMITE'S ROLE
Worker termites feed the colony and soldiers defend it. Winged reproductives fly from the parent colony to establish a new one. The king mates continuously with the queen, who is the colony's key member.

worker

soldier

reproductive

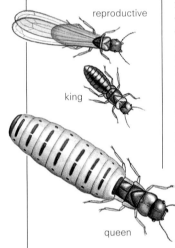

king

queen

TERMITES ■

Termites (order Isoptera), found throughout Australia, do everything on a grand scale. An Australian termite mound may rise to about 6 metres, and colonies often number in the millions. There are more than 300 species of termites in Australia, most in subtropical and tropical regions, but only about 15 are troublesome to humans. Most species feed on grass or decaying wood, and in so doing, help to create soil.

Although often referred to as white ants because of their size (3–12 mm long), colour and social habits, termites are not true ants and their development and habits are quite different. However, like true ants and some wasps and bees, they are social insects that live in colonies. Each species can exist in one of several forms, known as castes, and each caste performs specific functions within the colony. Like most social insects, survival of the colony is more important than survival of any individual, except the queen.

Social structures

The shapes and sizes of termite nests vary with species. Ground mounds may be tall and chimney-like, or wedge-shaped to prevent overheating and moisture loss. They vary in height from a few centimetres in the case of some species from the southern states, to about 6 metres for the spinifex termite (*Nasutitermes triodiae*) of the Northern Territory. External tree nests, known as arboreal nests, are built on trunks or large branches. The colony starts at the base of the tree but when the population increases the termites build a nest high up in the tree to accommodate it. Tree nests are sometimes built inside trees and tree stumps. Most nests are made of chewed soil, wood, saliva and droppings.

Within these dramatic exteriors, the nests are miracles of design. At the heart is the central royal chamber, where the queen lays up to a thousand eggs a day once she is five years old. She is attended by her consort, the king, and busy sterile workers. A nursery for young termites is also housed at the nest's centre, where moisture and temperature are least likely to fluctuate.

The termites control the temperature by transporting fluids up into the nest, either within their bodies or in the moist soil that they carry. The high level of humidity in the nest allows the termites to cultivate fungus as a rich source of protein.

Termite development

Termites undergo three stages of development: the egg, the nymph and the adult. Termite nymphs, which hatch from eggs, grow by a series of seven moults to become mature adult workers, soldiers, or sexually mature males and females called reproductives. Once the reproductives have formed their wings they become alates, and they await a cue from nature to emerge from the nest. Usually, just before a storm at dusk, the termites take flight, providing frogs, lizards, snakes, birds and predatory insects with a rare feast. On landing, the alates lose their wings and establish new colonies, where they are the queens and kings.

Kookaburras, kingfishers, echidnas and numbats all feed on termites, but some species of ants, such as driver ants, are their greatest enemies.

AIR-CONDITIONED TOWER
The temperature in the termite nest is regulated by a complex air-conditioning system, made up of chambers and passages, and channels in the outer ridges of the mound.

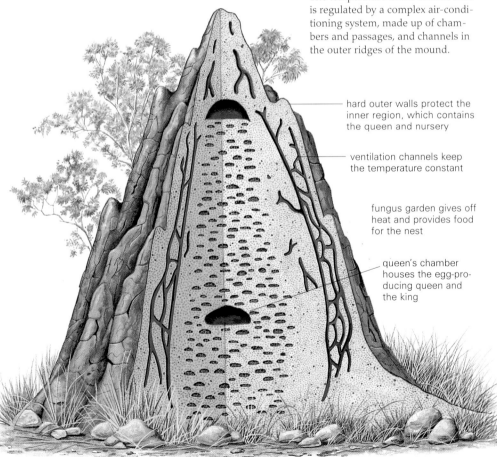

hard outer walls protect the inner region, which contains the queen and nursery

ventilation channels keep the temperature constant

fungus garden gives off heat and provides food for the nest

queen's chamber houses the egg-producing queen and the king

■ TERMITE WORKERS
The workers are the largest caste in the colony. Their tasks are to gather food and feed the other castes, including the queen, care for the eggs and young and help to build the nest. Pale and wingless, they have small jaws for chewing.

MANTIDS ▪

Often called praying mantids, these insects take their name from the Greek word 'mantis', meaning soothsayer. Their large, bulging, watchful eyes and the way they hold their raptorial forelegs in a prayer-like gesture seem to make them strangely human.

Mantids are solitary creatures. They lurk among grasses, flowers, shrubs and trees, not only in bush-lands but in inner city areas and towns throughout Australia.

Usually green or brown, mantids are elongated creatures 1–15 cm long. Their free-moving triangular head, which houses powerful chewing mouthparts, can swivel in an arc of almost 180 degrees. All males and some females have two pairs of wings: a pair of narrow, leathery forewings and a pair of membranous, fan-like hindwings. They fly during the day and night and are often spotted around electric lights, to which they are attracted. All mantids undergo incomplete metamorphosis (page 521).

There are 160 known species of praying mantids in Australia, and all of them eat a great many crop and garden pests. Adult mantids are themselves preyed upon by insectivorous mammals, birds, lizards and hunting wasps.

The commonly encountered small green mantid (*Orthodera ministralis*) is 4 cm long. It has two distinguishing features: its wide, flattened thorax and its blue-green colour. The large brown mantid (*Archimantis latistyla*) grows up to 10 cm long and is widely distributed throughout Australia, although it is particularly common inland. Around the Sydney region, the light green *Tenodera australasiae* is often found in spring sitting on native flowering plants, where it preys on bees and flies.

Camouflaged carnivore

Mantids are strictly carnivorous, but they seldom hunt. They prefer to wait with their grasping forelegs poised until other insects are within reach. To provide them with a camouflage against birds, mantids are the same colour and sometimes the same shape as the leaves, bark and grass stems on which they rest.

Some species can change colour. While waiting for prey they remain perfectly still, sometimes for hours, but their long, fine antennae are always alert to movement. When

the time is right, the mantids move with alarming suddenness, seizing their prey with their powerful forelegs. These limbs are armed with spines that pierce the victim as they snap shut like a clasp knife.

Dangerous liaisons

Mating is a risky business for the male mantid. Attracted by chemical substances, called pheromones, exuded by the female, he approaches his mate cautiously from behind and mounts her. At this point the female may turn her head and begin feeding on the male's head and body. Even when the male mantis has been decapitated, a chain of nerves extending the length of his body compel him to continue mating, and he transfers a small packet of sperm to the female before dying.

This amazing mating behaviour has been observed most often when mantids are kept in captivity; it does occur in the wild, but in that situation the male has a much better chance of escaping. Eating the male provides the female with much-needed protein for healthy development of the egg.

About two or three days after mating, the female exudes a frothy substance onto the surface of a branch or leaf. She lays some 100–400 eggs between the frothy layers, which then harden to form a protective purse, called an ootheca, in which the eggs develop. The ootheca insulates the cocoon in cold climates, and in arid regions it protects the eggs from dehydration.

After a few weeks the tiny nymphs hatch out and gather outside their old home. During this vulnerable time, many are carried away by

marauding ants – only a few survive the hazards of the first few weeks.

The young that survive instantly adopt the predatory instincts of the adults, feeding on tiny insects such as aphids. The nymphs undergo several moults, hanging upside down from a leaf or a twig and shedding their original skin.

Order: Mantodea

▪ **LARGE BROWN MANTID**
The female of this species, *Archimantis latistyla*, lays her eggs in a frothy discharge, which hardens into a protective capsule called an ootheca. Some females stay until the eggs have hatched, while others fly away.

▪ **PRAYING MANTID**
The distinctive head of the praying mantid, with its huge protruding compound eyes, make it easily recognisable. Here, it tilts its head to clean its forelegs.

■ EARWIG
Earwigs venture out to feed only at night. Those of the family Forficulidae are brown, winged and between 15 mm and 25 mm long.

EARWIGS ■

With its short legs and flattened body, the earwig is ideally shaped for a life spent lurking in crevices. It is instantly recognisable by a pair of pointed tail pincers, called cerci, which are used by the females to carry food and nesting material.

Australia has more than 60 earwig species. A few large species, such as the giant earwig (*Titanolabis colossea*), which is 10–45 mm long and found throughout Australia, may bite if handled. Some earwigs are wingless, but those with wings have two pairs, the short, toughened fore-wings protecting the longer but neatly folded hindwings.

During the daytime, earwigs shelter in cool, dark places, such as beneath bark, logs, decaying timber, rocks and stones, in forests and woodlands throughout Australia. At night, they feed on plants, fruit, decaying matter and other small insects. Under cover of darkness, earwigs sometimes fall prey to birds, bats and predatory insects.
Order: Dermaptera

ANIMAL LICE

Lice feed on blood or dead tissue of animals and birds. They are small, flat, wingless insects covered with rows of stout bristles for moving through fur and feathers. Their legs and claws are modified for clinging to their hosts.

Two species in particular are parasites of humans: the crab louse (*Pthirus pubis*), which invades pubic hair, and the body louse (*Pediculus*

humanus). Body lice in head hair are called head lice, and their eggs are called nits. Crab lice do not transmit diseases, but body lice are said to carry more diseases than any other insect. They can infest people living in unhygienic conditions, and are known to carry the bacteria that causes typhus (although it does not occur in Australia).
Order: Phthiraptera

BARK LICE

Closely related to animal lice, but markedly different in lifestyle, are the bark, or book, lice. When bark lice inhabit damp or damaged books they are known as book lice.

Bark lice (1–10 mm long) have large, bulbous heads and chisel-shaped mouths. Some species are wingless but most have two pairs of wings held roof-like over their abdomens. Bark lice undergo incomplete metamorphosis (page 521).

The introduced bark louse (*Atropos pulsatoria*) is the most commonly encountered species. It lives under bark and stones, in leaf litter and stored products. The larger native bark louse (*Myopsocus griseipennis*) is found in summer feeding on algae and fungi that grow on fences or tiles in cool, damp places. Many fungi-eating bark lice spread their spores from leaf to leaf. Bark lice are kept in check by nematodes, spiders, thrips, ants and parasitic wasps.
Order: Psocoptera

CRICKETS AND GRASSHOPPERS

More than 2800 species of grasshoppers and crickets have been recorded in Australia. These insects provide one of the most distinctive sounds of nature – a background buzz of trilling, chirping and clicking.

Both groups have enlarged and powerful hindlegs for jumping, with some species able to leap two metres or more. Most have four wings, with a leathery upper pair protecting the larger, more delicate lower pair. Both groups undergo an incomplete metamorphosis (page 521) from wingless nymph to winged adult.

Crickets and katydids can be distinguished from grasshoppers and locusts (migratory short-horned

grasshoppers) by their long, thin, whip-like antennae. Another difference is the way each group lays its eggs. Crickets and katydids lay individual eggs through a long, sword-shaped egg-laying organ called an ovipositor. Grasshoppers and locusts dig a hole in loose soil, using special appendages at the tip of their abdomen, and deposit masses of eggs encased in a frothy, protective coating.
Order: Orthoptera

BLACK FIELD CRICKET
Jet black, stout and 2–4 cm long, this is the most commonly encountered cricket in Australia. Found countrywide, in pastures, backyards and sometimes in the home, it spends its day under debris and vegetation or in cracks in the ground. At night it feeds on green and decaying plants and insect remains. The females lay up to 2000 eggs over a lifetime of several months.
Scientific name: *Teleogryllus* spp.

KATYDIDS ■
Most katydids are leaf-shaped, green (except as nymphs) and about 3 cm long, although some species are up to 8 cm long. They are more often heard than seen. During the day their leaf-imitating wings and habit of keeping still help them to hide from predators. At night they feed on leaves and flowers and, from high vantage points, the males serenade the females with complex compositions that could be mistaken for bird calls. These songs are unique, and can be used to tell species apart. There are about 300 species of katydids in Australia, found mainly in the warmer regions.
Family: Tettigoniidae

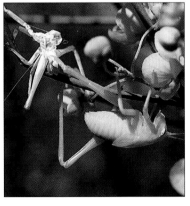

■ KATYDID NYMPH
This juvenile katydid, seen here feeding on a desert cassia, has just shed its outer skin. In the nymphal stages, katydids can take on the colour of whatever they feed on.

KING CRICKETS ◼

There are 15 Australian species of this large (2–7 cm long), fierce and mainly carnivorous insect. They are found mainly in eastern Australia. Most are wingless and live among the leaf litter of the forest floor, where at night they hunt for worms and insects.

The male king cricket has enlarged jaws. Both sexes are dark brown and stout with long, sharp, backward-pointing spines on their legs. They can give a strong bite if handled.
Family: Stenopelmatidae

MOLE CRICKETS

Mole crickets (3–3.5 cm long) are found in most parts of Australia. Their broad, shovel-like forelegs, especially adapted for digging the burrow in which they live, are also equipped with a series of 'teeth' to shear through vegetation – these crickets feed on roots and grasses and are especially fond of lawns.

At night the male sends forth one of the loudest courtship calls of all insects – a continuous, high-pitched buzz, broadcast from the horn-shaped burrow entrance, which is especially designed to amplify the sound. The female lays her eggs in

◼ COOLOOLA MONSTER
Rarely seen above ground, this unusual subterranean creature has legs and jaws adapted for digging. The female (below) has shorter, stouter legs and a more inflated abdomen than the male.

the burrow and protects the eggs and nymphs with a degree of maternal care rare among crickets. Australia has ten of the 50 mole cricket species in the world.
Family: Gryllotalpidae

COOLOOLA MONSTER ◼

When it was discovered in 1976, this cricket was considered distinctive enough to warrant the creation of a new insect family. Its 3 cm-long body is broad and fully adapted to a subterranean life, with short antennae, powerful legs for digging and even jaws that work like a shovel.

It lives in the sandy country near Noosa in south-eastern Queensland,

scrabbling below ground in search of invertebrate prey. The male, which has vestigial wings, comes out at night, but the wingless, almost blind female apparently never emerges into the light.
Family: Cooloolidae
Scientific name: *Cooloola propator*

◼ KING CRICKET
Wingless king crickets, a dark-coloured species, have antennae the same length as their body. They come out at night to hunt, making a meal of other insects, grubs and worms.

BUSH CONCERTS

Male grasshoppers and crickets produce sounds to attract females, some so high-pitched that humans cannot hear them. Crickets always call at dusk or at night, never during the day. The sound is made by rubbing a 'file' on one upper wing against a raised 'scraper' on the other. Sometimes a hardened area (called a 'mirror') on the wing amplifies the sound. Each species produces a unique series of chirps or clicks. Mole and field crickets click so rapidly – up to 200 times per second – that the sound appears to be continuous.

Unlike crickets, grasshoppers sing in the daylight. They have a rough 'file' on the inside of their back legs, which they rub along a scraper on the edge of their upper wings. Their calls usually consist of episodes of clickings that are shorter and quieter than those of crickets.

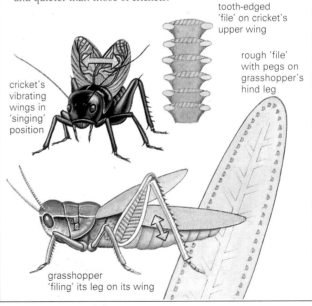

tooth-edged 'file' on cricket's upper wing

cricket's vibrating wings in 'singing' position

rough 'file' with pegs on grasshopper's hind leg

grasshopper 'filing' its leg on its wing

YELLOW-WINGED LOCUST

This widespread grasshopper species is known to everyone who has walked in grassland, because of its habit of making short, darting flights, displaying its bright yellow, black-bordered wings, at the same time making a loud clicking sound.

The male is about 3.5 cm long and the female 5 cm long. The locust is active during the day, feeding on grass. In southern Australia, it produces only one generation a year, but in the warmer north, where there are two generations annually, numbers can build to plague proportions. When the population is low the colour of the grasshopper is predominantly green; in dense populations the colour changes to brown. Yellow-winged locusts are a typical locust shape: compressed from side to side with short antennae and a downward-pointing head.

Scientific name: *Gastrimargus musicus*

SLANT-FACE GRASSHOPPER ■

This large, slender grasshopper, 5–6 cm long, is named for its long head, which comes to a point well above the eyes. It inhabits tall grasslands throughout most of Australia.

Depending on the light, its colour varies from green to pink, making it hard to spot as it clings to swaying stems. When approached the grasshopper takes suddenly to the air, and its large wings, dangling hindlegs and loud clicking noise make it briefly conspicuous before it disappears back into the grass.

Scientific name: *Acrida conica*

LEICHHARDT'S GRASSHOPPER ■

This grasshopper is found only in the escarpment country around Arnhem Land in the Northern Territory. The extremely bold, bright colours of Leichhardt's grasshopper are a warning to predators of the toxins stored in its body from a diet of aromatic or poisonous plants.

Leichhardt's grasshopper is about 4.5 cm long and is a typical grasshopper shape. It appears just before the wet season storms, and so features in Aboriginal lore as a harbinger of thunder.

The explorer Ludwig Leichhardt described the grasshopper in the 1840s, but because of its limited and isolated range it was virtually unseen by Europeans until 1970.

Scientific name: *Petasida ephippigera*

MONKEY GRASSHOPPERS

Monkey grasshoppers, which are 15–40 mm long, are very thin and always wingless, and tend to move more sluggishly than other grasshoppers. About 200 species are found in most parts of Australia, living mostly in trees and shrubs, where they are usually well camouflaged by their green or brown colouring. In dry parts of the country, some species match the brown shades of drying grass.

A very colourful tropical species belonging to the genus *Biroella* has the odd habit of sitting with its rear legs spread apart from its body.

Family: Eumastacidae

■ SLANT-FACE GRASSHOPPER
The slant-face grasshopper varies in colour, depending on where it is. Here, it takes on the straw colour of drying grass, which provides good camouflage.

■ LEICHHARDT'S GRASSHOPPER
One of the most strikingly coloured grasshoppers in Australia is the bold red and blue patterned Leichhardt's grasshopper, pictured here on a leaf.

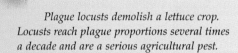

An ancient plague

'And the locusts ... covered the face of the whole Earth, so that the land was darkened ... there remained not any green thing in the trees, or in the herbs of the field, through all the land of Egypt.'
– EXODUS 10:14–15

As the Old Testament writer so eloquently testifies, locusts have been wreaking havoc for many thousands of years. The Australian plague locust (*Chortoicetes terminifera*) is not closely related to the African desert locust (which is probably descended from those that devastated Egypt in the time of Moses), but it does share many of the traits that can lead to serious locust plagues.

Desert-dwelling creatures must make quick, efficient use of the short-lived greening after rain. Most desert-adapted insects quickly grow and lay eggs to await the next green flush, but locusts can produce several consecutive generations at widely spaced feeding areas.

A locust plague can start with an isolated fall of rain in central Australia. The parched earth may already have a previous deposit of locust eggs in a state of arrested development. With the rain, seeds germinate on the surface and the water seeps down to awaken the eggs. The nymphs hatch and feed on young grasses, and then bunch together in long, advancing bands. Locusts respond to rain more quickly than most of their predators, so at this stage they thrive unchecked; at about three weeks most have reached the adult winged stage.

Moving on

Eventually the food becomes too dry to sustain the locusts; at this stage, either they will mate, lay eggs and die where they are, or the weather pattern will alert them to the possibility of rain elsewhere: how the locusts know when to migrate is a mystery, but when they do, it is often to areas where rain has fallen or is about to do so.

The departure of a locust swarm is spectacular. It usually takes place at sunset, and the whole horizon seems to lift, silhouetted against the sky. The locusts ride upper-level winds and fly up to 500 kilometres before landing in a new area.

They have out-raced their predators, and can lay their eggs in the new area in comparative safety. If green food is present, they will stay and lay again; otherwise they migrate once more. They usually migrate eastward or southward, getting closer to crop country with every flight. Each generation swells the

The female locust penetrates the soil to lay her eggs and squirts them with a frothy spume that hardens into a structure called a pod.

Plague locusts demolish a lettuce crop. Locusts reach plague proportions several times a decade and are a serious agricultural pest.

numbers in the swarm by about ten times. In a green year, with three or four generations, swarms reach plague proportions and can devastate grasslands and crops in the east. This is often the delayed price of drought-breaking rains.

Mistakes will happen

The timing of migrations is the key to the development of locust plagues in Australia. Locusts swarm with the assistance of winds at a height of several hundred metres. These winds may be blowing in a completely different direction from lower-level winds, and tend to take the locusts to areas where rain is likely, because migrations often coincide with fronts of low air pressure that generate strong winds carrying humid air.

Occasionally, something goes wrong with this normally perfect timing. In the summer of 1973–74, large locust populations built up in northern and western New South Wales, and were poised for one more migration, which would take them into lush crop country in Victoria. But – luckily for farmers – the weather proved the undoing of the locusts. The air depression was so severe that the locusts were blown along on upper winds of over 100 kilometres an hour, and did not land until they were well out to sea. Fishing boats in Bass Strait reported locusts falling into the sea and becoming food for the fishes, and one swarm flew all the way to Tasmania.

STICK AND LEAF INSECTS

For most stick insects and leaf insects, camouflage is the key to survival. Stick insects (also called phasmids) are very thin and long, and mimic brown or green sticks. Some are broader, spiny or more colourful, which makes them easier to spot, but these species are less common. In Australia leaf insects, which are leaf-shaped, are found only in far north Queensland.

During daylight hours phasmids remain perfectly still, cunningly disguised among the stems and leaves of trees and bushes. Most species tend to feed at night in order to escape detection by birds and lizards. Their diet is not restricted to one plant type but consists of a variety of leaves, which they chew with their well developed mouthparts.

Stick insects grow very slowly, with many species living for about a year. The smallest stick insects are only 3 cm long, while several species

STICK INSECT
The spur-legged stick insect (*Didymuria violescens*) can reach plague proportions and is capable of defoliating whole eucalypt forests. As their numbers increase, stick insects of this species abandon their green and brown camouflage and become more colourful.

SPINY STICK INSECT
The female of the species *Extatosoma tiaratum* has a broader, spinier body than the male. Females are often seen hanging upside down on plants with their abdomen curled over.

grow up to 30 cm long. Females are often much larger than males.

Some arid-zone species, such as the spiky clumped spinifex grass (*Triodia* spp.), are exceptionally thin and look just like certain grasses. *Triodia* is very hard to detect, even though it is about 8 cm long.

About 150 stick insect species are found throughout Australia. Of these, about half can fly and have large, often colourful hindwings, which are usually hidden under drab wing-covers. The others walk on long, spindly legs. In numerous species the females are either short-winged or wingless, and it is up to the males to fly around looking for them. However, if the sexes do not manage to find each other the females may lay unfertilised eggs that produce only females.

A female phasmid lays between 100 and 1000 eggs, which it generally just drops onto the ground from its perch. The eggs often look like seeds, and are so intricate that the species can be identified from the eggs alone. If conditions are poor, hatching can be delayed for several years. When the nymph emerges from the egg, it uncurls a skinny body, which is up to four times the length of its egg.

Some nymphs look like small, wingless adults, while others are quite distinct from adults. A few nymphs imitate ants in order to protect themselves from predators.
Order: Phasmatodea

SPINY STICK INSECT
Probably the best-known Australian stick insect species, spiny stick insects are found along much of the east coast of Australia. Children often keep them as pets. The females are large (16 cm long), wingless, and very broad and spiny. Their brown colour provides good camouflage among leaves and bracken.

Male spiny stick insects are quite rare. Because they are comparatively small (8 cm long), fully winged and skinny, they are easily mistaken for a different species. The newly hatched nymphs are thin and red and black in colour, and they move around with their abdomen curled up.
Scientific name: *Extatosoma tiaratum*

GIANT STICK INSECT
This is the longest stick insect in Australia, and one of the longest in the world. The females are 30 cm long and the males 15 cm long. They are found along the warmer parts of the east coast. Both sexes are winged and can fly. When at rest their mottled brown bodies imitate rough twigs, and their legs are held against their bodies to help the disguise. Their small wing-covers hide surprisingly large purple-brown wings, which they can suddenly unfurl to startle a predator.
Scientific name: *Acrophylla titan*

WEB-SPINNERS

Web-spinners, also called embiids, are one of very few insects that produce silk as adults. Very fine, almost shiny webs on fence posts, tree trunks and rotting timbers, and under stones, are more likely to be embiids' webs than spiders' webs.

Members of this obscure group of 65 species have small (4–15 mm long), elongated, dark bodies. They sometimes have four wings, but are more often wingless. A unique identifying feature of web-spinners is their swollen, bulbous feet.

They live in colonies in complex silken tunnels spun from glands in their front feet. Females care for the eggs inside their webs. Both sexes are adept at running through the web tunnels – both backwards and forwards – when faced with danger.

Adult female web-spinners feed on decaying leaves, mosses and bark. The winged males, which do not feed as adults, are sometimes attracted to lights at night.
Order: Embioptera

TRUE BUGS

Many insects are commonly referred to as 'bugs', but only true bugs have a specialised mouth – a rostrum. The rostrum is a series of sharp, slender tubes used for piercing and sucking. Evolved from chewing mouthparts, the rostrum allows true bugs to exploit otherwise unavailable food sources, such as sap and blood. True bugs include water bugs, plant hoppers, aphids, scale insects, mealy bugs and cicadas.

Most true bugs are herbivores, and many do considerable damage to crops and garden plants. A few are predators, like the assassin bug, which gives a painful, stabbing bite when handled, and some, like the bedbug, are bloodsuckers.

True bugs undergo incomplete, or gradual, metamorphosis (page 521), during which they moult three to seven times. The nymphs usually resemble the adults but in a few groups, such as the cicadas, the young look quite different.
Order: Hemiptera

ASSASSIN BUGS

These bugs (7 mm to 3 cm long) are stealthy hunters of Australia's subtropical and tropical regions, where they feed on other insects. Many assassin bugs are brightly coloured – either red and black or yellow and black – while others are brown or grey. Most emit a foul odour when threatened and can inflict a painful sting with their rostrum.

The bee killer (*Pristhesancus papuensis*) sits on flowering plants and waits for its preferred meal of bees, butterflies and flies. It pounces on its unsuspecting victim and sucks out its body fluids. Some other species, such as *Havinthus rufovarius*, conceal themselves beneath bark during the day and emerge at night to search for prey.

The feather-legged bug (*Ptilocnemus femoratus*) stations itself along an ant trail, raises its long legs to expose a gland, and lies in wait for its prey. When the ant licks the gland, it becomes paralysed and the bug drives its sharp rostrum into the ant, injecting a salivary secretion that liquefies the victim's tissues.
Superfamily: Reduvioidea

CRUSADER BUGS

The best known member of this group is the widely distributed species *Mictis profana*. It is 2.5 cm long, dark brown, and has a yellow cross on its wings, and is often seen flying on sunny days. It feeds on young acacia shoots, sucking the sap and causing the tips to wilt and die back. When threatened, the crusader bug squirts a foul-smelling fluid from the rear of its abdomen.
Family: Coreidae

SHIELD BUGS

Shield bugs are often called stink bugs because of the foul-smelling secretions they spray from their anal glands if they are disturbed.

To reproduce, the male mounts the back of the female and then turns around to continue mating end to end. The female shield bug, well known for her relentless maternal care of the eggs and young nymphs, lays clusters of 50–500 eggs on a branch. After several weeks or months, depending on the season, the tiny nymphs hatch and mass together. They moult several times before reaching maturity.

The cotton harlequin bug (*Tectocoris diophthalmus*) is found in New South Wales and Queensland, feeding on soft-wooded, juicy plants such as cultivated cotton, and native and introduced hibiscuses. The females are usually orange-yellow with dark spots, while the males are iridescent red, blue and green.

The predatory bug (*Cermatulus nasalis*) and the vine-moth bug (*Oechalia schellenbergii*) have strong rostrums that they use to impale unwary prey, especially slow-moving caterpillars. These predatory bugs keep crop pests in check.

Known as the bronze orange bug, the large native species *Musgraveia sulciventris* is commonly found in citrus orchards, where it causes

dieback of young shoots. The harlequin plant bug (*Dindymus versicolor*) is a widely distributed pest of figs, apples, pumpkins and melons, and the introduced green vegetable bug (*Nezara viridula*) is a serious pest of tomatoes, beans and lucerne. *N. viridula* has been dramatically reduced by tiny parasitic wasps.
Superfamily: Pentatomoidea

NEGRO BUGS

Negro bugs, or burrowing bugs, (6 mm long) are black or brown and bear a strong resemblance to some shiny black beetles. With powerful hindlegs and spines designed for digging, they rapidly burrow into soil when threatened. These bugs suck plant juices, and are often seen on flowers. Many species are root feeders and may appear above ground in vast numbers during the summer mating months. At night they congregate in large numbers on the ground beneath electric lights.
Family: Cydnidae

SHIELD BUG
The orange-yellow female cotton harlequin bug, *Tectocoris diophthalmus*, is known for the way she guards her cluster of eggs. The smaller male has bright red, blue and green markings.

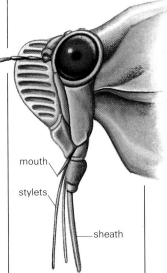
mouth
stylets
sheath

FEEDING STRAWS
The true bug's rostrum is drawn here to show the stylets – sharp 'straws' that penetrate tissue. In a living bug the stylets are enclosed in the sheath and dart from its tip to pierce and suck.

ASSASSIN BUG
An assassin bug pounces on an unsuspecting caterpillar and sucks the fluid from its body.

BEDBUGS

Bedbugs are small (2–5 mm long), flat bloodsuckers that hide in cracks and crevices during the day, coming out at night. Only one introduced species, *Cimex lectularius*, is known in Australia. Although bedbugs became rare due to better hygiene, their numbers have recently been increasing, brought in by travellers.
Superfamily: Cimicoidea

WATER BUGS ■

Water bugs are found in creeks and billabongs throughout Australia. Many are excellent swimmers, and certain species can remain under-water for long periods by carrying supplies of oxygen beneath their wing-covers. Water bugs feed on both live and drowned insects.

Water striders (family Gerridae), about 10 mm long, have long, slender legs for gliding in short bursts of speed across the water surface. They are so light that they do not break the water's surface tension.

Water boatmen (family Corixidae) also reach up to 10 mm in length, but swim using their paddle-like rear legs. Water boatmen are often confused with back-swimmers (family Notonectidae), which are up to 15 mm long, but back-swimmers swim on their backs and use their elongated hind legs like oars.

The great water bug, or fish killer (*Lethocerus insulanus*), feeds on small fishes and tadpoles. This huge bug, 5–7 cm long, is attracted to electric lights and may fly into car head-lights near water. *Diplonychus rusticus* is another large water bug from the same group. The female of this species seizes the male (4 cm long) when she is ready to lay her eggs and cements them to his back, where he carries them until they hatch.

■ MALE WATER BUG
In an unusual division of labour, the male great water bug carries the eggs on its back until they hatch.

■ LEAF-HOPPER
The bright green *Siphanta acuta* has broad, triangular wings, which it holds tent-like above its abdomen.

The water scorpion (*Laccotrephes tristis*), sometimes called the toe biter, is about 4 cm long and lives in the mud and among aquatic vegetation. Its stout forelegs are adapted for seizing and holding prey, and it has been known to nip the toes of humans squelching their way through mud. Its long, flexible tail, which makes it look a little like a scorpion, pokes out of the water and serves as a breathing tube. It lays its eggs on submerged plant stems and pieces of wood.
Superfamilies: Ochteoroidea, Nepoidea, Notonectoidea, Gericoidea, Corixoidea

LEAF-HOPPERS AND TREE-HOPPERS ■

Leaf-hoppers and tree-hoppers are widely distributed throughout Australia. The family Eurymelidae are strikingly coloured insects, 1–2 cm long, varying in colour from dark, iridescent blue with bright yellow, red and white patches to less flamboyant pastel shades. Those from the family Membracidae often have bizarre body shapes, prominent spines and ornamental 'horns'.

One of the most common hoppers, the gumtree hopper from the genus *Eurymela*, feeds on eucalypts and casuarinas. The females of these hoppers slit the tree bark in rows with their spear-shaped egg-laying organ (ovipositor), causing the trees to bleed and produce large quantities of weeping gum that sets hard in the sunshine. The females lay one egg in every slit. In warm weather the eggs hatch and the nymphs and adults crowd together on the stems.

Another well-known hopper is the green tree-hopper, *Sextius virescens*, which feeds on acacias, especially black wattle trees.

Leaf-hoppers are mostly small, green or yellowish-coloured insects. All seem to delight in sidling around the stems of plants. If disturbed, they can hop up to half a metre effortlessly. Many damage plants by drinking the sap and laying their eggs in the shoots, and in so doing can spread disease-carrying organisms to cultivated crops.

Tree-hoppers are often attended by ants, which feed on the sweet honeydew that they secrete. In return, the presence of the ants helps to protect the tree-hoppers from would-be predators.

Along bush trails in tropical and subtropical Australia, you may catch a glimpse of the familiar moth-like passion-vine hopper, *Scolypopa australis*, a member of the Raniciidae family. Its clear wings are heavily barred with black or brown. The nymphs and adults sit in rows along the stems of passion vines and other plants. The bright green species *Siphanta acuta* feeds on eucalypt leaves and is frequently seen in domestic gardens.
Superfamily: Cicadelloidea

SPITTLE BUGS ■

Spittle bugs, or froghoppers, feed on the sap of native plants. Although they are closely related to cicadas physically, their lifestyles are vastly different. Throughout the spittle bug's immature stages, the nymphs

■ SPITTLE BUGS
Spittle bug larvae cocoon themselves in a frothy substance, resembling spittle, which is often seen on plants.

cover themselves in a frothy, sticky fluid that protects them against enemies and the drying effects of the sun and the wind. As they reach maturity, the frothy mass shrinks.

When the adult insects emerge from their nymphal skin and their wings have dried, they jump about and take to the air.
Superfamily: Cercopoidea

LERP INSECTS

During their immature stages, lerp insects secrete sugary shelters called lerps that are often beautiful and intricate in design. The lerp of *Prototyora sterculiae* is shaped like a star; that of *Rhinocola costata* is scallop-shaped; that of *Eucalyptolyma maideni* looks like a tiny fern-frond; and *Cardiaspis tetrix* builds a covering of fine golden threads, rather like a miniature bird cage.

The lerp insects themselves are rarely seen. The adult female never leaves her shelter, but the male can fly – and does so to find a mate.

The sugar lerp insect, *Spondyliaspis eucalypti*, is the most widely distributed lerp in Australia. Many of its cone-shaped white lerps may be packed onto a single eucalypt leaf. When dislodged by birds or ants, or when their life cycle is complete, they fall to the ground and are popularly called manna. Aboriginal children relish their sugary coatings, steeping them in water to make a sweet drink.
Superfamily: Psylloidea

APHIDS ■

Aphids are usually green, pink or black and 1.5–8 mm long. Those known as greenflies are widespread pests of flowers, fruit trees and vegetables. About 157 species, many of which were introduced, have been recorded in Australia. Aphids use the protection offered by a strong

guard of ants and, like leaf-hoppers and tree-hoppers, they exude a sweet liquid honeydew to attract ants. An enormous number of aphids are destroyed by ladybird beetle larvae, as well as by minute parasitic wasps.

One of the most remarkable attributes of aphids is their rate of reproduction. Most aphids produce seven or more generations a year, depending on environmental and climatic conditions, and their numbers can increase at such a rate that literally millions may develop on a single shrub or tree.
Superfamily: Aphidoidea

MEALY BUGS

Oval-shaped, segmented female mealy bugs are seen on eucalypts during summer, often accompanied by ants. The male is so small and different that it may not be associated with the female. Mealy bugs, which vary in length from 1 mm to 1.5 cm, feed on plant juices.

Much larger than the males, the females are wingless and covered in white scales. After several moults they become immobile, and the tiny winged males fly onto the plants to mate with them. The eggs are usually incubated beneath the fleshy female. When she dies and falls to the ground, the exposed young nymphs are dispersed by winds to nearby plants.
Superfamily: Coccoidea

■ APHIDS
These tiny insects, some known as greenflies, are winged or wingless according to the season. Aphids often reproduce by parthenogenesis, in which 'stem mothers' produce young without male intervention.

■ CICADA
Colourful *Cyclochila australasiae* is one of Australia's best-known cicada species. It has several nicknames – 'blue prince' or 'masked devil' would suit this impressive specimen.

CICADAS ■

There are over 200 species of cicadas in Australia, all native to the country. They are the largest Australian hemipterans, and, like all of them, they have specialised piercing and sucking mouthparts, called rostrums (page 533). Their large compound eyes and three simple eyes (ocelli) are often prominent. Cicadas can be from 12 mm to 8 cm long. Some species are well known for their loud mating calls in summer.

The life cycle of the cicada begins when the female responds to the male's call. She finds him by circling the tree or shrub on the wing.

Mating can take several hours. Afterwards, the female cuts numerous slits in a branch with her spear-like egg-laying organ (ovipositor), and into these she lays her eggs. A few weeks later a shower of tiny nymphs fall to the ground, where they quickly burrow into the soil.

Most of a cicada's life is spent underground. Small cicadas have an annual cycle, but larger ones may spend several years below ground, feeding on the sap of tree roots. During warm weather, mature nymphs make their way to the surface, sometimes remaining just below it, waiting for favourable weather conditions. When they are ready, they climb the first upright support available, usually under the cover of night, and shed their nymphal skins. Slowly they unfurl their beautiful soft, moist wings. An hour or so later, the wings are dry and hard, and the cicadas climb or fly away, leaving their dried nymphal shells clinging to tree trunks.

Many birds feed on cicadas, as do cane toads, frogs, reptiles, predatory arthropods and insectivorous mammals, such as bats.

The cicadas that we are used to hearing belong to the Cicadidae family. Most have smooth, colourful bodies and are fitted with sound-making equipment. One well-known species, *Cyclochila australasiae*, has many colour variations. Among its common names are the green grocer, the yellow Monday, the masked devil (yellow with black mask), the blue prince and the chocolate soldier. Another member of this family is the large (8 cm) double drummer (*Thopha saccata*) and the floury baker (*Abricta curvicosta*), both of which make distinctive calls. The floury baker sounds like a scissors grinder, and the call of the double drummer is unmistakably loud.

Members of another family, the Tettigarctidae, are known as hairy cicadas because they are covered by short brown hairs. Hairy cicadas are found only in the high snow country of Australia, and just two species are known. They were probably more diverse and abundant before the continent warmed up. Unlike their more advanced relatives, they are completely silent.
Supertamily: Cicadoidea

THRIPS

Thrips are closely related to the true bugs. There are 400 introduced and native species in Australia. They are tiny (0.5–2 mm) insects with narrow, strap-like wings fringed with long hairs. To help them adhere to plants they have small balloon-like bladders at the ends of their legs that provide suction. They have relatively weak mouthparts that are adapted to piercing and rasping on living tissue, usually of plants and fungi, but occasionally of small insects and mites.

Some thrips live in leaf debris, but they are known to horticulturists and gardeners as annoying pests that damage fruit, vegetables and shrubs, and spread plant viruses. They feed on leaves or in the buds of flowers, impairing fruit development. Cultivated fruit trees, onions, cotton, cereal and tobacco crops are all attacked by thrips. Some native species feed on the flower nectar of eucalypts; others, like the plague thrips (*Thrips imaginis*), have developed a taste for flowers such as apple blossom and roses.

Adults are usually dark, and nymphs are pale, often white. After several moults, nymphs cease feeding and pupate in the ground. They emerge as adults and lay their eggs.

Thrips are not strong fliers and rely on air currents to transport them to new feeding areas. You can hijack them by flapping washing on a clothes line – flick them off, only to see them settle again.
Order: Thysanoptera

SOUND SYSTEM

Male cicadas sing to attract females. On each side of the male's body, an upper flap and a lower flap protect an internal chamber. The upper chamber contains a ribbed membrane, the tymbal, as the sound-producing structure and the lower pair contains a stretched membrane, the tympanum, as the sound-detecting organ. The latter is also present in females, which have more directional hearing than males. The species-specific song is produced by complex patterns of buckling of the individual ribs of the tymbals, which are amplified by a cavernous air space in the abdomen of males.

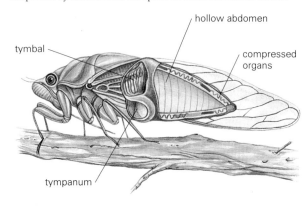

hollow abdomen
tymbal
compressed organs
tympanum

■ CICADA NYMPHS
The nymphs wait for warm conditions before emerging from the ground to shed their skins on tree trunks. They fly away as soon as their wings are dry.

LACEWINGS ◾

Lacewings are delicate, elongated insects with wingspans of 5 mm to 12 cm. Their wings are large and conspicuously veined, and are held roof-like above their body. They have bright, jewel-like compound eyes, which may be ruby red, blue or golden. Adult lacewings have soft exoskeletons and biting mouthparts. Some are equipped with raptorial forelimbs, which they hold in the prayer-like pose of praying mantids. All lacewings undergo complete metamorphosis (page 521).

Australian lacewings occur from deserts to subalpine regions, and many live in open woodlands and orchards near fresh water. Adults rest on flowers, leaves and bark. They are mainly nocturnal, and they often fly around electric lights during spring and summer evenings.

Unlike the delicate adults, the larvae of lacewings are robust, with conspicuous jaws. Some live in sandy soils, some on plants, some in termite mounds, and a few are semi-aquatic. All are active predators. Plant-dwellers feed on aphids and moths' eggs, piercing them with their long, curved jaws. The aquatic larvae feed on freshwater sponges. Many larvae can survive without food for up to two years.

Lacewings mate during warm weather and before rain. Their eggs are oval to spherical and are laid singly or in clusters, often on long stalks. The stalks are formed by the female exuding a drop of viscid fluid from the end of her abdomen. This fluid is drawn out into a fine thread that quickly hardens on contact with the air. An egg is immediately attached to the end of each supporting stalk. These stalks prevent the larvae eating one another after hatching.

The eggs of the lacewing *Nymphes myrmeleonides* resemble a pearl necklace and adhere to rocks and tree trunks near streams. The embryos of some species are equipped with an egg-breaker. This hard ridge is located on the shoulders of the embryo and is used to cut the embryo clear of the egg. Lacewings greatly benefit humans because their larvae destroy many pest insects, such as aphids, scale insects, mites and moths' eggs In some species the larvae, called antlions, dig conical pits in sandy soil to trap unwary pedestrians, especially ants.
Order: Neuroptera

◾ YELLOW-BODIED LACEWING
Many lacewing species are highly coloured, with gauze-like wings and large antennae. In flight they often resemble damselflies and dragonflies.

ALDERFLIES ◾

Alderflies closely resemble lacewings but have a softer, more flexible abdomen and wings that fold flat along the body. They have large, bulging, compound eyes, accompanied by three simple eyes, (ocelli), long antennae, and short legs with simple claws. Their wingspans range from 1 cm to 16 cm, and their mouthparts are well developed with strong jaws.

Of the 300 species described worldwide, only 20 are known in Australia. The widely distributed family Corydalidae is well represented in Australia; its most notable and colourful member is the large, handsome dobsonfly (*Archichauliodes guttiferus*). The black spots and splashes on the amber wings of this species are very noticeable as it rests on plants along riverbanks during the summer and autumn months.

Alderflies of the *Archichauliodes* genus mate facing in opposite directions on shrubs and trees overhanging rivers and creeks. The female lays her eggs, in clusters of several thousands, in cool, shaded areas. When the larvae hatch they tumble into the water, where they hide in the sediments. Furnished with long segmented gills, they scramble around the muddy bottom, pursuing tiny aquatic insects, such as mosquito larvae. After three years, they swim and crawl to the margins of the creek during high water and hide beneath fallen timber and rocks. When the water level drops, the alderfly larvae form mud-cells in the soil, where they pupate.

At dusk adult alderflies take to the wing in large numbers and fly above water, where they are heavily preyed upon by frogs, toads, lizards, and numerous predatory insects and spiders. Trout feed on both the larval and adult forms.
Order: Megaloptera

◾ ALDERFLY
Alderflies have large, delicate, semi-transparent wings with black veins. They are found only in cool climates, such as mountainous regions of south-eastern Australia, and Tasmania.

BEETLES

Nearly one in every three animal species is a beetle. If you set out to photograph a different Australian species every day of your life, you would be over 80 before you could snap them all! Land clearing, pesticide use and excessive collecting may have led to the extinction of some species already. A number of beetles are unique to Australia.

The largest beetles are as big as an adult's size eight shoe and as wide as an adult's hand; the smallest are smaller than a pinhead. All beetles have four wings. The elytra, or outer two wings, protect the softer inner wings, which are used for flying, and the tiny pores called spiracles through which beetles breathe.

Although most beetles are black or brown, some have brightly coloured outer wings. Beetles grow by complete metamorphosis (page 521), starting life as an egg, which hatches into a grub, then becomes a pupa, and finally an adult.
Order: Coleoptera

GROUND BEETLES
Only about half of the known Australian species in this family live on the ground. Of these, a quarter live on trees, logs and leaves and the other quarter on the edges of waterways or in swamps. Distributed throughout Australia, they vary greatly in size, from a few millimetres to several centimetres.

■ SCARAB BEETLES
Male scarab beetles, like many other insects, compete for mates. They are attracted by the female's pheromones.

Many ground beetles have long, slender legs and can pursue their prey quickly. Most are black and shiny, but some, such as the green carab beetle (*Calosoma schayeri*) are brightly coloured. They feed mainly on other small animals, which they catch with their prominent jaws. When threatened, the black and yellow bombardier beetle (*Pheropsophus verticalis*) releases a cloud of gas from its rear with a distinct 'pop'.
Family: Carabidae

ROVE BEETLES
Although rove beetles are sometimes confused with earwigs, they have no pincers. They are small (usually less than 1 cm), and their shortened wing cases cover only part of their long, slender bodies.

Many catch other small animals for food. The devil's coach-horse (*Creophilous erythrocephalus*), a black beetle with an orange head and a black spot between its eyes, is often found in animal corpses, hunting for maggots. A few species of rove beetles, known as inquillines, live in ant nests and are accepted by the ants.
Family: Staphylinidae

STAG BEETLES ■
Mainly found in the wetter parts of Australia, stag beetles may be large and brightly coloured. Their thorax is often broader than their abdomen, and their jaws are usually large. The adults are mainly active at night; the larvae live in rotten wood.
Family: Lucanidae

PASSALID BEETLES
Most passalids live in northern Australia in tunnels in rotten logs, where they break down dead timber. They have shiny, black, flattened bodies, and some have horns. Both adults and larvae make sounds, the adults by rubbing part of their hindwings against their abdomen, the larvae by rubbing the stump of their hindlegs against their middle legs.
Family: Passalidae

DUNG RECYCLERS
Australia's dung beetles evolved to eat the dung pellets of marsupials. One species, *Macroprocopris symbioticus*, lives in the anus of kangaroos and wallabies, holding on with large, hooked claws. When Europeans introduced cattle to Australia, the Australian dung beetle (shown below) couldn't cope with the dung that accumulated on rangelands, encouraging pests. Two beetles – the humpbacked dung beetle (*Onthophagus binodis*) and the bullhorned dung beetle (*Onthophagus taurus*) – were imported to break down the dung. These beetles destroy cattle dung pads, helping to control pests and recycle valuable nutrients.

■ STAG BEETLE PUPA
Stag beetles are found mainly in the wetter parts of Australia, where the larvae inhabit rotten wood. Pictured here is the pupa of *Rhyssonotus nebulosus*, cocooned inside a rainforest log.

SCARAB BEETLES

One of the largest of the beetle families, scarabs are stout and powerful. Although they often seem clumsy, they dig and fly well. Some are black, some brown, and others a vibrant green. Their hidden larvae feed on plant roots, dung and decaying animal matter.

Christmas beetles (*Anoplognathus* spp.) are perhaps the best known scarabs. They live mostly in eucalypt forests and woodlands along the east coast of Australia. Male rhinoceros or elephant beetles (subfamily Dynastinae) have curved horns. They are most abundant in northern and western Australia.
Family: Scarabaeidae

JEWEL BEETLES

These brilliantly coloured beetles, many with dominant shades of red, orange or yellow, and stripes or spots with a metallic sheen, are now protected in many states because of unscrupulous collecting. They are oval in shape, 8–30 mm long and widely distributed, especially in south-western Western Australia. The adult beetles fly strongly and are often active in hot weather, when they can be found on nectar-bearing flowers. Birds and other predators that find their bright colours attractive avoid them because they taste of bitter chemicals called buprestins.
Family: Buprestidae

CLICK BEETLES

Many species of these slender, elongated beetles are nocturnal and attracted to lights. They vary in size and are widely distributed throughout Australia.

If a click beetle falls on its back, it springs right side up with a loud click. It performs this 'trick' by means of special notches on the underside of its thorax. Some click beetle larvae, known as 'wireworms', are pests of crops.
Family: Elateridae

FIREFLIES

Despite their name, these insects are not flies but beetles. While they are flying at night they flash their luminescent abdomens to attract mates. Australian fireflies are rust-coloured, small (1–2 cm) and elongated, the body narrowing just before the point of attachment of the wing cases.
Family: Lampyridae

SOLDIER BEETLES

Soldier beetles are closely related to fireflies. They are 3–20 mm long, soft-bodied, and often yellow, black

and bluish-black. Found along the coast, especially of south-eastern Australia, they are active during the day, feeding on pollen, nectar, foliage, and occasionally other insects. Their bodies contain chemicals that predators, such as birds, quickly learn to avoid. The predatory larvae occur in leaf litter.
Family: Cantharidae

DERMESTID BEETLES

These small (2–10 mm), compact beetles are found throughout Australia. The larvae feed on animal corpses, hair or feathers. Many are pests: the museum beetle (*Anthrenus museorum*) destroys museum specimens; the black carpet beetle (*Attagenus unicolor*) ravages woollen

carpets; the larder beetle (*Dermestes lardarius*) contaminates stored food.
Family: Dermestidae

FURNITURE BEETLES

These dark-coloured beetles are about 5 mm long. The larvae tend to bore into the wood or bark of dead trees, a habit that can make them pests of furniture and house timbers. One species feeds on insect remains in spider nests. They are found in woods, forests and residential areas throughout Australia.
Family: Anobiidae

AUGER BEETLES

Black or brown augur beetles (3–22 mm long) are found in woodlands, forests and residential areas

JEWEL BEETLES
In Western Australia, male jewel beetles (*Julodimorpha bakewelli*) sometimes try to mate with discarded beer bottles, because the bottles resemble large female beetles. This attraction may prevent the males from mating normally.

CLICK BEETLE
The painted click beetle (*Ophidius histrio*) is found in Queensland and New South Wales. Click beetles are named for their clicking mechanism, which they use to right themselves if they tumble over and as a means of escape.

throughout Australia. They burrow into dying or newly felled trees, feeding on starch or sugar.

Australia has three major introduced auger beetle pests: the bamboo borer (*Dinoderus minutus*), which attacks cane furniture; the powderpost beetle (*Lyctus brunneus*), which can destroy structural house timber; and the lesser grain borer (*Rhyzopertha dominica*), which feeds on stored grain. The largest native species is the large auger beetle (*Bostrychopis jesuita*), which attacks wattles and eucalypts. Males of the two-spined auger beetle (*Xylobosca bispinosa*) block tunnel entrances with their wing cases to protect females as they lay their eggs.
Family: Bostrychidae

CLERID BEETLES
These beetles (3–20 mm long) may be brown, black, or a metallic green or blue, sometimes with a pattern. Nearly all adult and larval clerid species are predators, some invading the tunnels of auger beetles, others living in termite nests or carrion. Found throughout Australia, some species are introduced, some native.
Family: Cleridae

NITIDULID BEETLES
Nitidulids are small, flat beetles that eat rotten fruit, flowers, fungi, seeds and tree wounds. Some prey on the tiny scale insects that feed on plants. The introduced dried-fruit beetles (*Carpophilus* spp.), which are pests that devour stored dried fruit, sometimes eat fruit in orchards. Mostly brown or black, but sometimes bicoloured, nitidulids are distributed throughout Australia.
Family: Nitidulidae

■ LADYBIRD FEEDING
Ladybirds are useful biological controls because they eat insect pests. Australian species imported to California and Hawaii have been particularly successful in controlling the scale pests that suck sap from fruit trees. The bright orange spotted *Harmonia conformis* is shown here devouring an adult aphid.

LADYBIRDS ■
The larvae and adults of most ladybirds eat a range of plant pests, although some species do eat plants. Found throughout Australia, they are about 5 mm long, round, glossy and brightly coloured, often with spots. Some Australian species are used as biological control agents.
Family: Coccinellidae

TENEBRIONID BEETLES
Tenebrionids are smallish black beetles that live mainly on plant material and fungi. Adapted to arid environments, they survive well in many parts of Australia.

One of the most unusual tenebrionids is the pie-dish beetle (*Helaeus* spp.), named for its flat, plate-like shape. The yellow mealworm (*Tenebrio molitor*), sold as bird food, is a larval tenebrionid; other species, such as the confused flour beetle (*Tribolium confusum*) and the rust-red flour beetle (*Tribolium castaneum*), are pests that attack stored foods.
Family: Tenebrionidae

RHIPIPHORIDAN BEETLES
These dull-coloured beetles have parasitic larvae. When they hatch in flowers, on the underside of leaves or in soil, the larvae attach themselves to solitary bees or to wasps. They are carried to the nest, where they live on wasp larvae. Others parasitise cockroaches. Rhipiphordans occur throughout Australia.
Family: Rhipiphoridae

LONGICORN BEETLES ■
Longicorns (1–3 cm long) are black or brown beetles with antennae at least two-thirds the length of their bodies. The larvae eat bark, sap or heartwood. Some longicorns make squeaking sounds, either to alarm predators or attract a mate. They occur throughout Australia.
Family: Cerambycidae

LEAF BEETLES
Closely related to longicorn beetles, leaf beetles vary in size from 1 mm to 2.5 cm, and in colour, including some brilliant blues or greens. Found throughout Australia, they have elongated or rounded bodies.

The adults and larvae feed mainly on leaves. Some, such as the eucalyptus tortoise beetle (*Paropsis atomaria*), produce deadly hydrogen cyanide from special defence glands to repel bird attacks. The Tasmanian eucalyptus leaf beetle (*Chrysoph-tharta bimaculata*) defoliates eucalypt trees and can cause serious damage.
Family: Chrysomelidae

■ LONGICORN BEETLE
Adult longicorns often feed at night on flowers, foliage and bark.

WEEVILS ■
There are more species of weevil than of any other type of beetle. Found throughout Australia, they are 1 mm to 30 cm long and mostly black, brown or grey. They feed on plants and grain and can be serious pests. Most of Australia's native species perform important roles in breaking down dead timber and pollinating some native plants. When hoop pine plantations were established, the pine bark weevil (*Aesiotes notabilis*) became a pest of its host.
Superfamily: Curculionoidea

WHIRLIGIG BEETLES
These 2 cm-long black beetles swim on the surface of water, often in groups. Sometimes confused with other water-dwelling beetles, they can be recognised by their eyes, which have upper and lower parts. While adults eat insects that fall into the water, the larvae breathe with gills and eat other invertebrates.
Family: Gyrinidae

■ DIAMOND WEEVIL
This exceptional blue or green weevil shows the characteristic elongated snout (rostrum), ending in jaws.

SCORPION FLIES AND HANGING FLIES

There are about 500 species of the mecopteran group in the world and most come from just two families: the scorpion flies (Panorpidae) and the hanging flies (Bittacidae). Scorpion flies are named after the way the tip of the male's abdomen curls upward like a scorpion's sting, although it cannot sting. Hanging flies dangle from plants while holding on by their fore- or hindlegs. They are called flies but they are not true flies at all.

Mecopterans have two pairs of membranous wings, a long beak-shaped head, long thin antennae, and, in some species, long legs. They undergo complete metamorphosis (page 521). Many of the larvae live in moss or leaf litter, preying on other insects or scavenging on insect bodies. Some shelter in short burrows, surfacing only to feed. They pupate in the burrow. Most adults are predatory, catching other arthropods, such as flies, moths, bees, various larvae and spiders. Others eat nectar or other fluids, plant material, or dead insects. They mostly occur in moist environments, although some live in semi-desert areas.

Some mecopterans are remarkable for their reproductive behaviour, which involves elaborate courtship.

Males emit pheromones that draw females from long distances. When a female approaches, the male offers her a prey as a gift. She may accept the gift and mate with him or reject it and fly away. Some males masquerade as females, tricking suitors into offering them a meal. Since males do most of the hunting and so are most at risk of being captured by spiders or other enemies, perhaps this is a sly way of avoiding the dangers of catching their own meal.
Order: Mecoptera

FLEAS

All fleas are parasitic, living on the bodies of mammals and birds, and sucking their blood with needle-like projections called stylets.

Fleas can be as small as a pinhead, and their spiny, toughened, wingless bodies are flattened from side to side so that they can slip easily through the hairs or feathers of their hosts. Their forelegs, too, are modified for pushing through hair and feathers and their well developed knee and hip joints are designed to allow them to jump great distances.

Less than 100 of the approximately 2400 species of fleas in the world

■ SCORPION FLIES MATING
The male scorpion fly entices the female to mate by offering her food. He uses his long legs to transfer the prey from his mouth to hers during mating.

live in Australia, but most are unique to this country.

Fleas undergo complete metamorphosis (page 521). The eggs are laid on the host or in its nest, but the hatched larvae are not blood-suckers like their parents. They feed on organic debris in the bedding or nest of their host. After pupation, the new adult emerges to find a host.

The larvae, pupae and adults can all survive for long periods in harsh conditions without food. For example, pupae of the oriental rat flea (*Xenopsylla cheopis*) may live for up to a year waiting for the arrival of a suitable host. This is why people are sometimes plagued by fleas when they move into a deserted house: flea pupae present in carpets or between floorboards emerge as adults as soon as new hosts arrive.

Fleas are probably best known for the diseases they transmit. The human flea (*Pulex irritans*), the cat flea (*Ctenocephalides felis*) and the dog flea (*Ctenocephalides canis*) can all cause severe irritations if their hosts become sensitised to their bites. Bubonic plague can be transmitted from rats to humans by the bite of the oriental rat flea (*Xenopsylla cheopis*), but there have been very few outbreaks in Australia.

Fleas can be useful. In 1966 the European rabbit flea (*Spilopsyllus cuniculi*) was introduced into Australia to spread myxomatosis among the rabbit population. For some years the disease helped to control rabbit numbers, but it seems that rabbits have now developed an immunity to the infection.
Order: Siphonaptera

PERFORMING FLEAS
Fleas can jump extraordinary distances. They have well-developed hip and knee joints and, more importantly, an energy-releasing protein in their large hind legs. This superelastic substance, called resilin, is responsible for their amazing agility.

STYLOPS

Stylops are a small order of insects with about 500 species, of which fewer than 30 are Australian. They are parasitic on some insects and have unusual life cycles. The following is typical of some, but not all, species. The larvae emerge live from their mother's body. Active and fast-running, they seek out hosts, bore into them and then become legless, feeding and growing in the host's tissues. Males leave their host to pupate, emerging as adults with one pair of flight wings. The female lures the male by emitting a pheromone, which he detects with his antennae. Mating takes place on the host's body and the life cycle continues.
Order: Strepsiptera

■ MARCH FLY
The female march fly, or horse fly, feeds on blood, but the larger male, shown here, sucks all the nourishment it needs from plants.

TRUE FLIES

The flight mechanism of flies is energy-efficient and a brilliant example of natural aero-dynamics. Most insects fly with two pairs of wings, but flies use only the front pair. Their hindwings have evolved into small, club-like protuberances called halteres, which balance and stabilise the fly while aloft.

Flies undergo complete metamorphosis through the four life stages of egg, larva, pupa and adult (page 521). The larval stage of many flies is the maggot, and it is responsible for the evolutionary success of many fly families. Maggots can develop with remarkable speed, and so can take advantage of temporary nutrient-rich environments such as rotting fruit, excrement and carrion.

Several families of flies affect animals, including humans. Females of many biting flies, such as mosquitoes, need blood to produce eggs. Some flies transmit disease-causing organisms through their saliva, while others pick up such organisms from carrion, excrement and human garbage and carry them to new areas. Despite these problem flies, many others play an important role

in food webs, as both pollinators and controllers of other insect pests.

Flies are found in almost all habitats, including seashores, deserts, high mountains and polar regions, and many have immature stages that are aquatic. Some 110 000 species have been described worldwide, but probably several times that number await discovery. In Australia more than 7000 species have been described, but undoubtedly more than 20 000 live here. A few of the 90 families that occur in Australia are described below.
Order: Diptera

MOSQUITOES

Mosquitoes are 4–6 mm long and delicate, with scaly wings and a long proboscis. Adults of both sexes suck plant juices, but only females take blood as nutrients for their eggs.

The early stages of a mosquito's development occur in fresh or brackish water. The eggs are often laid in a floating raft and hatch into larvae, or 'wrigglers'. The larvae take in air through a siphon on their abdomen and must come periodically to the surface to breathe. Most larvae feed on algae and other small food particles, but some species prey on other mosquito larvae. The pupae float just beneath the water surface. When they emerge as adults, they climb onto their floating pupal skins and rest before flying away. There are approximately 250 species of mosquitoes in Australia. Females of most species feed on mammals and birds, while others take blood from reptiles and amphibians.

Mosquitoes carry a number of organisms that cause disease in humans: malaria, which is carried by *Anopheles* species, is no longer a problem in Australia, but there are occasional outbreaks of mosquito-borne Murray Valley encephalitis, dengue fever and epidemic polyarthritis. Mosquitoes carry dog heartworm, and they can transmit myxomatosis to rabbits.
Family: Culicidae

TRUE MIDGES

True midges occur in large numbers on warm summer evenings near fresh water and around lights. Adults (3–5 mm) resemble mosquitoes, but they do not bite. The aquatic larvae, some of which are called bloodworms, feed mostly on detritus and algae. They are a major food source for fish and other aquatic animals. One species damages rice seedlings in New South Wales.
Family: Chironomidae

GALL MIDGES

Gall midges are minute, delicate flies with long legs and antennae. Most have plant-feeding larvae that form tiny galls (swellings) on stems and leaves. Other larvae prey on aphids or are scavengers in decaying organic matter. They are abundant but not well known in Australia.
Family: Cecidomyiidae

BITING MIDGES

Biting midges are very small (often less than 1 mm long). Females of most species require a blood meal. They can be serious pests, especially near the coast, and their ability to pass through most screening has earned them the nickname 'no-see-ums'. Biting midges may cause allergic reactions and swelling. Some species take blood from the wing veins of large insects such as dragonflies. The larvae, found in creeks, mud, tree holes and brackish estuaries, are aquatic or semi-aquatic.
Family: Ceratopogonidae

MARCH FLIES ■

March flies, or horse flies, are up to 3 cm long. They are ferocious biters, and are particularly abundant near creeks and swamps, where their aquatic larvae develop. Their huge compound eyes often have a green iridescence, earning them the name 'greenheads'. As with most biting flies, only the female uses its proboscis to take blood.
Family: Tabanidae

CRANE FLIES

Crane flies, 1–2 cm long, are common in moist forests and gardens. With more than 800 species, they are one of the largest fly families in Australia. Their long, thin legs have earned them the name 'daddy longlegs', which they share with harvestmen and a common spider species.

Craneflies are sometimes mistaken for giant mosquitoes, but they do not bite. Adults may bob up and down on their legs, as if they are doing push-ups. The larvae may be found in soil and mud, and some species damage cultivated plants.
Family: Tipulidae

BLACK OR SAND FLIES

These small (3–4 mm) humpbacked flies gather around fast-flowing streams. The females of most species require a blood meal, and in early summer they can be ferocious biters of humans and livestock. The larvae cling to rocks and filter food from the passing current.
Family: Simuliidae

VAMPIRE INSECTS
The blood that the female mosquito sucks provides her eggs with important nutrients. The harmless male is not a blood-sucker.

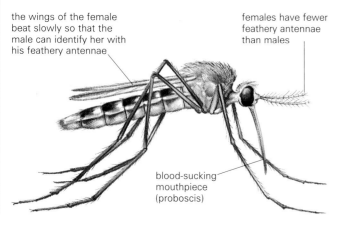

the wings of the female beat slowly so that the male can identify her with his feathery antennae

females have fewer feathery antennae than males

blood-sucking mouthpiece (proboscis)

FUNGUS GNATS

The larvae of most fungus gnats feed on fungi, such as mushrooms. The adults are small (5–10 mm), and are rather weak fliers. They are found primarily in moist forests.

The most remarkable members of the family are glow-worms, the light-producing larvae of the genus *Arachnocampa*. Known only from Australia and New Zealand, glow-worms are found in caves, rock overhangs, abandoned mines, and even moist, shaded road cuts. In the dark they emit a dull yellow light from luminescent organs at the tip of their abdomen. The light attracts tiny flying insect prey, which become entangled in mucilaginous webs secreted by the larvae.
Family: Mycetophilidae

ROBBER FLIES

Most adult robber flies are medium sized, but they can be quite large, with wingspans of up to 7.5 centimetres. They are often seen on twigs or tree trunks, waiting to swoop and capture prey in mid-air. The larvae, usually found in sandy soil, are also predatory. Australia has more than 600 species of robber flies.
Family: Asilidae

WATER CRUISERS

Water cruisers (3–8 mm long), which are sometimes called dance flies, are often seen flying back and forth over streams and pools. These flies are predatory, and the males of some species catch large insect prey to attract the females. On mating, the prey is transferred to the female, who takes the protein meal while coupling. This ritualised behaviour involves the male wrapping the prey in silk secreted by special glands on his forelegs. Some males trick females by wrapping flower petals or pieces of debris in silk, or even weaving an empty silken balloon so that the female gets nothing.
Family: Empididae

BEE FLIES

Bee flies are 5–30 mm long, densely hairy and robust. Adults are swift-flying nectar feeders, commonly seen hovering in front of flowers in open sunny areas.

Eggs are very small and females produce them in large numbers. After hatching, the young larvae actively search for other insect eggs or larvae to parasitise. Because of their larval habits, bee flies destroy many insect pests, and adults are important pollinators of plants.
Family: Bombyliidae

LONG-LEGGED FLIES

Long-legged flies (1–7 mm) are metallic blue-green with swept-back wings. They are often seen on foliage in sunny, moist habitats, or on tree trunks, river rocks and mud flats. They are mostly predatory on soft-bodied invertebrates. When courting, males often display bright silvery thoracic patches and/or 'flags' on their antennae or legs.
Family: Dolichopodidae

HOVER FLIES

Hover flies (8–20 mm) are superb fliers, often seen hovering in front of flowers in search of nectar. The larvae occur in a variety of habitats, including stagnant waters and leaf surfaces. The oval larva of the genus *Microdon* is a scavenger in ant nests. Hover flies pollinate many plants and control aphid pests on crops.
Family: Syrphidae

FERMENT FLIES OR VINEGAR FLIES

These small yellowish flies are common around rotting and fermented fruit, fungi, and sap flows. The larvae feed on bacteria and yeasts found in such substances. Because of their short generation time, ease of culture and physical variability, ferment fly species have been used extensively in the study of genetics.
Family: Drosophilidae

PLATYSTOMATID FLIES

Flies of this family are sometimes large (5–20 mm) and showy, with metallic coloration and patterned wings. The most spectacular species are the stalk-eyed flies of the genus *Achias*, which occur in northern Australia and New Guinea. The males have eyes at the ends of long stalks, which they use almost like

■ HOVER FLY
Many hover fly species have strong yellow and black banding on their abdomens, which helps them to mimic wasps and bees. The female hover fly shown here is laying an egg.

■ ROBBER FLY
Robber flies are fierce predators, capturing other insects on the wing. The fly grasps the prey with its strong legs and pierces it with its hard proboscis. The mouthparts of a robber fly are covered with a strong, bristly 'beard' to protect its head from its struggling victims.

horns or antlers, to defend their territory from other males.
Family: Platystomatidae

UPSIDE-DOWN FLIES

Upside-down flies (2–3 mm long) were first discovered in Australia but are now known to occur in Asia and Madagascar as well. The name of this curious fly comes from the fact that, on a vertical or inclined surface, its head always points toward the ground, whatever direction it is moving in. In Australia, adult upside-down flies are seen face downwards in the cunjevoi lily of the eastern rainforests.
Family: Neurochaetidae

FRUIT FLIES

Adult fruit flies (4–5 mm) are often brightly coloured with patterned wings. Females have a hard, blade-like egg-layer (ovipositor) that enables them to pierce plants and deposit their eggs. Several fruit fly species are serious pests of commercial fruit, especially the imported Mediterranean fruit fly or 'medfly' (*Ceratitus capitata*) and the native Queensland fruit fly (*Dacus tryoni*).
Family: Tephritidae

HOUSE FLIES AND BUSHFLIES

The family Muscidae (5–8 mm) includes the house fly (*Musca domestica*), which has spread worldwide in association with humans. Adults are attracted to faeces, garbage and human food, and often spread disease-carrying bacteria and viruses.

One of Australia's most notorious insects is the bushfly (*Musca vetustissima*). Bushflies are attracted to the human face, as they seek moisture from sweat, and from the eyes and

■ FRUIT FLY
The female fruit fly damages fruit when she deposits her eggs in its flesh.

lips. They are sensitive to cold and die off in southern Australia during winter but re-invade on hot springtime winds. They breed primarily in dung in warm conditions.

The introduction of cattle to the continent increased the amount of dung and consequently the number of bushfly larvae. In the 1960s the CSIRO introduced African dung beetles, which have greatly reduced bushfly populations in Australia.
Family: Muscidae

FLESH FLIES ■

Commonly found near carrion, flesh flies are 10–15 mm long with grey and black stripes. The eggs hatch within the females and the immature larvae are deposited into the rotting flesh. Since carrion does not last long, this gives the flesh fly larvae a distinct advantage in the race to reach maturity.
Family: Sarcophagidae

BLOWFLIES

Blowflies are usually 6–9 mm long and metallic blue-green. Their larvae develop on carrion and excrement.

The Australian sheep blowfly (*Lucilia cuprina*) is a serious pest of sheep, resulting in the loss of millions of dollars every year through sheep deaths and spoilt fleeces. Sheep are susceptible to flystrike when their fleeces are soiled with urine and faeces. Blowflies lay their eggs around the sheep's crutch or on wounds, and the larvae hatch and feed on the secretions, causing further infection. Skin lesions may develop and attract further strike, which can prove fatal. Preventive measures are mid-season 'crutching', or shearing around the breech and tail, and insecticidal dips.

The CSIRO has tried to control blowflies through parasites and genetic manipulation, and by swamping wild populations with

sterile irradiated males. However, the problem remains. The larvae of another blowfly species, the screw worm (*Chrysomya bezziana*), feed on the cattle wounds and can seriously damage livestock. Screw worms are not yet present in Australia, but they are widespread in Asia and Papua New Guinea and could enter the country from the north.
Family: Calliphoridae

TACHINID FLIES

These flies (5–15 mm) form a large but poorly known family. The larvae live as parasites inside the bodies of other insects and thus help control pest species. They have varied life histories. In some cases females deposit hundreds of tiny eggs on leaves. When an egg is swallowed by a caterpillar it hatches and feeds inside its host. The females of other species deposit eggs directly onto suitable hosts. Tachinid flies vary in form and size, but most adults are rather bristly. The brilliantly coloured species of the genus *Rutilia* are prominent in Australia.
Family: Tachinidae

BOTFLIES

Botflies (8–15 mm) are parasites inside the bodies of mammals, and feeding takes place only at the larval stage (adults have tiny nonfunctional mouthparts). Horse botfly eggs are deposited on horses' hair and, when licked, enter the horse's stomach, where they hatch and feed on secretions. The pupae then pass through the digestive tract.

The sheep botfly deposits tiny larvae in the nasal passages of sheep, and the larvae eat their way through the sinuses before pupating and being sneezed out. Some species were introduced to Australia already inside their hosts. Native botflies are found on kangaroos and wallabies.
Families: Gasterophilidae, Oestridae

LOUSE FLIES AND SHEEP KEDS

Superficially, louse flies look like lice or ticks. They are flat, bloodsucking parasites of mammals and birds, which cling to their host's hair or feathers with strong tarsal claws. The larvae develop inside the female louse fly, feeding on secretions. When it emerges from the female, the mature larva forms a pupa.

The sheep ked is an introduced species. Heavy infestations can cause anaemia and staining of wool. Australian native species occur on birds and marsupials.
Family: Hippoboscidae

■ FLESH FLY
Some female flesh flies have a 'uterus'. After mating, the fertilised eggs of the female hatch inside the uterus and immature larvae are deposited in the host, where they start feeding.

CADDIS FLIES

Caddis flies are not true flies, since they have two pairs of functional wings. They are most closely related to moths and butterflies, but their wings are covered in tiny hairs, not scales. When at rest, they hold their wings roof-like over their bodies. Their slender antennae are usually longer than their body (adults are up to 4 cm long). Since they fly mostly at night, they are easily mistaken for small, drab moths. You may spot their fast, erratic flight near water or around lights.

Almost all caddis flies inhabit fresh waters, but the larvae of one family, Chathamiidae, which is restricted to coastal Australia and New Zealand, are the only known marine forms. Life cycles are often no more than a month, although some Australian caddis flies can extend their life cycle over a very long period of time. Eggs laid in mountain streams often remain there through the winter, and those laid in the ephemeral waters of inland Australia may have to wait for fresh rain before they can hatch.

The female lays her eggs in or close to water. (Unusually, one of the marine species is known to lay her eggs within a sea star.) Within ten days or so, the larvae emerge. Some species are carnivorous, while others feed on aquatic plants. Herbivorous species construct cylindrical cases from sand grains, twigs or leaves, which they bind together with silk extruded from their mouths. They live inside these lightweight structures, dragging them along as they graze. Carnivorous larvae are usually free-living, but some weave clever silk structures in the form of tiny feeding nets, which they use to trap prey in the passing current.

Caddis flies provide food for a great number of aquatic animals, from dragonfly larvae to large fish. They are indispensable members of the food web: in mountain streams, where they may occur in large quantities, they form the staple diet of many fishes.
Order: Trichoptera

larval case made of sand grains

thick silky hairs on body and legs

long, narrow forewings and wider hindwings

long antennae

LARVA TO ADULT
Most caddis fly larvae inhabit fresh, flowing water. They construct curved cylindrical cases from grains of sand (top) and live inside them until they are ready to emerge (centre). The winged adult (bottom) has antennae that are longer than its body and two pairs of working wings, covered in hairs.

BUTTERFLIES AND MOTHS

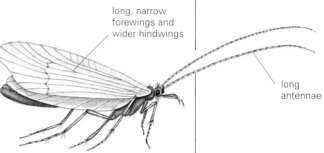

Moths and butterflies are known as lepidopterans, which means 'scaly wings'. The overlapping scales give these insects their colour. All butterflies and moths undergo complete metamorphosis (page 521) through egg, larva and pupa to adult.

Butterflies are usually brightly coloured and fly by day, while moths are mostly sombre and nocturnal – but there are many dull-coloured butterflies and some colourful, day-flying moths. The only structural difference between them is their antennae: most moths have short, thick antennae, in contrast to the slender, club-tipped antennae of butterflies. There are around 380 butterfly species in Australia, and no fewer than 22 000 species of moths.

Butterfly and moth larvae – caterpillars – eat plant foliage at a prodigious rate. Most adults, on the other hand, spend much of their life looking for mates and producing the next generation. Although they have a coiled, straw-like mouth for sucking up nectar, fruit juice and sap, some do not feed at all.

Of the six families of Australian butterflies, five are described in the following pages. The sixth, the beak family (Libytheidae), has only one species in Australia. This is the Australian beak (*Libythea geoffroy*), found in the north of the continent.

The skippers and darters (family Hesperiidae) are small, mainly brown, thick-bodied butterflies with short wings. They are easily confused with moths. Swallowtails (family Papilionidae) are large, strong-flying, often brightly coloured butterflies, common in the humid tropics. Some species have trailing hindwing tails like swallows, hence 'swallowtail'. Nymphalids (family Nymphalidae) have only two pairs of functional legs and a pupa that usually hangs upside down from a single attachment. Some species, including the wanderer, blue tiger and glasswing, are poisonous to birds. Whites and yellows (family Pieridae) are medium-sized butterflies with white or yellow wings. In some the upper side of the wings is a single colour and the underside is brightly patterned, a reversal of the typical wing coloration of butterflies. Blues and coppers (family Lycaenidae) are small, and often fly high in the crowns of trees.

Moths are represented by about 75 families, only a few of which can be discussed here. Some moth species can damage crops, pastures, stored food and clothes, but most are totally harmless. Indeed, like the butterflies, many pollinate flowers as they feed on their nectar.
Order: Lepidoptera

FLUTTERING BY
Moths and butterflies are among the most beautiful of insects. The gum leaf moth and the Ulysses butterfly are examples of the wide variety of wing sizes, shapes and colours found in this order.

545

BUTTERFLIES

ORANGE PALMDART

Caterpillars of the orange palmdart, a native of eastern Australia, make a mess of ornamental palm trees. Drawing together sections of frond with silken strands, they build tiny shelters from which they sally forth at night to nibble the foliage. Garden palms attacked by the caterpillars look untidy, but no real harm is done. Although bangalow palms and cabbage tree palms are the palmdart larva's native food, it also attacks some exotic palms.

While most females are dark brown with yellow patches, some are dark brown all over with no pattern. The males are dark brown with orange markings and the caterpillars are translucent blue or green. The wingspan of the orange palmdart is 3–4 cm.
Family: Hesperiidae
Scientific name: *Cephrenes augiades*

■ CAIRNS BIRDWING
This magnificent butterfly is aptly named: its wingspan is larger than that of many small birds. This female birdwing has just emerged from its pupal case.

CAIRNS BIRDWING ■

With a wingspan up to 17.5 cm – larger than that of many small birds – the Cairns birdwing is Australia's biggest butterfly. The sexes are strikingly different: males are iridescent green, yellow and velvet black; the much larger females are black, yellow and white. During the breeding season the males dance in circles around the females.

The Cairns birdwing lives in the rainforests of north Queensland, but often visits gardens in Cairns and other towns. Its caterpillars are brown or brown-black with rows of soft black spines. They feed on *Aristolochia* plants – native vines.
Family: Papilionidae
Scientific name: *Ornithoptera priamus*

RICHMOND BIRDWING

Similar to the Cairns birdwing but slightly smaller, the Richmond birdwing lives in the rainforests of southern Queensland and northern New South Wales. A hundred years ago this butterfly was quite common in Brisbane but now it is threatened by rainforest clearing and by the garden plant, Dutchman's pipe (see box, 'Gardeners, help!'). A campaign is under way to help this butterfly by encouraging people to grow its food-plant in gardens and schools.
Family: Papilionidae
Scientific name: *Ornithoptera richmondia*

ULYSSES SWALLOWTAIL

One of the largest and most spectacular of all Australian insects, the Ulysses swallowtail has a wingspan of 12 cm and a long tail on each hindwing. Its upper wings are iridescent blue with black margins, and its lower wings are dark brown. It favours sunny clearings in Queensland rainforests north of Sarina, and appears as a bright blue flash against the foliage. Adults are fond of the pink flowers of native *Euodia* species; the dark green caterpillars feed on the leaves.
Family: Papilionidae
Scientific name: *Papilio ulysses*

ORCHARD SWALLOWTAIL ■

The planting of orange and lemon trees around country homesteads has allowed the orchard swallowtail to extend its range far into outback Australia. A familiar garden butterfly in eastern and south-eastern Australia, its caterpillars thrive on orange and lemon tree leaves. Its native food is rainforest trees and shrubs, including native orange, crow's ash, leopard tree and wilga.

GARDENERS, HELP!

One of Australia's rarest butterflies is under threat from a garden plant. The Richmond birdwing lays its eggs on two rainforest vines that are closely related to the Dutchman's pipe. This garden plant has become a weed in the rainforests of southern Queensland where the birdwing lives. The birdwing cannot distinguish between the plants, and if it lays on the garden vine by mistake its caterpillars die because they cannot feed. The CSIRO has asked gardeners in the birdwing's habitats to help by growing the Richmond birdwing vine instead of Dutchman's pipe.

The male and female are so different that they look like separate species. Males are black with cream spots; the larger females are brown with red, white and blue markings and a wingspan of 11–13 cm, making this one of Australia's largest butterflies. Young caterpillars resemble bird droppings, apparently as a form of disguise. When larger, they become green and extrude two soft horns that smell pungently of citrus.
Family: Papilionidae
Scientific name: *Papilio aegeus*

■ ORCHARD SWALLOWTAIL
A frequent visitor to suburban gardens, the female orchard swallowtail has red, white and blue splashes on her wings.

BLUE TRIANGLE

The blue triangle always seems in a hurry, flying quickly and fluttering rapidly, pausing only briefly at flowers and rarely stopping to rest. It favours tubular flowers in clusters, like those of buddleia and lantana, and rapidly inserts its proboscis into many flowers in succession. Its triangular wings are blue with brown borders and have a wingspan of about 6.5–7.5 centimetres.

The blue triangle is found in rainforest, open forest and gardens in eastern Australia as far south as southern New South Wales. The bright green caterpillars are hard to spot among the foliage of rainforest trees, where they live. Their foodplants include native cinnamon, rib-fruited pepperberry, white bolly gum and camphor laurel.
Family: Papilionidae
Scientific name: *Graphium sarpedon*

COMMON EGGFLY

The common eggfly was discovered by Captain Cook's expedition of 1770. A wide-ranging butterfly, it lives in northern, eastern and central Australia, and also occurs in India and Southeast Asia. Individuals sometimes fly to New Zealand, where the butterfly is known as the blue moon because of its rarity and distinctive colour pattern.

Males are black with three pairs of blue-edged white spots; females are dark brown with three pairs of white spots and one pair of orange spots. The wingspan is 6.5–9 centimetres. The caterpillars, which are black with orange-yellow branched spines, feed on love flower, pigweed and lesser joyweed.
Family: Nymphalidae
Scientific name: *Hypolimnas bolina*

WANDERER ◼

The well known wanderer is not a native butterfly but a recent immigrant from North America, where it is called the monarch. Over the past hundred or more years it has spread across the islands of the Pacific to reach Australia, New Zealand and New Guinea. This vast migration was made possible by the previous spread of its food plants, brought to Australia and other countries as garden plants or unintentionally as weeds: they include swan plant, red-headed cotton bush and moth vine. These are all poisonous plants that render wanderer caterpillars and butterflies poisonous to birds.

Wanderer caterpillars are brightly coloured with black, white and yellow rings. The pupa is green, and

the adult butterfly, which has a wingspan of 7–10 cm, is bright orange with black veins and black borders to its wings.
Family: Nymphalidae
Scientific name: *Danaus plexippus*

COMMON CROW

At Katherine Gorge in the Northern Territory huge flocks of common crow butterflies have become a major tourist attraction. Hundreds of thousands of dark brown, white-spotted butterflies, with a wingspan of 7–8 cm, gather to pass the winter in shady gullies. Winter swarms have also been reported from gardens in Brisbane.

Also known as the oleander butterfly, the common crow is one of Australia's most common garden butterflies. Its orange and white, black-banded caterpillars feed on garden oleanders, native figs, caustic creeper and other plants that have a toxic milky sap.
Family: Nymphalidae
Scientific name: *Euploea core*

BLUE TIGER

The strong-flying blue tiger sometimes undertakes migrations, and flocks of many thousands may appear on islands off the Queensland coast. The butterflies are dark brown with pale blue streaks and spots, and with a wingspan of 7–8 centimetres. The caterpillars are banded black, white and grey, and adorned with four soft black horns. They feed on the leaves of two rainforest vines. The blue tiger lives in northern and eastern Australia as far south as Victoria, but it is rarely seen south of Sydney.
Family: Nymphalidae
Scientific name: *Danaus hamatus*

MEADOW ARGUS ◼

The meadow argus is our most widespread Australian butterfly, found throughout mainland Australia and Tasmania, and even reaching Lord Howe Island, Norfolk Island and New Zealand. It is particularly common in domestic gardens. Although small, the meadow argus is a very strong and direct flier. It likes to perch on bare, sunlit ground with its wings outstretched.

The plants the meadow argus feeds on are many and varied and include the garden snapdragon as well as weeds such as pigweed, purple top, plantain and centaury. Meadow argus caterpillars are black with branched spines, and the butterfly is brown with orange and cream markings and a wingspan of 4–5 centimetres.
Family: Nymphalidae
Scientific name: *Junonia villida*

◼ WANDERER
This boldly coloured butterfly feeds on garden plants and weeds and is shown here on lantana flowers. Male and female wanderers are similarly coloured: bright orange with black veins, black margins and white spots.

◼ MEADOW ARGUS
The pretty meadow argus butterfly is a familiar sight in gardens and at roadsides, settling sometimes on a flower and sometimes on the ground with its wings outstretched.

GLASSWING

Transparent upper wings are an unusual feature of the glasswing, which is a common butterfly in gardens. The lower wings are cream with black markings, and the wingspan is 5–6 cm.

Glasswing caterpillars, found feeding on poisonous wild passionfruit leaves, are orange-brown with black, branched spines. Both caterpillars and adults are poisonous to birds, and this explains why the glasswing flies in such a lazy carefree fashion.
Family: Nymphalidae
Scientific name: *Acraea andromacha*

AUSTRALIAN PAINTED LADY

The Australian painted lady is a dainty, orange-brown butterfly with a complex pattern of black streaks, bars and spots. Although small, it is a strong flier and often appears in New Zealand, having crossed the Tasman Sea. In some years it undertakes vast migrations. On one occasion, in 1888, the migrating flocks were so enormous that they darkened the skies of Victoria and trains were halted by crushed butterflies slicking their wheels.

The painted lady has a wingspan of 4–5 cm and occurs throughout Australia except in the far north. Caterpillars are brown, grey or green with branching spines. They feed on everlasting daisies, capeweed, Scotch thistle and other small plants. The pupa is grey or brown.
Family: Nymphalidae
Scientific name: *Vanessa kershawi*

COMMON BROWN ■

Forest glades supporting lush kangaroo grass are the favoured haunts of the common brown. It flies and perches close to the ground and is well disguised among dead leaves

■ COMMON BROWN
Side by side on some leaves, a pair of common brown butterflies quench their thirst.

■ CABBAGE WHITE
A male and female cabbage white (*Pieris rapae*) mate back to back on a flower. The life of an adult butterfly, whose main functions are reproduction and dispersal, is often very short.

when at rest. Males are first on the wing in spring, followed in summer by the females. By autumn only the females remain. They are larger than the males and more colourful, sporting pale yellow patches on their upper wings. The males are orange-brown with darker markings. Both sexes are dull brown on the undersides, providing disguise when at rest. The wingspan of the common brown is 5–6.5 cm.

The common brown is found mainly in eastern and south-eastern Australia. Its brown or green caterpillars feed upon various grasses, including kangaroo grass.
Family: Nymphalidae
Scientific name: *Heteronympha merope*

EVENING BROWN

The evening brown is a shy insect, active only at dawn and dusk, when it flies jerkily, close to the ground. At rest it sits with wings upright, exposing a brown undersurface like a dead leaf. When it perches among leaf litter it seems to vanish suddenly. The upper wings are handsomely shaded in brown and have a span of 6–8 centimetres.

The evening brown is found in northern and eastern Australia as far south as Sydney. The caterpillars are yellowish green with a pair of long horns on the head. They feed on various grasses, including blady grass, buffalo grass and sugar cane.
Family: Nymphalidae
Scientific name: *Melanitis leda*

TAILED EMPEROR

Fermenting fruit and dribbling sap are among the foods sought by the tailed emperor. A strong flier, it is large (7.5–9.5 cm across the wings), with a black and white pattern on the upper wings and complex brown and white markings below. The two small tails on each hindwing are a distinguishing feature.

Found in northern and eastern Australia, this butterfly frequents gardens and forests, laying its tiny yellow eggs on various wattles, cassias, kurrajongs and elms. The green caterpillar is easily identified by the four horns on its head.
Family: Nymphalidae
Scientific name: *Polyura pyrrhus*

CAPER WHITE

In outback Australia warrior bushes sometimes attract clouds of fluttering caper white butterflies – an unusual spectacle. The shrubs do not benefit from this attention and often they are completely defoliated by the caterpillars. When their numbers rise, caper whites frequently undergo immense migrations, with vast flocks travelling south to Victoria, far beyond the range of their food plants.

Caper whites have white upper wings with black margins; the underwings are white, yellow, or a mixture of white and yellow, but always with black markings. The wingspan is 4–6 centimetres. These butterflies are found almost entirely throughout Australia. Caper white caterpillars are brown or greenish with spots and hairs. Their food plants are the warrior bush and various native capers.
Family: Pieridae
Scientific name: *Anaphaeis java*

CABBAGE WHITE

The little green caterpillars that burrow into the hearts of cabbages are the larvae of the cabbage white butterfly. This pest, a native of Europe and northern Asia, appeared in Victoria in 1937. By 1943 it had spread north to Brisbane and west to Perth. It is now widespread in eastern, southern and western Australia and is often seen in gardens and on farms, where its food plants grow.

The cabbage white is white on top with a couple of black spots and black wing tips. The lower wing is dull yellow underneath and the wingspan is about 5 cm. Cabbage white caterpillars eat a variety of plants, including cabbage, broccoli, cauliflower, turnip, radish, nasturtium and related weeds, such as peppercresses.
Family: Pieridae
Scientific name: *Pieris rapae*

SMALL GRASS YELLOW

To the passing eye the small grass yellow appears as little more than a flash of yellow darting through the undergrowth. Viewed closely, its tiny yellow wings have dark brown borders. Seven Australian butterflies have almost the same yellow and brown pattern but when they are viewed under ultraviolet light, different markings are revealed. The butterflies themselves presumably detect such differences.

The small grass yellow is found throughout mainland Australia. Its tiny green caterpillars feed on cassias and native sensitive plant. The pupa is green; the wingspan of the adult butterfly is 2–3.5 cm.
Family: Pieridae
Scientific name: *Eurema smilax*

COMMON GRASS-BLUE

Also known as common blue, bean blue and lucerne blue, this is Australia's most common butterfly – but it is so tiny and flies so close to the ground that most people never see it. On wings only 1 cm long it flutters across lawns to feed on clover flowers. It also dwells in forest clearings where native peas grow. The butterfly is found throughout Australia, including Tasmania and some smaller islands. It has probably benefited from the conversion of forests into farms and lawns, for its caterpillars thrive on a variety of legume crops and weeds, including lucerne, garden beans and soybean, and a range of native peas. The species is sometimes a pest on farms. Its caterpillars resemble slugs and are green, grey or pink with

darker lines. Adult grass-blues are blue above with dark grey margins, although it loses much of the blue with age, resulting in a rather dull grey butterfly.
Family: Lycaenidae
Scientific name: *Zizina labradus*

COMMON IMPERIAL BLUE

The common imperial blue rarely roams far from the wattles that its caterpillars feed on. It is a small, fluttering butterfly, with a 3–5 cm wingspan and small tails on its hindwings. The wings are pale blue above with wide brown borders. The caterpillars are black with paler markings. This butterfly is found in south-eastern Australia from central Queensland to Victoria.
Family: Lycaenidae
Scientific name: *Jalmenus evagorus*

MOTHS

GIANT WOOD MOTH

The giant wood moth is the world's heaviest moth. With a wingspan of up to 25 cm and a weight of 30 grams, it is larger and heavier than a sparrow. Surprisingly few people know of this mighty insect, but its larva is one of the witchetty grubs eaten by Aborigines. The big white grubs bore into the trunks of eucalypts, from which Aborigines extract them with a hooked stick. When roasted over hot coals they have a rich nutty taste.

Female wood moths lay up to 20 000 tiny eggs in crevices in bark and the larvae feed on algae that grow inside the tunnels they bore into wood. The moths, with grey upper wings and dull brown lower wings, burst forth on hot summer nights, flutter about seeking mates, sometimes blundering into houses, and then soon die. They do not feed, drawing their energy from fat reserves in their thick abdomens.
Scientific name: *Xyleutes boisduvali*

ATLAS MOTH

Although not as heavy as the giant wood moth, the Atlas moth, sometimes called the Hercules moth, has much larger wings, making it the largest moth in Australia and one of the largest in the world. The females are orange-brown, with a wingspan of at least 25 cm; the smaller, red-brown males are just as spectacular and have long, trailing tails on their hindwings. The unusual wings display small transparent 'windows'.

The Atlas moth lives in rainforest in north Queensland and New Guinea. Attracted to lights, it may flutter powerfully against a torch carried in the dark. The caterpillars are pale blue with orange, yellow and red markings, and feed on such rainforest trees as bleeding heart, cheese tree and celerywood. They pupate inside an elaborate cocoon.
Scientific name: *Coscinocera hercules*

BOGONG MOTH

During late spring, hundreds of thousands of bogong moths migrate from southern Queensland and south-eastern Australia to the summits of the Australian Alps, where they congregate for several months in caverns and crevices.

Traditionally Aborigines used to trek into the mountains to feast on these fatty moths, which they cooked and pounded into cakes. The larvae of bogong moths are cutworms – pests of wheat, linseed and other crops. They are black, grey or brownish caterpillars that pupate into a brown or grey-black moth. The moths have a wingspan of 3–5.5 centimetres.
Scientific name: *Agrotis infusa*

■ ATLAS MOTH
The 'windows' on the wings of the Atlas moth, or Hercules moth, are clearly visible in the photograph above.

■ WOOD MOTH GRUB
Aborigines call the edible larvae of the giant wood moth 'witchetty grubs'. These white grubs burrow into the trunks of eucalypts.

NATIVE BUDWORM

Of the many pests that attack crops throughout Australia, the native budworm is one of the most serious. Hordes of these moths descend upon crops of tomatoes, maize, linseed, alfalfa, sorghum and sunflowers, each laying up to a thousand yellow eggs, which hatch in four to six days. The larvae eat leaves, fruits or buds, pupating in the soil after about 16 days. The moths have yellow-brown forewings, grey-white hindwings with a brown patch, and a wingspan of 3–4.5 cm. Sometimes they migrate hundreds of kilometres to find new sources of food, including the native everlasting daisy.

Scientific name: *Heliothis punctigera*

VINE HAWK MOTH

The voracious caterpillars of the vine hawk moth decimate balsam plants and grapevines. Up to 8 cm long, they are green or brown with large oval eyespots and a horn at the rear. The caterpillars pupate in the soil or under logs, and emerge as the handsome vine hawk moth. This moth inhabits most of Australia and also occurs in Asia and Europe. It is brown, with a pattern of black and white markings. A thick white stripe runs across the forewing and the hindwing is red at the base. Like all hawk moths the vine hawk has a stout body and narrow wings. The wingspan is 7–8 cm.

Scientific name: *Hippotion celerio*

LOOPERS AND SEMI-LOOPERS

The larvae of these moths have an unmistakable mode of travel. Rearing up on their hindlegs, they extend their long body forward, establish their forelegs, then arch or loop up the middle section of their body (on which there are no legs), bringing their hindlegs up to join their forelegs. Their front and back legs grasp exceptionally well.

Found throughout Australia, loopers chew the leaves of exotic and native garden plants. Usually leaf-green or twig-brown, the caterpillars are adept at disguise. Most of the moths, too, blend in well with bark or dead leaves; however, those that live in the rainforests of northern Queensland are often large and very colourful.

Families: Geometridae (loopers), Noctuidae (semi-loopers)

CASE MOTH

The caterpillar of the case moth shields itself from predators by living inside a bag of twigs spun together with silk. Dragging its home behind, it crawls from shrub to shrub, attaching new twigs as it grows, until the bag is as long as 12 cm. The caterpillar feeds on the leaves of eucalypts, tea trees, cotoneaster and pines.

The male case moth is a dull brown colour with slender wings and a hairy body. The wingless adult female remains inside her silk-and-

■ CUP MOTH LARVA
On its preferred spot on a eucalypt branch, the larva of the painted cup moth, *Doratifera oxleyi*, begins to build its cup-like pupa from silken thread.

twig bag until she lays eggs and dies. The case moth is also known as the bag moth or bagworm, and is found in eastern Australia.

Scientific name: *Oiketicus elongatus*

MAGPIE MOTH

The magpie moth is unusual in that it flies both by day and night. Its orange and black larvae feed on poisonous fireweeds, so the adult is probably poisonous to birds. When numbers are large this moth may migrate. It is found throughout eastern and southern Australia, where it often flutters into gardens.

The wings of the magpie moth are dark brown above with two white blotches on the forewing and one white blotch on the hindwing. The wingspan is 3.5–4.5 cm. Magpie moth caterpillars are orange and black with long erect hairs.

Scientific name: *Nyctemera amica*

CUP MOTHS

The larvae, and even the pupae, of these moths are more often recognised than the moths. They earn their common name from their pupa, which is cup-shaped with a lid that the young moth pushes open when it emerges. Commonly found on eucalypts, the larvae of *Doratifera vulnerans* and *D. oxleyi* feed voraciously on gum leaves and can, on occasion, strip whole trees. These larvae are often striking, with warning bright colours and patterns and retractable stinging spines that can give even humans quite a severe, numbing sting. The adult has a squat, furry body with a wingspan of 4 cm. Cup moths are found throughout Australia, but most occur in the tropics.

Family: Limacodidae

■ VINE HAWK MOTH
At dusk the grapevine hawk moth (*Hippotion celerio*) hovers as it feeds on nectar in a suburban garden.

SAWFLIES, WASPS, BEES AND ANTS

Sawflies, wasps, bees and ants are hymenopterans, meaning that they have membranous wings. Most have two pairs of transparent wings, the front pair larger than the back, joined by tiny hooks. Not all hymenopterans, however, have wings: most female ants and some female wasps are wingless. Female hymenopterans usually have hardened egg-laying organs called ovipositors, which in many cases are used to inject venom. All undergo complete metamorphosis (page 521).

Wasps, bees and ants – closely related to each other – are among the Earth's most beneficial insects. Honeybees are leading pollinators of trees and shrubs, wildflowers, pasture plants and crops. Wasps do a share of this work but, more importantly, a number of parasitic wasps help to control the populations of other insects, many of which could be destructive if their numbers were to get out of hand. Some ant species help to 'till' the soil, while others are agents of seed dispersal. More than 100 000 species of hymenopterans are known worldwide, almost 15 000 of them from Australia. Most are harmless to humans.

Hymenopterans have evolved a wide variety of lifestyles, from vegetable-eating sawflies, to parasitic wasps, to the highly complex social systems of ants and honeybees. All ants and some wasps and bees are social: that is, they live in colonies with different castes performing different functions. Although social wasps and ants are closely related, bees have evolved their social behaviour independently.
Order: Hymenoptera

SAWFLIES

Adult sawflies range in size from 3 mm to 3 cm and look like wasps without a waist. They are short-lived and rarely seen, but the larvae, especially those known as spitfires, are common. They are called sawflies because the female's serrated egg-depositing organ (ovipositor) doubles as a tool to cut into leaves.

Sawfly larvae feed on leaves for several months before pupating and changing into winged adults. Some are garden pests that feed on leaves.
Suborder: Symphyta

■ STEELBLUE SAWFLY
Sawfly larvae gather on a eucalyptus twig. They can become minor pests in gardens and plantations.

STEELBLUE SAWFLY ■
The steelblue sawfly is common in south-eastern Australia. Its larvae, called spitfires, are often seen by day clustered together on eucalypts. Wave a finger over the larvae and they will lift their heads and tails and spit out a sticky green fluid – a habit that gives them their name. The fluid is concentrated eucalyptus oil from the leaves they eat, and, although harmless to humans, it tastes unpleasant to birds. At night, they feed individually. To find each other, they tap on branches with the hardened tip of their abdomens.

Fully grown spitfires leave the tree and bury themselves in soft ground for the summer. They emerge in autumn and fly off to lay their eggs.

When a female steelblue sawfly is ready to lay, she selects a eucalypt leaf and scrapes off the hard waxy coating with the rough underside of her abdomen. She then lays a row of about 40 eggs into a slit that she has cut with her egg-laying organ (ovipositor). In a few weeks the young spitfires hatch and stay together for about six months.
Scientific name: *Perga dorsalis*

SIREX WASP
Sirex wasps, despite their common name, are sawflies. They were accidentally introduced into Australia in 1952 from Europe, where their larvae feed on fungi in pine trees –

fungi introduced by the female sawfly when she lays her eggs. With no natural predators in Australia, the sirex wasp became a major pest of the plantation pine species *Pinus radiata*. Two parasites have proved successful in controlling the pest: a worm that sterilises female sirex wasps and the wasps *Megarhyssa nortoni* and *Rhyssa persuasoria*, whose larvae eat the sirex larvae.
Scientific name: *Sirex noctilio*

WASPS

Most wasps are harmless and live solitary lives. Most, too, are parasites and predators, making them important regulators of insect pests.

Wasps are mainly distinguished by their narrow 'wasp-waist' between the thorax and abdomen, which gives the abdomen mobility for egg-laying and, sometimes, for stinging.

Males are usually smaller than females and seem to function solely as sperm donors. Male flower wasps are an exception: in this case, the males are larger than the wingless females. During mating they carry the females from flower to flower so that the females can feed on nectar – some males even feed

■ SAWFLY
These insects take their name from the way the female uses her saw-like ovipositor to cut into plants so that she can lay her eggs.

the females mouth to mouth. After mating, the female wasps return to the ground, where they feed off burrowing insects.

Wasps may be short and squat or long and thin with trailing ovipositors. Sizes range from 0.15 mm parasites to giant 3.5 cm hunting wasps.

Adult wasps usually feed on nectar and are important pollinators of plants. Their young are, in most cases, carnivorous.

Suborder: Apocrita

■ MUD-DAUBER
Before laying an egg, the female wasp places a paralysed caterpillar in one of the cells in her clay nest as nourishment for the grub that will later hatch there. Some species of mud-dauber have a long slender waist, as shown here.

SOCIAL WASPS
Of Australia's 30 native social, or paper-nest, wasps, the black and orange-banded wasps from the *Polistes* genus are the most common in northern and eastern Australia. Their small, multicelled nests are built by a mated queen under rocks and leaves or in the hollows of trees or buildings. Made of wood fragments mixed with saliva, the nest resembles paper when it dries. The queen lays an egg into each cell, but not all eggs are fertilised. Queens store sperm in their bodies. Eggs fertilised with the stored sperm produce females, and unfertilised eggs produce males. When the eggs hatch the queen feeds the larvae on chewed-up caterpillars. The first young of the season are females and help their mother raise more young. Males are produced only in the autumn, when they and newly hatched females fly from the nest to mate. The males then die and the females start new nests.

Family: Vespidae; Subfamily: Polistinae

■ ICHNEUMONID
A female ichneumonid (*Gotra* spp.) inserts her long ovipositor into the cocoon of a mottled cup moth to deposit her eggs, ensuring a ready supply of food for the larvae.

EUROPEAN WASP
This introduced wasp, which is now present in Tasmania, Victoria and New South Wales, continues to spread throughout southern Australia. The female builds a small paper nest, usually underground or in a hollow tree or building. Without the checks of predators, parasites and climate that operate in the wasp's native home, nests may grow to contain hundreds of thousands of wasps. Fruit-growers and bee-keepers consider them pests, as they eat fruit, bees and honey. Like bees, they inflict a painful sting.

Family: Vespidae; Subfamily: Vespinae
Scientific name: *Vespula germanica*

MUD-DAUBER ■
The 3 cm-long, black and orange female of this species builds mud cells in caves, hollow trees or, often, on the sides of houses. If there is no mud near the nest site she makes her own, flying to the nearest water to drink, then flying back and regurgitating the moisture on the ground near the nest. Here, she rolls the damp soil into little mud balls with her jaws and forelegs and moulds the mud into rows of hollow cells. She fills each cell with a paralysed caterpillar, lays an egg into the cell and seals it. The legless grubs that hatch from the eggs feed on the live caterpillars before pupating and emerging as adult wasps.

Family: Vespidae; Subfamily: Eumeninae;
Scientific name: *Eumenes bicincta*

CICADA-KILLER
The female cicada-killer digs a tunnel for her nest. Sometimes more than a metre long, the nest contains several cells, and into each of these she places a cicada or huntsman spider. Although the cicada killer is quite large – up to 3.5 cm long – her cicada victim may weigh twice as much as she does.

Family: Sphecidae; Subfamily: Nyssoninae. Scientific name: *Exeirus lateritius*

ICHNEUMONIDS ■
All ichneumonids are parasitic on the eggs or larvae of many arthropods. They are long, slender wasps, often brightly coloured, especially in red, black and white. Most females have a long ovipositor with which they lay eggs on or in their hosts.

The larvae of introduced sirex parasites (*Megarhyssa nortoni* and *Rhyssa persuasoria*) live inside the larvae of the pest sawfly, *Sirex noctilio* (page 551). The adult female ichneumonid uses its long egg-laying organ (ovipositor) to drill into the timber where sawfly larvae live.

The orange caterpillar parasite, *Netelia productus*, is often found around lights during the hours of darkness. The female ichneumonid lays her eggs on the skin of caterpillars. When the young larvae hatch, they feed on the living caterpillar.

Females of the orchid dupe wasp (*Lissopimpla excelsa*) lay their eggs in moth larvae. The male has developed a unique relationship with some terrestrial slipper orchids. The flowers' scent resembles that of a sexually receptive female wasp. Males try to mate with the flowers and in so doing pick up pollen packets on their back, which they carry to the next flower. Unlike most exchanges between insects and flowers, the deception does not seem to benefit the wasp at all.

Family: Ichneumonidae

BEES

Bees could be thought of as vegetarian wasps, since they feed their young on pollen and nectar rather than on other creatures. They have more hairs than wasps, especially on their back legs, which helps them to gather pollen. Most of the nearly 2000 species of bees in Australia are solitary. Only members of the family Apidae are social.

Among the solitary bees, females make their own nests in tunnels, which they dig in the ground or dead wood. Some solitary bees do share burrows with sister bees; while some defend the entrance against predators and parasites, others gather pollen and nectar. Inside the tunnel, each female bee usually forms her own individual cell and lays her own eggs.

Suborder: Apocrita

DANCE OF THE HONEYBEES

Honeybees tell their sister bees in the hive where they have found food or a new nest site by dancing. If food is nearby and easy to find, the returning honeybee dances in tight circles. The more vigorous the dance, the better the food. If the food is further away the bee dances in a figure of eight. The honeybee conveys distance and direction by altering the length and angle of the dance pattern. Most of these dances last little more than two minutes, but it may take half an hour to 'describe' a new nest site. Honeybees also dance to communicate messages within the hive, such as a need for more food, or to tell the queen when to leave the nest.

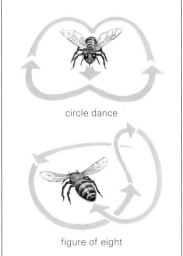

circle dance

figure of eight

HONEYBEES

Honeybees were introduced into Australia by the early European settlers. Now wild throughout most of southern Australia, their effect on the native fauna is not known. However, they do compete for nectar and nest spaces with other insects, and with birds and mammals.

Honeybees and their relatives in the Apidae family have the most complex social system of any insect. Each nest contains a single fertile female, the queen. She lays mainly fertilised eggs that hatch into sterile female worker bees. At first, these workers feed the young and build and maintain the wax cells of the nest. The wax is secreted in small scales from the bees' abdomens, and then worked into shape with their jaws. As they grow older, the female workers become foragers, leaving the nest to gather nectar and pollen. Some food is immediately fed to the adults and young in the nest, while the rest is stored.

A few of the queen's eggs are unfertilised. These become male drones, which do not help in the nest but are available for mating. A new nest is created when a fertile female, which has been fed a special diet of 'royal jelly' from the workers' salivary glands, leaves the nest with a swarm of workers, mates with a drone, and finds a new site.

Family: Apidae; Subfamily: Apinae
Scientific name: *Apis mellifera*

NATIVE HONEYBEES

Native honeybees, like European honeybee species, have a complex social system. They are a good deal smaller – about the size of a bushfly – and do not sting. Like honeybees, they form wax nests in hollow trees.

Family: Apidae; Subfamily: Meliponinae; Scientific name: *Trigona* spp.

CARPENTER BEES

These bees are so called because the female excavates her nest in the stems and branches of grass trees. Several females may share a communal nest, but egg-laying by one female in the nest appears to inhibit egg-laying by others. They concentrate instead on finding food, both for their adult nest-mates and for the developing young.

Family: Anthophoridae;
Subfamily: Xylocopinae
Scientific name: *Exoneura asimillima*

BLUE-BANDED BEES

Blue-banded bees are commonly seen in gardens throughout Australia, either searching for food among the flowers or sleeping. They sleep at night holding onto a plant stem with their jaws; sometimes several bees sleep together, lined up along a single stem.

Female blue-banded bees often nest in large groups, each within her own dug burrow. The nests are frequently parasitised by other bees of the genus *Thyreus*.

Family: Anthophoridae;
Subfamily: Anthophorinae
Scientific name: *Amegilla pulchra*

LEAF-CUTTING BEES

Leaf-cutting bees line their nests with sections of leaves. It is fascinating to watch a female at work on a rose leaf – a favourite plant of these bees. With a scissor-like action of her jaws and using her legs as compasses, she snips out a 1 cm semicircle from the edge of a leaf. She carries the cut leaf to her nest in a tunnel or under a rock. Here, she cements it into place with sticky secretions from her mouth. Scientists believe that this leafy lining helps to regulate humidity. The leaf-cutting bee dies before its young hatch.

Family: Megachilidae;
Subfamily: Megachilinae
Scientific name: *Megachile* spp.

CUCKOO BEES

Several species of so-called cuckoo bees lay their eggs in the nests of leaf-cutting bees. Their larvae do not feed on the bees or their larvae, but may destroy the original egg and eat the pollen and nectar in the nest, starving the rightful occupant.

Family: Megachilidae; Subfamily: Megachilinae
Scientific name: *Coelioxys* spp.

LEAF-CUTTING BEE
Nest-building species of these bees build complex nests lined with leaves that they have cut for this purpose. The female rolls the cut leaf into an arch and flies to the nest with it tucked between her legs.

ANTS

Australia has an astonishing diversity of ants, with probably more species than any other continent. About 1200 species have been formally named, but this represents only about a quarter of the Australian ant fauna. Ants are found throughout Australia, but they are most abundant and diverse in semi-arid and arid areas.

Ants are social insects that live in female-dominated colonies. For most of the year, a colony has one or several reproductive females, known as queens, and several to thousands of nonreproductive females, known as workers. Usually during late summer, small-headed virgin males are produced and, unlike the workers, they possess wings. At the same time, winged virgin females are produced. These are destined to become the queens of new colonies. Both the male and female winged ants then leave the colony. At the same time, reproductive ants of the same species from other colonies also leave their nests. Around dusk the winged ants fly together, forming spectacular mating swarms.

After mating, males die off, while females lose their wings and lay their eggs in a sheltered place. The larvae of this first laying will eventually provide the first worker ants of the new colony. In these initial stages the new queen maintains the colony. Later, the workers take over this role while the queen devotes her time solely to reproduction.

Most Australian ants collect food on the ground or in low vegetation. They usually eat a wide variety of invertebrates and plant materials, such as sap and seeds. However, some species eat only one or two types of food. For example, one species eats only termites. Foraging workers follow visual cues or chemical trails to find food, which is taken back to the nest and fed to the larvae. The larvae then feed the rest of the colony by regurgitating the food.

Most ant species nest in the soil or under stones and logs, where they are protected from extreme weather. Within the colony individual ants cooperate in an organised and integrated fashion, much as the specialised cells within the human body do. Often worker ants are specialised, either structurally or behaviourally, and perform different functions, such as caring for the queen and young, finding food, cleaning the nest and defending the colony. Individuals in the colony communicate with each other by pheromones, food regurgitation, sonar signals and body contact.
Suborder: Apocrita; Family: Formicidae

■ BULLDOG AND JUMPER ANTS ■
Some of the largest ants in the world belong to this group. All of them, except one species, are unique to Australia. Up to 3 cm long, bulldog and jumper ants can inflict a painful sting with their modified ovipositors. There are about a hundred species, all in the same genus, *Myrmecia*. They may be yellow, red, brown or black, and most have long, and slender mouthparts bearing a row of teeth. While adult ants feed on plant sap and honeydew from sap-sucking insects, their larvae are fed on the insects that they collect.
Subfamily: Myrmeciinae

■ BULLDOG ANT
Conspicuous by its large size, the bulldog ant (right) uses its sharp teeth and strong, pincer-like jaws for biting.

■ RED MEAT ANT
Some ants are quite aggressive: for example, the meat ant, *Iridomyrmex purpureus*, gives a fierce bite when disturbed. At the same time it releases an unpleasant smell to ward off attack.

■ HONEYPOT ANT
This rare photo shows the ant hanging from the ceiling of a storage chamber, its abdomen swollen with honey.

■ GREEN TREE ANTS
Found mainly in tropical regions of northern Australia, green tree ants combine forces to work as a group. They form a huge chain and drag leaves great distances to build their nest.

FIRE ANTS

Like bulldog and jumper ants, fire ants have stings, but they are rarely painful to humans. Most fire ants are less than 5 mm long, and several of the common groups, such as *Aphaenogaster* and *Pheidole* species, are red. *Pheidole* are common small ants in gardens. They have specialised workers, called soldiers, with greatly enlarged heads. The species in this group have a diverse range of nesting habits: some nest in soil, some in dead branches, and others in trees.
Subfamily: Myrmeciinae

GREENHEAD ANTS

Most greenheads, except for the common greenhead ant (*Rhytido-ponera metallica*) and related species, are rarely seen because of their secretive habits. The distinguishing features of greenhead ants are their metallic green bodies, their size (about 6 mm), and the painful sting they inflict when they defend themselves. *Rhytidoponera* species do not have a queen, but rather several reproductive workers, which are difficult to distinguish from non-reproductive workers.
Subfamily: Ponerinae

MEAT ANTS ■

Most small black ants that are commonly found in houses belong to this group, the best known being the Argentine ant (*Iridomyrmex humilis*).
Meat ants and other members of this subfamily do not sting. Instead, they employ a chemical defence, producing the familiar 'crushed ant' smell when disturbed.
The most conspicuous of all Australian ants is the meat ant

Iridomyrmex purpureus. This species builds large mound nests on the ground and decorates them with gravel and small pebbles. Inside the nests are several thousand workers. Despite their common name, these ants tend to feed more on plant material than on invertebrates.
Subfamily: Dolichoderinae

SUGAR ANTS, GREEN TREE ANTS AND HONEYPOTS ■

Collectively known as formicines, these ants do not sting. As a defence and aggression mechanism, they release formic acid from an opening at the tip of their abdomen.
Sugar ants (*Camponotus conso-brinus*) are often found in houses and are easily identified by their orange-and-brown-banded body and large size (12 mm long). Green tree ants (*Oecophylla smaragdina*) are common in the tropical regions of Australia. They form long chains of workers to build new nests close to existing ones by pulling together a number of leaves. Some workers collect larvae from the nest and squeeze a sticky silk from the grubs, which they use to bind the leaves together.
Honeypot ants (*Camponotus inflatus, Melophorus bagoti* and *M. cowleyi*) occur in arid areas of Australia. Workers collect honey-dew, which is secreted from winged insects such as cicadas and frog-hoppers, and nectar. They feed this to workers, whose swollen abdo-mens act as storage vessels or 'honeypots'. When food is scarce, members of the colony can dip into these reserves. Honeypot ants are a sought-after delicacy for Aborigines.
Subfamily: Formicinae

FARMERS, GARDENERS AND PHARMACISTS

Ants play a useful role in helping to maintain many types of Australian ecosystems. In sorting and grading different-sized grains of earth for their nests, they mix and aerate the soil, inadvertently preparing it for use by other animals and plants. More than 1500 native plant species rely solely on ants to disperse their seeds. These plants produce seeds with oily appendages that are tasty to ants. The ants carry the seeds back to the nest and give the food reward to the larvae. They discard the seeds, often by burying them in the nest.

Ants are armed with stings or formic acid sprays, effective deterrents when used against other insects, birds and mammals, including humans. Those ants that forage on plants for nectar, such as species of *Camponotus* and *Iridomyrmex*, may help to prevent herbivores from attacking plants. To encourage *Iridomyrmex* ants some plants provide them with a nesting site in the form of a swollen tuber. The ants' accumulated wastes form a supply of rich plant food.

Surprisingly, ants may also be an important new source of antibiotics, since they possess glands that produce antibacterial fluids. Their usefulness in the production of new drugs for humans is currently being researched using *Myrmecia* species.

CENTIPEDES AND MILLIPEDES

■ MILLIPEDE
Millipedes usually curl up into a spiral or ball when disturbed. This large millipede is hiding in leaf litter in the tropical rainforest.

Centipedes and millipedes are distinctly segmented arthropods. They have many legs and a pair of antennae. All are land-dwellers, most living in concealed moist places.

Insects rarely demonstrate parental care, but it is not uncommon among myriapods. Many centipedes guard their eggs and young by curling around them, and a large number of millipedes protect their eggs from predators in a nest of hard soil.
Class: Myriapoda

CENTIPEDES ■

■ CENTIPEDE
In a maternal embrace characteristic of some myriapods, the mother centipede of the genus *Ethmostigmus* curls her long body around her young to protect them.

Centipedes have long, flattened bodies, with each body segment bearing a single pair of long, strong legs that coordinate to give a surprising turn of speed. An adult has an average of 25 pairs of legs; the number varies from 15 to 177 pairs, depending on species. Centipedes are carnivorous. The first body segment carries a pair of strong fangs through which the centipede injects venom to paralyse its prey; even a human experiences pain and swelling when bitten.

Most centipedes live concealed under bark, in litter, under stones or in shallow burrows in the soil. At night they venture out to hunt for molluscs, worms and fellow arthropods. They are ferocious predators, and it is not unusual to see centipedes tackling large insects and even scorpions.

The largest centipedes in Australia are about 15 cm long, but the one most likely to be encountered is the 8 cm-long striped yellow or green common centipede (*Scolopendra morsitans*). When digging in the garden, the thin-bodied, many-legged earth centipedes (3–5 cm) or the shorter lithobiid centipedes (1–2 cm) may be seen.

You may also catch sight of long-legged, fast-running centipedes from the family Scutigeridae, as they scuttle among boulders at the beach or even climb up the inside walls of houses in the bush. Usually brightly coloured, often speckled and tinged with pink, blue or other colours, these centipedes can make a noise audible to humans by rubbing their legs together. They also have the curious habit, if they are seized, of shedding their legs, which then continue to twitch on the ground to divert the attention of an attacker.

A species that has attracted a great deal of interest in the United States belongs to the genus *Craterostigmus*. This curious centipede lives in the logs of Tasmania and New Zealand, where it feeds on termites. It is an ancient animal that was probably far more widespread when Australia was wetter. The *Craterostigmus* resembles a fossil found only in the United States, and is thought to be a possible link between ancient and modern centipedes.
Order: Chilopoda

MILLIPEDES ■

Millipedes are vegetarians that feed mostly on leaf mould and occasionally on roots of seedlings or small pot plants. Their long, cylindrical, smooth, hard bodies and strong heads push through the soil in search of food. Most body segments bear two pairs of small, slow-moving legs – up to as many as 375 pairs in some species.

Most millipedes are less than 4 cm long, although the robust, smooth, shiny and brownish-black members of the order Spirostreptida grow up to 12 cm or more. Not all are long and slender. The pill millipede, for example, is stout and has a smooth armour-like covering with which to protect itself when it curls up into a tight ball. The minute pincushion or dwarf millipede is also short and fat. Its thin-skinned body bears rows of scale-like bristles and tufts of barbed hairs. Pincushion millipedes have been seen travelling in enormous numbers in the Hamersley Range of Western Australia.

The accidentally introduced black Portuguese millipede (*Ommatoiulus moreletti*) has also been known to occur in plague proportions. In 1985, following heavy rains, a train in the Adelaide Hills was reduced to a crawl as hundreds of thousands of millipedes congregated on the railway line. These harmless millipedes sometimes occur in large numbers in houses as well.

Many millipedes are armed with chemical defences. While some produce dark toxic secretions distasteful to many birds, other tropical species spray corrosive droplets to distances of up to 70 cm, damaging the eyes of poultry or other aggressors.

A few plant-chewing millipedes are pests of plants, but most render a valuable service to the environment by converting plant debris to rich soil, and it is believed that dozens of species play important roles in forest ecology.
Order: Diplopoda

ARACHNIDS

Arachnids include the spiders, ticks, mites and scorpions, and the horseshoe crabs (Limulus spp.) which do not occur in Australia. Their bodies are divided into two – the prosoma and the opisthosoma. The first appendages are often a pair of pincer-like feeding structures (chelicerae), hence the arachnid subphylum, Chelicerata. The next pair of appendages, the pedipalps, is followed by the characteristic four pairs of walking legs. The opisthosoma contains the majority of the body organs, the genital opening and the anal opening, and with the openings to the respiratory book lungs and/or tracheae in between.
Subphylum: Chelicerata; Class: Arachnida

MITES AND TICKS

Ticks and mites have globular bodies, anterior feeding appendages and four pairs of legs (three in juveniles). Most are tiny. Over 2500 named species of mites occur in Australia, but there are perhaps ten times that.

Mites are very diverse in their lifestyles. Many are herbivorous, including some agricultural pests. Fungi also form the diet of some mites. Carnivorous mites feed on other small animals, such as nematodes and small arthropods including other mites. Many species are parasitic where they usually live on or in the surface of their hosts. Many mites feed on dead plant and animal matter and are important in nutrient recycling in soil. While the majority of mites are terrestrial, some have invaded fresh water and even the sea.

There are about 70 species of ticks in Australia. All live by sucking the blood of animals. They differ from mites in having special mouthparts with backward-pointing hooks they use to attach themselves to their host.
Class: Arachnida; Subclass: Acarina

SCABIES MITE

Human scabies is caused by scabies mites burrowing in the skin, where they feed and reproduce, causing an itchy rash. These mites are tiny, white, oval-shaped and covered with hairs and spines. Females lay two or three eggs a day and live for up to two months.

Mites are transmitted between humans by close contact or in shared bedding. They will also climb from livestock or pets on to humans, but such infestations do not usually become established. In domestic pets, scabies mites can cause mange (treatable by a vet).
Scientific name: *Sarcoptes scabiei*

HOUSE DUST MITES

House dust mites are common in houses, especially in mattresses. They are so small that specialised collecting methods are needed to prove their presence. They feed on the flakes of skin that we all shed every day.

Males and females mate continuously, for up to 48 hours, and the female stores sperm until it is required to fertilise eggs. A single house can contain millions of mites. Their droppings are tiny round pellets, so small and light that they float in the air, where they can cause asthma and other allergies if inhaled.
Scientific name: *Dermatophagoides* spp.

RED-LEGGED EARTH MITE

This minute creature resembles a tiny black spider with red legs. It is found in winter in south-eastern and south-western Australia. It feeds on plants such as clover and lucerne, causing extensive damage to pastures. It may feed on vegetables and lawns in gardens and sometimes floats in large masses on the surface of puddles.

Males spin silk webbing on the soil, where they deposit their sperm for females to pick up. As the weather becomes warm and dry in spring, the mites die out, leaving their eggs waiting in the soil for the first rains of autumn to trigger their hatching.
Scientific name: *Halotydeus destructor*

SPIDER MITES

The long, needle-like mouthparts of spider mites suck fluids from leaves, causing yellow discoloration on fruit trees and ornamental plants. The most common species is the two-spotted mite (*Tetranychus urticae*). Spider mites are so called because of the silk webs they spin on plants to hide their eggs and protect themselves from predators.
Scientific name: *Tetranychus* spp.

PARALYSIS TICK

This tick lives in a narrow coastal strip from eastern Victoria to north Queensland. It attacks many types of animals, including marsupials, humans and domestic pets. Eggs are laid in the soil and these hatch into tiny larvae that crawl up grass stems to seek a suitable host. Once they have attached themselves, they feed on the host's blood and then drop off to moult into adult males and females. The adults attach themselves to another host and, after feeding, the body of the female can swell greatly – to more than a centimetre in length.

During feeding, ticks inject saliva into their host. The saliva contains a toxin that can paralyse dogs and other animals and can be fatal if untreated (an effective antivenom is now available). Removal of ticks is best done by a medical or veterinary practitioner, since it is important not to break off the mouthparts that are embedded in the skin.
Scientific name: *Ixodes holocyclus*

BUSH TICK

This tick occurs in the east coast of New South Wales, south-eastern Queensland and north-eastern Victoria. It feeds on domestic and wild animals, and can seriously damage cattle by taking blood and irritating and blemishing their hides.

All adults are females that lay fertile eggs without mating. The bush tick rarely attacks humans and is not usually dangerous to animals except in heavy infestations.
Scientific name: *Haemaphysalis longicornis*

■ RED SPIDER MITE
This mite bears a marked resemblance to a spider; it takes its name from the web it weaves to protect its eggs. Mites are a type of arachnid.

■ PARALYSIS TICK
Adult female paralysis ticks are blood-suckers. After feeding on human or animal hosts, their bodies become grossly swollen with blood.

557

BABIES IN BACKPACKS
Females scorpions carry
their young beneath
their stinging tail for
several days after birth.
The young may take
a year or more to
reach maturity.

SCORPIONS

Massive claws, similar to those of a crab, and a curled tail are the most obvious features of the scorpion. The claws are modified palps – sensory appendages that the scorpion uses to seize its prey. Its tail, too, is a modification: the end segments of its abdomen are narrowed to form a tail with a sting at the tip. Like other primitive arachnids, scorpions breathe through internal gill-like structures called book lungs.

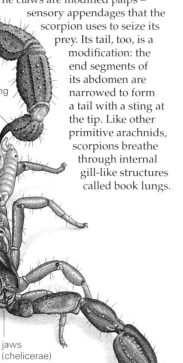

young scorpions

stinging tail

jaws (chelicerae)

claw (modified palp)

Australian scorpions reach a length of up to 12 cm. Thirty-five Australian scorpion species have been identified, all brownish or reddish in colour and occurring in most parts of the country. Species adapted to life in arid conditions avoid dehydration by living in burrows and hunting at night.

Their burrows usually consist of an arc-shaped slit in the ground with a spiral descent, but species living in hard, stony ground may simply create a shallow pit in soil beneath rocks. Some scorpions have flattened bodies so that they can squeeze into narrow cracks and crevices in the ground, or crawl under bark if they are tree-dwellers.

No Australian scorpion has venom that is fatal to humans, but some can deliver a painful sting – for example, the fairly common marbled scorpion, *Lychas marmoreus*.

Scorpions mostly eat insects, spiders and other arthropods. If food is plentiful, they sit at their burrow entrances at night and seize their prey as it passes. But when food is scarce they pursue whatever they can find; some species wander considerable distances from their retreats in search of a meal. To detect their prey they use sensory hairs on their body and a pair of sensory structures at the base of their

abdomen. Many crush their victims with their strong claws, reserving their sting for self-defence, but those taking on more powerful prey may sting repeatedly. They tear up their food with fine pincers on their jaws and then extract the body juices.

Warm weather stimulates mature males to go in search of a mate, attracted at first by smell. On meeting a female, the male rocks vigorously, and the couple then start a ritual known as promenading. With their powerful claws locked together, they 'waltz' over the ground, the male in the lead. Still dancing, he deposits his sperm packet on the ground and then pulls and lifts the female over it until it enters her genital opening. The sperm are then released, and the female departs to lay her eggs.

After a gestation period of 2–18 months, depending on the species, the female scorpion gives birth to as many as a hundred young. The young have a well-formed casing, but it is soft and their sting is blunt, so they scramble onto their mother's back and ride under the protection of her sting at least until they shed their first external skeleton.

Female scorpions can live for up to five years, but the males are often eaten by the females after mating.

Class: Arachnida; Order: Scorpiones

HARVESTMEN

Like scorpions, harvestmen are arachnids. They are often mistaken for daddy long-legs spiders – in fact, daddy long-legs is another of their

common names – but unlike spiders they do not have a waist between their cephalothorax (a fused head and thorax) and their abdomen. They are also unlike spiders in that they rarely venture into houses. Most have extremely long, slender walking legs and small, brownish grey bodies less than 1 cm long.

The name 'harvestman' comes from the northern hemisphere, where these creatures are most often seen at harvest time (July and August). In Australia, however, harvestman species are visible all the year round.

HARVESTMAN
Its disproportionately long legs account for the harvestman's other common name, daddy long-legs. Most species need moist conditions, but some have been found in arid regions of Australia.

Because they are susceptible to desiccation, most Australian harvestman species are restricted to moist parts of the country, but in these regions they are widespread. They live among fallen leaves, decaying bark and low-growing foliage, where they hunt for small insects and other arthropods.

Unlike most arachnids, harvestmen are partly scavengers, eating dead animal and plant matter as well as small invertebrates.

Their reproductive behaviour is also unusual. The male seduces the female by stroking her with his front pairs of legs and deposits sperm with a penis, rather than palps.
The female has a long egg-laying organ (an ovipositor), with which she lays her eggs in crevices beneath leaf litter and other debris.

Class: Arachnida; Order: Opiliones

PSEUDOSCORPIONS

Creeping around in leaf litter or skulking under tree bark and rocks are creatures no more than a centimetre long that look like small scorpions, but, although they have large claws with pincers, they have no tail. These pseudoscorpions, or false scorpions, differ from true scorpions in other ways too: having no tail, they store their venom at the end of their claws; they have a tubal breathing system, rather than gill-like book lungs; and they produce silk from the tips of their mouth appendages. Like true scorpions, many pseudoscorpions perform a promenading ritual when mating; however, the female does not bear live young but lays her eggs into a brood sac at her genital opening. She carries the sac with her until the young are ready to emerge.
Class: Arachnida;
Order: Pseudoscorpiones

A GREAT PRETENDER
Pseudoscorpions use the poison-bearing pincers on their large claws to kill their prey. They also use their pincers to tear up their victim's body and carry the parts to their jaws (chelicerae). Secretions from the jaws liquidise the prey, and the pseudoscorpion drinks the liquid.

SPIDERS

Master silk-spinners of the animal world, spiders depend on silk in every part of their lives: the young are cocooned in it, and adults use it to line burrows or weave webs, to form safety lines and to snare prey. Many insects spin silk from their mouths to make shelters and pupal cocoons, but spiders are unique in producing silk from abdominal glands and drawing it out of their bodies through special appendages called spinnerets. Spider silk is made of protein, and is strong and very elastic – it can be stretched by nearly a third without breaking.

Primitive spiders live in or on the ground because their gill-like lungs need coolness and moisture, but modern spiders have a more efficient breathing apparatus and have developed ways of catching prey in the air. Most spiders are nocturnal.

Like all arthropods, spiders shed their external skeletons in order to grow. Males are generally smaller than females. Female spiders live for 20 years or more, but male spiders survive for just one mating season.

Most spiders have eight eyes, although some have fewer. Each eye consists of a single simple lens. The arrangement of the eyes is distinctive for each spider family, and is often important for identification.

Pioneer balloonists
Ballooning for spiders is rather like parachuting for humans, but while humans descend from the skies, spiders glide upwards and then sail lightly down. When they emerge from their egg cases, young spiders of some species emit streams of fine silk from their spinnerets. The wind catches these silken streamers and the spiderlings' light little bodies become airborne. Adrift on air currents, they may travel thousands of metres up into the sky and drop down many kilometres from where they took off. Ballooning is a common method of dispersal amongst the modern spiders, but only a few primitive spiders use the technique.

Eco-friendly
Spiders make a valuable contribution to the recovery of damaged ecosystems. They are often among the first animals to colonise areas that have been devastated by volcanoes, earthquakes or landslides, and then birds and other animals move in from the edges of these regions to hunt the spiders.

Almost 2000 spider species have been identified in Australia.
Class: Arachnida; Order: Araneae

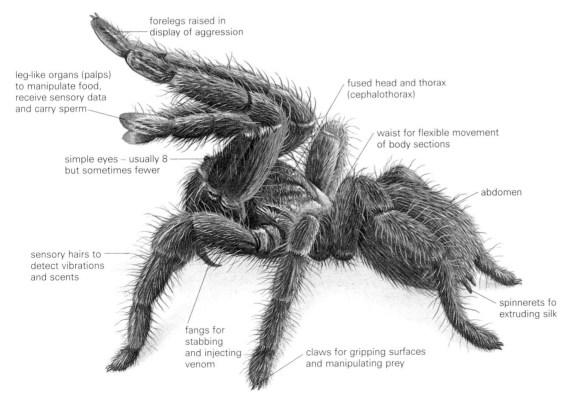

forelegs raised in display of aggression

leg-like organs (palps) to manipulate food, receive sensory data and carry sperm

fused head and thorax (cephalothorax)

simple eyes – usually 8 but sometimes fewer

waist for flexible movement of body sections

abdomen

sensory hairs to detect vibrations and scents

fangs for stabbing and injecting venom

claws for gripping surfaces and manipulating prey

spinnerets fo extruding silk

SPIDER ANATOMY
All spiders have four pairs of jointed legs and a protective plate called a carapace. Their large jaws (chelicerae) comprise fangs for injecting venom and fang bases for crushing insect prey. A male spider's leg-like sensory organs, or palps, have a tip that has been modified for carrying sperm.

Mating can be hazardous for male spiders, for when they have fulfilled their reproductive role they may be eaten by the female. This seems brutal, but once the males reach maturity their sole concern is to mate, and they do not need to eat; those that escape the female's jaws usually die of starvation. The main function of the female spider begins after copulation, and eating the body of her mate provides her with energy for the tasks ahead: laying eggs, building her egg sac, guarding the eggs and caring for the spiderlings.

PRIMITIVE SPIDERS

■ TRAPDOOR SPIDER
At dusk the trapdoor spider ascends, flips open the camouflaged lid of its burrow and emerges to ambush its unsuspecting prey.

Spiders may have been among the first creatures to live on land instead of in the sea. The primitive spiders show this ancestry in their two pairs of gill-like lungs, known as book lungs, which confine them to cool, moist underground burrows.

Primitive spiders spin silk to make egg sacs and linings for their burrows. At night they lurk at their burrow entrances, ready to pounce on their prey and strike it with their downward-stabbing fangs. Some of these spiders spread silken triplines outside their burrows to alert them to the movement of potential victims passing by.

Most primitive spiders have poor eyesight and so must rely on close-range capture. They are nocturnal and few stray far from their burrows. They are usually large and carry a good supply of venom, but they are rarely seen, except during the mating season. At such times the males are abroad – sometimes in daylight – in search of a partner.
Suborder: Mygalomorphae

TRAPDOOR SPIDERS ■

Several families of primitive spiders build trapdoors over their burrows, but the habit is most typical of trapdoor spiders. These spiders are dark brown, hairy and large: females may be 4 cm long and males 3 cm long. Species can be identified by the patterns on their abdomens, which also distinguish trapdoor spiders from the darker, unpatterned funnelwebs.

Many trapdoor spiders have evolved ingenious building systems to protect them from both predators and flooding. Their clever devices include blind or turreted entrances, double exits and burrow blockers. But most characteristic is the trapdoor – a plug of silk and soil, with bevel and hinge, that fits into the burrow entrance. Once its meal is within range, the spider rushes out, seizes the prey in its jaws and drags it into the burrow to eat it.

Trapdoor spiders live in most Australian habitats, from rainforests to deserts. These silent hunters are quite common but rarely seen.
Family: Idiopidae

MOUSE SPIDERS ■

The female mouse spider digs a large burrow with a shaft a metre or more deep, usually in the banks of creeks. The shaft has two entrances, each with a hinged door. In the mating season the male taps on one of the doors, and if the female is receptive she welcomes him in. Mating occurs in the burrow and, if the male is lucky, he escapes. After mating, the female excavates a side chamber with an internal hinged door about halfway down the shaft. In this chamber she conceals her egg sac. The spiderlings spend several weeks in the burrow before dispersing.

■ MOUSE SPIDER
The male *Missulena insignis* searches for a mate. Its colourful blue and red body and long palps are clearly visible.

Female mouse spiders are dark brown and stout, with a body up to 3.5 cm long. Male mouse spiders (1.5–2 cm long) are so colourful and different in shape from the females that, until early this century, they were thought to belong to a different species. The male's head region may be yellow, orange or red, and its abdomen blue, grey, plum red or black. The males, which are slender and long-limbed with exceptionally long palps, bite humans if disturbed.

Mouse spiders are common in temperate and subtropical Australia. They are usually nocturnal, but males travel a long way through forest floors and grasslands in search of females during the mating season.
Family: Actinopodidae

FUNNELWEB SPIDERS

These spiders live in damp, dark places along the coastal plain or nearby ranges of south-eastern Australia. They make their homes of silken tubing between crevices and in holes beneath rocks and logs, or in the ground. At night, females crawl to the entrances of their webbed tunnels and rest their front legs on triplines. When they detect prey, they lunge, stabbing and crushing their victims with their fangs.

Females (up to 5 cm long) rarely leave their retreats, but males roam about on spring and summer nights in search of females. The males (up to 3 cm long) have spurred legs to protect them during mating.

Some funnelwebs have a bite that can kill humans (see page 563). The notorious Sydney funnelweb (*Atrax robustus*) builds a burrow with a Y-shaped entrance and a silken tube extending from it. At the end of the tube it builds a resting chamber, which also serves as a brood site.
Family: Hexathelidae

BRUSH-FOOTED TRAPDOOR SPIDERS

These large spiders (average length 4 cm) excavate a burrow, sometimes with a trapdoor lid, under leaf litter. Fine, hairy brushes on their feet, oiled by special glands, give them suction-cup grip and allow them to climb smooth vertical surfaces.

Brush-footed trapdoor spiders are found in eucalypt forests, rainforests and arid regions. During the mating season some desert-dwelling species make barking or whistling sounds to attract one another.

The biggest brush-footed trapdoor spiders in Australia – 6 cm long, with fangs 1 cm long – catch frogs, lizards and even small birds and fledglings, earning them the name of bird-eating spiders.

Families: Barychelidae, Theraphosidae

HYPOCHILO-MORPHS

A living link between primitive and modern spiders, the hypochilomorphs pioneered the silk-making equipment that characterises modern spiders and revolutionised their lives. In these spiders, a pair of spinnerets became a spinning plate and brushes formed on their fourth pair of legs to control silk output. As a consequence, new uses for silk evolved.

The first of these was the building of above-ground snares to catch prey and retreats in which to hide. The reddish brown and black Tasmanian cave spider (*Hickmania troglodytes*) survives from these days. The female has a 10 mm long body and the male is smaller; both have long, thin legs. This spider builds a large horizontal sheet web to catch falling prey.

Despite its sophisticated use of silk, this cave-dweller retains the two pairs of gill-like lungs of the primitive spiders.

Suborder: Hypochilomorphae

MODERN SPIDERS

An abundant and diverse group, modern spiders differ from primitive spiders in several ways. Their breathing system has evolved to enable them to take in more oxygen: most modern spiders have insect-like tracheal tubes as well as a pair of gill-like lungs, though some have

■ HYPOCHILOMORPH
The Tasmanian cave spider hangs upside down beneath its filmy web, through which it pulls its prey.

only a tubal breathing system. No longer confined to burrows in damp earth, and with a good supply of oxygen, modern spiders can chase prey across the ground and up trees, and pursue winged insects into the forest canopy. Here they have evolved silk traps to snare prey, and lines to catch themselves if they fall.

Another refinement of modern spiders is the pincer-like action of the jaws for manipulating prey. The earliest modern spiders ran down their prey, but to conserve energy the spiders that evolved later

learned to lie in wait for prey. The early snare-making spiders developed a spinning plate for producing silk and bristles for combing it out. The wheel web builders are the most sophisticated of these spiders: their acute observation of flying insects and frugal energy use have resulted in a simple but highly effective web.

Suborder: Araneomorphae

WOLF SPIDERS ■

With their keen night vision, most wolf spiders forage at night in woodlands, grassland and across the plains of arid Australia. These large spiders – the body length of females is 15–35 mm and of males 10–25 mm – can run fast, catching their prey by relentless pursuit. Although strikingly patterned, their earthy colours blend in with their surroundings.

Wolf spiders shelter in burrows during the day. At dusk, females emerge, trailing fine, scent-laden silk draglines. A male 'tastes' his way towards a potential mate with sense organs on his palps. Once in view of the female, he waves his palps and forelegs to show his intentions and mating may occur.

Females carry their egg sacs with them when they are out hunting. During the day, they come to the entrance of the burrow and rotate the egg sacs in the sun to incubate the young. When the hatchlings emerge, they climb onto their mother's back, where they stay for the first few months, moulting as they grow and eating each other.

Family: Lycosidae

■ WOLF SPIDER
The mother wolf spider carries her young on her back until they are large enough to hunt. The spiderlings use special hairs on their mother's back to help them cling to her.

NURSERY-WEB SPIDERS

Often large – females can be up to 3 cm long – these hunting spiders are found throughout Australia, usually near fresh water. From the bank or the water surface, nursery-web spiders catch insects or dive to catch prey as large as tadpoles or small fishes. Like the similar-looking wolf spiders, females carry their egg sacs beneath them. Before the young hatch, the mother builds a nursery web, which she guards fiercely until the spiderlings are ready to disperse.
Family: Pisauridae

SAC SPIDERS

White, silken sacs serve as both retreats and brood chambers for these nocturnal hunting spiders. If disturbed, they are liable to bite, often causing considerable discomfort – localised swelling and burning pain, and sometimes headache, sickness and dizziness.

Sac spiders range in colour from fawn to dark brown, and have elongated bodies (1–3 cm long) and long legs. They are found in forested areas, grasslands and rocky outcrops all over Australia. They weave their sacs in blades of grass or in the folds of leaves, under bark or leaf litter, and in wall and ceiling corners.

The wandering habits of the white-tailed spider (*Lampona cylindrata*) – a species of sac spider – often bring it into contact with humans across southern Australia. It has a dark, cylindrical body – the female's is 2 cm long and the male's is 1 cm – with relatively short, reddish brown legs that darken with age. Young white-tails have pale blotches on the abdomen, which later disappear, leaving a single, distinctive white tip.

Like all sac spiders, white-tails hunt at night and often venture into buildings in search of their favourite prey – fellow spiders and their young. At dusk they emerge from concealed silken retreats to look for the webs of daddy long-legs, black house spiders and redbacks. In a game of deception, they pluck the threads of the web. Thinking it has caught an insect, the web owner rushes out and itself becomes a meal. White-tails also attack egg sacs, dissolving the silk with their digestive juices and feeding on their contents.

Although white-tails are relatively abundant, the recorded incidence of bites is low. Much of the impact of the spider's bite is caused by a bacterium in the venom (see page 563).
Families: Clubionidae, Gnaphosidae, Miturgida

REDBACK SPIDERS

Redbacks are reclusive, but more common than is realised. They range throughout Australia, haunting cool, dry places such as tree stumps, outhouses and abandoned containers. They are timid creatures and bite only if handled, and only the female is dangerous (see page 563).

When she is pregnant, the female's abdomen may reach the size of a large pea, but males are so small (3 mm long) that they are often mistaken for spiderlings. Females can lay a batch of eggs a month in summer, each one consisting of 12 egg sacs containing thousands of eggs. When they hatch, the spiderlings eat their fellows or disperse by ballooning (see page 559).

The redback constructs a strong, three-dimensional web in a hidden place, usually close to the ground. The web is supported by lateral guy ropes from which sticky trap-threads run to the ground. When an animal touches them, the threads release and recoil, suspending the victim in mid-air. Redbacks eat mostly beetles, but if they ensnare a creature that is too big for the trap, they dart out, smother the victim with silk, then bite it and suck it dry.
Family: Theridiidae

NURSERY-WEB SPIDER
Also known as water spiders, these creatures catch tadpoles and small fishes. The spider waits motionless on the water surface, its long legs spread. When the prey approaches, the spider dives down and grabs it, bites it and then drags it ashore for consumption.

Dubious fame

Two Australian spiders – the funnelweb and the redback – are notorious for their venom, but it is less well known that virtually all spiders are poisonous.

A funnelweb presents an awesome display of aggression, rearing up with venom dripping from its fangs before lunging at its victim.

The barking spider, found in tropical forests, has fangs as big as those of some snakes and can inflict an agonisingly painful bite.

A spider's venom usually consists of tissue-dissolving enzymes that are designed to help the spider to digest its prey. Only a few spiders produce venom that can harm humans, but all spiders should be treated with the utmost respect.

The Sydney area houses a spider that may well be the deadliest in the world – the Sydney funnelweb spider – and it is likely that a number of the many funnelweb species are deadly to humans.

Funnelwebs build their home of thick, silken tubing in crevices under rocks and logs or in the ground. Humans usually meet these large, hairy, purplish-black spiders when they are accidentally exposed in their shelters or when the males are roaming around in spring or summer looking for a mate. The male's venom is believed to be five times more toxic than the female's.

These spiders sometimes fall into backyard pools, where they appear to be drowned. In fact, they merely enter a torpid state, and they revive quickly if they are lifted from the water.

Funnelweb venom is something of a puzzle to scientists. It can be fatal to humans and other primates, attacking the nerve surfaces and producing a violent reaction within ten minutes, but the spider's normal predators, such as bandicoots, are resistant to it.

The female redback's scarlet stripe is a clear warning not to touch. Redbacks are common but timid, and bite only if they are handled.

Deadlier than the male

Australia's other well known dangerous spider is the redback. In this case it is the female's bite that is to be feared, though her fangs and venom glands are minute compared with those of the funnelweb, and often can penetrate only soft skin. Males are much smaller than females and their markings are more subdued. A bite from a male can produce a mild reaction, but a bite from a female can be painful enough to cause hysteria. Redback venom is much slower to act than funnelweb venom.

Redbacks range throughout Australia, haunting cool, dry places such as outhouses, hollows in tree stumps and the areas beneath ledges of rock. They are very common in disturbed habitats and settled areas, both urban and rural.

Safety first

Funnelweb and redback spiders probably enjoy their dubious fame largely because they are common in densely populated areas, but Australia has many other spiders to be wary of. Mouse spiders, which may be even more toxic than funnelwebs, are found in forested areas throughout Australia. The white-tailed spider, a roaming species that sometimes enters houses, is suspected of causing tissue death (necrosis) in some victims. The barking spider inflicts a huge, vicious bite.

When clearing up rubbish or working in rockeries or neglected areas of the garden, it is advisable to wear gardening gloves, stout footwear and long trousers. Outhouses, where spiders often lurk, should be cleaned up regularly.

SPOTTED RACING SPIDERS

Spotted racing spiders, also known as wasp-mimicking spiders, live in eucalypt woodlands in southern Australia. These little hunting spiders – body length up to 15 mm in females and 10 mm in males – are normally seen on the ground on sunny days in warmer months.

They move so rapidly, and their camouflage is so effective, that they can be seen only when they are stationary. They are easily identified by their black bodies, which are covered in numerous white to pale yellow spots and dashes, and a 'sprint-sit-sprint' way of moving over the leaf litter. The female lays her eggs in papery discs that she sticks underneath stones.

To protect themselves, spotted racing spiders mimic hunting wasps by holding their forelegs out in front of their bodies and waving them about to simulate antennae.

Family: Corinnidae
Scientific name: *Supunna* spp.

HUNTSMAN SPIDERS ▦

Found in most habitats throughout Australia, these spiders, in shades of grey and brown, have a distinctive, bulbous abdomen and are hairy all over. Body lengths range up to 4.5 cm in females and 3 cm in males, but it is their long legs that make these spiders look so big: angled forward, their legs can fan out to a span of up to 16 cm.

▦ HUNTSMAN SPIDER
A female huntsman spider defending her egg sac. Huntsmen's egg sacs are usually found under flaking tree bark.

SILKEN WRAP

As well as producing silk to build webs and cocoon their eggs, spiders also use it to wrap up their prey. Many spiders, such as the golden orb-weaver, catch relatively large prey in their webs. To immobilise their catch, they enfold it in a silken sheet before biting it and injecting a paralysing poison. The spider then either eats its meal straight away or saves it for later.

A favourite shelter for huntsmen is beneath the flaking bark of living or dead trees. Huntsman spiders can squeeze into such constricted spaces because of their flattened body and the crab-like arrangement of their legs. Like crabs, they can also scuttle sideways out of danger. As their name suggests, huntsmen run down or pounce on their prey rather than constructing silk traps in which to catch their victims.

Some species live in cracks in buildings or fence posts, or hidden in sheds. Old houses often have a resident huntsman or two living in the ceiling. The sudden appearance of these large spiders can cause even the stoutest heart to flutter.

The huntsman's intimidating appearance has earned it the misleading name 'tarantula'. (Tarantulas are South American spiders that resemble huntsmen and have a dangerous bite.) In fact, many huntsmen are comparatively unaggressive among themselves, and most are harmless to humans.

Some, such as the common huntsman, *Delena cancerides*, are relatively sociable. It is not unusual to find several generations sheltering together in vast numbers beneath bark, especially during flooding. Unusually for spiders, males are seldom eaten by their mates and often remain with the female after mating.

Huntsmen's egg sacs are normally found beneath bark. They are pure white and may be 3 cm or more in diameter. The female stays beside the egg sac or carries it about, and once the spiderlings are born she shares her catch with them. When they first clamber from the egg sac,

the spiderlings are pale green to jade green, and they retain this colouring for the first few moults.

Huntsman spiders of the genus *Neosparassus* are commonly known as badge spiders. They have a more arched form than the other huntsman species and a style of walking that carries the body raised rather than flattened close to the surface.

Badge spiders get their name from the brightly coloured badge-shaped pattern on the underside of the abdomen. The markings vary in intensity and shape and are generally black, white, yellow or orange. There are usually equally bright bands on the undersides of the legs. In sharp contrast to the colourful underside, these spiders are muted shades of brown on top, with little or no patterning, although some species have a prominent white band between the two rows of eyes.

Badge spiders are found in most regions of Australia. They usually forage during the night on the open ground and among low-growing vegetation. Although they are somewhat smaller than other huntsman species (female badge spiders have a body length of 18–22 mm and males are 12–18 mm long), their rounded body means that they cannot get into narrow spaces.

Some badge spiders live in abandoned cicada or wood-moth holes around the bases of tree trunks, and at least one species constructs a flimsy silken lid over the entrance to its adopted burrow.

Families: Heteropodidae

LYNX SPIDERS

Lynx spiders are sometimes confused with jumping spiders (next entry) simply because they jump. But unlike jumping spiders, which can jump upwards, lynx spiders merely leap down from surfaces onto their prey or in order to escape.

Lynx spiders are found in woodlands throughout Australia, hunting during the day in low, sun-dappled vegetation. The females have a body length of up to 12 mm and the more slender males can be up to 4 mm long. In other respects, males and females of a species are mostly similar. They have strong, heavily spined legs and are usually brown with a couple of abdominal stripes. Some species are green and unpatterned. The female places her white egg sac on a blade of grass or a leaf and remains with it until the spiderlings hatch.

Family: Oxyopidae
Scientific name: *Oxyopes* spp.

JUMPING SPIDERS ▨

These hunting spiders stalk their prey, making short dashes and then leaping on it. They live throughout Australia and all are harmless to humans, apart from the Queensland green jumping spider (*Mopsus mormon*), which bites.

Jumping spiders fasten themselves to a leaf or other surface with a silk safety line, and then, using their short, muscular legs, leap 20 times their own body length onto their prey in broad daylight. Large eyes give them good vision for hunting.

These spiders have a body length of up to 20 mm and a square or rectangular abdomen that is often brightly coloured, particularly in tropical species.

Males dance when courting, attracting females by signalling with their forelegs, waving them in a sequence characteristic for each species. If the female shows interest, the male raises his abdomen and dances towards her. After mating, the male jumps away to avoid being eaten.

The female places her egg sac, which is usually white, in a curved leaf or under tree bark or a stone, and then covers herself and the sac in a layer of silk.

Peacock jumping spiders (*Maratus* spp.), also known as flying spiders, are particularly striking members of this family. They are most commonly found in the woodlands of New South Wales. The males have vivid iridescent green, red and blue scale-like hairs on their abdomens.

The bodies of both males and females are about 5 mm long, and they have feather-like hairs that wrap around the abdomen. When the spider jumps, these hairs unfurl and the spider can glide through the air for several metres. To give balance and steerage while airborne, the spider's third pair of legs are elongated and covered with dense brushes.

When courting, the male dances in the sunlight so that his flashing colours can be fully appreciated by the watching female.
Family: Salticidae

ANT-MIMICKING SPIDERS ▨

A few Australian spider families in tropical and subtropical regions mimic ants. This subterfuge has distinct advantages, since ants tend

▨ PEACOCK JUMPING SPIDER
The male of this impressive species woos his mate by picking a sunny spot in which to dance and display his brilliantly coloured abdomen.

to be avoided by predators because they produce distasteful formic acid, and because they bite or sting. Ant-mimicking spiders are also safe from the ants they resemble because ants have poor eyesight and fail to detect the spiders in their midst.

Jumping spiders are the most convincing ant-mimics, particularly those of the genus *Myrmarachne*. These spiders look just like ants, down to having their tiny waists, and even behave like them.

Taking advantage of their disguise, some species plunder ants' nests to feed upon larvae. Some have given up jumping for prey, hunting along the margins of ant trails instead.
Families: Salticidae, Corinnidae, Zodariidae

CRAB SPIDERS

Found throughout Australia, crab spiders, which are only 10–15 mm long, resemble crabs and can move sideways as well as forwards. Their front two pairs of legs are longer

and stouter than the back pairs, and are armed with spines. Crab spiders wait with their hind legs grasping the surface and their front legs poised to attack, pouncing on victims with great speed. Once they have crushed the prey with their forelegs, they immobilise it with a bite.

Some colourful members of this family are known as flower spiders (*Diaea* spp.), because they match the blooms on which they sit during the day, stock-still, to ambush visitors. At night, flower spiders hide behind petals or leaves. Other crab spiders live in or under the bark of trees and are often hard to find because they are so well camouflaged.
Family: Thomisidae

NET-CASTING SPIDERS ▨

These remarkable spiders occur widely across Australia, mostly in woodlands, and can often be found in undisturbed corners of gardens along the eastern seaboard. They are grey to russet brown with long abdomens and stilt-like legs that have earned them their other common name, stick spiders. Females, with a body length of up to 25 mm, usually stay outdoors but males, which grow to 12 mm, sometimes venture inside buildings.

The net-casting spider has developed an ingenious technique for snaring prey. Dangling just above ground, it spins a sticky silk net that it holds between its front legs. With its enlarged eyes, which give it excellent vision, the spider sees prey approaching and throws the net over its victim. The captive becomes entangled and the spider then wraps it into a package. The spider bites the prey and then either eats it right away or hangs it up to be eaten later. A new net is needed for each catch.
Family: Deinopidae

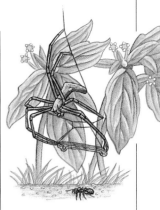

▨ NET-CASTING SPIDER
Dangling from a scaffold web just above ground, the spider spins an elastic net that it holds between its front legs.

With its excellent eyesight, the spider detects approaching prey and spreads its sticky silken net in anticipation.

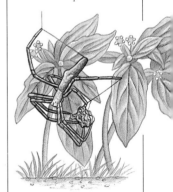

When its prey is within range, the spider throws its net over its victim. The captive is entangled and the spider then uses its hind legs to wrap it into a package. A bite paralyses the meal.

▨ ANT-MIMICKING SPIDER
Standing beside the species of ant that it mimics, the dissembling spider (right) raises its long front legs to resemble antennae.

BLACK HOUSE SPIDERS

These robust spiders frequent loose tree bark and rock crevices and are widely distributed in southern and eastern Australia. Two species, the most toxic of the family, *Badumna insignis*, and the small black house spider, *B. longinquus*, commonly inhabit buildings, spinning their untidy, lacy webs in the corners of rooms and window frames.

B. insignis is dark brown to black. The female's body is 20 mm long and the male is about half her size. *B. longinquus* is a little smaller than *B. insignis* and has a greyish body and grey-brown banded legs.

Females of both species can give humans a severe bite, causing pain, vomiting, dizziness and sweating, but these spiders never leave their webs and are aggressive only if they meet with interference.

The web radiates outwards from a funnel, made up of a muddle of ladders with dry silk poles and zigzag rungs; this is the spider's refuge. After the sun has gone down, the spider advances to the entrance of the funnel and extends its forelegs onto the mainstays of its web. When vibrations indicate that an insect has become entangled, the spider dashes out, trusses up the victim, bites it, and withdraws with it to the safety of the funnel to feed.

The male spider courts the female at her web by plucking at the outer threads with his front legs. The female then leaves her retreat to meet him. When she is sufficiently close, the male uses his front legs to tap out certain cues on the web; these make her immobile long enough for mating to take place.

■ BLACK HOUSE SPIDER
The tangled web of the black house spider radiates out from a funnel, to which the spider retreats for safety.

If the fertilised female does not then consume or chase away her mate, she may tolerate his presence in the brood area – a corner of the web or a nearby crevice – until the eggs are about to hatch. At that point her mood changes, and the male must retreat or suffer the consequences.

The black house spider can be a helpful housemate, as it catches unwelcome insects, such as flies and small cockroaches.
Family: Desidae

DADDY LONG-LEGS SPIDERS

Most Australian members of this family are little known, but the introduced common daddy long-legs spider (*Pholcus phalangioides*), with its distinctive long, spindly legs, often sits in the corner of a house ceiling or beneath a storeroom shelf. It builds a three-dimensional tangle web of dry silk, into which prey blunders and then becomes entrapped. The spider, feeling the presence of the struggling victim through the silken strands, moves quickly towards it, wraps it up and then delivers a fatal bite.

When disturbed, the common daddy long-legs sits at the centre of its web and rapidly vibrates it, so that both spider and web become a blur to the confused predator.

Both sexes of daddy long-legs are about the same size, with a cylindrical abdomen up to 12 mm long. They are pale yellowish brown with some darker markings, particularly on the abdomen.
Family: Pholcidae

RED-AND-BLACK SPIDERS

The bright red to yellow thorax and contrasting velvety black abdomen of the red-and-black spider warn predators that they may find it unpleasant to eat, or even poisonous. In fact, these spiders are harmless and should not be confused with the dangerous redback (page 562). (The redback has a vivid crimson stripe on its black abdomen, which is about the size of a pea.)

Both female and male red-and-black spiders have a body length of up to 10 mm, but the males have longer legs. They are found throughout Australia wherever there is vegetation. They build small, tangled sheet webs close to the ground, and usually under cover. Sometimes a number of webs are grouped together. The spiders hang beneath their webs and draw prey through the mesh. The female suspends her woolly egg sacs within her web.

Sexually active males in search of a mate can sometimes be seen making their way over the ground during the day, and females often bask in the sunshine near their webs. In southern Australia, both male and female red-and-black spiders are active as the weather warms up in spring, especially around the margins of rock outcrops.
Family: Nicodamidae

■ LARGE-JAWED SPIDER
These spiders are easily recognised by their long, slender abdomens and jaws that project well forward of their heads.

LARGE-JAWED SPIDERS

These spiders are also known as long-jawed spiders. Both females (body length 10 mm) and males (body length 8 mm) have prominent, strongly spined jaws. Their forelimbs are long and slender and they have long, cylindrical abdomens.

When a male locates a female in her web, he opens his jaws wide in anticipation of her threatening, open-jawed advance. The female immediately attempts to bite him, but she finds this impossible because the spines of his jaws lock into hers. This forces the forelimbs of both spiders out at right angles to their bodies, allowing the male's sperm-charged palps to reach beyond the combined distance of their locked jaws and into the female's genital opening.

Large-jawed spiders feed on flying insects, which they catch in wheel webs. They generally build their webs horizontally and close to areas of fresh water. The female hangs her long, slender, brown egg sacs alongside the web.

These spiders are found throughout eastern Australia, particularly in damp woodlands and swampy country in coastal regions of New South Wales and Queensland.
Family: Tetragnathidae
Scientific name: *Tetragnatha* spp.

BIRD-POO SPIDERS

Some of the web-building spiders have given up using webs to gather food in favour of a life of mimicry – in a variety of ingenious ways they imitate bird droppings. Since most predators do not find bird faeces very appetising, the disguise is a powerful protective device.

Female bird-poo spiders vary in body length from 3 mm to 3 cm. The males, which are minute in comparison, spend most of their time hidden among the vegetation, waiting for the females to mature, while the females spend their days, unnoticed, generally on a green leaf, waiting for prey. The females are usually shiny dark brown and white.

Bird-poo spiders inhabit the south and east of Australia. How they catch their prey depends in part on their habitat. For those that live in tropical rainforests, salt is the key. All creatures need salt for their metabolic functions, but in the tropics salt is hard to come by because of the constant leaching effect of heavy rain and high humidity. Because fresh bird droppings contain salt, many insects, especially butterflies, love to sip them. Doing so can be dangerous, however, for sometimes the 'bird poo' will snatch the insect and consume it.

Australia's best-known poo mimic is the bird-dung spider (*Celaenia kinbergii*), sometimes known as the orchard spider because it tends to live on fruit trees. Young females of the species build a tiny wheel web to catch their prey, but once they reach sexual maturity they become mimics of bird faeces by day – resting motionless on a leaf with their legs

▨ BIRD-POO SPIDER
Many bird-poo spiders enhance their bird-dropping appearance by spreading patches of dense white silk around them to mimic the splatter area.

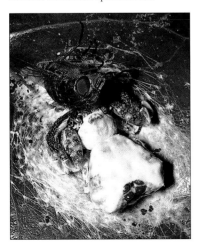

folded closely at their sides – and alchemists of fatal substances after the sun has set.

At dusk, the bird-dung spider sits on a leaf exuding an odour that copies the hormonal compounds of certain female moths. When a male moth picks up the scent it speeds towards it, flying in ever-decreasing spirals to find its source. When the moth is close, the spider grabs it with spiny legs and delivers a deadly bite. Each moth species produces a different hormonal compound and, depending on the time of year, the spider adjusts the odour it emits to mimic the sexual scent of a moth species that is currently mating.
Families: Araneidae, Thomisidae
Scientific names: *Celaenia, Phrynarachne, Archemorus* spp.

BOLAS SPIDERS

Instead of pouncing on their prey, nocturnal bolas spiders have a sophisticated method of trapping male moths with a single thread and a small, sticky silken ball (see box, 'Luring and trapping').

Bolas spiders live among the trees, a couple of metres above ground, in woodlands throughout Tasmania, South Australia, Victoria, New South Wales and Queensland.

The magnificent spider, *Dicrostichus magnificus*, from eastern Australia, is a particularly beautiful bolas spider. The female's body is about 14 mm long, and her abdomen is white with wavy brown lines on the upper surface, salmon-pink dots along the front edge and two yellow nodules on the back. The male is tiny, measuring only 1.5 mm long.
Family: Araneidae
Scientific names: *Dicrostichus, Ordgarius, Cladomelea* spp.

GOLDEN ORB-WEAVERS ▨

Australia's best-known wheel-web builders, golden orb-weavers create permanent webs, up to a metre in diameter, in open woodlands throughout the country. These wonderful webs, often spun from golden silk, are suspended more or less vertically from shrubs and trees well above the ground. They are extraordinarily strong, being resilient enough to enmesh sizeable insects and even predatory birds.

Females are conspicuous by their size (up to 4.5 cm in body length), their black and orange banded legs, and their silvery grey body. They can sit permanently in the centre of their webs because the stickiness of the web protects them, even in daylight. The tiny male golden orb-weaver,

which has a body length of no more than 8 mm, hangs around the outskirts of the female's web, often overlooked by the casual observer.

As a juvenile, the male feeds on small prey caught in the web, but on maturity he ventures into the centre of the web while the female is preoccupied with food, and mates with her. She may not even notice him!
Family: Araneidae
Scientific name: *Nephila* spp.

▨ GOLDEN ORB-WEAVER
Found throughout the continent, golden orb-weaving spiders and their finely constructed wheel webs are common in neglected corners of backyards.

LURING AND TRAPPING

At dusk, the female bolas spider emerges from her hideaway and suspends herself on a horizontal line of silk on a moth flight path. She then spins a length of thread, 50–70 mm long, which remains attached to her spinnerets but is controlled by her outstretched foreleg. At the end of the thread hangs a small, sticky ball of silk, called a bolas (after a type of lasso), and along the thread are tiny beads of liquid gum.

The spider exudes hormonal compounds that mimic those given off by females of certain moth species. As a male moth flies towards the spider in response, searching for a mate, the spider senses its wingbeats and swings its bolas in a wide arc. The beads of gum and the bolas stick to the moth which attempts to fly away but soon becomes exhausted. It is then hauled in, bitten, wrapped in silk – and eaten.

ST ANDREW'S CROSS SPIDERS

This spider, which is found among shrubs and tall grasses throughout Australia, makes a distinctive large wheel web with four spokes of zigzagged silk at the centre, forming a cross. When threatened, these spiders vibrate their webs vigorously so that they become invisible to predators. The cross, known as a stabilimentum, provides the support necessary to keep the web intact through such bouts of vibration.

Usually brightly banded in red, yellow, white and black, the females have a body length of about 15 mm, whereas the less colourful males are no more than 10 mm long. Males pluck at the female's web to signal their presence, and a duet of plucking ensues before mating takes place. Males are often maimed during copulation, and it is not unusual to see individuals with only a few legs.

The egg sacs, which are coloured to blend in with the surroundings, are suspended by strands of golden silk from vegetation near the web.
Family: Araneidae
Scientific name: *Argiope* spp.

■ ST ANDREW'S CROSS SPIDER
The female St Andrew's Cross spider remains at the centre of its web during the day, with its legs in pairs along the arms of the cross.

GARDEN ORB-WEAVERS

Most Australian city-dwellers are familiar with these spring and summer garden spiders – *Eriophora transmarinas* in the east of the country and *E. biapicatus* in the west. Their webs often stretch across pathways, causing concern, both to the people who walk into them and to the spiders that must repair them.

Garden orb-weaver females construct their wheel webs after the sun has set, taking less than an hour to complete them. These webs are among the most specialised of silk constructions, but the simplicity of their design means that the spiders can change location easily to take advantage of seasonal movements of insect prey. Because of their fragility, the webs need rebuilding every three or four days.

Moths are usually snared in garden orb-weaver webs as they fly towards house or street lights. Many manage to break free, because moth wings are covered in scales that easily become dislodged during the course of a struggle in the web, but those that are less fortunate are quickly trussed up in silk and then bitten. The spider either eats the moth immediately or hangs it from the web for a late supper.

Adult orb-weavers are heavily built and hairy. The female has a body length of 3 cm and the male is 2 cm long. Their colouring depends on where they live, for they take on the shades of their surroundings – the bark and leaves among which they hide during the day.

In common with most web spiders, the male lurks on the outskirts of the web. When courting, he announces his intentions from the margin of the female's web by plucking the silk, all the while nervously advancing. If she is receptive, she meets him about halfway, where mating may occurs. However, if she is hungry or already pregnant, the male may well become her next meal.
Family: Araneidae

SPINY SPIDERS

Spiny spiders have distinctive short legs and six prominent spines on their broad abdomens. These spines are sometimes long and sharp. Spiny spiders are probably the most hard-bodied of all spiders, and this, with their spines, makes them unappealing prey for wasps and birds.

The females have a body length of 10–15 mm and, as with many spider species, the males are a little smaller. The females of most common species are shiny black

■ SPINY SPIDER
The sharp spines on the body of this female spiny spider are clearly visible. Spiny spiders are sometimes known as Christmas or jewel spiders.

with white and bright orange or yellow markings, whereas the males are generally plain black.

Spiny spiders are found in bushland throughout mainland Australia, often near creeks and marshes. They frequently occur in huge colonies, with hundreds or even thousands of their vertical wheel webs interlocking. In some parts of southern Australia, it is difficult to walk along bush trails without brushing against their webs. During autumn, the females hang their egg sacs on plants close to their webs.
Family: Araneidae
Scientific name: *Gasteracantha* spp.

LEAF-CURLING SPIDERS

A variety of leaf-curling spiders are found in woodlands across Australia. Adult leaf-curling spiders create a leafy retreat within their orb web. They seek out a fallen leaf, or some other suitable object – sometimes a scrap of paper or an empty snail shell – and haul it up into their web on a thread of silk. Once the leaf is stabilised, the spider curls it up with silk and knits it into the main frame of the web.

Nestled in its new home, the spider then sits and waits for prey, protected from the weather and well camouflaged. Usually, all that can be seen of the spider is its forelegs poking out from the leaf.

The leaf also forms a brood chamber and nursery. As juveniles, leaf-curlers build a wheel web, but they do not create a leaf shelter.

Female leaf-curlers have a bulbous, marbled brown abdomen and grow to about 14 mm in body length. The slimmer male is similar in colouring, but grows to only 12 mm.
Family: Araneidae
Scientific name: *Phonognatha* spp.

CRUSTACEANS

Crustaceans live everywhere in the seas, from the ocean depths to the intertidal shores. Many live in fresh water, while a few have a land-based existence. Over 30 000 species have been described, ranging from water fleas smaller than a pinhead to crabs weighing as much as 17 kg, and many more are awaiting discovery. Some, such as crabs and shrimps, are predators, but most feed on plant and animal debris.

Crustaceans have a segmented body and an exoskeleton – a supportive structure on the outside of the body. This varies from a thin, transparent layer in some tiny crustaceans to a thick, shell-like carapace that covers the thorax in crayfish and crabs. There are appendages on the head for feeding and sensing the surroundings, and appendages on the thorax and abdomen for walking, swimming, respiration and mating. In many cases, one or more of the walking legs forms a claw.

Two classes of crustaceans are rare; two (the branchiopods and the maxillopods) consist of an assortment of so-called primitive animals; and the fifth group, the malacostracans, includes all the most commonly seen species, such as prawns, shrimps, rock lobsters and crabs.

Female crustaceans generally lay eggs that hatch as larvae, although in some cases the eggs hatch as miniature adults. The females of some crustaceans, such as crayfish and crabs, carry their eggs until they hatch. The larvae then grow into adults, forming part of the plankton while in the open sea.

Other crustaceans, for example, opossum shrimps, carry their young with them until they can fend for themselves. Hatchlings grow quickly and moult frequently, first casting their shells every few hours, then every few days. As they mature, the period between moults extends to weeks and eventually longer.
Subphylum: Crustacea

FAIRY SHRIMPS

These curious creatures, 3–4 cm long, have no carapace and swim upside down – that is, with their feet uppermost. They use their many pairs of swimming legs to funnel food particles towards their mouth.

Because they inhabit temporary pools and lakes in arid parts of Australia, fairy shrimps lay drought-resistant eggs that can survive, blown about in the dust, for as long as 25 years. When rain falls and puddles form, the eggs lying in the mud hatch out. The shrimps grow to maturity quickly in order to mate and lay their eggs before the puddle evaporates. The extraordinary brine shrimp, *Artemia salina*, can tolerate water that is ten times saltier than the sea.
Class: Branchiopoda; Order: Anostraca

SHIELD SHRIMPS

Australia's two shield shrimp species scramble about in the mud of freshwater pools feeding on food particles. In arid country, the olive green *Triops australiensis* appears in puddles after rain, when minute dried eggs hatch. The young quickly grow and in turn lay eggs before the mud dries out. The bright green *Lepidurus apus* lives in cooler, wetter regions.

The shield shrimp's body consists of a circular or oval carapace covering the legs and a narrow tail. Shield shrimps grow to 9 cm long.
Class: Branchiopoda; Order: Notostraca

WATER FLEAS

Water fleas are so named because they are flea-sized (0.25–6 mm) and their jerky way of swimming somewhat resembles jumping. The head, with swimming antennae, protrudes from the water flea's carapace.

Most of the hundred or so Australian species of water flea inhabit freshwater pools and streams, but a few live in the sea.
Class: Branchiopoda; Order: Cladocera

CLAM SHRIMPS

Clam shrimps look quite similar to bivalve molluscs, but they have a segmented body with many pairs of jointed legs inside the carapace. None of Australia's 20 species of clam shrimp is common. Usually less than 10 mm long, these creatures live in the soft mud on the bottom of freshwater lakes and ponds.
Class: Branchiopoda; Order: Conchostraca

ROCK LOBSTER ANATOMY
Despite its common name, the rock lobster is not a true lobster. It has five pairs of walking legs but no claws or nippers.

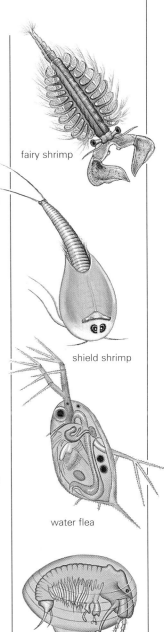

fairy shrimp

shield shrimp

water flea

clam shrimp

BRANCHIOPODS
The forms of these small animals are immensely varied, ranging from the fairy shrimp, which has no shell and swims upside down propelled by its many legs, to the clam shrimp, which is enclosed in a bivalve carapace and scrambles around on the bottom.

tail fan

long antennae for smelling and touching

segmented abdomen

swimmerets (beneath abdomen)

carapace to protect thorax and gills

walking legs (five pairs)

stalked, mobile eyes

short antennae

OSTRACODS

Ostracods are minute crustaceans, rarely growing to more than 2 mm long. They look rather like clam shrimps (page 569).

The few segments that comprise an ostracod's body are enclosed in a two-valved carapace that protects the animal from predators but opens wide enough for its antennae and legs to protrude. When danger threatens, the ostracod withdraws into its shell and closes it tightly.

Some larger species of ostracod inhabit the deeper parts of the sea, swimming about by flicking their long antennae. Most, however, do not swim but scramble around on the sea floor or on the bottom of lakes and ponds, using their antennae for crawling and burrowing. Australia is unusual in having a number of terrestrial species of ostracod that live among the leaf litter on damp forest floors.

Some ostracods are filter feeders, some eat organic material, and some prey on other small animals. By consuming rotten plant and animal matter, these creatures play an important part in maintaining the health of ecosystems.

Ostracods are found throughout Australia. Several of the most common ostracod species can be observed as green specks moving about at the bottom of puddles.

There are many species of marine ostracod in Australia. One marine family, the Cypridinidae, includes species that emit a bright blue light when they are disturbed at night. Others are scavengers, cleaning up the bodies of dead fishes in the sea.

Class: Maxillopoda; Subclass: Ostracoda

COPEPODS

The world's thousands of copepod species, which are usually less than 2 mm long, live almost anywhere there is water. They have only a short carapace and are extremely varied in form. While freshwater species are common in dams and lakes, copepods are often the dominant members of the marine plankton. Some marine copepods are parasites of fishes and other animals.

Some copepods consume plants, such as algae; some eat other tiny animals; and some are filter feeders, removing minute particles from the water. In turn, they are food for larger animals. Most copepods are swimmers, using their first pair of antennae like oars.

Class: Maxillopoda; Subclass: Copepoda

BARNACLES

Intertidal rocks on Australian shores are marked by the prolific growth of acorn barnacles – one of the two main forms of barnacle. They have so successfully adapted to living a protected life in one place that they are barely recognisable as crustaceans. Instead, they look like limpets or miniature volcanoes.

The barnacle larva attaches itself to a fixed or moving surface and creates chalky plates that gradually enclose it in a shell. As the barnacle grows to adulthood, it turns over so that it lies with its back to the object to which its shell is attached.

Many barnacles live in the intertidal zone and so spend a portion of the day out of the water. During these hours, the barnacle keeps its shell closed in order to stay moist. When submerged, it opens its shell and uses its six pairs of feathery legs to filter food from the water.

Acorn barnacles, the most abundant type, attach their plates to intertidal rocks, mangrove roots or wharf piles. One species of acorn barnacle that is commonly seen in southern Australia is the estuarine barnacle (*Elminius modestus*). Its soft body is enclosed in

■ MANTIS SHRIMP
These beautifully coloured tropical crustaceans live on reef flats, where they prey on fishes, crabs and molluscs.

a ring of four grey plates that grows to 6 mm across. The giant rock barnacle (*Austromegabalanus nigrescens*) is whitish or green-grey, turning black when eroded, and grows 5 cm high.

The goose barnacle (*Lepas anatifera*) grows in clusters on floating logs or buoys, and is seen only when it is washed up on beaches. Its body is enclosed in shiny, flat shell-plates on the end of a flexible stalk that can be 45 cm long. Other forms of goose barnacle live attached to rocks just beneath the tide line.

Class: Maxillopoda; Subclass: Cirripedia

MANTIS SHRIMPS

These creatures, which resemble prawns, live in burrows in coral or intertidal sandflats and are found Australia-wide. Their body consists of a thorax partly covered by a short carapace and a long abdomen ending in a tail fan. Tucked beneath the thorax they have strong claws, like those of a praying mantis, that can swiftly be extended. Behind the claws are six pairs of legs.

Mantis shrimps are aggressive predators, darting from their burrows or coral crevices and crushing their victims with their claws. Many species are brightly coloured, especially in the tropics, where some grow to 50 cm long, but they are commonly less than 15 cm in length.

Class: Malacostraca; Order: Stomatopoda

■ BARNACLES
Goose barnacles live largely in the open sea, attached by their stalks to the hulls of ships and pieces of floating debris. These ones are on a log that has been washed ashore.

MOUNTAIN SHRIMPS ▪

Found only in freshwater ponds and streams, mountain shrimps are confined to Australia and New Zealand and most species live in southern Australia. These shrimps are 5 mm to 5 cm long and are without a carapace, so their many body segments are quite easy to see.

The Tasmanian mountain shrimp, *Anaspides tasmaniae*, which lives in streams and pools in the mountains, is the largest member of the group. It half swims, half walks over vegetation on hairs at the ends of its flattened legs. The female lays her eggs on the stream or pool bottom, where they hatch as miniature adults.
Class: Malacostraca; Order: Anaspidacea

PERACARIDANS

There are thousands of peracaridan species, and new ones are constantly being discovered. These creatures live in marine, freshwater and terrestrial habitats. The most commonly seen groups are opossum shrimps, cumaceans, isopods and amphipods.

Unlike many other crustaceans, peracaridans have no larval stage. The male places sperm inside the female using specially adapted legs. When the eggs are laid, the female carries them in a brood pouch under her body between the walking legs, within which they hatch. After a couple of moults, the young emerge from the pouch as miniature adults.
Class: Malacostraca;
Superorder: Peracarida

OPOSSUM SHRIMPS
The common name of these crustaceans comes from the female's brooding behaviour. Like all peracaridans, she looks after both eggs and young in a brood pouch, as possums and kangaroos do.

Opossum shrimps, which grow to about 10 mm long, swim in dense swarms of hundreds or thousands, often close to the sea floor. Sometimes glassily transparent, sometimes brightly coloured, these shrimps are most likely to be seen simply as pairs of stalked black eyes darting about. One of the most colourful species is the red and white opossum shrimp, *Heteromysis harpaxoides,* which is common on the Great Barrier Reef. It lives in shells occupied by hermit crabs of the genus *Dardanus* (page 576). It is believed that the shrimp cleans the shell by feeding on its host's faeces. Other species of opossum shrimp live in association with sponges, anemones and corals.
Order: Mysidacea

CUMACEANS
Cumaceans have no distinct head. Their thorax is partly enclosed in a carapace, and they have a long, thin abdomen with a forked tail.

The largest cumaceans are no more than 15 mm long, and many are much smaller. They are found Australia-wide, living just below the surface of marine sand or mud, where they feed by filtering microscopic particles from the water.
Order: Cumacea

ISOPODS ▪
No species of isopod can be seen as typical. Many are marine, but some live in fresh water or on land. Some are free-living and others are parasitic. Australia's numerous species include representatives of most of the world's 95 isopod families – some flat and some cylindrical in shape. Identifying characteristics are that most of their seven pairs of legs are similar to each other and they have only one pair of tail limbs.

Sea lice are scavengers that feed on a variety of creatures and can reduce a dead fish to a skeleton in a few hours. They are called sea lice because they sometimes attack swimmers, causing bleeding from a small wound. Sea lice rest buried in sand but swim to search for food. Most shallow-water species are no more than 1 cm long, but members of the deep-sea genus *Bathynomus* can be as large as a football.

Fish lice are parasites that burrow into the flesh of fishes, attaching themselves to the gills or the inside of the mouth, where they feed on blood but cause little damage. Fish lice attach themselves to their host using strong hooks on their legs. They reach a length of up to 5 cm, and are often twisted and shiny white. Leatherjackets are particularly susceptible to fish lice.

Wood washed into the sea supports a variety of crustaceans. Like termites on land, gribble burrow into wood and can be serious pests in wharf pilings and boats. These marine isopods, up to 6 mm long, use their strong jaws to dig narrow burrows. Microflora in their gut enable them to digest the wood cellulose.

Marine pill bugs, which are grey or multi-coloured, roll into a ball when threatened. Australia's hundreds of species of marine pill bug live on the undersides of rocks and in coral crevices and can burrow into soft rock as well as mud.

The bodies of sandskaters are flattened, disc-shaped and patchily coloured, providing them with camouflage so they can swim or walk about on sand in the shallows without being seen. None of the legs is visible from above, but the first pair form claws. Australian species are no more than 10 mm long.

Sea centipedes feed on seaweed in shallow water on southern shores. Of the 27 species living in Australia, many are green or red to match the algae in which they hide.

The shiny grey pill bug (*Armadillidium vulgare*), found in gardens throughout Australia, was introduced from Europe, brought in with exotic plants. When threatened, this isopod rolls into a ball the size of a small ball bearing. Another European terrestrial isopod found throughout the continent is the slater (*Porcellio scaber*). It favours moist habitats, such as damp leaf litter.
Order: Isopoda

▪ MOUNTAIN SHRIMP
The Tasmanian mountain shrimp is found in chilly streams in the high country, where it feeds on decaying plant and animal material and algae.

▪ ISOPOD
Fish lice, which are parasites, are among Australia's many species of marine isopod. Here, a fish louse is attached to the head of a reef fish.

AMPHIPODS

There are almost 200 families of amphipods, and thousands of species. Few are larger than a mosquito. They are either long, thin and slow-moving or compact and agile, and their bodies are usually flattened from side to side. They are best characterised by three pairs of tail limbs and the frequent modification of the first two pairs of legs so that they can grasp food.

Skeleton shrimps (family Caprellidae) are thin and elongated and have large front legs that form nippers. Using smaller legs on their tiny abdomen, they attach themselves to seaweed while catching passing food with their nippers. They live in large numbers in shallows along the shore and take the colour of the seaweed.

Sandhoppers and garden hoppers belong to the family Talitridae. Pale scavengers that live among decaying seaweed thrown up on beaches, sandhoppers feed on the weed and dead fishes. Their bodies are modified for springing: by flicking their tails they can jump several times their own length to escape predators. Garden hoppers are brown terrestrial amphipods that live under rocks and litter in southern Australia and leap about when disturbed.

Order: Amphipoda

■ AMPHIPOD
The bodies of these tiny creatures, no more than a few millimetres long, are usually flattened from side to side. They have no carapace.

A HARD LIFE OUT OF WATER

While crustaceans live mainly in the sea, several isopod and amphipod families are terrestrial. In this environment, crustaceans have to compete with other terrestrial arthropods, such as insects and spiders. The crustaceans are at a considerable disadvantage because they breathe oxygen through gills that must be kept damp, so most terrestrial crustaceans spend their time beneath leaf litter on the forest floor to avoid the rays of the sun.

The slater and the pill bug (below) are only two of several hundred species of terrestrial isopod that live in Australian forests, grasslands and gardens. Few would believe that these familiar animals are not insects, but a count of their legs – seven pairs in all – confirms that they are indeed crustaceans.

KRILL ■

Krill are superficially similar to prawns, in that they have a body enclosed in a carapace and a long, muscular abdomen. However, their gills, at the bases of the legs, are exposed instead of being covered by the carapace. Unlike prawns, which spend most of their time close to the sea bottom and in estuaries, krill live in the open ocean.

These crustaceans are best known as the food of baleen whales. The whales scoop up vast mouthfuls of water and filter out the krill by expelling the water through horny food-filtering plates (called baleen) around their mouths.

The Antarctic krill (*Euphausia superba*) grows to about 8 cm, but the numerous krill species found in Australian waters are rarely more than 3 cm long.

Class: Malacostraca; Order: Euphausiacea

DECAPODS

Many well known crustaceans, such as prawns, rock lobsters and crabs, are decapods – meaning that they have ten limbs. These limbs are very noticeable; some, usually four pairs, are called walking legs, as they are used for moving about. Sometimes the front pair are not used for walking but are modified into claws.

Decapods fall into two groups. One group includes prawns (opposite page) and their relatives. The other group includes shrimps, freshwater crayfish, scampi, rock lobsters and crabs. The difference between the two lies in the way they treat their eggs. Prawn eggs are released by the female and develop while drifting in the sea. Those of crabs and their relatives are carried by the female under her abdomen (she is said to be 'in berry' during this time) until they hatch as larvae, which then swim in the open water.

Prawns also differ from other decapods in the way they move about. Prawns swim, using their swimmerets – appendages on their abdomen adapted for the purpose – whereas other decapods usually (but not always) walk or crawl.

Freshwater crayfish, some commonly known as yabbies (page 575) and scampi (page 574) are characterised by having one pair of strong claws, and then two pairs of legs,

■ KRILL
Many species of krill congregate in dense swarms of millions of individuals, forming part of the marine plankton.

which have tiny nippers at the end. All have a muscular tail.

Rock lobsters (page 575) live in the sea but are sometimes also referred to as crayfish. Like freshwater crayfish, rock lobsters have a thick exoskeleton and a muscular tail, but they have no claws or nippers of any sort. This differentiates them from true lobsters, which are not found in Australian waters.

Hermit crabs (page 576) and their crab-like allies, which include squat lobsters (page 576) and porcelain crabs (page 576), have one pair of claws and four pairs of walking legs. The back pair are so short that they are scarcely ever seen.

True crabs range in size from less than 2 mm across to as much as 40 cm across in the case of the Tasmanian giant crab, *Pseudocarcinus gigas*. Crabs are characterised by the lack of a tail fan and by their small abdomen. In males, the abdomen is visible as a tiny triangular area set into the underside of the body, and in females as a larger oval segmented plate bearing several hidden pairs of modified limbs, to which the eggs are attached.

The crab is covered by a tough carapace, from which the claws and four pairs of walking legs protrude. Crabs move sideways, generally with great speed and agility. In front, their antennae are relatively short and their eyes are small, stalked and mobile.

Almost all of the 30 or so crab families in the world occur in Australia, more in tropical than temperate environments. Species number over a thousand and most are marine, though one family, the freshwater crabs (page 577), can be found in lowland streams.

Class: Malacostraca; Order: Decapoda

PRAWNS

Prawns live along most coasts of Australia but are rare off cool, exposed southern shores. They have three pairs of nippers of similar size, and swim about close to the sea bottom using their swimmerets.

Female prawns lay their eggs in spawning grounds offshore, and the young moult through a series of larval stages while forming part of the plankton. After a few weeks, the young prawns swim to the sea floor and migrate into bays and estuaries, where they grow rapidly, feeding on the plentiful food on the muddy bottom. After almost a year the prawns migrate back into deeper water, where they lay their eggs. Most of the adults then die.

The most common prawns on the east coast are the king prawn (*Penaeus plebejus*), about 30 cm long, and translucent creamy yellow coloured with blue edges on the tail fan; and the school prawn (*Metapenaeus macleayi*), 16 cm long, with similar blue markings on its tail. The western king prawn (*Penaeus latisulcatus*) inhabits waters off the coasts of Western Australia, South Australia, the Northern Territory, Queensland and Asia.

The jumbo tiger prawn (*Penaeus monodon*), found throughout Asia and around the northern coast from Shark Bay in Western Australia to Sydney, grows to 33 cm and is brown with tiger-like stripes. The banana prawn (*Penaeus merguiensis*), of northern Australia and Asia, grows to 24 cm and is cream to yellow with a reddish tinge. The greentail prawn (*Metapenaeus bennettae*), also known as the greasyback, grows to 11 cm and lives in eastern Australia; it is the only member of the family that spends its life in estuarine waters.
Family: Penaeidae

GHOST SHRIMPS ■

Soft-bodied and pale, ghost shrimps are appropriately named, although they are also sometimes known as Bass yabbies or one-armed bandits. They are seldom seen, as they live buried in mud or sand, in coral crevices, or in rock fissures. They feed on bacteria and rotting seagrass. They have a flexible abdomen that is longer than the thorax.

Using one of their nippers, which is usually longer than the other, ghost shrimps construct extensive zigzag burrows with two openings. Some species in tropical lagoons grow to 30 cm long and build high, conical mounds of sand around the mouths of their burrows.

More than 30 ghost shrimp species live in Australian waters, but only *Trypaea australiensis* is commonly seen. This species grows to 6.5 cm and is found in large numbers on intertidal seagrass mudflats. The male's larger claw is stronger and more elaborate than the female's.
Family: Callianassidae

MUD LOBSTERS

Australia's mud lobsters are confined to the tropical mangrove forests, where they tunnel out a burrow 2 metres deep, leaving a tall chimney of mud around the entrance. All species are brown. They have two similar flattened claws and a small abdomen.

The Australian mud lobster (*Thalassina squamifera*) grows to 14 cm long. Its burrows are common across the muddy shores of northern Australia, but it is not often seen because it spends almost all its time deep in its water-filled burrow.
Family: Thalassinidae

WEED SHRIMPS

Herbert Hale, an early Australian marine biologist, described weed shrimps as 'an assortment of queer shrimps, many gaily coloured.' Many species are associated with seaweeds, and they take on the colours of these plants – bright red, green or purple. Even within one species, individual weed shrimps less than a metre or two from one another differ in colour, depending on their surroundings, and change colour when they move to another plant or are placed in a bucket.

The Australian weed shrimp (*Hippolyte australiensis*), which grows to 25 mm long, lives hidden in beds of seaweed along the southern coast. It is distinguished from many other species by a strong bend in the tail and a spike, notched underneath, between the eyes.
Family: Hippolytidae

SNAPPING SHRIMPS ■

When the tide is out, some rocky shores and mudflats resound with the clicks of snapping shrimps – sometimes called pistol shrimps. By snapping the short fingers at the end of its larger claw, the shrimp generates a pressure wave strong enough to deter a predator or to stun prey, such as other crustaceans and small fishes. Once the victim is immobilised, the shrimp grabs it with its claws and eats it. The shrimp's stalked eyes are hidden beneath a visor that extends from the front of the carapace.

Some species of snapping shrimp form an association with small tropical fishes known as gobies. The shrimp digs a deep burrow and allows the goby to retreat backwards into it whenever danger threatens. Hovering at the entrance to the burrow, the goby maintains contact with the shrimp's antennae, giving it warning of approaching trouble. These shrimps are often found in male–female pairs.

Of the several hundred species of snapping shrimp that inhabit Australian seashores, the green snapping shrimp, *Alpheus euphro-syne*, is the most common. It grows to 6.5 cm long and lives in burrows in intertidal seagrass flats along most sheltered coasts.
Family: Alpheidae

■ GHOST SHRIMP
The fragile, pale ghost shrimp digs its some-times extensive burrow in mudflats or in coral rubble around reefs.

■ SNAPPING SHRIMP
The goby and the snapping shrimp provide one another with protection. Here a shrimp is at work digging its burrow.

■ PALAEMONID
SHRIMP
Holthuis's shrimp,
a species of palaemonid,
lives on several kinds of
sea anemone and coral.
This female is carrying
eggs, which is referred to
as being 'in berry.'

■ PALAEMONID
SHRIMP
Holthuis's shrimp,
a species of palaemonid,
lives on several kinds of
sea anemone and coral.
This female is carrying
eggs, which is referred to
as being 'in berry.'

■ CORAL SHRIMP
The banded coral shrimp
is red and white with
long white feelers. This
one is cleaning parasites
from a green moray eel.

PALAEMONID SHRIMPS ■

Australia's hundreds of palaemonid shrimp species vary greatly in size, shape, habit and habitat. Palaemonids can be distinguished from most other shrimp families by the long claws that they bear on their second, rather than first, pair of legs.

One palaemonid species, the glass shrimp (*Palaemon serenus*), is common around the southern Australian coast. It grows to the size of a human thumb, but its body is glassy and transparent, so that it is usually detectable only as a pair of red wrist-bands on the claws and a pair of black eyes. It walks about on the bottom of rock pools and darts into seaweed when disturbed.

The largest and most widespread shrimp in the freshwater pools and streams of tropical Australia is the long-armed shrimp, *Macrobrachium rosenbergi*. It grows to almost 30 cm long, is bluish and has long claws. Similar, smaller species live in the rivers of southern Australia.

Many palaemonid shrimps live in close association with other marine animals, such as corals, sponges, anemones, molluscs and echinoderms, but the nature of these relationships is not fully known. These species are rarely seen in cool waters, but coral reefs are home to many. Most are no bigger than 20 mm and are brightly coloured or almost glassy, with patches of colour.
Family: Palaemonidae

CORAL SHRIMPS ■

Lurking in a crevice, the coral shrimp waves its long antennae to attract fishes, which swim towards it. These shrimps are cleaners: they nibble all over the surface of a fish, removing any parasites. While shrimps normally have two pairs of nippers, the coral shrimps have three, the third being much larger than the others. Unlike prawns, however, which also have three pairs of nippers, coral shrimps carry their eggs under their abdomen.

Stenopus species live in rock crevices and among coral from low-tide level to considerable depths. The banded coral shrimp (*Stenopus hispidus*) is a spiky creature up to 6 cm long, with red and white markings and long white feelers. Banded coral shrimps almost always occur in pairs as adults, with the male sometimes riding on the back of the female.
Family: Stenopodidae

FRESHWATER SHRIMPS

Most freshwater shrimps live in rivers or lakes, but some unusual Australian species live in dark, tropical limestone caves. Freshwater shrimps have tiny brushes on the tips of the first two pairs of legs, probably for scraping microscopic algae from rocks and mud to eat.

The common freshwater shrimp, *Paratya australiensis*, occurs in lakes, streams and ponds in eastern Australia, usually close to aquatic plants on the banks. Its body, up to 3 cm long, is so clear that the gut and heart within can be seen. The long spike extending forward between the eyes distinguishes this shrimp from yabbies.
Family: Atyidae

HINGE-BEAK SHRIMPS ■

These brilliantly coloured shrimps have the unusual feature of a hinged rostrum between the eyes. They grow to 8 cm long and are found at low-water levels on rocky coasts in temperate regions.

Rhynchocinetes rugulosus, which lives off the east coast, is olive green or blue, and strongly patterned with bars and circles. *R. australis*, found in Victoria and South Australia, is reddish orange.
Family: Rhynchocinetidae

■ HINGE-BEAK SHRIMP
Hinge-beak shrimps have the extraordinary feature of a hinged rostrum – the large beak-like protuberance.

SCAMPI

These pink or orange crustaceans resemble the true lobsters of the northern hemisphere, but are more like a marine version of a freshwater crayfish. They reach a total length of about 25 cm, and their claws are as long as the animal itself.

Most scampi belong to the genus *Metanephrops* and are characterised by a strong, toothed spike between their large eyes. They are found right around the Australian coast, but since they live offshore in deep waters, they are scarcely ever seen in their natural habitat.
Family: Nephropidae

FRESHWATER CRAYFISH

Hundreds of species of freshwater crayfish live in the streams, rivers, lakes and dams of Australia. Many river systems have their own particular crayfish species that is quite different from those in neighbouring catchments.

The first pair of walking legs of these heavy-bodied crustaceans form large claws or nippers, which they use for grasping food, digging burrows and defending themselves. Fresh-water crayfish vary markedly in colour, and range in size from 2.5 cm to 40 cm long.

Probably the best known species is the smooth freshwater crayfish, *Cherax destructor*, generally known as the yabby, which is widespread throughout inland south-eastern Australia. About 18 cm long, it is usually dull brown or green but bright blue forms are also known. The marron, *C. tenuimanus*, is a larger species native to southern Western Australia.

Australia has the world's largest freshwater crayfish – the Tasmanian giant crayfish, *Astacopsis gouldii*, which grows to 40 cm long and can weigh more than 3.5 kilograms. It lives in Tasmania's swamps and streams. Unfortunately, large specimens are rarely found today because of loss of habitat and overfishing. This crayfish's tail is covered with rows of spikes, similar to those of its mainland cousin, the Murray crayfish, *Euastacus armatus*, that lives in the Murray River basin, and grows to 30 cm long.
Family: Parastacidae

ROCK LOBSTERS

Rock lobsters are marine crustaceans; they are sometimes called crayfish, although crayfish are freshwater species. They have a thick, spiny carapace, a muscular tail and five pairs of walking legs. Unlike true lobsters, which do not occur in Australia, they are without claws or, indeed, nippers of any sort.

Twelve rock lobster species live in Australia. Most of them inhabit warm tropical waters, but the two species that are commercially fished in Australia – the southern rock lobster and the western rock lobster – are both from southern waters.

Rock lobsters live in crannies and caves on reefs along the coast in offshore waters. They usually hide during the day and search for food at night. They are opportunistic feeders and will eat any creatures that are available, from sea urchins to molluscs. Sometimes they even

prey on each other, particularly when the victim is incapacitated in some way.

In females, the paddle-shaped appendages under the abdomen, known as swimmerets, have inner spurs carrying bristles to which the fertilised eggs are attached. Females carry the eggs for 4–8 weeks, at which time the larvae hatch and are released to drift in the plankton on sea currents. After 11 months, the young drift back to the reefs. It takes about five years for youngsters to grow to adulthood.

The southern rock lobster, *Jasus novaehollandiae*, is a reddish species that grows to 50 cm long and is found in the waters off the southern coast of Australia. The tail is covered with small plates and the two branches at the end of the smaller

pair of feelers are very small. Deep-water forms are pale in colour.

The western rock lobster (*Panulirus cygnus*), which lives along the south-eastern coast of Western Australia, is much smoother and does not grow quite as large (45 cm). A distinguishing feature is that the two branches on its smaller pair of feelers are almost half as long as the stronger pair. This species takes almost four years to grow to legally edible size: a year in the plankton of the Indian Ocean and then three years living among the beds of seaweed on reefs below tidal levels.

The tropical painted rock lobster, *Panulirus versicolor*, is an exceedingly attractive species. It has black markings on its carapace and black and white stripes on its green abdomen.
Family: Palinuridae

■ ROCK LOBSTERS
Southern rock lobsters are gregarious. They live in groups under rock ledges or in crevices in caves on coastal and offshore reefs.

■ FRESHWATER CRAYFISH
Native to the Lamington Plateau in south-eastern Queensland, this blue freshwater crayfish lives in rainforest streams and launches itself fearlessly down waterfalls.

■ HERMIT CRAB
Some hermit crabs have adapted to living on land. This member of the genus *Coenobita* is feeding on a dead tern chick on the shores of a coral cay in the Great Barrier Reef.

■ BALMAIN BUG
Balmain bugs have no claws and so they use their flattened antennae to dig into sand and mud on the ocean floor.

BUGS ■

Bugs have a flattened carapace and broad, flattened antennae, and grow to about 20 cm long. Most species live in tropical waters but the Balmain bug (*Ibacus peronii*) occurs in southern waters. The Moreton Bay bug (*Thenus orientalis*), which is similar, is found in the north, particularly in Queensland. When not feeding, bugs hide in the sand.

The sculptured slipper lobster (*Parribacus antarcticus*), also a tropical species, is ochre or pale brown, and is not as flattened as the other two species. It has short, flat, plate-like antennae, grows to 25 cm long, and sometimes preys on giant clams.
Family: Scyllaridae

HERMIT CRABS ■

Hermit crabs are squatters, settling in an abandoned home – the shell of a dead snail. Hermit crabs have a soft abdomen that is usually twisted spirally, and their tail holds them firmly within the borrowed shell.

Using its two pairs of walking legs, the crab skilfully carries or drags its shell along. The first pair of limbs are strong claws; under threat, the crab retreats into the shell, plugging the opening with these claws, and is almost impossible to dislodge.

As the crab grows, it needs a larger home, so it inspects empty shells and moves into a suitable new one. Sometimes it rejects its new home, returns to the old one and resumes the search. Some hermit crabs prefer the shells of certain molluscs, but most use those of a range of species. The smallest species grow to only a few millimetres, but others need shells up to 30 cm long. Fights over empty shells are quite common.

Most hermit crabs live in shallow water or around tropical reefs, but the crazy crab, *Coenobita variabilis*, occurs above the high-tide mark in Australia's tropics. At night it leaves its burrow to feed. Its round, reddish left claw is larger than its right.

In Clarrie's hermit crab, *Pagurixus handrecki*, the right claw is stronger than the left, especially in males. This cream-brown hermit crab occurs in Victoria, living among sea-grasses and in shallow, rocky areas.

The tropical spotted red dardanus, *Dardanus megistos*, one of Australia's largest hermit crabs, grows to 30 cm long. Its red body is covered with blue-ringed white spots.
Families: Diogenidae, Paguridae, Coenobitidae

SQUAT LOBSTERS

These small animals have a flat shell, long, flat claws and a short abdomen folded under the body. Flapping the abdomen makes them strong swimmers, but they generally stay on the sea floor. Although they look like true crabs, they walk on three pairs of legs. The fourth pair, alongside the body, is almost invisible.

In cool water, some squat lobster species leave the sea bottom in swarms of hundreds of millions, so that the water appears to turn red.

There are dozens of species in Australia, especially in the tropics. The elegant *Allogalathea elegans*, which grows to 10 mm, lives among the arms of feather stars on coral reefs, its yellow and brown stripes matching the colour of its host.
Family: Galatheidae

PORCELAIN CRABS

Porcelain crabs can be mistaken for true crabs, but they have only three pairs of walking legs and a pair of claws. They hold their small last legs at their sides. The claws are flattened and a pair of the legs near the mouth has hairs for filtering food from the water. The long feelers of porcelain crabs reach well back over the body, unlike the short feelers of true crabs.

There are many colourful and active porcelain crab species in tropical Australia. In the south, these crabs can be seen only on exposed boulder shores. This is the habitat of *Petrocheles australiensis*, the reddish brown Australian porcelain crab.
Family: Porcellanidae

HAIRY STONE CRAB

The southern Australian coast is home to the crab-like *Lomis hirta*, the only species in its family. Dirty brown, its carapace, claws and legs are covered with granules and short hairs. It hides under rocks and if disturbed it flashes its blue feelers from between its flattened nippers.
Family: Lomisidae

SWIMMING CRABS

Swimming crabs have flat, paddle-like hind legs. Their flat, oval shell is wider than it is long, and is usually sharply toothed along its edges. Some species swim short distances across the sea floor but most prefer to burrow in mud or sand.

The blue swimmer crab or sand crab (*Portunus pelagicus*) has a mottled blue carapace and grows up to 20 cm wide. It lives throughout Australian coastal waters, particularly in estuaries.

The mud crab, *Scylla serrata*, has large claws and nine teeth on each side of its grey-green shell. It burrows in mud along mangrove shores in the north and east of the country.

■ SPONGE CRAB
To outwit possible predators, sponge crabs disguise themselves by attaching a living sponge to their carapace.

Around 1900, the European shore crab (*Carcinus maenas*) arrived in Victoria on ships. It is now common in sheltered bays in Victoria and Tasmania. The size of a small hand, it is dull green and its last leg ends in a flattened, pointed tip. It can be quite aggressive – hence one of its common names, the green meany. European shore crabs feed on other crabs and may be displacing native crab populations.
Family: Portunidae

FRESHWATER CRABS ■
The only two freshwater crabs in Australia are *Holthuisana transversa* and *H. angustifrons*; the former is the more widespread. They are a mottled green and brown and grow to a carapace width of 5 cm. They burrow in the banks of waterways throughout the northern part of the continent. They cope with dry periods by retreating to their burrows and plugging the entrance with mud, emerging the following wet season.
Family: Sundathelphusidae

SPANNER CRABS
Spanner crabs are longer than they are wide and have claws that resemble a spanner. Using their flattened legs, they burrow in sand and mud in shallow and offshore waters.

A common species is the red frog crab, *Ranina ranina*, which grows to 14 cm long. It is widely distributed from north-eastern Australia as far south as southern New South Wales.
Family: Raninidae

SHORE CRABS ■
These smooth, squarish, fast-moving crabs grow to 4.5 cm wide and are common on rocky and muddy shores. There are about a dozen species in Australia, distinguishable from one another by the shape and colouring of their carapace and claws, and by their habitat. On sheltered coasts in

South Australia, Victoria and Tasmania, up to three species of shore crab may occur together.
Family: Grapsidae

SPONGE CRABS ■
Sponge crabs carry with them a living sponge, which they craft to fit their back. This 'cap' is held in place by minute claws on their back legs, and it is such an effective form of camouflage that these crabs are rarely seen.

There are many species throughout reefs in Australia, the ridged sponge crab (*Stimdromia lateralis*) being one of the most common in southern waters. Up to 20 mm across, it has two triangular lobes extending over the eyes. The females carry their eggs, but these hatch as small crabs rather than planktonic larvae, as is usual in other crabs. Young sponge crabs pass through two moults under their mother's apron before being released to fend for themselves.
Family: Dromiidae

PEBBLE CRABS
Pebble crabs have roughly spherical bodies with a narrow front in which the eyes are deeply set. The legs are spindly and the claws long. Some species are smooth and shiny, while others are rough and knobbly. A few tropical deep-water species are beautifully coloured.

Commonly encountered in southern Australia is the smooth pebble crab, *Dittosa laevis*, a slate grey species that grows to 25 mm across. It lives in seagrass meadows. If disturbed, the crab adopts a threatening posture, holding its long claws erect.
Family: Leucosiidae

BLACK-FINGERED CRABS
Black-fingered crabs are the largest family of decapods in Australian waters, with nearly 50 genera recorded so far. They are so named because the tips of their claws are black or dark grey. The body is roughly oval and wider than it is long, and the legs are usually quite compact. Hundreds of colourful species occur on coral reefs, but they tend to stay hidden.

The Tasmanian giant crab, *Pseudocarcinus gigas*, belongs to this family and is one of the heaviest crabs known. Males, which have one claw considerably larger than the other, grow to 40 cm across and weigh up to 17 kg. The body is roughly the size of a flattened football, dull red in larger specimens and spotted in smaller ones. This crab lives in deep waters along the south coast of Australia.
Family: Xanthidae

■ FRESHWATER CRAB
These crabs live in damp forests in the north of Australia where they scavenge in the leaf litter.

■ SHORE CRAB
Most active at night, the variegated shore crab uses its powerful claws for fighting and for tearing molluscs from the rocks.

■ SOLDIER CRABS
When the tide is out, armies of these spherical blue crabs appear from beneath the sand to feed, leaving little pellets of sand behind them.

CRAB ANATOMY
Claws and four pairs of walking legs protrude from a crab's carapace. Its abdomen (not seen here) is tiny and it has no tail fan.

GHOST CRABS

Ghost crabs, semaphore crabs, sentinel crabs and fiddler crabs have eyes held erect on long stalks. Most species occur on tropical sandflats or in mangrove forests, where they dig deep burrows as permanent homes.

Members of the tropical genus *Ocypode* are called ghost crabs because they emerge from their burrows at night and run about on sandflats when the tide is out. These crabs, 3 cm across, can run at speeds of up to 15 km an hour.

The distinguishing feature of fiddler crabs (*Uca* spp.), which are 4 cm across, is that the males have one claw that is much larger than

the other. Each of the 16 species in Australia can be differentiated by the colour pattern on this claw. The flame fiddler crab (*U. flammula*), with a black carapace and red claw, occurs on creek banks in northern Western Australia and in the Northern Territory.
Family: Ocypodidae

SOLDIER CRABS ■

Unlike other crabs, which scuttle sideways, soldier crabs walk forwards. Each species has a bright blue body about the size and shape of a walnut, supported on stilt-like legs. When looking for food, soldier crabs swarm in vast numbers on flat

sandy beaches exposed at low tide. This moving carpet can instantly disappear if the crabs are frightened: they swiftly spiral themselves into the sand, digging with the legs on one side while walking backwards with the legs on the other.

Two species occur in Australia: *Mictyris platycheles* on the east coast and *M. longicarpus* in northwestern Australia, through the tropics southward to eastern Victoria.
Family: Mictyridae

PEA CRABS

Pea crabs are so named because of their shape and size, but some are much larger than the average pea. They live inside other marine animals, particularly bivalve molluscs.

The white pea crab (*Pinnotheres hickmani*) lives inside a live mussel's shell. It does no damage to its host, but simply feeds on the mucus that the mussel secretes in order to catch its planktonic food.
Family: Pinnotheridae

SPIDER CRABS ■

Spider crabs typically have pear-shaped bodies and very long legs, but numerous forms exist. Many species camouflage themselves by attaching seaweed, sponges or even marine invertebrates to spiked hairs on their backs and are thus known as decorator or masking crabs.

The seaweed crab (*Naxia aurita*) is one of several species of spider crab that live on southern Australian intertidal shores, but its seaweed camouflage makes it hard to see.

In deeper waters, scuba divers sometimes come across tangles of hundreds of Australian spider crabs (*Leptomithrax gaimardii*) gathered together for mating. The carapace of this species looks like a flat, spiky, dirty yellow pear. Its leg span can be as much as 40 cm.
Family: Majidae

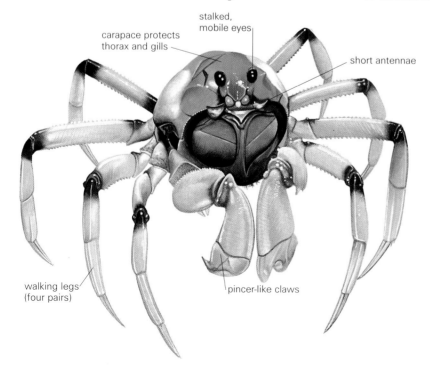

carapace protects thorax and gills

stalked, mobile eyes

short antennae

walking legs (four pairs)

pincer-like claws

■ SPIDER CRAB
Spider crabs are also called decorator crabs because they disguise themselves with marine debris and small sea creatures, such as sponges and algae.

MOLLUSCS

In Australia and its surrounding waters there are thought to be tens of thousands of species of molluscs, but the exact number is unknown. The phylum Mollusca is the largest invertebrate group after the arthropods, with over 100 000 species so far described worldwide. Some molluscs live on land, others in fresh water, but most are marine. Their appearance, behaviour and habitats differ widely, but all have soft, fleshy bodies and most breathe through gills.

There are seven main mollusc groups. The best known are the bivalves (clams, mussels, oysters and scallops), the cephalopods (squids, octopuses and nautiluses) and the gastropods (snails, slugs and limpets). The smaller groups are the monoplacophores, the aplacophores, the scaphopods (the tusk or tooth shells) and the polyplacophores (the chitons).

Limpet-like molluscs
The monoplacophores are small, limpet-like molluscs that live in the sediments on ocean floors. Until 40 years ago they were believed to be extinct, and none have yet been found in Australian waters.

Worm-like molluscs
Aplacophores are worm-like creatures, usually no more than 2.5 cm long. Most of the 250 or so known species are confined to deep water, although a few prefer the shallows.

Aplacophores have no shells, but the surfaces of their soft bodies are studded with spines of calcium carbonate. A few live mouth-down in muddy burrows, feeding on organic debris and tiny animals. A larger group of aplacophores, the solenogasters, creep along muddy surfaces and feed on hydroids and soft corals.

Tusk shells
Two species of Australian tusk shell, both 6 cm long, are prized by shell collectors: the brightly coloured *Dentalium formosum*, which has been recorded only by divers off Exmouth Gulf in Australia's north-west; and the green *Dentalium elephantinum*, found in the coral sand of the Great Barrier Reef. Of the 350 species that have been described worldwide, Australia has 107, including 30 that are unique to the continent.

Shaped like an elephant's tusk with an opening at each end, the tusk shell grows up to 15 cm long. The animal has no eyes and burrows almost vertically – mouth first – into sand, leaving only the tip of its shell and a small part of its mantle exposed. Most tusk shells live in deep water, sometimes as deep as 3000 metres, but a few tiny species are found close to shore. Once thought to be fishes' teeth, they are also known as tooth shells.

Armour-plated chitons
Finding chitons is relatively easy – on any rock in a seashore pool anywhere in southern Australia there are likely to be 10–15 different species. Picking them up is much harder: when disturbed they use a flat, muscular, mucus-secreting foot to clamp themselves so tenaciously to the rock that they are almost immovable. Of the 650 known living species Australia has at least 150,

and 90 per cent of these are found nowhere else. From the coast of southern Queensland southward and westward to the central coast of Western Australia, including the coast of Tasmania, Australia has a greater variety of these molluscs than anywhere else in the world.

A chiton is somewhat like a large, flattened slater, although it is not related to this land crustacean. Its most distinctive feature is a shell of several overlapping plates.

Although some have been dredged up from depths of 4000 metres, most chitons live in shallow waters and graze on rock-encrusting algae and animals. *Plaxiphora albida*, one of Australia's most common chiton species, lives on rocks in the intertidal zone. It grows up to 10 cm long, and is often encrusted with algae.

BUBBLE SHELL
Bubble shells (page 587) belong to the order Cephalaspidea. They are a large group of gastropods with a thin shell that does not completely cover them when they withdraw. This *Hydatina physis* was photographed in Sydney's northern beaches area.

CLEVER CEPHALOPODS
Of all the invertebrates, octopuses (pages 595–6) have the most advanced brains and eyes.

LESSER KNOWN MOLLUSCS
Chitons, aplacophores and tusk shells do not resemble each other at all, but all are molluscs.

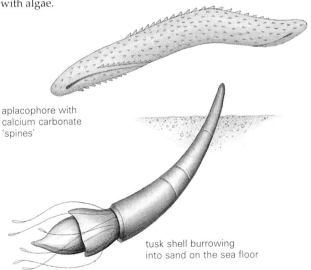

chiton with overlapping plates

aplacophore with calcium carbonate 'spines'

tusk shell burrowing into sand on the sea floor

BIVALVES

Stroll along any Australian beach and you will come across an array of beautiful shells. Many of these were once the homes of bivalves.

These soft-bodied creatures live inside a two-part shell, or valve, that is joined by a hinge. When the animal dies, the hinge usually breaks and single shells are cast up on the beach, often in their hundreds. Of some 10 000 bivalve species that exist worldwide, Australia has about two thousand.

A few bivalves live in fresh water, but most prefer saltwater environments between the high-tide mark and depths of about 200 metres. Some species live at greater depths, but pressure and cold make deep waters an unsuitable habitat for most bivalves.

Unlike the gastropod snails and slugs, which move around using a large muscular foot, bivalves stay put for much of their lives. They attach themselves to hard surfaces, as oysters do, or bury themselves in sand or mud, as pipis and razor clams do. Bivalves that burrow in mud and sand use the foot for digging, quickly burying themselves again if they are uncovered by wave action or dug up by humans.

Although fully equipped with internal organs, bivalves have no head, jaws or teeth: they feed by either filtering plankton from the currents or sifting food from the sand or mud where they live.

Bivalves have internal sex organs but no external sexual characteristics. Most are either male or female, but a few species are hermaphrodites, functioning as male and female simultaneously. Some bivalve groups change sex, spending their early lives as males and becoming females in adulthood. Some species produce millions of eggs and sperm that are released into the water for the currents to complete fertilisation. They develop into small planktonic larvae that eventually settle on the shore or sea floor, where they transform into miniature adults. In other bivalves far fewer eggs are stored in a brood pouch within the female. Only when sperm in the water enter the female through the inhalant siphon and flow over her eggs does fertilisation occur.

Class: Bivalvia

MUSSELS

Most of the world's 250 species of mussels live in the Arctic and Antarctic regions, but mussels are harvested for food all around the world. Most mussels prefer the intertidal and subtidal zones, and often gather in large colonies on rocks and wharf piles. Some bury themselves in the sand or mud, while others burrow into clay, rock and coral. Edible mussels (*Mytilus edulis*) attach themselves to rocks, wharf piles, and even rubble and mud surfaces. They occur around southern Australia from New South Wales to south-western Australia, where they are collected from the wild and cultivated on ropes.

Mussels vary in size. Their elongated, wedge-shaped shells are brown or black, or sometimes blue, green or red. They have a pearly interior. The shell's protective coating, called the periostracum, may be thick and hairy or thin and glossy.

Family: Mytilidae

ARK SHELLS

Most species of these boat-shaped shells live in the intertidal or subtidal zones, although there are a few that exist in very deep water. While some ark shells nestle or burrow into mud and sand, others attach themselves to solid objects.

The Sydney ark shell, *Anadara trapezia*, favours the sediments of seagrass flats and is found from south-eastern Queensland southward and westward to the southern coast of Western Australia. Its thick, white, ribbed shell grows up to 6 cm long and is covered by a dark brown periostracum. The Sydney ark shell is one of the few molluscs that have red blood with the oxygen-carrying pigment, haemoglobin – the blood of most molluscs is colourless or a very pale blue.

Family: Arcidae

PEARL OYSTERS

These rough, scaly bivalves are usually found in shallow warm waters in the intertidal zone. Most species prefer muddy or sandy areas, where they attach themselves by a tuft of strong filaments, called a byssus, to whatever solid object they can find – rock, coral, or occasionally seagrass.

The golden-lip pearl oyster, *Pinctada maxima* – about the size of a large dinner plate when fully grown – is the world's largest pearl oyster and is found in all Australian tropical waters. Before the 1950s, when Australia began culturing pearls, the oyster was killed for its shell to provide mother-of-pearl for buttons and ornaments. It is now used to grow cultured pearls (see 'Gems from the sea', opposite page).

The painted pearl oyster (*Pinctada fucata*) is common along the coasts of Queensland and New South Wales. It may also be found on ocean reefs and along the sandy mud flats of estuaries.

Family: Pteriidae

RAZOR CLAMS ■

Thin, translucent, wedge-shaped razor clams grow up to half a metre long. They are found from the intertidal zone to depths of 100 metres in tropical and temperate seas. The clams anchor themselves vertically in mud, sand or rubble with a silky, thread-like tuft (byssus).

The common razor clam, *Pinna bicolor*, is found along most of the Australian coastline. It usually

BIVALVE ANATOMY
Neatly fitted within the bivalve's hinged double shell are its respiratory system, its circulatory and its digestive system. To take in nutrients, the bivalve's gills filter food particles from water drawn in through the inhalant siphon. The particles are trapped in streams of mucus and carried by tiny hair-like cilia to the palps, which convey the food to the animal's mouth.

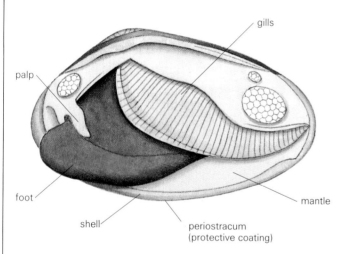

gills
palp
foot
shell
mantle
periostracum (protective coating)

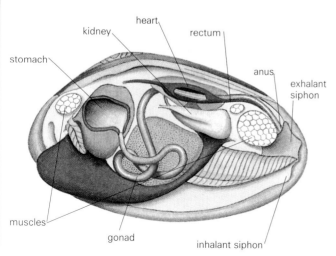

heart
kidney
rectum
stomach
anus
exhalant siphon
muscles
gonad
inhalant siphon

■ RAZOR CLAM
Pinna bicolor sits almost completely buried in the sandy mud, except for its thin, sharp upper edge, which protrudes slightly and often lacerates the feet of unsuspecting beachcombers.

dwells in the weed and mud flats of estuaries around the low-tide mark, and in mangrove swamps.
Family: Pinnidae

OYSTERS

Oysters thrive in the intertidal zone and shallow waters of temperate and tropical seas. Because they lose their foot and tuft (byssus) after the larval stage they cannot dig themselves out of sand, so they need to live on rocky shores, where they will not be smothered by shifting sand.

The outside of the oyster's round to elongated shell has a laminated appearance, and its inner surface looks rather like porcelain.

The Sydney rock oyster, *Crassostrea glomerata*, occurs naturally on rock platforms of ocean beaches and on rocks and mangroves in estuaries from Queensland south to Victoria. Oyster farmers place stones or sticks in the water and the larvae attach themselves to them. The larvae, called spats, are then moved to an area where there are more nutrients and the oysters stand a greater chance of survival to maturity.

The giant Pacific oyster, *Crassostrea gigas*, an import from Japan, is farmed in Tasmania. It has spread up the east coast of the mainland to southern Queensland, causing concern to growers of native oysters.
Family: Ostreidae

SCALLOPS ■

Although a few species of scallops cement themselves to solid surfaces below the tide mark, most are free-swimming or attach themselves to rocks, reefs or rubble by a tuft, or byssus. Most prefer shallow waters, but some live as deep as 300 metres. Scallop shells are circular, and are fluted or sculpted with knobs or spikes.The shells are joined by a strong internal ligament.

Along the edge of the scallop's mantle are 30–40 eyes; these register changes in the environment, and the scallop reacts immediately by swimming away to a safer area. Scallops swim by opening and shutting their shells rapidly. They often travel in shoals, and in this way they can migrate to new feeding grounds.

Scallops are found throughout the world's temperate and tropical waters. Several species are fished commercially in southern Australian waters. The most popular is *Pecten fumatus*, which is found from central Queensland down to Tasmania and across to southern Western Australia. The largest examples – up to 12 cm long – live in the cool waters of southern Australia.
Family: Pectinidae

■ SCALLOPS
Doughboy scallops (*Chlamys asperrimus*), covered in an encrusting orange sponge, take a grip on a larger king scallop (*Pecten meridionalis*). The brilliant blue eyes along the edge of their mantles are sensitive to movement, so they can detect an approaching enemy.

GEMS FROM THE SEA

A pearl forms when a foreign substance, such as a grain of sand, lodges itself inside an oyster. Gradually the oyster coats the intrusive body with nacre, the calcium-based lining of the inside of the shell that we call mother-of-pearl. Usually the result is a small, oddly shaped natural pearl.

Large, perfectly round pearls used to be extremely rare. In the thirteenth century AD the Chinese discovered how to culture pearls by introducing a fragment of wood, bone or metal into a mussel shell; they even produced minute pearl-encased statues of the Buddha! But the art of cultivating whole spherical pearls was not perfected until 1893, when the Japanese developed a method of 'seeding' oysters to make pearls.

Today almost all pearls are cultured. The largest, most lustrous and sought-after pearls in the world are produced by Australia's golden-lip pearl oyster (*Pinctada maxima*). It takes two years for *P. maxima* to grow a cultured pearl. The oyster is not killed to obtain the pearl: it can be re-seeded and returned to the water.

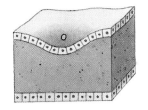

An irritant lodges between the shell (not shown) and the body.

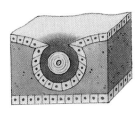

Many layers of calcium carbonate form around the foreign body.

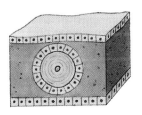

The fully formed pearl is completely encapsulated.

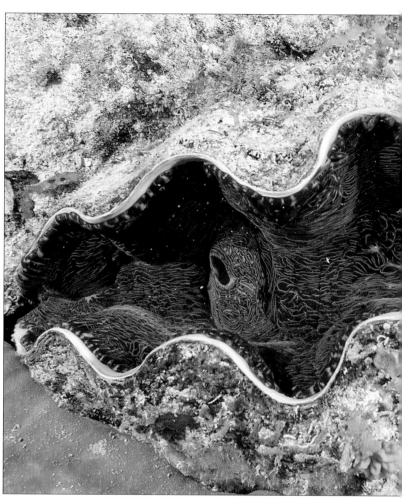

■ FRESHWATER
MUSSELS
In the past, the fresh-
water mussel *Velesunio
ambiguus* was a valuable
food source for the
Aborigines.

FRESHWATER MUSSELS ■

Species in this family are confined
to South America and Australasia,
where they live on the muddy or
gravelly beds of unpolluted freshwater rivers, lakes and dams.

Freshwater mussels incubate their
eggs in brood pouches until they
reach a larval stage. Still within the
adult, the larva develops a triangular shell fringed with curved hooks
and a long, thread-like tuft (byssus).
When the young mussel is ejected
into the water, it attaches its hooked
shell to a passing fish, on which it
feeds. After several weeks, it drops
off and grows into an adult mussel.

The balonne freshwater mussel,
Velesunio ambiguus, inhabits the
Murray–Darling River systems and
is found throughout Queensland,
New South Wales, Victoria and eastern South Australia. Its oval shell
grows up to 9 cm long and is covered with a black protective coating.
Family: Hyriidae

COCKLES

Cockles vary in size, thickness and
shape, but they usually have a
rounded triangular appearance.
When two intact shells are viewed
from the side they form a heart
shape. The outer shell surface is
ribbed and often knobbly.

Cockles live in sandy or muddy
sediments in intertidal and subtidal
zones. They are good burrowers,
and they can leap up from the seabed with the aid of their large foot.

The cream-coloured common
southern cockle, *Fulvia tenuicostata*,
up to 5.5 cm long, is found in temperate subtidal zones from New
South Wales to Tasmania through

to southern Western Australia. The
tiny Hamelin cockle, *Afrocardium
erugatum*, about 12 mm across,
lives in dense populations from
Geraldton to the Dampier Archipelago in Western Australia. Over
the centuries its shells have become
compressed into thick beds of shell
cement. Blocks are sawn from these
beds and used as building stones
for houses and fences.
Family: Cardiidae

GIANT CLAMS ■

These gargantuan bivalves are
found only in the tropical waters of
the Indian and Pacific Oceans. There
are only seven living species of giant
clam, six of which inhabit shallow
tropical Australian waters. They live
on sand and attach themselves to
coral by a thread-like tuft (byssus).

Tridacna gigas, the giant clam that
lives on the Great Barrier Reef, has
the largest shell of any bivalve in the
world. A specimen discovered there
in 1917 holds the record, measuring
114 cm by 74 cm and weighing in
at 262.9 kg. Giant clams lie among
the corals with their valves gaping
open to expose their colourful mantles to sunlight. Within these greatly

enlarged mantles, the clams 'farm'
algae called zooxanthellae, which
photosynthesise to provide some
of the clam's food.

Giant clams used to be popular
villains in underwater adventure
stories, their supposed habit of
snapping shut on unwary divers
providing many a moment of sus-
pense. In reality, clams close their
shells very slowly.

Poachers have decimated giant
clam populations in many areas by
taking the adductor muscle for food.
Giant clams are now fully protected
throughout Australia.
Family: Tridacnidae

FINGERNAIL SHELLS

These thin, elongated molluscs use
their large foot to dig vertically
into sand or mud, where they filter
food with their shells agape. In open
water, they swim by rapidly opening
and closing their shells.

The southern fingernail shell, *Solen
vaginoides*, lives in estuaries from
southern New South Wales south
to Tasmania and west to southern
Western Australia. At low tide these
shells bury themselves deeply and
rapidly, but when the tide is coming

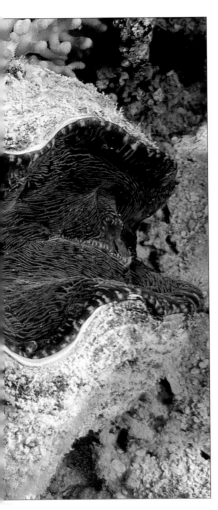

■ GIANT CLAMS

The reef clam *Tridacna maxima* (left) exposes its magnificently coloured fleshy mantle, filled with algae, to the sun. Using the sun's energy, the algae produce carbohydrates that supplement the clam's diet of plankton filtered from the water. *T. maxima* is the most common giant clam on the Great Barrier Reef.

The giant clam *Tridacna gigas* (below) gives a spectacular display of spawning. *T. gigas* is the largest of the giant clams. Found mainly in the northern half of the Great Barrier Reef, it lives loose on sand or in pockets of sand on the reef.

in, they rise closer to the surface of the water and extend their siphons from holes in the sediment.
Family: Solenidae

TELLINS

Tellins are sand-burrowers with long siphons that enable them to live deep in the sandy beds of intertidal and subtidal zones in tropical and subtropical waters. Their shells are yellow or pink and are often finely ridged. Cast ashore and opened out, they look like butterfly wings.

Tellina albinella, the little white tellin, ranges from New South Wales south to Tasmania and west to southern Western Australia. White with splashes of yellow, orange or pink, it grows to about 6 cm long.
Family: Tellinidae

WEDGE SHELLS ■

Most wedge shell species – usually white, brown, purple, mauve or orange – thrive on surf beaches. As the waves recede they thrust their foot deep into the sand, and within seconds their shells disappear and only the siphons are visible.

Several of the world's 50 species occur in Australia's subtropical and

tropical waters. Best known is the pipi (*Donax deltoides*), which lives above the low-tide mark on surf beaches from Queensland south and west to Western Australia. Only 6 cm long, pipis were bush tucker for Aborigines, and their shells are very common in shell middens in the sand dunes around Australia's coast.
Family: Donacidae

VENUS SHELLS

Venus shells – circular, oval, rectangular or triangular – are the largest and most diverse group of bivalves, with about 500 species worldwide. Most burrow a little way into mud or sand in shallow water.

The most colourful species live in tropical waters: one such is *Lioconcha castrensis*, the chocolate flamed Venus shell. It grows to about 5 cm across and lives in soft coral sand along the low-tide mark from north Western Australia northward and eastward to the central Queensland coast. Its smooth white shell is decorated with brown zigzag lines.

The frilled Venus shell, *Bassina disjecta*, is found from New South Wales to Tasmania and west to South Australia. Its white-to-cream

oval shell, up to 6 cm across, has pink frills. It usually feeds in sandy mud under water, but sometimes lives above the low-tide mark.
Family: Veneridae

ANGEL WINGS

Angel wings are thin, elongated, wing-shaped, and white with a thin, grey to black protective coating. Often too large for their shells, their soft bodies usually gape at both ends. They burrow into hard mud, clay, rock and timber by anchoring their foot with suction to a surface and twisting their shell in a rocking motion. As they grow, they grind a chamber in the surface, in which they eventually become enclosed.

They live above and below the low-tide mark. The Australian angel wing, *Barnea australasiae*, is often washed up on beaches from southeastern Queensland to Tasmania and west to southern Western Australia. The wood-boring angel wing, *Martesia striata*, prefers the warmer northern Australian waters.
Family: Pholadidae

SHIPWORMS

Shipworms are not worms but long, soft-bodied bivalves. Notorious attackers of wharves and other submerged timber structures, they have a pair of small shells at the front of their body that rotate to grind away timber. They feed on these wood shavings through their inhalant siphons. The naval shipworm, *Teredo navalis*, is found around the coasts of Australia as well as worldwide.

Northern Australian Aborigines break open dead mangrove wood to extract the shipworm's soft body, which they eat raw.
Family: Teredinidae

■ WEDGE SHELL
The pipi, *Donax deltoides*, shows its foot and its siphons. Its wedge-shaped shell is thick and smooth, and its protective coating is shiny.

GASTROPODS

Gastropods are prolific and wide-spread, and are found in shaded, moist rainforests and arid deserts, in freshwater rivers and lakes, and all the way to the oceans. A distinctive feature of gastropods is that before their shell starts to form they rotate their organs through 180 degrees. This is called torsion; it provides them with a better balanced shell, an improved water flow over the gills and sensory tentacles, and the ability to retreat completely into their shells.

Most gastropods carry a single spiral shell made of calcium carbonate. The shell protects their internal organs and prevents them from drying out. A flat, fleshy, muscular foot allows them to crawl and cling. Their heads are well formed and usually consist of sensory tentacles, eyes and a feeding apparatus – a rasp-like tongue called a radula.

Gastropods reproduce in many ways. Individuals can be male, female, or hermaphroditic. Some begin life as males and later become females. Some brood their eggs in pouches, while others release them directly into the water. In some species the egg capsules release the young straight into the sea. The eggs of still other species hatch into a larval stage before transforming into their adult form.

The class Gastropoda contains three subclasses: Prosobranchia, the shelled sea snails; Opisthobranchia, the sea slugs; and Pulmonata, the land snails and slugs.
Class: Gastropoda

A MISNOMER
The word gastropod means stomach-footed – but the large foot the gastropod moves on is not its stomach. All the inner organs are packed into the shell, if present. The body wall in the mantle secretes the shell and is tacked on to form a mantle cavity. Gastropods use their foot for crawling and gripping.

■ TURBAN SHELL
Jourdan's turban, *Turbo jourdani*, is confined to cooler waters off southern and western Australia. Like the button shell, it is popular for making jewellery.

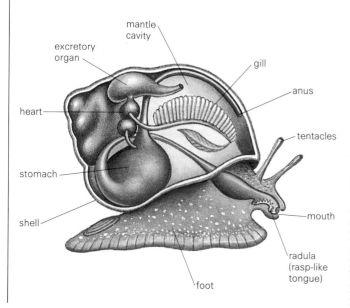

SHELLED SEA SNAILS

LIMPETS
Shaped like conical caps, limpets favour the rocky shores of cool seas and inhabit both the intertidal zone and the deeper waters below the low-tide mark. Desiccation is the main problem facing these hardy animals, since when the tide is out they are completely exposed. To meet the threat, a broad foot clamps their shell hard against the rock, sealing them off from the elements and preventing water loss. To escape predators, limpets sometimes raise their shell in a mushroom-like stance or sway from side to side before fleeing. Alternatively, they release their hold on rocks and tumble away.

Limpets feed submerged, usually at night. Moving their heads from side to side, they use their radula like a scythe to graze algae from rocks. They can travel up to 2 metres in search of food, but they always go back to their original resting place.
Families: Acmaeidae, Patellidae, Hipponicidae

ABALONES
Abalones, or ear shells, are abundant around Australia's southern coast-line, where they grip rocky surfaces with their wide, muscular foot. Some species live on wave-washed reefs just below the low-tide mark, while others can be found at depths of more than 25 metres.

Abalones are night-feeders: some species browse on algae that they scrape from rocks with their file-like radula, while others catch drifting algae with a specially adapted foot. They eliminate waste in the water that flows out from the characteristic holes around the edge of their ear-shaped, nacre-lined shell.

At breeding time, a whole population simultaneously releases millions of sperm and eggs into the water, where they meet and fertilise. After a larval stage of about a week, the young abalones settle on the rocks amid the stems and holdfasts of encrusting algae.
Family: Haliotidae

TOP SHELLS AND TURBAN SHELLS ■
Top and turban shells live along all coasts of Australia, some on coral reefs, others in sand and still others crawling about on mud. They are usually conical, rather like a child's spinning top. Both are omnivorous, feeding on plants and animals as well as organic debris.

Found along the tropical northern coastline, the button shell, *Trochus*

Labels on diagram:
mantle cavity
excretory organ
gill
anus
heart
tentacles
stomach
shell
mouth
radula (rasp-like tongue)
foot

niloticus, is one of Australia's largest top shells, reaching up to 12.5 cm across its base. Before World War II it was fished commercially to make mother-of-pearl buttons. Now only Torres Strait Islanders and Bardi Aborigines at One Arm Point, north of Broome, are allowed to collect the shells, which are made into shell jewellery for the Asian market.
Families: Trochidae, Turbinidae

CREEPERS

Creepers are slender, cone-shaped gastropods, perfectly designed for ploughing through sand and coral rubble. They are most abundant in tropical and subtropical regions, where they occur in large numbers and feed on organic debris, but little is known of their biology.
Families: Campanilidae, Cerithiidae, Potamididae

WHELKS

Although a few species have shells patterned with dots, dashes or lines, whelk shells are usually plain. They inhabit all seas from the intertidal zone to the abyssal depths. They either scavenge or hunt prey. The scavenging dog whelks (*Nassarius* spp.), patrol the intertidal sand flats and seagrass beds, waving their siphons from side to side as they search for dead animals.

If attacked, whelks quickly bury themselves or flip about by rapidly flexing their mobile bodies.
Family: Buccinidae

PERIWINKLES

Periwinkles live in the harsh zone between tide levels, where they must contend with nature's extremes – low tides and hot days in summer, cold nights and crashing seas in winter, and predatory birds all year round. Many are found covering the rocks along the shoreline well above the high-tide mark.

Some species fertilise their eggs internally, and a few of these keep them until the larvae have hatched in their mantle cavity and are quite advanced before releasing them into the sea. Other species lay their tough egg capsules on rocks, where they hatch into the water at high tide.
Families: Littorinidae, Neritidae

■ STROMB
The red-lipped or red-mouthed stromb, *Strombus luhuanus*, is often mistaken for the cone shell (page 587), but its characteristic notched red lip is unmistakable. Beneath its thick, dark, protective coating, the shell is white with stippled golden-brown bands.

STROMBS ■

Strombs inhabit tropical and subtropical areas of muddy sand and coral rubble. Their shells have thickened outer lips with a U-shaped notch at the front – a peephole for their characteristic stalked eyes.

Strombs do not glide; they move using a specially modified foot with a long, hook-like, serrated appendage (the operculum) to lift the shell and push it forward. They can also use the operculum as a weapon.

One well-known stromb, the spider shell, *Lambis lambis*, has tapered spines along the edge of its shell.
Family: Strombidae

COWRIES ■

Cowries are well represented in Australian seas. They are generally night feeders and hide during daylight in caves and crevices. Most tropical cowries graze on algae, but a few, such as the zoila cowries of southern Australian waters, are carnivorous and feed on sponges.

The female lays egg capsules containing many eggs and covers them with her large, fleshy foot. The free-swimming larvae hatch into the water and feed on microplankton until they settle on the sea floor and develop into adults.
Families: Cypraeidae, Ovulidae, Triviidae

MOON SNAILS

Moon snails prowl sand flats at low tide in search of their prey – buried clams. The snail holds the clam fast with its enlarged foot and then bores a hole in the clam shell. Scientists do not know whether the snail uses a chemical secretion to dissolve the shell or bores the hole with its rasp-like tongue (radula), but the result is the same – a very neat, small hole. The moon snail inserts its extended proboscis into the hole and feeds on the besieged bivalve.
Family: Naticidae

HELMET SHELLS

Helmet shells live in sandy habitats and feed on sea stars, sea urchins, sea biscuits and sea cucumbers.

Eating spiny sea urchins is a delicate art that the helmet shells have perfected. When it senses the presence of a juicy sea urchin, the helmet shell extends its proboscis and squirts out what is thought to be a neurotoxin to immobilise the urchin's waving spines. The gastropod then holds the urchin with its fleshy foot and devours its insides, either by rasping a hole through

■ COWRIE
The glossy white shell of this albino *Cypraea cribraria* is in dramatic contrast with its brilliant orange mantle. The high polish on the shell is maintained by the ornate and colourful mantle, which, in some species, has acid-secreting glands to protect it from predators.

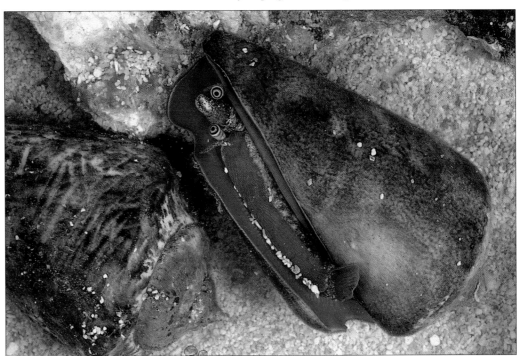

■ TRITON SHELL
The photographer has caught the triton *Ranella australasia* in the act of laying its eggs. Tritons have a long, elegant shell that is greatly valued by collectors.

■ UNDULATE VOLUTE
Amoria undulata is most common in the cooler waters off the coast of southern Australia. The colour and intricate patterning of its shell vary.

the urchin's tough exterior with its tongue (radula) before inserting its proboscis, or by simply inserting its proboscis through the urchin's anus.
Family: Cassidae

TUN SHELLS

Tun shells have thin, almost spherical shells and inhabit Australia's subtropical and tropical waters. They are little known, staying hidden under sand during daylight hours and emerging at night to feed on sea cucumbers. Once it finds its prey, the tun shell moves around it, tapping it with the sensory tentacles on its head. The sea cucumber reacts violently, trying to make itself bigger by sucking in water or attempting to swim away. Having decided which end to tackle first, the tun shell extends its proboscis and engulfs the cucumber whole – a process that takes only a few minutes.
Family: Tonnidae

TRITON SHELLS ■

The most famous of the tritons is the giant triton, *Charonia tritonis*, which grows up to 45 cm long. It lives below the tide level and feeds on the crown-of-thorns sea star, which has destroyed parts of the Great Barrier Reef. Unfortunately, it does not consume the sea star quickly enough to constitute a natural control.

All triton shells are carnivorous and feed on a variety of animals, including bivalves, other gastropods, sea stars, sea urchins, sea squirts and marine worms.
Family: Ranellidae

■ VIOLET SNAIL
With a cargo of goose barnacles, *Janthina janthina* cruises the ocean's surface below its raft of bubbles in search of its prey – the Portuguese man o'war and other surface-dwellers.

MUREX SHELLS AND DRUPES

Murex shells can be distinguished from the relatively smooth-shelled drupes by their intricate sculpture of spines and fronds. Both drupes and murex shells are voracious predators, feeding on molluscs, barnacles and worms. Many drill through the shells of their prey using a rasp-like radula (similar

to a tongue) and an acidic secretion from a gland near their mouths.

The coral drupella, *Drupella cornis*, feeds on live coral and has severely damaged coral reefs of the Ningaloo Marine Park, North West Cape, Western Australia. Along the coast of New South Wales the cart-rut shell, *Thais orbita*, and the mulberry whelk, *Morula marginalba*, are commonly found in rock pools.
Family: Muricidae

VIOLET SNAILS ■

The pelagic violet snail spends its entire life hanging upside down from a raft of bubbles. The snail forms the bubbles by lifting the front portion of its foot above the surface of the water and curling it back on itself, forming an air pocket. To encase the trapped air, it secretes mucus from special glands on its foot. As the bubbles accumulate a raft forms, beneath which the violet snail rides the ocean currents.

Separated from its raft the violet snail sinks and dies. In late summer hundreds of the fine, light, empty shells are sometimes washed up.
Family: Janthinidae

PAGODA AND VASE SHELLS

These large, heavy shells inhabit shallow tropical and subtropical waters. They have a long, narrow proboscis for feeding on marine worms. One of the largest members of this group, the giant conch (*Syrinx aruanus*), may grow up to 60 cm long. It can be found on sand flats around northern Australia from Western Australia to Queensland.
Family: Turbinellidae

VOLUTES

Volutes live in sandy habitats right around the Australian coastline. Many, such as those of the genus *Amoria*, are greatly sought after for their decorative shells.

Large baler shells (*Melo amphora* in tropical waters and *M. miltonis* in temperate seas) can reach 45 cm in length. The Aborigines used baler shells as water vessels, and the shell's common name was coined by early European settlers. Other volutes, such as the nucleus volute (*Lyria nucleus*) of Queensland, grow no larger than 2.5 cm.

Volutes are carnivores, feeding on other molluscs, or scavengers. Their young are fully developed when they hatch from the egg capsule.
Family: Volutidae

OLIVE SHELLS

Olives are smooth, torpedo-shaped shells ideally suited to crawling through the sandy or muddy shores where they live. Using the specially enlarged front part of their foot, they plough through sediments. They 'smell' the water in search of prey or carrion, holding their siphon erect with the tip above the sand.

Olive shells feed mostly on invertebrates, which they hold fast with their large foot. To escape predators, olive shells have been known to swim using this large foot as a kind of undulating fin.
Family: Olividae

CONE SHELLS

Cone shells are prized by collectors the world over. They inhabit all the coastlines of Australia and are found on rocky shores and coral reefs and in sandy habitats. All cone shells are carnivorous; most feed on worms, although some prefer molluscs and others fishes.

Conus geographus hunts small fishes and consumes them whole. Its venom is lethal to humans and has been responsible for several deaths. The beautifully marked textile cone, *Conus textile*, is also very dangerous and should be handled with great care. Both species occur along Australia's tropical coastline on coral reefs, often buried in sand under dead coral boulders.
Family: Conidae

AUGER SHELLS

Auger shells are found in tropical sandy lagoons, where they crawl through the sand in search of worms. Many species do not have a tongue-like radula covered with angled teeth, but rely on a modified proboscis to hold their prey by suction. Those with a radula use venom to immobilise prey, but they are quite small, and neither radula nor venom pose any threat to humans.
Family: Terebridae

SEA SLUGS

BUBBLE SHELLS

Bubble shells are found in both temperate and tropical areas of Australia, generally in soft sand or among the protective leaves of algae in shallow water. They have fragile, reduced shells that in most instances do not allow the animal to retreat fully. They are herbivorous and grow to about 2 cm long.

Bat wing slugs (family Gastropteridae) are slightly different; they have only a very small internal shell, so they must rely on their swimming abilities for protection.
Families: Bullinidae, Acteonidae, Hydatinidae, Bullidae, Haminoeidae, Gastropteridae

TAILED SLUGS

These slugs are cylindrical, often with two uneven tails, and are perfectly designed for burrowing in sand. Sensory bristles project from the front of their head-shield to detect prey, which they engulf voraciously. They secrete copious mucus to allow them to 'glide' through the sand without abrasion. Some can reach 6 cm in length.
Family: Aglajidae

■ CONE SHELL
The textile cone, *Conus textile*, derives its name from the textured patterning of its colourful shell. Its venomous proboscis emerges from the narrow end of the shell.

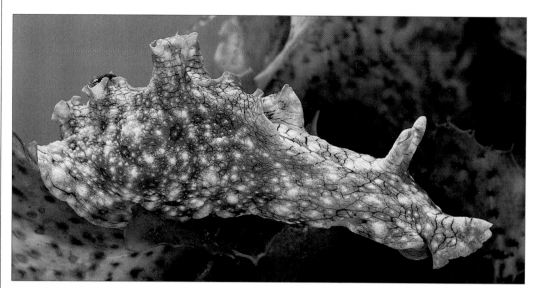

■ SEA HARE
Aplysia dactylomela, the black-tailed sea hare, is common along the east coast of Australia from the Great Barrier Reef to Victoria. People once believed that these strange-looking animals had demonic powers.

SEA BUTTERFLIES

Sea butterflies are very small (5–10 mm), free-swimming, open-ocean molluscs that spend their whole lives drifting with the marine currents. They have some very specialised features, including flotation devices and mucous feeding webs of sticky threads to trap their food. In some species, the females carry the developing young.
Family: Clavoliniidae

SEA HARES ■

Sea hares are generally large and fleshy with well-developed heads and reduced internal shells. They are slow-moving algae-grazers found along the entire Australian coastline on rocky reefs and in seagrass beds. They have a pair of wing-like structures on their backs that they use in an ungainly, undulating fashion to swim. During mating they may form long chains, each animal servicing the animal in front. The giant sea hare, *Aplysia gigantea*, is Australia's largest sea slug, up to 60 cm long and pitch black when mature. It lives in the cool southern waters of Western Australia.

Papery bubble shells (family Akeridae) live in silty, shallow water all around the coasts of Australia, including Tasmania. They have the sea hare's characteristic swimming flaps, but their shell resembles that of a bubble shell (page 587).
Families: Aplysiidae, Akeridae

SIDE-GILLED SLUGS

These slugs are so named because their gills lie along the right side of their body. Some species, such as the small umbrella shell, *Tylodina corticalis*, and the umbrella shell, *Umbraculum sinicum*, have an umbrella-like shell that protects their gills and internal organs.

Side-gilled slugs without a shell secrete toxic chemicals to defend themselves. Forskal's slug, *Pleuro-branchus forskalii*, for example, has glands on its body that secrete sulphuric acid strong enough to strip a layer of skin from your hand.
Families: Tylodinidea, Umbraculidae, Pleurobranchidae

SAP-SUCKING SLUGS ■

Small, very delicate and often green, sap-sucking slugs have a variety of body shapes. Some have a thin, reduced shell; others have no shell at all. The bivalve gastropods (family Juliidae) have two shells – like a clam, but with a gastropod's foot and head. They feed on algae.

Some sap-sucking slugs are solar powered. They store photosynthetic cells, collected from the plants they feed on, in their skin. These cells photosynthesise to make sugars that the slug uses as a source of food.
Families: Juliidae, Volvatellidae, Oxynoidae, Elysiidae, Polybranchiidae, Stiligeridae

■ SAP-SUCKING SLUG
This *Cyerce nigricans* is grazing on turtle weed. Its specially adapted radula is equipped with a single row of dagger-like teeth, with which the slug pierces algal cells and sucks out the nutritious contents.

Unlikely beauties

Sea slugs may not sound very attractive, but few animals can rival the beauty and range of shape found in this group of marine molluscs.

A colourful sea slug, the Spanish dancer, swirls the orange-red skirts for which it is named.

A Glaucus *sea slug feeds on the poisonous by-the-wind sailor but takes no harm from the stinging cells of its prey – it just recycles the cells and uses them in its own defence.*

Molluscs are perhaps the most diverse of all the animal phyla, and within the mollusc group the unromantically named sea slugs are a microcosm of this biodiversity.

Most sea slugs live in tropical waters, where they inhabit rocky reefs and beds of algae from the zone between high and low tide to the oceanic depths. They vary in length from a few millimetres to as much as 30 cm. Unlike most molluscs, they have no shell, either external or internal, except at the larval stage. They are only distantly related to the land slugs, which have also dispensed with a protective shell.

One group of sea slugs, members of the subclass Opisthobranchia, have the scientific name nudibranchs, meaning 'with naked gills' – a reference to the feathery gill plumes that many of these creatures bear on their back. These structures are highly sensitive to any contact.

Nudibranchs come in an astonishing range of patterns and shapes. Many are coloured in vibrant shades of violet, blue, orange or red, and even relatively drab species may have the most intricate body ornamentation, such as thick, coloured ridges or lumps, or tufts of gills that run down their sides and are protected by decorative appendages.

But nature is economical in its effects, and the colours and patterns of sea slugs are not there for decoration but to help the species to survive. Members of the spectacular Chromodoridae family, for example, secrete toxic chemicals that they ingest with their main foodstuff of sponges, and their brilliant colours act as a warning to predatory creatures to stay clear. Other sea slugs are less flamboyant in defence but equally successful; some cast sections of their body as a decoy, while others can camouflage themselves by taking on the colour of the organisms on which they feed.

Nudibranchs are versatile in attack as well as in defence. The voracious gymnodorids, which feed on sap-sucking slugs, follow a trail of mucus left by their intended prey, and then rear up and, with a quick lunge, snatch their victim and swallow it whole. The lion slug (*Melibe mirifica*) has a veil-like mouth that it spreads out like a fishing net to catch and draw in small crabs and shrimps.

Most remarkable of all are the aeolids, which feed on stinging hydroids and corals. Within their gut they can isolate the stinging cells of their prey and store them in projections on their backs for use in their own defence. The projections can also be detached and will stick to whatever they touch – an extremely effective stinging decoy.

The Spanish shawl has flashy gills to warn predators that it tastes bad.

LAND SNAILS AND SLUGS

Land snails and slugs are found in most habitats from rainforests to deserts, although slugs generally prefer wet areas. A few species live in mangrove swamps or on rocky shores. Many live in fresh water, either surfacing to breathe air or extracting oxygen directly from the water. Most are omnivorous.

Most land snails and all land slugs take in oxygen through lungs rather than gills. This has allowed them to become successful land-dwellers.

But life on land carries the danger of losing water from the body by evaporation, so pulmonates have developed several ways of retaining moisture. They minimise evaporation from moist surfaces around the lungs by breathing through a small pore in their side, and they are active mainly at night, when it is cooler and more humid – thus also escaping daylight predators. As a further protection during drier periods, snails often seal their shells with a layer of mucus and enter a state of near-suspended animation until wetter conditions return.

Land snails and slugs are hermaphrodites; each creature has both a male and a female reproductive system, although some individuals may function as male only or as female only. Some change sex as they grow older. Still others function as both sexes, producing eggs and sperm simultaneously. As well as the usual cross-fertilisation, land snails can fertilise their own eggs or reproduce without sperm.
Subclass: Pulmonata

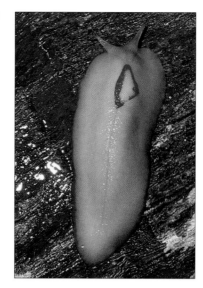

■ RED-TRIANGLE SLUG
Triboniophorus graeffei is the only red-triangle slug yet described in Australia.

SEMI-SLUGS

Generally, a snail has a shell and a slug does not, but this does not apply to the semi-slugs of coastal Australia, which have a thin, glassy shell, usually hidden beneath folds of tissue. The shell is too fragile and small to provide much protection.

But semi-slugs have other lines of defence. With their mantles drawn over their shells and their bodies hunched, they are difficult for predators to spot. If disturbed they release a thin, slippery mucus, sometimes yellow, orange or red, which may be noxious. Some species wriggle, presumably to make their bodies more difficult to grasp. As a last resort, the semi-slug sheds its tail, which goes on wriggling to distract the predator or provide it with a meal while the semi-slug escapes.
Family: Helicarionidae

RED-TRIANGLE SLUGS ■

These are large, flat slugs (up to 14 cm long) from eastern Australia. On their back they have a red or red-outlined triangle that marks their mantle and breathing pore. The rest of the slug may be white, grey, green, yellow, orange or red.

Red-triangle slugs, which are common between Brisbane and Sydney, graze on the algae on tree trunks, walls or glasshouses. They are found west to Mount Kaputar near Narrabri in New South Wales and as far north as the Atherton Tablelands in Queensland. So far only one species, *Triboniophorus graeffei*, is recognised from Australia, but there may be several undescribed species.
Family: Athoracophoridae

FOREST SNAILS ■

These snails are found all over Australia – in tropical rainforests, savannas and deserts – except in the extreme south-west and Tasmania. They are especially diverse in north-eastern Queensland, the Kimberley and central Australia.

Live forest snails are difficult to observe, but the shattered shells of *Hadra bipartita*, a black and brown rainforest giant, and other forest snails are often found around birds' nests. Greater bowerbirds use the empty shells of the large yellow savanna snail, *Xanthomelon pachystylum*, to adorn their bowers.
Family: Camaenidae

BUSH SNAILS

The common bush snail (*Bradybaena similaris*) was introduced into Australia from East Asia, and is now a minor pest of gardens between Brisbane and Sydney. It is usually less than 1.5 cm long, and so is often mistaken for a young garden snail (*Helix aspersa*). Bush snails can be distinguished from other snails, however, by a small lump between their two upper, eye-bearing tentacles. Known as the head wart, it is believed to release hormone-like substances before mating.
Family: Bradybaenidae

GARDEN AND WHITE SNAILS ■

None of these snails is native to Australia. Eleven species have been introduced from Europe, and many of them are pests of cereal crops, vineyards and market gardens. They are always associated with humans, and are rarely encountered away from cities or arable land.

The common garden snail (*Helix aspersa*) is abundant in well-watered

■ COMMON GARDEN SNAIL
Helix aspersa can be cultivated for eating. It is slightly smaller than the famed French escargot (*Helix pomatia*), which does not occur in Australia, but the taste is similar.

gardens in the southern half of the continent, extending north at higher altitudes. They are edible and are bred for the table in Australia in specialist snail farms.

White snails (*Candidula, Cernuella, Cochlicella* and *Theba* spp.) are widespread in southern Australia. Large numbers crawl up vertical surfaces and seal themselves in to avoid heat reflected from the ground.

Garden snails have unusual reproductive behaviour, impaling each other with chalky darts in the foot during courtship. The function of these darts is unknown, but they may transfer secretions from one snail to the other. The snails discard the darts after mating, and then secrete a new dart from a sac on the female part of the reproductive system over the following week or so.
Family: Helicidae

RAINFOREST SNAIL
This colourful forest snail of the *Helicarion* genus is feasting on fungi growing amid the lush subtropical rainforest of Nightcap National Park, near Byron Bay in north-eastern New South Wales.

INTRODUCED SLUGS

Most slugs encountered in domestic gardens were introduced into Australia from Europe and Asia. The major families of European slugs (Arionidae, Limacidae, Milacidae) have reduced mantles that sit immediately behind the head like small, badly made pancakes. The respiratory hole is clearly visible on the right-hand side.

The Testacellidae, one of only a few groups of truly carnivorous slugs, have tiny cap- or plate-like shells on the end of their tails. They live entirely in the soil, hunting soft-bodied prey such as earthworms.

Veronicellid slugs were introduced from Asia and are restricted to the warmer areas of Australia, such as

Darwin and eastern Queensland. They are completely shell-less and the mantle covers the upper surface of the slug. Veronicellids usually live in the soil but may surface after rain.
Families: Arionidae, Limacidae, Milacidae, Testacellidae, Veronicellidae

RIGHT-HANDED POND SNAILS

Right-handed pond snails live in slow-flowing rivers and dams all over Australia. How many species occur here is unknown, but at least two have been introduced from the northern hemisphere.

Some right-handed pond snail species have been implicated in the transmission of sheep liver fluke (*Fasciola hepatica*). Swimmer's itch, an irritating parasitic infection that is quite common in summer, is also transmitted by these snails.
Family: Lymnaeidae

LEFT-HANDED POND SNAILS

Snails with shells that open on the left-hand side are uncommon, but members of the Planorbidae family in Australia have shells that open in this way. Left-handed pond snails, which are also known as ramshorn snails, occur over the whole of Australia, and are usually found in heavily vegetated rivers, billabongs and dams.

Respiration in these snails is unusual, for two reasons: they have a false gill, and they have the red blood pigment, haemoglobin.

The false gill is an extension of the snail's mantle, protruding beyond the wall of the shell like a normal gill. Haemoglobin (which gives the red colour to human blood cells) is a more efficient carrier of oxygen than haemocyanin, which is the common blood pigment of molluscs.

These two factors allow left-handed pond snails to live and remain submerged in stagnant water, where the oxygen levels are low, whereas other aquatic pulmonates would be forced to come to the surface for air.
Family: Planorbidae

PULMONATE LIMPETS

Pulmonate limpets occur on rocky shores all around Australia, usually in the company of the more familiar

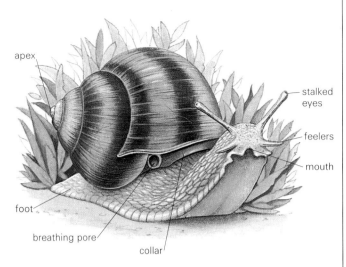

apex — stalked eyes — feelers — mouth — foot — breathing pore — collar

prosobranch limpets (page 584). The two strongly resemble each other because they have evolved in similar habitats, facing similar dangers. They each carry a cap-shaped shell that protects them from waves, predators and dehydration.

The shells of pulmonate limpets can be distinguished (but only on dislodged shells) by their subtle asymmetry – the right-hand edge of the shell is usually flared to accommodate the respiratory siphon.
Family: Siphonariidae

A MOBILE HOME
Like most gastropods, snails have a spiral shell of calcium carbonate. This shell is their permanent home, protecting their internal organs and preventing them from drying out.

LEOPARD SLUGS
To mate, a pair of the introduced slugs *Limax maximus* (up to 20 cm long) lower their entwined bodies on a thread of mucus, exchange sperm externally with their penises, and eat the thread as they crawl back up it.

CEPHALOPODS

Nautiluses, squids, cuttlefishes and octopuses have well-developed nervous systems and keen sight. Many are excellent swimmers, propelling themselves forward by drawing water into their mantle cavities and forcing it out through their siphon. Cephalopods have separate sexes.

Eggs are fertilised by the male within the female and laid on rocks, seaweed or coral, or in huge, gelatinous balls that float in the water.

Most cephalopods can rapidly change the colour, pattern or even texture of their skin to blend with their surroundings. Tiny sacs of red, yellow or black dye called chromatophores are connected to the animal's nervous system. When the chromatophores expand, they spread out into flattened discs and become visible. When they contract, they are reduced to tiny dots.

Most cephalopods secrete 'ink', which they use to trick predators: a frightened squid releases a glob of ink the same size as itself and then becomes translucent and darts away while the slower-witted predator bites into the glob of ink.
Class: Cephalopoda

■ NAUTILUS
The nautilus has survived almost unchanged for about 550 million years. Its eyes are large but not well developed, so the nautilus uses receptors at the end of its tentacles and near its gills to detect prey. This *Nautilus pompilius* is feeding on deep-sea shrimps.

NAUTILUSES ■

Nautiluses are the only cephalopods with a true external shell, measuring about 16 cm across and consisting of gas-filled chambers to keep the nautilus buoyant. The animal lives at the shell entrance and the number of chambers increases as it grows. Unlike other cephalopods, nautiluses have a simple eye. They have no suckers, ink sac or pigment cells.

Nautiluses live in deep tropical waters off the edges of reefs, rising to shallower waters at night to feed on dead marine creatures.

Two nautilus species, *Nautilus pompilius* and *N. stenomphalus*, live in Australian waters.
Family: Nautilidae

QUICK REACTIONS
Octopuses (left) and squids (below) share many features, including their highly developed eyes and their ability to shrink and change colour very rapidly.

eye

arms (eight)

suckers

siphon

tentacles

arms

eye

fins

SQUIDS

Squids are the living torpedoes of the ocean. Many are powerful swimmers, and some species undertake long migrations. They are generally streamlined and muscular and often occur in schools, swimming by flapping their fins or by jet propulsion using their siphon. Squids swim backward for long distances but can quickly jet forward to grab prey. Their shell consists of an inner 'pen' composed largely of chitin, a carbohydrate, and resembles clear plastic. Unlike cuttlefishes, squids usually have a pair of wing-like fins at the end of their body.
Order: Teuthoidea

GIANT SQUIDS

Many legends about deep-sea monsters probably originated with sightings of this gigantic creature, which inhabits most of the world's oceans. Information about giant squids comes mainly from specimens stranded on beaches or found in the stomachs of sperm whales.

Adults can reach a body length of up to 5 metres and weigh 1000 kg. A giant squid with its tentacles outstretched may be up to 18 metres in length. They are probably restricted to deep waters, but they have been washed up on Australian and New Zealand beaches: in 1887 a giant squid measuring 17.37 metres was beached in New Zealand.
Scientific name: *Architeuthis* spp.

NORTHERN CALAMARI

Also known as the bigfin reef squid, this inshore species is common in tropical northern Australian waters from Brisbane to Geraldton, Western Australia. It is dark in colour and its body is 20–35 cm in length. It is easily confused with a cuttlefish because of its large oval fins.

Individuals or small groups often gather around boat lights or lighted jetties at night. Sometimes they come within a metre of the beach in protected bays at night while hunting small fish and crustaceans.
Scientific name: *Sepioteuthis lessoniana*

SOUTHERN CALAMARI

The southern calamari is larger than its northern relative and has wider, more diamond-shaped fins. It ranges throughout Australia's southern waters from just south of Brisbane to north of Dampier, Western Australia. People who fish at night in southern waters are likely to be familiar with the southern calamari, which is attracted to jetty lights.

This species spawns year-round, depositing carpets of gelatinous, finger-shaped egg capsules in shallow water, often among seagrass beds.
Scientific name: *Sepioteuthis australis*

PENCIL SQUIDS

Pencil squids, also called mitre squids, pink squids or swordtip squids, assemble in large schools in the continental-shelf waters of northern Australia. Usually less than 25 cm in body length, they often swim around lighted boats close to shore. There are at least five known species, all very similar in appearance. Some occur in surface waters, while others live at depths of almost 100 metres.
Scientific name: *Photololigo* spp.

BAY SQUID

This 8–9 cm-long inshore squid is found right along the east coast of Australia from the Gulf of Carpentaria to Tasmania. It has small, rounded fins and a blunter 'tail end' than pencil squids. It is usually found in fairly shallow water, often within a few metres of the beach. In northern Queensland, the bay squid also lives in mangrove estuaries.
Scientific name: *Loliolus noctiluca*

ARROW SQUID

Also known as Gould's squid, aero squid, aeroplane squid, seine boat squid, torpedo squid or Gould's flying squid, the arrow squid is common in southern Australian offshore waters from south of Brisbane to Geraldton, Western Australia. It usually lives at depths of more than 500 metres, but occasionally comes close to shore, and even into estuaries. It is a powerful swimmer, and feeds on fishes, other arrow squids and crustaceans.

Unlike near-shore squids, which tend to lay hundreds of large eggs in 'fingers' attached to the sea floor, the arrow squid, and other oceanic squids, produce thousands of pinhead-sized eggs in a huge gelatinous ball that drifts in the open ocean.
Scientific name: *Notodarus gouldi*

NORTHERN CALAMARI
At night *Sepioteuthis lessoniana* swims into shallow waters inshore to feast on small fishes, shrimps and other crustaceans.

■ PFEFFER'S FLAMBOYANT CUTTLEFISH
Metasepia pfefferi has mottled black and yellow coloration with arms and fins outlined in bright yellow.

CUTTLEFISHES

Cuttlefishes are slightly flattened in cross-section and usually have a pair of long fins along the length of their body. The most familiar cuttlefishes belong to the genus *Sepia*, of which there are over 20 species in Australian waters. They usually have an internal cuttlebone, which is often found washed up on beaches, but some smaller species, such as the dumpling or bobtail squid and the pygmy cuttlefish, do not have cuttlebones. Most cuttlefishes live on the sea floor and lay their eggs in the sediments or attach them to structures such as coral.
Order: Sepioidea

AUSTRALIAN GIANT CUTTLEFISH ■
This is probably the most common cuttlefish in our southern waters. Weighing over 6 kg and with a body 50 cm long, it is restricted to coastal waters and bays, and ranges from Moreton Bay in southern Queensland throughout southern waters and up to around Learmonth in Western Australia. It lives around submerged coral caves, cliffs and ledges. *Sepia apama* is frequently eaten by Australian fur seals.
Scientific name: *Sepia apama*

PHARAOH'S CUTTLEFISH
Pharaoh's cuttlefish is 20–40 cm long, and is brown with zebra stripes (more obvious in males) and a blue iridescent stripe along the base of its fins. It is a common tropical Indo-Pacific species found in shallow waters from Townsville, across the Top End and down the west coast to Perth. It is particularly abundant in the Gulf of Carpentaria.
Scientific name: *Sepia pharaonus*

PFEFFER'S FLAMBOYANT CUTTLEFISH ■
This spectacular little cuttlefish has an unusually stout body – less than 8 cm long – compared with its arms. The cuttlebone is a distinctive diamond shape. It is a tropical shallow-water species, commonly found, well-camouflaged, scuttling along sand or silt bottoms using its arms and specialised flaps beneath its body. Little is known of its biology or life history.
Scientific name: *Metasepia pfefferi*

TASMANIAN DUMPLING SQUID
Shallow waters right around Australia house a number of dumpling squid species, sometimes called bobtail squid. The small Tasmanian dumpling squid ranges around southern Australia and Tasmania from New South Wales to Western Australia. It lives on the sea floor, particularly in seagrasses. It lacks a cuttlebone, and its 3 cm rounded body and semicircular fins are patterned with dark speckles.
Scientific name: *Euprymna tasmanica*

PYGMY CUTTLEFISHES
One pygmy cuttlefish, *Idiosepius pymaeus*, is the smallest of all the known cephalopods. It is common in the beaches and breakwaters of north-eastern Australia, particularly around Townsville, Queensland, and across the Top End to north-western Australia. Other favourite haunts are small mangrove tributaries, where it often swims attached to floating objects, such as leaves.

■ GIANT CUTTLEFISH
Sepia apama must have startled many an unsuspecting diver when it has come out of its cave to investigate the intruder. It can very rapidly take on its orange-red 'warning' colours (right).

Lacking a cuttlebone and looking like a miniature squid, it has a sticky organ on its back that it uses to attach itself to underwater objects. The female's body is about 2 cm long and the male's only 1 cm long.

There are at least two other species of pygmy cuttlefishes in Australia. The tropical species *I. paradoxa* has been collected from seagrass beds off Green Island on the Great Barrier Reef. In southern waters, the slightly larger *I. notoides* also inhabits seagrass beds, particularly in Western Port Bay, Victoria.
Scientific name: *Idiosepius* spp.

RAMSHORN SHELL
This tiny coiled shell, no more than 2.5 cm across, is the internal 'bone' of the tail-light squid, which lives in the deep sea throughout the Indo-Pacific region. The shell consists of up to 37 chambers which, when the animal is alive, are filled with gas to give buoyancy to its tail end.

The normal swimming position for the tail-light squid is to hang vertically in the water with its head facing down. An organ at the tail end emits a yellow-green light. This light can glow for hours on a captured tail-light squid that has been placed in an aquarium.
Scientific name: *Spirula spirula*

OCTOPUSES

Unlike squids and cuttlefishes, octopuses have no trace of a shell in their bodies. The smallest octopus species weighs less than a gram and could fit on a fingertip, while the giant Pacific octopus (*Octopus dofleini*) weighs more than 100 kg and has an armspan of up to 8 metres.

Some octopuses live in shallow water, on coral or rocky reefs, sand flats, mud flats, seagrass beds or mangroves. Others spend their lives in open water, never touching the sea floor. Still others cruise the deep sea up to 7 km below the surface. These are soft-bodied creatures with jelly-like skin and no ink sac – the ink decoy is useless against predators in these lightless depths.

The deep-sea cirrate octopuses have a pair of fins and small sensory fingers of skin called cirri next to their suckers for sensing prey in the dark. They swim with their arms spread out and use their fins to push themselves along, gliding through the water like frisbees.

At least 50 species of octopus have so far been found in the shallow waters surrounding Australia.
Order: Octopoda

DAY OCTOPUS ◼

With an armspan of around 2 metres and weighing up to 6 kg, this species is found throughout the tropical Pacific and Indian Oceans from Hawaii to East Africa. It lives on all northern Australian coral reefs, particularly the Great Barrier Reef. A master of camouflage, it uses colour patterns and skin sculpture to merge into backgrounds varying from smooth white sand to spiked corals. It has a black false eyespot beneath each real eye and zebra stripes on the undersides of its arms.

It feeds mainly on crabs and lobsters but also catches fishes and even young moray eels. The female lays up to 600 000 tiny eggs in strings called festoons. The minute hatchlings swim up into the surface waters, where they are carried away in the plankton by ocean currents.
Scientific name: *Octopus cyaneus*

COMMON SYDNEY OCTOPUS ◼

The common Sydney octopus occurs mainly along Australia's east coast from Brisbane to Eden in southern New South Wales. Slightly smaller than the day octopus, it is very common around Sydney Harbour. It

often sits at the mouth of its lair during the day. Its body is grey, the sides of its arms are orange and its pupils are white.

When feeding, usually at night, the octopus becomes a mottled orange-brown and can push up large digits of skin to impersonate seaweeds. Crabs are its preferred diet, but it also uses its toothed tongue to drill into mollusc shells and consume the fleshy contents. Females lay thousands of small eggs in festoons.
Scientific name: *Octopus tetricus*

NIGHT OCTOPUSES

Night octopuses feed after dark in the tropical and warm temperate coastal waters of northern Australia. With an armspan to 2 metres, a body size of 10–15 cm, and a weight of up to 2 kg, they have long front arms and are patterned in red and white.

Octopus alpheus is red with white spots. It lives on intertidal reefs, including the Great Barrier Reef, and feeds on crabs.

O. dierythraeus occurs in muddy coastal waters from Shark Bay, Western Australia to Brisbane. It has an alarm display of red spots on white. It feeds mainly by drilling mollusc shells, including young giant clams. Both species produce large eggs, and the young hatch as miniature adults and crawl away.

O. ornatus has a red body with longitudinal white stripes, and has a taste for other octopuses. The females lay thousands of small eggs and the young float in the sea with the plankton before coming to rest on the sea bed, where they mature.
Scientific name: *Octopus* spp.

SOUTHERN KEELED OCTOPUS

A number of octopus species can burrow into, and even swim through, sand and mud; one such is the southern keeled octopus from Victoria, Tasmania and South Australia. It has a ridge of skin around the edge of its body, forming a keel that helps to guide the octopus into and through the sand.

This octopus feeds on crustaceans and shellfish on sand or mud. It quickly buries itself under the sand when threatened, even popping up a single eye every now and then, like a periscope, to find out whether it is safe to emerge and keep foraging. The female lays large eggs, each attached by a stalk to a rocky surface or the inside of a discarded bottle.
Scientific name: *Octopus berrima*

◼ DAY OCTOPUS
When *Octopus cyaneus* emerges to forage among weeds, it uses its impressive camouflage apparatus to masquerade as part of the ocean floor. The 'tube' in the centre is the siphon that it uses for jet propulsion.

◼ COMMON SYDNEY OCTOPUS
An adult *Octopus tetricus* at the mouth of its lair pulls up rubble with its suckers to defend its home from an intruder.

■ PAPER NAUTILUS
After spawning, swarms of *Argonauta argo* some-times come inshore, where they die in shal-low waters. Here the animal's translucent shell-like egg case, with its characteristic sharp ridge, can be seen quite clearly.

BANDED ARM-DROPPING OCTOPUS

This bizarre octopus lives on inter-tidal flats across the northern coast of Australia. It has extremely long, banded arms that can be up to ten times its body length. It feeds on small crabs and shrimps in low-tide pools and sand flats at night.

It has developed a defence like that of a drop-tail lizard: if it is attacked it discards one or more arms at the base. The arm continues to wriggle for four or five hours, and will even crawl over an attacker. Meanwhile, the octopus crawls away and, within six to eight weeks, grows a new arm! This technique works so well that the banded arm-dropping octopus

can no longer produce and squirt the ink that other shallow-water octopuses use for self-defence.
Scientific name: *Ameloctopus litoralis*

BLUE-RINGED OCTOPUSES ■

When a blue-ringed octopus is at rest its pale blue circles and lines are not especially noticeable, but when the octopus is threatened the rings become vividly iridescent.

This display of colour serves as a warning: these octopuses have caused at least ten human deaths in Australia. The octopuses harbour bacteria in their salivary glands that produce a poison called tetrodotox-in. This toxin affects all muscles except that of the heart, so that the victim is fully conscious but cannot breathe. Mouth-to-mouth resuscita-tion can save victims, who seem to recover after about 24 hours.

Three blue-ringed octopuses inhabit Australian waters. The southern blue-ringed octopus, *Hapa-lochlaena maculosa*, has a body 4 cm long and an armspan of 15 cm and weighs about 50 grams. It lives around southern Australian coasts and has small rings 2–3 mm in diam-eter on its body and arms. It is often found on intertidal rock platforms and in shallow waters.

H. fasciata, the blue-lined octopus, is about the same size but occurs only off the coast of New South Wales and southern Queensland. The lines on its body and the linked rings on its arms are clearly visible.

The greater blue-ringed octopus, *H. lunulata*, is nearly twice the size of the other two. It occurs in north-ern Australia, particularly in the waters off the Northern Territory, and throughout the islands of the Indo-Malayan Archipelago. It has large rings up to 10 mm in diameter on its body and arms.
Scientific name: *Hapalochlaena* spp.

PAPER NAUTILUS ■

This pretty white shell is often mis-taken for that of a nautilus (page 592), but it is the protective egg case of the female argonaut octopus.

The female argonaut is 25–30 cm long, but the male is only about a tenth that size. Males have a special detachable arm that stores sperm; the arm breaks off and is passed to the female, and the male then dies. A single female may carry the detached arms of up to eight males, using the sperm to fertilise her eggs.

There are two species in Australia. Both spend their entire lives swim-ming in open water, never touching the sea floor. *Argonauta nodosa* has a rounded shell and is found in colder waters along southern Australian coasts, occasionally stranding in large numbers in Bass Strait and along the Victorian coast. *A. argo* is a warm-water paper nautilus that sometimes comes down the east coast of Australia. Its shell is more angular than that of *A. nodosa*, with a sharp ridge along its top.
Scientific name: *Argonauta nodosa, A. argo*

■ GREATER BLUE-RINGED OCTOPUS
This photograph of *Hapalochlaena lunulata* shows the vibrant electric-blue rings that give this poisonous octopus its name. When the animal senses dan-ger, special crystals in its skin pick up and refract the light to produce this dazzling alarm pattern.

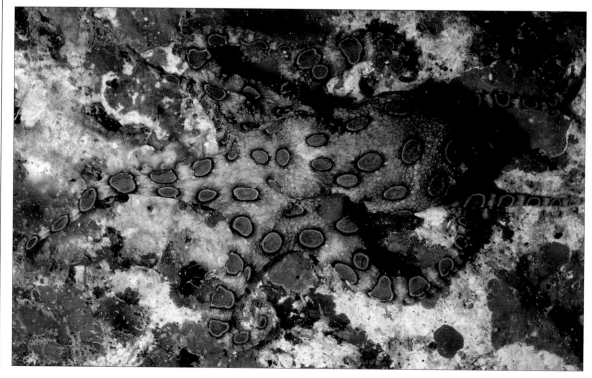

LAMPSHELLS

Lampshells are shelled marine animals with two shells, or 'valves'. They are often confused with bivalves. The main difference is that lampshells have one shell on top of their body and one below, whereas bivalves have one shell on either side of their body. Another difference is that, unlike bivalves, lampshells use a stalk called a pedicel to anchor themselves to the sea floor.

Lampshells have an internal skeleton, and their lower valve forms a beak like the spout of an Aladdin's lamp – hence the name 'lampshell'.

Lampshells are between 2 mm and 4.5 cm long, and their shells are usually grey, yellow or red. Depending on whether or not their valves are hinged, they fall into two classes: articulated and inarticulated.

Today there are about 280 species of lampshells – a mere fraction of the fossil family of some 30 000 lampshell species that inhabited the Earth's oceans around 400 million years ago, in the Paleozoic era. At least 11 species of lampshells are found in Australian waters.

Lampshells live in communities in temperate and cold waters, from the low-tide mark to the edge of the continental shelf. They attach themselves to rocks or to one another, anchor themselves into vertical burrows, or live freely on the muddy sea floor. They feed by filtering plankton through the feathery filaments on their two arms.

In most lampshells the sexes are separate. Some expel their eggs and sperm into the water, while others brood their larvae. After a brief swimming existence, the larvae secure themselves to a suitable site and metamorphose into adults.
Phylum: Brachiopoda

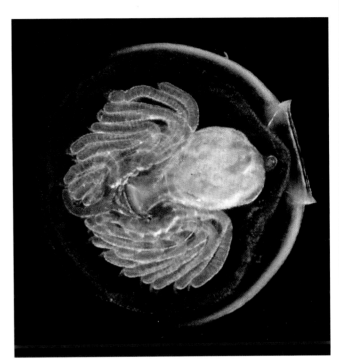

LAMPSHELL LARVAE
The unique, feathery, filament-lined arms – called brachia – of the lampshell form complex loops within its shell.

SEA MATS

Sea mats look like mosses – hence their name – but they are, in fact, colonies of hundreds, sometimes millions, of microscopic animals. Of the 3000–4000 marine species and 35 freshwater species, about 130 are the plant-like encrustations that are notorious for fouling the bottoms of boats, buoys and jetties.

Each individual animal, called a zooid, is less than 1.5 mm long, and its soft body is covered by a hardened case of calcium carbonate or chitin, a carbohydrate. These hidden bodies may be oval, or they may be shaped like tubes, boxes or vases. The sea mats' outer casings and colonies are just as diverse.

The most common sea mats are the encrusting and creeping colonies that attach themselves to rocks, shells or seaweed between the high-tide mark and shallow waters. Erect and branching colonies are more abundant in deeper water.

Sea mat colonies may reach up to a metre or more in diameter and height. Most are pale or white, but darker hues like purple also occur.

No sea mats are parasitic, but many species live either cooperatively or competitively with other organisms. Their primary food source is plant plankton, which the zooid traps with its tiny tentacles.

The most remarkable feature of all marine sea mats is their power of regeneration. Their soft body parts periodically break down into a brown mass, which, over time, is expelled from the body walls as waste, making way for the development of completely new organisms.

All freshwater and most marine sea mats are hermaphrodites, with most species brooding their large, yolky eggs. Each sea mat colony also grows by a form of nonsexual reproduction called 'budding'.
Phylum: Bryozoa

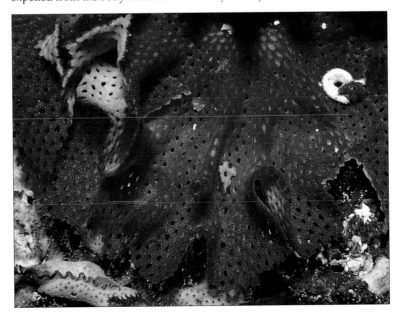

PURPLE BRYOZOAN
Most purple bryozoan colonies are small, but they can grow to more than 20 cm in diameter. This lace-like *Idodyctyum* species lies hidden in the deep water of ocean reefs.

feather star (crinoid)

sea star (asteroid)

brittle star (ophiuroid)

sea urchin (echinoid)

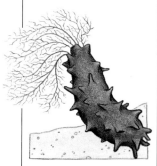

sea cucumber (holothuroid)

FIVE-STAR CREATURES
Superficially, the five classes of echinoderm do not resemble each other at all, but they share the same basic five-rayed structure.

ECHINODERMS

Echinoderms are relatively large, unusually shaped and often very colourful. Hundreds of species have been identified in Australian waters, and some are among the better known of the marine invertebrates. Echinoderms live only in salt water, and many species are found in tidal rock pools, along the surf lines of sandy beaches, and in tropical mudflats, seagrass beds, coral reefs and temperate-zone rocky reefs. Others are found in the depths of the seas, some living so deep that we know about them only through underwater video footage.

The name of the phylum Echinodermata means 'spiny-skinned' (from two Greek words, *echinos*, a hedgehog or sea urchin, and *dermis*, skin), but not all echinoderms have spines; most feather stars and sea cucumbers, for example, do not. Echinoderms have three main features that set them apart from other marine invertebrates – their unique skeletal structure, their five-rayed bodies, and the tubed feet that propel them along or collect food.

Unique features
All echinoderms have a skeleton made up of calcareous plates, or small bones (ossicles), but this skeletal structure varies in form among species. In some sea stars the ossicles are large, prominent and rigid, whereas in sea urchins they are hidden beneath the spines and the outer skin. The skeleton of a feather star or a brittle star is made up of thousands of body armour plates that give it flexibility, whereas the skeleton of the sea cucumber consists of minute calcareous plates distributed throughout the body wall.

The adult bodies of all echinoderms are based on a five-rayed structure arranged around a central point, usually the mouth. They are radially symmetrical, each of the five sections being a copy of the others. Although it is common to see sea stars with more than five arms – some have as many as 40 – all sea star species start life with five arms and add more as they grow.

The third distinctive feature of echinoderms is the water-driven vascular system that allows them to move on their tube-like feet. A remarkable system of hydraulic pumps and hoses allows each row of hollow feet to extend, push forward or back, and then retract to propel the animal along. Body fluid or sea water is pumped around the body to generate the pressure changes that drive the system.

The tube feet of echinoderms also have other uses: feather stars and brittle stars move food particles towards their mouths with their feet; sea urchins clean their skin with them; and sea urchins, sea stars and sea cucumbers have little suckers on the ends of their tube feet, with which they cling to rocks.

Some sea stars and sea urchins have tiny, pincer-like organs for keeping their outer skin clear of sediment and any encrusting animals. Called pedicellariae, these organs are on stalks and are located at the base of the spine and all over the outer surface of the animal.

In some species the pedicellariae have been modified for catching prey or for defence. The pedicellariae of the flowered sea urchin, *Toxopneustes pileolus* (page 604), are extremely toxic to humans.

Perpetuating the species
Except for a few hermaphrodites, echinoderms have separate sexes. Some female echinoderms brood their eggs until they hatch into tiny miniatures of the adults, but most species release millions of tiny eggs and sperm into the water.

Many of these eggs are never fertilised because they do not come into contact with sperm. From the few eggs that are fertilised, water-borne larvae are hatched. They stay in the larval state from a few days to several months, depending on the species. If the species has a very short larval life, the larvae do not need to feed. Most echinoderm larvae, however, have long lives and feed on phytoplankton – microscopic single-celled plants.

Some sea stars, brittle stars and sea cucumbers also reproduce nonsexually by splitting (see box, 'Reinventing the self', page 601).

IN SEARCH OF PREY
At dusk or turn of tide, a hungry sea star breaks cover and glides on pointed feet across the sandy sea floor.

FEATHER STARS

Feather stars, the most common of the crinoids, are delicate, flower-like animals found in both the southern and northern parts of Australia. The greatest number of species occur in the tropics, especially on coral reefs, such as the Great Barrier Reef.

The arms and feathery pinnules of feather stars look like birds' feathers – hence their common name. When spread out, the arms and pinnules form a broad net that traps food particles drifting past in the water currents. The particles then move along the pinnules to the arms, and the tube feet transfer them down the arms into the mouth.

Feather stars use their arms to crawl about, and some species even swim short distances by waving them. These animals must cling to hard surfaces in strong currents to feed. Many species hang on with thousands of sticky or serrated pinnules; others attach themselves by little grasping claws (cirri) that extend from the underside of their central body disc. Feather stars without cirri hang on with some of their arms and use the others to feed.

Some feather stars hide completely under rocks during the day, emerging at night to feed. Some stay in the open day and night, enabling them to feed continuously. Many others protect their soft, delicate body discs during the day but leave a few arms swaying out from beneath rocks to catch passing prey. Feather stars take in oxygen through large numbers of tube feet along each arm.

Class: Crinoidea

WHITE FEATHER STAR

The white feather star is a fairly common species that occurs under rocks on the southern coasts of Australia from northern New South Wales right around to Western Australia. It grows to about 10 cm across. It may have pale brown stripes running along its arms.
Scientific name: *Antedon incommoda*

LOVEN'S FEATHER STAR

The Loven's feather star is very similar in colour and habit to its close relative, the white feather star, but it is more slender and delicate in appearance and is generally a little smaller. Loven's feather stars are found from northern New South Wales round to the south-eastern part of South Australia.
Scientific name: *Antedon loveni*

GIANT BLACK FEATHER STAR

This, the largest of the Australian coral reef feather stars, is black all over. Although this feather star has only ten arms – fewer than many feather stars – it makes up for this by the length and breadth of these arms, which grow up to 25 cm long. The pinnules are also very long. The giant black feather star attaches itself to coral heads with its large, strong grasping claws.
Scientific name: *Tropiometra afra*

ROBUST FEATHER STAR

The robust feather star has more than 50 arms, each about 15 cm long. The upper sides of its arms are bright crimson, but the undersides may be much lighter in colour – almost white or grey. The robust feather star clings to coral heads with strong grasping claws and is often completely exposed during the day. It is commonly found on the Great Barrier Reef and elsewhere in tropical waters.
Scientific name: *Himmerometra robustipinna*

NOBLE FEATHER STAR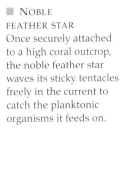

The noble feather star is also common on the Great Barrier Reef. It has more than 40 arms, each about 20 cm long, but these are far more delicate than those of the robust feather star or the giant black feather star. As it has no grasping claws, it uses a few of its arms and pinnules to grasp on to coral heads. Its colour is variable, but it is usually predominantly yellow with brown, white, black and green markings.
Scientific name: *Comanthina nobilis*

ORANGE FEATHER STAR

This feather star is the most conspicuous of the southern species. It grows up to 20 cm across and can have as many as 40 arms. Its colour ranges from orange through to brown, green, and even black.

During the day, when fish predators are active, the orange feather star hides most of its body under rocks and in crevices. When this creature is handled, its tiny pinnules break off and cling tightly to skin, gloves or wetsuits. These pinnules are difficult to remove because of their stickiness, but they are not dangerous or poisonous. The orange feather star is found right around the southern Australian coast from the waters of southern Queensland to Western Australia.
Scientific name: *Comanthus trichoptera*

■ NOBLE FEATHER STAR
Once securely attached to a high coral outcrop, the noble feather star waves its sticky tentacles freely in the current to catch the planktonic organisms it feeds on.

LILIES OF THE DEEP

Sea lilies, also known as stalked crinoids, are the most ancient and primitive of the echinoderms. Living at depths of 150 metres or more, they are usually seen only when they are trawled in deepwater fishing operations.

About 80 extant species have been recorded worldwide, but only a very few have been identified in Australia, mainly in tropical waters. Unlike feather stars, whose ancestors they are, sea lilies are fixed in position by their stalks. Millions of years ago they had stalks up to 20 metres in length, but today's species grow to only about 60 cm long.

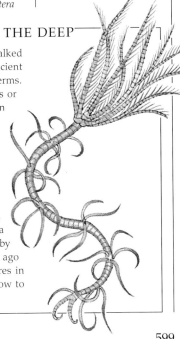

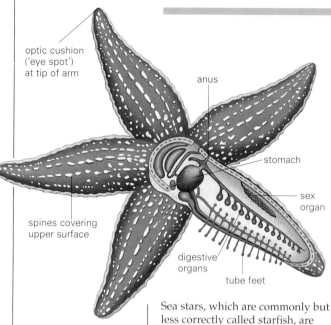

optic cushion ('eye spot') at tip of arm

anus

stomach

sex organ

spines covering upper surface

digestive organs

tube feet

SEA STARS

THE GROWTH OF A SEA STAR
All sea stars begin life with five arms. As they grow, so do new arms, and the adults of some species can end up with as many as forty. Under each of these arms sea stars have numerous tube feet that enable them to move about and deal with their prey.

Sea stars, which are commonly but less correctly called starfish, are probably the best known of all echinoderms. The most typical have five arms radiating from a central point. These are usually fattish at the base and taper to a blunt point at the tip. Some species have as many as 40 arms; others have almost vestigial arms, so that they are shaped more like a pentagon than a star. In all sea stars the mouth is in the centre of the body on the underside. A groove extending along each arm from the mouth contains the tube feet with which the sea star moves.

The feeding habits of sea stars are different from those of other echinoderms. They take in small prey, such as shrimps or snails, through the mouth into the stomach, which sits like a big sac inside the mouth. After digesting the item, they spit out the

hard body parts. In this way, they can eat several things at once. If a food item is too big to be taken inside the body, the sea star turns its stomach out through its mouth and spreads it over its prey. The stomach then releases digestive juices to break down the food.

Some sea star species use their hydraulically powered tube feet to prise open the shells of molluscs, such as mussels. Once the shell is open, the sea star turns its stomach inside out through its mouth and spreads it over the soft body of the mussel to digest it.

Sea stars have no lungs or gills. Instead, they absorb oxygen through tiny, delicate, fluid-filled sacs that pepper the surface of their bodies. They can also take up oxygen through their tube feet.

Sea stars are extremely sensitive to their environment. Like many other echinoderms, they have sensory cells in the suckers on their tube feet, through which they can detect chemical stimuli from food or predators. But sea stars also have 'eye spots', called optic cushions, on the tip of each arm, and can use them to detect changes in light intensity.
Class: Asteroidea

CROWN-OF-THORNS SEA STAR ■
The crown-of-thorns sea star is the world's only known venomous sea star. It can have up to 23 arms and grow to 70 cm in diameter, but most are about half this size. The upper

part of its body is covered with long, poisonous spines.

Crown-of-thorns sea stars are usually found in water deeper than 5 metres. In Australia they inhabit tropical waters from Dampier on the coast of Western Australia right around to the Great Barrier Reef in Queensland. They also live on coral reefs throughout the Indian Ocean.

This sea star feeds on live corals and has devoured many hectares of the Great Barrier Reef. It usually hides during the day, emerging to feed at night. Divers may detect its presence in an area by the white skeletons of freshly killed corals.
Scientific name: *Acanthaster planci*

COMB SEA STAR
The comb sea star has no suckers on the ends of its tube feet – it lives in sand and on soft sea bottoms and does not need suckers to hang onto rocks. It is one of several species that have long, horizontal spines along the margin of each arm to protect them from predators, such as fishes.

The comb sea star usually stays buried all day and at night crawls over the soft sea bed in search of prey. It eats mostly small bivalves, which it swallows whole.

This sea star is found in many parts of the world, including right around Australia's coastline. It grows to 17 cm in diameter, and is light to dark brown or even purple, with a much lighter underside.
Scientific name: *Astropecten polyacanthus*

■ CROWN-OF-THORNS SEA STAR
This voracious coral-eater generally moves about at night. Its tube feet enable it to right itself if turned over, but it tends to avoid the exposed reef crest where wave action is high.

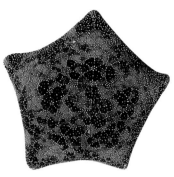

■ PINCUSHION SEA STAR
This species is found around the northern Australian coast from Western Australia to Queensland.

ELEVEN-ARMED SEA STAR

The eleven-armed sea star is very common all round the coast of southern Australia. It grows to 40 cm across and has between seven and 14 spiny arms. It moves very quickly over rocky reefs and soft-bottomed sea beds, seeking out sea urchins and small molluscs, which it consumes by turning its large stomach inside out. Its colour is a patchy blue, green, brown and white.

This sea star's arms are often different lengths. This is because it can reproduce by splitting in half, with each half regrowing its lost arms and becoming a complete sea star (see box, 'Reinventing the self').
Scientific name: *Coscinasterias calamaria*

JAPANESE SEA STAR

The introduced Japanese sea star arrived in Tasmanian waters in the ballast of ships during the 1980s. It grows up to 12 cm across and is variably coloured, with orange and blue predominating. Large breeding populations thrive on the muddy bottom of Tasmania's Derwent River, where they devour dead sea creatures, including fishes, and all types of small encrusting animals and other slow-moving animals, such as snails.

So far the Japanese sea star has not spread to the waters of the mainland states, but there is a concern that it may eventually threaten Australia's oyster and scallop fisheries.
Scientific name: *Asterias amurensis*

BLUE SEA STAR ■

This species inhabits waters around the northern half of Australia. The blue that gives this sea star its common name is very distinctive, but on some reefs and in deeper waters, grey, pink, yellow and khaki specimens have been found.

Although the blue sea star can grow to 30 cm across, it has a tiny stomach and feeds only on small encrusting animals and debris.

Young blue sea stars, which are bright white when small, are rarely seen, as they live hidden away in cracks and crevices to escape from predatory fishes.
Scientific name: *Linckia laevigata*

PINCUSHION SEA STAR ■

The pincushion sea star is most commonly found on coral reefs, where it feeds on corals and other encrusting organisms. It is slow-moving and has a thick body wall. The colours of this animal vary greatly, from yellow to green to brown and purple, but all provide good camouflage among the corals on the reef flats where these sea stars live.

The pincushion sea star derives its common name from its body, which is almost as thick as it is wide – so that it resembles a sea urchin without spines – and is covered with tiny, smooth, round, shiny ossicles that look like pinheads. It grows to about 20 cm in diameter.
Scientific name: *Culcita novaeguineae*

CARPET SEA STARS

Carpet sea stars abound on the southern Australian coastline. They live in reef flats and rock pools along the shores and come in a wide array of colours. The four most common species are *Patiriella calcar*, which has eight arms and occurs in combinations of almost all hues; *P. exigua*, which has only five arms and is generally a shade of blue-green; *P. brevispina*, which has six arms and is usually purple with bright orange tube feet; and *P. gunnii*, which also has six arms and, like *P. calcar*, comes in a wonderful array of colours.

Apart from *P. exigua*, which does not occur in Western Australia, all these species are found in the south-

ern Australian states, including Tasmania. On average, they are about 5 cm in diameter.

The genus *Patiriella* contains the world's smallest sea star, *P. parvivipara*, which reaches only 6 mm in diameter. This species is confined to a small area near Streaky Bay in South Australia. Unlike most sea stars, this species broods its young inside its body, and they are born as perfectly formed replicas of their parents and almost the same size.
Scientific name: *Patiriella* spp.

REINVENTING THE SELF

Some echinoderms have amazing powers of regeneration. Sea stars often regrow arms bitten off by predators. If disturbed, a brittle star often sheds all or part of an arm, which continues to wriggle for some time to distract the attacker and enable the rest of the brittle star to escape. The cast-off arm cannot grow into another brittle star, but another limb will grow from the lost or shortened arm on the main body.

Sea stars, brittle stars and sea cucumbers can reproduce by tearing themselves into two – a process that is called fission. Sea stars are the most common group of echinoderms to do this. Some brittle stars can reproduce nonsexually in the same way – by splitting their disc into two, one part with two arms and one with three; each half then heals and grows more arms. Some sea cucumbers can also reproduce nonsexually by simply splitting into two halves, each of which then rebuilds itself into a complete animal.

■ BLUE SEA STAR
The blue sea star is very common in sheltered, shallow waters on coral reefs in the northern half of Australia. It has strong powers of regeneration, easily growing new arms when they are severed. This one is unusual as it has additional arms growing above its body.

BRITTLE STARS AND BASKET STARS

■ SCHAYER'S
BRITTLE STAR
The arms of Schayer's
brittle star are banded
with light and dark grey
stripes and covered with
short spines.

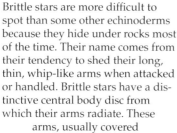

NOCTURNAL FEEDERS
When darkness falls,
basket stars spread out
their arms, both to move
around and to collect
their food of plankton
and underwater debris.

Brittle stars are more difficult to
spot than some other echinoderms
because they hide under rocks most
of the time. Their name comes from
their tendency to shed their long,
thin, whip-like arms when attacked
or handled. Brittle stars have a distinctive central body disc from
which their arms radiate. These
arms, usually covered
in spines, enable
brittle stars to move
more rapidly than
other echinoderms.
Brittle stars vary
greatly in size; some
are so tiny that a thousand
would fit inside a matchbox,
but in other species the central
disc can be as much as 3 cm across
and the arms up to 20 cm long.
Most brittle star species live alone,
but a few tiny species congregate in
large colonies on sea
fans. Some species
travel around
in couples, the
much larger female carry-
ing her tiny male partner
around on her disc.
Many brittle stars make their
homes on sponges, sea fans, corals,
and even other echinoderms, where
they find both food and shelter
without harming their host. This
relationship between animals is
known as commensalism (meaning
'sharing a table'), and it is very
common among marine animals.
Brittle stars take in oxygen from
the water using small, beating,

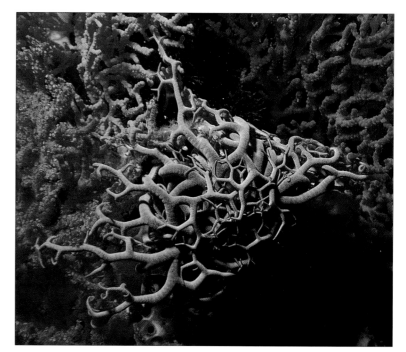

hair-like structures inside the body
disc, which work rather like gills to
move water in and out of slits at the
base of each arm.
Different brittle star species gather
food in different ways. Some are
scavengers, eating small living or
dead animals, while others pick up
small particles of food and transfer
them to their mouth with their
myriad tube feet, as feather stars
do. Some, again like feather stars,
extend their arms into water currents to trap drifting food particles.
Basket stars are not common, but
they are some of the most beautiful
of all echinoderms and are present
in both southern and northern
Australian waters. By day they hide
under rocks or among sea fans, their
long, many-branched arms bunched
up. At night they emerge and use
their arms as food baskets.
Class: Ophiuroidea

PINK BASKET STAR AND SOUTHERN BASKET STAR ■

These are the two basket star species
that are most likely to be seen. Both
are large species, 20–30 cm across
when fully spread out. They curl up
on sponges or fan corals during the
day, and feed at night.
The pink basket star is almost
always pink or orange, and is found
off the shores of South Australia
and Western Australia. The southern
basket star ranges from brown to
grey to red, with dark blotches on

■ BASKET STAR
Astroboa ernae is the largest of the
basket stars that live in the temperate
shallow waters of Australia's coastline.

its disc and dark bands on its arms.
It lives along the coast from New
South Wales to South Australia.
Scientific names: *Astroboa ernae* (pink
basket star), *Conocladus australis*
(southern basket star)

RAMSAY'S BRITTLE STAR

Ramsay's brittle star is common
under rocks between and just
below tidal levels on all southern
Australian shores. Its arms are banded in light and dark shades of red,
green, brown or grey. It skulks
under rocks, hiding from the many
predatory fish species that search
for food among the crevices.
Scientific name: *Ophiarachnella ramsayi*

SCHAYER'S BRITTLE STAR ■

Schayer's brittle star, another
common southern Australian
species, occupies the same habitat
as Ramsay's brittle star (previous
entry), but is smaller and less
colourful. It has much larger spines
on its arms than Ramsay's brittle
star. If disturbed at night, it often
becomes luminescent.
It is quite a large species, with a
body disc 2 cm in diameter or more
and arms 12 cm long. Its disc is light
greyish brown with white spots.
Scientific name: *Ophionereis schayeri*

SEA URCHINS

Sea urchins, sometimes called sea eggs, are found all around Australia, tucked into crevices on rocky shores and offshore reefs, or living among beds of algae and seagrasses. Sea urchins have five pairs of gills for taking up oxygen from the water.

The basic sea urchin form is a spherical shell, called a test, with the mouth on the bottom and the anus on the top. The test is studded with movable spines, all jacketed in a thin living tissue. Sizes vary from 1 cm to 20 cm in diameter. Some sea urchins, such as the needle-spined sea urchin, have very thin tests. Others, such as the slate-pencil sea urchin, have thick, well-armoured ones.

The sea urchin's spines are for protection against such predators as fishes, and some are very poisonous. To protect themselves against the settlement of encrusting animals, sea urchins have pedicellariae – little jaws with two or three teeth, mounted on mobile stalks located on the test at the base of the spines.

Sea urchins travel by using either their spines, which can move backwards or forwards, or their long tube feet, which poke out of their tests in five pairs of rows running from the top of the test near the anus to the bottom near the mouth. They pull themselves along by their tube feet in the same way as sea stars do.

Most sea urchins feed by scraping and pulling algae from rock surfaces, using a remarkable apparatus called an Aristotle's lantern (see illustration). This consists of five large rasping teeth joined together by muscles to make the teeth move up and down. Sea urchins feed mainly by grazing, but some species use these teeth to rasp off encrusting invertebrates, such as coral polyps. Some also use their tube feet, their spines and their pedicellariae to catch pieces of algae drifting past.

As with most echinoderms, sexes are separate in sea urchins; males and females release sperm and eggs into the water, and those eggs that become fertilised hatch and release tiny larvae. The larvae grow long arms covered in fine hairs, and they beat these rapidly in order to swim and catch the single-celled algae on which they feed. Once the juveniles settle on the sea bed, their long feeding arms turn into spines and they take on the appearance of miniature adult sea urchins.

Class: Echinoidea

NEEDLE-SPINED SEA URCHIN ◼

This species has long, thin, fragile spines, up to 20 cm long, and a small test (shell). Needle-spined sea urchins are very mobile and, when disturbed, they move menacingly in circles to deter predatory fishes. Their barbed spines are not toxic, but they can become deeply embedded in a human foot or hand, where they can set up infection.

The needle-spined sea urchin lives in the northern half of Australia around reefs and on groynes and rock walls. The adults are black and the juveniles are brownish with white-striped spines. Both adults and juveniles are easily recognised by a bright orange ring and vivid blue and white markings surrounding the anus on the upper side of the test.

Some animals use the spines of the needle-spined sea urchin as refuges. Small cardinal fishes in particular hide there as they feed on microscopic crustaceans swimming past.

Scientific name: *Diadema setosum*

GREEN SEA URCHIN

This is a common species found along the southern coast from Victoria to Western Australia, including Tasmania. Its green shell can be up to 7 cm in diameter and, while it is alive, its short, blunt, green spines are tipped with bright reddish orange. As well as algae, it feeds on the kelp or seagrass in which it wraps itself.

Green sea urchins are sometimes washed up in thousands on beaches after storms. They are a valuable source of food for a number of predatory animals.

Scientific name: *Holopneustes porosissimus*

SLATE-PENCIL SEA URCHIN

The slate-pencil sea urchin has just a few very thick, blunt spines that look rather like the old-fashioned slate pencils that were used when school children wrote on slate boards rather than paper.

For protection, this sea urchin has a thick, heavily armoured shell, 10 cm in diameter, instead of sharp spines. The species occurs on rocky reefs from Queensland southward to Tasmania. A very similar species, *Phyllacanthus irregularis*, inhabits the coastal waters of South Australia and Western Australia.

Scientific name: *Phyllacanthus parvispinus*

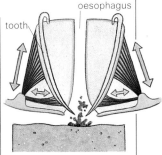

oesophagus

tooth

ARISTOTLE'S LANTERN
This cross-section of a sea urchin's mouth shows two of its five large rasping teeth, with the muscles that move them up and down to scrape up food. These teeth keep growing through the animal's life to compensate for wear.

◼ NEEDLE-SPINED SEA URCHIN
This needle-spined sea urchin is clinging to a mangrove root. Its spines can inflict pain on a human if it is handled incautiously.

■ FLOWERED
SEA URCHIN
This species takes its
common name from
its covering of hundreds
of red and white toothed
stalks, which look like
tiny flowers

BURROWING SEA URCHIN

This species, 8.5 cm in diameter, is
common on reefs as far south as
Rottnest Island in Western Australia
and on shallow coral reefs in the
tropical waters of northern Australia. It has fairly short, thick spines,
usually purple or green but with
sharp white tips.

The burrowing sea urchin bores
into the surface of reefs, devouring
small filaments of algae. In some
parts of the world, where its
predators have been overfished
or pollution has slowed coral
growth, populations have become
very dense, nibbling away hard reefs
faster than the corals can rebuild.
Scientific name: *Echinometra mathaei*

FLOWERED SEA URCHIN ■

The flowered sea urchin, light beige
and 12 cm in diameter, inhabits
Australia's northern coastline. It has
very short spines and is covered in
pretty white and red pedicellariae
(toothed stalks). Beautiful it may be,
but it is exceedingly poisonous to

■ PURPLE SEA URCHIN
The purple sea urchin belies its name
by sometimes being white, brown or
green. It is 7 cm in diameter.

humans; its pedicellariae are its first
line of defence, and are enlarged and
highly toxic. It should never be handled without protective gloves.
Scientific name: *Toxopneustes pileolus*

PURPLE SEA URCHIN ■

This is probably the most common
sea urchin species on southern
Australian shores, occurring from
southern Queensland to Western
Australia. It is usually found in
depressions or hollows along the
surf edge of shallow, rocky reefs,
where it feeds by grazing algae from
the rocks or by trapping bits of seaweed as they wash by. Populations
of purple sea urchins are sometimes
very dense, clustering together in
large numbers for protection from
the surf or from predators.
Scientific name: *Heliocidaris
erythrogramma*

HEART URCHINS AND SAND DOLLARS ■

Heart urchins and sand dollars
are irregularly shaped sea urchins
densely covered with short, fine
spines. Heart urchins are oval or
heart-shaped and look rather like
small, hairy coconuts (see box,
'Beachcombing bliss'). Sand dollars,
sometimes known as sea biscuits,
are flatter and coin-shaped.

The mouth and anus of the heart
urchin are at opposite ends of the
underside of the test (shell); in the
sand dollar they are both centrally
located on the underside. Both
groups can reach 10 cm in diameter.

From tidal areas to the deep sea,
heart urchins and sand dollars
burrow into soft sand and sediment.
Heart urchins use modified tube feet
around their mouths to pick up food
particles, while sand dollars use
their spines and tube feet to carry
food particles to their mouth from
all over the upper part of their body.
Scientific names: *Echinocardium
cordatum* (heart urchin), *Mellita
sexiesperforata* (sand dollar)

BEACHCOMBING BLISS

Heart urchins are common, but
they are not very often seen
because they live buried in sand.
Their tests (shells) are frequently
washed up on beaches, but are so
fragile that they are usually in
pieces. If you are lucky enough to
find the unbroken test of a heart
urchin (*Echinocardium cordatum*), you
will recognise it by its size (6–9 cm
long) and by the holes, in the shape
of a five-armed sea star, on its
upper surface for the tube feet.

Sand dollars are easier to find
alive, as they live closer to the beach
and are plentiful around northern
Australian coasts. At low tide they
can be discovered by following the
wide trails that they leave as they
burrow just below the surface.

■ SAND DOLLAR
The sand dollar is
perfectly adapted to its
environment of sand
and mud. When it feels
threatened, it disappears
from sight in the soft sea
bottom after two to three
minutes of burrowing.

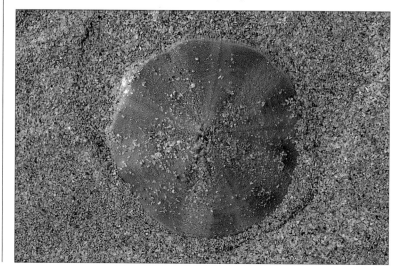

SEA CUCUMBERS

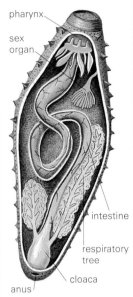

On first inspection, sea cucumbers look like soft sausages lying on the sea floor. They have a mouth at one end and an anus at the other, and they crawl about by means of their tube feet and the muscular expansion and contraction of their bodies. They vary in length from a couple of centimetres to more than a metre.

Sea cucumbers are often called sea slugs, but this name is more correctly applied to shell-less marine gastropods, such as sea hares and nudibranchs.

Some sea cucumber species live wholly or partly buried in sand or sediment, and others live in habitats ranging from rocky reefs to open sandy or shelly bottoms to the soft beds of intertidal areas. Very small sea cucumbers with soft bodies sometimes hide from fish predators during the day by wriggling under rocks, emerging at night to feed.

Like other echinoderms, sea cucumbers live in the deep sea, sometimes thousands of metres down, and we know of them only from samples taken by remote-controlled underwater vehicles. Sea cucumbers are found in all Australian waters, but there are more species in warmer tropical waters, where they can grow much larger than in cooler southern waters, and can reproduce in greater numbers.

Around the mouth of a sea cucumber is a ring of oral tentacles, which are actually specially adapted tube

THE MOMENT OF SPAWNING
When a sea cucumber spawns, in this case *Stichopus variegatus*, it arches its body up like a snake rearing its head.

feet that have been enlarged for feeding. Most species use these tentacles to pick up grains of sand and fragments of shell, which they then swallow. The sea cucumber digests any organic matter and then excretes the sand and shell particles.

Species with very soft bodies must remain buried both day and night to avoid predators, so they extend their tentacles at night to net food particles as they drift past. The more mobile species use their tentacles to mop up particles of food from sand, rocks and plants on the sea bed. They move the tentacles one by one into the mouth and suck them clean. One very small tropical sea cucumber, *Synaptula media*, lives solely by picking up particles trapped in the mucus that covers sponges.

The sea cucumber's respiratory system is inside an internal sac, called the cloaca, that opens into the anus. By contracting and expanding this sac, the sea cucumber draws water into and out of its anus and into respiratory trees, which are gill-like structures that extract the oxygen from the water.

A few sea cucumbers are hermaphrodites and some others brood their young, but most have separate sexes, like most echinoderms, and

fertilisation occurs in water. The fertilised eggs hatch to produce larvae that feed on single-celled algae, and the larvae turn into tiny forms of the adult before settling on the sea bed.

Sea cucumbers have some very unusual ways of avoiding or fighting off predators (see box, 'Defying death', page 606).
Class: Holothuroidea

GREEN SEA CUCUMBER ■
The green sea cucumber is a very common species on shallow coral reef flats around north-west to north-east Australia. Its colour varies from black to a very dark, almost iridescent green. It grows to about 20 cm long and is distinctly square in cross-section, with orange-tipped knobs or soft spines called papillae along each edge.

Like many members of the *Stichopus* group, the green sea cucumber disintegrates and turns to mush if it is picked up; this is part of its escape mechanism (see box, 'Defying death', page 606).
Scientific name: *Stichopus chloronatus*

SOFT SEA CUCUMBER
The soft sea cucumber is the most common species of sea cucumber in southern Australia and is found from the shores of New South Wales all the way around to the southern coast of Western Australia.

It lives just below low tide level in a number of habitats, including seagrass beds, sandy sea floors and the base of rocky reefs. It grows to about 25 cm long and can be almost any colour from yellow through to brown, grey or black.

The soft sea cucumber is easily recognised by the cone-like lumps on the upper part of its body.
Scientific name: *Stichopus mollis*

ANATOMY OF A
SEA CUCUMBER
The soft, leathery body wall of the sea cucumber protects the animal's digestive, respiratory and reproductive organs.

pharynx
sex organ
intestine
respiratory tree
cloaca
anus

■ GREEN SEA CUCUMBER
This particular *Stichopus* specimen was photographed on the Great Barrier Reef in the clear waters off Heron Island.

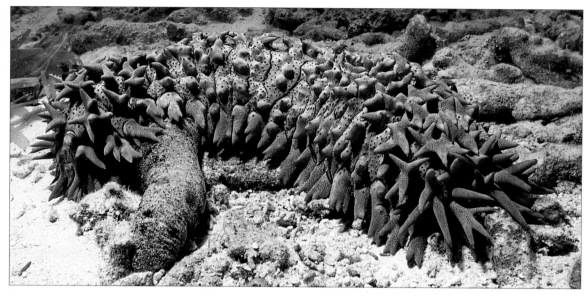

■ PRICKLY REDFISH
In some parts of the world the prickly redfish is called the pineapple sea cucumber because it resembles the fruit. Its scientific name, *Thelenota ananas*, derives from this resemblance: *ananas* is French for pineapple.

PRICKLY REDFISH ■

The spectacular prickly redfish is the largest of the sea cucumber species. It is commonly found on reefs in the tropical waters around the shores of north-west to north-east Australia.

It looks as though it is covered with thorns – but this is deceptive, as its 'prickles' are actually quite soft to the touch. It lives in sheltered sandy or shelly sea beds and varies in colour from a bright red to a dull brown. The prickly redfish grows to about 70 cm long and, because it is so large, it moves very slowly, even for a sea cucumber.

Scientific name: *Thelenota ananas*

DEFYING DEATH

Sea cucumbers are able to self-destruct and regenerate as a defence against predators. Some discharge a large, sticky, tangled mass of tubules, or hollow threads, from the anus to enlace or scare off attacking fishes or crabs. These tubules grow again to be ready for the next enemy onslaught.

More spectacularly, some other species of sea cucumber shoot their entire respiratory, reproductive and digestive organs out of the anus, either to frighten the attacker or to satisfy its hunger, allowing the rest of the body to escape. Amazingly, these species can regrow all their internal organs.

Yet another group, members of the genus *Stichopus*, literally disintegrate and then regrow vital parts of their bodies.

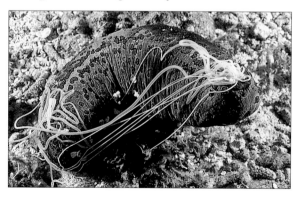

EYED SEA CUCUMBER

Characteristic brown circles surrounded by a white ring, with a black spot in the centre, give the eyed sea cucumber its common name. It is normally found just below low tide level on coral reefs around the shores of north-west to north-east Australia.

When disturbed, it promptly discharges a thick mass of very sticky tubules from its anus towards its attacker. The eyed sea cucumber grows to about 40 cm in length.

Scientific name: *Bohadschia argus*

GRAEFFE'S SEA CUCUMBER ■

Graeffe's sea cucumber reaches about 30 cm in length, and is easily identified by its brown speckled body and long black tentacles with white caps. It occurs on coral reefs and is particularly common on the Great Barrier Reef. It is one of the sea cucumber species that, if threatened, ejects its innards (see box, 'Defying death').

Scientific name: *Bohadschia graeffei*

SANDY SEA CUCUMBER

This species is abundant around much of the northern Australian coast, including the Great Barrier Reef. Small (10–15 cm) specimens are usually covered in sand grains, which accounts for their name, but they are actually black, and smooth to the touch. They are often exposed at low tide, and it is not known whether the sand covering is to reflect the sun's rays or to disguise the sea cucumber from predators.

Larger specimens (up to 40 cm) are shiny and black and do not have the sand covering. They are usually found on deeper parts of reefs.

Both large and small sandy sea cucumbers release a red fluid from their skin when handled. This defence mechanism helps to distinguish them from other black species of sea cucumber, such as the black-fringed sea cucumber (below).

Scientific name: *Holothuria atra*

BLACK-FRINGED SEA CUCUMBER

This species is covered in delicate tubed feet that give it a fringed appearance. It is common on many tropical coral reefs and lives in tidal pools and on reef flats. It is found on the north-eastern coast of Australia as far south as northern New South Wales and grows to about 60 cm long. When disturbed, the black-fringed sea cucumber releases sticky white tubules from its anus.

Scientific name: *Holothuria leucospilota*

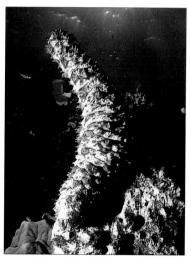

■ GRAEFFE'S SEA CUCUMBER
Unlike most sea cucumbers, Graeffe's sea cucumber prefers reef slopes to open soft or sandy bottoms.

LIVING LINKS

Mammals, birds, reptiles, amphibians and fishes are vertebrates – that is, they have a flexible backbone protecting a nerve cord that carries messages to and from a complex brain enclosed in a skull made of bone or cartilage. But invertebrates, which do not have backbones, were living on Earth for many millions of years before vertebrates evolved. So where did the vertebrates come from?

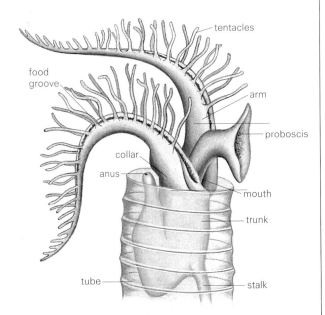

The earliest vertebrates and their ancestors were almost certainly soft-bodied and left barely a trace in the fossil record, but the study of a few invertebrates living today provides some clues to vertebrate ancestry.

The following detail from the evolutionary tree shows that the closest relatives of the vertebrates are the invertebrate lancelets and tunicates in the great phylum Chordata:

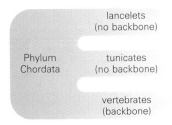

Phylum Chordata	lancelets (no backbone)
	tunicates (no backbone)
	vertebrates (backbone)

Chordates differ from all other animals in four ways. First, their nerve cord runs along the back of the body, whereas in most invertebrates it runs along the underside. Second, at some stage all chordates have a firm rod of cells (the notochord) beneath the nerve cord. Third, all have a gland that stores iodine in the same way as the vertebrate thyroid gland. Finally, all chordates have gill slits at some stage of their life.

All vertebrates have these four characteristics. As embryos, they all have a notochord, which is gradually replaced by a backbone, along the back of their body; all have a thyroid gland; and (at least at the embryo stage) all have gill slits.

Hemichordates: half-way there

Acorn worms (class Enteropneusta) and pterobranchs (class Pterobranchia) belong to a separate phylum, Hemichordata. Hemichordates do not possess a notochord, although they have the other three main chordate characteristics – a nerve cord running along the back of the body, a gland possibly related to the vertebrate thyroid, and gill slits. About 20 hemichordate species have been identified in Australia.

Acorn worms have separate sexes, but some pterobranchs are hermaphrodites. Whether single-sex or hermaphroditic, hemichordates release eggs and sperm into the water before fertilisation takes place. The fertilised eggs begin to divide in the same way as those of echinoderms and chordates, and they hatch as larvae covered with hair-like cilia. Some of the larvae look very like the larvae of the familiar echinoderms, the sea stars.

Hemichordates feed by trapping nutrients in mucus, which they draw into their mouths with bands of beating cilia, on a proboscis (acorn worms) or on grooved tentacles (pterobranchs).

Acorn worms are sluggish and solitary, and usually well hidden. They lead sedentary lives in U-shaped burrows in the sea floor, where they reach lengths of 2 cm to 2.5 metres. Outgoing tides reveal their coiled castings in the sand. *Ptychodera flava*, bright yellow and up to 10 cm long, is a distinctive species, often found under boulders or just below the surface of the sand.

Pterobranchs are delicate colonial animals that live in branched tubes attached to rocky surfaces.

Chordates: vertebrate beginnings

Lancelets and tunicates (phylum Chordata) are marine invertebrates. Both could be ancestors of the vertebrates, since they have a distinctive chordate feature – the notochord – that links them to the vertebrates.

Lancelets (subphylum Cephalochordata) are sometimes called amphioxus, which used to be the scientific name for the best known lancelet genus, now called *Branchiostoma*. Lancelets reach lengths of about 5–7 cm, and resemble the larvae of the simplest of the fishes, the lampreys. Australia has eight lancelet species – two in southern waters and the rest in northern tropical waters. The larvae drift in

TUBE-DWELLERS
Fully extended from the tube in which it lives, the pterobranch's arms collect food particles in their tentacles and funnel them along the food groove to the mouth. If the animal is disturbed, it shrinks back into its tube.

BURROWERS
The acorn worm *Ptychodera flava* has an acorn-like head and large gill slits. It lives in sandy, sheltered coastal areas and burrows with its proboscis.

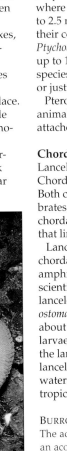

nerve cord and notochord

gill slits

LITTLE LANCES
Lancelets are commonly referred to as amphioxus, which means 'sharp at both ends'. Their elongated, slender shape is characteristic.

oceans and tropical lagoons, but the adults settle in one spot, wriggling backwards vertically into the sand until only their front end is showing. Here they filter food through a web of tentacles and then through fine slits that are the precursors of fishes' gills.

Tunicates (subphylum Tunicata) are found from shallow tidal zones to deep ocean waters. They have gill slits and a gland in the pharynx that stores iodine, and most have a larval form with a trunk and a tail containing a nerve cord running along the back above the notochord. So, at some stage, tunicates have the four main chordate characteristics.

Sea squirts (class Ascidiacea) are the best known of the tunicates. They have sac-like bodies with two openings called siphons and an outer coating that is chemically similar to plant cellulose. They feed by pumping water into one siphon and out of the other, straining food particles through perforations in the pharynx wall – the gill slits.

Adult sea squirts live attached to marine surfaces such as rocks. They can be mistaken for plants, but they are quite highly evolved animals.

A MYSTERY PHYLUM

Arrow worms (phylum Chaetognatha) are widespread and abundant in the world's oceans, but no one really knows where they fit into the evolutionary puzzle.

Ranging from 2.5 cm to 10 cm in length, they are torpedo-shaped and are usually transparent to milky white, although a few deep-sea species are reddish. They spend their lives in the ocean currents, which carry them around the world. They are hermaphodites, but their eggs are fertilised with sperm from another individual and are then shed into the sea, where they hatch as miniature adults.

Arrow worms are fierce predators, driving themselves forward by their tail fin to capture their prey. Their head region is usually sheathed, but the sheath retracts to reveal a mouth armed with long spines and file-like teeth that gape open to snatch and shred prey. They are important in the food web, making up 1–30 per cent of the plankton.

Most of the 20 Australian arrow worm species are found in tropical waters to depths of about 100 metres, but some live in southern waters and two cold-water species inhabit the Antarctic ice fields.

They have both male and female sex organs, but these mature at different times, so self-fertilisation rarely occurs. Some of the embryos develop in the sea, others within the parent. The embryos grow into free-swimming tadpole-like larvae that eventually attach themselves to a surface with sticky glands at the front of their trunk. They then absorb their tails.

Some sea squirts are solitary and grow up to 20 cm tall; others are as small as 1 mm and bud or subdivide to form colonies several metres across. Some are delicate and transparent, others are quite tough and opaque. Some are brilliantly coloured, while others camouflage themselves with weed or sand.

In Australia, along the rocky shores of the south-eastern coast from Fraser Island in Queensland to St Vincent Gulf in South Australia, stretches of solitary cunjevois (*Pyura stolonifera*) are a familiar sight at low tide. Under water their aperture opens, revealing a bright red throat.

In winter, long-stalked sea tulips are washed up along the shores of Tasmania. *P. gibbosa draschi* and *P. australis* are both common around the southern coast, and *P. gibbosa gibbosa* extends northward as far as Sydney Harbour. The colonial sea squirts *Botryllus schlosseri* and *B. leachi*, which look like embroidered daisies, are also common.

Salps and doliolids (class Thaliacea) and larvaceans (class Larvacea) are tunicates that ride the world's ocean currents, often in huge swarms. Salps and doliolids have both solitary and colonial life stages. Translucent and gelatinous, they are usually 1–12 cm long but can reach 60 cm or more. The hair-like cilia lining their gill slits draw

UNLIKELY ANCESTORS
Sea squirts look like plants, but they are believed to be ancestors of the vertebrates. *Botrylloides magnicoecum* is a common Australian species.

in water at one end of their bodies and expel it at the other, generating a continuous jet that propels the animals through the water. The gill slits strain food particles out of the water as it passes. Some salps have luminescent organs, and large swarms can be seen from aircraft, and even from satellites.

Larvaceans are solitary and grow no larger than 5 mm, including the tail. They resemble sea squirt larvae, but their tails are permanent. They build a 'house' with secreted mucus and filter their food by driving a stream of water through the 'house' with their whipping tails.

Strange relations
Many scientists believe that the tunicates are the most likely candidates for vertebrate – and therefore human – ancestry, because they have four of the main characteristics of chordates: a nerve cord running along the back (not the belly) of their body; at some stage, a firm rod of cells – the notochord, which resembles a rudimentary backbone – beneath the nerve cord; gill slits; and a gland in the pharynx that stores iodine in the same way as the vertebrate thyroid.

Even stranger is our link with the echinoderms – sea stars and their kin. Unusually among the invertebrates, echinoderms share with chordates a fundamental similarity – the way their fertilised egg divides and develops into an embryo. Next time you find a sea star, pause to reflect on our common origins.

GLOSSARY AND INDEX

GLOSSARY

abdomen: in arthropods, the rear section of the body.

abyssal: at great ocean depth, usually more than 1000 metres below sea level.

aestivation: a process in which an animal becomes inactive during hot, dry weather and its metabolic processes slow down, saving it energy and water. Some animals aestivate for months, or even years, surviving extremes of both heat and cold.

algae: simple plants, ranging from single cells to large seaweeds, that photosynthesise but have no supporting or conducting tissues to transport materials.

amphibian: a class of animal that includes frogs, toads and salamanders; frogs and the introduced cane toad are the only amphibians in Australia. Their larval stages differ from the adult forms and are usually aquatic.

amphibious: living both in water and on land.

antennae: paired sensory appendages, usually long, thin and jointed, on the head of some arthropods.

arboreal: living in trees.

bacteria: (plural of bacterium), simple microscopic organisms without a defined nucleus; a bacterium may consist of a single cell or a chain of cells.

baleen: long, flexible, horny plates growing from the upper jaw of toothless whales. They form a sieve that collects zooplankton from the water that the whale sucks into its mouth.

barbels: fleshy projections near the jaws of some turtles or fishes.

basal: at the base.

benthic: bottom-dwelling aquatic or marine forms.

biological control: pest control using other organisms – animals, plants, fungi, bacteria or viruses.

bioluminescence: the production of light by living organisms.

biomass: the weight (usually dry) of organisms collected from an area or volume; can be total biomass or biomass of a particular species or part of an organism, such as the leaves of a plant.

bivalves: a group of molluscs having two shells hinged together, such as oysters and mussels.

book-lungs: the gill-like respiratory organs on the underside of the abdomen of spiders and scorpions.

brackish: water that is slightly salty, as in an estuary.

brigalow: the dense acacia scrub or low forest that dominates large areas of inland Queensland and northern New South Wales.

bristles: in birds, modified feathers, with little or no vane. They act as a 'basket' to increase the width of the bill or as sensory structures to locate prey.

brood pouch: a body recess or pouch in which young animals live until they can fend for themselves.

broombush: *Melaleuca uncinata*, a native shrub growing 3 metres tall, found in dry areas.

browser: an animal that feeds on woody plants, such as shrubs and trees (*compare* grazer).

byssus: strong threads used by some bivalves, such as mussels, for attachment to rocks or sediments.

calcareous: made of calcium carbonate.

camp: the traditional roosting site of a bat colony.

canine teeth: usually pointed and sharp, one on either side of both jaws behind the incisors; particularly well developed in flesh-eating mammals.

canopy: the continuous cover provided by the upper leaves and branches of trees in a forest.

carapace: a protective plate of chitin covering the head and thorax of arthropods such as crustaceans and spiders, or the top part of a turtle's shell.

carnivore: a flesh-eating animal, equipped with powerful jaws and sharp canine teeth.

carrion: dead animal matter.

cartilage: a hard but flexible material often associated with bones; found in some vertebrates but sometimes forming the entire skeleton, as in sharks.

cephalothorax: the fused head and thorax of spiders and some crustaceans.

cere: a swollen, fleshy patch at the base of the upper bill of some birds.

chelicerae: (plural of chelicera), the first pair of head appendages of mites, ticks, scorpions, harvestmen and spiders, often referred to as jaws; the chelicerae are used for capturing, crushing or poisoning prey.

chitin: a tough, flexible organic substance that is a major component of an arthropod's exoskeleton.

chromatophores: pigment cells in the skin of animals, which in some enable them to change colour.

chromosomes: thread-like structures in the nucleus of cells that carry the genes.

cilia: (plural of cilium), minute hair-like structures on the surface of cells, often used for movement in single-celled organisms and in small animals.

claypans: shallow depressions containing clay and silt sediments, in which water collects after rain.

cloaca: a single body opening for the reproductive, digestive and excretory systems. Certain invertebrates, fishes, frogs, reptiles, birds, monotremes and marsupials have only a cloaca (often called a vent in birds and reptiles).

colonial: living as a group of separate or fused individuals.

commensal: living with or on another species and obtaining food without harming the host species (*compare* parasitic).

communal: living or laying eggs together in one place.

continental islands: islands (not volcanic or coral) that were once attached to the mainland but have become separated by rising sea levels, eg Tasmania

continental shelf: the sloping seabed that in Australia extends from the shore to about 200 metres below sea level.

continental slope: the steep slope that extends offshore from the edge of the continental shelf to the abyssal plain at about 2000 metres depth.

coverts: the small feathers covering the larger wing and tail feathers at their base.

cuticle: the protective nonliving external covering of some invertebrates; in arthropods, the cuticle forms the exoskeleton.

cyanobacteria: bacteria that can photosynthesise; they are also known as blue-green algae, but are not true algae.

dentition: the number, type and arrangement of teeth in a species.

detritus: fragments of the dead bodies of animals and plants.

dispersal: the spreading of an organism into new areas to exploit new resources.

diurnal: active during daylight.

DNA : deoxyribonucleic acid – the molecule that forms the code for the genetic blueprint that is passed from one generation to the next.

dry season: a dry, hot season in northern Australia from April or May to September or October.

ecdysis: the process of moulting (shedding) the exoskeleton in arthropods.

echolocation: a way in which some animals, such as certain bats and whales, can locate objects by uttering sounds and judging distance by listening to the echoes that bounce back.

ecosystem: the interaction between animals, plants, fungi, bacteria, landscape, water, air and so on.

ectotherm: an animal whose body temperature depends on the environmental temperature; reptiles, fishes and invertebrates are ectothermic.

embryo: the earliest stages of life, when cells have begun to divide but the organism is still contained within an egg or the uterus.

encrusting animal: an animal that attaches itself to a surface such as rocks or seaweed.

endemic: native to a particular area and found nowhere else.

endotherm: an animal that maintains a constant body temperature by internal metabolic processes; birds and mammals are endothermic.

ephemeral: transitory; not lasting.

epiphytes: plants that grow on other plants, usually high up on the branches of trees.

escarpment: a plateau that drops dramatically to a lower land formation, eg the Arnhem Land Plateau.

estuarine: found in wide tidal mouths (estuaries) of rivers; water here often varies in saltiness.

evolution: the development of new species from pre-existing ones by small genetic changes.

exoskeleton: a protective and supportive covering of some invertebrate animals, particularly arthropods.

exotic: not native.

eyeshine: light reflected from a special lining at the back of the eye; it enables nocturnal species to see in low light by using the available light twice: going in and coming out.

eyespots: light receptors acting solely as very primitive eyes; *also* body markings that look like large eyes to potential predators.

feral: wild; usually refers to introduced species that have become uncontrolled. In Australia, feral species are harmful because native populations are unaccustomed to such predators or competitors.

filter feeding: filtering food particles from water.

fin spine: a sharp, pointed projection that supports the fin of a fish.

flagella: (plural of flagellum), long, hair-like microscopic structures with a whip-like action; often used to propel an organism along in water.

fledge: to leave the nest.

fledging: the life stage of a bird just before it can fly.

fledgling: a bird that has left the nest but cannot yet fly properly.

flood plains: flat land regularly inundated after heavy rain.

food-plant: the plant on which an animal feeds; in butterflies, the food-plants on which the larvae feed.

food web: a diagrammatic representation of food consumption. A food web is likely to include organic particles from the bodies of bacteria, algae, plants, and microscopic and larger herbivorous, carnivorous, scavenging and parasitic animals, all of which are linked in a web by who eats whom.

free-living: independent, not parasitic.

gallery forest: forest along river ravines that differs from surrounding vegetation.

gams: associations of juvenile albatrosses that collect to practise courtship dances.

gemmule: a heavily armoured reproductive unit that can suspend growth until suitable conditions arise; often applied to sponges.

genetic manipulation: a procedure by which genes may be altered to express different characteristics than originally existed.

gestation period: period of pregnancy, from fertilisation of the egg until birth.

gibber: pebbles or boulders, especially wind-polished stones that occur in arid regions.

gills: the breathing structures of fishes and some aquatic invertebrates; usually flimsy surfaces, often divided into feathery projections, each rich in blood vessels that absorb oxygen from passing water.

gill slits: openings to the gills in fishes and other aquatic chordates, usually paired and positioned at the rear sides of the head.

Gondwana: an ancient large landmass or super-continent that comprised all the modern southern hemisphere continents, including Australia, South America, Africa, Antarctica and India. It began to fragment 120–40 million years ago. About 38 million years ago Australia became isolated from Gondwana and began to drift northward.

gravid: pregnant, or egg-bearing; frequently applied to fishes or reptiles.

grazer: an animal that feeds on low-growing vegetation such as grasses (*compare* browser)

hatchery: a place where the eggs and young of fishes or invertebrates (eg oysters) are artificially cultivated.

hawk: to obtain food by observing and catching prey while remaining in flight.

herbivore: a plant-eating animal.

hermaphroditic: containing both female and male sex organs within the one animal. Eggs and sperm may be produced simultaneously or at different stages of the life cycle.

hibernate: to enter a deep sleep of weeks or months in which body processes are greatly reduced and body temperature drops, so that stored body fats are used very slowly.

hinterland: land lying behind and next to the coast.

holdfast: the part of a seaweed or other organism that holds it attached to the seabed.

home range: the area where an animal usually lives and moves; may include an animal's burrow or shelter as well as hunting or foraging sites, and may be defended territorially. Usually there is little overlap between the home ranges of individuals or families.

honeydew: the sweet secretions of some plant-sucking insects, such as aphids.

host: an organism that carries another organism in or on its body (*see* commensal, parasitic).

hybrid: the offspring of two different species or varieties within a species; the former are usually sterile.

incisors: sharp, flattened teeth at the front of mammals' jaws, adapted for biting or gnawing food.

Indo-Pacific: the large tropical and subtropical oceanic region that includes the Indian Ocean (including the Red Sea) and the Pacific Ocean.

insectivorous: feeding on insects.

intertidal zone: the area of the seashore between high and low tides.

introduced: not native; exotic; an animal that has been deliberately or inadvertently brought to a location outside its normal range by humans.

irradiated: exposed to radiation.

kelp: a group of brown seaweeds with large fronds and well-developed holdfasts.

lactation: the discharge of milk from mammary glands, which is stimulated by the sucking of the infants. Milk production is controlled by hormones.

larvae: (plural of larva), an early developmental stage of some animals quite different in form from the adult; common in aquatic invertebrates, insects, fishes and amphibians.

lateral line: a line of pit-like organs along both sides of a fish's body and sometimes branching out around its head. The pits lead into canals containing a jelly-like substance that responds to changes in pressure, allowing the fish to detect nearby objects.

laterally compressed: flattened from side to side.

leaf litter: a layer of dead leaves that lie on the ground until they decompose.

lerp: a sugar coating exuded onto leaves by psyllids to protect their larvae; sometimes applied to the psyllid insects themselves.

lichen: an organism composed of one or more fungi and one or more unicellular algae living together with mutual benefit as a single organism.

lignum: a dense shrub found around swamps and in depressions where water collects after rain.

lipids: organic molecules that are insoluble in water; includes fats, oils, waxes and steroid hormones.

long-line fishing: fishing from ocean-going boats with lines many kilometres long and set with numerous fish hooks at intervals.

lore: the area between a bird's bill and its eye.

mallee: a dry-country eucalypt in which many branches grow directly from the ground.

mandibles: jaws; the horny mouthparts in insects and crustaceans; the lower and upper part of the bill in birds; the lower jaw in all other vertebrates.

mangroves: a tropical or subtropical habitat dominated by trees with aerial roots. The trees, which are regularly submerged in salty or brackish water, are often found lining estuaries.

manna: lerps secreted by sap-sucking insects, known as psyllids, to protect their larvae; many may be packed onto a single eucalypt leaf.

mantle: in molluscs, the thin flaps of skin that extend from the main body mass and over its upper surface. In most molluscs the mantle secretes calcium to make the shell.

mantle cavity: a tuck in the skin, at the rear end or the side of the body in most molluscs and at the front end in gastropods. It houses the gills in aquatic molluscs and the lungs in land snails and slugs.

medusa: the free-swimming bell-shaped form of a cnidarian, such as a sea jelly.

membrane: thin, sheet-like tissue that covers, connects or lines cells, organs and other structures in plants and animals.

metabolism: chemical processes that build up and break down organic molecules to release energy for body functions.

metamorphosis: a dramatic change of form – eg from a caterpillar to a butterfly.

microplankton: microscopic free-living organisms transported by currents in the sea or fresh water.

migrant: an animal that makes regular seasonal and large-scale geographical movements.

migrate: to move regularly to certain areas according to the season or time of day.

migratory: making regular seasonal and geographical movements.

monogamous: having only one mate.

mucilaginous: sticky, mucus-like.

mulga: scrub vegetation dominated by species of acacia; particularly common in arid Australia.

mutualistic relationship: regular and intimate association between two organisms that provides benefits to each other.

native: found in a particular area naturally; not introduced by humans. It may also be found elsewhere (*compare* endemic).

nematocyst: a structure in the cells occurring on the tentacles of cnidarians, such as sea jellies, used in the capture of food or for defence. On contact these structures release threads that can inject a toxin.

neurotoxin: a poison affecting the nervous system.

niche: the position occupied by an organism within a community; not necessarily a physical place.

nictitating membrane: a thin, transparent fold of skin over the eyes of reptiles, birds, amphibians, sharks and some mammals; can be drawn across the eye to clean and moisten the surface without impairing vision.

nomad: an animal that makes erratic seasonal and geographical movements.

oestrus: of female mammals; on heat, sexually receptive to males.

omnivore: an animal that eats a wide variety of foods, including both animals and plants.

ovipositor: an egg-laying organ at the rear of the abdomen of female insects.

palps: in mites, ticks, scorpions, sea spiders, harvest-men and spiders, jointed appendages between the chelicerae and the four pairs of walking legs, used to manipulate food, to sense the environment or for depositing sperm. In bivalves, fleshy appendages used to direct food into the mouth.

parasitic: feeding on or in another organism, causing it some degree of harm (*compare* commensal).

parthenogenesis: the process by which some female animals can produce female young without fertilisation from males; common in rotifers, crustaceans, many groups of insects and a few reptiles. Exceptionally, in hymenoptera (bees, ants and wasps) males, rather than females, are produced from unfertilised eggs.

pathogen: an organism that causes disease.

pelagic : fast-swimming, open-water species.

periostracum: a horny protective coating over the shell of gastropods and bivalves.

pharynx: muscular structure in the gut just behind the mouth. In some worms, the pharynx may be everted out of the mouth to envelop prey. In cephalochordates, urochordates and fishes, the pharynx opens to the gill slits.

pheromones: chemical substances emitted to attract mates, mark trails and promote social cohesion; most commonly found in mammals and insects.

photosynthesis: the process by which plants, algae and some bacteria harvest energy from sunlight to convert carbon dioxide and water into sugars; results in the release of oxygen.

pinnules: rows of tiny, long, thin projections from a long support shaft, such as the feathery side branches of feather-stars' arms.

plankton: tiny free-living organisms floating in the sea or fresh water. Animal plankton is sometimes known as zooplankton, plant plankton as phyto-plankton. Plankton often forms the basis of food webs in aquatic ecosystems. Marine larvae are often referred to as planktonic.

plastron: plates on the underside of a turtle's shell.

pod: a group of whales, seals or dolphins.

pollinate: to fertilise plants by transferring pollen from the male to the female parts of flowers. Many Australian animals feed on nectar, and the pollen that powders their body as they feed is brushed off onto the next flower they visit.

polygamy: (adjective polygamous), the mating of one male with several females (polygyny) or one female with several males (polyandry).

polyp: an attached or stationary life stage of cnidarians; the polyp has a cup-shaped form and tentacles around the outer rim.

population: a group of animals of the same species that share a particular habitat at the same time.

preen: in birds, to groom their feathers with their bill to keep them in prime condition for flight and to discourage parasites.

prehensile: adapted for grasping or gripping objects.

primary flight feathers: the outer wing feathers of birds, which maximise the flying surface and function with the tail feathers to control manoeuvrability in the air.

proboscis: an organ that protrudes out of the mouth of an animal, often long and flexible.

protrusible mouth: extendable mouth.

pupate: the process by which a larva becomes sedentary, often within a cocoon, and changes into an adult insect.

purse seining: a method of fishing with huge draw-string-like nets (up to a kilometre long), used for catching pelagic fishes such as tunas, but sometimes responsible for drowning dolphins.

radially symmetrical: with body parts arranged symmetrically and radiating from a central axis.

radula: a rasp-like 'tongue' within the mouth of most molluscs (but absent in bivalves), used for feeding.

raft: a flock of sea birds roosting or resting on water.

range: the extent of an area occupied by an animal.

rangelands: uncultivated semi-arid land, usually vegetated with grasses, herbs and shrubs.

raptorial: having a raptor-like structure – ie a structure adapted for seizing prey.

ray: a flexible structure, often segmented and branched, that supports the fin of a fish.

refuge: an area where a remnant population occurs when conditions in its former range have become unsuitable (sometimes called a refugium).

riverine: living or growing in rivers.

roosting: resting, often at night; applicable to birds and bats.

rufous: a reddish brown colour.

ruminants: mammals with a rumen, eg cows, sheep and deer. A rumen is a large fermentation chamber in the stomach. Food is regurgitated from the rumen for further chewing; when reswallowed, the food bypasses the rumen and goes directly to other parts of the stomach.

saline: salty.

savanna: grasslands dotted with trees and subject to seasonal rainfall, usually found in the tropics or subtropics.

scales: the small bony or horny plates forming a body covering in reptiles and fishes. In reptiles, the scales are derived from the inner layer of the skin (the outer layer being periodically shed), whereas fish scales are derived from the outer layer of the skin.

scavenger: an animal that feeds on the bodies of dead animals and plants.

school: a group of aquatic animals, often fishes or squids, that swim together while feeding or migrating. Schooling is an effective protection against predators.

scrape: a shallow depression scratched out of the earth by a bird's feet for feeding or nesting.

scutes: the large scales on the shells of turtles or protruding from the sides of fishes, such as mackerel.

seagrasses: flowering plants, often with long, strap-like leaves, that grow on the bottom of shallow, sheltered coastal waters, where they can survive submerged throughout their life cycle.

sedentary: remaining within a restricted area throughout an animal's lifetime or a stage of its life, often permanently attached.

sedges: a family of grass-like plants that grow in boggy conditions.

semi-desert: semi-arid; an area with a slightly higher rainfall than a true desert, and able to sustain more plant life.

shellfish: shelled marine and freshwater invertebrates, especially molluscs and crustaceans.

shield: a coloured piece of hardened flesh between the eyes and above the beak of birds.

shoal: a dense group of swimming fish.

siphon: a tubular funnel or hole on the body surface of molluscs and sea squirts, through which water passes in and out of the body and from which the animal extracts food particles and oxygen.

social: living, or at least spending considerable time, within a group.

solitary: living alone, not in a colony, herd or group.

spawn: to shed eggs and/or sperm directly into water.

speciation: the genetic splitting of a population into two or more groups; the groups cannot interbreed, and so become different species.

spicules: small, often sharp spikes of calcium carbonate or silica, found in sponges, soft corals, sea squirts and sea cucumbers.

subalpine: mountainous regions just below the alpine region and just within the limit of tree growth.

subtidal: below the low-tide mark; generally refers to waters less than 50 metres deep.

swim bladder: an internal gas-filled bladder that maintains buoyancy in bony fishes.

swimmerets: specialised appendages on the abdomen of many crustaceans, used for swimming and, in some species, for the carrying of eggs by females.

symbiotic relationship: regular and intimate association between two organisms; often – but not always – restricted to associations that provide mutual benefit.

taxonomist: a person who names, describes and classifies organisms according to their evolutionary relationships to one another.

test: the hard shell or tough outer covering of certain invertebrates, eg sea urchins, sea squirts.

thorax: the central part of an insect's or crustacean's body, between its head and its abdomen.

tined: pronged.

Top End: the northern part of the Northern Territory, Queensland and Western Australia.

torpor: a sleep of a day or so during which metabolic processes slow down and body temperature drops a few degrees; similar to hibernation but lasting for a shorter period. Torpor is a strategy to conserve energy during short-term food or water deficiencies.

toxic: chemically poisonous.

triplines: threads of silk that radiate from a spider's burrow to ensnare passing prey.

tubercles: small rounded bumps on the skin of animals, usually reptiles.

tubules: any tube-like structure, eg tracheal tubules in insects. *Also* the sticky mass of tangled hollow threads that sea cucumbers discharge from the anus in response to potential predator attacks.

understorey: the layer of vegetation that grows beneath the cover of higher vegetation.

vagrant: an animal found in an area other than its usual habitat, a stray.

veliger: the planktonic larval stage of many molluscs, having a long, veil-like membrane.

vestigial: having the traces of a particular structure; refers to organs that become smaller during evolution because the function they served has decreased in importance or become obsolete – eg the legs of burrowing lizards; the appendix of humans.

vine thickets: small patches of rainforest, subject to seasonally dry weather.

vivarium: a enclosed space where a living terrestrial animal is kept captive and studied; the equivalent of an aquarium for water-dwelling animals.

water column: the volume of water extending from the surface to the bottom.

wattles: fleshy lobes or appendages hanging from the throat or chin of certain birds.

wet season: a season in northern Australia, usually from October or November to March or April, during which conditions are hot, wet and humid.

World Heritage Listing: the official inscription on the World Heritage List of a place with a natural and/or cultural heritage that is considered of outstanding universal value.

zooid: a complex individual component that largely acts independently but is connected to others to form a colonial organism – eg some cnidarians, bryozoans and sea squirts.

INDEX

painted button-quail, 168, *168*
painted cup moth, *550*
painted finch, 279, *279*
painted firetail *see* painted finch
painted honeyeater, 244–5, *244*
painted lady butterflies, 548
painted latchet, 438
painted morwong, *465*
painted pearl oyster, 580
painted snipe, 169, *169*
painted turtle, 304
Palaemon serenus, 574
palaemonid shrimps, 574, *574*
pale field rat, 99, *99*
pale-flecked garden sunskink, 333, *333*
pale-headed mannikin, 281
pale-headed rosella, 202, *203*
pale-headed snake, 350–1
pale-lipped shadeskink, 339
pale-snouted ground gecko, 314
pale white-eye, 290
pale-yellow robin, 249, *249*
pallid cuckoos, 208, *209*
Pallimnarchus, 30
palm cockatoo, 195, *195*
palmdart butterfly, orange, 546
Palorchestes azeal, 30, 31
pandanus pigeon *see* bar-shouldered
    dove
Pandion haliaetus, 155, *155*
pantropical spotted dolphin, 113,
    113
Panulirus cygnus, 575
P. versicolor, 575
Papilio aegeus, 546, *546*
P. ulysses, 545, 546
paper nautilus, 596, *596*
papery bubble shells, 588
Papsula abbotti, 144
Papuan frogmouth, 216, *216*
Papuan sheath-tail bat, 88
Parablennius intermedius, 476
P. tasmanianus, 476, *476*
Paracanturus hepatus, 480, *480*
Paracirrhites arcatus, 464, *464*
P. forsteri, 464
Paracrinia haswelli, 375, *375*
Paradelma orientalis, 316, *316*, *317*
paradise riflebird, 268, *268*, 269
Parahydrophis mertoni, 361, *361*
paralysis tick, 557, *557*
Paramecia spp., 493, 496
Parantechinus apicalis, 68, 72, *72*
Parapercis clathrata, 474
P. cylindrica, 474
P. haackei, 474
P. nebulosa, 474
P. ramsayi, 473–4
Paraplagiusa unicolor, 485
Paraplesiops bleekeri, 443, *443*
P. meleagris, 443
Paraploactis trachyderma, 436, *436*
Parapriacanthus elongatus, 457
P. ransonnetti, 457, *457*
Paraquula melbournensis, 452
Parascyllium spp., 397, *397*
parasites, 495, 496, 611
parasitic lamprey, 395, *395*
parasitic wasps, 551, 552, *552*

parasitic worms, 508, 509, *509*, 510,
    510, 511, 513, 518
Parasuta spp., 357, *357*
Parataeniophorus spp., 428
Paratya australiensis, 574
Parazen pazificus, 432
Pardachirus pavoninus, 485
Pardalotus punctatus, 233, *233*
P. quadragintus, 233, *233*
P. rubricatus, 233, *233*
P. striatus, 233, *233*
Parika scaber, 487
Paristiopterus gallipavo, 461
P. labiosus, 461
parma wallaby, 46, *46*
Paropsis atomaria, 540
Parotosuchus, 26
Parribacus antarcticus, 576
parrotfishes, 469–70, *469*
parrots and cockatoos, 193–207,
    193–207
parthenogenesis, 309, 611
partridge pigeon, 189, *189*
Parupeneus barberinus, 457
P. cyclostomus, 456
P. indicus, 457
P. macronema, 357
P. multifasciatus, 456–7
P. pleurostigma, 457
P. signatus, 456, *456*
Parvancorina, 23
passalid beetles, 538
Passer domesticus, 277, *277*
P. montanus, 277, *277*
passerines *see* songbirds
passion-vine hopper, 534
Pataecus fronto, 436–7, *436*
Patiriella brevispina, 601
P. calcar, 601
P. exigua, 601
P. gunnii, 601
P. parvivipara, 601
Pavo cristatus, 127
pavo razorfish, 467
pea crab, 578
peaceful dove, 190, *190*
peacock jumping spider, 565, *565*
peacock sole, 485
peafowl, 127
peanut worm, 494, 512, *512*
pearl oysters, 580
pearl perch, 444, *444*
pearlfish, 423
pearls, 580, 581, *581*
pearly coral bream, 455
pebble crabs, 577
Pecten fumatus, 581
P. meridionalis, *581*
pectoral sandpiper, 173, *173*
Pedicullus humanus, 528
Pedionomus torquatus, 168, *168*
Pegasus lancifer, 432, *432*
P. volitans, 432
Pelagia noctiluca, 501
pelagic cods, 422
pelagic gecko, 309
pelagic sea snake *see* yellow-bellied sea
    snake
pelagic thresher shark, 400

Pelagodroma marina, 142, *142*
Pelamis platurus, 360–1, *360*
Pelecaniformes, 138
Pelecanus conspicillatus, 146–7, *146*, *147*
pelicans, 138, 146–7, *146*, *147*
Pempheris compressa, 457
P. klunzingeri, 457
P. multiradiata, 457
Penaeus latisulcatus, 573
P. merguiensis, 573
P. monodon, 573
P. plebejus, 573
pencil squid, 593
penguins, 136–7, *136*, *137*, 214
peninsula brown snake, 351
pennyfish, 440
Pentaceropsis recurvirostris, 461, *461*
Pentapodus vitta, 455
Peponocephala electra, 114, *114*
peracaridans, 571–2, *571*, *572*
Perameles bougainville, 77, 80
P. eremiana, 78
P. gunnii, 80, *80*
P. nasuta, 80–1, *80*
Perca fluviatilis, 445, *445*
perch-like fishes, 440–84, *440–84*
Percy Island whipsnake, 349
peregrine falcons, *154*, 160, 161, *161*
perentie, 326, 327
Perga dorsalis, 551, *551*
Perionyx excavatus, 518
Periplaneta americana, 525
P. fuliginosa, 525
periwinkles, 585
Peronedys anguillaris, 476
Peron's tree frog, *384*, 385, *385*
Perth herrings, 415
Perth lined lerista, 336
pesticides, 161
pet shop turtle *see* Mary River turtle
Petalura ingentissima, 523, *523*
Petasida ephippigera, 530, *530*
Petauroides volans, 64, 66, *66*
Petaurus australis, 63, *63*
P. breviceps, 63, *63*
P. gracilis, 63, *63*
P. norfolcensis, 63, *63*
petrels, 138–40, *138*, *139*
Petrocheles australiensis, 576
Petrogale assimilis, 53, *53*, 54
P. brachyotis, 54, *54*
P. burbidgei, 54, *54*
P. coenensis, 54, *54*
P. concinna, 54, *54*
P. godmani, 54, *54*
P. herberti, 54, *54*
P. inornata, 52, 54, *54*
P. lateralis, 53, *53*
P. mareeba, 54, *54*
P. penicillata, 54, *54*
P. persephone, 53, *53*
P. sharmani, 54
P. xanthopus, 52, 53, *53*
Petroica goodenovii, 249, *249*
P. multicolor, 248–9, *248*
P. phoenicea, 249, *249*
P. rodinogaster, 249, *249*
P. rosea, 249, *249*
Petrophassa albipennis, 189, *189*

P. rufipennis, 189, *189*
Petropseudes dahli, 65, *65*
Petroscirtes breviceps, 476, *476*
P. lupus, 476
P. variabilis, 476
pets, 35, 193, 207, 509, 511
    see also cats; dogs
Pezoporus wallicus, 193, 207, *207*
Pfeffer's flamboyant cuttlefish, 594, *594*
Phaethon lepturus, 142
P. rubricauda, 142, *142*
Phalacrocorax carbo, 146, *146*
P. fuscescens, 146, *146*
P. melanoleucos, 145, *145*
P. sulcirostris, 146, *146*
P. varius, 146, *146*
Phalanger mimicus, 61, *61*
phalaropes, 175, *175*
Phalaropus fulicaria, 175, *175*
P. lobatus, 175
Phaps chalcoptera, 188, *188*
P. elegans, 188, *188*
P. histrionica, 188, *188*
pharaoh's cuttlefish, 594
Phascogale calura, 74, *74*
P. tapoatafa, 74, 74
phascogales, 68, 74, *74*
Phascolarctos cinereus, 13, 34, 39, 40, *40*
Phascolosoma noduliferum, 512, *512*
Phasianus colchicus, 127
phasmids *see* stick insects
pheasant, common, 127
pheasant coucal, 208, 210, *210*
Pheidole spp., 555
Pheropsophus verticalis, 538
Philemon argenticeps, 240, *240*
P. buceroides, 240, *240*
P. citreogularis, 240, *240*
P. corniculatus, 240, *240*
Philomachus pugnax, 174–5, *174*, *175*
Philoria frosti, 376, *376*
P. sphagnicolus, 365, 376, *376*
Phoebetria fusca, 141
P. palpebrata, 141
Pholcus phalangioides, 566
Phonognatha spp., 568
Photoblepharon palpebratus, 429, *429*
Photololigo spp., 593
Phrynarachne spp., 567
Phtheirichthys lineatus, 449
Phycodurus eques, 434
Phylidonyris albifrons, 245, *245*
P. melanops, 245, *245*
P. nigra, 245, *245*
P. novaehollandiae, 238, 245, *245*
P. pyrrhoptera, 245, *245*
Phyllacanthus irregularis, 603
P. parvispinus, 603
Phyllodoce novaehollandiae, 514
phyllodocids, 514
Phyllopteryx taeniolatus, 434
Phyllorhiza punctata, 502
Phyllurus caudiannulatus, 311
P. platurus, 311
Physalia physalis, 501, *501*
Physeter catodon, 111, 116, *116*
Physignathus lesueurii, 321, *321*
pictorella mannikin, 281, *281*
pie-dish beetle, 540

633

PICTURE CREDITS

The photographs reproduced in the *Encyclopedia of Australian Wildlife* came from the sources listed below.
Positions of the photographs on the page: *t* = top; *c* = centre; *b* = bottom; *l* = left; *r* = right.
Abbreviations: Auscape = Auscape International; ANT = ANTPhoto.com; APL = Australian Picture Library; PLA = Photolibrary.com

Front cover D. Parer & E. Parer-Cook/Auscape. **Back cover** *ct* D. Fleetham-OSF/Auscape; *br* Jean-Paul Ferrero/Auscape; *all others* PhotoEssentials. **Spine** Glen Threlfo/Auscape. **1** Pavel German/Wildlife Images. **2–3** Becca Saunders/Auscape. **4–5** Michael Aw. **6–7** Jean-Paul Ferrero/Auscape. **8–9** Bob Wickham/PLA. **13** Jean-Paul Ferrero/Auscape. **16** *t* Andrew Gregory/APL; *b both* Oliver Strewe/APL. **17** *t* Gerry Whitmont/APL; *c* Derek Roff/APL; *bl* Robin Morrison/Reader's Digest; *br* Lightstorm/APL. **18–19** Mike Berceanu/PLA. **20–21** Pavel German/Wildlife Images. **21** Ted Mead/PLA. **22** *t* Reg Morrison; *b* Bruce G. Thomson/ANT. **32–33** Jean-Paul Ferrero/Auscape. **36** *t* Gary Lewis/PLA; *b* Jiri Lochman/Lochman Transparencies. 37 *t* Dave Watts; *b* Esther Beaton. **38** *t* Reg Morrison/Auscape; *c* Bob Walden/APL; *b* D. Parer & E. Parer-Cook/Auscape. **39** Jean-Paul Ferrero/Auscape. **40** *t* Fredy Mercay/ANT; *b* Fritz Prenzel/APL. **41** *t* John Cancalosi/Auscape; *b* Gary Bell/oceanwideimages.com. **42** Lance Nelson/Stock Photos. **43** *t* John Carnemolla/APL; *b both* Jean-Paul Ferrero/Auscape. **44** *t* Kathie Atkinson; *b* Martin Harvey/ANT. **45** *t* John Cancalosi/Auscape; *b* International Photographic Library. **46** *t* Kathie Atkinson; *b* Jean-Paul Ferrero/Auscape. **47** *tl* Wade Hughes/Lochman Transparencies; *tr* Jiri Lochman/Lochman Transparencies; *b* Kathie Atkinson. **48** *t* Dave Watts; *b* Frith/Cianelli. **49** *t* Jean-Paul Ferrero/Auscape; *b* Pavel German/Wildlife Images. **50** Dave Watts/ANT. **51** *t* Jean-Paul Ferrero/Auscape; *b* Dominic Chaplin. **52** N.N. Birks/Auscape. **53** *t* Klaus Toft; *b* Dave Watts/ANT. **54** *t* Babs & Bert Wells; *c* Mike Prociv/Wetro-pics; *b* Jiri Lochman/Lochman Transparencies. **55** Michael Trenerry. **56** Dave Watts. **57** *t* Jiri Lochman/Lochman Transparencies; *b* M.W. Gillam/Auscape. **58** *t* Jean-Paul Ferrero/Auscape; *b all* C. & S. Pollitt/ANT. **59** Michael Morcombe/Lochman Transparencies. **60** *t* Tony Joyce/APL; *b* Pavel German/Wildlife Images. **61** *t* Hans & Judy Beste; *b* Luke Leung. **62** *t* Mike Prociv/Wetro-pics; *b* Jean-Paul Ferrero/Auscape. **63** *t* C. & S. Pollitt/ANT; *b* Pavel German/ANT. **64** *t* Dave Watts/ANT; *b* Michael Trenerry. **65** *t* Andrew Dennis/ANT; *b* Jean-Paul Ferrero/Auscape. **66** *t* Dick Whitford; *c* Jean-Paul Ferrero/Auscape; *b* Pavel German/Wildlife Images. **67** *t* John Cancalosi/Auscape; *b* Kathie Atkinson. **68** *t* Murdoch Books; *b* C. Andrew Henley. **69** Mark Newman. **70** *t* Dave Watts/ANT; *b* Jean-Paul Ferrero/Auscape. **71** *t* Kathie Atkinson; *bl* Jiri Lochman/Lochman Transparencies; *br* Murdoch Books. **72** *t* Horizon Photo Library; *b* Bruce G. Thomson/ANT. **73** *t* Mike Prociv/Wetro-pics; *b* C. Andrew Henley. **74** *t* Jean-Paul Ferrero/Auscape; *b* Gunther Schmida. **75** *t* Babs & Bert Wells; *b* Reg Morrison/Auscape. **76** Kathie Atkinson. **77** *t both* Dave Watts/ANT; *bl* Babs & Bert Wells; *br* Hans & Judy Beste. **78** *t* Jiri Lochman/Lochman Transparencies; *b* Dick Whitford. **79** *t* Jiri Lochman/Lochman Transparencies; *b* C. & S. Pollitt/ANT. **80** *t* I.R. McCann/Macdown Productions/ANT; *b* Reg Morrison/Auscape. **81** *l* Jean-Paul Ferrero/Auscape; *r* G. Harold/Auscape. **82** *tl* Martin Harvey/ANT; *tr* N.H.P.A./ANT; *b* Jean-Paul Ferrero/Auscape. **83** Jiri Lochman/Lochman Transparencies. **84** *tl* Pavel German/ANT; *tr* Mike Prociv/Wetro-pics; *b* Darran Leal. **85** *t* Michael Trenerry; *b* Jean-Paul Ferrero/Auscape. **86** *t* N.N. Birks/Auscape; *b* Graham D. Anderson/ANT. **87** *t* Kathie Atkinson; *b* G.B. Baker/ANT. **88** *t* G.B. Baker/ANT; *b* Pavel German/Wildlife Images. **89** *t* Dave Roberts/SPL/PLA; *bl* G.A. Hoye; *br* G.B. Baker/ANT. **90** D. Parer & E. Parer-Cook/Auscape. **91** *t* Andrew Dennis/ANT; *b* Bob Walden/APL. **92** *t* Pavel German/Wildlife Images; *c* Dave Watts/ANT; *b* G.B. Baker/ANT. **93** *t* C. & S. Pollitt/ANT; *b* Kathie Atkinson. **94** Jiri Lochman/Lochman Transparencies. **95** *t & br* Mike Prociv/Wetro-pics; *bl* Dick Whitford/ANT. **96** *t* Dave Watts/ANT; *b* David E. Carter/ANT. **97** *t* Dave Watts/ANT; *b* Jiri Lochman/Lochman Transparencies. **98** *t* Babs & Bert Wells; *b* Jiri Lochman/Lochman Transparencies. **99** *t* Jiri Lochman/Lochman Transparencies; *b* C. Andrew Henley/Auscape. **100** *t* C. Andrew Henley/Auscape; *b* Ferrero-Labat/Auscape. **101** *t* N.H.P.A./ANT; *b* C. Andrew Henley/Auscape. **102** *t* Duane Yates; *b* Jean-Paul Ferrero/Auscape. **103** *t* Peter & Margy Nicholas/Lochman Transparencies; *c* Jason Edwards/Bio-Images; *b* Volvox/APL. **104** *tl* Zefa/APL; *tr* Jean-Paul Ferrero/Auscape; *b* Colin Blobel/ANT. **105** *t* Jean-Paul Ferrero/Auscape; *b* Dave Watts/ANT. **106** *t* Jiri Lochman/Lochman Transparencies; *b* Jean-Paul Ferrero/Auscape. **107** John Carnemolla/APL. **108** *t* Otto Rogge/ANT; *b* Leo Meier/APL. **109** *t* Ken Griffiths/ANT; *b* Jiri Lochman/Lochman Transparencies. **110** *t* Wayne Lawler/Auscape; *b* Kathie Atkinson. **111** Stephen R. Burnell. **112** *t* Mark Spencer/Auscape; *bl* Doug Perrine/Auscape; *br* International Photographic Library. **113** *both* Kevin Aitken/ANT. **114** *t* D. Parer & E. Parer-Cook/Auscape; *b* Dave Watts/ANT. **115** D. Parer & E. Parer-Cook/Auscape. **116** François Gohier/Auscape. **117** *t* Mark Spencer/Auscape; *b* François Gohier/Auscape. **118** *t* Lorix J. Bertling; *b* Pacific Stock/PLA. **119** Richard Smyth. **120–21** Leo Meier/APL. **124** Jason Edwards/Bio-Images. **125** *t* Jean-Paul Ferrero/Auscape; *b* Esther Beaton. **126** *t* Esther Beaton; *b* Fredy Mercay/ANT. **127** *t* Leo Meier/APL; *b* I.R. McCann/Macdown Productions/ANT. **128** Ford Kristo/ANT. **129** *t* D. Parer & E. Parer-Cook/Auscape; *b* Jiri Lochman/Lochman Transparencies. **130** *t* Tony Howard/ANT; *c* Eric Vanderduys; *b* C. Andrew Henley/Auscape. **131** John Cancalosi/Auscape. **132** *both* Jean-Paul Ferrero/Auscape. **133** *t* Graeme Chapman; *c* Jean-Paul Ferrero/Auscape; *b* Darran Leal. **134** *t* John Cancalosi/Auscape; *b* Ken Griffiths/ANT. **135** Graeme Chapman. **136** *t* Ralph & Daphne Keller/ANT; *b* Jonathan Chester/ANT. **137** *t & br* Minden Pictures/APL; *bl* Tui De Roy/Auscape. **138** *t* Jiri Lochman/Lochman Transparencies; *b* Peter Fullagar/Auscape. **139** *t* Ian Hutton; *b* Kathie Atkinson. **140** *t* Brian Chudleigh/ANT; *b* Mike Turner/PLA. **141** *t* Hans & Judy Beste; *b* M.F. Soper/ANT. **142** *t* Graham Robertson/Auscape; *b* Jean-Paul Ferrero/Auscape. **143** *t* Kathie Atkinson; *b* D. Parer & E. Parer-Cook/Auscape. **144** *all* Kathie Atkinson. **145** *t* Andrew Dennis/ANT; *b* Brian Chudleigh/ANT. **146** *t* Keith K.Vagg/ANT; *b* David Dare Parker. **147** *t* C. & S. Pollitt/ANT; *b* Mark Jones/Auscape. **148** Jiri Lochman/Lochman Transparencies. **149** *t* Jay Sarson/Lochman Transparencies; *b* Tom & Pam Gardner. **150** *t* Brian Chudleigh/ANT; *b* Hans & Judy Beste. **151** *t* Leo Meier/APL; *b* Jean-Paul Ferrero/Auscape. **152** *t* Steve Sadler; *b* Geoff Taylor/Lochman Transparencies.

153 *t* M.P. Kahl/Auscape; *b* Jean-Paul Ferrero/Auscape. **154** Jean-Michel Labat/Auscape. **155** *t* I.R. McCann/Macdown Productions/ANT; *b* N.N. Birks/Auscape. **156** *t* Frank Park/ANT; *b* Jack & Lindsay Cupper/Auscape. **157** *t* Dave Watts/ANT; *b* Leo Meier/APL. **158** *t* Jack & Lindsay Cupper/Auscape; *b* John Carnemolla/APL. **159** N.N. Birks/Auscape. **160** *t* Michael Brabenetz; *b* N.N. Birks/Auscape. **161** *t & br* Dave Watts/ANT; *bl* Jean-Michel Labat/Auscape. **162** John Cooper/Austral. **163** *t* G. Wane; *b* Hans & Judy Beste. **164** *t* Jean-Paul Ferrero/Auscape; *b* Hans & Judy Beste. **165** *t* Jean-Paul Ferrero/Auscape; *b* M.F. Soper/ANT. **166** Jason Edwards/Bio-Images. **167** I.R. McCann/Macdown Productions/ANT. **168** *t* Bob Walden/APL; *b* Hans & Judy Beste. **169** *t* Dave Watts/ANT; *b* Jean-Paul Ferrero/Auscape. **170** Peter Cook/Auscape. **171** *t* Bill Belson/Lochman Transparencies; *b* Leo Meier/APL. **172** *t* Bob Walden/APL; *b* Tom & Pam Gardner. **173** *t* Bob Walden/APL; *b* Brian Chudleigh/ANT. **174** *t* Klaus Uhlenhut/ANT; *b* Brian Chudleigh/ANT. **175** *t* Brian Chudleigh/ANT; *b* Hellio-Van Ingen/Auscape. **176** Raoul Slater/Lochman Transparencies. **177** *t* Horizon Photo Library; *b* Bill Bachman/ANT. **178** *t* I.R. McCann/Macdown Productions/ANT; *b* Nigel Dennis/ANT. **179** *t* Owen Wilson/Austral; *b* Dave Watts/ANT. **180** *t* Jiri Lochman/Lochman Transparencies; *b* Graeme Chapman. **181** *t* Jiri Lochman/Lochman Transparencies; *b* Ralph & Daphne Keller/ANT. **182** *t* Brian Chudleigh/ANT; *b* Jean-Paul Ferrero/Auscape. **183** *t* Cyril Webster/ANT; *b* Kathie Atkinson. **184** *t* Dave Watts/ANT; *b* Jean-Paul Ferrero/Auscape. **185** *t* Steve Sadler; *b* Kathie Atkinson. **186** *t* Jiri Lochman/Lochman Transparencies; *b* Klaus Uhlenhut/ANT. **187** *both* Cyril Webster/ANT. **188** *t* Glen Threlfo/Auscape; *b* Cyril Webster/ANT. **189** *t* Raoul Slater/Lochman Transparencies; *b* Jiri Lochman/Lochman Transparencies. **190** *tl* I.R. McCann/Macdown Productions/ANT; *tr* Cyril Webster/ANT; *b* Glen Carruthers. **191** Brian J. Coates/ANT. **192** *tl & b* Glen Threlfo/Auscape; *tr* Frithfoto/ANT. **193** Steve Sadler. **194** Gerry Whitmont. **194–95** Frank Park/ANT. **195** Frithfoto/ANT. **196** *t* Gerry Whitmont; *b* Peter Marsack/Lochman Transparencies. **197** *t* Jiri Lochman/Lochman Transparencies; *b* John Cancalosi/Auscape. **198** Hans & Judy Beste. **198–99** Horizon Photo Library. **199** *t* Bruce G. Thomson/ANT; *b* Raoul Slater/Lochman Transparencies. **200** *t* Michael Trenerry; *b* Cyril Webster/ANT. **201** *t* John Shaw/Auscape; *b* Darran Leal. **202** Jean-Paul Ferrero/Auscape. **203** *t* M.F. Soper/ANT; *b* Graeme Chapman. **204** Michael & Irene Morcombe. **205** *t* Murdoch Books; *b* N.N. Birks/Auscape. **206** *t* Graeme Chapman; *b* Fredy Mercay/ANT. **207** *t* Graeme Chapman; *b* Dave Watts/ANT. **208** Raoul Slater/Lochman Transparencies. **209** I.R. McCann/Macdown Productions/ANT. **210** *t* Brian J. Coates/ANT; *b both* Cyril Webster/ANT. **211** Dave Watts/ANT. **212** *tl* Michael Leach/Oxf Science/PLA; *tr* Densey Clyne; *b* Dave Watts/ANT. **213** *t* Jean-Paul Ferrero/Auscape; *b* Hans & Judy Beste. **214** *tl* Darran Leal; *tr* N.N. Birks/Auscape; *b* Albert Visage. **215** *t* Cyril Webster/ANT; *b* Barry Silkstone. **216** *t* G.A.Wood/ANT; *b* Gary & Robyn Wilson/ANT. **217** *t* Tom & Pam Gardner; *b* Ross Whiteford. **218** *t* Mike Prociv/Wetro-pics; *b* Graham D. Anderson. **219** *t* Frithfoto/ANT; *bl* Dave Watts/ANT; *br* Ken Stepnell. **220** Glen Threlfo/Auscape. **221** *t* Leo Meier/APL; *b* Hans & Judy Beste. **222** *t* Cyril Webster/ANT; *b* Frithfoto/ANT. **223** *t* Brian Chudleigh/ANT; *b* Bill Bachman/ANT. **224** Graeme Chapman. **225** Glen Threlfo/Auscape. **226** *t* Bob Walden/APL; *c & b* Ken Griffiths/ANT. **227** *t* Roger Brown/Auscape; *b* Michael & Irene Morcombe. **228** *t* Bill Belson/Lochman Transparencies; *b* Raoul Slater/Lochman Transparencies. **229** Jean-Paul Ferrero/Auscape. **230** *t* Geoff Higgins/PLA; *c* Frank Park/ANT; *b* Graeme Chapman. **231** *t* Cyril Webster/ANT; *b* Frank Park/ANT. **232** *t* D. & M. Trounson/ANT; *b* Graeme Chapman. **233** Raoul Slater. **234** *t* Geoff Higgins/PLA; *b* Cyril Webster/ANT. **235** *t* Alan Gibb/ANT; *b* Graeme Chapman. **236** *t* Frithfoto/ANT; *b* Ralph & Daphne Keller/ANT. **237** G. Little. **238** *t* Roger Brown/Auscape; *b* Jean-Paul Ferrero/Auscape. **239** *t* I.R. McCann/Macdown Productions/ANT; *b* Trevor A. Waite. **240** Graeme Chapman. **241** *t* Fredy Mercay/ANT; *bl* Graham D. Anderson/ANT; *br* Tom & Pam Gardner. **242** D. & V. Blagden/ANT. **243** *t* Babs & Bert Wells; *b* Geoff Higgins/PLA. **244** *t* Tom & Pam Gardner; *b* Michael & Irene Morcombe. **245** *t* Malcolm McNaughton; *b* Trevor A. Waite. **246** *t* Michael & Irene Morcombe; *c* Graeme Chapman; *b* Tom & Pam Gardner. **247** *t* Peter Knowles/PLA; *b* Michael & Irene Morcombe. **248** *t* Michael & Irene Morcombe; *b* Hans & Judy Beste. **249** *t* Frank Park/ANT; *b* Roger Brown/Auscape. **250** *t* Cyril Webster/ANT; *b* Michael & Irene Morcombe. **251** Glen Threlfo/Auscape. **252** *t* Frank Park/ANT; *b* Cyril Webster/ANT. **253** *t* Roger Brown/Auscape; *b* Michael & Irene Morcombe. **254** *t* Graeme Chapman; *b* Roger Brown/Auscape. **255** Roger Brown/Auscape. **256** *both* Graeme Chapman. **257** Keith K. Vagg/ANT. **258** *t* Frithfoto/ANT; *b* Roger Brown/Auscape. **259** *t* Jean-Paul Ferrero/Auscape; *b* Jim Frazier. **260** *both* Graeme Chapman. **261** *both* Bob Walden/APL. **262** *t* Graeme Chapman; *b* Frithfoto. **263** *t* Cyril Webster/ANT; *b* Raoul Slater/Lochman Transparencies. **264** *t* John McCann; *b* Cyril Webster/ANT. **265** Geoff Higgins/PLA. **266** *tl* Matt Jones/Auscape; *tr* Graeme Chapman; *b* Roger Brown/Auscape. **267** *t* Jean-Paul Ferrero/Auscape; *b* Geoff Higgins/PLA. **268** Hans & Judy Beste. **269** *t* Frithfoto; *b* Michael & Irene Morcombe. **270** *t* Bob Walden/APL; *b* Jean-Paul Ferrero/Auscape. **271** *t* C. Andrew Henley/Auscape; *b* Michael Gough. **272** *t* Roger Brown/Auscape; *b* Hans & Judy Beste. **273** John McCann. **274** *t* Graeme Chapman; *b* C.B. & D.W. Frith. **275** N.H.P.A./ANT. **276** Bob Walden/APL. **277** *t* John Carnemolla/APL; *b* Graeme Chapman. **278** *tl* Cyril Webster/ANT; *tr* Babs & Bert Wells; *b* Bruce G. Thomson/ANT. **279** *t* Ralph & Daphne Keller/ANT; *b* Murdoch Books. **280** *t* Hans & Judy Beste; *b* C. Andrew Henley/Auscape. **281** *t* Cyril Webster/ANT; *b* Graeme Chapman. **282** Wesley Tolhurst/APL. **283** *t* Michael & Irene Morcombe; *b* Graham D. Anderson/ANT. **284** *t* John Cancalosi/Auscape; *b* Michael & Irene Morcombe. **285** *t* Albert Visage; *b* Derek Roff/APL. **286** *both* Graeme Chapman. **287** *t & c* Graeme Chapman; *b* Bob Walden/APL. **288** *t* Graham Robertson/Auscape; *bl* Evan Collis/APL; *br* Jim Frazier. **289** *t* Gerry Whitmont; *b* Graeme Chapman. **290** *t* J. Hicks; *b* Trevor A. Waite. **291** *t* Brian Chudleigh/ANT; *b* Michael & Irene Morcombe. **292** *t* Bob Walden/APL; *b* Brian Chudleigh/ANT. **293** *t* Jim Frazier; *b* Albert Visage/Auscape. **294–95** Jean-Paul Ferrero/Auscape. **298** Jim Frazier. **299** *t* 1996 Quest Australia Productions; *b* Michael Cermak/ANT. **300** Jean-Paul Ferrero/Auscape. **301** *t* Peter Eggler; *b* Gary Bell/oceanwideimages.com. **302** *t* Klaus Uhlenhut ANT; *b* Alby Ziebell/Auscape. **303** John Cann. **304** *t* Jiri Lochman/Lochman Transparencies; *b* John Cann. **305** John Cann. **306** Michael Trenerry.

307 *t* Harald Ehmann/Wildworks Australia; *b* Jean-Paul Ferrero/Auscape. **308** *t* Harald Ehmann/Wildworks Australia; *b* Gunther Schmida. **309** *t* Jiri Lochman/Lochman Transparencies; *b* Harald Ehmann/Wildworks Australia. **310** *t* J.C. Wombey; *b* Steve Swanson. **311** *tl* Fredy Mercay/ANT; *tr* Jiri Lochman/Lochman Transparencies; *b* Hans & Judy Beste. **312** *all* Steve Wilson. **313** *t* Kathie Atkinson; *b* Steve Wilson. **314** *both* Gunther Schmida. **315** Steve Wilson. **316** *t* Gunther Schmida; *b* Jean-Paul Ferrero/Auscape. **317** *t* Steve Wilson; *b* Harald Ehmann. **318** Ken Griffiths/ANT. **319** *t* G. Harold/Auscape; *bl* Mike Prociv/Wetro-pics; *br* Steve Sadler. **320** *t* Otto Rogge/ANT; *b* Gunther Schmida. **321** *t* Jiri Lochman/Lochman Transparencies; *b* Horizon Photo Library. **322** *t* Michael Trenerry; *b* J.C. Wombey. **323** *t* Jean-Paul Ferrero/Auscape; *b* Reg Morrison. **324** *t* Pavel German/Wildlife Images; *b* Otto Rogge/ANT. **325** *t* Marie Lochman/Lochman Transparencies; *b* Ken Griffiths/ANT. **326** *t* Derek Roff/APL; *b* Mike Prociv/Wetro-pics. **327** Steve Wilson. **328** *t* Michael Trenerry; *b* Gunther Schmida. **329** *t* R.G.W. Jenkins/ANT; *b* Harald Ehmann/Wildworks Australia. **330** *t* Gunther Schmida/ANT; *b* Steve Wilson. **331** *tl* Leo Meier/APL; *tr* Derek Roff/APL; *b* Pavel German/Wildlife Images. **332** *t* Steve Wilson; *b* Michael Trenerry. **333** *t* Ken Griffiths/ANT; *b* Mike Prociv/Wetro-pics. **334** *t* Steve Wilson; *b* Mike Prociv/Wetro-pics. **335** *both* G. Harold/Auscape. **336** *t* Harald Ehmann/Wildworks Australia; *b* Mike Prociv/Wetro-pics. **337** *t* H. Cogger; *b* R.W. Murray/APL. **338** *both* Harald Ehmann/Wildworks Australia. **339** *t* Frithfoto/ANT; *b* Harald Ehmann/Wildworks Australia. **340** *both* Harald Ehmann/Wildworks Australia. **341** Gunther Schmida/ANT. **342** *t* Esther Beaton; *b* Kathie Atkinson. **343** *t* Jim Frazier; *b* Steve Wilson. **344** *t* Klaus Uhlenhut/ANT; *b* John Cann. **345** *t* Ken Griffiths/ANT; *c* Cyril Webster/ANT; *b* Leo Meier/APL. **346** *t* Leo Meier/APL; *b* Steve Swanson. **347** *t* Harald Ehmann/Wildworks Australia; *b* Leo Meier/APL. **348** *both* Harald Ehmann/Wildworks Australia. **349** *t* G. Shea; *b* Gunther Schmida/ANT. **350** *t* J.C. Wombey; *b* Gunther Schmida. **351** *both* Gunther Schmida. **352** *t* Steve Wilson; *b* Michael Cermak/ANT. **353** *t* Harald Ehmann/Wildworks Australia; *b* Kathie Atkinson. **354** *t* R.W. Murray/APL; *b* Jiri Lochman/Lochman Transparencies. **355** *t* Ken Griffiths/ANT; *b* Steve Wilson. **356** *t* R.G.W. Jenkins/ANT; *b* Gunther Schmida. **357** *t* Frithfoto/ANT; *b* Marie Lochman/Lochman Transparencies. **358** Steve Swanson. **359** *t* P. G. Horner; *b* International Photographic Library. **360** *t* Harald Ehmann/Wildworks Australia; *b* P. G. Horner. **361** Jürgen Freund/Auscape. **362–63** C. Andrew Henley/Auscape. **366** *both* Harald Ehmann/Wildworks Australia. **367** *both* Michael Mahony. **368** *t* Harald Ehmann/Wildworks Australia; *b* Jiri Lochman/Lochman Transparencies. **369** Harald Ehmann/Wildworks Australia. **370** *t* Harald Ehmann/Wildworks Australia; *b* Jiri Lochman/Lochman Transparencies. **371** *t* Neville Coleman; *b* Kathie Atkinson. **372** *t* Gunther Schmida; *b* C. Andrew Henley/Auscape. **373** *t* Neville Coleman; *b* Michael Mahony. **374** Harald Ehmann/Wildworks Australia. **375** *t* G.A. Hoye; *b* Steve Wilson. **376** *t* Gunther Schmida; *b* Ross Knowles. **377** *t* Pavel German/Wildlife Images; *bl* Ross Knowles/APL; *br* Michael J. Tyler. **378** *t* Hans & Judy Beste; *b* Harald Ehmann/Wildworks Australia. **379** *t* Michael Trenerry; *b* Michael Mahony. **380** Alwyn Y. Pepper. **381** *t* Michael Mahony; *b* Gary Bell/oceanwideimages.com. **382** *tl* Leo Meier/APL; *tr* Neville Coleman; *b* Hans & Judy Beste. **383** *t* Jiri Lochman/Lochman Transparencies; *b* Gunther Schmida. **384** *both* Michael Trenerry. **385** *t* Neville Coleman; *b* Harald Ehmann/Wildworks Australia. **386** Ross Knowles. **387** *t* Michael Trenerry; *b* Densey Clyne. **388** Harald Ehmann/Wildworks Australia. **389** *t* Jean-Paul Ferrero/Auscape; *b* Kathie Atkinson. **390–91** Gary Bell/oceanwideimages.com. **395** Yves Lanceau/Auscape. **397** *t* Eva Boogaard/Lochman Transparencies; *b* Becca Saunders. **398** *t* Kevin Deacon/Auscape; *b* Gary Bell/oceanwideimages.com. **399** Ron & Valerie Taylor. **400** Gary Bell/oceanwideimages.com. **401** *t* G. Allen; *b* Tom Campbell's Photographic. **402** *l* Ian Gordon/Auscape; *r* Ron & Valerie Taylor. **403** & **404** *all* Rudie H. Kuiter. **405** *t* Norbert Wu/ANT; *b* Rudie H. Kuiter. **406** *t* Rudie H. Kuiter; *b* Eva Boogaard/Lochman Transparencies. **407** H.G. de Couet/Auscape. **408** *t* Eva Boogaard/Lochman Transparencies; *b* Rudie H. Kuiter. **409** Gunther Schmida. **410** *t* Gunther Schmida/ANT; *b* Gunther Schmida. **411** Gary Bell/oceanwideimages.com. **412** Gunther Schmida. **413** *t* Gary Bell/oceanwideimages.com; *b* Mike Neumann/PLA. **414** *t* Ron & Valerie Taylor; *b* Norbert Wu/ANT. **415** *t* Gunther Schmida; *b* Patrick Baker/Lochman Transparencies. **416** *t* Rudie H. Kuiter; *b* Yves Lanceau/Auscape. **417** *t* Gunther Schmida; *b* Ron & Valerie Taylor. **418** *t* & *c* Gunther Schmida; *b* Reg Morrison. **419** *t* D. Parer & E. Parer-Cook/Auscape; *b* G. Allen. **420** *tl* Peter & Margy Nicholas/Lochman Transparencies; *tr* Mike Turner/PLA; *b* Rudie H. Kuiter. **421** *t* Norbert Wu/TSW/PLA; *b both* Norbert Wu/ANT. **422** Ian Loney. **423** *t* Rudie H. Kuiter; *b* Kelvin Aitken/ANT. **424** *t* G. Allen; *c* Norbert Wu/ANT; *b* Rudie H. Kuiter. **425** Eva Boogaard/Lochman Transparencies. **426** *t* Gunther Schmida; *b* Rudie H. Kuiter. **427** *t* Norbert Wu/ANT; *b* Gunther Schmida. **428** *t* Rudie H. Kuiter; *b* G. Allen. **429** *t* Jean-Paul Ferrero/Auscape; *b* Rudie H. Kuiter. **430** *t* Ron & Valerie Taylor; *b* Rudie H. Kuiter. **431** *t* G. Allen; *b* Peter David/Planet Earth Pictures. **432** *t* Kevin Cullimore/Planet Earth Pictures; *b* Mark Spencer/Auscape. **433** *t* Alby Ziebell/Auscape; *b* Ron & Valerie Taylor. **434** *t* Becca Saunders/Auscape; *c* Mark Spencer/Auscape; *b* Rudie H. Kuiter. **435** *t* Gunther Schmida; *b* Larry Tackett/Planet Earth Pictures. **436** *t* Rudie H. Kuiter; *b* Mark Spencer. **437** *t* Ian Loney; *b* Graham Edgar. **438** Pacific Stock/PLA. **439** Ian Loney. **440** *t* Gunther Schmida; *b* Kelvin Aitken/ANT. **441** *t* Jean-Paul Ferrero/Auscape; *b* Rudie H. Kuiter. **442** *t* Gary Bell/oceanwideimages.com; *b* Ron & Valerie Taylor. **443** *t* Mark Spencer; *c* Gunther Schmida; *b* Rudie H. Kuiter. **444** *t* Rudie H. Kuiter; *b* Gunther Schmida/ANT. **445** *t* Gunther Schmida; *b* Kelvin Aitken/ANT. **446** *t* Michael Aw; *bl* Rudie H. Kuiter; *br* Ron & Valerie Taylor. **447** *t* Rudie H. Kuiter; *b* Neville Coleman. **448** *t* Jean-Paul Ferrero/Auscape; *b* Gary Bell/oceanwideimages.com. **449** *t* Gary Bell/oceanwideimages.com; *bl* Gary Bell/oceanwideimages.com; *br* Norbert Wu/ANT. **450** *both* Rudie H. Kuiter. **451** Ron & Valerie Taylor/ANT. **452** *both* Gary Bell/oceanwideimages.com. **453** *t* Becca Saunders/Auscape; *b* Mike Turner/PLA. **454** Kelvin Aitken/ANT. **455** *t* Neville Coleman; *b* Ann Storrie. **456** Eva Boogaard/Lochman Transparencies. **457** Mark Aldred. **458** *tl* Gunther Schmida; *tr* Rudie H. Kuiter; *b* Rudie H. Kuiter/ANT. **459** *t* Gunther Schmida; *b* Jean-Michel Labat/Auscape. **460** *t* Mike Turner/PLA; *b* Becca Saunders/Auscape. **461** *t* Labat-Lanceau/Auscape; *b* Eva Boogaard/Lochman Transparencies. **462** *both* Gary Bell/oceanwideimages.com. **463** *t*, *bc* & *inset br* Gary Bell/oceanwideimages.com; *inset bl* Bill Wood/APL. **464** *t* Graham Edgar; *b* Pete Atkinson/ANT. **465** *t* Bill & Peter Boyle/Auscape; *b* Kevin Deacon/Auscape. **466** Michael Aw. **467** *t* Kevin Deacon/Auscape; *b* Kelvin Aitken/ANT. **468** *t* Rudie H. Kuiter; *b* D. Parer & E. Parer-Cook/Auscape. **469** *t* Mike Thomas/ANT; *b* Ron & Valerie Taylor. **470** Gunther Schmida. **471** *t* Craig Madden; *c* Ron & Valerie Taylor; *b* Mark Welsh. **472** *t* Norbert Wu/ANT; *b* John & Val Butler/Lochman Transparencies. **473** *t* Kelvin Aitken/ANT; *b* Michael Aw. **474** *t* Rudie H. Kuiter; *b* Becca Saunders. **475** Gary Bell/oceanwideimages.com. **476** *t* Gary Bell/oceanwideimages.com; *b* G. Allen. **477** *t* Rudie H. Kuiter; *b* Bill & Peter Boyle/Auscape. **478** *t* Klaus Uhlenhut/ANT; *b* Gunther Schmida. **478–79** Pacific Stock/PLA. **479** *bl* Becca Saunders; *br* Rudie H. Kuiter. **480** *t* Pavel German/ANT; *c* Paddy Ryan/ANT; *b* Rudie H. Kuiter. **481** Mark Spencer. **482** Darrell Ray Jones/Corbis/APL. **483** *t* Becca Saunders/Auscape; *b* Neil Wehlack/Lochman Transparencies. **485** *t* International Photographic Library; *b* Rudie H. Kuiter/ANT. **486** *t* Peter & Margy Nicholas/Lochman Transparencies; *b* Alby Ziebell/Auscape. **487** *t* Ann Storrie; *b* Pete Atkinson/ANT. **488** *t* Mike Thomas/ANT; *b* Volvox/APL. **489** *tl* Volvox/APL; *tr* Norbert Wu/ANT; *b* Gary Bell/oceanwideimages.com. **490–91** Leo Meier/APL. **496** *both* Ron Oldfield. **498** *t* Eva Boogaard/Lochman Transparencies; *b* Kathie Atkinson. **499** Kevin Deacon/Ocean Earth Images. **500** *both* L. Newman & A. Flowers. **501** Kathie Atkinson. **502** *t* Neil Wehlack/Lochman Transparencies; *b* Ben Cropp/Auscape. **503** *t* Gary Bell/oceanwideimages.com; *b* Kathie Atkinson. **504** *t* Ron & Valerie Taylor/ANT; *c* Kelvin Aitken/ANT; *b* Clay Bryce/Lochman Transparencies. **505** *t* Fritz Prenzel/APL; *b* Gary Bell/oceanwideimages.com. **506** *t* Bill Wood; *b* Gary Bell/oceanwideimages.com. **507** Bill Wood. **508** *both* L. Newman & A. Flowers. **509** *t* Sinclair Stammers/SPL/PLA; *b* Leo Meier/APL. **510** *t* Kathie Atkinson; *b* L. Newman & A. Flowers. **511** Sinclair Stammers/SPL/PLA. **512** L. Newman & A. Flowers. **513** *t* L. Newman & A. Flowers; *bl* & *br* Kathie Atkinson. **514** *both* Kathie Atkinson. **515** *t* Kathie Atkinson/Auscape. **515** *b both* Kathie Atkinson. **516** *t* Eva Boogaard/Lochman Transparencies; *b* Pete Atkinson/ANT. **517** *t* Kathie Atkinson; *b* Kelvin Aitken/ANT. **518** *t* Jean-Paul Ferrero/Auscape; *bl* Michael Trenerry; *br* Kathie Atkinson. **519** Kathie Atkinson. **520–21** Jim Frazier. **521** Horizon Photo Library. **522** Kathie Atkinson/Auscape. **523** Cyril Webster/ANT. **524** *t* Michael Trenerry; *b* Paul Zborowski. **525** *t* Reg Morrison; *b* C. Andrew Henley/Auscape. **526** Jiri Lochman/Lochman Transparencies. **527** *t* Bert Brunet; *b* Hans & Judy Beste. **528** *t* Peter Wilson/APL; *b* Reg Morrison. **529** *t* Kathie Atkinson; *b* Densey Clyne. **530** *t* Jiri Lochman/Lochman Transparencies; *b* Leo Meier/APL. **531** *t both* Otto Rogge/ANT; *b* Jim Frazier/ANT. **532** *t* Hans & Judy Beste; *b* Otto Rogge/ANT. **533** *both* Densey Clyne. **534** *t* D. Knowles/Lochman Transparencies; *b* Densey Clyne. **535** *t* Jean-Paul Ferrero/Auscape; *b* Peter Wilson/APL. **536** *t* Fredy Mercay/ANT; *b* Reg Morrison. **537** *both* Pavel German/Wildlife Images. **538** *t* G. Harold/Auscape; *bl* Pavel German/Wildlife Images; *br* Kathie Atkinson. **539** *t* Jiri Lochman/Lochman Transparencies; *b* D. Knowles/Lochman Transparencies. **540** *t* Steve Wilson/ANT; *bl* C. Andrew Henley/Auscape; *br* T.J. Hawkeswood/ANT. **541** Jiri Lochman/Lochman Transparencies. **542** Pavel German/Wildlife Images. **543** *t* Horizon Photo Library; *b* Densey Clyne. **544** *t* Michael Brabenetz; *b* Jiri Lochman/Lochman Transparencies. **545** *l* Gunther Schmida; *r* A.H. Tolhurst/APL. **546** *l* Densey Clyne; *rt* Glen Threlfo/Auscape; *rb* Brett Gregory/Auscape. **547** *t* Kathie Atkinson; *b* Densey Clyne. **548** *t* Anne & Jacques Six/Auscape; *b* Kathie Atkinson. **549** *t* Jean-Paul Ferrero/Auscape; *b* Reg Morrison. **550** *t* C. Andrew Henley/Auscape; *b* A.P. Smith/ANT. **551** *t* Jiri Lochman/Lochman Transparencies; *b* Jean-Paul Ferrero/Auscape. **552** *t* Jiri Lochman/Lochman Transparencies; *b* C. Andrew Henley/Auscape. **553** Horizon Photo Library. **554** *t* Kathie Atkinson/Auscape; *b* G. Harold/Auscape. **555** *tl* Densey Clyne/ANT; *tr* Klaus Uhlenhut/ANT; *b* Gunther Schmida. **556** *t* Wayne Lawler/Auscape; *b* Kathie Atkinson. **557** *t* Leo Meier/APL; *b* Kathie Atkinson. **558** Kathie Atkinson. **560** *t* C. Andrew Henley/Auscape; *c* Densey Clyne; *b* Otto Rogge/ANT. **561** *t* Reg Morrison/Auscape; *b* Pavel German/Wildlife Images. **562** Martin Dohrn/SPL/PLA. **563** *tl* Reg Morrison/Auscape; *tr* Jim Frazier; *b* Pavel German. **564** *t* Leo Meier/APL; *b* Jean-Paul Ferrero/Auscape. **565** *t* G. Harold/Auscape; *b* Michael Cermak/ANT. **566** *t* Jean-Paul Ferrero/Auscape; *b* Jiri Lochman/Lochman Transparencies. **567** *t* Marie Lochman/Lochman Transparencies; *b* Densey Clyne. **568** *t* Brett Gregory/Auscape; *b* Densey Clyne. **570** *t* Rudie H. Kuiter; *b* G. Wheeler/ANT. **571** *t* Reg Morrison; *b* Kathie Atkinson. **572** *tl* Michael Marmach/Museum of Victoria; *tr* Geoff Taylor/Lochman Transparencies; *b* Densey Clyne. **573** *t* Ralph & Daphne Keller/ANT; *b* Rudie H. Kuiter. **574** *t* Mark Spencer; *bl* G. Saueracker/Lochman Transparencies; *br* Becca Saunders. **575** *t* Gary Bell/oceanwideimages.com; *b* Roger Brown/Auscape. **576** *t* Kathie Atkinson; *b* Rudie H. Kuiter. **577** *tl* Kelvin Aitken/ANT; *tr* G.A. Wood/ANT; *b* Clay Bryce/Lochman Transparencies. **578** *t* Fritz Prenzel/APL; *b* Kelvin Aitken/ANT. **579** *t* Eva Boogaard/Lochman Transparencies; *b* Kathie Atkinson. **581** *both* Becca Saunders/Auscape. **582** Kathie Atkinson. **582–83** Kelvin Aitken/ANT. **583** *t* D. Parer & E. Parer-Cook/Auscape; *b* Kathie Atkinson. **584** Clay Bryce/Lochman Transparencies. **585** *t* Kathie Atkinson; *b* Kathie Atkinson/Auscape. **586** *tl* Isobel Bennett; *tr* Kathie Atkinson; *b* Kelvin Aitken/ANT. **587** L. Newman & A. Flowers. **588** *t* Jean-Paul Ferrero/Auscape; *b* Kathie Atkinson/Auscape. **589** *tl* Reg Morrison/Auscape; *tr* & *b* Norbert Wu/ANT. **590** *t* Neville Coleman; *b* Kathie Atkinson. **591** *l* Jean-Paul Ferrero/Auscape; *r* Kathie Atkinson. **592** Kevin Deacon/Ocean Earth Images. **593** International Photographic Library. **594** *t* Ron & Valerie Taylor; *c* Kevin Deacon/Ocean Earth Images; *b* Gary Bell/oceanwideimages.com. **595** *t* Kathie Atkinson; *b* Ron & Valerie Taylor. **596** *t* Ron & Valerie Taylor; *b* L. Newman & A. Flowers. **597** *both* L. Newman & A. Flowers. **598** Sipa Press/Austral. **599** Alby Ziebell/Auscape. **600** Kevin Deacon/Auscape. **601** *t* L. Newman & A. Flowers; *c* Becca Saunders/Auscape; *b* G. Saueracker/Lochman Transparencies. **602** *t* Wayne Storrie; *b* Mark Spencer. **603** D. Parer & E. Parer-Cook/Auscape. **604** *tl* Gary Bell/oceanwideimages.com; *tr* D. Parer & E. Parer-Cook/Auscape; *b* Jean-Paul Ferrero/Auscape. **605** *t* Fenton Walsh/ANT; *b* L. Newman & A. Flowers. **606** *t* Clay Bryce/Lochman Transparencies; *bl* Kelvin Aitken/ANT; *br* Ann Storrie/Auscape. **607** L. Newman & A. Flowers. **608** *t* Becca Saunders; *b* L. Newman & A. Flowers. **609** Bob Walden/APL.

Textured backgrounds **pp. 77, 89, 137, 214, 288, 331, 421, 434, 463, 471, 504, 531, 563, 589**: Images © 1997 PhotoDisc, Inc.

Product code 041 3202
Concept Code AU0108/L